Tools for Student Success!

MyMathLab

MyMathLab is a series of text-specific, easily customizable online courses for Prentice Hall textbooks in mathematics and statistics. Powered by CourseCompass™ (Pearson Education's online teaching and learning environment) and MathXL® (our online homework, tutorial, and assessment system), MyMathLab gives you the tools you need to deliver all or a portion of your course online, whether your students are in a lab setting or working from home. MyMathLab provides a rich and flexible set of course materials, featuring free-response exercises that are algorithmically generated for unlimited practice and mastery. Students can also use online tools, such as video lectures, animations, and a multimedia textbook, to independently improve their understanding and performance. Instructors can use MyMathLab's homework and test managers to select and assign online exercises correlated directly to the textbook, and they can also create and assign their own online exercises and import TestGen tests for added flexibility. MyMathLab's online gradebook—designed specifically for mathematics and statistics—automatically tracks students' homework and test results and gives the instructor control over how to calculate final grades. Instructors can also add offline (paper-and-pencil) grades to the gradebook. MyMathLab is available to qualified adopters. For more information, visit our website at www.mymathlab.com or contact your Prentice Hall sales representative.

MathXL®

MathXL® is a powerful online homework, tutorial, and assessment system that accompanies Prentice Hall textbooks in mathematics or statistics. With MathXL, instructors can create, edit, and assign online homework and tests using algorithmically generated exercises correlated at the objective level to the textbook. They can also create and assign their own online exercises and import TestGen tests for added flexibility. All student work is tracked in MathXL's online gradebook. Students can take chapter tests in MathXL and receive personalized study plans based on their test results. The study plan diagnoses weaknesses and links students directly to tutorial exercises for the objectives they need to study and retest. Students can also access supplemental animations and video clips directly from selected exercises. MathXL is available to qualified adopters. For more information, visit our website at www.mathxl.com, or contact your Prentice Hall sales representative.

More Tools for Student Success!

STUDENT STUDY PACK

Includes:

- the *Student Solutions Manual*
- access to the *Prentice Hall Tutor Center*
- the *CD Lecture Series Videos*

Student Solutions Manual

Provides full, worked-out solutions to:

- the odd-numbered section exercises
- all (even and odd) exercises in the Cumulative Review Exercises (within the section exercises), Mid-Chapter Tests, Chapter Review Exercises, Chapter Practice Tests, and Cumulative Review Tests

Chapter Test Prep Video CD

Provides step-by-step video solutions to each problem in each *Chapter Practice Test* in the textbook.

CD Lecture Series Videos

Each section includes:

- a 20-minute mini-lecture
- several worked-out section exercises (identified by a CD icon)

Prentice Hall Tutor Center

Staffed by developmental math faculty, the Tutor Center provides live tutorial support via phone, fax, or email.

ELEMENTARY ALGEBRA

For College Students

EARLY GRAPHING

ELEMENTARY ALGEBRA

For College Students

EARLY GRAPHING

Third Edition

Allen R. Angel

Monroe Community College

with assistance from

Aimee L. Calhoun
Donna R. Petrie

Monroe Community College

PEARSON

Prentice Hall

Upper Saddle River, New Jersey 07458

Executive Editor: *Paul Murphy*
Project Manager: *Dawn Nuttall*
Editor in Chief: *Christine Hoag*
Production Editor: *Lynn Savino Wendel*
Executive Managing Editor: *Kathleen Schiaparelli*
Senior Managing Editor: *Linda Mihatov Behrens*
Media Project Manager, Developmental Math: *Audra J. Walsh*
Media Production Editor: *Ashley Booth*
Assistant Managing Editor, Science and Math Supplements: *Karen Bosch*
Manufacturing Buyer: *Maura Zaldivar*
Manufacturing Manager: *Alexis Heydt-Long*
Director of Marketing: *Patrice Jones*
Senior Marketing Manager: *Kate Valentine*
Marketing Assistant: *Jennifer de Leeuwerk*
Editorial Assistant/Print Supplements Editor: *Abigail Rethore*
Editor in Chief, Development: *Carol Trueheart*
Art Director: *John Christiana*
Interior Designer: *Studio Indigo*
Cover Designer: *Michael J. Fruhbeis*
Art Editor: *Thomas Benfatti*
Creative Director: *Juan R. López*
Director of Creative Services: *Paul Belfanti*
Director, Image Resource Center: *Melinda Patelli*
Manager, Rights and Permissions: *Zina Arabia*
Manager, Visual Research: *Beth Brenzel*
Image Permission Coordinator: *Craig A. Jones*
Photo Researcher: *Teri Stratford*
Compositor: *Prepare, Inc.*
Art Studios: *Precision Graphics and Laserwords*

© 2008, 2004, 2000 Pearson Education, Inc.
Pearson Prentice Hall
Pearson Education, Inc.
Upper Saddle River, NJ 07458

10 9 8 7 6 5 4 3 2 1

ISBN 0-13-613417-3 (AIE)
ISBN 0-13-613416-5 (Student Edition)

Pearson Education, LTD., *London*
Pearson Education Australia PTY, Limited, *Sydney*
Pearson Education Singapore, Pte. Ltd
Pearson Education North Asia Ltd, *Hong Kong*
Pearson Education Canada, Ltd., *Toronto*
Pearson Educación de Mexico, S.A. de C.V.
Pearson Education –Japan, *Tokyo*
Pearson Education Malaysia, Pte. Ltd

To my wife, Kathy,
and my sons, Robert and Steven

Contents

Preface

This book was written for college students and other adults who have never been exposed to algebra or those who have been exposed but need a refresher course. My primary goal was to write a book that students can read, understand, and enjoy. To achieve this goal I have used short sentences, clear explanations, and many detailed, worked-out examples. I have tried to make the book relevant to college students by using practical applications of algebra throughout the text.

Features of the Text

Full-Color Format

Color is used pedagogically in the following ways:

- Important definitions and procedures are color screened.
- Color screening or color type is used to make other important items stand out.
- Artwork is enhanced and clarified with use of multiple colors.
- The full-color format allows for easy identification of important features by students.
- The full-color format makes the text more appealing and interesting to students.

Readability

One of the most important features of the text is its readability. The book is very readable, even for those with weak reading skills. Short, clear sentences are used and more easily recognized, and easy-to-understand language is used whenever possible.

Accuracy

Accuracy in a mathematics text is essential. To ensure accuracy in this book, mathematicians from around the country have read the pages carefully for typographical errors and have checked all the answers.

Connections

Many of our students do not thoroughly grasp new concepts the first time they are presented. In this text we encourage students to make connections. That is, we introduce a concept, then later in the text briefly reintroduce it and build upon it. Often an important concept is used in many sections of the text. Students are reminded where the material was seen before, or where it will be used again. This also serves to emphasize the importance of the concept. Important concepts are also reinforced throughout the text in the Cumulative Review Exercises and Cumulative Review Tests.

Chapter Opening Application

Each chapter begins with a real-life application related to the material covered in the chapter. By the time students complete the chapter, they should have the knowledge to work the problem.

Goals of this Chapter

This feature on the chapter opener page gives students a preview of the chapter and also indicates where this material will be used again in other chapters of the book. This material helps students see the connections among various topics in the book and the connection to real-world situations.

The Use of Icons

At the begining of each exercise set the icon for MathXL®, *Math*_XL_, and for MyMathLab, **MyMathLab**, are illustrated. Both of these icons will be explained shortly.

Keyed Section Objectives

Each section opens with a list of skills that the student should learn in that section. The objectives are then keyed to the appropriate portions of the sections with blue numbers such as **1**.

Problem Solving

Polya's five-step problem-solving procedure is discussed in Section 1.2. Throughout the book, problem solving and Polya's problem-solving procedure are emphasized.

Practical Applications

Practical applications of algebra are stressed throughout the text. Students need to learn how to translate application problems into algebraic symbols. The problem-solving approach used throughout this text gives students ample practice in setting up and solving application problems. The use of practical applications motivates students.

Detailed, Worked-Out Examples

A wealth of examples have been worked out in a step-by-step, detailed manner. Important steps are highlighted in color, and no steps are omitted until after the student has seen a sufficient number of similar examples.

Now Try Exercises

In each section, after each example, students are asked to work an exercise that parallels the example given in the text. These Now Try Exercises make the students *active*, rather than passive, learners and they reinforce the concepts as students work the exercises. Through these exercises, students have the opportunity to immediately apply what they have learned. After each example, Now Try Exercises are indicated in green type such as ▶ **Now Try Exercise 27**. They are also indicated in green type in the exercise sets, such as 27.

Study Skills Section

Many students taking this course have poor study skills in mathematics. Section 1.1, the first section of this text, discusses the study skills needed to be successful in mathematics. This section should be very beneficial for your students and should help them to achieve success in mathematics.

Helpful Hints
The Helpful Hint boxes offer useful suggestions for problem solving and other varied topics. They are set off in a special manner so that students will be sure to read them.

Helpful Hints—Study Tip
The Helpful Hint–Study Tip boxes offer valuable information on items related to studying and learning the material.

Avoiding Common Errors
Errors that students often make are illustrated. The reasons why certain procedures are wrong are explained, and the correct procedure for working the problem is illustrated. These Avoiding Common Errors boxes will help prevent your students from making those errors we see so often.

Using Your Calculator
The Using Your Calculator boxes, placed at appropriate locations in the text, are written to reinforce the algebraic topics presented in the section and to give the student pertinent information on using a scientific calculator to solve algebraic problems.

Using Your Graphing Calculator
Using Your Graphing Calculator boxes are placed at appropriate locations throughout the text. They reinforce the algebraic topics taught and sometimes offer alternate methods of working problems. This book is designed to give the instructor the option of using or not using a graphing calculator in his or her course. Some of the Using Your Graphing Calculator boxes contain graphing calculator exercises, whose answers appear in the answer section of the book. The illustrations shown in the Using Your Graphing Calculator boxes are from a Texas Instruments TI-84 Plus calculator. The Using Your Graphing Calculator boxes are written assuming that the student has no prior graphing calculator experience.

Exercise Sets

The exercise sets are broken into three main categories: Concept/Writing Exercises, Practice the Skills, and Problem Solving. Many exercise sets also contain Challenge Problems and/or Group Activities. Each exercise set is graded in difficulty. The early problems help develop the student's confidence, and then students are eased gradually into the more difficult problems. A sufficient number and variety of examples are given in each section for the student to successfully complete even the more difficult exercises. The number of exercises in each section is more than ample for student assignments and practice.

Concept/Writing Exercises
Most exercise sets include exercises that require students to write out the answers in words. These exercises improve students'

understanding and comprehension of the material. Many of these exercises involve problem solving and conceptualization and help develop better reasoning and critical thinking skills. Writing exercises are indicated by the symbol ↘.

Problem Solving Exercises
These exercises have been added to help students become better thinkers and problem solvers. Many of these exercises involve real-life applications of algebra. It is important for students to be able to apply what they learn to real-life situations. Many problem-solving exercises help with this.

Challenge Problems
These exercises, which are part of many exercise sets, provide a variety of problems. Many were written to stimulate student thinking. Others provide additional applications of algebra or present material from future sections of the book so that students can see and learn the material on their own before it is covered in class. Others are more challenging than those in the regular exercise set.

CD Lecture Exercises
The exercises that are worked out in detail on the CD Lecture Videos are marked with the CD icon, 💿. This will prove helpful for your students.

Cumulative Review Exercises
All exercise sets (after the first two) contain questions from previous sections in the chapter and from previous chapters. These Cumulative Review Exercises will reinforce topics that were previously covered and help students retain the earlier material, while they are learning the new material. For the students' benefit, Cumulative Review Exercises are keyed to the section where the material is covered, using brackets, such as [3.4].

Group Activities
Many exercise sets have group activity exercises that lead to interesting group discussions. Many students learn well in a cooperative learning atmosphere, and these exercises will get students talking mathematics to one another.

Mid-Chapter Tests
In the middle of each chapter is a new Mid-Chapter Test. Students should take each Mid-Chapter Test to make sure they understand the material presented in the chapter up to that point. In the student answers, brackets such as [2.3] are used to indicate the section where the material was first presented.

Chapter Summary
At the end of each chapter is a newly formatted, comprehensive chapter summary that includes important chapter facts and examples illustrating these important facts.

Chapter Review Exercises
At the end of each chapter are review exercises that cover all types of exercises presented in the chapter. The review exercises are keyed, using color numbers and brackets, such as [1.5], to the sections where the material was first introduced.

Chapter Practice Tests

The comprehensive end-of-chapter practice test will enable the students to see how well they are prepared for the actual class test. The section where the material was first introduced is indicated in brackets in the student answers.

Cumulative Review Tests

These tests, which appear at the end of each chapter after the first, test the students' knowledge of material from the beginning of the book to the end of that chapter. Students can use these tests for review, as well as for preparation for the final exam. These exams, like the Cumulative Review Exercises, will serve to reinforce topics taught earlier. In the answer section, after each answer, the section where that material was covered is given using brackets.

Answers

The *odd answers* are provided for the exercise sets. *All answers* are provided for the Using Your Graphing Calculator Exercises, Cumulative Review Exercises, Mid-Chapter Tests, Chapters Review Exercises, Chapter Practice Tests, and Cumulative Review Tests. Answers are not provided for the Group Activity exercises since we want students to reach agreement by themselves on the answers to these exercises.

National Standards

Recommendations of the *Curriculum and Evaluation Standards for School Mathematics*, prepared by the National Council of Teachers of Mathematics (NCTM), and *Beyond Crossroads: Implementing Mathematics Standards in the First Two Years of College*, prepared by the American Mathematical Association of Two Year Colleges (AMATYC), are incorporated into this edition.

Prerequisite

This text assumes no prior knowledge of algebra. However, a working knowledge of arithmetic skills is important. Fractions are reviewed early in the text, and decimals and percent are reviewed in Appendix A.

Modes of Instruction

The format and readability of this book lends itself to many different modes of instruction. The constant reinforcement of concepts will result in greater understanding and retention of the material by your students.

The features of the text and the large variety of supplements available make this text suitable for many types of instructional modes, including

- lecture
- distance learning
- self-paced instruction
- modified lecture
- cooperative or group study
- learning laboratory

Changes in the Third Edition

When I wrote the third edition I considered many letters and reviews I got from students and faculty alike. I would like to thank all of you who made suggestions for improving the third edition. I would also like to thank the many instructors and students who wrote to inform me of how much they enjoyed, appreciated, and learned from the text. Some of the changes made in the third edition of the text include the following:

- Chapter 3, "Applications of Algebra," has been shortened from five sections to four sections and has been rewritten to make the material more understandable for students. Sections 3.1 and 3.4 have been reorganized to make the material clearer and flow more smoothly. The chapter also has many new and exciting real-life applications.

- The material on formulas has been moved from Chapter 3 to Chapter 2, where it now reinforces the material on solving equations.

- More emphasis is placed on solving equations containing decimal numbers and fractions in Chapter 2.

- Addition and subtraction of fractions and decimals have been enhanced and improved in Chapter 1.

- Material on rounding decimal numbers has been added to the decimal number appendix.

- A *Chapter Test Prep Video CD* now comes with the book. This video CD shows the worked-out solution to each exercise in the Chapter Practice Test for each chapter. This is yet another aid to improve student learning and understanding.

- *Every* example in the book now has a corresponding Now Try Exercise associated with it. Students are encouraged to work the exercise immediately after they finish studying the respective example. This gives students an opportunity to reinforce the concepts or topics covered in the example.

- A new feature called *Mid-Chapter Test* has been added to the middle of each chapter. These tests are designed to see how well students understand the topics covered in the first part of the chapter. If a student misses a question, the student should review the appropriate material. The section where the material was introduced is given in brackets next to the answer in the back of the book.

- More *Helpful Hints* and *Avoiding Common Errors* boxes have been added where appropriate.

- The Chapter Summary has been rewritten to include examples of important facts and concepts covered in the chapter. The left-hand column gives the fact or concept, and the right-hand column gives an example of the fact or concept. The new chapter summary should be an aid to students in reviewing the chapter and preparing for a test.

- New and exciting examples and exercises have been added throughout the book.

  ○ New exercises were added to many exercise sets to ensure that every example in the book now has exercises that correspond to that given example.

  ○ In some sections, more difficult exercises have been added at the end, or easier exercises have been added at the beginning of the exercise set so that there is a continuous increase in the level of difficulty of the exercises.

  ○ Every effort has been made to include applications that are of interest to students.

  ○ Variables other than *x* and *y* are used more often in examples and exercises.

- *Goals of This Chapter* have replaced *A Look Ahead*. The information provided gives students an overview of what they will see and are expected to learn in the chapter.

- *Using Your Graphing Calculator* boxes now show keystrokes for the TI-84 Plus calculator. Note that the same keystrokes are appropriate for the TI-83 Plus calculator.

- The *Mathematics in Action* feature has been removed to conserve space.

- More art and photos have been added to the text to make the material either more understandable or more interesting for students.

- The basic colors used in the text have been softened to make the text more attractive and easier for students to read.

Supplements for the Third Edition

FOR INSTRUCTORS

Printed Supplements

Annotated Instructor's Edition (0-13-613417-3)

Contains all the content found in the student edition, plus the following:

- Answers to exercises are printed on the same text page with graphing answers in a special Graphing Answer Section in the back of the text.

- *Teaching Tips* throughout the text are placed at key points in the margins.

- **NEW!** An extra *Instructor Example* is now provided in the margin next to each student example. These extra examples are meant to be used as additional examples in the classroom.

Instructor's Solutions Manual (0-13-158068-X)

This manual contains complete solutions to every exercise in the text.

Instructor's Resource Manual with Tests (0-13-158069-8)

- **NEW!** Now includes a Mini-Lecture for every section of the text.

- Provides several test forms, both free response and multiple choice, for every chapter, as well as cumulative tests and final exams.

- Answers to all items also included.

Media Supplements

TestGen (0-13-158070-1)

TestGen enables instructors to build, edit, print, and administer tests using a computerized bank of questions developed to cover all the objectives of the text. TestGen is algorithmically based, allowing instructors to create multiple but equivalent versions of the same question or test with the click of a button. Instructors can also modify test bank questions or add new questions. Tests can be printed or administered online. The software is available on a dual-platform Windows/Macintosh CD-ROM.

CD Lecture Series Videos—Lab Pack (0-13-158071-X)

For each section, there are about 20 minutes of lecture along with several of the section exercises worked out. The exercises that are worked out are identified in the student edition by the icon 💿.

NEW! MyMathLab Instructor Version (0-13-147898-2)

MyMathLab is a series of text-specific, easily customizable online courses for Prentice Hall textbooks in mathematics and statistics. Powered by CourseCompass™ (Pearson Education's online teaching and learning environment) and MathXL® (our online homework, tutorial, and assessment system), MyMathLab gives you the tools you need to deliver all or a portion of your course online, whether your students are in a lab setting or working from home.

NEW! MathXL® Instructor Version (0-13-147895-8)

MathXL® is a powerful online homework, tutorial, and assessment system that accompanies Prentice Hall textbooks in mathematics or statistics. With MathXL, instructors can create, edit, and assign online homework and tests using algorithmically generated exercises correlated at the objective level to the textbook.

FOR STUDENTS

NEW! Student Study Pack (0-13-234886-1)

Includes

- The *Student Solutions Manual*
- Access to the *Prentice Hall Tutor Center*
- The *CD Lecture Series Videos*

Printed Supplements

Student Solutions Manual (0-13-158067-1)

Provides full, worked-out solutions to

- The odd-numbered section exercises
- All (even and odd) exercises in the Cumulative Review Exercises (within the section exercises), Mid-Chapter Tests, Chapter Review Exercises, Chapter Practice Tests, and Cumulative Review Tests

Media Supplements

NEW! Chapter Test Prep Video CD (0-13-159447-8)

Provides step-by-step video solutions to each problem in each *Chapter Practice Test* in the textbook. Packaged with a new text, inside the back cover.

NEW! MathXL® Tutorials on CD (0-13-158073-6)

This interactive tutorial CD-ROM provides algorithmically generated practice exercises that are correlated at the objective level to the exercises in the textbook. Every practice exercise is accompanied by an example and a guided solution designed to involve students in the solution process. Selected exercises may also include a video clip to help students visualize concepts. The software provides helpful feedback for incorrect answers and can generate printed summaries of students' progress.

Prentice Hall Tutor Center: www.prenhall.com/tutorcenter (0-13-064604-0)

Staffed by developmental math faculty, the Tutor Center provides live tutorial support via phone, fax, or e-mail. Tutors are available Sunday through Thursday 5 P.M. EST to midnight, 5 days a week, 7 hours a day. The Tutor Center may be accessed through a registration number that may be bundled with a new text or purchased separately with a used book. Comes automatically within *MyMathLab*.

InterAct Math Tutorial Web site: www.interactmath.com

Get practice and tutorial help online! This interactive tutorial Web site provides algorithmically generated practice exercises that correlate directly to the exercises in the textbook. Students can retry an exercise as many times as they like with new values each time for unlimited practice and mastery. Every exercise is accompanied by an interactive guided solution that provides helpful feedback for incorrect answers, and students can also view a worked-out sample problem that steps them through an exercise similar to the one they're working on.

Acknowledgments

Writing a textbook is a long and time-consuming project. Many people deserve thanks for encouraging and assisting me with this project. Most importantly, my special thanks goes to my wife Kathy and sons, Robert and Steven. Without their constant encouragement and understanding, this project would not have become a reality. I would also like to thank my daughter-in-law, Kathy, for her support.

I would like to thank Aimee Calhoun and Donna Petrie of Monroe Community College for their conscientiousness and attention to detail they provided in checking pages, artwork, and answers. Special thanks to Aimee, who has been involved in all aspects of the project.

I want to thank Rafiq Ladhani and his team at Edutorial for accuracy reviewing the pages and checking all answers.

I would like to thank several people at Prentice Hall, including Paul Murphy, Executive Editor; Dawn Nuttall, Project Manager; Thomas Benfatti, Art Editor; John Christiana, Art Director; and Lynn Savino Wendel, Production Editor, for their many valuable suggestions and conscientiousness with this project.

I want to thank those who worked with me on the print supplements for this book.

- Student and Instructor's Solutions Manuals: Doreen Kelly, *Mesa Community College, AZ*
- Instructor's Resource Manual: Kevin Bodden and Randy Gallaher, *Lewis and Clark Community College, IL*

I would like to thank the following reviewers of the last two editions for their thoughtful comments and suggestions:

Darla Aguilar, *Pima Community College, AZ*
Frances Alvarado, *University of Texas–Pan American, TX*
Jose Alvarado, *University of Texas–Pan American, TX*
Ben Anderson, *Darton College, GA*
Mary Lou Baker, *Columbia State Community College, TN*
Sharon Berrian, *Northwest Shoals Community College, AL*
Dianne Bolen, *Northeast Mississippi Community College, MS*
Julie Bonds, *Sonoma State University, CA*
Clark Brown, *Mojave Community College, AZ*
Connie Buller, *Metropolitan Community College, NE*
Marc D. Campbell, *Daytona Beach Community College, FL*
Julie Chesser, *Owens Community College, OH*
Kim Christensen, *Maple Woods Community College, MO*
Barry Cogan, *Macomb Community College, MI*
Pat C. Cook, *Weatherford College, TX*
Lisa DeLong Cuneo, *Pennsylvania State University–Dubois, PA*
Stephan Delong, *Tidewater Community College, VA*
Deborah Doucette, *Erie Community College (North), NY*

William Echols, *Houston Community College, TX*
Dale Felkins, *Arkansas Technical University, AR*
Reginald Fulwood, *Palm Beach Community College, FL*
Susan Grody, *Broward Community College, FL*
Abdollah Hajikandi, *State University of New York–Buffalo, NY*
Olga Cynthia Harrison, *Baton Rouge Community College, LA*
Richard Hobbs, *Mission College, CA*
Joe Howe, *St. Charles Community College, MO*
Laura L. Hoye, *Trident Technical College, SC*
Barbara Hughes, *San Jacinto Community College (Central), TX*
Mary Johnson, *Inver Hills Community College, MN*
Jane Keller, *Metropolitan Community College, NE*
Mike Kirby, *Tidewater Community College, VA*
William Krant, *Palo Alto College, TX*
Gayle L. Krzemien, *Pikes Peak Community College, CO*
Mitchel Levy, *Broward Community College, FL*
Mitzi Logan, *Pitt Community College, NC*
Jason Mahar, *Monroe Community College, NY*

Kimberley A. Martello, *Monroe Community College, NY*
Constance Meade, *College of Southern Idaho, ID*
Lynnette Meslinsky, *Erie Community College, NY*
Elizabeth Morrison, *Valencia Community College, FL*
Elsie Newman, *Owens Community College, OH*
Charlotte Newsom, *Tidewater Community College, VA*
Charles Odion, *Houston Community College, TX*
Jean Olsen, *Pikes Peak Community College, CO*
Jeanne Pirie, *Erie Community College (North), NY*
Behnaz Rouhani, *Athens Technical College, GA*
Brian Sanders, *Modesto Junior College, CA*
Glenn R. Sandifer, *San Jacinto Community College (Central), TX*
Rebecca Schantz, *Prairie State College, IL*
Cristela Sifuentez, *University of Texas–Pan American, TX*
Fereja Tahir, *Illinois Central College, IL*
Burnette Thompson, Jr., *Houston Community College, TX*
Mary Vachon, *San Joaquin Delta College, CA*
Andrea Vorwark, *Maple Woods Community College, MO*
Ronald Yates, *Community College of Southern Nevada, NV*

To the Student

Algebra is a course that cannot be learned by observation. To learn algebra you must become an active participant. You must read the text, pay attention in class, and, most importantly, you must work the exercises. The more exercises you work, the better.

The text was written with you in mind. Short, clear sentences are used, and many examples are given to illustrate specific points. The text stresses useful applications of algebra. Hopefully, as you progress through the course, you will come to realize that algebra is not just another math course that you are required to take, but a course that offers a wealth of useful information and applications.

This text makes full use of color. The different colors are used to highlight important information. Important procedures, definitions, and formulas are placed within colored boxes.

The boxes marked **Helpful Hints** should be studied carefully, for they stress important information. The boxes marked **Avoiding Common Errors** should also be studied carefully. These boxes point out errors that students commonly make, and provide the correct procedures for doing these problems.

After each example you will see a Now Try Exercise reference, such as ▶ **Now Try Exercise 27**. The exercise indicated is very similar to the example given in the book. You may wish to try the indicated exercise after you read the example to make sure you truly understand the example. In the exercise set, the Now Try exercises are written in green, such as 27.

In the exercise sets, the exercises marked with a pencil, ✎, indicate writing exercises—that is, exercises that require a written answer. The exercises marked with a CD, ⊙, indicate that these exercises are worked out on the CD Lecture Videos.

Ask your professor early in the course to explain the policy on when the calculator may be used. Pay particular attention to the 🖩 **Using Your Calculator** boxes. You should also read the 🖩 **Using Your Graphing Calculator** boxes even if you are not using a graphing calculator in class. You may find the information presented here helps you better understand the algebraic concepts.

Other questions you should ask your professor early in the course include: What supplements are available for use? Where can help be obtained when the professor is not available? Supplements that may be available include: the Student Solutions Manual; the CD Lecture Series Videos; the Chapter Test Prep Video CD; MathXL® *MathXL*; MyMathLab *MyMathLab*; and the Prentice Hall Mathematics Tutor Center. All these items are discussed under the heading of Supplements in Section 1.1, as well as in the Preface.

You may wish to form a study group with other students in your class. Many students find that working in small groups provides an excellent way to learn the material. By discussing and explaining the concepts and exercises to one another, you reinforce your own understanding. Once guidelines and procedures are determined by your group, make sure to follow them.

One of the first things you should do is to read Section 1.1, Study Skills for Success in Mathematics. Read this section slowly and carefully, and pay particular attention to the advice and information given. Occasionally, refer back to this section. This could be the most important section of the book. Carefully read the material on doing your homework and on attending class.

At the end of all Exercise Sets (after the first two) are **Cumulative Review Exercises**. You should work these problems on a regular basis, even if they are not assigned. These problems are from earlier sections and chapters of the text, and they will refresh your memory and reinforce those topics. If you have a problem when working these exercises, read the appropriate section of the text or study your notes that correspond to that material. The section of the text where the Cumulative Review Exercise was introduced is indicated in brackets, [ ], to the left of the exercise. After reviewing the material, if you still have a problem, make an appointment to see your professor. Working the Cumulative Review Exercises throughout the semester will also help prepare you to take your final exam.

Near the middle of each chapter is a **Mid-Chapter Test**. You should take each Mid-Chapter Test to make sure you understand the material up to that point. The section where the material was first introduced is given in brackets after the answer in the answer section of the book.

At the end of each chapter are a **Chapter Summary**, **Chapter Review Exercises**, a **Chapter Practice Test**, and a **Cumulative Review Test.** Before each examination you should review this material carefully and take the Chapter Practice Test (you may want to review the *Chapter Test Prep Video CD* also). If you do well on the Chater Practice Test, you should do well on the class test. The questions in the Review Exercises are marked to indicate the section in which that material was first introduced. If you have a problem with a Review Exercise question, reread the section indicated. You may also wish to take the Cumulative Review Test that appears at the end of every chapter.

In the back of the text there is an **answer section** that contains the answers to the *odd-numbered* exercises, including the Challenge Problems. Answers to *all* Using Your Graphing Calculator Exercises, Cumulative Review Exercises, Mid-Chapter Tests, Chapter Review Exercises, Chapter Practice Tests, and Cumulative Review Tests are provided. Answers to the Group Activity exercises are not provided, for we wish students to reach agreement by themselves on answers to these exercises. The answers should be used only to check your work. For the Mid-Chapter Tests, Chapter Practice Tests, and Cumulative Review Tests, after each answer the section number where that type of exercise was covered is provided.

I have tried to make this text as clear and error free as possible. No text is perfect, however. If you find an error in the text, or an example or section that you believe can be improved, I would greatly appreciate hearing from you. If you enjoy the text, I would also appreciate hearing from you. You can submit comments at *http://247.prenhall.com*.

Allen R. Angel

1

Real Numbers

GOALS OF THIS CHAPTER

This chapter will provide you with the foundation that you need in order to succeed in this course and all other mathematics courses you will take. Learning proper study skills is the first step in building this foundation. *Please read Section 1.1 carefully and follow the advice given.* The emphasis of this chapter is to provide you with an understanding of the real number system.

In this chapter, you will learn a five-step problem-solving procedure that will be used throughout the book. Once you have learned the material in this chapter, you will be able to tackle the subsequent chapters in the book with confidence.

IN ADDITION TO YEARLY PREMIUMS, certain medical insurance policies require a co-payment for each visit made to a doctor's office. Others require that the individual pay a certain dollar amount in medical expenses each year, after which the insurance company pays a large percentage of the remaining costs. On pages 10 and 11, we use a problem-solving technique to determine the portion of a medical bill a person is responsible for and how much of that bill the insurance company will pay.

1.1 Study Skills for Success in Mathematics

1. Recognize the goals of this text.
2. Learn proper study skills.
3. Prepare for and take exams.
4. Learn to manage time.
5. Purchase a calculator.

This section is extremely important. Take the time to read it carefully and follow the advice given. For many of you this section may be the most important section of the text.

Most of you taking this course fall into one of three categories: (1) those who did not take algebra in high school, (2) those who took algebra in high school but did not understand the material, or (3) those who successfully completed algebra in high school but have been out of school for some time and need to take the course again. Whichever the case, you will need to acquire study skills for mathematics courses.

Before we discuss study skills, we will present the goals of this text. These goals may help you realize why certain topics are covered in the text and why they are covered as they are.

TEACHING TIP
Before discussing the goals of the text, have students list their reasons for enrolling in the course. Then have them share their reasons with other students.

1 Recognize the Goals of This Text

The goals of this text include:

1. Presenting traditional algebra topics
2. Preparing you for more advanced mathematics courses
3. Building your confidence in, and your enjoyment of, mathematics
4. Improving your reasoning and critical thinking skills
5. Increasing your understanding of how important mathematics is in solving real-life problems
6. Encouraging you to think mathematically, so that you will feel comfortable translating real-life problems into mathematical equations, and then solving the problems.

In addition to teaching you the mathematical content, our goals are to teach you to be more *mathematically literate*, which is also called *quantitatively literate*. We wish to teach you to *communicate mathematically*, to teach you *to understand and interpret data* in a variety of formats, to teach you measurement and geometric concepts, to teach you to *reason more logically*, and to teach you to be able to represent real world applications mathematically, which is called *modeling*. Throughout the book we will strive to increase your mathematical understanding to help you become more successful in mathematics, in your future job, and throughout life.

Another goal of this text is to help you become more familiar with technology that may help you in this and future mathematics courses, and throughout life. To do so, we use Calculator Boxes throughout the book for both scientific and graphing calculators.

We also realize that some of you may have some mathematics anxiety. We have written the book to try to help you overcome that anxiety by building your confidence in mathematics.

It is important to realize that this course is the foundation for more advanced mathematics courses. A thorough understanding of algebra will make it easier for you to succeed in later mathematics courses and in life.

2 Learn Proper Study Skills

Have a Positive Attitude

You may be thinking to yourself, "I hate math," or "I wish I did not have to take this class." You may have heard of "math anxiety" and feel you fit this category. The first thing to do to be successful in this course is to change your attitude to a more positive one. You must be willing to give this course, and yourself, a fair chance.

Based on past experiences in mathematics, you may feel that this is difficult. However, mathematics is something you need to work at. Many of you are more mature now than when you took previous mathematics courses. Your maturity and desire to learn are extremely important and can make a tremendous difference in your ability to succeed in mathematics. I believe you can be successful in this course, but you also need to believe it.

Prepare for and Attend Class

To be prepared for class, you need to do your homework assignments completely. If you have difficulty with the homework, or some of the concepts, write down questions to ask your instructor. If you were given a reading assignment, read the appropriate material carefully before class.

After the material is explained in class, read the corresponding sections of the text slowly and carefully, word by word.

You should plan to attend every class. Generally, the more absences you have, the lower your grade will be. Every time you miss a class, you miss important information. If you must miss a class, contact your instructor ahead of time, and get the reading assignment and homework. If possible, before the next class, try to copy a friend's notes to help you understand the material you missed.

In algebra and other mathematics courses, the material you learn is cumulative. The new material is built on material that was presented previously. You must understand each section before moving on to the next section, and each chapter before moving on to the next chapter. Therefore, do not let yourself fall behind. Seek help as soon as you need it—do not wait! You will greatly increase your chance of success in this course by following the study skills presented in this section.

While in class, pay attention to what your instructor is saying. If you don't understand something, ask your instructor to repeat the material. If you don't ask questions, your instructor will not know that you have a problem understanding the material.

In class, take careful notes. Write numbers and letters clearly, so that you can read them later. Make sure your x's do not look like y's and vice versa. It is not necessary to write down every word your instructor says. Copy the major points and the examples that do not appear in the text. You should not be taking notes so frantically that you lose track of what your instructor is saying.

Read the Text

Mathematics textbooks should be read slowly and carefully, word by word. If you don't understand what you are reading, reread the material. When you come across a new concept or definition, you may wish to underline or highlight it, so that it stands out. Then it will be easier to find later. When you come across an example, read and follow it line by line. Don't just skim it. Also, work the **Now Try Exercises** that appear in the text following each example. The Now Try Exercises are designed so that you have the opportunity to immediately apply new ideas. Make notes of anything you don't understand to ask your instructor.

This textbook has special features to help you. I suggest that you pay particular attention to these highlighted features, including the **Avoiding Common Errors** boxes, the **Helpful Hint** boxes, and important procedures and definitions identified by color. The Avoiding Common Errors boxes point out the most common errors made by students. Read and study this material very carefully and make sure that you understand what is explained. If you avoid making these common errors, your chances of success in this and other mathematics classes will be increased greatly. The Helpful Hints offer many valuable techniques for working certain problems. They may also present some very useful information or show an alternative way to work a problem.

Do the Homework

Two very important commitments that you must make to be successful in this course are attending class and doing your homework regularly. Your assignments must be worked conscientiously and completely. Do your homework as soon as possible, so the material presented in class will be fresh in your mind. It is through doing homework that you truly learn the material. While working homework you will become aware of the types of problems that you need further help with. If you do not work the assigned exercises, you will not know what questions to ask in class.

TEACHING TIP
Compare doing homework with practicing a sport: Math homework is to a test as football practice is to a game.

When you do your homework, make sure that you write it neatly and carefully. Pay particular attention to copying signs and exponents correctly.

Don't forget to check the answers to your homework assignments. This book contains the answers to the odd-numbered exercises in the back of the book. In addition, the answers to all the Cumulative Review Exercises, Mid-Chapter Tests, Chapter Review Exercises, Chapter Practice Tests, and Cumulative Review Tests are in the back of the book. The section number where the material is first introduced is provided next to the exercises for the Cumulative Review Exercises and Chapter Review Exercises. The section number where the material is first introduced is provided with the answers in the back of the book for the Mid-Chapter Tests, Chapter Practice Tests, and Cumulative Review Tests. Answers to the Group Activity Exercises are not provided because we want you to arrive at the answers as a group.

Ask questions in class about homework problems you don't understand. You should not feel comfortable until you understand all the concepts needed to work every assigned problem successfully.

Study for Class

Study in the proper atmosphere, in an area where you will not be constantly disturbed, so that your attention can be devoted to what you are reading. The area where you study should be well ventilated and well lit. You should have sufficient desk space to spread out all your materials. Your chair should be comfortable. You should try to minimize distractions while you are studying. You should not study for hours on end. Short study breaks are a good idea.

Before you begin studying, make sure that you have all the materials you need (pencils, markers, calculator, etc.). You may wish to highlight the important points covered in class or in the book.

It is recommended that students study and do homework for at least two hours for each hour of class time. Some students require more time than others. It is important to spread your studying time out over the entire week rather than studying during one large block of time.

When studying, you should not only understand how to work a problem but also know *why* you follow the specific steps you do to work the problem. If you do not have an understanding of why you follow the specific process, you will not be able to transfer the process to solve similar problems.

This book has Mid-Chapter Tests in the middle of each chapter. These exercises reinforce material presented in the first half of the chapter. They will also help you determine if you need to go back and review the topics covered in the first half of the chapter. For any of the Mid-Chapter Test questions that you get incorrect, turn to the section provided with the answers in the back of the book and review that section. This book also has Cumulative Review Exercises at the end of every section after Section 1.2. These exercises reinforce material presented earlier in the course, and you will be less likely to forget the material if you review it repeatedly throughout the course. The exercises will also help prepare you for the final exam. Even if these exercises are not assigned for homework, I urge you to work them as part of your studying process.

3 Prepare for and Take Exams

If you study a little bit each day you should not need to cram the night before an exam. Begin your studying early. If you wait until the last minute, you may not have time to seek the help you may need if you find you cannot work a problem.

To prepare for an exam:

1. Read your class notes.

2. Review your homework assignments.

3. Study formulas, definitions, and procedures you will need for the exam.

4. Read the Avoiding Common Errors boxes and Helpful Hint boxes carefully.

5. Read the summary at the end of each chapter.

6. Work the Chapter Review Exercises at the end of each chapter. If you have difficulties, restudy those sections. If you still have trouble, seek help.

7. Work the Mid-Chapter Test and the Chapter Practice Test.

8. Rework quizzes previously given if the material covered in the quizzes will be included on the test.

9. If your exam is a cumulative exam, work the Cumulative Review Test.

Prepare for Midterm and Final Exam

When studying for a comprehensive midterm or final exam follow the procedures discussed for preparing for an exam. However, also:

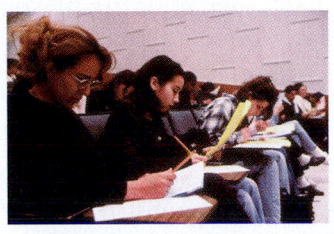

1. Study all your previous tests and quizzes carefully. Make sure that you have learned to work the problems that you may have previously missed.

2. Work the Cumulative Review Tests at the end of each chapter. These tests cover the material from the beginning of the book to the end of that chapter.

3. If your instructor has given you a worksheet or practice exam, make sure that you complete it. Ask questions about any problems you do not understand.

4. Begin your studying process early so that you can seek all the help you need in a timely manner.

Take an Exam

Make sure you get sufficient sleep the night before the test. Arrive at the exam site early so that you have a few minutes to relax before the exam. If you rush into the exam, you will start out nervous and anxious. After you are given the exam, you should do the following:

1. Carefully write down any formulas or ideas that you want to remember.

2. Look over the entire exam quickly to get an idea of its length. Also make sure that no pages are missing.

3. Read the test directions carefully.

4. Read each question carefully. Show all of your work. Answer each question completely, and make sure that you have answered the specific question asked.

5. Work the questions you understand best first; then go back and work those you are not sure of. Do not spend too much time on any one problem or you may not be able to complete the exam. Be prepared to spend more time on problems worth more points.

6. Attempt each problem. You may get at least partial credit even if you do not obtain the correct answer. If you make no attempt at answering the question, you will lose full credit.

7. Work carefully step by step. Copy all signs and exponents correctly when working from step to step, and make sure to copy the original question from the test correctly.

8. Write clearly so that your instructor can read your work. If your instructor cannot read your work, you may lose credit. When appropriate, make sure that your final answer stands out by placing a box around it.

9. If you have time, check your work and your answers.

10. Do not be concerned if others finish the test before you or if you are the last to finish. Use any extra time to check your work.

Stay calm when taking your test. Do not get upset if you come across a problem you can't figure out right away. Go on to something else and come back to that problem later.

4 Learn to Manage Time

As mentioned earlier, it is recommended that students study and do homework for at least two hours for each hour of class time. Finding the necessary time to study is not always easy. The following are some suggestions that you may find helpful.

1. Plan ahead. Determine when you will study and do your homework. Do not schedule other activities for these periods. Try to space these periods evenly over the week.

2. Be organized, so that you will not have to waste time looking for your books, your pencil, your calculator, or your notes.

3. If you are allowed to use a calculator, use it for tedious calculations.

4. When you stop studying, clearly mark where you stopped in the text.

5. Try not to take on added responsibilities. You must set your priorities. If your education is a top priority, as it should be, you may have to reduce time spent on other activities.

6. If time is a problem, do not overburden yourself with too many courses.

Use Supplements

This text comes with a large variety of supplements. Find out from your instructor early in the semester which supplements are available and might be beneficial for you to use. Supplements should not replace reading the text, but should be used to enhance your understanding of the material. If you miss a class, you may want to review the video on the topic you missed before attending the next class.

The supplements available are: the Student Solutions Manual which works out the odd section exercises as well as all the end-of-chapter exercises; the CD Lecture Series Videos, which show about 20 minutes of lecture per section and include the worked out solutions to the exercises marked with this icon ●; the Chapter Test Prep Video CD, which works out every problem in every Chapter Practice Test; *Math XL* MathXL®, a powerful online tutorial and homework system, which is also available on CD; *MyMathLab* MyMathLab, the online course which houses MathXL plus a variety of other supplements; and the Prentice Hall Mathematics Tutor Center, which provides live tutorial support via phone, fax or email.

Seek Help

Be sure to get help as soon as you need it! Do not wait! In mathematics, one day's material is usually based on the previous day's material. So, if you don't understand the material today, you may not be able to understand the material tomorrow.

Where should you seek help? There are often a number of resources on campus. Try to make a friend in the class with whom you can study. Often, you can help one another. You may wish to form a study group with other students in your class. Discussing the concepts and homework with your peers will reinforce your own understanding of the material.

You should know your instructor's office hours, and you should not hesitate to seek help from your instructor when you need it. Make sure you read the assigned material and attempt the homework before meeting with your instructor. Come prepared with specific questions to ask.

There are often other sources of help available. Many colleges have a mathematics lab or a mathematics learning center where tutors are available. Ask your instructor early in the semester where and when tutoring is available. Arrange for a tutor as soon as you need one.

5 Purchase a Calculator

You may wish to purchase a scientific or graphing calculator for this course. Ask your instructor if he or she recommends a particular calculator for this or a future mathematics class. Also ask your instructor if you may use a calculator in class, on homework, and on tests. If so, you should use your calculator whenever possible to save time.

TEACHING TIP
You may want to suggest that students exchange phone numbers or e-mail addresses with a study partner.

TEACHING TIP
You may wish to recommend a type of calculator for students to purchase and a place to purchase one at a good price.

If a calculator contains a LOG key or SIN key, it is a scientific calculator. You *cannot* use the square root key √ to identify scientific calculators since both scientific calculators and nonscientific calculators may have this key. You should pay particular attention to the **Using Your Calculator** boxes in this book. The boxes explain how to use your calculator to solve problems. If you are using a graphing calculator, pay particular attention to the **Using Your Graphing Calculator** boxes. You may also need to use the reference manual that comes with your calculator at various times.

A Final Word

You can be successful at mathematics if you attend class regularly, pay attention in class, study your text carefully, do your homework daily, review regularly, and seek help as soon as you need it. Good luck in your course.

---

14. Read slowly and carefully; do not just skim the text.   **16.** so that you will be able to solve similar types of problems

EXERCISE SET 1.1

MathXL®   MyMathLab

Do you know: **1.–10., 12., 15., 17.** Answers will vary.

1. your professor's name and office hours?

2. your professor's office location and telephone number?

3. where and when you can obtain help if your professor is not available?

4. the name and phone number of a friend in your class?

5. what supplements are available to assist you in learning?

6. if your instructor is recommending the use of a particular calculator?

7. when you can use your calculator in this course?

8. if your instructor is requiring the use of MyMathLab?

If you do not know the answer to questions 1–8, you should find out as soon as possible.

9. What are your goals for this course?

10. What are your reasons for taking this course?

11. List the things you need to do to prepare properly for class.
Do all the homework carefully and completely; preview the new material to be covered in class.

12. Are you beginning this course with a positive attitude? It is important that you do!

13. For each hour of class time, how many hours outside of class are recommended for studying and doing homework?

14. Explain how a mathematics text should be read.

15. Two very important commitments that you must make to be successful in this course are **(a)** doing homework regularly and completely and **(b)** attending class regularly. Explain why these commitments are necessary.

16. When studying, you should not only understand how to work a problem, but also why you follow the specific steps you do. Why is this important?

17. Have you given any thought to studying with a friend or a group of friends? Can you see any advantages in doing so? Can you see any disadvantages in doing so?

18. Write a summary of the steps you should follow when taking an exam.   See page 5.

13. At least 2 hours of study and homework time for each hour of class time is generally recommended.

---

indicates an exercise worked out on the CD Lecture Series Videos.

indicates a writing exercise. That is, an exercise that requires a written answer.

1.2 Problem Solving

1 Learn the five-step problem-solving procedure.

2 Solve problems involving bar, line, and circle graphs.

3 Solve problems involving statistics.

1 Learn the Five-Step Problem-Solving Procedure

One of the main reasons we study mathematics is that we can use it to solve many real-life problems. Throughout the book, we will be problem solving. To solve most real-life problems mathematically, we need to be able to express the problem in mathematical symbols. This is an important part of the problem-solving procedure that we will present shortly. In Chapter 3, we will also spend a great deal of time explaining how to express real-life applications mathematically.

We will now give the general five-step **problem-solving procedure** that was developed by George Polya and presented in his book *How to Solve It*. You can approach any problem by following this general procedure.

George Polya

Guidelines for Problem Solving

1. **Understand the problem.**

   - Read the problem *carefully* at least twice. In the first reading, get a general overview of the problem. In the second reading, determine **(a)** exactly what you are being asked to find and **(b)** what information the problem provides.
   - Make a list of the given facts. Determine which are pertinent to solving the problem.
   - Determine whether you can substitute smaller or simpler numbers to make the problem more understandable.
   - If it will help you organize the information, list the information in a table.
   - If possible, make a sketch to illustrate the problem. Label the information given.

2. **Translate the problem to mathematical language.**

   - This will generally involve expressing the problem in terms of an algebraic expression or equation. (We will explain how to express application problems as equations in Chapter 3.)
   - Determine whether there is a formula that can be used to solve the problem.

3. **Carry out the mathematical calculations necessary to solve the problem.**

4. **Check the answer obtained in step 3.**

   - Ask yourself, "Does the answer make sense?" "Is the answer reasonable?" If the answer is not reasonable, recheck your method for solving the problem and your calculations.
   - Check the solution in the original problem if possible.

5. **Make sure you have answered the question.**

   - State the answer clearly.

In step 2 we use the words *algebraic expression*. An **algebraic expression**, sometimes just referred to as an **expression**, is a general term for any collection of numbers, letters (called variables), grouping symbols such as parentheses ( ) or brackets [ ], and **operations** (such as addition, subtraction, multiplication, and division). In this section we will not be using variables, so we will discuss their use later.

Examples of Expressions

$$3 + 4, \qquad 6(12 \div 3), \qquad (2)(7)$$

The following examples show how to apply the guidelines for problem solving. We will sometimes provide the steps in the examples to illustrate the five-step procedure. However, in some problems it may not be possible or necessary to list every step in the procedure. In some of the examples, we use decimal numbers and percents. If you need to review procedures for adding, subtracting, multiplying, or dividing decimal numbers, or if you need a review of percents, read Appendix A before going on.

EXAMPLE 1 ▶ **Buying Games** Georgia May is deciding which would be less expensive, buying her son's birthday presents on eBay or buying them at a local toy store. Founded in 1995, eBay is The World's Online Marketplace® for the sale of goods and services by a diverse community of individuals and small businesses. The eBay community includes more than 100 million registered members from around the world. The local toy store is only minutes from Georgia's house. Therefore, the cost of gasoline for her car will not factor into her decision. On eBay, the three games Georgia would like to purchase cost $5.99, $9.95, and $19.95. Shipping costs for the games would total $11.10. There would be no sales tax on this purchase. At the local toy store, the total cost for the same three games would be $57.89 plus 8.25% sales tax.

a) Which would be less expensive for Georgia, purchasing the games on eBay or at the local toy store?

b) How much would Georgia save by making the less expensive purchase?

Solution   **a) Understand the problem**   A careful reading of the problem shows that the task is to determine if it would be less expensive for Georgia to purchase the games on eBay or at the local toy store. Make a list of all the information given and determine which information is needed to solve the problem.

Information Given	Pertinent to Solving the Problem?
eBay includes more than 100 million registered members	no
$5.99, $9.95, and $19.95 cost of the games on eBay	yes
$11.10 shipping costs on eBay	yes
no sales tax on the eBay purchase	yes
cost of gasoline not a factor in Georgia's decision	yes
$57.89 cost of the games at the local toy store	yes
8.25% sales tax at the local toy store	yes

To determine if purchasing the games on eBay or at the local toy store would be less expensive, it is not necessary to know that eBay includes more than 100 million registered members. Solving this problem involves calculating the total cost of the games on eBay, including the shipping costs, and calculating the total cost of the games at the local toy store, including the sales tax. To calculate the sales tax, you need to determine 8.25% of the cost of the games at the local toy store. When performing calculations, numbers given in percent are changed to decimal numbers.

Translate the problem into mathematical language

total cost of games on eBay = cost of each individual game + shipping costs

total cost of games at local toy store = total cost of games + 8.25% sales tax

Carry out the calculations

total cost of games on eBay = $5.99 + $9.95 + $19.95 + $11.10 = $46.99

total cost of games at local toy store = $57.89 + 0.0825($57.89)

$$= \$57.89 + \$4.78 = \$62.67$$

Check the answer   The total costs of $46.99 and $62.67 are reasonable based on the information given.

Answer the question asked   It would be less expensive for Georgia to purchase the games on eBay.

b) Understand   To determine how much Georgia would save by making the less expensive purchase, you need to subtract the total cost of the games on eBay from the total cost of the games at the local toy store.

Translate   amount Georgia would save = total cost at toy store − total cost on eBay

Carry Out $62.67 − $46.99 = $15.68

Check   The answer $15.68 seems reasonable.

Answer   Georgia would save $15.68 by purchasing the games on eBay.

▸ **Now Try Exercise 27**

EXAMPLE 2 ▸ **Processor Speed** In November 2004, the fastest Intel processor, the Pentium 4, could perform about 3.8 billion operations per second (3.8 gigahertz, symbolized 3.8 GHz). How many operations could it perform in 0.4 second?

Solution Understand We are given the name of the processor, a speed of about 3.8 billion (3,800,000,000) operations per second, and 0.4 second. To determine the answer to this problem, the name of the processor, Pentium 4, is not needed.

To obtain the answer, will we need to multiply or divide? Often a fairly simple problem seems more difficult because of the numbers involved. When very large or very small numbers make the problem seem confusing, try substituting commonly used numbers in the problem to determine how to solve the problem. Suppose the problem said that the processor can perform 6 operations per second. How many operations can it perform in 2 seconds? The answer to this question should be more obvious. It is 6×2 or 12. Since we multiplied to obtain this answer, we also will need to multiply to obtain the answer to the given problem.

Translate

number of operations in 0.4 second = 0.4(number of operations per second)

Carry Out $= 0.4(3,800,000,000)$

$= 1,520,000,000$ *From a calculator*

Check The answer, 1,520,000,000 operations, is less than the 3,800,000,000 operations per second, which makes sense because the processor is operating for less than a second.

Answer In 0.4 second, the processor can perform about 1,520,000,000 operations.

▸ **Now Try Exercise 21**

TEACHING TIP

Before discussing the solution to Example 2 ask, "How many could it perform in 2 seconds? $\frac{1}{2}$ second? $\frac{1}{4}$ second? $\frac{1}{10}$ second?

Between which 2 numbers should our answer be? Why?

INSTRUCTOR EXAMPLE

If a computer processor can perform 3.2 billion operations per second, how many operations can it perform in 0.3 second?

Ans.: 960,000,000 operations

EXAMPLE 3 ▸ **Medical Insurance** Brook Matthews's medical insurance policy is similar to that of many workers. Her policy requires that she pay the first $100 of medical expenses each calendar year (called a deductible). After the deductible is paid, she pays 20% of the medical expenses (called a co-payment) and the insurance company pays 80%. (There is a maximum co-payment of $600 that she must pay each year. After that, the insurance company pays 100% of the fee schedule.) On January 1, Brook sprained her ankle playing tennis. She went to the doctor's office for an examination and X rays. The total bill of $325 was sent to the insurance company.

a) How much of the bill will Brook be responsible for?

b) How much will the insurance company be responsible for?

Solution   **a)** Understand   First we list all the *relevant* given information.

Given Information

$100 deductible

20% co-payment after deductible

80% paid by insurance company after deductible

$325 doctor bill

All the other information is not needed to solve the problem. Brook will be responsible for the first $100 and 20% of the remaining balance. The insurance company will be responsible for 80% of the balance after the deductible. Before we can find what Brook owes, we need to first find the balance of the bill after the deductible. The balance of the bill after the deductible is $325 − $100 = $225.

Translate

Brook's responsibility = deductible + 20% of balance of bill after the deductible

INSTRUCTOR EXAMPLE

Consider the same situation as in Example 3 with the following change: Brook's total bill of $575 was sent to the insurance company.

a) How much of the bill will Brook be responsible for?

b) How much will the insurance company be responsible for?

Ans.:

a) $195

b) $380

Carry Out

$$\begin{aligned}
\text{Brook's responsibility} &= 100 + 20\%(225) \\
&= 100 + 0.20(225) \\
&= 100 + 45 \\
&= 145
\end{aligned}$$

Check and Answer   The answer appears reasonable. Brook will be responsible for $145.

b) The insurance company will be responsible for 80% of the balance after the deductible.

$$\begin{aligned}
\text{insurance company's responsibility} &= 80\% \text{ of balance after deductible} \\
&= 0.80(225) \\
&= 180
\end{aligned}$$

Thus, the insurance company is responsible for $180. This checks because the sum of Brook's responsibility and the insurance company's responsibility is equal to the doctor's bill.

$$\$145 + \$180 = \$325$$

We could have also found the answer to part **(b)** by subtracting Brook's responsibility from the total amount of the bill, but to give you more practice with percents we decided to show the solution as we did.

▶ **Now Try Exercise 33**

---

2 Solve Problems Involving Bar, Line, and Circle Graphs

Problem solving often involves understanding and reading graphs and sets of data (or numbers). We will be using bar, line, and circle (or pie) graphs and sets of data, throughout the book. We will illustrate a number of such graphs in this section and explain how to interpret them. To work Example 4, you must interpret a bar graph and work with data.

EXAMPLE 4 ▶ **Walking It Off** Experts suggest that people walk 10,000 steps daily. Depending on stride length, each mile ranges between 2000 and 2500 steps. **Figure 1.1** is a bar graph that shows the number of steps it takes to burn off calories from a garden salad with fat-free dressing, a 12-ounce can of soda, a doughnut, and a cheeseburger.

a) Using the bar graph in **Figure 1.1**, estimate the number of steps it takes to burn off calories from a cheeseburger.

b) If Cliff Jackson can walk a mile in 2000 steps, how many miles will he have to walk in order to burn off the calories from the cheeseburger he ate for lunch?

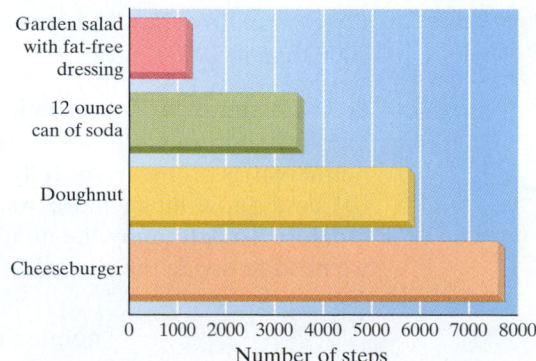

FIGURE 1.1   *Source*: USA Today

Solution   **a)** Using the bar to the right of Cheeseburger in **Figure 1.1**, we estimate that the number of steps it takes to burn off calories from a cheeseburger is about 7600. Notice that we are using the front face of the bar to get our estimate. Whenever we are working with a three-dimensional bar graph, as is the case here, we will use the front face to determine the reading.

b) Understand   Since it takes Cliff 2000 steps to walk a mile, it follows that he would need to take 4000 steps to walk 2 miles, 6000 steps to walk 3 miles, and so on. To determine how many miles Cliff will have to walk in order to burn off the calories from the cheeseburger, we need to divide as follows.

Translate   miles to walk $= \dfrac{\text{number of steps to burn off calories}}{2000}$

Carry Out   miles to walk $= \dfrac{7600}{2000} = 3.8$

Check and Answer   The answer appears reasonable. Cliff will need to walk 3.8 miles in order to burn off the calories from the cheeseburger that he ate for lunch.

▸ **Now Try Exercise 35**

In Example 5, we will use the symbol $\approx$, which is read "**is approximately equal to.**" If, for example, the answer to a problem is 34.12432, we may write the answer as $\approx$34.1.

EXAMPLE 5 ▸   **The Super Bowl**   The **line graph** in **Figure 1.2** shows the cost of a 30-second commercial during Super Bowls from 1997 to 2005. The advertising prices are set by the TV network.

a) Estimate the cost of 30-second commercials in 1997 and 2004.

b) How much more was the cost for a 30-second commercial in 2004 than in 1997?

c) How many times greater was the cost of a 30-second commercial in 2004 than in 1997?

Solution   **a)** When reading a line graph where the line has some thickness, as in **Figure 1.2**, we will use the center of the line to make our estimate. By observing the dashed lines on the graph, we can estimate that the cost of a 30-second commercial was about $1.2 million (or $1,200,000) in 1997 and about $2.3 million (or $2,300,000) in 2004.

b) We use the problem-solving procedure to answer the question.

Understand   To determine how much more the cost of a 30-second commercial was in 2004 than in 1997, we need to subtract.

Translate   difference in cost = cost in 2004 − cost in 1997

Carry Out   = $2,300,000 − $1,200,000 = $1,100,000

Check and Answer   The answer appears reasonable. The cost was $1,100,000 more in 2004 than in 1997.

c) Understand   If you examine parts (b) and (c), they may appear to ask the same question, but they do not. In Section 1.1, we indicated that it is important to read a mathematics problem carefully, word by word. The two parts are different in that part (b) asks "how much more was the cost" whereas part (c) asks "how many <u>times</u> greater." To determine the number of times greater the cost was in 2004 than in 1997, we need to divide the cost in 2004 by the cost in 1997, as shown below.

Translate   number of times greater $= \dfrac{\text{cost in 2004}}{\text{cost in 1997}}$

Super Bowl Commercial Cost

Source: *St. Petersburg Times*

FIGURE 1.2

INSTRUCTOR EXAMPLE

Using the graph in Example 5,
  a) estimate the cost of 30-second commercials in 1999 and 2005.
  b) determine how much more the cost of a 30-second commercial was in 2005 than in 1999.
  c) determine how many times greater the cost of a 30-second commercial was in 2005 than in 1999.

Ans.:
  a) $1.6 million in 1999, $2.4 million in 2005
  b) $800,000
  c) 1.5 times greater

Carry Out

$$\text{number of times greater} = \frac{2{,}300{,}000}{1{,}200{,}000} \approx 1.92$$

Check and Answer   By observing the graph, we see that the answer is reasonable. The cost of a 30-second commercial during the Super Bowl in 2004 was about 1.92 times the cost in 1997.

▶ **Now Try Exercise 37**

EXAMPLE 6 ▶ **Stay-at-Home Parents** The following information was provided in a press release on November 30, 2004, by the U.S. Census Bureau. **Figure 1.3** is a circle graph that shows the reasons why married mothers with children under the age of 15 have stayed out of the labor force for the past year. Use **Figure 1.3** to determine the number of married mothers with children under the age of 15 who have stayed out of the labor force for the following reasons: to care for home and family, ill/disabled, retired, going to school, could not find work, and other.

Reasons for Married Mothers with Children Under Age 15 Staying Out of the Labor Force for the Past Year

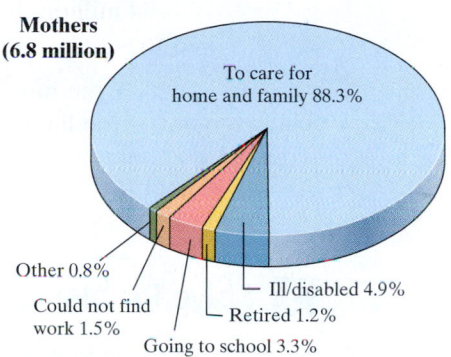

Source: U.S. Census Bureau, Current Population Survey, Annual Social and Economic Supplement, 2003.

FIGURE 1.3

Solution   **Understand**   The circle graph in **Figure 1.3** indicates that there were 6.8 million married mothers with children under the age of 15 who were out of the labor force. Of these mothers, 88.3% were out of the labor force to care for home and family, 4.9% were ill/disabled, 1.2% were retired, 3.3% were going to school, 1.5% could not find work, and 0.8% were out of the labor force for other reasons. The sum of these percents is 100%. (Notice that 88.3% of the total area of the circle indicates to care for home and family, 4.9% indicates ill/disabled, 1.2% indicates retired, 3.3% indicates going to school, 1.5% indicates could not find work, and 0.8% indicates other.) To determine the number of married mothers with children under the age of 15 out of the labor force to care for home and family, we need to find 88.3% of the total number of married mothers with children under the age of 15 who were out of the labor force. To do this, we multiply as follows.

Translate

$$\begin{pmatrix} \text{to care for home} \\ \text{and family} \end{pmatrix} = \begin{pmatrix} \text{percent out of the labor force} \\ \text{to care for home and family} \end{pmatrix} \begin{pmatrix} \text{total number out} \\ \text{of the labor force} \end{pmatrix}$$

Carry Out

$$\text{to care for home and family} = 0.883(6.8 \text{ million})$$

$$= 6.0044 \text{ million}$$

Thus, 6.0044 million married mothers with children under the age of 15 were out of the labor force to care for home and family.

To find the number of married mothers with children under the age of 15 who were out of the labor force for being ill/disabled, we do a similar calculation.

$$\text{ill/disabled} = 0.049(6.8 \text{ million})$$
$$= 0.3332 \text{ million}$$

We do similar calculations to find the number of married mothers with children under the age of 15 who were retired, going to school, could not find work, or for other reasons were out of the labor force.

$$\text{retired} = 0.012(6.8 \text{ million})$$
$$= 0.0816 \text{ million}$$
$$\text{going to school} = 0.033(6.8 \text{ million})$$
$$= 0.2244 \text{ million}$$
$$\text{could not find work} = 0.015(6.8 \text{ million})$$
$$= 0.102 \text{ million}$$
$$\text{other reasons} = 0.008(6.8 \text{ million})$$
$$= 0.0544 \text{ million}$$

Check If we add the six amounts, we obtain the 6.8 million total. Therefore, our answer is correct.

$$6.0044 \text{ million} + 0.3332 \text{ million} + 0.0816 \text{ million} + 0.2244 \text{ million}$$
$$+ 0.102 \text{ million} + 0.0544 \text{ million} = 6.8 \text{ million}$$

Answer In 2003, the number of married mothers with children under the age of 15 who were out of the labor force were as follows: 6.0044 million to care for home and family; 0.3332 million were ill/disabled; 0.0816 million were retired; 0.2244 million were going to school; 0.102 million could not find work; for other reasons, 0.0544 million.

▸ **Now Try Exercise 39**

3 Solve Problems Involving Statistics

Because understanding statistics is so important in our society, we will now discuss certain statistical topics and use them in solving problems.

The *mean* and *median* are two **measures of central tendency**, which are also referred to as *averages*. An average is a value that is representative of a set of data (or numbers). If you take a statistics course you will study these averages in more detail, and you will be introduced to other averages.

The **mean** of a set of data is determined by adding all the values and dividing the sum by the number of values. For example, to find the mean of 6, 9, 3, 12, 12, we do the following.

$$\text{mean} = \frac{6 + 9 + 3 + 12 + 12}{5} = \frac{42}{5} = 8.4$$

We divided the sum by 5 since there are five values. The mean is the most commonly used average and it is generally what is thought of when we use the word *average*.

Another average is the median. The **median** is the value in the middle of a set of **ranked data**. The data may be ranked from smallest to largest or largest to smallest. To find the median of 6, 9, 3, 12, 12, we can rank the data from smallest to largest as follows.

3, 6, 9, 12, 12

↑
Middle value

The value in the middle of the ranked set of data is 9. Therefore, the median is 9. Note that half the values will be above the median and half will be below the median.

If there is an even number of pieces of data, the median is halfway between the two middle pieces. For example, to find the median of 3, 12, 5, 12, 17, 9, we can rank the data as follows.

3, 5, 9, 12, 12, 17

↑
Middle values

Since there are six pieces of data (an even number), we find the value halfway between the two middle pieces, the 9 and the 12. To find the median, we add these values and divide the sum by 2.

$$\text{median} = \frac{9 + 12}{2} = \frac{21}{2} = 10.5$$

Thus, the median is 10.5. Note that half the values are above and half are below 10.5.

EXAMPLE 7 ▸ **The Mean Grade** Alfonso Ramirez's first six exam grades are 90, 87, 76, 84, 78, and 62.

    a) Find the mean for Alfonso's six grades.

    b) If one more exam is to be given, what is the minimum grade that Alfonso can receive to obtain at least a B average (a mean average of 80 or better)?

    c) Is it possible for Alfonso to obtain an A average (90 or better)? Explain.

Solution   **a)** To obtain the mean, we add the six grades and divide by 6.

$$\text{mean} = \frac{90 + 87 + 76 + 84 + 78 + 62}{6} = \frac{477}{6} = 79.5$$

b) We will show the problem-solving steps for this part of the example.

Understand   The answer to this part may be found in a number of ways. For the mean average of seven exams to be 80, the total points for the seven exams must be 7(80) or 560. Can you explain why? The minimum grade needed can be found by subtracting the sum of the first six grades from 560.

Translate   minimum grade needed = 560 − sum of first six exam grades

Carry Out

$$= 560 - (90 + 87 + 76 + 84 + 78 + 62)$$
$$= 560 - 477$$
$$= 83$$

Check   We can check to see that a seventh grade of 83 gives a mean of 80 as follows.

$$\text{mean} = \frac{90 + 87 + 76 + 84 + 78 + 62 + 83}{7} = \frac{560}{7} = 80$$

Answer   A seventh grade of 83 or higher will result in at least a B average.

c) We can use the same reasoning as in part **(b)**. For a 90 average, the total points that Alfonso will need to attain is 90(7) = 630. Since his total points are 477, he will need 630 − 477 or 153 points to obtain an A average. Since the maximum number of points available on most exams is 100, Alfonso would not be able to obtain an A in the course.

▸ **Now Try Exercise 41**

1. understand, translate, calculate, check, state answer   **2.** a collection of numbers, letters, grouping symbols, and operations

EXERCISE SET 1.2

Concept/Writing Exercises

3. is approximately equal to   **4.** substitute smaller or larger numbers   **5.** Rank the data. The median is the value in the middle.   **7.** Divide the sum of the data by the number of pieces of data.

  1. Outline the five-step problem-solving procedure.

  2. What is an expression?

  3. What does the symbol ≈ mean?

  4. If a problem is difficult to solve because the numbers in the problem are very large or very small, what can you do that may help make the problem easier to solve?

  5. Explain how to find the median of a set of data.

  6. What measure of central tendency do we generally think of as "the average"?   the mean

  7. Explain how to find the mean of a set of data.

  8. Consider the set of data 2, 3, 5, 6, 30. Without doing any calculations, can you determine whether the mean or the median is greater? Explain your answer.   mean

9. To get a grade of B, a student must have a mean average of 80. Walter Kirby has a mean average of 79 for 10 quizzes. He approaches his teacher and asks for a B, reasoning that he missed a B by only one point. What is wrong with his reasoning?   missed by 10 points

10. Consider the set of data 3, 3, 3, 4, 4, 4. If one 4 is changed to 5, which of the following will change, the mean and/or the median? Explain.   mean

Practice the Skills

In this exercise set, use a calculator as needed to save time.

11. Test Grades Jenna Webber's test grades are 78, 97, 59, 74, and 74. For Jenna's grades, determine the **(a)** mean and **(b)** median.   **a)** 76.4   **b)** 74

12. Bowling Scores William Krant's bowling scores for five games were 161, 131, 187, 163, and 145. For William's games, determine the **(a)** mean and **(b)** median.   **a)** 157.4   **b)** 161

13. Electric Bills The Malones' electric bills for January through June, 2006, were $96.56, $108.78, $87.23, $85.90, $79.55, and $65.88. For these bills, determine the **(a)** mean and **(b)** median.   **a)** $87.32   **b)** $86.57

14. Grocery Bills Antoinette Payne's monthly grocery bills for the first five months of 2006 were $204.83, $153.85, $210.03, $119.76, and $128.38. For Antoinette's grocery bills, determine the **(a)** mean and **(b)** median.   **a)** $163.37   **b)** $153.85

15. Dry Summers The following figure shows the 10 driest summers in the Southeast from 1895 through 2004. Determine the **(a)** mean and **(b)** median inches of rainfall for the 10 years shown.   **a)** 11.593   **b)** 11.68

Driest Summers in the Southeast

Source: Gloria Forthun, Southeast Regional Climate Center
Records are from 1895 through 2004. The Southeast is Va., N.C., S.C., Ga., Fla., and Ala.

16. Homes for Sale Eight homes are for sale in a community. The sale prices are $124,100, $175,900, $142,300, $164,800, $146,000, $210,000, $112,200, and $153,600. Determine the **(a)** mean and **(b)** median sale price of the eight homes.   **a)** $153,612.50   **b)** $149,800

Problem Solving

17. Commissions Barbara Riedell earns a 5% commission on appliances she sells. Her sales last week totaled $9400. Find her week's earnings. $470

18. Empire State Building May 1, 1931, was the opening day of the Empire State Building. It stands 1454 feet or 443 meters high. Use this information to determine the approximate number of feet in a meter.   ≈3.28

19. Sales Tax a) The sales tax in Jefferson County is 8%. What was the sales tax that Scott Reed paid on a used car that cost $16,700 before tax? $1336

b) What is the total cost of the car including tax? $18,036

20. Checking Account The balance in Debbie Ogilvie's checking account is $312.60. She purchased five DVDs at $17.11 each including tax. If she pays by check, what is the new balance in her checking account? $227.05

21. Computer Processor Suppose a computer processor can perform about 2.3 billion operations per second. How many operations can it perform in 0.7 second?   1,610,000,000 operations

22. Buying a Computer Pat Sullivan wants to purchase a computer that sells for $950. He can either pay the total amount at the time of purchase or agree to pay the store $200 down and $33 per month for 24 months.

a) If he pays the down payment and monthly charge, how much will he pay for the computer? $992

b) How much money can he save by paying the total amount at the time of purchase? $42

23. Energy Values The following table gives the approximate energy values of some foods and the approximate energy consumption of some activities, in kilojoules (kJ). Determine how long it would take for you to use up the energy from the following.

a) a hamburger by running   19.375 min

b) a chocolate milkshake by walking   88 min

c) a glass of skim milk by cycling   10 min

Energy Value, Food	(kJ)	Energy Consumption, Activity	(kJ/min)
Chocolate milkshake	2200	Walking	25
Fried egg	460	Cycling	35
Hamburger	1550	Swimming	50
Strawberry shortcake	1440	Running	80
Glass of skim milk	350		

See Exercise 23.b)

A green numbered exercise, such as **21.** indicates a Now Try Exercise.

32. b) ≈1.47 feet per second   c) 88 feet per second   33. b) $172

24. **Jet Ski** The rental cost of a jet ski from Don's Ski Rental is $20 per half-hour, and the rental cost from A. J.'s Ski Rental is $50 per hour. Suppose you plan to rent a jet ski for 3 hours.

   a) Which is the better deal?   Don's

   b) How much will you save? $30

 25. **Gas Mileage** When the odometer in Tribet LaPierre's car reads 16,741.3, he fills his gas tank. The next time he fills his tank it takes 10.5 gallons, and his odometer reads 16,935.4. Determine the number of miles per gallon that his car gets.   ≈18.49 mpg

26. **Income Taxes** The federal income tax rate schedule for a *joint return* in 2005 is illustrated in the following table.

Adjusted Gross Income	Taxes
$0–$14,600	10% of income
$14,600–$59,400	$1460.00 + 15% in excess of $14,600
$59,400–$119,950	$8180.00 + 25% in excess of $59,400
$119,950–$182,800	$23,317.50 + 28% in excess of $119,950
$182,800–$326,450	$40,915.50 + 33% in excess of $182,800
$326,450 and up	$88,320.00 + 35% in excess of $326,450

Source: www.irs.gov

   a) If the Donovins' adjusted gross income in 2005 was $34,612 determine their taxes. $4461.80

   b) If the Ortegas' 2005 adjusted gross income was $75,610 determine their taxes. $12,232.50

27. **Buying Tires** Eric Weiss purchased four tires through the Internet. He paid $62.30 plus $6.20 shipping and handling per tire. There was no sales tax on this purchase. When he received the tires, Eric had to pay $8.00 per tire for mounting and balancing. At a local tire store, his total cost for the four tires with mounting and balancing would have been $425 plus 8% sales tax. How much did Eric save by purchasing the tires through the Internet? $153

28. **Baseball Salaries** Manny Ramirez, of the Boston Red Sox, was the highest paid professional baseball player in 2004, earning $22.5 million. Pedro Martinez, also of the Boston Red Sox, was the highest paid pitcher, earning $17.5 million. In 2004, Ramirez batted 568 times and Martinez pitched 217 innings. Determine approximately how much more Martinez received per inning pitched than Ramirez did per at bat.   ≈$41,032.49

29. **Balance** Consider the figure shown. Assuming the green and red blocks have the same weight, where should a single green block, ▮, be placed to make the scale balanced? Explain how you determined your answer.   on the 3 on the right

30. **Taxi Ride** A taxicab charges $2 upon a customer's entering the taxi, then 30 cents for each $\frac{1}{4}$ mile traveled and 20 cents for each 30 seconds stopped in traffic. David Lopez takes a taxi ride for a distance of 3 miles where the taxi spends 90 seconds stopped in traffic. Determine David's cost of the taxi ride. $6.20

31. **Leaky Faucet** A faucet that leaks 1 ounce of water per minute wastes 11.25 gallons in a day.

   a) How many gallons of water are wasted in a (non-leap) year?   4106.25 gal

   b) If water costs $5.20 per 1000 gallons, how much additional money per year is being spent on the water bill?   ≈$21.35

32. **Conversions a)** What is 1 mile per hour equal to in feet per hour? One mile contains 5280 feet.   5280 feet per hour

   b) What is 1 mile per hour equal to in feet per second?

   c) What is 60 miles per hour equal to in feet per second?

33. **Medical Insurance** Mel LeBar's medical insurance policy requires that he pay a $150 deductible each calendar year. After the deductible is paid, he pays 20% of the medical expenses and the insurance company pays 80%. On January 1, Mel's daughter accidentally closed the car door on his finger. He went to the doctor's office for an examination and X rays. The total bill of $365 was sent to the insurance company. If Mel had not as yet paid any of the deductible,

   a) how much of the bill will Mel be responsible for? $193

   b) how much will the insurance company be responsible for?

34. **Insurance** Drivers under the age of 25 who pass a driver education course generally have their auto insurance premium decreased by 10%. Most insurers will offer this 10% deduction until the driver reaches 25. A particular driver education course costs $70. Don Beville, who just turned 18, has auto insurance that costs $630 per year.

   a) Excluding the cost of the driver education course, how much would Don save in auto insurance premiums, from the age of 18 until the age of 25, by taking the driver education course? $441

   b) What would be his net savings after the cost of the course? $371

35. **Math Scores** The bar graph below shows some 2003 scores from the Program for International Student Assessment, a test for 15-year-olds. The scale was constructed so that an average score is 500.

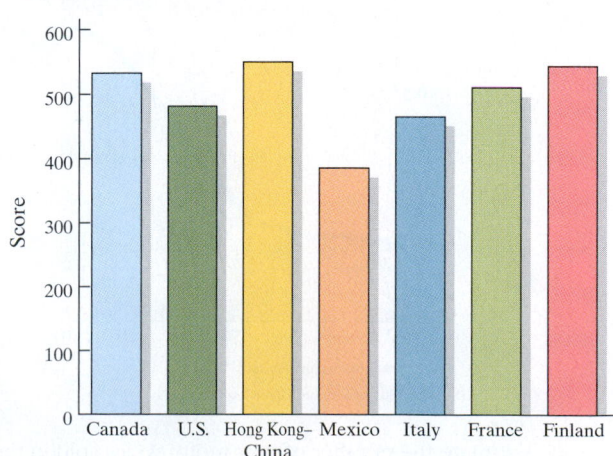

Math Scores

Source: New York Times

a) Which country had the highest math score shown? Estimate the score.   Hong Kong-China; 550

b) Which country had the lowest math scores shown? Estimate the score.   Mexico; 385

c) Estimate the difference between the scores for Hong Kong–China and Mexico.   165

36. **Commercial Airlines** The bar graph shows the total scheduled passengers on U.S. commercial airlines from 1999 to 2004 with the forecasted totals through 2016. From the bar graph, estimate

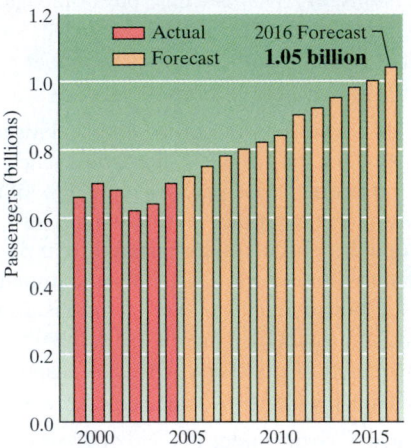

Total Scheduled Passengers on U.S. Commercial Airlines

Note: Data are for fiscal years beginning in October; 2004 figure is an estimate

Source: Federal Aviation Administration

a) the total number of scheduled passengers on U.S. commercial airlines in 2000.   0.7 billion

b) the forecasted total number of scheduled passengers on U.S. commercial airlines in 2015.   1.0 billion

c) how many times greater is the forecasted total number of scheduled passengers on U.S. commercial airlines in 2015 than in 2000?   ≈1.43 times greater

37. **Motorcycle Sales** The line graph below shows the U.S. sales of new motorcycles from 1992 to 2004.

U.S. Sales of New Motorcycles

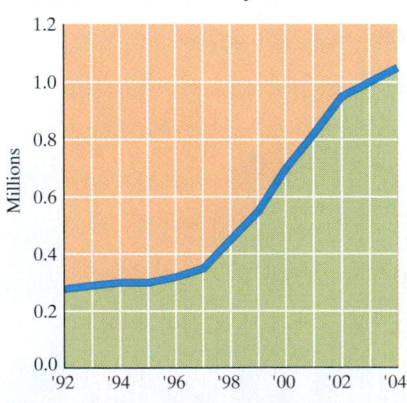

Note: 2004 figure is an estimate.

Source: Motorcycle Industry Council

a) Estimate the number of new motorcycles sold in the U.S. in 1992 and in 2004.   0.275 million or 275,000; 1.05 million or 1,050,000

b) How many more new motorcycles were sold in the U.S. in 2004 than in 1992?   0.775 million or 775,000

c) How many times greater was the number of new motorcycles sold in 2004 than in 1992?   ≈3.82 times greater

38. **NBA Draft** The line graph below shows the number of high school students selected in the NBA draft's first round from 1995 to 2004.

a) During which consecutive years did the number of high school students selected in the NBA draft's first round remain constant?   1997–1998 and 1999–2000

During which consecutive years did the number of high school students selected in the NBA draft's first round

b) increase the most?   2003–2004

c) decrease the most?   2001–2002

High School Students Selected in the NBA Draft's First Round from 1995–2004

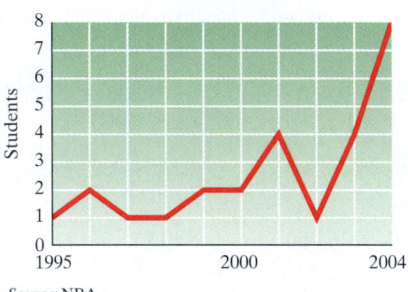

Source: NBA

39. **Adoption** The following information was provided by *www.census.gov*. In 2004, approximately 1.7 million U.S. households contained adopted children. The circle graph below shows the percent of these households that had one adopted child, two adopted children, and three or more adopted children. Estimate the number of U.S. households in 2004 that had

a) one adopted child.   1.394 million

b) two adopted children.   0.255 million

c) three or more adopted children.   0.051 million

U.S. Households with Adopted Children (1.7 million households)

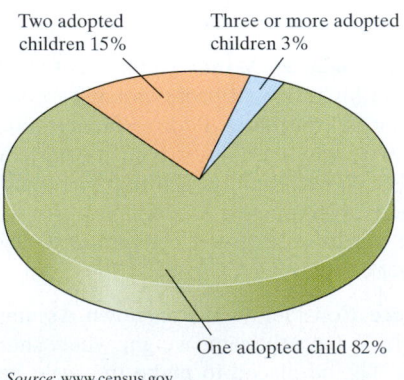

Two adopted children 15%

Three or more adopted children 3%

One adopted child 82%

Source: www.census.gov

40. **Jeopardy!** As of this writing, Ken Jennings, a software engineer from Salt Lake City, Utah, is the record holder for the most money ever won on a television game show. The circle graph on the next page shows the outcome of the 160 Daily

Doubles that Ken attempted on his *Jeopardy!* run. Use the circle graph to determine

a) the number of Daily Doubles Ken answered correctly. 133

b) the number of Daily Doubles Ken answered incorrectly. 27

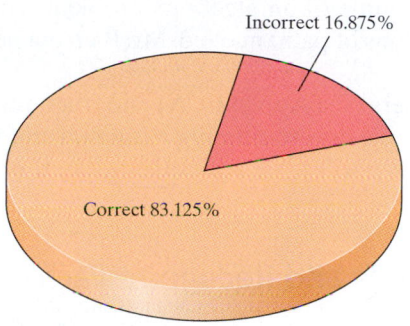

**Ken Jennings's Jeopardy Daily Doubles
(160 Total)**

Incorrect 16.875%

Correct 83.125%

Source: www.tvgameshows.net/jenningswinnings.htm

41. Test Grades A mean of 60 on all exams is needed to pass a course. On his first five exams Lamond Paine's grades are 50, 59, 67, 80, and 56.

a) What is the minimum grade that Lamond can receive on the sixth exam to pass the course? 48

b) An average of 70 is needed to get a C in the course. Is it possible for Lamond to get a C? If so, what is the minimum grade that Lamond can receive on the sixth exam? no

42. Test Grades A mean of 80 on all exams is needed to earn a B in a course. On her first four exams, Heather Feldman's grades are 95, 88, 82, and 85.

a) What is the minimum grade that Heather can receive on the fifth exam to earn a B in the course? 50

b) A mean of 90 is needed to earn an A in the course. Is it possible for Heather to get an A? If so, what is the minimum grade that Heather can receive on the fifth exam? yes; 100

43. Level of Education The following bar graph shows the median annual earnings by level of education in 2003 in the United States. Which degree has median annual earnings that are approximately 2.3 times the median annual earnings of someone with less than a high school diploma? Bachelor's degree

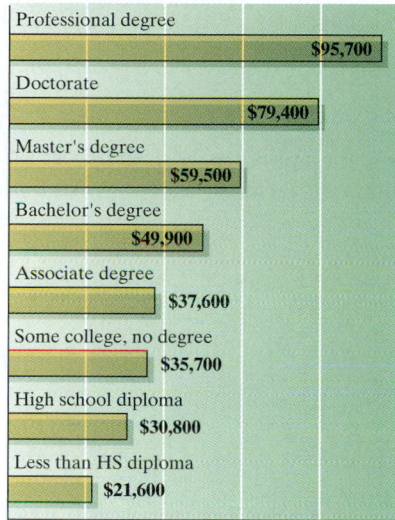

**Median Annual Earnings
by Level of Education**

Professional degree	$95,700
Doctorate	$79,400
Master's degree	$59,500
Bachelor's degree	$49,900
Associate degree	$37,600
Some college, no degree	$35,700
High school diploma	$30,800
Less than HS diploma	$21,600

Sources: College Board,
U.S. Census Bureau (2003 data)

44. Exams Mike Ambrosino's mean average on six exams is 78. Find the sum of his scores. 468

45. Construct Data Construct a set of five pieces of data with a mean of 70 and no two values the same. One example is 50, 60, 70, 80, 90

Challenge Problem

46. Reading Meters The figure shows how to read an electric (or gas) meter.

Step 1. Start with the dial on the right. If the arrow falls between two numbers, use the smaller number on the dial (except when the dial is between 9 and 0, then use the 9). Notice the arrows above the meters indicate the direction the dial is moving (clockwise, then counterclockwise).

Step 2. If the pointer is directly on a number, check the dial to the *right* to make sure it has passed 0 and is headed toward 1. If the dial to the right has not passed 0, use the next lower number. The number on the meters on the right is 16064.

1   6   0   6   4

Source: Southern California Edison, Understanding Your Electricity Bill

Suppose your previous month's reading was as shown on the previous page, and this month's meter reading is as shown below.

a) Determine this month's meter reading. 16504

b) Determine your electrical cost for this month by first subtracting last month's meter reading from this month's meter reading (measured in kilowatt hours), and then multiplying the difference by the cost per kilowatt hour of electricity. Assume electricity costs 24.3 cents per kilowatt hour. ≈$106.92

1.3 Fractions

1 Learn multiplication symbols and recognize factors.

2 Simplify fractions.

3 Multiply fractions.

4 Divide fractions.

5 Add and subtract fractions.

6 Change mixed numbers to fractions and vice versa.

Students taking algebra for the first time often ask, "What is the difference between arithmetic and algebra?" When doing arithmetic, all the quantities used in the calculations are known. In algebra, however, one or more of the quantities are unknown and must be found. Consider the following:

Mr. Piersma has 1 gallon of paint. In order to paint his bedroom, he needs 3 gallons of paint. How many additional gallons does he need?

Although elementary, this is an example of an algebraic problem. The unknown quantity is the number of additional gallons of paint needed. Mr. Piersma needs 2 more gallons of paint.

An understanding of decimal numbers (see Appendix A) and fractions is essential to success in algebra. You will need to know how to simplify a fraction and how to add, subtract, multiply, and divide fractions. We will review these topics in this section. We will also explain the meaning of factors.

1 Learn Multiplication Symbols and Recognize Factors

In algebra we often use letters called **variables** to represent numbers. Letters commonly used as variables are x, y, and z, but other letters can be used as variables. Variables are usually shown in italics. So that we do not confuse the variable x with the multiplication sign, we often use different notation to indicate multiplication.

Multiplication Symbols

If a and b represent any two mathematical quantities, then each of the following may be used to indicate the product of a and b ("a times b").

$$ab \quad a \cdot b \quad a(b) \quad (a)b \quad (a)(b)$$

EXAMPLES

3 times 4 may be written:	3 times x may be written:	x times y may be written:
	$3x$	xy
3(4)	3(x)	x(y)
(3)4	(3)x	(x)y
(3)(4)	(3)(x)	(x)(y)

Now we will introduce the term *factors*, which we shall be using throughout the text. Below we define factors.

Factors

The numbers or variables that are multiplied in a multiplication problem are called **factors**.

If $a \cdot b = c$, then a and b are *factors* of c.

For example, in $3 \cdot 5 = 15$, the numbers 3 and 5 are factors of the product 15. In $2 \cdot 15 = 30$, the numbers 2 and 15 are factors of the product 30. Note that 30 has many other factors. Since $5 \cdot 6 = 30$, the numbers 5 and 6 are also factors of 30. Since $3x$ means 3 times x, both the 3 and the x are factors of $3x$.

2 Simplify Fractions

Now we have the necessary information to discuss **fractions**. The top number of a fraction is called the **numerator**, and the bottom number is called the **denominator**. In the fraction $\frac{3}{5}$, the 3 is the numerator and the 5 is the denominator.

Helpful Hint

Consider the fraction $\frac{3}{5}$. There are equivalent methods of expressing this fraction, as illustrated below.

$$\frac{3}{5} = 3 \div 5 = 5\overline{)3}$$

In general, $\frac{a}{b} = a \div b = b\overline{)a}$

Now we will discuss how to simplify a fraction.

A fraction is **simplified** (or **reduced to its lowest terms**) when the numerator and denominator have no common factors other than 1. To simplify a fraction, follow these steps.

To Simplify a Fraction

1. Find the largest number that will divide (without remainder) both the numerator and the denominator. This number is called the **greatest common factor** (GCF).

2. Then divide both the numerator and the denominator by the greatest common factor.

If you do not remember how to find the greatest common factor of two or more numbers, read Appendix B.

EXAMPLE 1 ▶ Simplify   **a)** $\frac{10}{25}$ **b)** $\frac{6}{18}$.

INSTRUCTOR EXAMPLE

Simplify $\frac{24}{28}$.

Ans.: $\frac{6}{7}$

Solution

a) The largest number that divides both 10 and 25 is 5. Therefore, 5 is the greatest common factor. Divide both the numerator and the denominator by 5 to simplify the fraction.

$$\frac{10}{25} = \frac{10 \div 5}{25 \div 5} = \frac{2}{5}$$

b) Both 6 and 18 can be divided by 1, 2, 3, and 6. The largest of these numbers, 6, is the greatest common factor. Divide both the numerator and the denominator by 6.

$$\frac{6}{18} = \frac{6 \div 6}{18 \div 6} = \frac{1}{3}$$

Note in Example **1b)** that both the numerator and denominator could have been written with a factor of 6. Then the common factor 6 could be divided out.

$$\frac{6}{18} = \frac{1 \cdot \cancel{6}}{3 \cdot \cancel{6}} = \frac{1}{3}$$

▶ **Now Try Exercise 23**

When you work with fractions you should simplify your answers.

3 Multiply Fractions

To multiply two or more fractions, multiply their numerators together and multiply their denominators together.

To Multiply Fractions

$$\frac{a}{b} \cdot \frac{c}{d} = \frac{ac}{bd}$$

EXAMPLE 2 ▶ Multiply $\frac{3}{13}$ by $\frac{5}{11}$.

Solution $\frac{3}{13} \cdot \frac{5}{11} = \frac{3 \cdot 5}{13 \cdot 11} = \frac{15}{143}$

▶ **Now Try Exercise 51**

Before multiplying fractions, to help avoid having to simplify an answer, we often divide both a numerator and a denominator by a common factor.

EXAMPLE 3 ▶ Multiply   **a)** $\frac{8}{17} \cdot \frac{5}{16}$ **b)** $\frac{27}{40} \cdot \frac{16}{9}$.

Solution

a) Since the numerator 8 and the denominator 16 can both be divided by the common factor 8, we divide out the 8 first. Then we multiply.

$$\frac{8}{17} \cdot \frac{5}{16} = \frac{\overset{1}{\cancel{8}}}{17} \cdot \frac{5}{\underset{2}{\cancel{16}}} = \frac{1 \cdot 5}{17 \cdot 2} = \frac{5}{34}$$

b)

$$\frac{27}{40} \cdot \frac{16}{9} = \frac{\overset{3}{\cancel{27}}}{40} \cdot \frac{16}{\underset{1}{\cancel{9}}}$$ *Divide both 27 and 9 by 9.*

$$= \frac{\overset{3}{\cancel{27}}}{\underset{5}{\cancel{40}}} \cdot \frac{\overset{2}{\cancel{16}}}{\underset{1}{\cancel{9}}}$$ *Divide both 40 and 16 by 8.*

$$= \frac{3 \cdot 2}{5 \cdot 1} = \frac{6}{5}$$

▶ **Now Try Exercise 53**

The numbers 0, 1, 2, 3, 4, . . . are called **whole numbers**. The three dots after the 4 which is called an *ellipsis*, indicate that the whole numbers continue indefinitely in the same manner. Thus, the numbers 468 and 5043 are also whole numbers. Whole numbers will be discussed further in Section 1.4. To multiply a whole number by a fraction, write the whole number with a denominator of 1 and then multiply.

EXAMPLE 4 ▶ **Lawn Mower Engine** Some engines run on a mixture of gas and oil. A particular lawn mower engine requires a mixture of $\frac{5}{64}$ gallon of oil for each gallon of gasoline used. A lawn care company wishes to make a mixture for this engine using 12 gallons of gasoline. How much oil must be used?

Solution   We must multiply 12 by $\frac{5}{64}$ to determine the amount of oil that must be used. First we write 12 as $\frac{12}{1}$, then we divide both 12 and 64 by their greatest common factor, 4, as follows.

$$12 \cdot \frac{5}{64} = \frac{12}{1} \cdot \frac{5}{64} = \frac{\overset{3}{\cancel{12}}}{1} \cdot \frac{5}{\underset{16}{\cancel{64}}} = \frac{3 \cdot 5}{1 \cdot 16} = \frac{15}{16}$$

Thus, $\frac{15}{16}$ gallon of oil must be added to the 12 gallons of gasoline to make the proper mixture.

▶ **Now Try Exercise 101**

4 Divide Fractions

To divide one fraction by another, invert the divisor (the second fraction if written with ÷) and proceed as in multiplication.

To Divide Fractions

$$\frac{a}{b} \div \frac{c}{d} = \frac{a}{b} \cdot \frac{d}{c} = \frac{ad}{bc}$$

Sometimes, rather than being asked to obtain the answer to a problem by adding, subtracting, multiplying, or dividing, you may be asked to evaluate an expression. To **evaluate** an expression means to obtain the answer to the problem using the operations given.

INSTRUCTOR EXAMPLE

Evaluate $\frac{4}{7} \div \frac{7}{8}$.

Ans.: $\frac{32}{49}$

EXAMPLE 5 ▶ Evaluate **a)** $\frac{3}{5} \div \frac{5}{6}$ **b)** $\frac{3}{8} \div 12$.

Solution

a) $\frac{3}{5} \div \frac{5}{6} = \frac{3}{5} \cdot \frac{6}{5} = \frac{3 \cdot 6}{5 \cdot 5} = \frac{18}{25}$

b) Write 12 as $\frac{12}{1}$. Then invert the divisor and multiply.

$$\frac{3}{8} \div 12 = \frac{3}{8} \div \frac{12}{1} = \frac{\overset{1}{\cancel{3}}}{8} \cdot \frac{1}{\underset{4}{\cancel{12}}} = \frac{1}{32}$$

▶ **Now Try Exercise 59**

5 Add and Subtract Fractions

Fractions that have the same (or a common) *denominator can be added or subtracted.* To add (or subtract) fractions with the same denominator, add (or subtract) the numerators and keep the common denominator.

To Add and Subtract Fractions

$$\frac{a}{c} + \frac{b}{c} = \frac{a+b}{c} \quad \text{or} \quad \frac{a}{c} - \frac{b}{c} = \frac{a-b}{c}$$

INSTRUCTOR EXAMPLE

a) Add $\frac{6}{8} + \frac{1}{8}$.

b) Subtract $\frac{10}{17} - \frac{5}{17}$.

Ans.:

a) $\frac{7}{8}$

b) $\frac{5}{17}$

EXAMPLE 6 ▶ **a)** Add $\frac{6}{15} + \frac{2}{15}$.   **b)** Subtract $\frac{8}{13} - \frac{5}{13}$.

Solution **a)** $\frac{6}{15} + \frac{2}{15} = \frac{6+2}{15} = \frac{8}{15}$ **b)** $\frac{8}{13} - \frac{5}{13} = \frac{8-5}{13} = \frac{3}{13}$

▶ **Now Try Exercise 67**

To add (or subtract) fractions with unlike denominators, we must first rewrite each fraction with the same, or a common, denominator. The smallest number that is divisible by two or more denominators is called the **least common denominator** or **LCD**. *If you have forgotten how to find the least common denominator review Appendix B now.*

EXAMPLE 7 ▶ Add $\frac{1}{2} + \frac{1}{5}$.

Solution   We cannot add these fractions until we rewrite them with a common denominator. Since the lowest number that both 2 and 5 divide into (without remainder) is 10, we will first rewrite both fractions with the least common denominator of 10.

$$\frac{1}{2} = \frac{1}{2} \cdot \frac{5}{5} = \frac{5}{10} \quad \text{and} \quad \frac{1}{5} = \frac{1}{5} \cdot \frac{2}{2} = \frac{2}{10}$$

Now we add.

$$\frac{1}{2} + \frac{1}{5} = \frac{5}{10} + \frac{2}{10} = \frac{7}{10}$$

▶ **Now Try Exercise 75**

Note that multiplying both the numerator and denominator by the same number is the same as multiplying by 1. Thus, the value of the fraction does not change.

EXAMPLE 8 ▶ How much larger is $\frac{3}{4}$ inch than $\frac{2}{3}$ inch?

Solution   To find the difference, we need to subtract $\frac{2}{3}$ inch from $\frac{3}{4}$ inch.

$$\frac{3}{4} - \frac{2}{3}$$

The least common denominator is 12. Therefore, we rewrite both fractions with a denominator of 12.

$$\frac{3}{4} = \frac{3}{4} \cdot \frac{3}{3} = \frac{9}{12} \quad \text{and} \quad \frac{2}{3} = \frac{2}{3} \cdot \frac{4}{4} = \frac{8}{12}$$

Now we subtract.

$$\frac{3}{4} - \frac{2}{3} = \frac{9}{12} - \frac{8}{12} = \frac{1}{12}$$

Thus, $\frac{3}{4}$ inch is $\frac{1}{12}$ inch greater than $\frac{2}{3}$ inch.

▶ **Now Try Exercise 87**

Avoiding Common Errors

It is important to remember that dividing out a common factor in the numerator of one fraction and the denominator of a different fraction can be performed only when multiplying fractions. *This process cannot be performed when adding or subtracting fractions.*

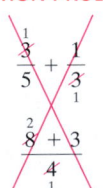

CORRECT	INCORRECT
MULTIPLICATION PROBLEMS	ADDITION PROBLEMS

---

6 **Change Mixed Numbers to Fractions and Vice Versa**

Consider the number $5\frac{2}{3}$. This is an example of a **mixed number**. A mixed number consists of a whole number followed by a fraction. The mixed number $5\frac{2}{3}$ means $5 + \frac{2}{3}$. We can change $5\frac{2}{3}$ to a fraction as follows.

$$5\frac{2}{3} = 5 + \frac{2}{3} = \frac{15}{3} + \frac{2}{3} = \frac{15 + 2}{3} = \frac{17}{3}$$

Notice that we expressed the whole number, 5, as a fraction with a denominator of 3, then added the fractions.

INSTRUCTOR EXAMPLE

Change $6\frac{5}{7}$ to a fraction.

Ans.: $\frac{47}{7}$

EXAMPLE 9 ▶ Change $7\frac{3}{8}$ to a fraction.

Solution $$7\frac{3}{8} = \boxed{7} + \frac{3}{8} = \boxed{\frac{56}{8}} + \frac{3}{8} = \frac{56 + 3}{8} = \frac{59}{8}$$

▶ **Now Try Exercise 37**

Now consider the fraction $\frac{17}{3}$. This fraction can be converted to a mixed number as follows.

$$\frac{17}{3} = \boxed{\frac{15}{3}} + \frac{2}{3} = \boxed{5} + \frac{2}{3} = 5\frac{2}{3}$$

Notice we wrote $\frac{17}{3}$ as a sum of two fractions, each with the denominator of 3. The first fraction being added, $\frac{15}{3}$, is the equivalent of the largest integer that is less than $\frac{17}{3}$.

INSTRUCTOR EXAMPLE

Change $\frac{63}{8}$ to a mixed number.

Ans.: $7\frac{7}{8}$

EXAMPLE 10 ▶ Change $\frac{43}{6}$ to a mixed number.

Solution $$\frac{43}{6} = \boxed{\frac{42}{6}} + \frac{1}{6} = \boxed{7} + \frac{1}{6} = 7\frac{1}{6}$$

▶ **Now Try Exercise 43**

TEACHING TIP
You may wish to teach your students that $43 \div 6 = 7$, remainder 1, and $\frac{43}{6} = 7\frac{1}{6}$.

Helpful Hint

Notice in Example 10 the fraction $\frac{43}{6}$ is simplified because the greatest common divisor of the numerator and denominator is 1. Do not confuse simplifying a fraction with changing a fraction with a value greater than 1 to a mixed number. The fraction $\frac{43}{6}$ can be converted to the mixed number $7\frac{1}{6}$. However, $\frac{43}{6}$ is a simplified fraction.

Now we will work examples that contain mixed numbers.

EXAMPLE 11 ▶ **Plumbing** To repair a plumbing leak, a coupling $\frac{1}{2}$ inch long is glued to a piece of plastic pipe. After the gluing, the piece of plastic pipe showing is $2\frac{9}{16}$ inches, as shown in **Figure 1.4**. How long is the combined length?

Solution **Understand and Translate** We need to add $2\frac{9}{16}$ inches and $\frac{1}{2}$ inch to obtain the combined lengths. We will place the two numbers one above the other. After we write both fractions with a common denominator, we add the numbers.

FIGURE 1.4

Carry Out

$$\begin{array}{r} 2\frac{9}{16} \\ + \frac{1}{2} \\ \hline \end{array} \quad \rightarrow \quad \begin{array}{r} 2\frac{9}{16} \\ + \frac{8}{16} \\ \hline 2\frac{17}{16} \end{array}$$

Since $2\frac{17}{16} = 2 + \frac{17}{16} = 2 + 1\frac{1}{16} = 3\frac{1}{16}$, the sum is $3\frac{1}{16}$.

Check and Answer The answer appears reasonable. Thus, the total length is $3\frac{1}{16}$ inches.

▶ **Now Try Exercise 105**

INSTRUCTOR EXAMPLE

If $6\frac{2}{3}$ feet of fencing is added to a $50\frac{3}{4}$-foot-long fence, how long is the new length?

Ans.: $57\frac{5}{12}$ ft

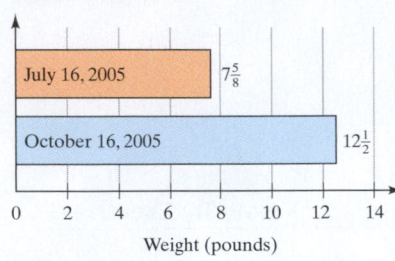

Jonathan's Growth

July 16, 2005 $7\frac{5}{8}$

October 16, 2005 $12\frac{1}{2}$

Weight (pounds)

FIGURE 1.5

EXAMPLE 12 ▶ Gaining Weight The graph in **Figure 1.5** shows the weight of the Seeburgers' baby boy, Jonathan, on July 16, 2005, and on October 16, 2005. How much weight had Jonathan gained during this time period?

Solution   Understand and Translate   To find the increase, we need to subtract Jonathan's weight on July 16, 2005, from his weight on October 16, 2005. We will subtract vertically.

Carry Out

$$
\begin{array}{r}
12\frac{1}{2} \\
-\ 7\frac{5}{8} \\
\hline
\end{array}
\qquad \rightarrow \qquad
\begin{array}{r}
12\frac{4}{8} \\
-\ 7\frac{5}{8} \\
\hline
\end{array}
$$

Since we wish to subtract $\frac{5}{8}$ from $\frac{4}{8}$, and $\frac{5}{8}$ is greater than $\frac{4}{8}$, we write $12\frac{4}{8}$ as $11\frac{12}{8}$.

To get $11\frac{12}{8}$, we take 1 unit from the number 12 and write it as $\frac{8}{8}$. This gives

$11 + 1 + \frac{4}{8} = 11 + \frac{8}{8} + \frac{4}{8} = 11 + \frac{12}{8} = 11\frac{12}{8}$. Now we subtract as follows.

$$
\begin{array}{r}
12\frac{1}{2} \\
-\ 7\frac{5}{8} \\
\hline
\end{array}
\rightarrow
\begin{array}{r}
12\frac{4}{8} \\
-\ 7\frac{5}{8} \\
\hline
\end{array}
\rightarrow
\begin{array}{r}
11\frac{12}{8} \\
-\ 7\frac{5}{8} \\
\hline
4\frac{7}{8}
\end{array}
$$

Check and Answer   By examining the graph, we see that the answer is reasonable. Thus, Jonathan gained $4\frac{7}{8}$ pounds during this time period.

▶ **Now Try Exercise 97**

Although it is not necessary to change mixed numbers to fractions when adding or subtracting mixed numbers, it is necessary to change mixed numbers to fractions when multiplying or dividing mixed numbers. We illustrate this procedure in Example 13.

EXAMPLE 13 ▶ Cutting Wood A carpenter is cutting a rectangular piece of wood 4 feet wide by $10\frac{2}{3}$ feet long into four equal strips, as shown in **Figure 1.6**. Find the dimensions of each strip.

Solution   Understand and Translate   We know from **Figure 1.6** that one side will have a width of 4 feet. To find the length of the strips, we need to divide $10\frac{2}{3}$ by 4.

Carry Out

$$10\frac{2}{3} \div 4 = \frac{32}{3} \div \frac{4}{1} = \frac{\overset{8}{\cancel{32}}}{3} \cdot \frac{1}{\underset{1}{\cancel{4}}} = \frac{8}{3} = 2\frac{2}{3}$$

Check and Answer   If you multiply $2\frac{2}{3}$ by 4 you obtain the original length, $10\frac{2}{3}$.

Thus, the calculation is correct. The dimensions of each strip will be 4 feet by $2\frac{2}{3}$ feet.

▶ **Now Try Exercise 99**

4 ft

$10\frac{2}{3}$ ft

FIGURE 1.6

EXERCISE SET 1.3

Concept/Writing Exercises

4. $5(x)$, $(5)x$, $(5)(x)$, $5x$, $5 \cdot x$ **5.** Divide out the common factors.   **6. b)** numbers continue in the same manner   **7. a)** the smallest number divisible by the two denominators

1. a) What are variables?   letters that represent numbers
   b) What letters are often used to represent variables? x, y, z

2. What are factors?   numbers or variables that are multiplied together

3. In a fraction, what is the name of the **a)** top number and **b)** bottom number?   **a)** numerator   **b)** denominator

4. Show five different ways that "5 times x" may be written.

5. Explain how to simplify a fraction.

6. a) What are the three dots in $4, 5, 6, 7, \ldots$ called?   ellipsis
   b) What do the three dots following the 7 mean?

7. a) What is the least common denominator of two or more fractions?
   b) Write two fractions and then give the LCD of the two fractions you wrote.   Answers will vary.

8. What is the LCD of the fractions $\frac{3}{8}$ and $\frac{7}{10}$? Explain.   40

In Exercises 9 and 10, which part a) or b) shows simplifying a fraction? Explain.

9. a) $\frac{\overset{1}{\cancel{2}}}{5} \cdot \frac{1}{\underset{2}{\cancel{4}}}$ **b)** $\frac{\overset{1}{\cancel{2}}}{\underset{2}{\cancel{4}}}$ b)

10. a) $\frac{\overset{1}{\cancel{4}}}{\underset{3}{\cancel{12}}}$ **b)** $\frac{7}{\underset{3}{\cancel{12}}} \cdot \frac{\overset{1}{\cancel{4}}}{5}$ a)

In Exercises 11 and 12, one of the procedures a) or b) is incorrect. Determine which is the incorrect procedure and explain why.

11. a) $\frac{\overset{1}{\cancel{4}}}{5} + \frac{3}{\underset{2}{\cancel{8}}}$ **b)** $\frac{\overset{1}{\cancel{4}}}{5} \cdot \frac{3}{\underset{2}{\cancel{8}}}$ a) is incorrect

12. a) $\frac{4}{\underset{3}{\cancel{15}}} \cdot \frac{\overset{1}{\cancel{5}}}{7}$ **b)** $\frac{4}{\underset{3}{\cancel{15}}} + \frac{\overset{1}{\cancel{5}}}{7}$ b) is incorrect

In Exercises 13 and 14, indicate any parts where a common factor can be divided out as a first step in evaluating each expression. Explain your answer.

13. a) $\frac{4}{5} + \frac{1}{4}$ **b)** $\frac{4}{5} - \frac{1}{4}$ **c)** $\frac{4}{5} \cdot \frac{1}{4}$ **d)** $\frac{4}{5} \div \frac{1}{4}$ c)

14. a) $6 + \frac{5}{12}$ **b)** $6 \cdot \frac{5}{12}$ **c)** $6 - \frac{5}{12}$ **d)** $6 \div \frac{5}{12}$ b)

15. Explain how to multiply fractions.

16. Explain how to divide fractions.   invert the divisor, then multiply

17. Explain how to add or subtract fractions.

18. Give an example of a mixed number.   Answers will vary: $3\frac{1}{2}$

19. Is the fraction $\frac{24}{5}$ simplified? Explain your answer.   yes

20. Is the fraction $\frac{20}{3}$ simplified? Explain your answer.   yes

21. Can the fraction $\frac{13}{5}$ be written as a mixed number? Explain your answer.   yes

22. Can the fraction $\frac{8}{3}$ be written as a mixed number? Explain your answer.   yes

15. divide out common factors, multiply numerators, multiply denominators
17. write fractions with common denominator, add or subtract numerators, keep common denominator

Practice the Skills

Simplify each fraction. If a fraction is already simplified, so state.

23. $\frac{10}{15}$ $\frac{2}{3}$ **24.** $\frac{40}{10}$ 4   **25.** $\frac{3}{12}$ $\frac{1}{4}$ **26.** $\frac{19}{25}$ simplified   **27.** $\frac{36}{76}$ $\frac{9}{19}$ **28.** $\frac{16}{72}$ $\frac{2}{9}$

29. $\frac{9}{21}$ $\frac{3}{7}$ **30.** $\frac{60}{105}$ $\frac{4}{7}$ **31.** $\frac{18}{49}$ simplified   **32.** $\frac{100}{144}$ $\frac{25}{36}$ **33.** $\frac{12}{25}$ simplified   **34.** $\frac{42}{138}$ $\frac{7}{23}$

Convert each mixed number to a fraction.

35. $2\frac{13}{15}$ $\frac{43}{15}$ **36.** $5\frac{1}{3}$ $\frac{16}{3}$ **37.** $7\frac{2}{3}$ $\frac{23}{3}$ **38.** $4\frac{3}{4}$ $\frac{19}{4}$ **39.** $3\frac{5}{18}$ $\frac{59}{18}$ **40.** $6\frac{2}{9}$ $\frac{56}{9}$ **41.** $9\frac{6}{17}$ $\frac{159}{17}$ **42.** $3\frac{3}{32}$ $\frac{99}{32}$

Write each fraction as a mixed number.

43. $\frac{7}{4}$ $1\frac{3}{4}$ **44.** $\frac{18}{7}$ $2\frac{4}{7}$ **45.** $\frac{13}{4}$ $3\frac{1}{4}$ **46.** $\frac{9}{2}$ $4\frac{1}{2}$ **47.** $\frac{32}{7}$ $4\frac{4}{7}$ **48.** $\frac{110}{20}$ $5\frac{1}{2}$ **49.** $\frac{86}{14}$ $6\frac{1}{7}$ **50.** $\frac{72}{14}$ $5\frac{1}{7}$

Find each product or quotient. Simplify the answer.

51. $\frac{2}{3} \cdot \frac{4}{5}$ $\frac{8}{15}$ **52.** $\frac{6}{13} \cdot \frac{7}{17}$ $\frac{42}{221}$ **53.** $\frac{5}{12} \cdot \frac{4}{15}$ $\frac{1}{9}$ **54.** $\frac{36}{48} \cdot \frac{16}{45}$ $\frac{4}{15}$

55. $\frac{3}{4} \div \frac{1}{2}$ $\frac{3}{2}$ or $1\frac{1}{2}$ **56.** $\frac{15}{16} \cdot \frac{4}{3}$ $\frac{5}{4}$ or $1\frac{1}{4}$ **57.** $\frac{3}{8} \div \frac{3}{4}$ $\frac{1}{2}$ **58.** $\frac{3}{8} \cdot \frac{10}{11}$ $\frac{15}{44}$

59. $\frac{10}{3} \div \frac{5}{9}$ 6   **60.** $\frac{5}{9} \div 30$ $\frac{1}{54}$ **61.** $\frac{15}{4} \cdot \frac{2}{3}$ $\frac{5}{2}$ or $2\frac{1}{2}$ **62.** $\frac{5}{12} \div \frac{4}{3}$ $\frac{5}{16}$

63. $5\frac{3}{8} \div 1\frac{1}{4}$ $\frac{43}{10}$ or $4\frac{3}{10}$ **64.** $\left(2\frac{1}{5}\right)\left(\frac{7}{8}\right)$ $\frac{77}{40}$ or $1\frac{37}{40}$ **65.** $\frac{28}{13} \cdot \frac{2}{7}$ $\frac{8}{13}$ **66.** $4\frac{4}{5} \div \frac{8}{15}$ 9

Add or subtract. Simplify each answer.

67. $\frac{3}{8} + \frac{2}{8}$ $\frac{5}{8}$

68. $\frac{18}{36} - \frac{1}{36}$ $\frac{17}{36}$

69. $\frac{3}{14} - \frac{1}{14}$ $\frac{1}{7}$

70. $\frac{1}{4} + \frac{3}{4}$ 1

71. $\frac{4}{5} + \frac{6}{15}$ $\frac{6}{5}$ or $1\frac{1}{5}$

72. $\frac{7}{8} - \frac{5}{6}$ $\frac{1}{24}$

73. $\frac{8}{17} + \frac{2}{34}$ $\frac{9}{17}$

74. $\frac{3}{7} + \frac{17}{35}$ $\frac{32}{35}$

75. $\frac{1}{3} + \frac{1}{4}$ $\frac{7}{12}$

76. $\frac{1}{6} - \frac{1}{18}$ $\frac{1}{9}$

77. $\frac{7}{12} - \frac{2}{9}$ $\frac{13}{36}$

78. $\frac{3}{7} + \frac{5}{12}$ $\frac{71}{84}$

79. $3\frac{1}{8} - \frac{5}{12}$ $\frac{65}{24}$ or $2\frac{17}{24}$

80. $5\frac{6}{7} + 4\frac{5}{8}$ $\frac{587}{56}$ or $10\frac{27}{56}$

81. $6\frac{1}{3} - 3\frac{1}{2}$ $\frac{17}{6}$ or $2\frac{5}{6}$

82. $2\frac{3}{8} + 3\frac{3}{4}$ $\frac{49}{8}$ or $6\frac{1}{8}$

83. $9\frac{2}{5} - 6\frac{1}{2}$ $\frac{29}{10}$ or $2\frac{9}{10}$

84. $4\frac{5}{9} - \frac{7}{8}$ $\frac{265}{72}$ or $3\frac{49}{72}$

85. $5\frac{9}{10} + 3\frac{1}{3}$ $\frac{277}{30}$ or $9\frac{7}{30}$

86. $8\frac{2}{7} - 3\frac{1}{3}$ $\frac{104}{21}$ or $4\frac{20}{21}$

87. How much larger is $\frac{5}{6}$ mile than $\frac{3}{8}$ mile? $\frac{11}{24}$ mile

88. How much larger is $\frac{1}{5}$ meter than $\frac{1}{7}$ meter? $\frac{2}{35}$ meter

Problem Solving

89. Height Gain The following graph shows Rebecca Bersagel's height, in inches, on her 8th and 12th birthdays. How much had Rebecca grown in the 4 years? $8\frac{15}{16}$ in.

Rebecca Bersagel's Height

90. Road Paving The following graph shows the progress of the Davenport Paving Company in paving the Memorial Highway. How much of the highway was paved from June through August? $6\frac{7}{8}$ mi

Highway Paved in Selected Months

In many problems you will need to subtract a fraction from 1, where 1 represents "the whole" or the "total amount." Exercises 91–94 are answered by subtracting the given fraction from 1.

91. Putting Success During the 2004 season, $\frac{31}{50}$ of all putts from six feet were made by PGA Tour players. What fraction of all putts from six feet were not made? $\frac{19}{50}$

Source: USA Today

92. Global Warming The probability that an event does not occur may be found by subtracting the probability that the event does occur from 1. If the probability that global warming is occurring is $\frac{7}{9}$, find the probability that global warming is not occurring. $\frac{2}{9}$

93. High School Diploma Use the following circle graph to determine the fraction of people ages 25 and older with no high school diploma who were unemployed in January, 2005. $\frac{3}{40}$

Employment Status of People Ages 25 and Older with No High School Diploma in January, 2005

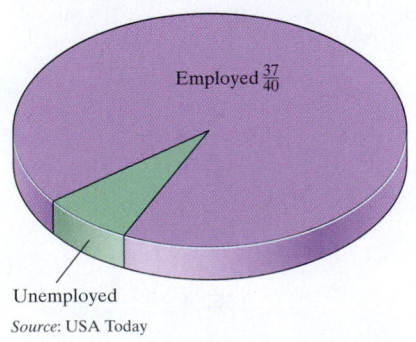

Source: USA Today

94. Home Heating The following circle graph shows the fraction of U.S. homes that used electricity to heat their homes in 2003. Determine the fraction of U.S. homes that did not use electricity. $\frac{687}{1000}$

How Americans Heat Their Homes, 2003

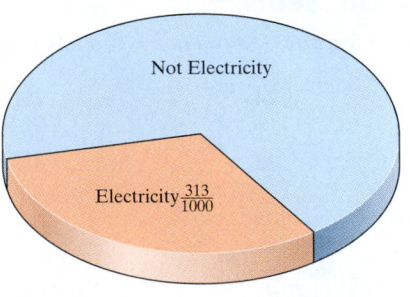

Source: www.census.gov

In Exercises 95–110, answer the questions asked.

95. Albino's Growth An albino python at Cypress Gardens, Florida, was 3 feet, $3\frac{1}{4}$ inches when born. Its present length is 15 feet, $2\frac{1}{2}$ inches. How much has it grown since birth?   11 ft, $11\frac{1}{4}$ in. or $143\frac{1}{4}$ in. or ≈ 11.94 ft

96. Cream Pie A Boston cream pie weighs $1\frac{5}{16}$ pounds. If the pie is to be divided equally among 6 people, how much will each person get? $\frac{7}{32}$ lb

97. Running Denise started a running program in January when she could run a mile in $10\frac{1}{2}$ minutes. After 6 months, Denise could run a mile in $8\frac{2}{5}$ minutes. By how many minutes did Denise improve in 6 months? $2\frac{1}{10}$ minutes

98. Baking Turkey The instructions on a turkey indicate that a 12- to 16-pound turkey should bake at 325°F for about 22 minutes per pound. Josephine Nickola is planning to bake a $13\frac{1}{2}$-pound turkey. Approximately how long should the turkey be baked? 297 min or 4 hr 57 min

99. Wood Cut Debbie Anderson cuts a piece of wood measuring $3\frac{1}{8}$ inches into two equal pieces. How long is each piece? $1\frac{9}{16}$ in.

100. Pants Inseam The inseam on a new pair of pants is 30 inches. If Don O'Neal's inseam is $28\frac{3}{8}$ inches, by how much will the pants need to be shortened? $1\frac{5}{8}$ in.

101. Drug Amount A nurse must give $\frac{1}{16}$ milligram of a drug for each kilogram of patient weight. If Mr. Krisanda weighs (or has a mass of) 80 kilograms, find the amount of the drug Mr. Krisanda should be given. 5 mg

102. Chopped Onions A recipe for pot roast calls for $\frac{1}{4}$ cup chopped onions for each pound of beef. For $5\frac{1}{2}$ pounds of beef, how many cups of chopped onions are needed? $1\frac{3}{8}$ cups

103. Shampoo A bottle of shampoo contains 15 fluid ounces. If Tierra Bentley uses $\frac{3}{8}$ of an ounce each time she washes her hair, how many times can Tierra wash her hair using this bottle? 40 times

104. Fencing Matt Mesaros wants to fence in his backyard as shown. The three sides to be fenced measure $16\frac{2}{3}$ yards, $22\frac{2}{3}$ yards, and $14\frac{1}{8}$ yards.

16$\frac{2}{3}$ yd
22$\frac{2}{3}$ yd
14$\frac{1}{8}$ yd

a) How much fence will Matt need? $53\frac{11}{24}$ yd
b) If Matt buys 60 yards of fence, how much will be left over? $6\frac{13}{24}$ yd

105. Windows An insulated window for a house is made up of two pieces of glass, each $\frac{1}{4}$-inch thick, with a 1-inch space between them. What is the total thickness of this window? $1\frac{1}{2}$ in.

106. Truck Weight A flatbed tow truck weighing $4\frac{1}{2}$ tons is carrying two cars. One car weighs $1\frac{1}{6}$ tons, the other weighs

$1\frac{3}{4}$ tons. What is the total weight of the tow truck and the two cars? $7\frac{5}{12}$ tons

107. Cutting Wood A 28-inch length of wood is to be cut into $4\frac{2}{3}$ inch strips. How many whole strips can be made? Disregard loss of wood due to cuts made. 6

108. Fasten Bolts A mechanic wishes to use a bolt to fasten a piece of wood $4\frac{1}{2}$ inches thick to a metal tube $2\frac{1}{3}$ inches thick. If the thickness of the nut is $\frac{1}{8}$ inch, find the length of the shaft of the bolt so that the nut fits flush with the end of the bolt (see the figure below). $6\frac{23}{24}$ in.

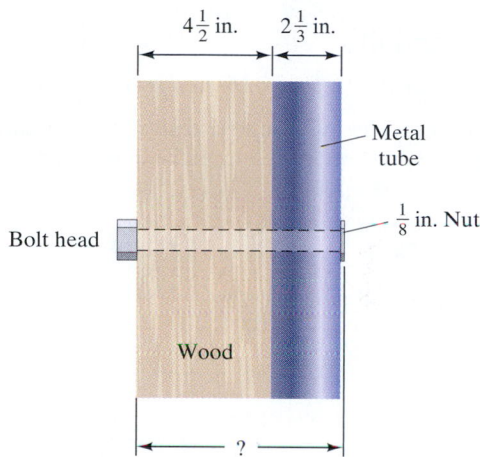
$4\frac{1}{2}$ in. $2\frac{1}{3}$ in.
Metal tube
$\frac{1}{8}$ in. Nut
Bolt head
Wood
?

109. Computer Cabinet Karen Kraatz is considering purchasing a mail order computer. The catalog describes the computer as $7\frac{1}{2}$ inches high and the monitor as $14\frac{3}{8}$ inches high. Karen is hoping to place the monitor on top of the computer and to place the computer and monitor together in the opening where the computer is shown.

$22\frac{1}{2}$"
$26\frac{1}{2}$"
$2\frac{1}{2}$"
$1\frac{1}{4}$"

a) Will there be sufficient room to do this? yes
b) If so, how much extra space will she have? $\frac{5}{8}$ in.
c) Find the total height of the computer desk $52\frac{3}{4}$ in.

110. Soda If five 2-liter bottles of soda are split evenly among 30 people, how many liters of soda will each person get? $\frac{1}{3}$ liter

Challenge Problems

111. Add or subtract the following fractions using the rule discussed in this section. Your answer should be a single fraction, and it should contain the symbols given in the exercise.

a) $\dfrac{*}{a} + \dfrac{?}{a}$ $\dfrac{*+?}{a}$

b) $\dfrac{\odot}{?} - \dfrac{\square}{?}$ $\dfrac{\odot - \square}{?}$

c) $\dfrac{\triangle}{\square} + \dfrac{4}{\square}$ $\dfrac{\triangle + 4}{\square}$

d) $\dfrac{x}{3} - \dfrac{2}{3}$ $\dfrac{x-2}{3}$

e) $\dfrac{12}{x} - \dfrac{4}{x}$ $\dfrac{8}{x}$

112. Multiply the following fractions using the rule discussed in this section. Your answer should be a single fraction and it should contain the symbols given in the exercise.

a) $\dfrac{\triangle}{a} \cdot \dfrac{\square}{b}$ $\dfrac{\triangle\square}{ab}$

b) $\dfrac{6}{3} \cdot \dfrac{\triangle}{\square}$ $\dfrac{2\triangle}{\square}$

c) $\dfrac{x}{a} \cdot \dfrac{y}{b}$ $\dfrac{xy}{ab}$

d) $\dfrac{3}{8} \cdot \dfrac{4}{y}$ $\dfrac{3}{2y}$

e) $\dfrac{3}{x} \cdot \dfrac{x}{y}$ $\dfrac{3}{y}$

113. Drug Dosage An allopurinal pill comes in 300-milligram doses. Dr. Muechler wants a patient to get 450 milligrams each day by cutting the pills in half and taking $\frac{1}{2}$ pill three times a day. If he wants to prescribe enough pills for a 6-month period (assume 30 days per month), how many pills should he prescribe?   270 pills

Group Activity

Discuss and answer Exercise 114 as a group.

114. a) flakes, 2 cups; milk, 6 tbsp   **b)** flakes, 2 cups; milk, $7\frac{1}{3}$ tbsp   **c)** flakes, 2 cups; milk, $\frac{1}{2}$ cup or 8 tbsp   **d)** flakes, 2 cups; milk, $8\frac{2}{3}$ tbsp   **e)** flakes are same, milk is different — $\frac{1}{3}$ cup is not twice 2 tbsp

114. Potatoes The following table gives the amount of each ingredient recommended to make 2, 4, and 8 servings of instant mashed potatoes.

Servings	2	4	8
Water	$\frac{2}{3}$ cup	$1\frac{1}{3}$ cups	$2\frac{2}{3}$ cups
Milk	2 tbsp	$\frac{1}{3}$ cup	$\frac{2}{3}$ cup
Butter*	1 tbsp	2 tbsp	4 tbsp
Salt†	$\frac{1}{4}$ tsp	$\frac{1}{2}$ tsp	1 tsp
Potato flakes	$\frac{2}{3}$ cup	$1\frac{1}{3}$ cup	$2\frac{2}{3}$ cups

*or margarine
†Less salt can be used if desired.

Determine the amount of potato flakes and milk needed to make 6 servings by the different methods described. When working with milk, 16 tbsp = 1 cup.

a) Group member 1: Determine the amount of potato flakes and milk needed to make 6 servings by multiplying the amount for 2 servings by 3.

b) Group member 2: Determine the amounts by adding the amounts for 2 servings to the amounts for 4 servings.

c) Group member 3: Determine the amounts by finding the average (mean) of 4 and 8 servings.

d) As a group, determine the amount by subtracting the amount for 2 servings from the amount for 8 servings.

e) As a group, compare your answers from parts **a)** through **d)**. Are they all the same? If not, can you explain why? (This might be a little tricky.)

Cumulative Review Exercises

115. Answers will vary.

[1.1] **115.** What is your instructor's name and office hours?

[1.2] **116.** What is the mean of 9, 8, 15, 32, 16?   16

117. What is the median of 9, 8, 15, 32, 16?   15

[1.3] **118.** What are variables?   letters used to represent numbers

1.4 The Real Number System

1 Identify sets of numbers.

2 Know the structure of the real numbers.

We will be talking about and using various types of numbers throughout the text. This section introduces you to some of those numbers and to the structure of the real number system.

1 Identify Sets of Numbers

A **set** is a collection of **elements** listed within braces. The set $\{a, b, c, d, e\}$ consists of five elements, namely a, b, c, d, and e. A set that contains no elements is called an **empty set** (or **null set**). The symbols $\{\ \}$ or $\varnothing$ are used to represent the empty set.

There are many different sets of numbers. Two important sets are the natural numbers and the whole numbers. The whole numbers were introduced earlier.

Natural numbers: $\{1, 2, 3, 4, 5, \ldots\}$

Whole numbers: $\{0, 1, 2, 3, 4, 5, \ldots\}$

TEACHING TIP
As a class, you may want to choose the empty set notation which will be used by the class.

An aid in understanding sets of numbers is the real number line (**Fig. 1.7**).

FIGURE 1.7

The real number line continues indefinitely in both directions. The numbers to the right of 0 are positive and those to the left of 0 are negative. Zero is neither positive nor negative (**Fig. 1.8**).

FIGURE 1.8

Figure 1.9 illustrates the natural numbers marked on a number line. The natural numbers are also called the **counting numbers** or the **positive integers**.

FIGURE 1.9

Another important set of numbers is the integers.

Integers: $\{\ldots, -5, -4, -3, -2, -1, 0, 1, 2, 3, 4, 5, \ldots\}$

Negative integers   Positive integers

The integers consist of the negative integers, 0, and the positive integers. The integers are marked on the number line in **Figure 1.10**.

FIGURE 1.10

TEACHING TIP
You may wish to point out that the word *rational* contains the word ratio, and a rational number is a ratio of two integers, denominator not zero.

Can you think of any numbers that are not integers? You probably thought of "fractions" or "decimal numbers." Fractions and certain decimal numbers belong to the set of rational numbers. The set of **rational numbers** consists of all the numbers that can be expressed as a quotient (or a ratio) of two integers, with the denominator not 0.

Rational numbers: {quotient of two integers, denominator not 0}

All integers are rational numbers since they can be written with a denominator of 1. For example, $3 = \frac{3}{1}$, $-12 = \frac{-12}{1}$, and $0 = \frac{0}{1}$. All fractions containing integers in the numerator and denominator (with the denominator not 0) are rational numbers. For example, the fraction $\frac{3}{5}$ is a quotient of two integers and is a rational number.

When a fraction that is a ratio of two integers is converted to a decimal number by dividing the numerator by the denominator, the quotient will always be either a *terminating decimal number*, such as 0.3 and 3.25, or a *repeating decimal number* such as 0.3333 . . . and 5.2727 . . . . The three dots at the end of a number like 0.3333 . . . indicate that the numbers continue to repeat in the same manner indefinitely. All terminating decimal numbers and all repeating decimal numbers are rational numbers which can be expressed as a quotient of two integers. For example, $0.3 = \frac{3}{10}$, $3.25 = \frac{325}{100}$, $0.3333\ldots = \frac{1}{3}$ and $5.2727\ldots = \frac{522}{99}$. Some rational numbers are illustrated on the number line in **Figure 1.11**.

FIGURE 1.11

Most of the numbers that we use are rational numbers. However, some numbers are not rational. Numbers such as the square root of 2, written $\sqrt{2}$, are not rational numbers. Any number that can be represented on the number line that is not a rational number is called an **irrational number**. Irrational numbers are non-terminating, non-repeating decimal numbers. For example, $\sqrt{2}$ cannot be expressed exactly as a decimal number. Irrational numbers can only be *approximated* by decimal numbers. $\sqrt{2}$ is *approximately* 1.41. Thus, we may write $\sqrt{2} \approx 1.41$. Some irrational numbers are illustrated on the number line in **Figure 1.12**. Rational and irrational numbers will be discussed further in later chapters.

FIGURE 1.12

2   Know the Structure of the Real Numbers

Notice that many different types of numbers can be illustrated on a number line. Any number that can be represented on the number line is a **real number**.

Real numbers: {all numbers that can be represented on a real number line}

The symbol $\mathbb{R}$ is used to represent the set of real numbers. All the numbers mentioned thus far are real numbers. The natural numbers, the whole numbers, the integers, the rational numbers, and the irrational numbers are all real numbers. There are some types of numbers that are not real numbers, but these numbers are not discussed in this chapter. **Figure 1.13** illustrates the relationships between the various sets of numbers within the set of real numbers.

In **Figure 1.13a**, we can see that when we combine the rational numbers and the irrational numbers we get the real numbers. When we combine the integers with the noninteger rational numbers (such as $\frac{1}{2}$ and 0.42), we get the rational numbers. When we combine the whole numbers and the negative integers, we get the integers.

Consider the natural number 5. If we follow the branches in **Figure 1.13a** upward, we see that the number 5 is also a whole number, an integer, a rational number, and a real number. Now consider the number $\frac{1}{2}$. It belongs to the noninteger rational numbers. If we follow the branches upward, we can see that $\frac{1}{2}$ is also a rational number and a real number.

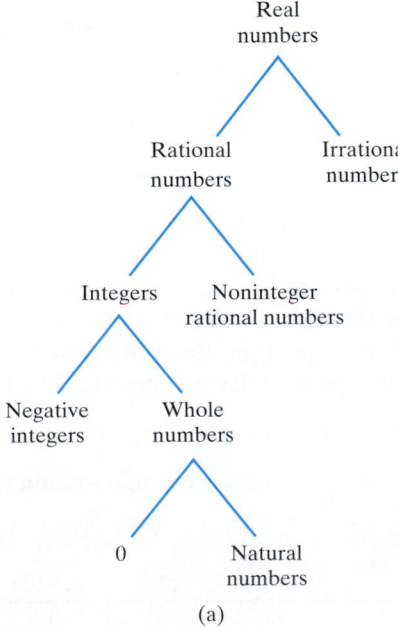

Real Numbers	
Rational numbers	Irrational numbers
(Integers and noninteger rational numbers)	(Certain* square roots and other special numbers)
−12 4 0	$\sqrt{2}$ $\sqrt{5}$
$\frac{3}{8}$ $\frac{1}{3}$ −1.24	π $\sqrt{12}$
−1$\frac{3}{5}$ −2.463	

*Other higher roots like $\sqrt[3]{2}$ and $\sqrt[4]{5}$ are also irrational numbers.

(a)

(b)

FIGURE 1.13

EXAMPLE 1 ▶ Consider the following set of numbers.

$$\left\{\sqrt{11}, -\frac{3}{8}, -0.6, -4, 7\frac{1}{2}, 12, 0, \sqrt{5}, -48, 3.9, -\sqrt{7}\right\}$$

List the elements of the set that are

a) natural numbers. b) whole numbers. c) integers.

d) rational numbers. e) irrational numbers. f) real numbers.

Solution We will list the elements from left to right as they appear in the set. However, the elements may be listed in any order.

a) 12 b) 12, 0 c) −4, 12, 0, −48

d) $-\dfrac{3}{8}, -0.6, -4, 7\dfrac{1}{2}, 12, 0, -48, 3.9$ e) $\sqrt{11}, \sqrt{5}, -\sqrt{7}$

f) $\sqrt{11}, -\dfrac{3}{8}, -0.6, -4, 7\dfrac{1}{2}, 12, 0, \sqrt{5}, -48, 3.9, -\sqrt{7}$

▶ **Now Try Exercise 51**

---

2. the empty or null set 5. 0 is an element of the whole numbers, but not of the natural numbers 6. the set of counting numbers, the set of positive integers 7. a)-c) All natural numbers are whole numbers, rational numbers, and real numbers. 8. a) quotient of two integers, denominator not 0 8. b) can be written with a denominator of 1

EXERCISE SET 1.4
MathXL® MyMathLab

Concept/Writing Exercises

1. What is a set? a collection of elements

2. What is a set that contains no elements called?

3. Describe a set that is an empty set. Answers will vary.

4. Give two symbols used to represent the empty set. { } and ∅

5. How do the sets of natural numbers and whole numbers differ?

6. What are two other names for the set of natural numbers?

7. Explain why the natural number 7 is also a
   a) whole number.
   b) rational number.
   c) real number.

8. a) What is a rational number?
   b) Explain why every integer is a rational number.

9. Is 0 a member of the set of
   a) integers? Yes
   b) positive integers? No
   c) negative integers? No
   d) rational numbers? Yes

10. Write a paragraph or two describing the structure of the real number system. Explain how whole numbers, counting numbers, integers, rational numbers, irrational numbers, and real numbers are related. Answers will vary.

Practice the Skills

In Exercises 11–15, list each set of numbers.

11. Integers $\{\ldots, -3, -2, -1, 0, 1, 2, 3, \ldots\}$

12. Counting numbers $\{1, 2, 3, 4, \ldots\}$

13. Whole numbers $\{0, 1, 2, 3, \ldots\}$

14. Positive integers $\{1, 2, 3, 4, \ldots\}$

15. Negative integers $\{\ldots, -3, -2, -1\}$

16. Natural numbers $\{1, 2, 3, 4, \ldots\}$

In Exercises 17–48, indicate whether each statement is true or false.

17. 0 is a whole number. T

18. −1 is a negative integer. T

19. −7.3 is a real number. T

20. $\dfrac{3}{5}$ is an integer. F

21. 0.6 is an integer. F

22. 0 is a natural number. F

23. $\sqrt{2}$ is a rational number. F

24. $\sqrt{3}$ is a real number. T

25. $-\dfrac{1}{5}$ is a rational number. T

26. $-2\dfrac{1}{3}$ is a rational number. T

27. 0 is a rational number. T

28. 9.2 is a rational number. T

29. $4\dfrac{5}{8}$ is an irrational number.   F

30. 0 is not a positive number.   T

31. $-\sqrt{5}$ is an irrational number.   T

32. Every counting number is a rational number.   T

33. The symbol $\varnothing$ is used to represent the empty set.   T

34. Every integer is negative.   F

35. Every real number is a rational number.   F

36. Every negative integer is a real number.   T

37. Every rational number is a real number.   T

38. When zero is added to the set of counting numbers, the set of whole numbers is formed.   T

39. Some real numbers are not rational numbers.   T

40. Some irrational numbers are not real numbers.   F

41. Every negative number is a negative integer.   F

42. All real numbers can be represented on a number line.   T

43. The symbol $\mathbb{R}$ is used to represent the set of real numbers.   T

44. Any number to the left of zero on a number line is a negative number.   T

45. Every number greater than zero is a positive integer.   F

46. Irrational numbers cannot be represented on a number line.   F

47. When the negative integers, the positive integers, and 0 are combined, the integers are formed.   T

48. The natural numbers, counting numbers, and positive integers are different names for the same set of numbers.   T

49. Hotels Some of the older hotels in Europe have elevators that list negative numbers for floors below the lobby level. For example, a floor might be designated as -2. In the United States and in many countries, floor number 13 is omitted because of superstition. Considering the numbers -2 and 13, list those that are

a) positive integers.   13

b) rational numbers. $-2, 13$

c) real numbers. $-2, 13$

d) whole numbers.   13

50. Address We generally think of house addresses as being integers greater than 0. Have you ever seen a house number that was not an integer greater than 0? There are quite a few

51. e) $\sqrt{7}, -\sqrt{3}$ **52. e)** $\sqrt{3}, \sqrt{7}$

such addresses in cities and towns across America. The house numbers 0 and $2\dfrac{1}{2}$ appear on Legare Street in Charleston, SC. Considering the numbers 0 and $2\dfrac{1}{2}$, list those that are

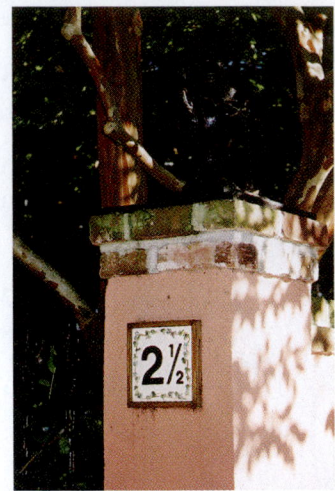

a) integers   0

b) rational numbers $0, 2\dfrac{1}{2}$

c) real numbers $0, 2\dfrac{1}{2}$

51. Consider the following set of numbers.

$$\left\{ -\frac{5}{7}, 0, -2, 3, 6\frac{1}{4}, \sqrt{7}, -\sqrt{3}, 1.63, 77 \right\}$$

List the numbers that are

a) positive integers. $3, 77$

b) whole numbers. $0, 3, 77$

c) integers. $0, -2, 3, 77$

d) rational numbers. $-\dfrac{5}{7}, 0, -2, 3, 6\dfrac{1}{4}, 1.63, 77$

e) irrational numbers.

f) real numbers. $-\dfrac{5}{7}, 0, -2, 3, 6\dfrac{1}{4}, \sqrt{7}, -\sqrt{3}, 1.63, 77$

52. Consider the following set of numbers.

$$\left\{ -6, 7, 12.4, -\frac{9}{5}, -2\frac{1}{4}, \sqrt{3}, 0, 9, \sqrt{7}, 0.35 \right\}$$

List the numbers that are

a) positive integers. $7, 9$

b) whole numbers. $7, 0, 9$

c) integers. $-6, 7, 0, 9$

d) rational numbers. $-6, 7, 12.4, -\dfrac{9}{5}, -2\dfrac{1}{4}, 0, 9, 0.35$

e) irrational numbers.

f) real numbers. $-6, 7, 12.4, -\dfrac{9}{5}, -2\dfrac{1}{4}, \sqrt{3}, 0, 9, \sqrt{7}, 0.35$

Problem Solving

Give three examples of numbers that satisfy the given conditions.

55. $-\sqrt{2}, -\sqrt{3}, -\sqrt{7}$ **61.** $\sqrt{2}, \sqrt{3}, -\sqrt{5}$ **64.** $-\dfrac{1}{2}, -\dfrac{5}{8}, -\sqrt{5}$

53.–64. Answers will vary.

53. An integer but not a negative integer. $0, 1, 2$

54. A real number but not an integer. $\dfrac{1}{2}, -\dfrac{1}{2}, 0.6$

55. An irrational number and a negative number.

56. A real number and a rational number. $1, \dfrac{1}{2}, -\dfrac{3}{5}$

57. A rational number but not a natural number. $-\dfrac{2}{3}, \dfrac{1}{2}, 6.3$

58. An integer and a rational number. $-5, 0, 4$

59. A negative integer and a rational number. $-13, -5, -1$

60. A negative integer and a real number. $-1, -2, -3$

61. A real number but not a positive rational number.

62. A rational number but not a negative number. $1.5, 3, 6\dfrac{1}{4}$

63. A real number but not an irrational number. $-7, 1, 5$

64. A negative number but not a negative integer.

Three dots inside a set indicate that the set continues in the same manner. For example, $\{1, 2, 3, \ldots, 84\}$ is the set of natural numbers from 1 up to and including 84. In Exercises 65 and 66, determine the number of elements in each set.

65. $\{8, 9, 10, 11, \ldots, 94\}$ 87

66. $\{-4, -3, -2, -1, 0, 1, \ldots, 64\}$ 69

Challenge Problems

The diagrams in Exercises 67 and 68 are called **Venn diagrams** *(named after the English mathematician John Venn). Venn diagrams are used to illustrate sets. For example, in the diagrams, circle A contains all the elements in set A, and circle B contains all the elements in set B. For each diagram, determine a) set A, b) set B, c) the set of elements that belong to both set A and set B, and d) the set of elements that belong to either set A or set B.*

69. a) set B continues beyond 4   **70. b)** an infinite number

67.

A ... B

1, 4, 3   5, 8   2, 6, 7

a) {1, 3, 4, 5, 8}

b) {2, 5, 6, 7, 8}

c) {5, 8}

d) {1, 2, 3, 4, 5, 6, 7, 8}

69. Consider the sets $A = \{1, 2, 3, 4\}$ and $B = \{1, 2, 3, 4, \dots\}$.

a) Explain the difference between set A and set B.

b) How many elements are in set A?   4

c) How many elements are in set B?   infinite number

d) Set A is an example of a *finite set*. Can you guess the name given to a set like set B?   infinite set

68.

A ... B

△, P, ?   □, *   R, L, W

a) {△, P, ?, *}

b) {*, □, L, W, R}

c) {*}

d) {△, P, ?, *, □, L, W, R}

70. How many decimal numbers are there

a) between 1.0 and 2.0;   an infinite number

b) between 1.4 and 1.5? Explain your answer.

71. How many fractions are there

a) between 1 and 2;   an infinite number

b) between $\frac{1}{3}$ and $\frac{1}{5}$? Explain your answer.   an infinite number

---

Group Activity

72. a) $\cup$: {1, 2, 3, 4, 5, 6, 7, 8, 9}, $\cap$: {2, 3, 8}   **72. b)** $\cup$: {a, b, c, d, g, h, i, j, m, p}, $\cap$: {b, c, d}
72. c) $\cup$: {red, blue, green, yellow, pink, orange, purple}, $\cap$: $\varnothing$

Discuss and answer Exercise 72 as a group.

72. Set A **union** set B, symbolized $A \cup B$, consists of the set of elements that belong to set A or set B (or both sets). Set A **intersection** set B, symbolized $A \cap B$, consists of the set of elements that both set A and set B have in common. Note that the elements that belong to both sets are listed only once in the union of the sets.
Consider the pairs of sets below.

Group member 1: $A = \{2, 3, 4, 6, 8, 9\}$ $B = \{1, 2, 3, 5, 7, 8\}$

Group member 2: $A = \{a, b, c, d, g, i, j\}$ $B = \{b, c, d, h, m, p\}$

Group member 3: $A = \{red, blue, green, yellow\}$ $B = \{pink, orange, purple\}$

a) Group member 1: Find the union and intersection of the sets marked Group member 1.
b) Group member 2: Find the union and intersection of the sets marked Group member 2.
c) Group member 3: Find the union and intersection of the sets marked Group member 3.
d) Now as a group, check each other's work. Correct any mistakes.
e) As a group, using group member 1's sets, construct a Venn diagram like those shown in Exercises 67 and 68.

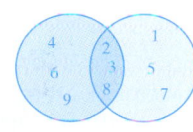

Cumulative Review Exercises

[1.3]   **73.** Convert $5\frac{2}{5}$ to a fraction. $\frac{27}{5}$

74. Write $\frac{16}{3}$ as a mixed number. $5\frac{1}{3}$

75. Subtract $\frac{7}{8} - \frac{2}{3}$. $\frac{5}{24}$

76. Divide $\frac{3}{5} \div 6\frac{3}{4}$. $\frac{4}{45}$

1.5 Inequalities

1 Determine which is the greater of two numbers.

2 Find the absolute value of a number.

1 Determine Which Is the Greater of Two Numbers

The number line, which shows numbers increasing from left to right, can be used to explain inequalities (see **Fig. 1.14**). When comparing two numbers, **the number to the right on the number line is the greater number, and the number to the left is the lesser number**. The symbol $>$ is used to represent the words "is greater than." The symbol $<$ is used to represent the words "is less than."

Lesser   Greater

FIGURE 1.14

The statement that the number 3 is greater than the number 2 is written $3 > 2$. Notice that 3 is to the right of 2 on the number line in **Figure 1.14** on page 35. The statement that the number 0 is greater than the number -1 is written $0 > -1$. Notice that 0 is to the right of -1 on the number line.

Instead of stating that 3 is greater than 2, we could state that 2 is less than 3, written $2 < 3$. Notice that 2 is to the left of 3 on the number line. The statement that the number -1 is less than the number 0 is written $-1 < 0$. Notice that -1 is to the left of 0 on the number line.

EXAMPLE 1 ▶ Insert either $>$ or $<$ in the shaded area between each pair of numbers to make a true statement.

a) -4 ▨ -2 **b)** $-\dfrac{3}{2}$ ▨ 2.5 **c)** $\dfrac{1}{2}$ ▨ $\dfrac{1}{4}$ **d)** -2 ▨ 4

Solution   The points given are shown on the number line (**Fig. 1.15**).

FIGURE 1.15

a) $-4 < -2$; notice that -4 is to the left of -2.

b) $-\dfrac{3}{2} < 2.5$; notice that $-\dfrac{3}{2}$ is to the left of 2.5.

c) $\dfrac{1}{2} > \dfrac{1}{4}$; notice that $\dfrac{1}{2}$ is to the right of $\dfrac{1}{4}$.

d) $-2 < 4$; notice that -2 is to the left of 4.

▶ **Now Try Exercise 35**

EXAMPLE 2 ▶ Insert either $>$ or $<$ in the shaded area between each pair of numbers to make a true statement.

a) -3 ▨ 3 **b)** -3 ▨ -4 **c)** -4 ▨ 0 **d)** -1.08 ▨ -1.8

Solution   The numbers given are shown on the number line (**Fig. 1.16**).

FIGURE 1.16

a) $-3 < 3$; notice that -3 is to the left of 3.

b) $-3 > -4$; notice that -3 is to the right of -4.

c) $-4 < 0$; notice that -4 is to the left of 0.

d) $-1.08 > -1.8$; notice that -1.08 is to the right of -1.8.

▶ **Now Try Exercise 43**

2 Find the Absolute Value of a Number

The concept of absolute value can be explained with the help of the number line shown in **Figure 1.17** on page 37. The **absolute value** of a number can be considered the distance between the number and 0 on a number line. Thus, the absolute value of 3, written $|3|$, is 3 since it is 3 units from 0 on a number line. Similarly, the absolute value of -3, written $|-3|$, is also 3 since -3 is 3 units from 0.

$$|3| = 3 \quad \text{and} \quad |-3| = 3$$

FIGURE 1.17

Since the absolute value of a number measures the distance (without regard to direction) of a number from 0 on the number line, *the absolute value of every number will be either positive or zero.*

Number	Absolute Value of Number
6	$\lvert 6 \rvert = 6$
-6	$\lvert -6 \rvert = 6$
0	$\lvert 0 \rvert = 0$
$-\dfrac{1}{2}$	$\left\lvert -\dfrac{1}{2} \right\rvert = \dfrac{1}{2}$

The negative of the absolute value of a nonzero number will always be a negative number. For example,

$$-\lvert 2 \rvert = -(2) = -2 \quad \text{and} \quad -\lvert -3 \rvert = -(3) = -3$$

EXAMPLE 3 ▶ Insert either $>$, $<$, or $=$ in each shaded area to make a true statement.

a) $\lvert 3 \rvert$ ▨ 3 **b)** $\lvert -2 \rvert$ ▨ $\lvert 2 \rvert$ **c)** -2 ▨ $\lvert -4 \rvert$

d) $\lvert -2 \rvert$ ▨ $\lvert -4 \rvert$ **e)** $\left\lvert -\dfrac{2}{5} \right\rvert$ ▨ $\lvert -0.42 \rvert$

Solution

a) $\lvert 3 \rvert = 3$.   **b)** $\lvert -2 \rvert = \lvert 2 \rvert$, since both $\lvert -2 \rvert$ and $\lvert 2 \rvert$ equal 2.

c) $-2 < \lvert -4 \rvert$, since $\lvert -4 \rvert = 4$.

d) $\lvert -2 \rvert < \lvert -4 \rvert$, since $\lvert -2 \rvert = 2$ and $\lvert -4 \rvert = 4$.

e) When an absolute value contains a fraction, we can compare it to an absolute value containing a decimal number by rewriting the fraction as a decimal number and comparing the absolute values of the decimal numbers.

$$\left\lvert -\frac{2}{5} \right\rvert = \lvert -0.40 \rvert = 0.40$$

$$\lvert -0.42 \rvert = 0.42$$

Therefore, $\left\lvert -\dfrac{2}{5} \right\rvert < \lvert -0.42 \rvert$ because $0.40 < 0.42$.

▶ **Now Try Exercise 57**

We will use absolute value in Sections 1.6 and 1.7 to add and subtract real numbers. The concept of absolute value is very important in higher-level mathematics courses. If you take a course in intermediate algebra, you will learn a more formal definition of absolute value.

EXERCISE SET 1.5

MathXL®   MyMathLab

Concept/Writing Exercises

2. the distance between the number and 0 on a number line   **3. a)** 4 is 4 units from 0.   **b)** −4 is 4 units from 0.   **c)** 0 is 0 units from 0.   **4.** Yes, 0. The absolute value of 0 is 0.

1. a) Draw a number line. **a) and b)** ◄─┼─●─┼─●─┼─┼─┼─┼─►
−5 −4 −3 −2 −1 0 1 2

  b) Mark the numbers −2 and −4 on your number line.

  c) Is −2 less than −4 or is −2 greater than −4? Explain.   >

  In parts **d)** and **e)** write a correct statement using −2 and −4 and the symbol given.

  d) <   −4 < −2

  e) >   −2 > −4

2. What is the absolute value of a number?

3. a) Explain why the absolute value of 4, |4|, is 4.

  b) Explain why the absolute value of −4, |−4|, is 4.

  c) Explain why the absolute value of 0, |0|, is 0.

4. Are there any real numbers whose absolute value is not a positive number? Explain your answer.

5. Suppose a and b represent any two real numbers. If $a > b$ is true, will $b < a$ also be true? Explain and give some examples using specific numbers for a and b.   yes

6. Will $|a| - |a| = 0$ always be true for any real number a? Explain.   yes

7. Suppose a and b represent any two real numbers. Suppose $a < b$ is true. Will $|a| < |b|$ also be true? Explain and give an example to support your answer.   No, −4 < −3 but |−4| > |−3|.

8. Suppose a and b represent any two real numbers. Suppose $a > b$ is true. Will $|a| > |b|$ also be true? Explain and give an example to support your answer.   No, −3 > −4 but |−3| < |−4|.

9. Suppose a and b represent any two real numbers. Suppose $|a| < |b|$ is true. Will $a < b$ also be true? Explain and give an example to support your answer.   No, |−3| < |−4| but −3 > −4.

10. Suppose a and b represent any two real numbers. Suppose $|a| > |b|$ is true. Will $a > b$ also be true? Explain and give an example to support your answer.   No, |−4| > |−3| but −4 < −3.

Practice the Skills

Evaluate.

11. |7| 7

12. |−6| 6

13. |−15| 15

14. |0| 0

15. −|0| 0

16. |54| 54

17. −|−5| −5

18. −|92| −92

19. −|21| −21

20. −|−34| −34

Insert either < or > in each shaded area to make a true statement.

21. 6 ▮ 2   >

22. 4 ▮ −2   >

23. −4 ▮ 0   <

24. −6 ▮ −4   <

25. $\frac{1}{2}$ ▮ $-\frac{2}{3}$ >

26. $\frac{3}{5}$ ▮ $\frac{4}{5}$ <

27. 0.7 ▮ 0.8   <

28. −0.2 ▮ −0.4   >

29. $-\frac{1}{2}$ ▮ −1   >

30. −0.1 ▮ −0.9   >

31. −5 ▮ 5   <

32. $-\frac{3}{4}$ ▮ −1   >

33. −2.1 ▮ −2   <

34. −1.83 ▮ −1.82   <

35. $\frac{4}{5}$ ▮ $-\frac{4}{5}$ >

36. −9 ▮ −12   >

37. $-\frac{3}{8}$ ▮ $\frac{3}{8}$ <

38. −4.09 ▮ −5.3   >

39. 0.49 ▮ 0.43   >

40. −1.0 ▮ −0.7   <

41. −0.086 ▮ −0.095   >

42. $\frac{1}{2}$ ▮ $-\frac{1}{2}$ >

43. 0.001 ▮ 0.002   <

44. −0.006 ▮ −0.007   >

45. $\frac{5}{8}$ ▮ 0.6   >

46. 2.7 ▮ $\frac{10}{3}$ <

47. $-\frac{4}{3}$ ▮ $-\frac{1}{3}$ <

48. $\frac{9}{2}$ ▮ $\frac{7}{2}$ >

49. −0.8 ▮ $-\frac{3}{5}$ <

50. −0.7 ▮ −0.2   <

51. 0.3 ▮ $\frac{1}{3}$ <

52. $\frac{9}{20}$ ▮ 0.42   >

53. $-\frac{17}{30}$ ▮ $-\frac{16}{20}$ >

54. $\frac{13}{15}$ ▮ $\frac{8}{9}$ <

55. −(−6) ▮ −(−5)   >

56. $-\left(-\frac{12}{13}\right)$ ▮ $\frac{7}{8}$ >

Insert either <, >, or = in each shaded area to make a true statement.

57. 5 ▮ |−2| >

58. |−12| ▮ |−13| <

59. $\frac{3}{4}$ ▮ |−4| <

60. |−4| ▮ −3   >

61. |0| ▮ |−4| <

62. |−2.1| ▮ |−1.8| >

63. 4 ▮ $\left|-\frac{9}{2}\right|$ <

64. |−5| ▮ −|−6| >

65. $\left|-\frac{4}{5}\right|$ ▮ $\left|-\frac{5}{4}\right|$ <

66. $\left|\frac{2}{5}\right|$ ▮ |−0.40| =

67. |−4.6| ▮ $\left|-\frac{23}{5}\right|$ =

68. $\left|-\frac{8}{3}\right|$ ▮ |−3.5| <

Insert either $>$, $<$, *or* $=$ *in each shaded area to make a true statement.*

69. $\dfrac{2}{3} + \dfrac{2}{3} + \dfrac{2}{3} + \dfrac{2}{3}$ ▨ $4 \cdot \dfrac{2}{3}$ =

70. $\dfrac{3}{4} + \dfrac{3}{4}$ ▨ $\dfrac{3}{4} \cdot \dfrac{3}{4}$ >

71. $\dfrac{1}{2} \cdot \dfrac{1}{2}$ ▨ $\dfrac{1}{2} \div \dfrac{1}{2}$ <

72. $5 \div \dfrac{2}{3}$ ▨ $\dfrac{2}{3} \div 5$ >

73. $\dfrac{5}{8} - \dfrac{1}{2}$ ▨ $\dfrac{5}{8} \div \dfrac{1}{2}$ <

74. $3\dfrac{1}{5} + \dfrac{1}{3}$ ▨ $3\dfrac{1}{5} \cdot \dfrac{1}{3}$ >

Arrange the numbers from smallest to largest.

75. $0.46, \dfrac{4}{9}, |-5|, -|-1|, \dfrac{3}{7}$ $-|-1|, \dfrac{3}{7}, \dfrac{4}{9}, 0.46, |-5|$

76. $-\dfrac{3}{4}, -|0.6|, -\dfrac{5}{9}, -1.74, |-1.9|$ $-1.74, -\dfrac{3}{4}, -|0.6|, -\dfrac{5}{9}, |-1.9|$

77. $\dfrac{2}{3}, 0.6, |-2.6|, \dfrac{19}{25}, \dfrac{5}{12}$ $\dfrac{5}{12}, 0.6, \dfrac{2}{3}, \dfrac{19}{25}, |-2.6|$

78. $-|-5|, |-9|, -\left|-\dfrac{12}{5}\right|, 2.7, \dfrac{7}{12}$ $-|-5|, \dfrac{7}{12}, -\left|-\dfrac{12}{5}\right|, 2.7, |-9|$

Problem Solving

79. What numbers are 4 units from 0 on a number line?   4, −4

80. What numbers are 100 units from 0 on the number line?   100, −100

In Exercises 81–88, give three real numbers that satisfy all the stated criteria. If no real numbers satisfy the criteria, so state and explain why.

81. less than 4 and greater than 6   not possible

82. greater than 4 and less than 6   Answers will vary: $4\frac{1}{2}, 5, 5.5$.

83. less than −2 and greater than −6

84. greater than −5 and greater than −9

85. greater than −3 and greater than 3   Answers will vary: 4, 5, 6.

86. less than −3 and less than 3   Answers will vary: −4, −5, −6.

87. greater than $|-2|$ and less than $|-6|$ Answers will vary: 3, 4, 5.

88. greater than $|-3|$ and less than $|3|$ not possible

89. **a)** Consider the word *between*. What does this word mean?

b) List three real numbers between 4 and 6

c) Is the number 4 between the numbers 4 and 6? Explain.   no

d) Is the number 5 between the numbers 4 and 6? Explain.   yes

e) Is it true or false that the real numbers between 4 and 6 are the real numbers that are both greater than 4 and less than 6? Explain.   true

90. **Property Crime Rates** The following line graph shows the U.S. property crime rates per 1000 households from 1973 to 2003.

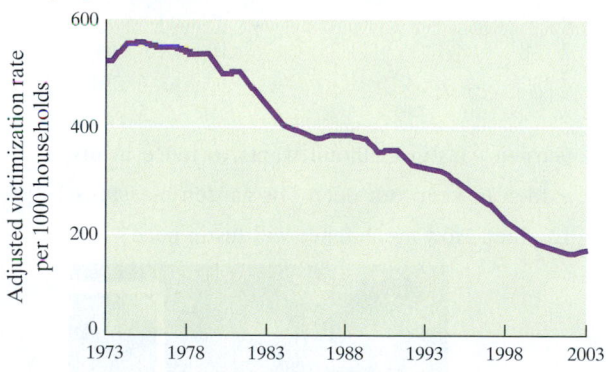

Propery Crime Rates

Note: Property crimes include burglary, theft, and motor vehicle theft.

Source: www.ojp.usdoj.gov

Estimate the year(s) when the property crime rate was

a) first less than 400 per 1000 households.   1984

b) first less than 200 per 1000 households.   2000

c) greater than 400 per 1000 households and less than 600 per 1000 households.   1973–1983

91. **Peanuts** The following bar graph shows the percent of the recommended daily allowance of certain nutrients in 1 ounce of dry-roasted, salted peanuts. Use the bar graph to determine which nutrients provide

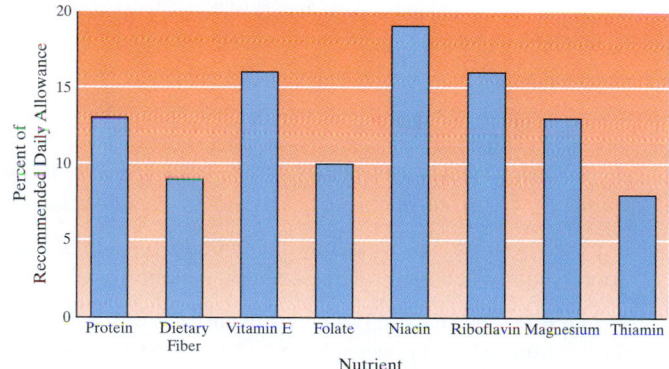

Source: Nutritional Wellness

a) less than 10% of the recommended daily allowance.

b) greater than 15% of the recommended daily allowance.   vitamin E, niacin, and riboflavin

83. Answers will vary: −3, −4, −5.   **84.** Answers will vary: −4, 0, 3.

89. a) does not include the endpoints   **b)** Answers will vary: $4.1, 5, 5\dfrac{1}{2}$.

91. a) dietary fiber and thiamin

Challenge Problems

92. A number greater than 0 and less than 1 (or between 0 and 1) is multiplied by itself. Will the product be less than, equal to, or greater than the original number selected? Explain why this is always true.   less than

93. A number between 0 and 1 is divided by itself. Will the quotient be less than, equal to, or greater than the original number selected? Explain why this is always true.   greater than

94. What two numbers can be substituted for x to make $|x| = 3$ a true statement?   3, −3

95. Are there any values for x that would make $|x| = -3$ a true statement? Explain.   no

96. a) To what is $|x|$ equal if x represents a real number greater than or equal to 0? x

b) To what is $|x|$ equal if x represents a real number less than 0? $-x$

c) Fill in the following shaded areas to make a true statement. $x, -x$

$$|x| = \begin{cases} \rule{1em}{0.8em} & , x \geq 0 \\ \rule{1em}{0.8em} & , x < 0 \end{cases}$$

Group Activity

Discuss and answer Exercise 97 as a group.

97. a) Group member 1: Draw a number line and mark points on the line to represent the following numbers.

$$|-2|, \qquad -|3|, \qquad -\left|\frac{1}{3}\right|$$

b) Group member 2: Do the same as in part **a)**, but on your number line mark points for the following numbers.

$$|-4|, \qquad -|2|, \qquad \left|-\frac{3}{5}\right|$$

97. a)–d)

$$\begin{array}{c} -|-3| \\ -|3| \quad -|2| \quad -\left|\frac{1}{3}\right| |0| -\frac{3}{5} \quad |-2| \quad \left|\frac{16}{5}\right| |-4| \end{array}$$

(number line from −3 to 4)

c) Group member 3: Do the same as in parts **a)** and **b)**, but mark points for the following numbers.

$$|0|, \qquad \left|\frac{16}{5}\right|, \qquad -|-3|$$

d) As a group, construct one number line that contains all the points listed in parts **a)**, **b)**, and **c)**.

Cumulative Review Exercises

[1.3] **98.** Add $2\frac{3}{5} + 3\frac{1}{3}$. $\frac{89}{15}$ or $5\frac{14}{15}$

[1.4] **99.** List the set of integers. $\{\ldots, -3, -2, -1, 0, 1, 2, 3, \ldots\}$

100. List the set of whole numbers. $\{0, 1, 2, 3, \ldots\}$

101. Consider the following set of numbers.

$$\left\{5, -2, 0, \frac{1}{3}, \sqrt{3}, -\frac{5}{9}, 2.3\right\}$$

List the numbers that are

a) natural numbers.   5

b) whole numbers.   5, 0

c) integers.   5, −2, 0

d) rational numbers. $5, -2, 0, \frac{1}{3}, -\frac{5}{9}, 2.3$

e) irrational numbers. $\sqrt{3}$

f) real numbers. $5, -2, 0, \frac{1}{3}, \sqrt{3}, -\frac{5}{9}, 2.3$

Mid-Chapter Test: 1.1–1.5

1. At least two hours of study and homework for each hour of class time is generally recommended.

To find out how well you understand the chapter material to this point, take this brief test. The answers, and the section where the material was initially discussed, are given in the back of the book. Review any questions that you answered incorrectly.

1. For each hour of class time, how many hours outside of class are recommended for studying and doing homework?

2. Phone Bills   Jason Wisely's monthly phone bills for the first six months of 2005 were $78.83, $96.57, $62.23, $88.79, $101.75, and $55.62. For Jason's phone bills, determine the **a)** mean and **b)** median.   **a)** $80.63   **b)** $83.81

3. Checking Account   The balance in Elizabeth Mater's checking account is $652.70. She deposited $230.75 and then purchased three books at $19.62 each, including tax. If she pays by check, what is the new balance in her checking account? $824.59

4. Boat Rental   The rental cost of a boat from Natwora's Boat Rental is $7.50 per 15 minutes, and the rental cost from Gurney's Boat Rental is $18 per half hour. Suppose you plan to rent a boat for 4 hours.

a) Which is the better deal?   Natwora's

b) How much will you save? $24

5. Water Rate   The water rate in Livingston County is $1.85 per 1000 gallons of water used. What is the water bill for a resident of Livingston County who uses 33,700 gallons of water? $62.35

Perform the indicated operation.

6. $\frac{3}{7} \cdot \frac{7}{18}$ $\frac{1}{6}$

7. $\frac{9}{16} \div \frac{12}{13}$ $\frac{39}{64}$

8. $\frac{5}{8} + \frac{3}{5}$ $\frac{49}{40}$ or $1\frac{9}{40}$

9. $6\frac{1}{4} - 3\frac{1}{5}$ $\frac{61}{20}$ or $3\frac{1}{20}$

10. Garden   Justin Calhoun wants to fence in his rectangular garden to keep out deer. His garden measures $14\frac{2}{3}$ feet by $12\frac{1}{2}$ feet. How much fence will Justin need? $54\frac{1}{3}$ ft

In Exercises 11–15, indicate whether each statement is true or false.

11. 0 is a natural number. F   **12.** −8.6 is a real number. T

13. $3\frac{2}{3}$ is an irrational number. F

14. Every integer is a real number. T

15. Every whole number is a counting number. F

16. Evaluate $-\left|-\dfrac{7}{10}\right|$. $-\dfrac{7}{10}$

Insert either <, >, *or* = *in each shaded area to make a true statement.*

17. -0.005 ▨ -0.006 >   **18.** $\dfrac{7}{8}$ ▨ $\dfrac{5}{6}$ >

19. $|-9|$ ▨ $|-12|$ <   **20.** $\left|-\dfrac{3}{8}\right|$ ▨ $|-0.375|$ =

1.6 Addition of Real Numbers

1. Add real numbers using a number line.

2. Add fractions.

3. Identify opposites.

4. Add using absolute values.

5. Add using calculators.

There are many practical uses for negative numbers. A submarine diving below sea level, a bank account that has been overdrawn, a business spending more than it earns, and a temperature below zero are some examples.

The four basic **operations** of arithmetic are addition, subtraction, multiplication, and division. In the next few sections, we will explain how to add, subtract, multiply, and divide numbers. We will consider both positive and negative numbers. In this section, we discuss the operation of addition.

1 Add Real Numbers Using a Number Line

To add numbers, we make use of a number line. Represent the first number to be added (first *addend*) by an arrow starting at 0. The arrow is drawn to the right if the number is positive. If the number is negative, the arrow is drawn to the left. From the tip of the first arrow, draw a second arrow to represent the second addend. The second arrow is drawn to the right or left, as just explained. The sum of the two numbers is found at the tip of the second arrow. Note that with the exception of 0, *any number without a sign in front of it is positive.* For example, 3 means +3 and 5 means +5.

EXAMPLE 1 ▶ Evaluate $3 + (-4)$ using a number line.

Solution *Always begin at 0.* Since the first addend, the 3, is positive, the first arrow starts at 0 and is drawn 3 units to the right (**Fig. 1.18**).

FIGURE 1.18

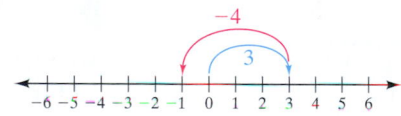

FIGURE 1.19

The second arrow starts at 3 and is drawn 4 units to the left, since the second addend is negative (**Fig. 1.19**). The tip of the second arrow is at −1. Thus,

$$3 + (-4) = -1$$

▶ **Now Try Exercise 27**

EXAMPLE 2 ▶ Evaluate $-4 + 2$ using a number line.

Solution Begin at 0. Since the first addend is negative, −4, the first arrow is drawn 4 units to the left. From there, since 2 is positive, the second arrow is drawn 2 units to the right. The second arrow ends at −2 (**Fig. 1.20**).

FIGURE 1.20

$$-4 + 2 = -2$$

▶ **Now Try Exercise 37**

EXAMPLE 3 ▸ Evaluate $-3 + (-2)$ using a number line.

Solution   Start at 0. Since both numbers being added are negative, both arrows will be drawn to the left (**Fig. 1.21**).

FIGURE 1.21

$$-3 + (-2) = -5$$

▸ **Now Try Exercise 39**

In Example 3, we can think of the expression $-3 + (-2)$ as combining a *loss* of 3 and a *loss* of 2 for a total *loss* of 5, or -5.

EXAMPLE 4 ▸ Add $5 + (-5)$ using a number line.

Solution   The first arrow starts at 0 and is drawn 5 units to the right. The second arrow starts at 5 and is drawn 5 units to the left. The tip of the second arrow is at 0. Thus, $5 + (-5) = 0$ (**Fig. 1.22**).

FIGURE 1.22

$$5 + (-5) = 0$$

▸ **Now Try Exercise 31**

EXAMPLE 5 ▸ **Below-Zero Temperatures** At the beginning of the five o'clock news broadcast on a winter day in Rochester, New York, the chief meteorologist reported that the temperature was three degrees below zero Fahrenheit. During the weather segment twenty minutes later, the chief meteorologist stated that the temperature had dropped four degrees since the beginning of the news broadcast. Find the temperature at 5:20 P.M.

Solution   A vertical number line (**Fig. 1.23**) may help you visualize this problem.

$$-3 + (-4) = -7°F$$

▸ **Now Try Exercise 117**

FIGURE 1.23

0°F
−3°F
−3°F
−4°F
−7°F

2 Add Fractions

We introduced fractions, and explained how to add positive fractions, in Section 1.3. To add fractions, where one or more of the fractions is negative, we use the same general procedure discussed in Section 1.3. Whenever the denominators are not the same, we must obtain a common denominator. Once we obtain the common denominator, we obtain the answer by adding the numerators while keeping the common denominator.

For example, suppose after obtaining a common denominator, we have $-\dfrac{19}{29} + \dfrac{13}{29}$.

To obtain the numerator of the answer, we may add $-19 + 13$ on the number line to obtain -6. The denominator of the answer is the common denominator, 29. Thus, the answer is $-\dfrac{6}{29}$. We show these calculations as follows.

$$-\frac{19}{29} + \frac{13}{29} = \frac{-19 + 13}{29} = \frac{-6}{29} = -\frac{6}{29}$$

Let's look at one more example. Suppose after obtaining a common denominator, we have $-\dfrac{7}{40} + \left(-\dfrac{5}{40}\right)$. To obtain the numerator of the answer, we may add $-7 + (-5)$ on the number line to obtain -12. The denominator of the answer is 40.

Thus, the answer before being simplified is $-\dfrac{12}{40}$. The final answer simplifies to $-\dfrac{3}{10}$. We show these calculations as follows.

$$-\frac{7}{40} + \left(-\frac{5}{40}\right) = \frac{-7 + (-5)}{40} = \frac{-12}{40} = -\frac{3}{10}$$

EXAMPLE 6 ▶ Add $\frac{7}{16} + \left(-\frac{2}{3}\right)$.

Solution　First, we determine that the least common denominator is 48. Changing each fraction to a fraction with a denominator of 48 yields

$$\frac{7}{16} \cdot \boxed{\frac{3}{3}} + \left(-\frac{2}{3}\right) \cdot \boxed{\frac{16}{16}}$$

$$\text{or}\quad \frac{21}{48} + \left(-\frac{32}{48}\right)$$

Now the fractions being added have a common denominator. To add these fractions, we keep the common denominator and add the numerators to get

$$\frac{7}{16} + \left(-\frac{2}{3}\right) = \frac{21}{48} + \left(-\frac{32}{48}\right) = \frac{21 + (-32)}{48}$$

Now we add $21 + (-32)$ on a number line to get the numerator of the fraction, -11; see **Figure 1.24**.

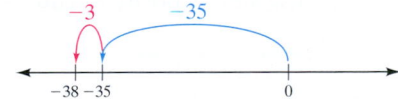

FIGURE 1.24

$$\text{Thus, } \frac{7}{16} + \left(-\frac{2}{3}\right) = \frac{21}{48} + \left(-\frac{32}{48}\right) = \frac{21 + (-32)}{48} = -\frac{11}{48}.$$

▶ **Now Try Exercise 77**

EXAMPLE 7 ▶ Add $-\frac{7}{8} + \left(-\frac{3}{40}\right)$.

Solution　The least common denominator (or LCD) is 40. Rewriting the first fraction with the LCD gives the following.

$$-\frac{7}{8} + \left(-\frac{3}{40}\right) = -\frac{7}{8} \cdot \boxed{\frac{5}{5}} + \left(-\frac{3}{40}\right)$$

$$= -\frac{35}{40} + \left(-\frac{3}{40}\right) = \frac{-35 + (-3)}{40}$$

Now we add $-35 + (-3)$ to get the numerator of the fraction, -38; see **Figure 1.25**.

FIGURE 1.25

$$\text{Thus, } -\frac{7}{8} + \left(-\frac{3}{40}\right) = \frac{-35}{40} + \left(\frac{-3}{40}\right) = \frac{-35 + (-3)}{40} = -\frac{38}{40} = -\frac{19}{20}.$$

▶ **Now Try Exercise 85**

Helpful Hint

In Example 6, **Figure 1.24**, we illustrated that starting at 0 and moving 21 units to the right, then moving 32 units to the left, ends at a negative 11. Thus, $21 + (-32) = -11$.

When the numbers are large, you are not expected to actually mark and count the units. For example, you will not need to count 32 units to the left from 21 to obtain the answer -11.

In objective 3, we will show you how to obtain $21 + (-32) = -11$ without having to draw number lines. We present adding on a number line here to help you understand the concept of addition of signed numbers, and to help you in determining, without doing any calculations, whether the sum of two signed numbers will be a positive number, a negative number, or zero.

3 Identify Opposites

Now let's consider **opposites**, or **additive inverses**.

> ### Opposites (or Additive Inverses)
> Any two numbers whose sum is zero are said to be **opposites** (or **additive inverses**) of each other. In general, if we let a represent any real number, then its opposite is $-a$ and $a + (-a) = 0$.

In Example 4, the sum of 5 and -5 is 0. Thus, -5 is the opposite of 5 and 5 is the opposite of -5.

EXAMPLE 8 ▶ Find the opposite of each number. **a)** 3 **b)** -4 **c)** $-\dfrac{7}{8}$

Solution

  a) The opposite of 3 is -3, since $3 + (-3) = 0$.
  b) The opposite of -4 is 4, since $-4 + 4 = 0$.
  c) The opposite of $-\dfrac{7}{8}$ is $\dfrac{7}{8}$, since $-\dfrac{7}{8} + \dfrac{7}{8} = 0$.

▶ **Now Try Exercise 15**

4 Add Using Absolute Values

Now that we have had some practice adding signed numbers on a number line, we give a rule (in two parts) for using absolute value to add signed numbers. Remember that the absolute value of a nonzero number will always be positive. The first part of the rule follows.

> ### Adding Real Numbers with the Same Sign
> To add real numbers with the same sign (either both positive or both negative), add their absolute values. The sum has the same sign as the numbers being added.

EXAMPLE 9 ▶ Add $4 + 8$.

Solution Since both numbers have the same sign, both positive, we add their absolute values: $|4| + |8| = 4 + 8 = 12$. Since both numbers being added are positive, the sum is positive. Thus, $4 + 8 = 12$.

▶ **Now Try Exercise 49**

EXAMPLE 10 ▶ Add $-6 + (-9)$.

Solution Since both numbers have the same sign, both negative, we add their absolute values: $|-6| + |-9| = 6 + 9 = 15$. Since both numbers being added are negative, their sum is negative. Thus, $-6 + (-9) = -15$.

▶ **Now Try Exercise 51**

   The sum of two positive numbers will always be positive and the sum of two negative numbers will always be negative.

> ### Adding Two Signed Numbers with Different Signs
> To add two signed numbers with different signs (one positive and the other negative), subtract the smaller absolute value from the larger absolute value. The answer has the sign of the number with the larger absolute value.

TEACHING TIP
Point out that the negative sign can be thought of as meaning "the opposite of." Then show how this meaning is useful in some cases such as $-(-3)$ which means the opposite of negative three, or three.

INSTRUCTOR EXAMPLE
Find the opposite of each number.
  a) 6 **b)** $-\dfrac{3}{5}$
Ans.:
  a) -6 **d)** $\dfrac{3}{5}$

INSTRUCTOR EXAMPLE
Add $12 + 7$.
Ans.: 19

INSTRUCTOR EXAMPLE
Add $-5 + (-10)$.
Ans.: -15

EXAMPLE 11 ▶ Add 10 + (−6).

Solution The two numbers being added have different signs, so we subtract the smaller absolute value from the larger: $|10| - |-6| = 10 - 6 = 4$. Since $|10|$ is greater than $|-6|$ and the sign of 10 is positive, the sum is positive. Thus, $10 + (-6) = 4$.

▶ **Now Try Exercise 53**

EXAMPLE 12 ▶ Add 12 + (−18).

Solution The numbers being added have different signs, so we subtract the smaller absolute value from the larger: $|-18| - |12| = 18 - 12 = 6$. Since $|-18|$ is greater than $|12|$ and the sign of −18 is negative, the sum is negative. Thus, $12 + (-18) = -6$.

▶ **Now Try Exercise 55**

EXAMPLE 13 ▶ Add −21 + 20.

Solution The two numbers being added have different signs, so we subtract the smaller absolute value from the larger: $|-21| - |20| = 21 - 20 = 1$. Since $|-21|$ is greater than $|20|$, the sum is negative. Therefore, $-21 + 20 = -1$.

▶ **Now Try Exercise 61**

Now let's look at some additional examples that contain fractions and decimal numbers.

EXAMPLE 14 ▶ Add $-\dfrac{3}{5} + \dfrac{4}{7}$.

Solution We can write each fraction with the least common denominator, 35.

$$-\frac{3}{5} + \frac{4}{7} = -\frac{3}{5} \cdot \frac{7}{7} + \frac{4}{7} \cdot \frac{5}{5}$$
$$= \frac{-21}{35} + \frac{20}{35} = \frac{-21 + 20}{35}$$

Since $|-21|$ is greater than $|20|$, the final answer will be negative. In Example 13, we found that $-21 + 20 = -1$. Thus, we can write

$$\frac{-21}{35} + \frac{20}{35} = \frac{-21 + 20}{35} = \frac{-1}{35} = -\frac{1}{35}$$

Thus, $-\dfrac{3}{5} + \dfrac{4}{7} = -\dfrac{1}{35}$.

▶ **Now Try Exercise 87**

Examples 15 and 16 contain decimal numbers. If you have forgotten how to perform the basic operations of addition, subtraction, multiplication, and division of decimal numbers, read Appendix A now.

EXAMPLE 15 ▶ Add −37.45 + (−26.98).

Solution Since both numbers have the same sign, both negative, we add their absolute values: $|-37.45| + |-26.98| = 37.45 + 26.98$.

$$\begin{array}{r} 37.45 \\ + \ 26.98 \\ \hline 64.43 \end{array}$$

Since two negative numbers are being added, the sum is negative. Therefore, $-37.45 + (-26.98) = -64.43$.

▶ **Now Try Exercise 67**

EXAMPLE 16 ▶ **Net Profit or Loss**   The B.J. Donaldson Printing Company had a loss of $4005.69 for the first 6 months of the year and a profit of $29,645.78 for the second 6 months of the year. Find the net profit or loss for the year.

Solution **Understand and Translate** This problem can be represented as $-4005.69 + 29{,}645.78$. Since the numbers have different signs, we subtract the smaller absolute value from the larger.

Carry Out $|29{,}645.78| - |-4005.69| = 29{,}645.78 - 4005.69$

$$
\begin{array}{r}
29{,}645.78 \\
-\ \ \ 4005.69 \\
\hline
25{,}640.09
\end{array}
$$

Since $|29{,}645.78|$ is greater than $|-4005.69|$ and the sign of $29{,}645.78$ is positive, the sum is positive. Thus, $-4005.69 + 29{,}645.78 = 25{,}640.09$.

Check and Answer   The answer is reasonable. Thus, the net profit for the year was $25,640.09.

▶ **Now Try Exercise 121**

The sum of two signed numbers with different signs may be either positive or negative. The sign of the sum will be the same as the sign of the number with the larger absolute value.

Helpful Hint

Architects often make a scale model of a building before starting construction of the building. This "model" helps them visualize the project and often helps them avoid problems.

Mathematicians also construct models. A mathematical *model* may be a physical representation of a mathematical concept. It may be as simple as using tiles or chips to represent specific numbers. For example, below we use a model to help explain addition of real numbers. This may help some of you understand the concepts better.

We let a red chip represent $+1$ and a green chip represent -1.

● $= +1$ ● $= -1$

If we add $+1$ and -1, or a red and a green chip, we get 0.
Now consider the addition problem $3 + (-5)$. We can represent this as

$$\underbrace{\bullet\ \bullet\ \bullet}_{3} + \underbrace{\bullet\ \bullet\ \bullet\ \bullet\ \bullet}_{-5}$$

If we remove 3 red chips and 3 green chips, or three zeros, we are left with 2 green chips, which represents a sum of -2. Thus, $3 + (-5) = -2$,

$$\cancel{\bullet}\ \cancel{\bullet}\ \cancel{\bullet} + \cancel{\bullet}\ \cancel{\bullet}\ \cancel{\bullet}\ \bullet\ \bullet$$

Now consider the problem $-4 + (-2)$. We can represent this as

$$\underbrace{\bullet\ \bullet\ \bullet\ \bullet}_{-4} + \underbrace{\bullet\ \bullet}_{-2}$$

Since we end up with 6 green chips, and each green chip represents -1, the sum is -6. Therefore, $-4 + (-2) = -6$.

5   Add Using Calculators

Throughout the book we will provide information about calculators in the Using Your Calculator Boxes. Some will be for scientific calculators; some will be for graphing calculators, also called graphers; and some will be for both. To the left are pictures of a scientific calculator (on left) and a graphing calculator (on right). Graphing calculators can do everything that a scientific calculator can do and more. Ask your instructor if he or she is recommending a particular calculator for this course. If you plan on taking additional mathematics courses, you may want to consider purchasing the calculator that will be used in those courses.

TEACHING TIP
Point out that scientific calculators know the rules for order of operation which we will discuss in Section 1.9. Then say, "Check if your calculator is a scientific calculator by entering $10 - 4 \times 2 =$. Did you get 2 or 12? If your answer is 12, the calculator is not a scientific calculator."

It is important that you understand the procedures for adding, subtracting, multiplying, and dividing real numbers *without* using a calculator. *You should not need to rely on a calculator to work problems.* If you are permitted to use a calculator, you can, however, use the calculator to help save time on difficult calculations. If you have an understanding of the basic concepts, you should be able to tell if you have made an error entering information on the calculator if the answer shown does not seem reasonable.

Following is the first of many Using Your Calculator Boxes and the first of many Using Your Graphing Calculator Boxes. Note that *no new material* will be presented in the boxes. The boxes are provided to help you use your calculator, if you are using one in this course. Do not be concerned if you do not know what all the calculator keys do. Your instructor will tell you which calculator keys you will need to know how to use.

In Using Your Graphing Calculator Boxes, when we show keystrokes or graphing screens (called windows), they will be for the Texas Instruments TI-84 Plus calculator. The same instructions will apply for the Texas Instruments TI-83 Plus calculator, although we will not indicate this in the Using Your Graphing Calculator Boxes. You should read your graphing calculator manual for more detailed instructions.

USING YOUR CALCULATOR   Entering Negative Numbers

Most scientific calculators contain a $\boxed{+/-}$ key, which is used to enter a negative number. To enter the number -5, press $5\ \boxed{+/-}$ and a -5 will be displayed. Now we show how to evaluate some addition problems on a scientific calculator.

Addition of Real Numbers

EVALUATE	KEYSTROKES*	ANSWER DISPLAYED
$-9 + 24$	$9\ \boxed{+/-}\ \boxed{+}\ 24\ \boxed{=}$	15
$15 + (-22)$	$15\ \boxed{+}\ 22\ \boxed{+/-}\ \boxed{=}$	-7
$-30 + (-16)$	$30\ \boxed{+/-}\ \boxed{+}\ 16\ \boxed{+/-}\ \boxed{=}$	-46

*With some scientific calculators the negative sign is entered before the number, as is done with graphing calculators.

USING YOUR GRAPHING CALCULATOR   Entering Negative Numbers

Graphing calculators have two keys that look similar, as shown below.

$\boxed{(-)}$ $\qquad\qquad\qquad\qquad\qquad$ $\boxed{-}$
↑ $\qquad\qquad\qquad\qquad\qquad\qquad\qquad$ ↑
Used to make a number negative $\qquad\qquad\qquad$ *Used to subtract*

Addition of Real Numbers

EVALUATE	KEYSTROKES	ANSWER DISPLAYED
$-9 + 24$	$\boxed{(-)}\ 9 + 24\ \boxed{ENTER}$	15
$15 + (-22)$	$15 + \boxed{(-)}\ 22\ \boxed{ENTER}$	-7
$-30 + (-16)$	$\boxed{(-)}\ 30 + \boxed{(-)}\ 16\ \boxed{ENTER}$	-46

To make a number negative on a graphing calculator, you first press the $\boxed{(-)}$ key, then enter the number.

EXERCISE SET 1.6
MathXL®   MyMathLab

Concept/Writing Exercises

1. addition, subtraction, multiplication, division
2. a) two numbers that sum to 0   b) One example is 3 and -3.

1. What are the four basic operations of arithmetic?

2. a) What are opposites or additive inverses?
   b) Give an example of two numbers that are opposites.

3. a) Are the numbers $-\dfrac{2}{3}$ and $\dfrac{3}{2}$ opposites? Explain.   no

b) If the numbers in part a) are not opposites, what number is the opposite of $-\dfrac{2}{3}$? $\dfrac{2}{3}$

4. If we add a positive number and a negative number, will the sum be positive, negative, or can it be either? Explain.
   can be either

5. If we add two negative numbers, will the sum be a positive number or a negative number? Explain.   negative

6. a) If we add −24,692 and 30,519, will the sum be positive or negative? Without performing any calculations, explain how you determined your answer.   positive

   b) Repeat part a) for the numbers 24,692 and −30,519.

   c) Repeat part a) for the numbers −24,692 and −30,519.

7. Explain how to add two numbers with like signs.

8. Explain how to add two numbers with unlike signs.

9. Mr. Dabskic charged $162 worth of groceries on his charge card. He later made a payment of $85.

   a) Explain why the balance remaining on his card may be found by the addition −162 + 85.

   b) Find the sum of −162 + 85.   −77

   c) In part b), you should have obtained a sum of −77. Explain why this −77 indicates that Mr. Dabskic owes $77 on his credit card.

10. Mrs. Goldstein owed $163 on her credit card. She charged another item costing $56.

    a) Explain why the new balance on her credit card may be found by the addition −163 + (−56).

    b) Find the sum of −163 + (−56).   −219

    c) In part b), you should have obtained a sum of −219. Explain why this −219 indicates that Mrs. Goldstein owes $219 on her credit card.

6. b) negative   c) negative
7., 8., 9. a) and c) Answers will vary. 10. a) and c) Answers will vary.

In Exercises 11 and 12, are the calculations shown correct? If not, explain why not.

11. $\dfrac{-5}{12} + \dfrac{9}{12} = \dfrac{-5+9}{12} = \dfrac{4}{12} = \dfrac{1}{3}$ correct

12. $\dfrac{-6}{70} + \left(\dfrac{-9}{70}\right) = \dfrac{-6+(-9)}{70} = \dfrac{-15}{70} = -\dfrac{3}{14}$ correct

Practice the Skills

Write the opposite of each number.

81. $-\dfrac{16}{15}$ or $-1\dfrac{1}{15}$ 91. $-\dfrac{23}{21}$ or $-1\dfrac{2}{21}$

13. 9   −9

14. −7   7

15. −28   28

16. 3   −3

17. 0   0

18. $-3\dfrac{1}{2}$ $3\dfrac{1}{2}$

19. $\dfrac{5}{3}$ $-\dfrac{5}{3}$

20. $-\dfrac{1}{4}$ $\dfrac{1}{4}$

21. $2\dfrac{3}{5}$ $-2\dfrac{3}{5}$

22. −1   1

23. 3.72   −3.72

24. −0.721   0.721

Add.

25. 5 + 6   11

26. −8 + 2   −6

27. 4 + (−3)   1

28. 9 + (−12)   −3

29. −4 + (−2)   −6

30. −3 + (−5)   −8

31. 6 + (−6)   0

32. −8 + 8   0

33. −4 + 4   0

34. −6 + 6   0

35. −8 + (−2)   −10

36. 6 + (−5)   1

37. −7 + 3   −4

38. −6 + 9   3

39. −8 + (−5)   −13

40. 0 + (−3)   −3

41. 0 + 0   0

42. 0 + (−0)   0

43. −6 + 0   −6

44. −9 + 13   4

45. 18 + (−9)   9

46. −7 + 7   0

47. −33 + (−31)   −64

48. −27 + (−9)   −36

49. 7 + 9   16

50. 12 + 3   15

51. −8 + (−4)   −12

52. −25 + (−36)   −61

53. 6 + (−3)   3

54. 52 + (−25)   27

55. 13 + (−19)   −6

56. 34 + (−40)   −6

57. 180 + (−200)   −20

58. −452 + 312   −140

59. −11 + (−20)   −31

60. −33 + (−92)   −125

61. −67 + 28   −39

62. 183 + (−183)   0

63. 184 + (−93)   91

64. −19 + 176   157

65. 80.5 + (−90.4)   −9.9

66. −24.6 + (−13.9)   −38.5

67. −124.7 + (−19.3)   −144.0

68. 106.3 + (−110.9)   −4.6

69. −123.56 + (−18.35)   −141.91

70. −72.79 + 33.47   −39.32

71. −99.36 + 45.71   −53.65

72. −84.15 + (−29.98)   −114.13

Add.

73. $\dfrac{3}{5} + \dfrac{1}{7}$ $\dfrac{26}{35}$

74. $\dfrac{5}{8} + \dfrac{3}{5}$ $\dfrac{49}{40}$ or $1\dfrac{9}{40}$

75. $\dfrac{5}{12} + \dfrac{6}{7}$ $\dfrac{107}{84}$ or $1\dfrac{23}{84}$

76. $\dfrac{2}{9} + \dfrac{3}{10}$ $\dfrac{47}{90}$

77. $-\dfrac{8}{11} + \dfrac{4}{5}$ $\dfrac{4}{55}$

78. $-\dfrac{4}{9} + \dfrac{5}{27}$ $-\dfrac{7}{27}$

79. $-\dfrac{7}{10} + \dfrac{11}{90}$ $-\dfrac{26}{45}$

80. $\dfrac{8}{9} + \left(-\dfrac{1}{3}\right)$ $\dfrac{5}{9}$

81. $-\dfrac{7}{30} + \left(-\dfrac{5}{6}\right)$

82. $-\dfrac{7}{9} + \left(-\dfrac{1}{5}\right)$ $-\dfrac{44}{45}$

83. $\dfrac{9}{25} + \left(-\dfrac{3}{50}\right)$ $\dfrac{3}{10}$

84. $-\dfrac{1}{15} + \left(-\dfrac{5}{6}\right)$ $-\dfrac{9}{10}$

85. $-\dfrac{4}{5} + \left(-\dfrac{5}{75}\right)$ $-\dfrac{13}{15}$

86. $\dfrac{5}{36} + \left(-\dfrac{5}{24}\right)$ $-\dfrac{5}{72}$

87. $-\dfrac{9}{24} + \dfrac{5}{7}$ $\dfrac{19}{56}$

88. $-\dfrac{9}{40} + \dfrac{4}{15}$ $\dfrac{1}{24}$

89. $-\dfrac{5}{12} + \left(-\dfrac{3}{10}\right)$ $-\dfrac{43}{60}$

90. $\dfrac{7}{16} + \left(-\dfrac{5}{24}\right)$ $\dfrac{11}{48}$

91. $-\dfrac{13}{14} + \left(-\dfrac{7}{42}\right)$

92. $-\dfrac{11}{27} + \left(-\dfrac{7}{18}\right)$ $-\dfrac{43}{54}$

In Exercises 93–108, a) determine by observation whether the sum will be a positive number, zero, or a negative number; b) find the sum using your calculator; and c) examine your answer to part b) to see whether it is reasonable and makes sense.

93. 587 + (−197)   390

94. −140 + (−629)   −769

95. −84 + (−289)   −373

96. −647 + 352   −295

97. −947 + 495   −452

98. 762 + (−762)   0

99. −496 + (−804)   −1300

100. −354 + 1090   736

101. $-375 + 263$ -112 **102.** $1127 + (-84)$ 1043 **103.** $-1833 + (-2047)$ -3880 **104.** $-426 + 572$ 146

105. $3124 + (-2013)$ 1111 **106.** $-9095 + (-647)$ -9742 **107.** $-1025 + (-1025)$ -2050 **108.** $7513 + (-4361)$ 3152

Indicate whether each statement is true or false.

109. The sum of two negative numbers is always a negative number. T

110. The sum of a negative number and a positive number is sometimes a negative number. T

111. The sum of two positive numbers is never a negative number. T

112. The sum of a positive number and a negative number is always a negative number. F

113. The sum of a positive number and a negative number is always a positive number. F

114. The sum of a number and its opposite is always equal to zero. T

Problem Solving

Write an expression that can be used to solve each problem and then solve.

115. Credit Card David Nurkiewicz owed $94 on his bank credit card. He charged another item costing $183. Find the amount that David owed the bank. $277

116. Charge Card Mrs. Chu charged $142 worth of goods on her charge card. Find her balance after she made a payment of $87. $55

117. Football A football team lost 18 yards on one play and then lost 3 yards on the following play. What was the total loss in yardage? 21 yd

118. Overdrawn Checking Account Mrs. Jahn is unaware that her checking account has been overdrawn by $56. While shopping, she writes a check for $162. Find the total amount by which Mrs. Jahn has overdrawn her account. $218

119. Drilling for Water A company is drilling a well. During the first week they drilled 27 feet, and during the second week they drilled another 34 feet before they struck water. How deep is the well? 61 ft

120. Coffee Bar The Frenches opened a coffee bar. Their income and expenses for their first three months of operation are shown in the following graph.

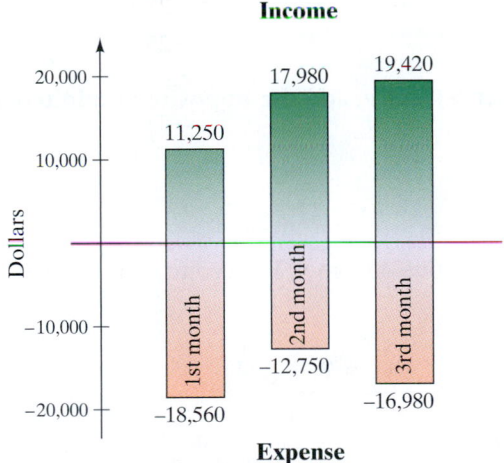

Income

a) Find the net profit or loss (the sum of income and expenses) for the first month. loss of $7310

b) Find the net profit or loss for the second month.

c) Find the net profit or loss for the third month.

121. High Mountain The Web site *www.guinnessworldrecords.com* lists Mauna Kea in Hawaii as the tallest mountain in the world when measured from its base to its peak. The base of Mauna Kea is 19,684 feet below sea level. The total height of the mountain from its base to its peak is 33,480 feet. How high is the peak of Mauna Kea above sea level? 13,796 ft

120. b) profit of $5230   **c)** profit of $2440

122. Net Profit or Loss The Crafty Scrapbook Company had a loss of $3000 for the first 4 months of the year and a profit of $37,400 for the last 8 months of the year. Find the net profit or loss for the year. $34,400 net profit

123. Surplus or Deficit The following graph shows the surplus or deficit for Preferred Care, Inc. in Rochester, New York, for the years 1994 through 2004.

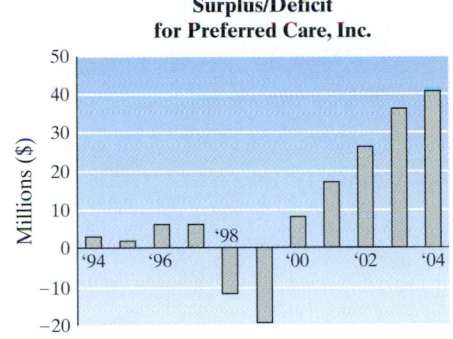

**Surplus/Deficit
for Preferred Care, Inc.**

Source: Rochester Democrat & Chronicle

a) Estimate the surplus or deficit for Preferred Care, Inc. in 1998. −$12 million

b) Estimate the surplus or deficit for Preferred Care Inc. for each of the years 1999, 2000, and 2001. Then estimate the surplus or deficit from 1999 through 2001 by adding these three estimates. 1999–2001: surplus, $5 million

124. Stocks The following chart shows percent changes from the first quarter of 2004 through the first quarter of 2005 for stocks based in the Buffalo–Niagara, New York region.

Percent change from previous quarter for stocks based in the Buffalo–Niagara, New York region

1st quarter 2004	−3.2%
2nd quarter 2004	Unchanged
3rd quarter 2004	1.2%
4th quarter 2004	12.2%
1st quarter 2005	−2.6%

Source: The Buffalo News

Determine the percent change for stocks based in the Buffalo–Niagara, New York, region from the first quarter of 2004 through the first quarter of 2005 by adding the individual percents. 7.6%

Challenge Problems

Evaluate each exercise by adding the numbers from left to right. We will discuss problems like this shortly.

125. $(-4) + (-6) + (-12)$ -22

126. $5 + (-7) + (-8)$ -10

127. $29 + (-46) + 37$ 20

128. $4 + (-5) + 6 + (-8)$ -3

129. $(-12) + (-10) + 25 + (-3)$ 0

130. $(-4) + (-2) + (-15) + (-27)$ -48

131. $\dfrac{1}{2} + \left(-\dfrac{1}{3}\right) + \dfrac{1}{5}$ $\dfrac{11}{30}$

132. $-\dfrac{3}{8} + \left(-\dfrac{2}{9}\right) + \left(-\dfrac{1}{2}\right)$ $-\dfrac{79}{72}$ or $-1\dfrac{7}{72}$

Find the following sums. Explain how you determined your answer. (Hint: Pair small numbers with large numbers from the ends inward.)

133. $1 + 2 + 3 + \cdots + 10$ 55

134. $1 + 2 + 3 + \cdots + 20$ 210

Cumulative Review Exercises

[1.3] **135.** Multiply $\left(\dfrac{4}{7}\right)\left(2\dfrac{3}{8}\right)$. $\dfrac{19}{14}$ or $1\dfrac{5}{14}$

136. Subtract $3 - \dfrac{5}{16}$. $\dfrac{43}{16}$ or $2\dfrac{11}{16}$

[1.4] **137.** True or False: Every number less than zero is a negative integer.   F

[1.5] *Insert either* $<$, $>$, *or* $=$ *in each shaded area to make a true statement.*

138. $|-3|$ ▨ 2 $>$

139. 8 ▨ $|-12|$ $<$

1.7 Subtraction of Real Numbers

1 Subtract numbers.

2 Subtract numbers mentally.

3 Evaluate expressions containing more than two numbers.

1 Subtract Numbers

Any subtraction problem can be rewritten as an addition problem using the additive inverse.

> ### To Subtract Real Numbers
>
> In general, if a and b represent any two real numbers, then
> $$a - b = a + (-b)$$

This rule says that to subtract b from a, add the opposite or additive inverse of b to a.

EXAMPLE 1 ▶ Evaluate $9 - (+4)$.

Solution   We are subtracting a positive 4 from 9. To accomplish this, we add the opposite of $+4$, which is -4, to 9.

$$9 - (+4) = 9 + (-4) = 5$$

Subtract   Positive 4   Add   Negative 4

We evaluated $9 + (-4)$ using the procedures for *adding* real numbers presented in Section 1.6.

▶ **Now Try Exercise 13**

Often in a subtraction problem, when the number being subtracted is a positive number, the $+$ sign preceding the number being subtracted is not shown. For example, in the subtraction $9 - 4$,

$$9 - \boxed{4} \text{ means } 9 - \boxed{(+4)}$$

Thus, to evaluate $9 - 4$, we must add the opposite of 4, which is -4, to 9.

$$9 - 4 = 9 + (-4) = 5$$

Subtract Positive 4   Add Negative 4

This procedure is illustrated in Example 2.

INSTRUCTOR EXAMPLE
Evaluate $6 - 2$.
Ans.: 4

EXAMPLE 2 ▶ Evaluate $5 - 3$.

Solution   We must subtract a positive 3 from 5. To change this problem to an addition problem, we add the opposite of 3, which is -3, to 5.

Subtraction   Addition
problem   problem
$$5 - 3 = 5 + (-3) = 2$$

Subtract Positive 3   Add   Negative 3

▶ **Now Try Exercise 15**

INSTRUCTOR EXAMPLE
Evaluate.
 a) $7 - 10$ b) $-11 - 13$
Ans.:
 a) -3 b) -24

EXAMPLE 3 ▶ Evaluate.

 a) $4 - 9$ **b)** $-4 - 2$

Solution

 a) Add the opposite of 9, which is -9, to 4.

$$4 - 9 = 4 + (-9) = -5$$

 b) Add the opposite of 2, which is -2, to -4.

$$-4 - 2 = -4 + (-2) = -6$$

▶ **Now Try Exercise 17**

In Example 4, we subtract numbers that contain decimal points.

INSTRUCTOR EXAMPLE
Evaluate $27.54 - 29.86$.
Ans.: -2.32

EXAMPLE 4 ▶ Evaluate $16.32 - 18.75$.

Solution   Add the opposite of 18.75, which is -18.75, to 16.32.

$$16.32 - 18.75 = 16.32 + (-18.75) = -2.43$$

▶ **Now Try Exercise 53**

In Examples 5 and 6, we will show how to subtract a negative number.

INSTRUCTOR EXAMPLE
Evaluate $15 - (-19)$.
Ans.: 34

EXAMPLE 5 ▶ Evaluate $4 - (-2)$.

Solution   We are asked to subtract a negative 2 from 4. To do this, we add the opposite of -2, which is 2, to 4.

$$4 - (-2) = 4 + 2 = 6$$

Subtract Negative 2   Add Positive 2

▶ **Now Try Exercise 19**

Helpful Hint

By examining Example 5, we see that

$$4 - (-2) = 4 + 2$$

Two negative   Plus
signs together

Whenever we subtract a negative number, we can replace the two negative signs with a plus sign.

EXAMPLE 6 ▶ Evaluate.

a) $7 - (-5)$ **b)** $-15 - (-12)$

Solution

a) Since we are subtracting a negative number, adding the opposite of -5, which is 5, to 7 will result in the two negative signs being replaced by a plus sign.

$$7 - (-5) = 7 + 5 = 12$$

b) $-15 - (-12) = -15 + 12 = -3$

▶ **Now Try Exercise 29**

Helpful Hint

We will now indicate how we may illustrate subtraction using colored chips. Remember from the preceding section that a red chip represents $+1$ and a green chip -1.

● $= +1$ ● $= -1$

Consider the subtraction problem $2 - 5$. If we change this to an addition problem, we get $2 + (-5)$. We can then add, as was done in the preceding section. The figure below shows that $2 + (-5) = -3$.

Now consider $-2 - 5$. This means $-2 + (-5)$, which can be represented as follows:

Thus, $-2 - 5 = -7$.
Now consider the problem $-3 - (-5)$. This can be rewritten as $-3 + 5$, which can be represented as follows:

Thus, $-3 - (-5) = 2$.
Some students still have difficulty understanding why when you subtract a negative number you obtain a positive number. Let's look at the problem $3 - (-2)$. This time we will look at it from a slightly different point of view. Let's start with 3:

From this we wish to subtract a negative 2. To the $+3$ shown above we will add two zeros by adding two $+1 - 1$ combinations. Remember, $+1$ and -1 sum to 0.

+3   0   0

Now we can subtract or "take away" the two -1's as shown:

From this we see that we are left with $3 + 2$ or 5. Thus, $3 - (-2) = 5$.

EXAMPLE 7 ▶ Subtract 12 from 3.

Solution

$$3 - 12 = 3 + (-12) = -9$$

▶ **Now Try Exercise 57**

Helpful Hint

Example 7 asked us to "subtract 12 from 3." Some of you may have expected this to be written as $12 - 3$ since you may be accustomed to getting a positive answer. However, the correct way of writing this is $3 - 12$. Notice that the number following the word "from" is our starting point. That is where the calculation begins. For example:

Subtract 2 from 7 means $7 - 2$.   From 7, subtract 2 means $7 - 2$.

Subtract 5 from -1 means $-1 - 5$.   From -1, subtract 5 means $-1 - 5$.

Subtract -4 from -2 means $-2 - (-4)$.   From -2, subtract -4 means $-2 - (-4)$.

Subtract -3 from 6 means $6 - (-3)$.   From 6, subtract -3 means $6 - (-3)$.

Subtract a from b means $b - a$.   From a, subtract b means $a - b$.

EXAMPLE 8 ▶ Subtract 5 from 5.

Solution $5 - 5 = 5 + (-5) = 0$

▶ **Now Try Exercise 59**

EXAMPLE 9 ▶ Subtract -6.48 from 4.25.

Solution $4.25 - (-6.48) = 4.25 + 6.48 = 10.73$

▶ **Now Try Exercise 61**

Now we will perform subtraction problems that contain fractions.

EXAMPLE 10 ▶ Subtract $\dfrac{5}{9} - \dfrac{13}{15}$.

Solution   Begin by changing the subtraction problem to an addition problem.

$$\frac{5}{9} - \frac{13}{15} = \frac{5}{9} + \left(-\frac{13}{15}\right)$$

Now rewrite the fractions with the LCD, 45, and add the fractions as was done in the last section.

$$\frac{5}{9} + \left(-\frac{13}{15}\right) = \frac{5}{9} \cdot \frac{5}{5} + \left(-\frac{13}{15}\right) \cdot \frac{3}{3}$$

$$= \frac{25}{45} + \left(-\frac{39}{45}\right) = \frac{25 + (-39)}{45} = \frac{-14}{45} = -\frac{14}{45}$$

Thus, $\dfrac{5}{9} - \dfrac{13}{15} = -\dfrac{14}{45}$.

▶ **Now Try Exercise 85**

EXAMPLE 11 ▶ Subtract $-\dfrac{7}{18}$ from $-\dfrac{9}{15}$.

Solution   This problem is written $-\dfrac{9}{15} - \left(-\dfrac{7}{18}\right)$.

We can simplify this as follows.

$$-\frac{9}{15} - \left(-\frac{7}{18}\right) = -\frac{9}{15} + \frac{7}{18}.$$

The LCD of 15 and 18 is 90. Rewriting the fractions with a common denominator gives

$$-\frac{9}{15} \cdot \frac{6}{6} + \frac{7}{18} \cdot \frac{5}{5} = -\frac{54}{90} + \frac{35}{90} = \frac{-54 + 35}{90}$$

$$= \frac{-19}{90} = -\frac{19}{90}.$$

▶ **Now Try Exercise 87**

Let us now look at some applications that involve subtraction.

INSTRUCTOR EXAMPLE
Scott Shafer's checkbook indicated a balance of $567.23 before he wrote a check for $250.69. Find the balance in his checkbook.
Ans.: $316.54

EXAMPLE 12 ▶ **A Gift Card Balance** Brigitte Martineau's gift card indicates a balance of $86.23 before she makes purchases totaling $127.49. Find the amount that Brigitte owes the cashier after she uses her gift card.

Solution   Understand and Translate   We can obtain the amount that Brigitte owes by subtracting 127.49 from 86.23.

Carry Out $86.23 - 127.49 = 86.23 + (-127.49) = -41.26$

Check and Answer   The negative indicates a deficit, which is what we expect. Therefore, Brigitte owes the cashier $41.26.

▶ **Now Try Exercise 131**

INSTRUCTOR EXAMPLE
On a particular January day, the high temperature in Fargo, North Dakota, was −5°F. On the same day, the high temperature in Dallas, Texas, was 64°F. Find the difference in their temperatures.
Ans.: 69°F

EXAMPLE 13 ▶ **Temperature Difference** On January 4, 2005, the high temperature for the day in Laredo, Texas, was 88°F. On the same day, the low temperature in Wolf Point, Montana, was −29°F. Find the difference in their temperatures.

Solution   Understand and Translate   The word *difference* in the example title indicates subtraction. We can obtain the difference in their temperatures by subtracting as follows.

Carry Out $88 - (-29) = 88 + 29 = 117$

Check and Answer   Therefore, the high temperature in Laredo is 117°F greater than the low temperature in Wolf Point.

▶ **Now Try Exercise 135**

Laredo, Texas

EXAMPLE 14 ▶ **Measuring Snow** A kindergarten class in Richfield, Minnesota, has a snow gauge placed outside its window that is left untouched for two days. Suppose that on the first day $6\frac{3}{8}$ inches of snow falls. On the second day, no snow falls, but $1\frac{1}{2}$ inches of the first day's snowfall melts. How much snow remains after the second day?

INSTRUCTOR EXAMPLE
A board measures $2\frac{5}{16}$ feet. What will be the length of the board if $\frac{3}{8}$ foot is cut from the board?
Ans.: $1\frac{15}{16}$ ft

Solution   Understand and Translate   From the first amount, $6\frac{3}{8}$ inches, we must subtract $1\frac{1}{2}$ inches.

Carry Out   On page 26, we subtracted mixed numbers using the mixed numbers themselves. Addition and subtraction of mixed numbers can also be done by changing the mixed numbers to improper fractions. We illustrate the procedure here. We begin by changing the subtraction problem to an addition problem. We then change the mixed numbers to fractions, and then rewrite each fraction with the LCD, 8.

$$6\frac{3}{8} - 1\frac{1}{2} = 6\frac{3}{8} + \left(-1\frac{1}{2}\right)$$

$$= \frac{51}{8} + \left(-\frac{3}{2}\right)$$

$$= \frac{51}{8} + \left(-\frac{3}{2}\right) \cdot \frac{4}{4}$$

$$= \frac{51}{8} + \left(-\frac{12}{8}\right)$$

$$= \frac{51 + (-12)}{8} = \frac{39}{8} \quad \text{or} \quad 4\frac{7}{8}$$

Check and Answer   Thus, after the second day there were $4\frac{7}{8}$ inches of snow remaining. Based upon the numbers given in the problem, the answer seems reasonable.

▶ **Now Try Exercise 133**

INSTRUCTOR EXAMPLE
Evaluate.
a) $-29 - 23$ b) $9 - (-3)$
Ans.:
a) -52 b) 12

EXAMPLE 15 ▶ Evaluate.

a) $15 + (-4)$ b) $-16 - 3$ c) $19 + (-14)$
d) $7 - (-9)$ e) $-9 - (-3)$ f) $8 - 13$

Solution   Parts **a)** and **c)** are addition problems, whereas the other parts are subtraction problems. We can rewrite each subtraction problem as an addition problem to evaluate.

a) $15 + (-4) = 11$ b) $-16 - 3 = -16 + (-3) = -19$
c) $19 + (-14) = 5$ d) $7 - (-9) = 7 + 9 = 16$
e) $-9 - (-3) = -9 + 3 = -6$ f) $8 - 13 = 8 + (-13) = -5$

▶ **Now Try Exercise 31**

2 Subtract Numbers Mentally

In the previous examples, we rewrote subtraction problems as addition problems. We did this because we know how to add real numbers. After this chapter, when we work out a subtraction problem, we will not show this step. *You need to practice and thoroughly understand how to add and subtract real numbers. You should understand this material so well that, when asked to evaluate an expression like $-4 - 6$, you will be able to compute the answer mentally. You should understand that $-4 - 6$ means the same as $-4 + (-6)$, but you should not need to write this using addition to find the value of the expression, -10.*

Let's evaluate a few subtraction problems without showing the process of changing the subtraction to addition.

INSTRUCTOR EXAMPLE
Evaluate $-21 - 13$.
Ans.: -34

EXAMPLE 16 ▶ Evaluate.

a) $-7 - 5$ b) $4 - 12$ c) $18 - 25$ d) $-20 - 12$

Solution

a) $-7 - 5 = -12$ b) $4 - 12 = -8$ c) $18 - 25 = -7$ d) $-20 - 12 = -32$

▶ **Now Try Exercise 33**

In Example 16 **a)**, we may have reasoned that $-7 - 5$ meant $-7 + (-5)$, which is -12, but we did not need to show it.

EXAMPLE 17 ▶ Evaluate $-\dfrac{3}{5} - \dfrac{7}{8}$.

Solution   The least common denominator is 40. Write each fraction with the LCD, 40.

$$-\frac{3}{5} \cdot \frac{8}{8} - \frac{7}{8} \cdot \frac{5}{5} = -\frac{24}{40} - \frac{35}{40} = \frac{-24 - 35}{40} = -\frac{59}{40} = -1\frac{19}{40}$$

▶ **Now Try Exercise 77**

Notice in Example 17, when we had $-\dfrac{24}{40} - \dfrac{35}{40}$, we could have written $\dfrac{-24 + (-35)}{40}$, but at this time we elected to write it as $\dfrac{-24 - 35}{40}$. Since $-24 - 35$ is -59, the answer is $-\dfrac{59}{40}$ or $-1\dfrac{19}{40}$.

3 Evaluate Expressions Containing More Than Two Numbers

In evaluating expressions involving more than one addition and subtraction, work from left to right unless parentheses or other grouping symbols appear.

EXAMPLE 18 ▶ Evaluate.

a) $9 - 12 + 3$ **b)** $-7 - 15 - 6$ **c)** $-5 + 1 - 8$

Solution   We work from left to right.

a) $\underline{9 - 12} + 3$ **b)** $\underline{-7 - 15} - 6$ **c)** $\underline{-5 + 1} - 8$

$= -3 \;\;\;+ 3$ $= -22 \;\;- 6$ $= -4 \;\;- 8$

$= 0$ $= -28$ $= -12$

▶ **Now Try Exercise 119**

After this section you will generally not see an expression like $3 + (-4)$. Instead, the expression will be written as $3 - 4$. Recall that $3 - 4$ means $3 + (-4)$ by our definition of subtraction. **Whenever we see an expression of the form $a + (-b)$, we can write the expression as $a - b$.** For example, $12 + (-15)$ can be written as $12 - 15$ and $-6 + (-9)$ can be written as $-6 - 9$.

As discussed earlier, **whenever we see an expression of the form $a - (-b)$, we can rewrite it as $a + b$.** For example, $6 - (-13)$ can be rewritten as $6 + 13$ and $-12 - (-9)$ can be rewritten as $-12 + 9$.

> **Rewriting Expressions**
>
> In general, for any real numbers a and b,
> $$a + (-b) = a - b, \text{ and}$$
> $$a - (-b) = a + b$$

Using the given information, the expression $9 + (-12) - (-8)$ may be simplified to $9 - 12 + 8$.

EXAMPLE 19 ▶

a) Evaluate $-5 - (-9) + (-12) + (-3)$.

b) Simplify the expression in part **a)**.

c) Evaluate the simplified expression in part **b)**.

Solution

a) We work from left to right. The shading indicates the additions being performed to get to the next step.

$$-5 - (-9) + (-12) + (-3) = \boxed{-5 + 9} + (-12) + (-3)$$
$$= \boxed{4 + (-12)} + (-3)$$
$$= -8 + (-3)$$
$$= -11$$

b) The expression simplifies as follows:

$$-5 - (-9) + (-12) + (-3) = -5 + 9 - 12 - 3$$

c) Evaluate the simplified expression from left to right. Begin by adding $-5 + 9$ to obtain 4.

$$-5 + 9 - 12 - 3 = \boxed{4 - 12} - 3$$
$$= -8 - 3$$
$$= -11$$

When you come across an expression like the one in Example 19 **a)**, you should simplify it as we did in part **b)** and then evaluate the simplified expression.

▶ **Now Try Exercise 129**

USING YOUR CALCULATOR   **Subtraction on a Scientific Calculator**

In the Using Your Calculator box on page 47, we indicated that the $\boxed{+/-}$ key is usually pressed after a number is entered to make the number negative. Following are some examples of subtraction on a scientific calculator.

EVALUATE	KEYSTROKES	ANSWER DISPLAYED
$-5 - 8$	$5\ \boxed{+/-}\ \boxed{-}\ 8\ \boxed{=}$	-13
$2 - (-7)$	$2\ \boxed{-}\ 7\ \boxed{+/-}\ \boxed{=}$	9

Subtraction on a Graphing Calculator

In the Using Your Graphing Calculator box on page 47, we mentioned that on a graphing calculator we press the $\boxed{(-)}$ key before the number is entered to make the number negative. The $\boxed{-}$ key on a graphing calculator is used to perform subtraction. Following are some examples of subtraction on a graphing calculator.

EVALUATE	KEYSTROKE	DISPLAY
$-5 - 8$	$\boxed{(-)}\,5\ \boxed{-}\ 8\ \boxed{ENTER}$	-13
$2 - (-7)$	$2\ \boxed{-}\ \boxed{(-)}\,7\ \boxed{ENTER}$	9

EXERCISE SET 1.7   MathXL®   MyMathLab

Concept/Writing Exercises

1. $2 - 7$ **2.** $-4 - (-6)$ **3.** $- ?$ **4.** $\square - \ast$
5. a) Answers will vary.   **6. a)** $a - b$ **c)** -6 **7. a)** $a + b$

1. Write an expression that illustrates 7 subtracted from 2.

2. Write an expression that illustrates -6 subtracted from -4.

3. Write an expression that illustrates ? subtracted from .

4. Write an expression that illustrates $\ast$ subtracted from $\square$.

5. a) Explain how to subtract a number b from a number a.

   b) Write an expression using addition that can be used to subtract 14 from 5. $5 + (-14)$

   c) Evaluate the expression you determined in part **b)**. -9

6. a) Express the subtraction $a - (+b)$ in a simplified form.

   b) Simplify the expression $3 - (+9)$. $3 - 9$

   c) Evaluate the simplified expression obtained in part **b)**.

7. a) Express the subtraction $a - (-b)$ in a simplified form.

   b) Write a simplified expression that can be used to evaluate $-4 - (-12)$. $-4 + 12$

   c) Evaluate the simplified expression obtained in part **b)**. 8

8. When we add three or more numbers without parentheses, how do we evaluate the expression?   left to right

9. a) Simplify $3 - (-6) + (-5)$ by eliminating two signs next to one another and replacing them with a single sign. (See Example 19b).) Explain how you determined your answer. $3 + 6 - 5$

   b) Evaluate the simplified expression obtained in part **a)**. 4

10. a) Simplify $-12 + (-5) - (-4)$. Explain how you determined your answer. $-12 - 5 + 4$

   b) Evaluate the simplified expression obtained in part **a)**. -13

In Exercises 11 and 12, are the following calculations correct? If not, explain why.

11. $\dfrac{4}{9} - \dfrac{3}{7} = \dfrac{28}{63} - \dfrac{27}{63} = \dfrac{28 - 27}{63} = \dfrac{1}{63}$ Correct

12. $-\dfrac{5}{12} - \dfrac{7}{9} = -\dfrac{15}{36} - \dfrac{28}{36} = \dfrac{-15 - 28}{36} = -\dfrac{43}{36}$ Correct

Practice the Skills

Evaluate.

13. $8 - (+2)$ 6

14. $17 - (+8)$ 9

15. $12 - 5$ 7

16. $9 - 4$ 5

17. $8 - 9$ -1

18. $-6 - 3$ -9

19. $9 - (-3)$ 12

20. $17 - (-5)$ 22

21. $-6 - 6$ -12

22. $-4 - (-3)$ -1

23. $0 - 7$ -7

24. $9 - (-9)$ 18

25. $8 - 8$ 0

26. $10 - 10$ 0

27. $-3 - 1$ -4

28. $-5.7 - (-3.1)$ -2.6

29. $-8 - (-5)$ -3

30. $4 - 9$ -5

31. $6 - (-3)$ 9

32. $6 - 10$ -4

33. $-9 - 11$ -20

34. $37 - 40$ -3

35. $0 - (-9.8)$ 9.8

36. $-6.3 - 4.7$ -11.0

37. $-4.8 - (-5.1)$ 0.3

38. $-4 - (-4)$ 0

39. $14 - 7$ 7

40. $9 - 9$ 0

41. $-8 - (-12)$ 4

42. $-6 - (-2)$ -4

43. $18 - (-4)$ 22

44. $-25 - 16$ -41

45. $-9 - 2$ -11

46. $-35 - (-8)$ -27

47. $-90.7 - 40.3$ -131.0

48. $-52.6 - 37.9$ -90.5

49. $-45 - 37$ -82

50. $-50 - (-40)$ -10

51. $70 - (-70)$ 140

52. $130 - (-90)$ 220

53. $42.3 - 49.7$ -7.4

54. $81.3 - 92.5$ -11.2

55. $-7.85 - (-3.92)$ -3.93

56. $-12.43 - (-9.57)$ -2.86

57. Subtract 15 from 4. -11

58. Subtract 7 from 1. -6

59. Subtract 21 from 21. 0

60. Subtract 13 from 13. 0

61. Subtract -12.4 from -6.3. 6.1

62. Subtract 17.3 from -9.8. -27.1

63. Subtract -7.9 from 10.3. 18.2

64. Subtract -23 from -23. 0

65. Subtract 24 from 13. -11

66. Subtract -11.7 from -5.2. 6.5

67. Subtract 7.8 from -10.3. -18.1

68. Subtract -9.6 from 3.4. 13.0

87. $-\dfrac{7}{60}$ **88.** $-\dfrac{47}{80}$

Evaluate.

69. $\dfrac{5}{9} - \dfrac{3}{8}$ $\dfrac{13}{72}$

70. $\dfrac{4}{5} - \dfrac{5}{6}$ $-\dfrac{1}{30}$

71. $\dfrac{8}{15} - \dfrac{7}{45}$ $\dfrac{17}{45}$

72. $\dfrac{5}{12} - \dfrac{7}{8}$ $-\dfrac{11}{24}$

73. $-\dfrac{7}{10} - \dfrac{5}{12}$ $-\dfrac{67}{60}$ or $-1\dfrac{7}{60}$

74. $-\dfrac{1}{4} - \dfrac{2}{3}$ $-\dfrac{11}{12}$

75. $-\dfrac{4}{15} - \dfrac{3}{20}$ $-\dfrac{5}{12}$

76. $-\dfrac{5}{4} - \dfrac{7}{11}$ $-\dfrac{83}{44}$ or $-1\dfrac{39}{44}$

77. $-\dfrac{7}{12} - \dfrac{5}{40}$ $-\dfrac{17}{24}$

78. $-\dfrac{5}{6} - \dfrac{3}{32}$ $-\dfrac{89}{96}$

79. $\dfrac{3}{8} - \dfrac{6}{48}$ $\dfrac{1}{4}$

80. $\dfrac{17}{18} - \dfrac{13}{20}$ $\dfrac{53}{180}$

81. $-\dfrac{4}{9} - \left(-\dfrac{3}{5}\right)$ $\dfrac{7}{45}$

82. $\dfrac{5}{20} - \left(-\dfrac{1}{8}\right)$ $\dfrac{3}{8}$

83. $\dfrac{3}{16} - \left(-\dfrac{5}{8}\right)$ $\dfrac{13}{16}$

84. $-\dfrac{5}{12} - \left(-\dfrac{3}{8}\right)$ $-\dfrac{1}{24}$

85. Subtract $\dfrac{7}{9}$ from $\dfrac{4}{7}$. $-\dfrac{13}{63}$

86. Subtract $\dfrac{7}{15}$ from $\dfrac{5}{8}$. $\dfrac{19}{120}$

87. Subtract $-\dfrac{3}{10}$ from $-\dfrac{5}{12}$.

88. Subtract $-\dfrac{5}{16}$ from $-\dfrac{9}{10}$.

In Exercises 89–106, a) determine by observation whether the difference will be a positive number, zero, or a negative number; b) find the difference using your calculator; and c) examine your answer to part b) to see whether it is reasonable and makes sense.

89. $378 - 279$ 99

90. $483 - 569$ -86

91. $-482 - 137$ -619

92. $178 - (-377)$ 555

93. $843 - (-745)$ 1588

94. $864 - (-762)$ 1626

95. $-408 - (-604)$ 196

96. $-623 - 111$ -734

97. $-1024 - (-576)$ -448

98. $-104.7 - 27.6$ -132.3

99. $165.7 - 49.6$ 116.1

100. $-40.2 - (-12.6)$ -27.6

101. Subtract 364 from 295. -69

102. Subtract -433 from -932. -499

103. Subtract 647 from -1023. -1670

104. Subtract 2432 from -4120. -6552

105. Subtract -7.62 from -7.62. 0

106. Subtract 36.7 from -103.2. -139.9

Evaluate.

107. $7 + 5 - (+8)$ 4

108. $15 - (+9) - (+5)$ 1

109. $-6 + (-6) + 6$ -6

110. $9 - 4 + (-2)$ 3

111. $-13 - (+5) + 3$ -15

112. $7 - (+4) - (-3)$ 6

113. $-9 - (-3) + 4$ -2

114. $15 + (-7) - (-3)$ 11

115. $5 - (-9) + (-1)$ 13

116. $12 + (-5) - (-4)$ 11

117. $17 + (-8) - (+14)$ -5

118. $-7 + 6 - 3$ -4

119. $-36 - 5 + 9$ -32

120. $45 - 3 - 7$ 35

121. $-2 + 7 - 9$ -4

122. $-2 - 7 - 13$ -22

123. $25 - 19 + 3$ 9

124. $-4 - 1 + 5$ 0

125. $-4 - 6 + 5 - 7$ -12

126. $-9 - 3 - (-4) + 5$ -3

127. $17 + (-3) - 9 - (-7)$ 12

128. $32 + 5 - 7 - 12$ 18

129. $-9 + (-7) + (-5) - (-3)$ -18

130. $6 - 9 - (-3) + 12$ 12

Problem Solving

131. Lands' End The Lands' End catalog department had 300 ladies' blue cardigan sweaters in stock on December 1. By December 9, the department had taken orders for 343 of the sweaters.

   a) How many sweaters were on back order?   43

   b) If the catalog department wanted 100 sweaters in addition to those already ordered, how many sweaters would it need to back order?   143

132. Leadville, Co According to the *Guinness Book of World Records*, the city with the greatest elevation in the United States is Leadville, Colorado at 10,152 feet. The city with the lowest elevation in the United States, at 184 feet below sea level, is Calipatria, California. What is the difference in the elevation of these cities?   10,336 ft

Leadville, Colorado

133. Measuring Rainfall At Kim Christensen's house, a rain gauge is placed in the yard and is left untouched for 2 days. Suppose that on the first day, $2\frac{1}{4}$ inches of rain falls. On the second day, no rain falls, but $\frac{3}{8}$ inch of the first day's rainfall evaporates. How much water remains in the gauge after the second day? $1\frac{7}{8}$ in.

134. Death Valley A medical supply package is dropped into Death Valley, California, from a helicopter 1605.7 feet above sea level. The package lands at a location in Death Valley 267.4 feet below sea level. What vertical distance did the package travel?   1873.1 feet

135. Temperature Change The greatest change in temperature ever recorded within a 24-hour period occurred at Browning, Montana, on January 23, 1916. The temperature fell from 44°F to −56°F. How much did the temperature drop?   100°F

136. Going Home Two college students are driving on an expressway, going home for spring break. Shawntoya travels 58.5 miles in 1 hour. Marcelino travels 67.3 miles in 1 hour.

   a) If Shawntoya and Marcelino start at the same parking lot and travel in opposite directions, how far apart will they be in 1 hour?   125.8 mi

   b) If Shawntoya and Marcelino start at the same parking lot and travel in the same direction, how far apart will they be in 1 hour?   8.8 mi

137. Golf The chart below shows some final scores at the Masters golf tournament, held in Augusta, Georgia, in 2006.

The Masters, 2006

Golfer	Score (above or below par)
P. Mickelson	−7
T. Clark	−5
T. Woods	−4
V. Singh	−3
S. Cink	−2
D. Howell	+2
L. Donald	+8
O. Browne	+9

Source: www.masters.org

   a) If par for the Masters is 288 strokes, determine P. Mickelson's score in 2006.   281

   b) What was the difference in the strokes between T. Clark and S. Cink in 2006?   3 strokes less

138. Inseam Christine Henry purchases a new pair of pants whose inseam is $32\frac{1}{2}$ inches. If $2\frac{3}{4}$ inches are cut from the inseam of the pants, what will be the new inseam of the pants? $29\frac{3}{4}$ in.

Challenge Problems

Find each sum.   **141. a)** 8 units

139. $1 - 2 + 3 - 4 + 5 - 6 + 7 - 8 + 9 - 10$ −5

140. $1 - 2 + 3 - 4 + 5 - 6 + \cdots + 99 - 100$ −50

141. Consider a number line.

   a) What is the distance, in units, between −11 and −3?

   b) Write a subtraction problem to represent this distance (the distance is to be positive). $-3 - (-11)$

142. Stock Amy Tait buys a stock for $50. Will the stock be worth more if it decreases by 10% and then increases by 10%, or if it increases by 10% and then decreases by 10%, or will the value be the same either way?   same

143. Rolling Ball A ball rolls off a table and follows the path indicated in the figure. Suppose the maximum height reached by the ball on each bounce is 1 foot less than on the previous bounce.

3 ft   2 ft   1 ft   Ball is stopped here.

a) Determine the total vertical distance traveled by the ball.   9 ft

b) If we consider the ball moving in a downward direction as negative, and the ball moving in an upward direction as positive, what was the net vertical distance traveled (from its starting point) by the ball?   −3 ft

Cumulative Review Exercises

[1.4] **144.** List the set of counting numbers.   {1, 2, 3, …}

145. Explain the relationship between the set of rational numbers, the set of irrational numbers, and the set of real numbers.   The set of rational numbers together with the set of irrational numbers form the set of real numbers.

[1.5] *Insert either* >, <, *or* = *in each shaded area to make the statement true.*

146. $|-3|$ ▮ -5 >

147. $-|-9|$ ▮ $-|-5|$ <

[1.7] **148.** Subtract $\dfrac{7}{8}$ from $\dfrac{5}{6}$. $-\dfrac{1}{24}$

1.8 Multiplication and Division of Real Numbers

1   Multiply numbers.

2   Divide numbers.

3   Remove negative signs from denominators.

4   Evaluate divisions involving 0.

TEACHING TIP
You may wish to mention that multiplication and division of decimal numbers are covered in Appendix A.

1 Multiply Numbers

The following rules are used in determining the sign of the product when two numbers are multiplied.

> **The Sign of the Product of Two Real Numbers**
>
> 1. The product of two numbers with **like** signs is a **positive** number.
> 2. The product of two numbers with **unlike** signs is a **negative** number.

By this rule, the product of two positive numbers or two negative numbers will be a positive number. The product of a positive number and a negative number will be a negative number.

INSTRUCTOR EXAMPLE
Evaluate.
a) 6(−9)   b) (−8)(−4)
Ans.:
a) −54   b) 32

EXAMPLE 1 ▶ Evaluate.

a) $4(-5)$ b) $(-6)(7)$ c) $(-9)(-3)$

Solution

a) Since the numbers have unlike signs, the product is negative.

$$4(-5) = -20$$

b) Since the numbers have unlike signs, the product is negative.

$$(-6)(7) = -42$$

c) Since the numbers have like signs, both negative, the product is positive.

$$(-9)(-3) = 27$$

▶ **Now Try Exercise 17**

EXAMPLE 2 ▸ Evaluate.

a) $(-8)(5)$ b) $(-4)(-8)$ c) $0(6)$

d) $0(-2)$ e) $4.2(-9.7)$ f) $(-3.62)(-6.18)$

Solution

a) $(-8)(5) = -40$ b) $(-4)(-8) = 32$ c) $0(6) = 0$

d) $0(-2) = 0$ e) $4.2(-9.7) = -40.74$ f) $(-3.62)(-6.18) = 22.3716$

Note that zero multiplied by any real number equals zero.

▸ **Now Try Exercise 29**

Helpful Hint

At this point some students begin confusing problems like $-2 - 3$ with $(-2)(-3)$ and problems like $2 - 3$ with $2(-3)$. If you do not understand the difference between problems like $-2 - 3$ and $(-2)(-3)$, make an appointment to see your instructor as soon as possible.

Subtraction Problems	Multiplication Problems
$-2 - 3 = -5$	$(-2)(-3) = 6$
$2 - 3 = -1$	$(2)(-3) = -6$

EXAMPLE 3 ▸ Evaluate.

a) $\left(\dfrac{-1}{8}\right)\left(\dfrac{-3}{5}\right)$ b) $\left(\dfrac{3}{20}\right)\left(\dfrac{-3}{10}\right)$

Solution

a) $\left(\dfrac{-1}{8}\right)\left(\dfrac{-3}{5}\right) = \dfrac{(-1)(-3)}{8(5)} = \dfrac{3}{40}$ b) $\left(\dfrac{3}{20}\right)\left(\dfrac{-3}{10}\right) = \dfrac{3(-3)}{20(10)} = -\dfrac{9}{200}$

▸ **Now Try Exercise 41**

Sometimes you may be asked to perform more than one multiplication in a given problem. When this happens, the sign of the final product can be determined by counting the number of *negative* numbers being multiplied. *The product of an even number of negative numbers will always be positive. The product of an odd number of negative numbers will always be negative.* Can you explain why?

EXAMPLE 4 ▸ Evaluate.

a) $(-5)(-3)(1)(-4)$ b) $(-2)(-4)(-1)(3)(-4)$

Solution

a) Since there are three negative numbers (an odd number of negative numbers), the product will be negative, as illustrated.

$$(-5)(-3)(1)(-4) = (15)(1)(-4)$$
$$= (15)(-4)$$
$$= -60$$

b) Since there are four negative numbers (an even number of negative numbers), the product will be positive, as illustrated.

$$(-2)(-4)(-1)(3)(-4) = (8)(-1)(3)(-4)$$
$$= (-8)(3)(-4)$$
$$= (-24)(-4)$$
$$= 96$$

▸ **Now Try Exercise 35**

2 Divide Numbers

The rules for dividing numbers are very similar to those used in multiplying numbers.

The Sign of the Quotient of Two Real Numbers

1. The quotient of two numbers with **like** signs is a **positive** number.
2. The quotient of two numbers with **unlike** signs is a **negative** number.

Therefore, the quotient of two positive numbers or two negative numbers will be a positive number. The quotient of a positive number and a negative number will be a negative number.

INSTRUCTOR EXAMPLE
Evaluate.

a) $\dfrac{-36}{4}$ b) $\dfrac{-45}{-9}$

Ans.:
a) -9 b) 5

EXAMPLE 5 ▶ Evaluate.

a) $\dfrac{10}{-5}$ b) $\dfrac{-45}{5}$ c) $\dfrac{-36}{-6}$

Solution

a) Since the numbers have unlike signs, the quotient is negative.
$$\frac{10}{-5} = -2$$

b) Since the numbers have unlike signs, the quotient is negative.
$$\frac{-45}{5} = -9$$

c) Since the numbers have like signs, both negative, the quotient is positive.
$$\frac{-36}{-6} = 6$$

▶ **Now Try Exercise 55**

INSTRUCTOR EXAMPLE
Evaluate $\dfrac{-2}{7} \div \dfrac{-1}{2}$.

Ans.: $\dfrac{4}{7}$

EXAMPLE 6 ▶ Evaluate.

a) $-16 \div (-2)$ b) $\dfrac{-2}{3} \div \dfrac{-5}{7}$

Solution

a) Since the numbers have like signs, both negative, the quotient is positive.
$$\frac{-16}{-2} = 8$$

b) Invert the *divisor*, $\dfrac{-5}{7}$, and then multiply.

$$\frac{-2}{3} \div \frac{-5}{7} = \left(\frac{-2}{3}\right)\left(\frac{7}{-5}\right) = \frac{-14}{-15} = \frac{14}{15}$$

▶ **Now Try Exercise 77**

INSTRUCTOR EXAMPLE
Repeat Example 7 for

a) $-12.37 \div 3.2$ b) $\dfrac{-53.5}{-3.4}$

Ans.:
a) ≈ -3.87 b) ≈ 15.74

EXAMPLE 7 ▶ Evaluate, round your answer to the nearest hundredth when appropriate.

a) $-18.86 \div 4.1$ b) $\dfrac{-27.2}{-2.6}$

Solution

a) Since the numbers have unlike signs, the quotient is negative.
$$\frac{-18.86}{4.1} = -4.6$$

b) Since the numbers have like signs, both negative, the quotient is positive.

$$\frac{-27.2}{-2.6} \approx 10.46$$

The answer in part **b)** was rounded to two decimal places, or hundredths. If you have forgotten how to round decimal numbers, review Appendix A now.

▶ **Now Try Exercise 69**

Helpful Hint

For multiplication and division of two real numbers:

$$\left.\begin{array}{c}(+)(+) = + \\ (-)(-) = +\end{array}\right\} \quad \left.\begin{array}{c}\dfrac{(+)}{(+)} = + \\ \dfrac{(-)}{(-)} = +\end{array}\right\} \quad \textit{Like signs give positive products and quotients.}$$

$$\left.\begin{array}{c}(+)(-) = - \\ (-)(+) = -\end{array}\right\} \quad \left.\begin{array}{c}\dfrac{(+)}{(-)} = - \\ \dfrac{(-)}{(+)} = -\end{array}\right\} \quad \textit{Unlike signs give negative products and quotients.}$$

3 Remove Negative Signs from Denominators

We now know that the quotient of a positive number and a negative number is a negative number. The fractions $-\dfrac{3}{4}, \dfrac{-3}{4}$, and $\dfrac{3}{-4}$ all represent the same negative number, negative three-fourths.

The Quotient of a Positive Number and a Negative Number

If a and b represent any real numbers, $b \neq 0$, then

$$\frac{a}{-b} = \frac{-a}{b} = -\frac{a}{b}$$

In mathematics we generally do not write a fraction with a negative sign in the denominator. When a negative sign appears in a denominator, we can move it to the numerator or place it in front of the fraction. For example, the fraction $\dfrac{5}{-7}$ should be written as either $-\dfrac{5}{7}$ or $\dfrac{-5}{7}$. Fractions also can be written using a slash, /. For example, the fraction $-\dfrac{5}{7}$ may be written $-5/7$ or $-(5/7)$.

EXAMPLE 8 ▶ Evaluate $\dfrac{3}{7} \div \left(\dfrac{-12}{35}\right)$.

Solution
$$\frac{3}{7} \div \left(\frac{-12}{35}\right) = \frac{\overset{1}{\cancel{3}}}{\cancel{7}} \cdot \left(\frac{\overset{5}{\cancel{35}}}{\underset{4}{\cancel{-12}}}\right) = \frac{1(5)}{1(-4)} = \frac{5}{-4} = -\frac{5}{4}$$

▶ **Now Try Exercise 73**

The operations on real numbers are summarized in **Table 1.1**.

TABLE 1.1	Summary of Operations on Real Numbers			
Signs of Numbers	Addition	Subtraction	Multiplication	Division
Both Numbers Are Positive	Sum Is Always Positive	Difference May Be Either Positive or Negative	Product Is Always Positive	Quotient Is Always Positive
Examples				
6 and 2	$6 + 2 = 8$	$6 - 2 = 4$	$6 \cdot 2 = 12$	$6 \div 2 = 3$
2 and 6	$2 + 6 = 8$	$2 - 6 = -4$	$2 \cdot 6 = 12$	$2 \div 6 = \dfrac{1}{3}$
One Number Is Positive and the Other Number Is Negative	Sum May Be Either Positive or Negative	Difference May Be Either Positive or Negative	Product Is Always Negative	Quotient Is Always Negative
Examples				
6 and −2	$6 + (-2) = 4$	$6 - (-2) = 8$	$6(-2) = -12$	$6 \div (-2) = -3$
−6 and 2	$-6 + 2 = -4$	$-6 - 2 = -8$	$-6(2) = -12$	$-6 \div 2 = -3$
Both Numbers Are Negative	Sum Is Always Negative	Difference May Be Either Positive or Negative	Product Is Always Positive	Quotient Is Always Positive
Examples				
−6 and −2	$-6 + (-2) = -8$	$-6 - (-2) = -4$	$-6(-2) = 12$	$-6 \div (-2) = 3$
−2 and −6	$-2 + (-6) = -8$	$-2 - (-6) = 4$	$-2(-6) = 12$	$-2 \div (-6) = \dfrac{1}{3}$

4 Evaluate Divisions Involving 0

Now let's look at divisions involving the number 0. What is $\dfrac{0}{1}$ equal to? Note that $\dfrac{6}{3} = 2$ because $3 \cdot 2 = 6$. We can follow the same procedure to determine the value of $\dfrac{0}{1}$. Suppose that $\dfrac{0}{1}$ is equal to some number, which we will designate by $\boxed{?}$.

$$\text{If} \quad \frac{0}{1} = \boxed{?} \quad \text{then} \quad 1 \cdot \boxed{?} = 0$$

Since only $1 \cdot 0 = 0$, the $\boxed{?}$ must be 0. Thus, $\dfrac{0}{1} = 0$. Using the same technique, we can show that zero divided by any nonzero number is zero.

Zero Divided by a Nonzero Number

If a represents any real number except 0, then

$$0 \div a = \frac{0}{a} = 0$$

Now what is $\dfrac{1}{0}$ equal to?

$$\text{If} \quad \frac{1}{0} = \boxed{?} \quad \text{then} \quad 0 \cdot \boxed{?} = 1$$

But since 0 multiplied by any number will be 0, there is no value that can replace ?. We say that $\frac{1}{0}$ is **undefined**. Using the same technique, we can show that any real number, except 0, divided by 0 is undefined.

Division by Zero

If a represents any real number except 0, then

$$a \div 0 \quad \text{or} \quad \frac{a}{0} \quad \text{is undefined}$$

TEACHING TIP
It may be helpful to use a table and a calculator to divide 1 by numbers closer and closer to 0. Then have students evaluate $\frac{1}{0}$ on their calculator.

What is $\frac{0}{0}$ equal to?

$$\text{If} \quad \frac{0}{0} = \boxed{?} \quad \text{then} \quad 0 \cdot \boxed{?} = 0$$

Since the product of any number and 0 is 0, the ? can be replaced by any real number. Therefore, the quotient $\frac{0}{0}$ cannot be determined, and so there is no answer. Thus, we will not use it in this course.*

Summary of Division Involving 0

If a represents any real number except 0, then

$$\frac{0}{a} = 0 \quad \text{and} \quad \frac{a}{0} \text{ is undefined}$$

INSTRUCTOR EXAMPLE
Indicate whether each quotient is 0 or undefined.

a) $\frac{0}{6}$ **b)** $\frac{2}{0}$

Ans.:

a) 0   **b)** undefined

EXAMPLE 9 ▶ Indicate whether each quotient is 0 or undefined.

a) $\frac{0}{2}$ **b)** $\frac{5}{0}$ **c)** $\frac{0}{-4}$ **d)** $\frac{-2}{0}$

Solution   The answer to parts **a)** and **c)** is 0. The answer to parts **b)** and **d)** is undefined.

▶ **Now Try Exercise 95**

USING YOUR CALCULATOR   Multiplication and Division on a Scientific Calculator

Below we show how numbers may be multiplied and divided on many calculators.

EVALUATE	KEYSTROKES	ANSWER DISPLAYED
$6(-23)$	6 × 23 +/− =	−138
$\dfrac{-240}{-16}$	240 +/− ÷ 16 +/− =	15

Multiplication and Division on a Graphing Calculator

EVALUATE	KEYSTROKES	ANSWER DISPLAYED
$6(-23)$	6 × (−) 23 ENTER	−138
$\dfrac{-240}{-16}$	(−) 240 ÷ (−) 16 ENTER	15

Since a positive number multiplied by a negative number will be negative, to obtain the product of $6(-23)$, you can multiply, $(6)(23)$ and write a negative sign before the answer. Since a negative number divided by a negative number is positive, $\dfrac{-240}{-16}$ could have been found by dividing $\dfrac{240}{16}$.

---

*At this level, some professors prefer to call $\frac{0}{0}$ *indeterminate* while others prefer to call $\frac{0}{0}$ *undefined*. In higher-level mathematics courses, $\frac{0}{0}$ is sometimes referred to as the *indeterminate form*.

EXERCISE SET 1.8

1.–2. like signs: product or quotient is positive; unlike signs: product or quotient is negative

Concept/Writing Exercises

3. even number of negative numbers: product is positive, odd number: negative **5. b)** undefined
7. a) $3 - 5$, subtraction; $3(-5)$, multiplication **8. a)** $-4 - 2$, subtraction; $(-4)(-2)$, multiplication

1. State the rules used to determine the sign of the product of two real numbers.

2. State the rules used to determine the sign of the quotient of two real numbers.

3. When multiplying three or more real numbers, explain how to determine the sign of the product of the numbers.

4. What is the product of 0 and any real number? 0

5. a) What is $\dfrac{0}{a}$ equal to where a is any nonzero real number? 0

   b) What is $\dfrac{a}{0}$ equal to where a is any nonzero real number?

6. How do we generally rewrite a fraction of the form $\dfrac{a}{-b}$, where a and b represent any positive real numbers? $-\dfrac{a}{b}$ or $\dfrac{-a}{b}$

7. a) Explain the difference between $3 - 5$ and $3(-5)$.

   b) Evaluate $3 - 5$ and $3(-5)$. $-2, -15$

8. a) Explain the difference between $-4 - 2$ and $(-4)(-2)$.

   b) Evaluate $-4 - 2$ and $(-4)(-2)$. $-6, 8$

9. a) Explain the difference between $x - y$ and $x(-y)$ where x and y represent any real numbers.

   If x is 5 and y is -2, find the value of

   b) $x - y$, 7   c) $x(-y)$, and 10   d) $-x - y$. -3

10. If x is -9 and y is 7, find the value of

    a) xy, -63 b) $x(-y)$, 63

    c) $x - y$, and -16 d) $-x - y$. 2

9. a) $x - y$, subtraction; $x(-y)$, multiplication

Determine the sign of each product. Explain how you determined the sign.

11. $(8)(4)(-5)$ negative

12. $(-9)(-12)(20)$ positive

13. $(-102)(-16)(24)(19)$ positive

14. $(1054)(-92)(-16)(-37)$ negative

15. $(-40)(-16)(30)(50)(-13)$ negative

16. $(-1)(3)(-462)(-196)(-312)$ positive

Practice the Skills

Find each product.

17. $(-5)(-4)$ 20

18. $-4(2)$ -8

19. $6(-3)$ -18

20. $6(-2)$ -12

21. $(-8)(-10)$ 80

22. $(-3)(2)$ -6

23. $-2.1(6)$ -12.6

24. $-1(8.7)$ -8.7

25. $6(7)$ 42

26. $-9(-4)$ 36

27. $9(-9)$ -81

28. $(7)(-8)$ -56

29. $(-5)(-6)$ 30

30. $0(-5)$ 0

31. $(-9)(0)(-6)$ 0

32. $5(-4)(2)$ -40

33. $(21)(-1)(4)$ -84

34. $2(8)(-1)(-3)$ 48

35. $-1(-3)(3)(-8)$ -72

36. $(2)(-4)(-5)(-1)$ -40

37. $(-4)(5)(-7)(1)$ 140

38. $(-3)(2)(5)(3)$ -90

39. $(-1)(3)(0)(-7)$ 0

40. $(-6)(6)(4)(-4)$ 576

Find each product.

41. $\left(\dfrac{-1}{2}\right)\left(\dfrac{3}{5}\right)$ $-\dfrac{3}{10}$

42. $\left(\dfrac{1}{3}\right)\left(\dfrac{-3}{5}\right)$ $-\dfrac{1}{5}$

43. $\left(\dfrac{-5}{9}\right)\left(\dfrac{-7}{15}\right)$ $\dfrac{7}{27}$

44. $\left(\dfrac{4}{5}\right)\left(\dfrac{-3}{10}\right)$ $-\dfrac{6}{25}$

45. $\left(\dfrac{6}{-3}\right)\left(\dfrac{4}{-2}\right)$ 4

46. $\left(\dfrac{9}{-10}\right)\left(\dfrac{6}{-7}\right)$ $\dfrac{27}{35}$

47. $\left(\dfrac{3}{4}\right)\left(\dfrac{-2}{15}\right)$ $-\dfrac{1}{10}$

48. $\left(\dfrac{9}{10}\right)\left(\dfrac{7}{-8}\right)$ $-\dfrac{63}{80}$

Find each quotient.

49. $\dfrac{42}{6}$ 7

50. $25 \div 5$ 5

51. $-16 \div (-4)$ 4

52. $\dfrac{-18}{9}$ -2

53. $\dfrac{-36}{-9}$ 4

54. $\dfrac{30}{-6}$ -5

55. $\dfrac{36}{-2}$ -18

56. $\dfrac{-15}{-1}$ 15

57. $\dfrac{-19.8}{-2}$ 9.9

58. $-15.6/(-3)$ 5.2

59. $40/(-4)$ -10

60. $\dfrac{63}{-7}$ -9

61. $\dfrac{-66}{11}$ -6

62. $\dfrac{-25}{-5}$ 5

63. $\dfrac{48}{-6}$ -8

64. $\dfrac{-10}{10}$ -1

65. $-64.8 \div (-4)$ 16.2

66. $-86.4/(-2)$ 43.2

67. Divide 0 by 4. 0

68. Divide 26 by -13. -2

69. Divide 30.8 by -5.6. -5.5

70. Divide -67.64 by 7.6. -8.9

71. Divide -30 by -5. 6

72. Divide -36 by -6. 6

Find each quotient.

73. $\dfrac{3}{12} \div \left(\dfrac{-5}{8}\right)$ $-\dfrac{2}{5}$

74. $4 \div \left(\dfrac{-6}{13}\right)$ $-\dfrac{26}{3}$ or $-8\dfrac{2}{3}$

75. $\dfrac{-5}{12} \div (-3)$ $\dfrac{5}{36}$

76. $\dfrac{6}{15} \div \left(\dfrac{7}{30}\right)$ $\dfrac{12}{7}$ or $1\dfrac{5}{7}$

77. $\dfrac{-15}{21} \div \left(\dfrac{-15}{21}\right)$ 1

78. $\dfrac{-4}{9} \div \left(\dfrac{-6}{7}\right)$ $\dfrac{14}{27}$

79. $(-12) \div \dfrac{5}{12}$ $-\dfrac{144}{5}$ or $-28\dfrac{4}{5}$

80. $\dfrac{-16}{3} \div \left(\dfrac{5}{-9}\right)$ $\dfrac{48}{5}$ or $9\dfrac{3}{5}$

Evaluate.

81. $-4(8)$ -32

82. $\dfrac{-18}{-2}$ 9

83. $\dfrac{-100}{-5}$ 20

84. $-50 \div (-10)$ 5

85. $-7(2)$ −14
86. $6.4(-8)$ −51.2
87. $27.9 \div (-3)$ −9.3
88. Divide 130 by -10. −13
89. $-100 \div 5$ −20
90. $4(-2)(-1)(-5)$ −40
91. Divide -90 by -90. 1
92. $(6)(1)(-3)(4)$ −72

Indicate whether each quotient is 0 or undefined.

93. $0 \div 8.6$ 0
94. $\dfrac{-2.7}{0}$ undefined
95. $\dfrac{5}{0}$ undefined
96. $\dfrac{0}{1}$ 0

97. $0 \div (-7)$ 0
98. $\dfrac{6}{0}$ undefined
99. 8 divided by 0 undefined
100. 0 divided by 12 0

 In Exercises 101–116, a) determine by observation whether the product or quotient will be a positive number, zero, a negative number, or undefined; b) find the product or quotient on your calculator (an error message indicates that the quotient is undefined); c) examine your answer in part b) to see whether it is reasonable and makes sense.

101. $92(-38)$ −3496
102. $-168 \div 42$ −4
103. $-240/15$ −16
104. $0/12$ 0
105. $243 \div (-27)$ −9
106. $(323)(-115)$ −37,145
107. $(-49)(-126)$ 6174
108. $(1530)(0)$ 0
109. $0 \div 5335$ 0
110. $-86.4 \div (-36)$ 2.4
111. $8.2 \div 0$ undefined
112. $-37.74 \div 0$ undefined
113. $8 \div (2.5)$ 3.2
114. $(1.1)(9.72)(6.3)$ 67.3596
115. $(-3.0)(4.2)(-18)$ 226.8
116. $-288.86/1.43$ −202

Indicate whether each statement is true or false.

117. The product of two negative numbers is a negative number. F
118. The product of a positive number and a negative number is a negative number. T
119. The quotient of two numbers with unlike signs is a positive number. F
120. The quotient of two negative numbers is a positive number. T
121. The product of an even number of negative numbers is a positive number. T

122. Zero divided by 1 is 1. F
123. The product of an odd number of negative numbers is a negative number. T
124. Six divided by 0 is 0. F
125. Zero divided by 1 is undefined. F
126. The product of 0 and any real number is 0. T
127. Five divided by 0 is undefined. T
128. Division by 0 does not result in a real number. T

Problem Solving

129. Football A high school football team is penalized three times, each time with a loss of 15 yards, or -15 yards. Find the total loss due to penalties. 45 yard loss or −45 yards

130. Submarine Dive A submarine is at a depth of -160 feet (160 feet below sea level). It dives to 3 times that depth. Find its new depth. −480 ft

131. Credit Card Leona De Vito's balance on her credit card is $-\$520$ (she owes \$520). She pays back $\dfrac{1}{5}$ of this balance.
a) How much did she pay back? \$104
b) What is her new balance? −\$416

132. Money Owed Brian Philip owes his Dad \$500. After he makes four payments of \$40 each, how much will he still owe? \$340

133. Garage Sale Four sisters made a total of \$775.40 at a garage sale. After they each give their husbands \$50 and split the remaining amount equally, how much will each woman receive? \$143.85

134. Wind Chill On Monday in Minneapolis the wind chill was $-30°$F. On Tuesday the wind chill was only $\dfrac{1}{3}$ of what it was on Monday. What was the wind chill on Tuesday? −10°F

135. Test Score Because of incorrect work, Josue Nunez lost 4 points on each of the five questions on his math test.
a) How many points did Josue lose altogether?
b) If the maximum score possible was 100%, what is Josue's test score? 80

136. Reciprocals Most calculators have a *reciprocal key*, $\boxed{1/x}$.
a) Press a number key between 1 and 9 on your calculator. Then press the $\boxed{1/x}$ key. Indicate what happened when you pressed this key. get $\frac{1}{\text{number}}$ as a decimal
b) Press the $\boxed{1/x}$ key a second time. What happens now?
c) What do you think will happen if you enter 0 and then press the $\boxed{1/x}$ key? Explain your answer.
d) Enter 0 and then press the $\boxed{1/x}$ key to see whether your answer to part **c)** was correct. If not, explain why.

137. Heart Rate The Johns Hopkins Medical Letter states that to find a person's *target heart rate* in beats per minute, follow this procedure. Subtract the person's age from 220, then multiply this difference by 60% and 75%. The difference multiplied by 60% gives the lower limit and the difference multiplied by 75% gives the upper limit.
a) Find the target heart rate range of a 50-year-old.
b) Find your own target heart rate. Answers will vary.

135. a) 20 point loss or −20 points **136. b)** get number **c)** and **d)** get error
137. a) 102–128 beats per minute

Challenge Problems

We will learn in the next section that $2^3 = 2 \cdot 2 \cdot 2$ *and* $x^n = \underbrace{x \cdot x \cdot x \cdots \cdot x}_{\text{(n factors of x)}}.$

Use this information to evaluate each expression.

138. 3^4 81

139. $(-5)^3$ -125

140. $\left(\dfrac{2}{3}\right)^3$ $\dfrac{8}{27}$

141. 1^{100} 1

142. $(-1)^{81}$ -1

143. Will the product of $(-1)(-2)(-3)(-4) \cdots (-10)$ be a positive number or a negative number? Explain how you determined your answer.   positive, 10 negative numbers

144. Will the product of $(1)(-2)(3)(-4)(5)(-6) \cdots (33)(-34)$ be a positive number or a negative number? Explain how you determined your answer.   negative, 17 negative numbers

Group Activity

Discuss and answer Exercise 145 as a group, according to the instructions.

145. a) Each member of the group is to do this procedure separately. At this time do not share your number with the other members of your group.

1. Choose a number between 2 and 10.
2. Multiply your number by 9.
3. Add the two digits in the product together.
4. Subtract 5 from the sum.
5. Now choose the corresponding letter of the alphabet that corresponds with the difference found. For example, 1 is a, 2 is b, 3 is c, and so on.

6. Choose a *one-word* country that starts with that letter.
7. Now choose a *one-word* animal that starts with the last letter of the country selected.
8. Finally, choose a color that starts with the last letter of the animal chosen.

b) Now share your final answer with the other members of your group. Did you all get the same answer?

c) Most people will obtain the answer *orange.* As a group, write a paragraph or two explaining why.   Country will start with D. Most students will select Denmark. They will most likely select kangaroo which leads to orange.

Cumulative Review Exercises

[1.5] **146.** Insert either $<$, $>$, or $=$ in the shaded area to make a true statement.
$$|-3.6| \quad \boxed{} \quad |-2.7| \quad >$$

[1.6] **147.** Add $-\dfrac{7}{12} + \left(-\dfrac{1}{10}\right).$ $-\dfrac{41}{60}$

[1.7] **148.** Subtract -18 from -20. -2

149. Evaluate $6 - 3 - 4 - 2$ -3

150. Evaluate $5 - (-2) + 3 - 7$ 3

1.9 Exponents, Parentheses, and the Order of Operations

1 Learn the meaning of exponents.

2 Evaluate expressions containing exponents.

3 Learn the difference between $-x^2$ and $(-x)^2$.

4 Learn the order of operations.

5 Learn the use of parentheses.

6 Evaluate expressions containing variables.

1 Learn the Meaning of Exponents

To understand certain topics in algebra, you must understand exponents. Exponents are introduced in this section and are discussed in more detail in Chapter 4.

In the expression 4^2, the 4 is called the **base**, and the 2 is called the **exponent**. The number 4^2 is read "4 squared" or "4 to the second power" and means

$$\underbrace{4 \cdot 4}_{\text{2 factors of 4}} = 4^{2} \quad \text{base} \downarrow \quad \leftarrow \text{exponent}$$

The number 4^3 is read "4 cubed" or "4 to the third power" and means

$$\underbrace{4 \cdot 4 \cdot 4}_{\text{3 factors of 4}} = 4^3$$

In general, the number b to the *n*th power, written b^n, means

$$\underbrace{b \cdot b \cdot b \cdot \cdots \cdot b}_{\text{n factors of b}} = b^n$$

Thus, $b^4 = b \cdot b \cdot b \cdot b$ or $bbbb$ and $x^3 = x \cdot x \cdot x$ or xxx.

2 Evaluate Expressions Containing Exponents

Let's evaluate some expressions that contain exponents.

EXAMPLE 1 ▶ Evaluate.   **a)** 3^2 **b)** 2^5 **c)** 1^5 **d)** $(-6)^2$ **e)** $(-2)^3$ **f)** $\left(\dfrac{2}{3}\right)^2$

Solution

  a) $3^2 = 3 \cdot 3 = 9$

  b) $2^5 = 2 \cdot 2 \cdot 2 \cdot 2 \cdot 2 = 32$

  c) $1^5 = 1 \cdot 1 \cdot 1 \cdot 1 \cdot 1 = 1$ (1 raised to any power equals 1; why?)

  d) $(-6)^2 = (-6)(-6) = 36$

  e) $(-2)^3 = (-2)(-2)(-2) = -8$

  f) $\left(\dfrac{2}{3}\right)^2 = \left(\dfrac{2}{3}\right)\left(\dfrac{2}{3}\right) = \dfrac{4}{9}$

▶ **Now Try Exercise 29**

It is not necessary to write exponents of 1. For example, when writing xxy, we write x^2y and not x^2y^1. **Whenever we see a variable or number without an exponent, we always assume that the variable or number has an exponent of 1.**

EXAMPLES OF EXPONENTIAL NOTATION

  a) $xyxx = x^3y$ **b)** $xyzzy = xy^2z^2$
  c) $3aabbb = 3a^2b^3$ **d)** $5xyyyy = 5xy^4$
  e) $4 \cdot 4rrs = 4^2r^2s$ **f)** $5 \cdot 5 \cdot 5mmn = 5^3m^2n$

Notice in parts **a)** and **b)** that the order of the factors does not matter.

Helpful Hint

Note that $x + x + x + x + x + x = 6x$ and $x \cdot x \cdot x \cdot x \cdot x \cdot x = x^6$. Be careful that you do not get addition and multiplication confused.

3 Learn the Difference Between $-x^2$ and $(-x)^2$

An exponent refers only to the number or variable that directly precedes it unless parentheses are used to indicate otherwise. For example, in the expression $3x^2$, only the x is squared. In the expression $-x^2$, only the x is squared. We can write $-x^2$ as $-1x^2$ because any real number may be multiplied by 1 without affecting its value.

$$-x^2 = -1x^2$$

By looking at $-1x^2$ we can see that only the x is squared, not the -1. If the entire expression $-x$ were to be squared, we would need to use parentheses and write $(-x)^2$. Note the difference in the following two examples:

$$-x^2 = -(x)(x)$$
$$(-x)^2 = (-x)(-x)$$

Consider the expressions -3^2 and $(-3)^2$. How do they differ?

$$-3^2 = -(3)(3) = -9$$
$$(-3)^2 = (-3)(-3) = 9$$

Helpful Hint

The expression $-x^2$ is read "negative x squared," or "the opposite of x squared." The expression $(-x)^2$ is read "negative x, quantity squared."

EXAMPLE 2 ▶ Evaluate.

a) -5^2　　　　　　b) $(-5)^2$　　　　　　c) -2^3　　　　　　d) $(-2)^3$

Solution

a) $-5^2 = -(5)(5) = -25$　　　　　b) $(-5)^2 = (-5)(-5) = 25$

c) $-2^3 = -(2)(2)(2) = -8$　　　　　d) $(-2)^3 = (-2)(-2)(-2) = -8$

▶ **Now Try Exercise 21**

EXAMPLE 3 ▶ Evaluate.

a) -2^4　　　　　　b) $(-2)^4$

Solution

a) $-2^4 = -(2)(2)(2)(2) = -16$　　　　b) $(-2)^4 = (-2)(-2)(-2)(-2) = 16$

▶ **Now Try Exercise 33**

USING YOUR CALCULATOR Use of $\boxed{x^2}$, $\boxed{y^x}$, and $\boxed{\wedge}$ Keys

The $\boxed{x^2}$ key is used to square a value. For example, to evaluate 5^2, we would do the following.

	KEYSTROKES	ANSWER DISPLAYED
Scientific Calculator	5 $\boxed{x^2}$	25
Graphing Calculator	5 $\boxed{x^2}$ $\boxed{\text{ENTER}}$	25

To evaluate $(-5)^2$ on a calculator, we would do the following.

	KEYSTROKES	ANSWER DISPLAYED
*Scientific Calculator	5 $\boxed{+/-}$ $\boxed{x^2}$	25
Graphing Calculator	$\boxed{(}$ $\boxed{(-)}$ 5 $\boxed{)}$ $\boxed{x^2}$ $\boxed{\text{ENTER}}$	25

To raise a value to a power greater than 2, we use the $\boxed{y^x}$** or $\boxed{\wedge}$ key. To use these keys you enter the number, then press either the $\boxed{y^x}$ or $\boxed{\wedge}$ key, then enter the exponent. Following we show how to evaluate 2^5 and $(-2)^5$.

	EVALUATE	KEYSTROKES	ANSWER DISPLAYED
Scientific Calculator	2^5	2 $\boxed{y^x}$ 5 $\boxed{=}$	32
*Scientific Calculator	$(-2)^5$	2 $\boxed{+/-}$ $\boxed{y^x}$ 5 $\boxed{=}$	-32
Graphing Calculator	2^5	2 $\boxed{\wedge}$ 5 $\boxed{\text{ENTER}}$	32
Graphing Calculator	$(-2)^5$	$\boxed{(}$ $\boxed{(-)}$ 2 $\boxed{)}$ $\boxed{\wedge}$ 5 $\boxed{\text{ENTER}}$	-32

Possibly the easiest way to raise negative numbers to a power may be to raise the positive number to the power and then write a negative sign before the final answer if needed. *A negative number raised to an odd power will be negative, and a negative number raised to an even power will be positive.* Can you explain why this is true?

*Some newer scientific calculators have a $\boxed{(-)}$ key. To evaluate a negative expression raised to a power on these calculators, follow the instructions for the graphing calculator.
**Some calculators use a $\boxed{x^y}$ key instead of a $\boxed{y^x}$ key.

TEACHING TIP
We did not include information about radicals in the order of operations. Radicals are not discussed until Chapter 9.

4 Learn the Order of Operations

Now that we have introduced exponents we can present the **order of operations**. Can you evaluate $2 + 3 \cdot 4$? Is it 20? Or is it 14? To answer this, you must know the order of operations to follow when evaluating a mathematical expression. You will often have to evaluate expressions containing multiple operations.

Order of Operations To Evaluate Mathematical Expressions, Use the Following Order

1. First, evaluate the information within **parentheses** ( ), brackets [ ], or braces { }. These are **grouping symbols**, for they group information together. A fraction bar, $-$, also serves as a grouping symbol. If the expression contains nested parentheses (one pair of parentheses within another pair), evaluate the information in the innermost parentheses first.

2. Next, evaluate all **exponents**.

3. Next, evaluate all **multiplications** or **divisions** in the order in which they occur, working from left to right.

4. Finally, evaluate all **additions** or **subtractions** in the order in which they occur, working from left to right.

Some students remember the word PEMDAS or the phrase "Please Excuse My Dear Aunt Sally" to help them remember the order of operations. PEMDAS helps them remember the order: **P**arentheses, **E**xponents, **M**ultiplication, **D**ivision, **A**ddition, **S**ubtraction. Remember, this does not imply multiplication before division or addition before subtraction.

We can now evaluate $2 + 3 \cdot 4$. Since multiplications are performed before additions,

$$2 + 3 \cdot 4 \quad \text{means} \quad 2 + (3 \cdot 4) = 2 + 12 = 14$$

USING YOUR CALCULATOR

We now know that $2 + 3 \cdot 4$ means $2 + (3 \cdot 4)$ and has a value of 14. What will a calculator display if you key in the following?

$$2 \boxed{+} 3 \boxed{\times} 4 \boxed{=}$$

The answer depends on your calculator. *Scientific and graphing calculators* will evaluate an expression following the rules just stated.

	KEYSTROKES	ANSWER DISPLAYED
Scientific Calculator	$2 \boxed{+} 3 \boxed{\times} 4 \boxed{=}$	14
Graphing Calculator	$2 \boxed{+} 3 \boxed{\times} 4 \boxed{\text{ENTER}}$	14

Nonscientific calculators will perform operations in the order they are entered.

		ANSWER DISPLAYED
Nonscientific Calculator	$2 \boxed{+} 3 \boxed{\times} 4 \boxed{=}$	20

Remember that in algebra, unless otherwise instructed by parentheses, we always perform multiplications and divisions before additions and subtractions. In this course you should be using either a scientific or graphing calculator.

5 Learn the Use of Parentheses

Parentheses or brackets may be used (1) to change the order of operations to be followed in evaluating an algebraic expression or (2) to help clarify the understanding of an expression.

To evaluate the expression $2 + 3 \cdot 4$, we would normally perform the multiplication, $3 \cdot 4$, first. If we wished to have the addition performed before the multiplication, we could indicate this by placing parentheses around $2 + 3$:

$$(2 + 3) \cdot 4 = 5 \cdot 4 = 20$$

Consider the expression $1 \cdot 3 + 2 \cdot 4$. According to the order of operations, multiplications are to be performed before additions. We can rewrite this expression as $(1 \cdot 3) + (2 \cdot 4)$. Note that the order of operations was not changed. The parentheses were used only to help clarify the order to be followed.

Sometimes it may be necessary to use more than one set of parentheses to indicate the order to be followed in an expression. As indicated in step 1 of the Order of Operations box, when one set of parentheses is within another set of parentheses, we call this **nested parentheses**. For example, the expression $6(2 + 3(4 + 1))$ has nested parentheses. Often, to make an expression with nested parentheses easier to follow, brackets, [ ], or braces, { }, are used in place of multiple parentheses. Thus, we could write the expression $6(2 + 3(4 + 1))$ as $6[2 + 3(4 + 1)]$. Whenever we are given an expression with nested parentheses, we always evaluate the numbers in the *innermost parentheses first*. Color shading is used in the following examples to indicate the order in which the expression is evaluated.

$$6[2 + 3(\,4 + 1\,)] = 6[2 + \,3(5)\,] = 6[\,2 + 15\,] = \,6[17]\, = 102$$

$$4[3(\,6 - 4\,) \div 6] = 4[\,3(2)\, \div 6] = 4[\,6 \div 6\,] = \,4[1]\, = 4$$

$$\{2 + [(\,8 \div 4\,)^2 - 1]\}^2 = [2 + (\,2^2\, - 1)]^2 = [2 + (\,4 - 1\,)]^2 = (\,2 + 3\,)^2 = \,5^2\, = 25$$

Now we will work some examples, but before we do, read the following Helpful Hint.

Helpful Hint

If parentheses are not used to change the order of operations, multiplications and divisions are always performed before additions and subtractions. When a problem has only multiplications and divisions, work from left to right. Similarly, when a problem has only additions and subtractions, work from left to right.

INSTRUCTOR EXAMPLE
Evaluate $3 + 2 \cdot 4^2 - 8$.
Ans.: 27

EXAMPLE 4 ▶ Evaluate $6 + 3 \cdot 5^2 - 4$.

Solution   Colored shading is used to indicate the order in which the expression is to be evaluated.

$$6 + 3 \cdot \boxed{5^2} - 4 \qquad \textit{Exponent}$$
$$= 6 + \boxed{3 \cdot 25} - 4 \qquad \textit{Multiply.}$$
$$= \boxed{6 + 75} - 4 \qquad \textit{Add.}$$
$$= 81 - 4$$
$$= 77$$

▶ **Now Try Exercise 61**

INSTRUCTOR EXAMPLE
Evaluate $-5 + 4[-3 + (100 \div 5^2)]$.
Ans.: −1

EXAMPLE 5 ▶ Evaluate $-7 + 2[-6 + (36 \div 3^2)]$.

Solution

$$-7 + 2[-6 + (36 \div \boxed{3^2})] \qquad \textit{Exponent}$$
$$= -7 + 2[-6 + (\boxed{36 \div 9})] \qquad \textit{Divide.}$$
$$= -7 + 2[\boxed{-6 + 4}] \qquad \textit{Add.}$$
$$= -7 + \boxed{2[-2]} \qquad \textit{Multiply.}$$
$$= -7 - 4$$
$$= -11$$

▶ **Now Try Exercise 75**

EXAMPLE 6 ▶ Evaluate $(8 \div 2) + 7(5 - 2)^2$.

Solution

$$
\begin{aligned}
(8 \div 2) + 7(\,5 - 2\,)^2 \qquad &\text{\textit{Parentheses}} \\
= 4 + 7\,(3)^2 \qquad &\text{\textit{Exponent}} \\
= 4 + 7 \cdot 9 \qquad &\text{\textit{Multiply.}} \\
= 4 + 63 \\
= 67
\end{aligned}
$$

▶ **Now Try Exercise 81**

EXAMPLE 7 ▶ Evaluate $-8 - 81 \div 9 \cdot 2^2 + 7$.

Solution

$$
\begin{aligned}
-8 - 81 \div 9 \cdot 2^2 + 7 \qquad &\text{\textit{Exponent}} \\
= -8 - 81 \div 9 \cdot 4 + 7 \qquad &\text{\textit{Divide.}} \\
= -8 - 9 \cdot 4 + 7 \qquad &\text{\textit{Multiply.}} \\
= -8 - 36 + 7 \qquad &\text{\textit{Subtract.}} \\
= -44 + 7 \\
= -37
\end{aligned}
$$

▶ **Now Try Exercise 79**

EXAMPLE 8 ▶ Evaluate.

a) $-4^2 + 6 \div 3$ **b)** $(-4)^2 + 6 \div 3$

Solution

a)
$$
\begin{aligned}
- 4^2 + 6 \div 3 \qquad &\text{\textit{Exponent}} \\
= -16 + 6 \div 3 \qquad &\text{\textit{Divide.}} \\
= -16 + 2 \\
= -14
\end{aligned}
$$

b)
$$
\begin{aligned}
(-4)^2 + 6 \div 3 \qquad &\text{\textit{Exponent}} \\
= 16 + 6 \div 3 \qquad &\text{\textit{Divide.}} \\
= 16 + 2 \\
= 18
\end{aligned}
$$

▶ **Now Try Exercise 85**

EXAMPLE 9 ▶ Evaluate $\dfrac{3}{8} - \dfrac{2}{5} \cdot \dfrac{1}{12}$.

Solution   First perform the multiplication.

$$
\begin{aligned}
\frac{3}{8} - \left(\frac{\overset{1}{2}}{5} \cdot \frac{1}{\underset{6}{12}} \right) \qquad &\text{\textit{Multiply.}} \\
= \frac{3}{8} - \frac{1}{30} \qquad &\text{\textit{Subtract.}} \\
= \frac{45}{120} - \frac{4}{120} \\
= \frac{41}{120}
\end{aligned}
$$

▶ **Now Try Exercise 91**

EXAMPLE 10 ▶ Write the following statements as mathematical expressions using parentheses and brackets and then evaluate: Multiply 12 by 3. Add 8 to this product. Subtract 7 from this sum. Divide this difference by 6.

Solution

$$12 \cdot 3 \qquad\qquad \text{\color{red}Multiply 12 by 3.}$$
$$(12 \cdot 3) + 8 \qquad\qquad \text{\color{red}Add 8.}$$
$$[(12 \cdot 3) + 8] - 7 \qquad\qquad \text{\color{red}Subtract 7.}$$
$$\{[(12 \cdot 3) + 8] - 7\} \div 6 \qquad\qquad \text{\color{red}Divide the difference by 6.}$$

Now evaluate.

$$\{[(\ 12 \cdot 3\ ) + 8] - 7\} \div 6$$
$$= \{[36 + 8] - 7\} \div 6$$
$$= \{44 - 7\} \div 6$$
$$= 37 \div 6$$
$$= \frac{37}{6}$$

▶ **Now Try Exercise 135**

As shown in Example 10, sometimes brackets, [ ], and braces, { }, are used in place of parentheses to help avoid confusion. If only parentheses had been used, the preceding expression would appear as $(((12 \cdot 3) + 8) - 7) \div 6$.

USING YOUR CALCULATOR   Using Parentheses

When evaluating an expression on a calculator where the order of operations is to be changed, you will need to use parentheses. If you are not sure whether they are needed, it will not hurt to add them. Consider $\dfrac{8}{4 - 2}$. Since we wish to divide 8 by the difference $4 - 2$, we need to use parentheses.

EVALUATE	KEYSTROKES	ANSWER DISPLAYED
$\dfrac{8}{4 - 2}$	$8 \div (\ 4 - 2\ ) = {}^{*}$	4

What would you obtain if you evaluated $8 \div 4 - 2 =$ on a scientific calculator? Why would you get that result?

To evaluate $\left(\dfrac{2}{5}\right)^2$ on a scientific calculator, we press the following keys.

EVALUATE	KEYSTROKES	ANSWER DISPLAYED
$\left(\dfrac{2}{5}\right)^2$	$2 \div 5 = x^2 {}^{**}$	.16
	or $(\ 2 \div 5\ ) x^2$	.16

What would you obtain if you evaluated $2 \div 5\ x^2$ on a scientific calculator? Why?

* If using a graphing calculator, replace $=$ with ENTER . Everything else remains the same.
** On a graphing calculator, replace $=$ with ENTER and press ENTER after x^2 .

6 Evaluate Expressions Containing Variables

Now we will evaluate some expressions for given values of the variables.

EXAMPLE 11 ▶ Evaluate $5x - 4$ when $x = 3$.

Solution   Substitute 3 for x in the expression.

$$5x - 4 = 5(3) - 4 = 15 - 4 = 11$$

▶ **Now Try Exercise 115**

EXAMPLE 12 ▶ Evaluate **a)** x^2 **b)** $-x^2$ and **c)** $(-x)^2$ when $x = 3$.

Solution   Substitute 3 for x.

a) $x^2 = 3^2 = 3(3) = 9$ **c)** $(-x)^2 = (-3)^2 = (-3)(-3) = 9$

b) $-x^2 = -3^2 = -(3)(3) = -9$

▶ **Now Try Exercise 105**

EXAMPLE 13 ▶ Evaluate **a)** y^2 **b)** $-y^2$ and **c)** $(-y)^2$ when $y = -4$.

Solution   Substitute -4 for y.

a) $y^2 = (-4)^2 = (-4)(-4) = 16$ **c)** $(-y)^2 = [-(-4)]^2 = (4)^2 = 16$

b) $-y^2 = -(-4)^2 = -(-4)(-4) = -16$

▶ **Now Try Exercise 107**

Note that $-x^2$ will always be a negative number for any nonzero value of x, and $(-x)^2$ will always be a positive number for any nonzero value of x. Can you explain why? See Exercise 6 on page 77.

Avoiding Common Errors

The expression $-x^2$ means $-(x^2)$. When asked to evaluate $-x^2$ for any real number x, many students will incorrectly treat $-x^2$ as $(-x)^2$. For example, to evaluate $-x^2$ when $x = 5$,

CORRECT

$-5^2 = -(5^2) = -(5)(5)$
$= -25$

INCORRECT

$-5^2 = (-5)(-5)$
$= 25$

EXAMPLE 14 ▶ Evaluate $2x^2 + 4x + 1$ when $x = \dfrac{1}{4}$.

Solution   Substitute $\dfrac{1}{4}$ for each x in the expression, then evaluate using the order of operations.

$$2x^2 + 4x + 1 = 2\left(\frac{1}{4}\right)^2 + 4\left(\frac{1}{4}\right) + 1 \quad \textit{Substitute.}$$

$$= 2\left(\frac{1}{16}\right) + 4\left(\frac{1}{4}\right) + 1 \quad \textit{Exponent}$$

$$= \frac{1}{8} + 1 + 1 \quad \textit{Multiply.}$$

$$= \frac{1}{8} + 2 \quad \textit{Add.}$$

$$= 2\frac{1}{8}$$

▶ **Now Try Exercise 123**

EXAMPLE 15 ▶ Evaluate $-y^2 + 3(x + 2) - 5$ when $x = -3$ and $y = -2$.

Solution   Substitute -3 for each x and -2 for each y, then evaluate using the order of operations.

$$-y^2 + 3(x + 2) - 5 = -(-2)^2 + 3(-3 + 2) - 5 \quad \textit{Substitute.}$$

$$= -(-2)^2 + 3(-1) - 5 \quad \textit{Parentheses}$$

$$= -(4) + 3(-1) - 5 \quad \textit{Exponent}$$

$$= -4 - 3 - 5 \quad \textit{Multiply.}$$

$$= -7 - 5 \quad \textit{Subtract, left to right.}$$

$$= -12$$

▶ **Now Try Exercise 131**

USING YOUR CALCULATOR   Evaluating Expressions on a Scientific Calculator

Later in this course you will need to evaluate an expression like $3x^2 - 2x + 5$ for various values of x. Below we show how to evaluate such expressions.

EVALUATE

KEYSTROKES

a) $3x^2 - 2x + 5$, for $x = 4$

$3(4)^2 - 2(4) + 5$

$3\boxed{\times}4\boxed{x^2}\boxed{-}2\boxed{\times}4\boxed{+}5\boxed{=}45$

b) $3x^2 - 2x + 5$, for $x = -6$

$3(-6)^2 - 2(-6) + 5$

$3\boxed{\times}6\boxed{+/-}\boxed{x^2}\boxed{-}2\boxed{\times}6\boxed{+/-}\boxed{+}5\boxed{=}125$

c) $-x^2 - 3x - 5$, for $x = -2$

$-(-2)^2 - 3(-2) - 5$

$1\boxed{+/-}\boxed{\times}2\boxed{+/-}\boxed{x^2}\boxed{-}3\boxed{\times}2\boxed{+/-}\boxed{-}5\boxed{=}-3$

Remember in part **c)** that $-x^2 = -1x^2$.

USING YOUR GRAPHING CALCULATOR   Evaluating Expressions on a Graphing Calculator

All graphing calculators have a procedure for evaluating expressions. You generally need to enter the value to be used for the variable and the expression to be evaluated. After the $\boxed{\text{ENTER}}$ key is pressed, the graphing calculator displays the answer. The procedure varies from calculator to calculator. Below we show how an expression is evaluated on a TI-84 Plus. On this calculator the store key, $\boxed{\text{STO}\blacktriangleright}$, is used to store a value. Stored values and expressions are separated using a colon, which is obtained by pressing $\boxed{\text{ALPHA}}$ followed by $\boxed{\cdot}$.

EVALUATE

KEYSTROKES ON TI-84 PLUS

$3x^2 - 2x + 5$ for $x = -6$

Display shown: $-6 \rightarrow x$ $: 3\ x^2 - 2\ x + 5$ 125

Notice that to obtain an x^2 on the display, we press the $\boxed{\text{X, T, }\theta, n}$ key to select the variable x, then we press the $\boxed{x^2}$ key, which is used to square the variable or number selected.

A nice feature of graphing calculators is that to evaluate an expression for different values of a variable you do not have to re-enter the expression each time. For example, on the TI-84 Plus if you press $\boxed{\text{2}^{\text{nd}}}$ followed by $\boxed{\text{ENTER}}$ it displays the expression again. You then change the value stored for x to the new value and press $\boxed{\text{ENTER}}$ to evaluate the expression with the new value of the variable.

Each brand of calculator uses different keys and procedures. We have given just a quick overview. Please read the manual that comes with your graphing calculator for a complete explanation of how to evaluate expressions.

*This key can be used to generate any of these letters (θ is a Greek letter). From this point on, in displays of keystrokes, to generate an x we will just show $\boxed{x}$ rather than $\boxed{\text{X, T, }\theta, n}$.

EXERCISE SET 1.9

Concept/Writing Exercises

1. In the expression a^b, what is the a called and what is the b called?   base, exponent

2. Explain the meaning of
   a) 3^2 2 factors of 3
   b) 5^4 4 factors of 5
   c) x^n n factors of x

3. a) What is the exponent on a number or variable that has no exponent illustrated?   1
   b) In the expression $5x^3y^2z$, what is the exponent on the 5, the x, the y, and the z?   1, 3, 2, 1

4. Write a simplified expression for the following.
   a) $x + x + x + x + x$ $5x$
   b) $x \cdot x \cdot x \cdot x \cdot x$ x^5

8. left to right **10.** to change order or to clarify

5. Write a simplified expression for the following.

   a) $y + y + y + y$ $4y$

   b) $y \cdot y \cdot y \cdot y$ y^4

6. a) Explain why $-x^2$ will always be a negative number for any nonzero real number selected for x. $-x^2$ means $-(x^2)$

   b) Explain why $(-x)^2$ will always be a positive number for any nonzero real number selected for x.

7. List the order of operations to be followed when evaluating a mathematical expression.

8. When an expression has only additions and subtractions or only multiplications or divisions, how is it evaluated?

9. If you evaluate $4 + 5 \times 2$ on a calculator and obtain an answer of 18, is the calculator a scientific calculator? Explain.   no

10. List two reasons why parentheses are used in an expression.

11. Determine the results obtained on a scientific calculator if the following keys are pressed.

   a) 15 $-$ 10 $\div$ 5 $=$ 13

   b) $($ 15 $-$ 10 $)$ $\div$ 5 $=$ 1

   c) Which keystrokes, **a)** or **b)**, are used to evaluate $\dfrac{15 - 10}{5}$? Explain.   **b)**

12. Determine the results obtained on a scientific calculator if the following keys are pressed.

   a) 20 $\div$ 5 $-$ 3 $=$ 1

   b) 20 $\div$ $($ 5 $-$ 3 $)$ $=$ 10

   c) Which keystrokes, **a)** or **b)**, are used to evaluate $\dfrac{20}{5 - 3}$? Explain.   **b)**

6. b) $(-x)^2$ means $(-x)(-x)$, product positive if $x < 0$ or $x > 0$ **7.** parentheses, exponents, multiplication or division, addition or subtraction

In Exercises 13 and 14, **a)** *write the step-by-step procedure you would use to evaluate the expression, and* **b)** *evaluate the expression.*

13. $[10 - (16 \div 4)]^2 - 6^3$ **b)** -180

14. $[(8 \cdot 3) - 4^2]^2 - 5$ **b)** 59

In Exercises 15 and 16, **a)** *write the step-by-step procedure you would use to evaluate the expression for the given value of the variable, and* **b)** *evaluate the expression for the given value of the variable.*

15. $-4x^2 + 3x - 6$ when $x = 5$ **b)** -91

16. $-5x^2 - 2x + 8$ when $x = -2$ **b)** -8

Practice the Skills

Evaluate.

17. 5^2 25

18. 2^3 8

19. 1^7 1

20. 4^1 4

21. -8^2 -64

22. 7^3 343

23. $(-3)^2$ 9

24. -6^3 -216

25. $(-1)^3$ -1

26. 2^5 32

27. -10^2 -100

28. 5^3 125

29. $(-9)^2$ 81

30. $(-3)^3$ -27

31. 3^3 27

32. -7^2 -49

33. $(-4)^4$ 256

34. -4^4 -256

35. -2^4 -16

36. $3^2(4)^2$ 144

37. $\left(\dfrac{3}{4}\right)^2$ $\dfrac{9}{16}$

38. $\left(\dfrac{5}{8}\right)^3$ $\dfrac{125}{512}$

39. $\left(-\dfrac{1}{2}\right)^5$ $-\dfrac{1}{32}$

40. $\left(-\dfrac{2}{3}\right)^4$ $\dfrac{16}{81}$

41. $5^2 \cdot 3^2$ 225

42. $(-1)^4(2)^4$ 16

43. $4^3 \cdot 3^2$ 576

44. $(-2)^3(-1)^9$ 8

In Exercises 45–56, **a)** *determine by observation whether the answer should be positive or negative and explain your answer;* **b)** *evaluate the expression on your calculator; and* **c)** *determine whether your answer in part* **b)** *is reasonable and makes sense.*

45. 7^3 343

46. 4^6 4096

47. 6^4 1296

48. -2^5 -32

49. $(-3)^5$ -243

50. 10^3 1000

51. $(-5)^4$ 625

52. $(1.3)^3$ 2.197

53. $-(-9)^2$ -81

54. $(-3.3)^3$ -35.937

55. $-\left(\dfrac{3}{8}\right)^2$ -0.140625

56. $\left(-\dfrac{3}{4}\right)^3$ -0.421875

Evaluate.

57. $3 + 2 \cdot 6$ 15

58. $7 - 5^2 + 2$ -16

59. $6 - 6 + 8$ 8

60. $(8^2 \div 4) - (20 - 4)$ 0

61. $-7 + 2 \cdot 6^2 - 8$ 57

62. $6 + 2 \cdot 3^2 - 10$ 14

63. $-3^3 + 27$ 0

64. $(-2)^3 + 8 \div 4$ -6

65. $(4 - 3) \cdot (5 - 1)^2$ 16

66. $-10 - 6 - 3 - 2$ -21

67. $3 \cdot 7 + 4 \cdot 2$ 29

68. $4^2 - 3 \cdot 4 - 6$ -2

69. $5 - 2(7 + 5)$ -19

70. $8 + 3(6 + 4)$ 38

71. $-32 - 5(7 - 10)^2$ -77

72. $-40 - 3(4 - 8)^2$ -88

73. $\dfrac{3}{4} + 2\left(\dfrac{1}{5}\right)^2$ $\dfrac{83}{100}$

74. $-\dfrac{2}{3} - 3\left(\dfrac{3}{4}\right)^2$ $-\dfrac{113}{48}$ or $-2\dfrac{17}{48}$

75. $-4 + 3[-1 + (12 \div 2^2)]$ 2

76. $-2 + 4[-3 + (48 \div 4^2)]$ -2

77. $(6 \div 3)^3 + 4^2 \div 8$ 10

78. $4 + (4^2 - 13)^4 - 3$ 82

79. $-7 - 48 \div 6 \cdot 2^2 + 5$ -34

80. $-7 - 56 \div 7 \cdot 2^2 + 4$ -35

81. $(9 \div 3) + 4(7 - 2)^2$ 103

82. $(12 \div 4) + 5(6 - 4)^2$ 23

83. $[4 + ((5 - 2)^2 \div 3)^2]^2$ 169

84. $(20 \div 5 \cdot 5 \div 5 - 5)^2$ 1

85. $(-3)^2 + 8 \div 2$ 13

86. $-3^2 + 8 \div 2$ -5

87. $2[1.55 + 5(3.7)] - 3.35$ 36.75

88. $(8.4 + 3.1)^2 - (3.64 - 1.2)$ 129.81

89. $\left(\dfrac{2}{5} + \dfrac{3}{8}\right) - \dfrac{3}{20}$ $\dfrac{5}{8}$

90. $\left(\frac{5}{6}\cdot\frac{4}{5}\right)+\left(\frac{2}{3}\cdot\frac{5}{8}\right)$ $\frac{13}{12}$ or $1\frac{1}{12}$ **91.** $\frac{3}{4}-4\cdot\frac{5}{40}$ $\frac{1}{4}$ **92.** $\frac{1}{8}-\frac{1}{4}\cdot\frac{3}{2}+\frac{3}{5}$ $\frac{7}{20}$

93. $\frac{4}{5}+\frac{3}{4}\div\frac{1}{2}-\frac{2}{3}$ $\frac{49}{30}$ or $1\frac{19}{30}$ **94.** $\frac{12-(4-6)^2}{6+4^2\div2^2}$ $\frac{4}{5}$ **95.** $\frac{-4-[2(9\div3)-5]}{6^2-3^2\cdot7}$ $\frac{5}{27}$

96. $\frac{[(7-3)^2-4]^2}{9-16\div8-4}$ 48 **97.** $\frac{-[4-(6-12)^2]}{[(9\div3)+4]^2+2^2}$ $\frac{32}{53}$ **98.** $\frac{[(5-(3-7))-2]^2}{2[(16\div2^2)-(8\cdot4)]}$ $-\frac{7}{8}$

99. $\{5-2[4-(6\div2)]^2\}^2$ 9 **100.** $\{-6-[3(16\div4^2)]\}^2$ 81 **101.** $-\{4-[-3-(2-5)]^2\}$ -4

102. $3\{4[(3-4)^2-3]^3-1\}$ -99 **103.** $\{4-3[2-(9\div3)]^2\}^2$ 1 **104.** $2\{5[(4-6)^3-1]^2-3\}$ 804

Evaluate **a)** x^2, **b)** $-x^2$, *and* **c)** $(-x)^2$ *for the following values of x.*

105. 5 $25,-25,25$ **106.** 8 $64,-64,64$ **107.** -2 $4,-4,4$ **108.** -5 $25,-25,25$

109. 6 $36,-36,36$ **110.** 7 $49,-49,49$ **111.** $-\frac{1}{3}$ $\frac{1}{9},-\frac{1}{9},\frac{1}{9}$ **112.** $\frac{3}{4}$ $\frac{9}{16},-\frac{9}{16},\frac{9}{16}$

Evaluate each expression for the given value of the variable or variables.

113. $x+6; x=-2$ 4 **114.** $2x-4x+5; x=3$ -1 **115.** $-7z-3; z=6$ -45

116. $3(x-2); x=5$ 9 **117.** $a^2-6; a=-3$ 3 **118.** $b^2-8; b=5$ 17

119. $3p^2-6p-4; p=2$ -4 **120.** $2r^2-5r+3; r=1$ 0 **121.** $-4x^2-2x+1; x=-1$ -1

122. $-t^2-4t+5; t=-4$ 5 **123.** $-x^2-2x+5; x=\frac{1}{2}$ $\frac{15}{4}$ or $3\frac{3}{4}$ **124.** $2x^2-4x-10; x=\frac{3}{4}$ $-\frac{95}{8}$ or $-11\frac{7}{8}$

125. $4(3x+1)^2-6x; x=5$ 994 **126.** $3n^2(2n-1)+5; n=-4$ -427

127. $r^2-s^2; r=-2, s=-3$ -5 **128.** $p^2-q^2; p=5, q=-3$ 16

129. $5(x-6y)+3x-7y; x=1, y=-5$ 193 **130.** $4(x+y)^2+2(x+y)+3; x=2, y=4$ 159

131. $3(x-4)^2-(3y-4)^2; x=-1, y=-2$ -25 **132.** $6x^2+3xy-y^2; x=2, y=-3$ -3

Problem Solving

134. $[(9+4)\div2]+10; \frac{33}{2}$ or $16\frac{1}{2}$ **135.** $\{[(10\cdot4)+9]-6\}\div7; \frac{43}{7}$ or $6\frac{1}{7}$ **136.** $10\{[(6\cdot3)+27]\div8\}; \frac{225}{4}$ or $56\frac{1}{4}$

Write the following statements as mathematical expressions using parentheses and brackets, and then evaluate.   **139.** all real numbers   **142.** $1.€

133. Multiply 6 by 3. From this product, subtract 4. From this difference, subtract 2. $[(6\cdot3)-4]-2; 12$

134. Add 4 to 9. Divide this sum by 2. Add 10 to this quotient.

135. Multiply 10 by 4. Add 9 to this product. Subtract 6 from this sum. Divide this difference by 7.

136. Multiply 6 by 3. To this product, add 27. Divide this sum by 8. Multiply this quotient by 10.

137. Add $\frac{4}{5}$ to $\frac{3}{7}$. Multiply this sum by $\frac{2}{3}$. $\left(\frac{4}{5}+\frac{3}{7}\right)\cdot\frac{2}{3}; \frac{86}{105}$

138. Multiply $\frac{3}{8}$ by $\frac{4}{5}$. To this product, add $\frac{7}{120}$. From this sum, subtract $\frac{1}{60}$. $\left[\left(\frac{3}{8}\cdot\frac{4}{5}\right)+\frac{7}{120}\right]-\frac{1}{60}; \frac{41}{120}$

139. For what value or values of x does $-(x^2)=-x^2$?

140. For what value or values of x does $x=x^2$? $0, 1$

141. **Road Trip** If a car travels at 65 miles per hour, the distance it travels in t hours is $65t$. Determine how far a car traveling at 65 miles per hour travels in 2.5 hours. 162.5 mi

142. **Sales Tax** If the sales tax on an item is 8%, the sales tax on an item costing d dollars can be found by the expression $0.08d$. Determine the sales tax on a scrapbook that costs $19.99.

143. **Projectile Height** An object is projected upward with an initial velocity of 48 feet per second from the top of a 70-foot building. The height of the object above the ground at any time t, in seconds, can be found by the expression $-16t^2+48t+70$. Determine the height of the object after 2 seconds. 102 ft

144. **Car Cost** If the sales tax on an item is 8%, then the total cost of an item c, including sales tax, can be found by the expression $c+0.08c$. Find the total cost of a car that costs $17,000.

145. In the Using Your Calculator box on page 74, we showed that to evaluate $\left(\frac{2}{5}\right)^2$ we press the following keys:

2 $\div$ 5 $=$ x^2

We obtained an answer of .16. Indicate what a scientific (or graphing) calculator would display if the following keys are pressed. (On a graphing calculator, press ENTER instead of $=$ and end part **b)** with ENTER). Explain your reason for each answer. Check your answer on your calculator.

a) 2 $\div$ 5 x^2 $=$ .08

b) $($ 2 $\div$ 5 $)$ x^2 .16

146. We will discuss using zero as an exponent in Section 6.1. On your calculator find the value of 4^0 by using your y^x, x^y, or $\wedge$ key and record its value. Evaluate a few other numbers raised to the zero power. Can you make any conclusions about a real number (other than 0) raised to the zero power?   equals 1   **144.** $18,360

Challenge Problems

147. Grass Growth The rate of growth of grass in inches per week depends on a number of factors, including rainfall and temperature. For a certain region of the country, the growth per week can be approximated by the expression $0.2R^2 + 0.003RT + 0.0001T^2$, where R is the weekly rainfall, in inches, and T is the average weekly temperature, in degrees Fahrenheit. Find the amount of growth of grass for a week in which the rainfall is 2 inches and the average temperature is 70°F.   1.71 in.

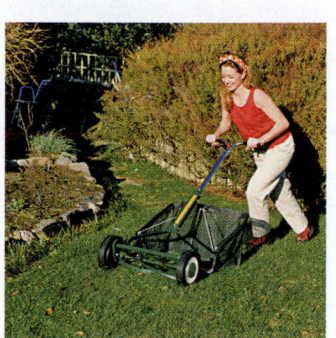

Insert one pair of parentheses to make each statement true.

148. $14 + 6 \div 2 \times 4 = 40$ $(14 + 6) \div 2 \times 4 = 40$

149. $12 - 4 - 6 + 10 = 24$ $12 - (4 - 6) + 10 = 24$

150. $24 \div 6 \div 2 + 2 = 1$ $24 \div 6 \div (2 + 2) = 1$

Group Activity

*Discuss and answer Exercises 151–154 as a group, according to the instructions. Each question has four parts. For parts **a)**, **b)**, and **c)**, simplify the expression and write the answer in exponential form. Use the knowledge gained in parts **a)–c)** to answer part **d)**. (General rules that may be used to solve exercises like these will be discussed in Chapter 6.)*

a) *Group member 1: Do part **a)** of each exercise.*

b) *Group member 2: Do part **b)** of each exercise.*

c) *Group member 3: Do part **c)** of each exercise.*

d) *As a group, answer part **d)** of each exercise. You may need to make up other examples like parts **a)–c)** to help you answer part **d)**.*

151. a) $2^2 \cdot 2^3$ 2^5
  b) $3^2 \cdot 3^3$ 3^5
  c) $2^3 \cdot 2^4$ 2^7
  d) $x^m \cdot x^n$ x^{m+n}

152. a) $\dfrac{2^3}{2^2}$ $2^1 = 2$
  b) $\dfrac{3^4}{3^2}$ 3^2
  c) $\dfrac{4^5}{4^3}$ 4^2
  d) $\dfrac{x^m}{x^n}$ x^{m-n}

153. a) $(2^3)^2$ 2^6
  b) $(3^3)^2$ 3^6
  c) $(4^2)^2$ 4^4
  d) $(x^m)^n$ x^{mn}

154. a) $(2x)^2$ 2^2x^2
  b) $(3x)^2$ 3^2x^2
  c) $(4x)^3$ 4^3x^3
  d) $(ax)^m$ a^mx^m

Cumulative Review Exercises

[1.2] **155. Dogs** The graph shows the number of dogs in various houses selected at random in a neighborhood.

Dogs in Selected Houses

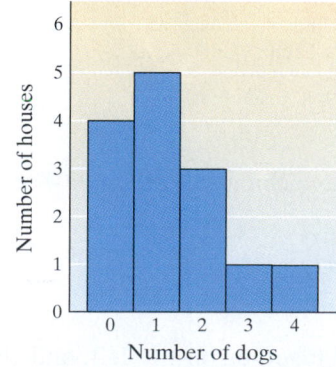

a) How many houses have two dogs?   3

b) Make a chart showing the number of houses that have no dogs, one dog, two dogs, and so on.

c) How many dogs in total are there in all the houses?

d) Determine the mean number of dogs in all the houses surveyed.   ≈1.29

156. Taxi Cost Yellow Cab charges $2.40 for the first $\dfrac{1}{2}$ mile plus 20 cents for each additional $\dfrac{1}{8}$ mile or part thereof. Find the cost of a 3-mile trip. $6.40

[1.6] **157.** Add $-\dfrac{7}{12} + \dfrac{4}{9}$. $-\dfrac{5}{36}$

[1.8] **158.** Divide $\left(\dfrac{-5}{7}\right) \div \left(\dfrac{-3}{14}\right)$. $\dfrac{10}{3}$ or $3\dfrac{1}{3}$

155. b)

Dogs	Houses
0	4
1	5
2	3
3	1
4	1

155. c) 18

1.10 Properties of the Real Number System

Here, we introduce various properties of the real number system. We will use these properties throughout the text.

1 Learn the Commutative Property

The **commutative property of addition** states that the order in which any two real numbers are added does not matter.

> ### Commutative Property of Addition
> If a and b represent any two real numbers, then
> $$a + b = b + a$$

Notice that the commutative property involves a change in *order*. For example,

$$4 + 3 = 3 + 4$$
$$7 = 7$$

The **commutative property of multiplication** states that the order in which any two real numbers are multiplied does not matter.

> ### Commutative Property of Multiplication
> If a and b represent any two real numbers, then
> $$a \cdot b = b \cdot a$$

For example,

$$6 \cdot 3 = 3 \cdot 6$$
$$18 = 18$$

The commutative property **does not hold** *for subtraction or division.* For example, $4 - 6 \neq 6 - 4$ and $6 \div 3 \neq 3 \div 6$.

2 Learn the Associative Property

The **associative property of addition** states that, in the addition of three or more numbers, parentheses may be placed around any two adjacent numbers without changing the results.

> ### Associative Property of Addition
> If a, b, and c represent any three real numbers, then
> $$(a + b) + c = a + (b + c)$$

Notice that the associative property involves a change of *grouping*. For example,

$$(3 + 4) + 5 = 3 + (4 + 5)$$
$$7 + 5 = 3 + 9$$
$$12 = 12$$

In this example, the 3 and 4 are grouped together on the left, and the 4 and 5 are grouped together on the right.

The **associative property of multiplication**, states that, in the multiplication of three or more numbers, parentheses may be placed around any two adjacent numbers without changing the results.

Associative Property of Multiplication

If a, b, and c represent any three real numbers, then

$$(a \cdot b) \cdot c = a \cdot (b \cdot c)$$

For example,

$$(6 \cdot 2) \cdot 4 = 6 \cdot (2 \cdot 4)$$
$$12 \cdot 4 = 6 \cdot 8$$
$$48 = 48$$

Since the associative property involves a change of grouping, when the associative property is used, the content within the parentheses changes.

The associative property **does not hold** *for subtraction or division.* For example, $(4 - 1) - 3 \neq 4 - (1 - 3)$ and $(8 \div 4) \div 2 \neq 8 \div (4 \div 2)$.

Often when we add numbers we group the numbers so that we can add them easily. For example, when we add $70 + 50 + 30$ we may first add the $70 + 30$ to get 100. We are able to do this because of the commutative and associative properties. Notice that

$$(70 + 50) + 30 = 70 + (50 + 30) \qquad \text{\textit{Associative property of addition}}$$
$$= 70 + (30 + 50) \qquad \text{\textit{Commutative property of addition}}$$
$$= (70 + 30) + 50 \qquad \text{\textit{Associative property of addition}}$$
$$= 100 + 50 \qquad \text{\textit{Addition facts}}$$
$$= 150$$

Notice in the second step that the same numbers remained in parentheses but the order of the numbers changed, $50 + 30$ to $30 + 50$. Since this step involved a change in order (and not grouping), this is the commutative property of addition.

3 Learn the Distributive Property

A very important property of the real numbers is the **distributive property of multiplication over addition**. We often shorten the name to the **distributive property**.

Distributive Property

If a, b, and c represent any three real numbers, then

$$a(b + c) = ab + ac$$

For example, if we let $a = 2$, $b = 3$, and $c = 4$, then

$$2(3 + 4) = (2 \cdot 3) + (2 \cdot 4)$$
$$2 \cdot 7 = 6 + 8$$
$$14 = 14$$

Therefore, we may either add first and then multiply, or multiply first and then add. Another example of the distributive property is

$$2(x + 3) = 2 \cdot x + 2 \cdot 3 = 2x + 6$$

The distributive property can be expanded in the following manner:

$$a(b + c + d + \cdots + n) = ab + ac + ad + \cdots + an$$

For example, $3(x + y + 5) = 3x + 3y + 15$.

The distributive property will be discussed in more detail in Chapter 2.

Helpful Hint

The *commutative property* changes *order*.

The *associative property* changes *grouping*.

The *distributive property* involves *two operations*, usually multiplication and addition.

INSTRUCTOR EXAMPLE

Name each property illustrated.

a) $-3 + (-5) = -5 + (-3)$

b) $6(x - 9) = 6x - 54$

c) $rg = gr$

d) $6 + (w + 1) = (6 + w) + 1$

Ans.:

a) Commutative property of addition

b) Distributive property

c) Commutative property of multiplication

d) Associative property of addition

EXAMPLE 1 ▶ Name each property illustrated.

a) $4 + (-2) = -2 + 4$

b) $5(r + s) = 5 \cdot r + 5 \cdot s = 5r + 5s$

c) $x \cdot y = y \cdot x$

d) $(-12 + 3) + 4 = -12 + (3 + 4)$

Solution

a) Commutative property of addition

b) Distributive property

c) Commutative property of multiplication

d) Associative property of addition

▶ **Now Try Exercise 29**

Helpful Hint

Do not confuse the distributive property with the associative property of multiplication. Make sure you understand the difference.

Distributive Property	Associative Property of Multiplication
$3(4 + x) = 3 \cdot 4 + 3 \cdot x$	$3(4 \cdot x) = (3 \cdot 4)x$
$= 12 + 3x$	$= 12x$

For the distributive property to be used, there must be two *terms* within parentheses, separated by a plus or minus sign as in $3(4 + x)$.

4 Learn the Identity Properties

Now we will discuss the **identity properties**. When the number 0 is added to any real number, the real number is unchanged. For example, $5 + 0 = 5$ and $0 + 5 = 5$. For this reason we call 0 the **identity element of addition**. When any real number is multiplied by 1, the real number is unchanged. For example, $7 \cdot 1 = 7$ and $1 \cdot 7 = 7$. For this reason we call 1 the **identity element of multiplication**. The identity property for addition states that when 0 is added to any real number, the sum is the real number you started with. The identity property for multiplication states that when any real number is multiplied by 1, the product is the real number you started with. These properties are summarized below.

Identity Properties

If a represents any real number, then

$$a + 0 = a \quad \text{and} \quad 0 + a = a \qquad \textit{Identity property of addition}$$

and

$$a \cdot 1 = a \quad \text{and} \quad 1 \cdot a = a \qquad \textit{Identity property of multiplication}$$

We often use the identity properties without realizing we are using them. For example, when we reduce $\dfrac{15}{50}$, we may do the following:

$$\frac{15}{50} = \frac{3 \cdot 5}{10 \cdot 5} = \frac{3}{10} \cdot \frac{5}{5} = \frac{3}{10} \cdot 1 = \frac{3}{10}$$

When we showed that $\dfrac{3}{10} \cdot 1 = \dfrac{3}{10}$, we used the identity property of multiplication.

5 Learn the Inverse Properties

The last properties we will discuss in this chapter are the **inverse properties**. On page 44, we indicated that numbers like 3 and -3 were opposites or *additive inverses* because $3 + (-3) = 0$ and $-3 + 3 = 0$. Any two numbers whose sum is 0 are called *additive inverses* of each other. In general, for any real number a its additive inverse is $-a$.

We also have multiplicative inverses. Any two numbers whose product is 1 are called *multiplicative inverses* of each other. For example, because $4 \cdot \dfrac{1}{4} = 1$ and $\dfrac{1}{4} \cdot 4 = 1$, the numbers 4 and $\dfrac{1}{4}$ are *multiplicative inverses* (or *reciprocals*) of each other. In general, for any real number a, its multiplicative inverse is $\dfrac{1}{a}$. The inverse properties are summarized below.

> **Inverse Properties**
>
> If a represents any real number, then
>
> $$a + (-a) = 0 \quad \text{and} \quad -a + a = 0 \qquad \textit{Inverse property of addition}$$
>
> and
>
> $$a \cdot \frac{1}{a} = 1 \quad \text{and} \quad \frac{1}{a} \cdot a = 1\,(a \neq 0) \qquad \textit{Inverse property of multiplication}$$

We often use the inverse properties without realizing we are using them. For example, to evaluate the expression $6x + 2$, when $x = \dfrac{1}{6}$ we may do the following:

$$6x + 2 = 6\left(\frac{1}{6}\right) + 2 = 1 + 2 = 3$$

When we multiplied $6\left(\dfrac{1}{6}\right)$ and replaced it with 1, we used the inverse property of multiplication. We will be using both the identity and inverse properties throughout the book, although we may not specifically refer to them by name.

INSTRUCTOR EXAMPLE
Name each property illustrated.

a) $5y + (-5y) = 0$

b) $4(x - 7) = (4 \cdot x) + (4 \cdot -7) = 4x - 28$

Ans.:

a) Inverse property of addition

b) Distributive property

EXAMPLE 2 ▶ Name each property illustrated.

a) $2(x + 6) = (2 \cdot x) + (2 \cdot 6) = 2x + 12$

b) $3x \cdot 1 = 3x$

c) $(3 \cdot 6) \cdot 5 = 3 \cdot (6 \cdot 5)$

d) $y \cdot \dfrac{1}{y} = 1$

e) $2a + (-2a) = 0$

f) $3y + 0 = 3y$

Solution

a) Distributive property

b) Identity property of multiplication

c) Associative property of multiplication

d) Inverse property of multiplication

e) Inverse property of addition

f) Identity property of addition

▶ **Now Try Exercise 35**

INSTRUCTOR EXAMPLE

In parts **a)**–**c)**, follow the directions as in Example 3.

a) Associative property of multiplication

$(3 \cdot 6) \cdot 9 =$

b) Distributive property

$7(x - 4) =$

c) Identity property of addition

$6b + 0 =$

Ans.:

a) $3 \cdot (6 \cdot 9)$

b) $7x - 28$

c) $6b$

EXAMPLE 3 ▶ In parts **a)**–**f)**, the name of a property is given followed by part of an equation. Complete the equation, to the right of the equal sign, to illustrate the given property.

a) Associative property of multiplication

$(5 \cdot 4) \cdot 7 =$

c) Identity property of multiplication

$6y \cdot 1 =$

e) Identity property of addition

$2a + 0 =$

b) Inverse property of addition

$3c + (-3c) =$

d) Distributive property

$3(x + 5) =$

f) Inverse property of multiplication

$b \cdot \dfrac{1}{b} =$

Solution

a) $5 \cdot (4 \cdot 7)$ **b)** 0 **c)** $6y$ **d)** $3x + 15$ **e)** $2a$ **f)** 1

▶ **Now Try Exercise 55**

EXERCISE SET 1.10   MathXL®   MyMathLab

Concept/Writing Exercises

6. $2(3 + 4) = 2(3) + 2(4)$ **7.** Answers will vary.   **8. b)** $x(y + z) = xy + xz$

 1. Explain the commutative property of addition and give an example of it.   Answers will vary; $3 + 4 = 4 + 3$

 2. Explain the commutative property of multiplication and give an example of it.   Answers will vary; $5(6) = 6(5)$

 3. Explain the associative property of addition and give an example of it.   Answers will vary; $(2 + 3) + 4 = 2 + (3 + 4)$

 4. Explain the associative property of multiplication and give an example of it.   Answers will vary; $(2 \cdot 3) \cdot 4 = 2 \cdot (3 \cdot 4)$

 5. a) Explain the difference between $x + (y + z)$ and $x(y + z)$.   Answers will vary.

  b) Find the value of $x + (y + z)$ when $x = 4$, $y = 5$, and $z = 6$.   15

  c) Find the value of $x(y + z)$ when $x = 4$, $y = 5$, and $z = 6$.   44

 6. Explain the distributive property and give an example of it.

 7. Explain how you can tell the difference between the associative property of multiplication and the distributive property.

8. a) Write the associative property of addition using $x + (y + z)$. $x + (y + z) = (x + y) + z$

  b) Write the distributive property using $x(y + z)$.

9. What number is the additive identity element?   0

10. What number is the multiplicative identity element?   1

Practice the Skills

*In Exercises 11–22, for the given expression, determine **a)** the additive inverse, and **b)** the multiplicative inverse.*

11. 6 **a)** -6 **b)** $\dfrac{1}{6}$

12. 5 **a)** -5 **b)** $\dfrac{1}{5}$

13. -3 **a)** 3 **b)** $-\dfrac{1}{3}$

14. -7 **a)** 7 **b)** $-\dfrac{1}{7}$

15. x **a)** $-x$ **b)** $\dfrac{1}{x}$

16. z **a)** $-z$ **b)** $\dfrac{1}{z}$

17. 1.6 **a)** -1.6 **b)** $\dfrac{1}{1.6}$ or 0.625

18. -0.125 **a)** 0.125 **b)** $-\dfrac{1}{0.125}$ or -8

19. $\dfrac{1}{5}$ **a)** $-\dfrac{1}{5}$ **b)** 5

20. $\dfrac{1}{8}$ **a)** $-\dfrac{1}{8}$ **b)** 8

21. $-\dfrac{5}{6}$ **a)** $\dfrac{5}{6}$ **b)** $-\dfrac{6}{5}$

22. $-\dfrac{2}{9}$ **a)** $\dfrac{2}{9}$ **b)** $-\dfrac{9}{2}$

Practice the Skills

Name each property illustrated.

23. $6(x + 7) = 6x + 42$ distributive

24. $3 + y = y + 3$ commutative, addition

25. $(x + 3) + 5 = x + (3 + 5)$ associative, addition

26. $1(x + 3) = (1)(x) + (1)(3) = x + 3$ distributive

27. $5 \cdot y = y \cdot 5$ commutative, multiplication

28. $-4x + 4x = 0$ inverse property of addition

29. $p \cdot (q \cdot r) = (p \cdot q) \cdot r$ associative, multiplication

30. $2(x + 4) = 2x + 8$ distributive

31. $4(d + 3) = 4d + 12$ distributive

32. $3 + (4 + t) = (3 + 4) + t$ associative, addition

33. $3z \cdot 1 = 3z$ identity property of multiplication

34. $0 + 3y = 3y$ identity property of addition

35. $2y \cdot \dfrac{1}{2y} = 1$ inverse property of multiplication

36. $x \cdot y = y \cdot x$ commutative, multiplication

In Exercises 37–58, the name of a property is given followed by part of an equation. Complete the equation, to the right of the equal sign, to illustrate the given property.

37. commutative property of addition

$-4 + 1 = \quad 1 + (-4)$

38. inverse property of addition

$(-7a) + 7a = \quad 0$

39. associative property of multiplication

$-6 \cdot (4 \cdot 2) = \quad (-6 \cdot 4) \cdot 2$

40. associative property of addition

$-5 + (6 + 8) = \quad (-5 + 6) + 8$

41. distributive property

$-2(x + y) = \quad -2x - 2y$

42. distributive property

$4(x + 3) = \quad 4x + 12$

43. commutative property of multiplication

$x \cdot y = \quad y \cdot x$

44. identity property of multiplication

$(1)\left(-\dfrac{1}{3}b\right) = \quad -\dfrac{1}{3}b$

45. commutative property of addition

$4x + 3y = \quad 3y + 4x$

46. associative property of multiplication

$-9 \cdot (3 \cdot 8) = \quad (-9 \cdot 3) \cdot 8$

47. associative property of addition

$(a + b) + 3 = \quad a + (b + 3)$

48. commutative property of multiplication

$(x + 2)3 = \quad 3(x + 2)$

49. associative property of addition

$(3x + 4) + 6 = \quad 3x + (4 + 6)$

50. commutative property of addition

$3(x + y) = \quad 3(y + x)$

51. commutative property of multiplication

$3(m + n) = \quad (m + n)3$

52. associative property of multiplication

$(3x)y = \quad 3(xy)$

53. distributive property

$4(x + y + 3) \quad 4x + 4y + 12$

54. distributive property

$3(x + y + 2) = \quad 3x + 3y + 6$

55. inverse property of addition

$3n + (-3n) = \quad 0$

56. identity property of addition

$0 + 2x = \quad 2x$

57. identity property of multiplication

$\left(\dfrac{5}{2}n\right)(1) = \quad \dfrac{5}{2}n$

58. inverse property of multiplication

$\left(\dfrac{x}{2}\right)\left(\dfrac{2}{x}\right) = \quad 1$

Problem Solving

Indicate whether the given processes are commutative. That is, does changing the order in which the actions are done result in the same final outcome? Explain each answer.

59. Putting sugar and then cream in coffee; putting cream and then sugar in coffee. yes

60. Applying suntan lotion and then sunning yourself; sunning yourself and then applying suntan lotion. no

61. Putting your contacts in and then washing your hair; washing your hair and then putting your contacts in. yes

62. Putting on your sweater and then your coat; putting on your coat and then your sweater. no

63. Writing on the chalkboard and then erasing the chalkboard; erasing the chalkboard and then writing on the chalkboard. no

64. Getting your hands dirty and then washing your hands; washing your hands and then getting your hands dirty. no

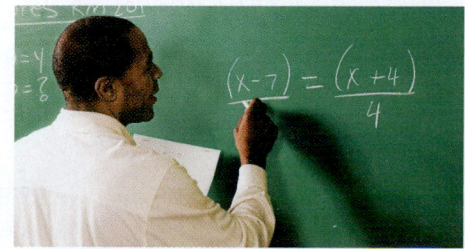

In Exercises 65–70, indicate whether the given processes are associative. For a process to be associative, the final outcome must be the same when the first two actions are performed first or when the last two actions are performed first. Explain each answer.

65. Cleaning the kitchen sink, dusting the bedroom furniture, and doing the laundry.   yes

66. In a store, buying cereal, soap, and dog food.   yes

67. Turning on a DVD player, inserting a DVD, and watching the DVD.   no

68. Putting on a shirt, a tie, and a sweater.   no

69. Starting a car, moving the shift lever to drive, and then stepping on the gas.   no

70. Putting cereal, milk, and sugar in a bowl.   yes

71. The commutative property of addition is $a + b = b + a$. Explain why $(3 + 4) + x = x + (3 + 4)$ also illustrates the commutative property of addition.   treat $(3 + 4)$ as one value

72. The commutative property of multiplication is $a \cdot b = b \cdot a$. Explain why $(3 + 4) \cdot x = x \cdot (3 + 4)$ also illustrates the commutative property of multiplication.   treat $(3 + 4)$ as one value

Challenge Problems

73. Consider $x + (3 + 5) = x + (5 + 3)$. Does this illustrate the commutative property of addition or the associative property of addition? Explain.   commutative

74. Consider $x + (3 + 5) = (3 + 5) + x$. Does this illustrate the commutative property of addition or the associative property of addition? Explain.   commutative

75. Consider $x + (3 + 5) = (x + 3) + 5$. Does this illustrate the commutative property of addition? Explain.   no, associative property of addition

76. The commutative property of multiplication is $a \cdot b = b \cdot a$. Explain why $(3 + 4) \cdot (5 + 6) = (5 + 6) \cdot (3 + 4)$ also illustrates the commutative property of multiplication.   Treat $(3 + 4)$ as one value and $(5 + 6)$ as a second value.

Cumulative Review Exercises

[1.3]   **77.** Add $2\frac{3}{5} + \frac{2}{3}$. $\frac{49}{15}$ or $3\frac{4}{15}$

78. Subtract $3\frac{5}{8} - 2\frac{3}{16}$. $\frac{23}{16}$ or $1\frac{7}{16}$

[1.6]   **79.** Add $102.7 + (-113.9)$. -11.2

80. Write the opposite of $\frac{7}{8}$. $-\frac{7}{8}$

Chapter 1 Summary

IMPORTANT FACTS AND CONCEPTS	EXAMPLES

Section 1.2

Guidelines for Problem Solving

1. **Understand the problem.**
2. **Translate the problem to mathematical language.**
3. **Carry out the mathematical calculations necessary to solve the problem.**
4. **Check the answer obtained in step 3.**
5. **Make sure you have answered the question.**

See page 8 for more details on problem solving.

Jacob Thomas can pay either $725 cash for a desk or pay $300 down and $20 a month for 24 months. How much money can he save by paying cash?

Solution: Understand We need to determine how much he would pay if he paid $300 down and $20 a month for 24 months. This amount would then be compared to $725.

Translate

$$\begin{pmatrix} \text{amount if} \\ \text{paid over 24} \\ \text{months} \end{pmatrix} = \$300 + \begin{pmatrix} \text{additional} \\ \text{amount paid} \\ \text{over 24 months} \end{pmatrix}$$

Carry Out

$$= \$300 + \$20(24)$$
$$= \$300 + \$480$$
$$= \$780$$

The difference in the amounts is $780 - \$725 = \$55$.

Check and Answer

The answer appears reasonable. Jacob can save $55 by paying the total amount at the time of purchase.

IMPORTANT FACTS AND CONCEPTS	EXAMPLES

Section 1.2 (continued)

An **algebraic expression** is a general term for any collection of numbers, variables, grouping symbols, and operations.	$8(24 \div 4), 3x - 5, a^2 - 6$

Bar graph

Logging onto Travel Web Sites in November, 2004

Visitors in November 2004 (in millions)

Source: USA Today

Line graph

Digital Images Not Printed

(billions)

Source: Rochester Democrat & Chronicle

Circle graph

Registered Nurses in the U.S., 2003

Men 8%

Women 92%

Source: www.census.gov

The symbol $\approx$ is read **"is approximately equal to."**	$57.91536 \approx 57.92$

Measures of central tendency or **averages** are values that are representative of a set of data.	The mean and median are averages.
The **mean** of a set of data is determined by adding all the values and dividing the sum by the number of values.	The mean of Adam Michael's test grades of 82, 95, 76, 92, and 88 is $\dfrac{82 + 95 + 76 + 92 + 88}{5} = \dfrac{433}{5} = 86.6$.
The **median** is the value in the middle of a set of **ranked data**.	The median of Adam's five test grades given above is 88 (circled). $76, 82, \textcircled{88}, 92, 95$

IMPORTANT FACTS AND CONCEPTS	EXAMPLES

Section 1.3

Multiplication Symbols

If a and b represent any two mathematical quantities, then each of the following may be used to indicate the product of a and b ("a times b").

$$ab \quad a \cdot b \quad a(b) \quad (a)b \quad (a)(b)$$

5 times z may be written:

$$5z, \quad 5 \cdot z, \quad 5(z), \quad (5)z \quad \text{or} \quad (5)(z)$$

The numbers or variables that are multiplied in a multiplication problem are called **factors**.

If $a \cdot b = c$, then a and b are *factors* of c.

In $7 \cdot 9 = 63$, the numbers 7 and 9 are factors of 63.

The numbers $0, 1, 2, 3, 4, \ldots$ are called **whole numbers**.

12, 105, and 0 are whole numbers.

The top number of a fraction is called the **numerator**, and the bottom number is called the **denominator**.

In the fraction $\dfrac{6}{11}$, the 6 is the numerator and the 11 is the denominator.

To Simplify a Fraction

1. Find the largest number that will divide (without remainder) both the numerator and the denominator. This number is called the **greatest common factor** (GCF).

2. Then divide both the numerator and the denominator by the greatest common factor.

The GCF of 36 and 48 is 12. Therefore,

$$\frac{36}{48} = \frac{36 \div 12}{48 \div 12} = \frac{3}{4}$$

To Multiply Fractions

$$\frac{a}{b} \cdot \frac{c}{d} = \frac{ac}{bd}$$

$$\frac{3}{4} \cdot \frac{3}{5} = \frac{9}{20}$$

To Divide Fractions

$$\frac{a}{b} \div \frac{c}{d} = \frac{a}{b} \cdot \frac{d}{c} = \frac{ad}{bc}$$

$$\frac{9}{7} \div \frac{4}{5} = \frac{9}{7} \cdot \frac{5}{4} = \frac{45}{28}$$

To Add and Subtract Fractions with Like Denominators

$$\frac{a}{c} + \frac{b}{c} = \frac{a+b}{c} \quad \text{or} \quad \frac{a}{c} - \frac{b}{c} = \frac{a-b}{c}$$

1. $\dfrac{3}{13} + \dfrac{7}{13} = \dfrac{3+7}{13} = \dfrac{10}{13}$

2. $\dfrac{4}{5} - \dfrac{1}{5} = \dfrac{4-1}{5} = \dfrac{3}{5}$

The smallest number that is divisible by two or more denominators is called the **least common denominator** or **LCD**.

To add (or subtract) fractions with unlike denominators, first rewrite each fraction with a common denominator.

In the fractions $\dfrac{7}{9}$ and $\dfrac{2}{5}$, 45 is the LCD.

Subtract $\dfrac{7}{9} - \dfrac{2}{5}$.

$$\frac{7}{9} - \frac{2}{5} = \frac{7}{9} \cdot \frac{5}{5} - \frac{2}{5} \cdot \frac{9}{9}$$

$$= \frac{35}{45} - \frac{18}{45} = \frac{17}{45}$$

A **mixed number** consists of a whole number followed by a fraction.

$7\dfrac{4}{5}$ is a mixed number.

Change a mixed number to a fraction.

$$6\frac{2}{3} = 6 + \frac{2}{3} = \frac{18}{3} + \frac{2}{3} = \frac{20}{3}$$

Change a fraction to a mixed number.

$$\frac{52}{7} = \frac{49}{7} + \frac{3}{7} = 7 + \frac{3}{7} = 7\frac{3}{7}$$

IMPORTANT FACTS AND CONCEPTS	EXAMPLES

Section 1.4

A **set** is a collection of **elements** listed within braces.	The set {2, 4, 6, 8} consists of four elements, namely 2, 4, 6, and 8.
A set that contains no elements is called an **empty set** (or **null set**).	The set of dogs that can fly is an empty set.

Natural numbers: {1, 2, 3, 4, 5, ...}	23, 16, and 1231 are natural numbers.
The natural numbers are also called the **positive integers** or the **counting numbers**.	
Whole numbers: {0, 1, 2, 3, 4, 5, ...}	35, 0, and 257 are whole numbers.
Integers: {..., −3, −2, −1, 0, 1, 2, 3 ...} $\underbrace{\text{Negative integers}}$ $\underbrace{\text{Positive integers}}$	−101, 0, and 236 are integers.
Rational numbers: {quotient of two integers, denominator not 0}	$-3, 2.8, 9\frac{1}{2}, 0, 15, -\frac{9}{13}$, and −3.6 are rational numbers.
Irrational numbers: {numbers that can be represented on the number line that are not rational numbers}	$\sqrt{13}$ and $-\sqrt{7}$ are irrational numbers.
Real numbers: {all numbers that can be represented on a number line}	$5.7, -\frac{3}{8}, -16, 0, \sqrt{5}, 3\frac{1}{7}, -2.1, -\sqrt{2}$, and 31 are real numbers.

Section 1.5

The symbol > is used to represent the words "is greater than." The symbol < is used to represent the words "is less than."	**1.** $3.8 > 3.08$ **2.** $-7 < -1$
The **absolute value** of a number can be considered the distance between the number and 0 on a number line. The absolute value of every number will be either *positive* or *zero*.	**1.** $\lvert 12 \rvert = 12$ **2.** $\lvert 0 \rvert = 0$ **3.** $\lvert -100 \rvert = 100$

Section 1.6

Add Using a Number Line: Represent the first number to be added (first *addend*) by an arrow starting at 0 on the number line. The arrow is drawn to the right if the number is positive, and to the left if the number is negative. From the tip of the first arrow, draw a second arrow to represent the second addend. The second arrow is drawn to the right or left, as just explained. The sum of the two numbers is found at the tip of the second arrow.	Add $5 + (-7)$. 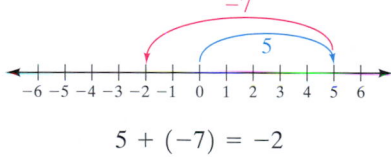 $$5 + (-7) = -2$$
Any two numbers whose sum is zero are said to be **opposites** (or **additive inverses**) of each other.	**1.** The opposite of 8 is −8. **2.** The opposite of $-\frac{5}{6}$ is $\frac{5}{6}$.
Add Using Absolute Value: **To add real numbers with the same sign**, add their absolute values. The sum has the same sign as the numbers being added.	Add $-4 + (-9)$. $$\lvert -4 \rvert + \lvert -9 \rvert = 4 + 9 = 13$$ Since both numbers being added are negative, the sum is negative. Thus, $-4 + (-9) = -13$.
To add two signed numbers with different signs, subtract the smaller absolute value from the larger absolute value. The answer has the sign of the number with the larger absolute value.	Add $-25 + 10$. $$\lvert -25 \rvert - \lvert 10 \rvert = 25 - 10 = 15$$ Since $\lvert -25 \rvert$ is greater than $\lvert 10 \rvert$, the sum is negative. Thus, $-25 + 10 = -15$.

IMPORTANT FACTS AND CONCEPTS	EXAMPLES

Section 1.7

To Subtract Real Numbers

In general, if a and b represent any two real numbers, then

$$a - b = a + (-b)$$

In evaluating expressions involving more than one addition and subtraction, work from left to right unless parentheses or other grouping symbols appear.

1. $8 - (+4) = 8 + (-4) = 4$
2. $-7 - 5 = -7 + (-5) = -12$
3. $-12 - (-6) = -12 + 6 = -6$
4. $-8 + 5 - 11 = -3 - 11 = -14$

Section 1.8

The Sign of the Product of Two Real Numbers

1. The product of two numbers with **like** signs is a **positive** number.
2. The product of two numbers with **unlike** signs is a **negative** number.

1. $-8(-7) = 56$

2. $5(-6) = -30$

The Sign of the Quotient of Two Real Numbers

1. The quotient of two numbers with **like** signs is a **positive** number.
2. The quotient of two numbers with **unlike** signs is a **negative** number.

1. $\dfrac{-81}{-9} = 9$

2. $\dfrac{-35}{7} = -5$

The Quotient of a Positive Number and a Negative Number

If a and b represent any real numbers, $b \neq 0$, then

$$\frac{a}{-b} = \frac{-a}{b} = -\frac{a}{b}$$

$$\frac{3}{-8} = \frac{-3}{8} = -\frac{3}{8}$$

Summary of Division Involving 0

If a represents any real number except 0, then

$$\frac{0}{a} = 0 \qquad \frac{a}{0} \text{ is undefined}$$

1. $\dfrac{0}{12} = 0$

2. $\dfrac{5}{0}$ is undefined

Section 1.9

In general, the number b to the nth power, written b^n, means

$$\underbrace{b \cdot b \cdot b \cdots b}_{n \text{ factors of } b} = b^n$$

$$x^5 = x \cdot x \cdot x \cdot x \cdot x$$

Order of Operations

1. First, evaluate the information within **parentheses ( )**, brackets **[ ]**, or braces **{ }**. These are **grouping symbols**. A fraction bar, —, also serves as a grouping symbol. If the expression contains nested parentheses, evaluate the information in the innermost parentheses first.

2. Next, evaluate all **exponents**.

3. Next, evaluate all **multiplications** or **divisions** in order from left to right.

4. Finally, evaluate all **additions** or **subtractions** in order from left to right.

$$-16 - 3(6 - 8)^2$$
$$= -16 - 3(-2)^2$$
$$= -16 - 3(4)$$
$$= -16 - 12$$
$$= -28$$

IMPORTANT FACTS AND CONCEPTS	EXAMPLES

Section 1.10

Commutative Property of Addition

If a and b represent any two real numbers, then
$$a + b = b + a$$

$$9 + 6 = 6 + 9$$
$$15 = 15$$

Commutative Property of Multiplication

If a and b represent any two real numbers, then
$$a \cdot b = b \cdot a$$

$$6 \cdot 7 = 7 \cdot 6$$
$$42 = 42$$

Associative Property of Addition

If a, b, and c represent any three real numbers, then
$$(a + b) + c = a + (b + c)$$

$$(1 + 2) + 3 = 1 + (2 + 3)$$
$$3 + 3 = 1 + 5$$
$$6 = 6$$

Associative Property of Multiplication

If a, b, and c represent any three real numbers, then
$$(a \cdot b) \cdot c = a \cdot (b \cdot c)$$

$$(5 \cdot 4) \cdot 3 = 5 \cdot (4 \cdot 3)$$
$$20 \cdot 3 = 5 \cdot 12$$
$$60 = 60$$

Distributive Property

If a, b, and c represent any three real numbers, then
$$a(b + c) = ab + ac$$

$$4(y + 9) = 4 \cdot y + 4 \cdot 9 = 4y + 36$$

Identity Properties

If a represents any real number, then

1. $a + 0 = a$ and $0 + a = a$ *Identity property of addition*

and

2. $a \cdot 1 = a$ and $1 \cdot a = a$ *Identity property of multiplication*

1. $15 + 0 = 0 + 15 = 15$

2. $8 \cdot 1 = 1 \cdot 8 = 8$

Inverse Properties

If a represents any real number, then

1. $a + (-a) = 0$ and $-a + a = 0$ *Inverse property of addition*

and

2. $a \cdot \dfrac{1}{a} = 1$ and $\dfrac{1}{a} \cdot a = 1 (a \neq 0)$ *Inverse property of multiplication*

1. $9 + (-9) = -9 + 9 = 0$

2. $6 \cdot \dfrac{1}{6} = \dfrac{1}{6} \cdot 6 = 1$

Chapter 1 Review Exercises

[1.2] *Solve.*   **3. b)** $974.24

1. **Final Exam Review** Eraj Basnayake bought doughnuts for his math classes for their final exam review sessions. His first class ate 32 doughnuts. His second class ate 29 doughnuts. His third class ate 36 doughnuts, and his fourth class ate 31 doughnuts. If he purchased 13 dozen doughnuts, how many did he have left over? 28

2. **Inflation** Assume that the rate of inflation is 5% per year for the next two years. What will be the cost of goods two years from now, adjusted for inflation, if the goods cost $500.00 today? $551.25

3. **Sales Tax** The sales tax in Cattaraugus County is 8.25%.
   a) What was the sales tax that Andrew Jacob paid on a laptop computer that cost $899.99 before tax? $74.25
   b) What is the total cost of the laptop computer including tax?

4. **Fax Machine** Neeta Gandhi wants to purchase a fax machine that sells for $300. She can either pay the total amount at the time of purchase, or she can agree to pay the store $30 down and $25 a month for 12 months. How much money can she save by paying the total amount at the time of purchase? $30

5. **Test Grades** On Angie Smajstrla's first five exams her grades were 75, 79, 86, 88, and 64. Find the **a)** mean and **b)** median of her grades. **a)** 78.4 **b)** 79

6. **Little League** The number of points scored by a Little League football team in their last six games were 21, 3, 17, 10, 9, and 6. Find the **a)** mean and **b)** median of the points. **a)** 11 **b)** 9.5

7. Commute Times In March, 2005, the U.S. Census Bureau released a report that included the following bar graph. The bar graph shows some of the longest average commute-to-work times in the United States. Estimate the average one-way commute time in

a) New York.   30 minutes

b) Illinois.   27 minutes

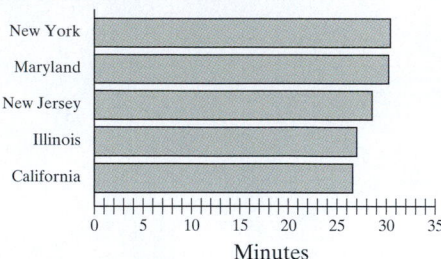

Some of the Longest Average Commute-to-Work Times

Source: US Census Bureau

Number of Schools to Which Freshmen at Four-Year Colleges Applied

Source: Higher Education Research Institute at the University of California-Los Angeles

8. College Applications The graphs on the right show the number of schools to which freshmen at four-year colleges applied in 1967 and 2003.

a) If there were 1.6 million freshmen at four-year colleges in 1967, determine the number of these freshmen who applied to two or fewer colleges.   1.0192 million

b) If there were 2.1 million freshmen at four-year colleges in 2003, determine the number of these freshmen who applied to six or more colleges.   0.5187 million

[1.3] *Perform each indicated operation. Simplify your answers.*

9. $\dfrac{3}{5} \cdot \dfrac{5}{6}$ $\dfrac{1}{2}$

10. $3\dfrac{5}{7} + 2\dfrac{1}{3}$ $\dfrac{127}{21}$ or $6\dfrac{1}{21}$

11. $\dfrac{5}{12} \div \dfrac{3}{5}$ $\dfrac{25}{36}$

12. $\dfrac{5}{6} + \dfrac{1}{3}$ $\dfrac{7}{6}$ or $1\dfrac{1}{6}$

13. $3\dfrac{1}{6} - 1\dfrac{1}{4}$ $\dfrac{23}{12}$ or $1\dfrac{11}{12}$

14. $7\dfrac{3}{8} \div \dfrac{5}{12}$ $\dfrac{177}{10}$ or $17\dfrac{7}{10}$

[1.4] **15.** List the set of natural numbers. $\{1, 2, 3, \dots\}$

16. List the set of whole numbers. $\{0, 1, 2, 3, \dots\}$

17. List the set of integers. $\{\dots -3, -2, -1, 0, 1, 2, 3, \dots\}$

18. Describe the set of rational numbers.

19. Consider the following set of numbers.

$$\left\{ 3, -5, -12, 0, \dfrac{1}{2}, -0.62, \sqrt{7}, 426, -3\dfrac{1}{4} \right\}$$

List the numbers that are

a) positive integers.   3, 426

b) whole numbers.   3, 0, 426

c) integers.   3, −5, −12, 0, 426

d) rational numbers.

e) irrational numbers. $\sqrt{7}$

f) real numbers.

d) $3, -5, -12, 0, \dfrac{1}{2}, -0.62, 426, -3\dfrac{1}{4}$

f) $3, -5, -12, 0, \dfrac{1}{2}, -0.62, \sqrt{7}, 426, -3\dfrac{1}{4}$

20. Consider the following set of numbers.

$$\left\{ -2.3, -8, -9, 1\dfrac{1}{2}, \sqrt{2}, -\sqrt{2}, 1, -\dfrac{3}{17} \right\}$$

List the numbers that are

a) natural numbers.   1

b) whole numbers.   1

c) negative integers.   −8, −9

d) integers.   −8, −9, 1

e) rational numbers. $-2.3, -8, -9, 1\dfrac{1}{2}, 1, -\dfrac{3}{17}$

f) irrational numbers. $\sqrt{2}, -\sqrt{2}$

g) real numbers.

g) $-2.3, -8, -9, 1\dfrac{1}{2}, \sqrt{2}, -\sqrt{2}, 1, -\dfrac{3}{17}$

18. {quotient of two integers, denominator not 0}

[1.5] *Insert either $<$, $>$, or $=$ in each shaded area to make a true statement.*

21. -7 ▨ -5 $<$

22. -2.6 ▨ -3.6 $>$

23. 0.50 ▨ 0.509 $<$

24. 4.6 ▨ 4.06 $>$

25. -6.3 ▨ -6.03 $<$

26. 5 ▨ $|-3|$ $>$

27. $\left| -\dfrac{9}{2} \right|$ ▨ $|-4.5|$ $=$

28. $|-10|$ ▨ $|-7|$ $>$

[1.6–1.7] *Evaluate.*

29. $-9 + (-5)$ -14

30. $-6 + 6$ 0

31. $0 + (-3)$ -3

32. $-10 + 4$ -6

33. $-8 - (-2)$ -6

34. $-2 - (-4)$ 2

35. $4 - (-4)$ 8

36. $12 - 12$ 0

37. $2 - 7$ -5

38. $7 - (-7)$ 14

39. $0 - (-4)$ 4

40. $-7 - 5$ -12

41. $\dfrac{4}{3} - \dfrac{3}{4}$ $\dfrac{7}{12}$ **42.** $\dfrac{1}{2} + \dfrac{3}{5}$ $\dfrac{11}{10}$ or $1\dfrac{1}{10}$ **43.** $\dfrac{5}{9} - \dfrac{3}{4}$ $-\dfrac{7}{36}$ **44.** $-\dfrac{5}{7} + \dfrac{3}{8}$ $-\dfrac{19}{56}$

45. $-\dfrac{5}{12} - \dfrac{5}{6}$ $-\dfrac{5}{4}$ or $-1\dfrac{1}{4}$ **46.** $-\dfrac{6}{7} + \dfrac{5}{12}$ $-\dfrac{37}{84}$ **47.** $\dfrac{2}{9} - \dfrac{3}{10}$ $-\dfrac{7}{90}$ **48.** $\dfrac{5}{12} - \left(-\dfrac{3}{5}\right)$ $\dfrac{61}{60}$ or $1\dfrac{1}{60}$

Evaluate.

49. $9 - 4 + 3$ 8   **50.** $-8 - 9 + 4$ -13 **51.** $-5 - 4 - 3$ -12 **52.** $-2 + (-3) - 2$ -7

53. $7 - (+4) - (-3)$ 6   **54.** $6 - (-2) + 3$ 11

[1.8] *Evaluate.*

55. $7(-9)$ -63 **56.** $(-8.2)(-3.1)$ 25.42   **57.** $(-4)(-5)(-6)$ -120 **58.** $\left(\dfrac{3}{5}\right)\left(\dfrac{-2}{7}\right)$ $-\dfrac{6}{35}$

59. $\left(\dfrac{10}{11}\right)\left(\dfrac{3}{-5}\right)$ $-\dfrac{6}{11}$ **60.** $\left(\dfrac{-5}{8}\right)\left(\dfrac{-3}{7}\right)$ $\dfrac{15}{56}$ **61.** $0\left(\dfrac{4}{9}\right)$ 0   **62.** $(-4)(-6)(-2)(-3)$ 144

Evaluate.

63. $15 \div (-3)$ -5 **64.** $12 \div (-2)$ -6 **65.** $-14.72 \div 4.6$ -3.2 **66.** $-37.41 \div (-8.7)$ 4.3

67. $-88 \div (-11)$ 8   **68.** $-4 \div \left(\dfrac{-4}{9}\right)$ 9   **69.** $\dfrac{28}{-3} \div \left(\dfrac{9}{-2}\right)$ $\dfrac{56}{27}$ or $2\dfrac{2}{27}$ **70.** $\dfrac{14}{3} \div \left(\dfrac{-6}{5}\right)$ $-\dfrac{35}{9}$ or $-3\dfrac{8}{9}$

Indicate whether each quotient is 0 or undefined.

71. $0 \div 5$ 0   **72.** $0 \div (-6)$ 0   **73.** $-12 \div 0$ undefined

74. $-4 \div 0$ undefined   **75.** $\dfrac{8.3}{0}$ undefined   **76.** $\dfrac{0}{-9.8}$ 0

[1.6–1.8, 1.9] *Evaluate.*

77. $-5(3 - 8)$ 25   **78.** $2(4 - 8)$ -8 **79.** $(3 - 6) + 4$ 1

80. $(-4 + 3) - (2 - 6)$ 3   **81.** $[6 + 3(-2)] - 6$ -6 **82.** $(-5 - 3)(4)$ -32

83. $[12 + (-4)] + (6 - 8)$ 6   **84.** $9[3 + (-4)] + 5$ -4 **85.** $-4(-3) + [4 \div (-2)]$ 10

86. $(-3 \cdot 4) \div (-2 \cdot 6)$ 1   **87.** $(-3)(-4) + 6 - 3$ 15   **88.** $[-2(3) + 6] - 4$ -4

[1.9] *Evaluate.*

89. -6^2 -36 **90.** $(-6)^2$ 36   **91.** 2^4 16   **92.** $(-3)^3$ -27

93. $(-1)^9$ -1 **94.** $(-2)^5$ -32 **95.** $\left(\dfrac{-4}{5}\right)^2$ $\dfrac{16}{25}$ **96.** $\left(\dfrac{2}{5}\right)^3$ $\dfrac{8}{125}$

97. $5^3 \cdot (-2)^2$ 500   **98.** $(-2)^4\left(\dfrac{1}{2}\right)^2$ 4   **99.** $\left(-\dfrac{2}{3}\right)^2 \cdot 3^3$ 12   **100.** $(-4)^3(-2)^2$ -256

Evaluate.

101. $-5 + 3 \cdot 4$ 7   **102.** $4 \cdot 6 + 4 \cdot 2$ 32   **103.** $(3.7 - 4.1)^2 + 6.2$ 6.36

104. $10 - 36 \div 4 \cdot 3$ -17 **105.** $6 - 3^2 \cdot 5$ -39 **106.** $[6.9 - (3 \cdot 5)] + 5.8$ -2.3

107. $\dfrac{6^2 - 4 \cdot 3^2}{-[6 - (3 - 4)]}$ 0   **108.** $\dfrac{4 + 5^2 \div 5}{6 - (-3 + 2)}$ $\dfrac{9}{7}$ or $1\dfrac{2}{7}$ **109.** $3[9 - (4^2 + 3)] \cdot 2$ -60

110. $(-3^2 + 4^2) + (3^2 \div 3)$ 10   **111.** $2^3 \div 4 + 6 \cdot 3$ 20   **112.** $(4 \div 2)^4 + 4^2 \div 2^2$ 20

113. $(8 - 2^2)^2 - 4 \cdot 3 + 10$ 14   **114.** $4^3 \div 4^2 - 5(2 - 7) \div 5$ 9   **115.** $-\{-4[27 \div 3^2 - 2(4 - 2)]\}$ -4

116. $2\{4^3 - 6[4 - (2 - 4)] - 3\}$ 50

Evaluate each expression for the given values.

117. $3x - 7$; $x = 4$ 5   **118.** $6 - 4x$; $x = -5$ 26

119. $2x^2 - 5x + 3$; $x = 6$ 45   **120.** $5y^2 + 3y - 2$; $y = -1$ 0

121. $-x^2 + 2x - 3$; $x = -2$ -11 **122.** $-x^2 + 2x - 3$; $x = 2$ -3

123. $-3x^2 - 5x + 5$; $x = 1$ -3 **124.** $-x^2 - 8x - 12y$; $x = -3$, $y = -2$ 39

[1.6–1.9] **a)** *Use a calculator to evaluate each expression, and* **b)** *check to see whether your answer is reasonable.*

125. $278 + (-493)$ -215 **126.** $324 - (-29.6)$ 353.6   **127.** $\dfrac{-17.28}{6}$ -2.88

128. $(-62)(-1.9)$ 117.8   **129.** $(-4)^8$ 65,536   **130.** $-(4.2)^3$ -74.088

[1.10] *Name each indicated property.*

131. $(7 + 4) + 9 = 7 + (4 + 9)$ associative, addition   **132.** $-5(a + 2) = -5a - 10$ distributive

133. $6x + 3x = 3x + 6x$ commutative, addition   **134.** $(x + 4)3 = 3(x + 4)$ commutative, multiplication

135. $4(x + 3) = 4x + 12$ distributive   **136.** $(x + 7) + 4 = x + (7 + 4)$ associative, addition

137. $8b \cdot 1 = 8b$ identity, multiplication   **138.** $-8y + 8y = 0$ inverse, addition

Chapter 1 Practice Test

To find out how well you understand the chapter material, take this practice test. The answers, and the section where the material was initially discussed, are given in the back of the book. Each problem is also fully worked out on the **Chapter Test Prep Video CD**. *Review any questions that you answered incorrectly.*

1. **Shopping** While shopping, Mia Nguyen purchases two half-gallons of milk for $1.30 each, one Boston cream pie for $4.75, and three 2-liter bottles of soda for $1.10 each.

   a) What is her total bill before tax? $10.65

   b) If there is a 7% sales tax on the bottles of soda, how much is the sales tax? $0.23

   c) How much is her total bill including tax? $10.88

   d) How much change will she receive from a $50 bill? $39.12

2. **TV Commercials** The following line graph shows the cost for a 30-second commercial during the same time slot on the same channel for 12 consecutive years. How many times greater was the cost for a 30-second commercial in the twelfth year than in the first year? $\approx$ 2.5 times greater

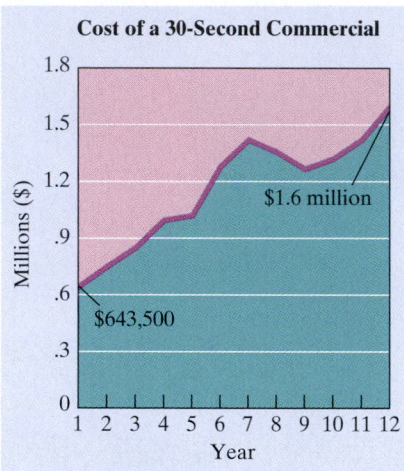

Cost of a 30-Second Commercial

$1.6 million

$643,500

3. **Radio** The following graph shows the median number of listeners for various radio stations during a specific time.

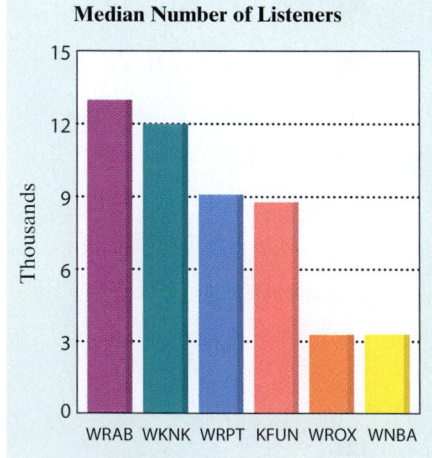

Median Number of Listeners

a) Determine the median number of listeners who listened to WRAB during this time.

b) The median number of listeners who listened to KFUN during this time was approximately 8.8 thousand. Explain what this means.   During this specific time, half the time KFUN had more than 8.8 thousand listeners and half the time KFUN had less than 8.8 thousand listeners.

3. a) $\approx$ 13 thousand

4. Consider the following set of numbers.
$$\left\{-6, 42, -3\tfrac{1}{2}, 0, 6.52, \sqrt{5}, \tfrac{5}{9}, -7, -1\right\}$$
List the numbers that are

   a) natural numbers.   42

   b) whole numbers.   42, 0

   c) integers. $-6, 42, 0, -7, -1$

   d) rational numbers. $-6, 42, -3\tfrac{1}{2}, 0, 6.52, \tfrac{5}{9}, -7, -1$

   e) irrational numbers. $\sqrt{5}$

   f) real numbers. $-6, 42, -3\tfrac{1}{2}, 0, 6.52, \sqrt{5}, \tfrac{5}{9}, -7, -1$

Insert either $<$, $>$, or $=$ in each shaded area to make a true statement.

5. -9.9 ▨ -9.09 $<$

6. $|-3|$ ▨ $|-2|$ $>$

Evaluate.

7. $-7 + (-8)$ -15

8. $-6 - 5$ -11

9. $15 - 12 - 17$ -14

10. $(-4 + 6) - 3(-2)$ 8

11. $(-4)(-3)(2)(-1)$ -24

12. $\left(\dfrac{-2}{9}\right) \div \left(\dfrac{-7}{8}\right)$ $\dfrac{16}{63}$

13. $\left(-18 \cdot \dfrac{1}{2}\right) \div 3$ -3

14. $-\dfrac{3}{8} - \dfrac{4}{7}$ $-\dfrac{53}{56}$

15. $-6(-2 - 3) \div 5 \cdot 2$ 12

16. $\left(-\dfrac{2}{3}\right)^5$ $-\dfrac{32}{243}$

17. $[6 + ((9 - 3)^2 \div 18)^2]^2$ 100

✎ 18. Explain why $-x^2$ will always be a negative value for any nonzero real number selected for x.

Evaluate the expression for the given values.

19. $5x^2 - 8$; $x = -3$ 37

20. $-x^2 - 6x + 3$; $x = -2$ 11

21. $6x - 3y^2 + 4$; $x = 3, y = -2$ 10

22. $-x^2 + xy + y^2$; $x = 1, y = -2$ 1

Name each indicated property.

23. $x + 3 = 3 + x$ commutative, addition

24. $4(x + 9) = 4x + 36$ distributive

25. $(2 + x) + 4 = 2 + (x + 4)$ associative, addition

18. $-x^2$ means $-(x^2)$ and x^2 will always be positive for any nonzero value of x. Therefore, $-x^2$ will always be negative.

2 Solving Linear Equations and Inequalities

The major emphasis of this chapter is to teach you how to solve linear equations. *To be successful in solving linear equations, you need to have a thorough understanding of adding, subtracting, multiplying, and dividing real numbers.* This material was discussed in Chapter 1.

The first four sections of this chapter will give you the building blocks you will need for solving linear equations. Section 2.5 combines the material previously presented to teach you how to solve a variety of linear equations. In the last few sections of this chapter, you will learn about formulas, ratios, proportions, and solving linear inequalities.

You will be using principles learned in this chapter throughout the book and in real life.

PROPORTIONS ARE VERY USEFUL in everyday living. In Exercise 65 on page 162, we use a proportion to determine how many cups of onions are needed for a recipe.

2.1 Combining Like Terms

1 Identify terms.

2 Identify like terms.

3 Combine like terms.

4 Use the distributive property.

5 Remove parentheses when they are preceded by a plus or minus sign.

6 Simplify an expression.

1 Identify Terms

In Section 1.3, we indicated that letters called **variables** are used to represent numbers. A variable can represent a variety of different numbers.

As was indicated in Chapter 1, an **expression** (sometimes referred to as an **algebraic expression**) is a collection of numbers, variables, grouping symbols, and operation symbols.

Examples of Expressions

$$7, \quad x^2 - 6, \quad 4x - 3, \quad 2(x + 5) + 6, \quad \frac{x + 3}{4}$$

When an algebraic expression consists of several parts, the parts that are *added* are called the **terms** of the expression. Consider the expression $2x - 3y - 5$. The expression can be written as $2x + (-3y) + (-5)$, and so the expression $2x - 3y - 5$ has three terms: $2x$, $-3y$, and -5. The expression $3x^2 + 2xy + 5(x + y)$ also has three terms: $3x^2$, $2xy$, and $5(x + y)$.

When listing the terms of an expression, it is not necessary to list the $+$ sign at the beginning of a term.

Expression	Terms
$-2x + 3y - 8$	$-2x, 3y, -8$
$3y^2 - 2x + \dfrac{1}{2}$	$3y^2, -2x, \dfrac{1}{2}$
$7 + x + 4 - 5x$	$7, x, 4, -5x$
$3(x - 1) - 4x + 2$	$3(x - 1), -4x, 2$
$\dfrac{x + 4}{3} - 5x + 3$	$\dfrac{x + 4}{3}, -5x, 3$

The numerical part of a term is called its **numerical coefficient** or simply its **coefficient**. In the term $6x$, the 6 is the numerical coefficient. Note that $6x$ means the variable x is multiplied by 6.

Term	Numerical Coefficient
$5x$	5
$-\dfrac{1}{2}x$	$-\dfrac{1}{2}$
$4(x - 3)$	4
$\dfrac{2x}{3}$	$\dfrac{2}{3}$, since $\dfrac{2x}{3}$ means $\dfrac{2}{3}x$
$\dfrac{x + 4}{3}$	$\dfrac{1}{3}$, since $\dfrac{x + 4}{3}$ means $\dfrac{1}{3}(x + 4)$

Whenever a term appears without a numerical coefficient, we assume that the numerical coefficient is 1.

Examples

x means $1x$

x^2 means $1x^2$

xy means $1xy$

$(x + 2)$ means $1(x + 2)$

$-x$ means $-1x$

$-x^2$ means $-1x^2$

$-xy$ means $-1xy$

$-(x + 2)$ means $-1(x + 2)$

TEACHING TIP
Emphasize that it is important to list the minus sign when identifying the term.

TEACHING TIP
Point out that the language of mathematics often assumes the reader knows certain things by the absence of a symbol. For instance, $5x$ is assumed to have a positive sign associated with it because no sign is given.

TEACHING TIP
Point out that variables are used when different numbers can be used in a situation and constants are used when only one number can be used. For instance, if you are charged a monthly fee of $9.95 for internet service and an hourly fee of $1.25, your charge is represented by $1.25x + 9.95$.

If an expression has a term that is a number (without a variable), we refer to that number as a **constant term**, or simply a **constant**. In the expression $x^2 + 3x - 4$, the -4 is a constant term, or a constant.

2 Identify Like Terms

Like terms (also called similar terms) are terms that have the same variables with the same exponents, respectively. Constants, such as 4 and -6, are like terms. Some examples of like terms and unlike terms follow. Note that if two terms are like terms, only their numerical coefficients may differ.

Like Terms	Unlike Terms	
$3x$, $-4x$	$3x$, 2	*(One term has a variable, the other is a constant.)*
$4y$, $6y$	$3x$, $4y$	*(Variables differ)*
5, -6	x, 3	*(One term has a variable, the other is a constant.)*
$3(x + 1)$, $-2(x + 1)$	$2x$, $3xy$	*(Variables differ)*
$3x^2$, $4x^2$	$3x$, $4x^2$	*(Exponents differ)*
$5ab$, $2ab$	$4a$, $2ab$	*(Variables differ)*

EXAMPLE 1 ▶ Identify any like terms.

a) $2x + 3x + 4$ **b)** $2x + 3y + 2$ **c)** $x + 3 + y - \dfrac{1}{2}$ **d)** $x + 3x^2 - 4x^2$

e) $5x - x + 6$ **f)** $3 - 2x + 4x - 6$ **g)** $12 + x^2 - x + 7$

Solution

a) $2x$ and $3x$ are like terms.

b) There are no like terms.

c) 3 and $-\dfrac{1}{2}$ are like terms.

d) $3x^2$ and $-4x^2$ are like terms.

e) $5x$ and $-x$ (or $-1x$) are like terms.

f) 3 and -6 are like terms; $-2x$ and $4x$ are like terms.

g) 12 and 7 are like terms.

▶ **Now Try Exercise 5**

3 Combine Like Terms

We often need to simplify expressions by combining like terms. **To combine like terms** means to add or subtract the like terms in an expression. To combine like terms, we can use the procedure that follows.

To Combine Like Terms
1. Determine which terms are like terms.
2. Add or subtract the coefficients of the like terms.
3. Multiply the number found in step 2 by the common variable(s).

Examples 2 through 7 illustrate this procedure.

EXAMPLE 2 ▸ Combine like terms: $5x + 4x$.

Solution $5x$ and $4x$ are like terms with the common variable x. Since $5 + 4 = 9$, then $5x + 4x = 9x$.

▸ **Now Try Exercise 9**

EXAMPLE 3 ▸ Combine like terms: $\frac{3}{5}x - \frac{2}{3}x$.

Solution   Since $\frac{3}{5} - \frac{2}{3} = \frac{9}{15} - \frac{10}{15} = -\frac{1}{15}$, then $\frac{3}{5}x - \frac{2}{3}x = -\frac{1}{15}x$.

▸ **Now Try Exercise 15**

EXAMPLE 4 ▸ Combine like terms: $6.47b - 8.39b$.

Solution   Since $6.47 - 8.39 = -1.92$, then $6.47b - 8.39b = -1.92b$.

▸ **Now Try Exercise 35**

EXAMPLE 5 ▸ Combine like terms: $3x + x + 5$.

Solution   The $3x$ and x are like terms.

$$3x + x + 5 = 3x + 1x + 5 = 4x + 5$$

▸ **Now Try Exercise 19**

Because of the commutative property of addition, the order of the terms in the answer is not critical. Thus, $5 + 4x$ is also an acceptable answer to Example 5. When writing answers, we generally list the terms containing variables in alphabetical order from left to right, and list the constant term last.

The commutative and associative properties of addition will be used to rearrange the terms in Examples 6 and 7.

EXAMPLE 6 ▸ Combine like terms: $3b + 6a - 5 - 2a$.

Solution   The only like terms are $6a$ and $-2a$.

$$3b + 6a - 5 - 2a = 6a - 2a + 3b - 5 \qquad \textit{Rearrange terms.}$$
$$= 4a + 3b - 5 \qquad \textit{Combine like terms.}$$

▸ **Now Try Exercise 21**

EXAMPLE 7 ▸ Combine like terms: $-2x^2 + 3y - 4x^2 + 3 - y + 5$.

Solution

$-2x^2$	and	$-4x^2$	are like terms.
$3y$	and	$-y$	are like terms.
3	and	5	are like terms.

Grouping the like terms together gives

$$-2x^2 + 3y - 4x^2 + 3 - y + 5 = -2x^2 - 4x^2 + 3y - y + 3 + 5$$
$$= -6x^2 + 2y + 8$$

▸ **Now Try Exercise 29**

4 Use the Distributive Property

We introduced the distributive property in Section 1.10. Because this property is so important, we will study it again. But before we do, let's briefly review the subtraction of real numbers. Recall from Section 1.7 that

$$6 - 3 = 6 + (-3)$$

In general,

Subtraction of Real Numbers

For any real numbers a and b,

$$a - b = a + (-b)$$

We will use the fact that $a + (-b)$ means $a - b$ in discussing the distributive property.

Distributive Property

For any real numbers a, b, and c,

$$a(b + c) = ab + ac$$

TEACHING TIP
Before discussing Example 8a, have students rewrite the expression $2(x + 4)$ as an addition problem: $2(x + 4) = (x + 4) + (x + 4) = 2x + 8$. Then ask, "How would we simplify this problem using the Distributive Property?"

INSTRUCTOR EXAMPLE
Use the distributive property to remove parentheses.
a) $6(x + 2)$
b) $-4(r + 3)$
Ans.:
a) $6x + 12$
b) $-4r - 12$

EXAMPLE 8 ▶ Use the distributive property to remove parentheses.

a) $2(x + 4)$ b) $-5(p + 3)$

Solution

a) $2(x + 4) = 2x + 2(4) = 2x + 8$

b) $-5(p + 3) = -5p + (-5)(3) = -5p + (-15) = -5p - 15$

Note in part **b)** that, instead of leaving the answer $-5p + (-15)$, we wrote it as $-5p - 15$, which is the proper form of the answer.

▶ **Now Try Exercise 61**

INSTRUCTOR EXAMPLE
Use the distributive property to remove parentheses.
a) $8(w - 7)$
b) $-3(r - 9)$
Ans.:
a) $8w - 56$
b) $-3r + 27$

EXAMPLE 9 ▶ Use the distributive property to remove parentheses.

a) $3(x - 2)$ b) $-2(4x - 3)$

Solution

a) By the definition of subtraction, we may write $x - 2$ as $x + (-2)$.

$$3(x - 2) = 3[x + (-2)] = 3x + 3(-2)$$
$$= 3x + (-6)$$
$$= 3x - 6$$

b) $-2(4x - 3) = -2[4x + (-3)] = -2(4x) + (-2)(-3) = -8x + 6$

▶ **Now Try Exercise 63**

The distributive property is used often in algebra, so you need to understand it well. You should understand it so well that you will be able to simplify an expression using the distributive property without having to write down all the steps that we listed in working Examples 8 and 9. Study closely the Helpful Hint that follows.

Helpful Hint

With a little practice, you will be able to eliminate some of the intermediate steps when you use the distributive property. When using the distributive property, there are eight possibilities with regard to signs. Study and understand the eight possibilities that follow.

Positive Coefficient

a) $2(x) = 2x$

$2(x + 3) = 2x + 6$

$2(+3) = +6$

b) $2(x) = 2x$

$2(x - 3) = 2x - 6$

$2(-3) = -6$

c) $2(-x) = -2x$

$2(-x + 3) = -2x + 6$

$2(+3) = +6$

d) $2(-x) = -2x$

$2(-x - 3) = -2x - 6$

$2(-3) = -6$

Negative Coefficient

e) $(-2)(x) = -2x$

$-2(x + 3) = -2x - 6$

$(-2)(+3) = -6$

f) $(-2)(x) = -2x$

$-2(x - 3) = -2x + 6$

$(-2)(-3) = +6$

g) $(-2)(-x) = 2x$

$-2(-x + 3) = 2x - 6$

$(-2)(+3) = -6$

h) $(-2)(-x) = 2x$

$-2(-x - 3) = 2x + 6$

$(-2)(-3) = +6$

TEACHING TIP
Have students write $4(x + y + z)$ as an addition problem and then simplify. After they compare the original expression with the simplified one ask, "Can the distributive property be used when we have 3 terms?"

The distributive property can be expanded as follows:

$$a(b + c + d + \cdots + n) = ab + ac + ad + \cdots + an$$

Examples of the Expanded Distributive Property

$$3(x + y + z) = 3x + 3y + 3z$$
$$2(x + y - 3) = 2x + 2y - 6$$

INSTRUCTOR EXAMPLE
Use the distributive property to remove parentheses.
a) $-\dfrac{2}{3}(5t + 9)$
b) $-4(2x + 3y - 5z)$
Ans.:
a) $-\dfrac{10}{3}t - 6$
b) $-8x - 12y + 20z$

EXAMPLE 10 ▸ Use the distributive property to remove parentheses.

a) $4(x - 3)$ **b)** $-6(5y - 1)$ **c)** $-\dfrac{1}{2}(4r + 5)$ **d)** $-7(2x + 4y - 9z)$

Solution

a) $4(x - 3) = 4x - 12$ **b)** $-6(5y - 1) = -30y + 6$

c) $-\dfrac{1}{2}(4r + 5) = -2r - \dfrac{5}{2}$ **d)** $-7(2x + 4y - 9z) = -14x - 28y + 63z$

▸ **Now Try Exercise 79**

The distributive property can also be used from the right, as in Example 11.

INSTRUCTOR EXAMPLE
Use the distributive property to remove parentheses from the expression $(3a - 4b)2$.
Ans.: $6a - 8b$

EXAMPLE 11 ▸ Use the distributive property to remove parentheses from the expression $(2x - 8y)4$.

Solution   We distribute the 4 on the right side of the parentheses over the terms within the parentheses.

$$(2x - 8y)4 = 2x(4) - 8y(4)$$
$$= 8x - 32y$$

▸ **Now Try Exercise 83**

Example 11 could have been rewritten as $4(2x - 8y)$ by the commutative property of multiplication, and then the 4 could have been distributed from the left to obtain the same answer, $8x - 32y$.

Helpful Hint

Students sometimes try to use the distributive property when it cannot be used. For the distributive property to be used, there must be a + or − between the terms *within parentheses* and the terms within parentheses must be *multiplied* by some number or expression. Study the following correct simplifications carefully.

$$4(2xy) = 8xy \qquad \textit{(distributive property is not used)}$$
$$4(2x + y) = 8x + 4y \qquad \textit{(distributive property is used)}$$
$$(2x + y) - 4 = 2x + y - 4 \qquad \textit{(distributive property is not used)}$$
$$(2x + y)(-4) = -8x - 4y \qquad \textit{(distributive property is used)}$$

5 Remove Parentheses When They Are Preceded by a Plus or Minus Sign

In the expression $(4x + 3)$, how do we remove parentheses? Recall that the coefficient of a term is assumed to be 1 if none is shown. Therefore, we may write

$$(4x + 3) = 1(4x + 3)$$
$$= 1(4x) + (1)(3)$$
$$= 4x + 3$$

Note that $(4x + 3) = 4x + 3$. **When no sign or a plus sign precedes parentheses, the parentheses may be removed without having to change the expression inside the parentheses.**

Examples

$$(x + 3) = x + 3$$
$$(2x - 3) = 2x - 3$$
$$+(2x - 5) = 2x - 5$$
$$+(x + 2y - 6) = x + 2y - 6$$

Now consider the expression $-(4x + 3)$. How do we remove parentheses in this expression? Here, the coefficient in front of the parentheses is -1, so each term within the parentheses is multiplied by -1.

$$-(4x + 3) = -1(4x + 3)$$
$$= -1(4x) + (-1)(3)$$
$$= -4x + (-3)$$
$$= -4x - 3$$

Thus, $-(4x + 3) = -4x - 3$. **When a minus sign precedes parentheses, the signs of all the terms within the parentheses are changed when the parentheses are removed.**

Examples

$$-(x + 4) = -x - 4$$
$$-(-2x + 3) = 2x - 3$$
$$-(5x - y + 3) = -5x + y - 3$$
$$-(-4c - 3d - 5) = 4c + 3d + 5$$

6 Simplify an Expression

Combining what we learned in the preceding discussions, we have the following procedure for **simplifying an expression**.

To Simplify an Expression

1. Use the distributive property to remove any parentheses.

2. Combine like terms.

EXAMPLE 12 ▶ Simplify $6 - (2x + 3)$.

Solution

$$6 - (2x + 3) = 6 - 2x - 3 \qquad \textit{Use the distributive property.}$$
$$= -2x + 3 \qquad \textit{Combine like terms.}$$

Note: $3 - 2x$ is the same as $-2x + 3$; however, we generally write the term containing the variable first.

▶ **Now Try Exercise 89**

EXAMPLE 13 ▶ Simplify $-\left(\dfrac{2}{3}x - \dfrac{1}{4}\right) + 3x$.

Solution

$$-\left(\frac{2}{3}x - \frac{1}{4}\right) + 3x = -\frac{2}{3}x + \frac{1}{4} + 3x \qquad \textit{Distributive property}$$

$$= -\frac{2}{3}x + 3x + \frac{1}{4} \qquad \textit{Rearrange terms.}$$

$$= -\frac{2}{3}x + \frac{9}{3}x + \frac{1}{4} \qquad \textit{Write x terms with the LCD, 3.}$$

$$= \frac{7}{3}x + \frac{1}{4} \qquad \textit{Combine like terms.}$$

▶ **Now Try Exercise 101**

Notice in Example 13 that $\dfrac{7}{3}x$ and $\dfrac{1}{4}$ could not be combined because they are not like terms.

EXAMPLE 14 ▶ Simplify $\dfrac{3}{4}x + \dfrac{1}{3}(5x - 2)$.

Solution

$$\frac{3}{4}x + \frac{1}{3}(5x - 2) = \frac{3}{4}x + \frac{1}{3}(5x) + \frac{1}{3}(-2) \qquad \textit{Distributive property}$$

$$= \frac{3}{4}x + \frac{5}{3}x - \frac{2}{3}$$

$$= \frac{9}{12}x + \frac{20}{12}x - \frac{2}{3} \qquad \textit{Write x terms with the LCD, 12.}$$

$$= \frac{29}{12}x - \frac{2}{3} \qquad \textit{Combine like terms.}$$

▶ **Now Try Exercise 103**

EXAMPLE 15 ▶ Simplify $3(2a - 5) - 3(b - 6) - 4a$.

Solution

$$3(2a - 5) - 3(b - 6) - 4a = 6a - 15 - 3b + 18 - 4a \qquad \textit{Distributive property}$$
$$= 6a - 4a - 3b - 15 + 18 \qquad \textit{Rearrange terms.}$$
$$= 2a - 3b + 3 \qquad \textit{Combine like terms.}$$

▶ **Now Try Exercise 107**

Helpful Hint

Keep in mind the difference between the concepts of *term* and *factor*. When two or more expressions are **multiplied**, each expression is a **factor** of the product. For example, since $4 \cdot 3 = 12$, the 4 and the 3 are factors of 12. Since $3 \cdot x = 3x$, the 3 and the x are factors of $3x$. Similarly, in the expression $5xyz$, the 5, x, y, and z are all factors.

In an expression, the parts that are **added** are the **terms** of the expression. For example, the expression $2x^2 + 3x - 4$, has three terms, $2x^2$, $3x$, and -4. Note that the terms of an expression may have factors. For example, in the term $2x^2$, the 2 and the x^2 are factors because they are multiplied.

EXERCISE SET 2.1

MathXL®   MyMathLab
MathXL®   MyMathLab

Concept/Writing Exercises

1. a) What are the terms of an expression?

   b) What are the terms of $3x - 4y - 5$? $3x, -4y, -5$

   c) What are the terms of $6xy + 3x - y - 9$?

2. a) What is the name given to the numerical part of a term? List the coefficient of the following terms.

   b) $4x$ 4   **c)** x 1   **d)** $-x$ -1

   e) $\dfrac{3x}{5}$ $\dfrac{3}{5}$ **f)** $\dfrac{4}{7}(3t - 5)$ $\dfrac{4}{7}$

3. Consider the expression $2x - 5$.

   a) What is the x called?   a variable

   b) What is the -5 called?   a constant

   c) What is the 2 called?   coefficient

4. a) What are like terms? Determine whether the following are like terms. If not, explain why.

   b) $3x, 4y$ no   **c)** $7, -2$ yes

   d) $5x^2, 2x$ no   **e)** $4x, -5xy$ no

1. a) the parts that are added   **c)** $6xy, 3x, -y, -9$

2. a) numerical coefficient or coefficient

4. a) have same variable with same exponents

6. a) Parentheses may be removed without changing the expression.

5. Determine whether the following are like terms. If not, explain why.

   a) $5x, -7x$ yes   **b)** $7y, 2$ no

   c) $-3(t + 2), 6(t + 2)$ yes   **d)** $4pq, -9pq$ yes

6. a) When no sign or a plus sign precedes an expression within parentheses, explain how to remove parentheses.

   b) Write $+(x - 8)$ without parentheses. $x - 8$

7. a) When a minus sign precedes an expression within parentheses, explain how to remove parentheses.

   b) Write $-(x - 8)$ without parentheses. $-x + 8$

8. a) What are the factors of an expression?

   b) Explain why 3 and x are factors of $3x$.   multiplied together

   c) Explain why 5, x, and y are all factors of the expression $5xy$.   multiplied together

7. a) The signs of all terms inside the parentheses change when the parentheses are removed.

8. a) the parts that are multiplied

Practice the Skills

29. $10x^2 - 10y^2 - 7$ **30.** $-7x^2 - 7y + 5$ **47.** $21.72x - 7.11$ **51.** $5w^3 + 2w^2 + w + 3$

Combine like terms when possible. If not possible, rewrite the expression as is.

9. $6x + 3x$ $9x$

10. $4x - 5x$ $-x$

11. $3x + 6$ $3x + 6$

12. $4x + 3y$ $4x + 3y$

13. $y + 3 + 4y$ $5y + 3$

14. $4x - 7x + 4$ $-3x + 4$

15. $\dfrac{3}{4}a - \dfrac{6}{11}a$ $\dfrac{9}{44}a$

16. $\dfrac{3}{4}p - \dfrac{2}{7}p$ $\dfrac{13}{28}p$

17. $2 - 6x + 5$ $-6x + 7$

18. $-7 - 4m - 6$ $-4m - 13$

19. $-2w - 3w + 5$ $-5w + 5$

20. $-8y - 4y - 7$ $-12y - 7$

21. $-x + 2 - x - 2$ $-2x$

22. $8x - 2y - 1 - 3x$ $5x - 2y - 1$

23. $3 + 6x - 3 - 6x$ 0

24. $y - 2y + 5$ $-y + 5$

25. $5 + 2x - 4x + 6$ $-2x + 11$

26. $5s - 3s - 2s$ 0

27. $4r - 6 - 6r - 2$ $-2r - 8$

28. $-6t + 5 + 2t - 9$ $-4t - 4$

29. $3x^2 - 9y^2 + 7x^2 - 5 - y^2 - 2$

30. $-4x^2 - 6y - 3x^2 + 6 - y - 1$

31. $-2x + 4x - 3$ $2x - 3$

32. $4 - x + 4x - 8$ $3x - 4$

33. $b + 4 + \dfrac{3}{5}$ $b + \dfrac{23}{5}$

34. $\dfrac{3}{4}x + 2 + x$ $\dfrac{7}{4}x + 2$

35. $5.1n + 6.42 - 4.3n$ $0.8n + 6.42$

36. $2x^2 + 3y^2 + 4x + 5y^2$ $2x^2 + 4x + 8y^2$ **37.** $\dfrac{1}{2}a + 3b + 1$ $\dfrac{1}{2}a + 3b + 1$

38. $x + \dfrac{1}{2}y - \dfrac{3}{8}y$ $x + \dfrac{1}{8}y$

39. $13.4x + 1.2x + 8.3$ $14.6x + 8.3$

40. $-4x^2 - 3.1 - 5.2$ $-4x^2 - 8.3$

41. $-x^2 + 2x^2 + y$ $x^2 + y$

42. $1 + x^2 + 6 - 3x^2$ $-2x^2 + 7$

43. $2x - 7y - 5x + 2y$ $-3x - 5y$

44. $3x - 7 - 9 + 4x$ $7x - 16$

45. $4 - 3n^2 + 9 - 2n$ $-3n^2 - 2n + 13$

46. $9x + y - 2 - 4x$ $5x + y - 2$

47. $-19.36 + 40.02x + 12.25 - 18.3x$

48. $52x - 52x - 63.5 - 63.5$ -127

49. $\dfrac{3}{5}x - 3 - \dfrac{7}{4}x - 2$ $-\dfrac{23}{20}x - 5$

50. $\dfrac{1}{2}y - 4 + \dfrac{3}{4}x - \dfrac{1}{5}y$ $\dfrac{3}{4}x + \dfrac{3}{10}y - 4$

51. $5w^3 + 2w^2 + w + 3$

52. $4p^2 - 3p^2 + 2p - 5p$ $p^2 - 3p$

53. $2z - 5z^3 - 2z^3 - z^2$ $-7z^3 - z^2 + 2z$

54. $5ab - 3ab$ $2ab$

55. $6x^2 - 6xy + 3y^2$ $6x^2 - 6xy + 3y^2$

56. $x^2 - 3xy - 2xy + 6$ $x^2 - 5xy + 6$

57. $4a^2 - 3ab + 6ab + b^2$ $4a^2 + 3ab + b^2$ **58.** $4b^2 - 8bc + 5bc + c^2$ $4b^2 - 3bc + c^2$

Use the distributive property to remove parentheses.

59. $5(x + 2)$ $5x + 10$

60. $2(-y + 5)$ $-2y + 10$

61. $5(x + 4)$ $5x + 20$

62. $-2(y + 8)$ $-2y - 16$

63. $3(x - 6)$ $3x - 18$

64. $-2(x - 4)$ $-2x + 8$

65. $-\dfrac{1}{2}(2x - 4)$ $-x + 2$

66. $-4(x + 6)$ $-4x - 24$

67. $1(-4 + x)$ $x - 4$

68. $\frac{2}{3}(m - 9)$ $\frac{2}{3}m - 6$

69. $\frac{4}{5}(s - 5)$ $\frac{4}{5}s - 4$

70. $5(x - y + 5)$ $5x - 5y + 25$

71. $-0.3(3x + 5)$ $-0.9x - 1.5$

72. $-(x - 3)$ $-x + 3$

73. $-\frac{1}{3}(3r - 12)$ $-r + 4$

74. $-2(x + y - z)$ $-2x - 2y + 2z$

75. $0.7(2x + 0.5)$ $1.4x + 0.35$

76. $-(x + 4y)$ $-x - 4y$

77. $-(-x + y)$ $x - y$

78. $(3x + 4y - 6)$ $3x + 4y - 6$

79. $-(2x + 4y - 8)$ $-2x - 4y + 8$

80. $-3(2a + 3b - 7)$ $-6a - 9b + 21$

81. $1.1(3.1x - 5.2y + 2.8)$

82. $-4(-2m - 3n + 8)$ $8m + 12n - 32$

83. $(2x - 9y)5$ $10x - 45y$

84. $(8b - 1)7$ $56b - 7$

85. $(x + 3y - 9)$ $x + 3y - 9$

86. $(-p + 2q - 3)$ $-p + 2q - 3$

87. $-3(-x + 2y + 4)$ $3x - 6y - 12$

88. $2.3(1.6x + 5.1y - 4.1)$

$3.68x + 11.73y - 9.43$

Simplify.   **81.** $3.41x - 5.72y + 3.08$

89. $5 - (3x + 4)$ $-3x + 1$

90. $7 - (2x - 9)$ $-2x + 16$

91. $-2(3 - x) + 7$ $2x + 1$

92. $-(3x - 3) + 5$ $-3x + 8$

93. $6x + 2(4x + 9)$ $14x + 18$

94. $3(x + y) + 2y$ $3x + 5y$

95. $2(x - y) + 2x + 3$ $4x - 2y + 3$

96. $6 + (x - 5) + 3x$ $4x + 1$

97. $4(2c - 3) - 3(c - 4)$ $5c$

98. $4 + (2y + 2) + y$ $3y + 6$

99. $8x - (x - 3)$ $7x + 3$

100. $-(x - 5) - 3x + 4$ $-4x + 9$

101. $-\left(\frac{3}{4}x - \frac{1}{3}\right) + 2x$ $\frac{5}{4}x + \frac{1}{3}$

102. $-\left(\frac{7}{8}x - \frac{1}{2}\right) - 3x$ $-\frac{31}{8}x + \frac{1}{2}$

103. $\frac{2}{3}x + \frac{1}{2}(5x - 4)$ $\frac{19}{6}x - 2$

104. $\frac{4}{5}x + \frac{1}{7}(3x - 1)$ $\frac{43}{35}x - \frac{1}{7}$

105. $-(3s + 4) - (s + 2)$ $-4s - 6$

106. $6 - 2(x + 3) + 5x$ $3x$

107. $4(x - 1) + 2(3 - x) - 4$ $2x - 2$

108. $4(3b - 2) - 5(c - 4) - 6b$

109. $4(m + 3) - 4m - 12$ 0

110. $-3(a + 2b) + 3(a + 2b)$ 0

111. $0.4 - (y + 5) + 0.6 - 2$ $-y - 6$

112. $4 - (2 - x) + 3x$ $4x + 2$

113. $4 + (3x - 4) - 5$ $3x - 5$

114. $2y - 6(y - 2) + 3$ $-4y + 15$

115. $4(x + 2) - 3(x - 4) - 5$ $x + 15$

116. $6 - (a - 5) - (2b + 1)$

117. $-0.2(6 - x) - 4(y + 0.4)$

118. $-5(2y - 8) - 3(1 + x) - 7$

119. $-6x + 7y - (3 + x) + (x + 3)$

120. $3(t - 2) - 2(t + 4) - 6$ $t - 20$

121. $\frac{1}{2}(x + 3) + \frac{1}{3}(3x + 6)$ $\frac{3}{2}x + \frac{7}{2}$

122. $\frac{2}{3}(r - 2) - \frac{1}{2}(r + 4)$ $\frac{1}{6}r - \frac{10}{3}$ **108.** $6b - 5c + 12$ **116.** $-a - 2b + 10$ **117.** $0.2x - 4y - 2.8$ **118.** $-3x - 10y + 30$ **119.** $-6x + 7y$

Problem Solving

If $\square + \square + \square + \odot + \odot$ *can be represented as* $3\square + 2\odot$, *write an expression to represent each of the following.*

123. $\square + \ominus + \ominus + \square + \ominus$ $2\square + 3\ominus$

124. $\otimes + \textcircled{\smile} + \otimes + \textcircled{\smile} + \textcircled{\smile} + \textcircled{\smile}$ $2\otimes + 4\textcircled{\smile}$

125. $x + y + \triangle + \triangle + x + y + y$ $2x + 3y + 2\triangle$

126. $2 + x + 2 + \ominus + \ominus + 2 + y$ $x + y + 2\ominus + 6$

Combine like terms.

127. $3\triangle + 5\square - \triangle - 3\square$ $2\triangle + 2\square$

128. $8\textcircled{\smile} - 4\boxdot - 2\boxdot - 3\textcircled{\smile}$ $5\textcircled{\smile} - 6\boxdot$

In Exercises 129 and 130, consider the following. The positive factors of 6 are 1, 2, 3, and 6 since

$$1 \cdot 6 = 6$$
$$2 \cdot 3 = 6$$
$$\uparrow \quad \uparrow$$
factors

129. List all the positive factors of 18. $1, 2, 3, 6, 9, 18$

130. List all the positive factors of 24. $1, 2, 3, 4, 6, 8, 12, 24$

Challenge Problems

Simplify.

131. $4x^2 + 5y^2 + 6(3x^2 - 5y^2) - 4x + 3$ $22x^2 - 25y^2 - 4x + 3$

132. $2x^2 - 4x + 8x^2 - 3(x + 2) - x^2 - 2$ $9x^2 - 7x - 8$

133. $2[3 + 4(x - 5)] - [2 - (x - 3)]$ $9x - 39$

134. $\frac{1}{4}\left[3 - 2(y + 1)\right] - \frac{1}{3}\left[2 - (y - 6)\right]$ $-\frac{1}{6}y - \frac{29}{12}$

Cumulative Review Exercises

[1.5] *Evaluate.*

   135. $|-7|$ 7

   136. $-|-16|$ −16

[1.7] **137.** Evaluate $-4 - 3 - (-6)$.   −1

[1.9] **138.** Write a paragraph explaining the order of operations.

     139. Evaluate $-x^2 + 5x - 6$ when $x = -1$.   −12

     138. Answers will vary.

2.2 The Addition Property of Equality

1   Identify linear equations.

2   Check solutions to equations.

3   Identify equivalent equations.

4   Use the addition property to solve equations.

5   Solve equations by doing some steps mentally.

TEACHING TIP
Have students identify characteristics of linear equations in one variable. Be sure they notice that it is an equation which has 1 variable that is multiplied by a number and some constants. Then point out that linear equations can have the variable on both sides, such as $x + 4 = 2x - 6$.

1   Identify Linear Equations

A statement that shows two algebraic expressions are equal is called an **equation**. For example, $4x + 3 = 2x - 4$ is an equation. In this chapter, we learn to solve **linear equations** in one variable.

> **Linear Equation**
>
> A **linear equation** in one variable is an equation that can be written in the form
>
> $$ax + b = c$$
>
> where a, b, and c are real numbers and $a \neq 0$.

Examples of Linear Equations

$$x + 4 = 7$$
$$2x - 4 = 6$$

2   Check Solutions to Equations

The **solution to an equation** is the number or numbers that when substituted for the variable or variables make the equation a true statement. For example, the solution to $x + 4 = 7$ is 3. We will shortly learn how to find the solution to an equation, or to **solve an equation**. But before we do this we will learn how to *check* the solution to an equation.

    The solution to an equation may be **checked** by substituting the value that is believed to be the solution for the variable in the original equation. If the substitution results in a true statement, your solution is correct. If the substitution results in a false statement, then either your solution or your check is incorrect, and you need to go back and find your error. Try to check all your solutions. Checking the solutions will improve your arithmetic and algebra skills.

    When we show the check of a solution we shall use the notation, $\stackrel{?}{=}$. This notation is used when we are questioning whether a statement is true. For example, if we use

$$2 + 3 \stackrel{?}{=} 2(3) - 1$$

we are asking "Does $2 + 3 = 2(3) - 1$?"

    To check whether 3 is the solution to $x + 4 = 7$, we substitute 3 for each x in the equation.

TEACHING TIP
In the explanations and Examples 1–3, we have written "is a solution" rather than "is the solution". At this point students are not aware that there is only one solution to a linear equation.

Check:

$$x = 3$$
$$x + 4 = 7$$
$$3 + 4 \stackrel{?}{=} 7$$
$$7 = 7 \qquad \textit{True}$$

Since the check results in a true statement, 3 is a solution.

EXAMPLE 1 ▶ Consider the equation $2x - 4 = 6$. Determine whether 3 is a solution.

Solution   To determine whether 3 is a solution to the equation, we substitute 3 for x.

Check:

$$x = 3$$
$$2x - 4 = 6$$
$$2(3) - 4 \stackrel{?}{=} 6$$
$$6 - 4 \stackrel{?}{=} 6$$
$$2 = 6 \qquad \textit{False}$$

Since we obtained a false statement, 3 is not a solution.

▶ **Now Try Exercise 13**

Now check to see if 5 is a solution to the equation in Example 1. Your check should show that 5 is a solution.

We can use the same procedures to check more complex equations, as shown in Examples 2 and 3.

EXAMPLE 2 ▶ Determine whether 18 is a solution to the following equation.

$$3x - 2(x + 3) = 12$$

Solution   To determine whether 18 is a solution, we substitute 18 for each x in the equation. If the substitution results in a true statement, then 18 is a solution.

Check:

$$x = 18$$
$$3x - 2(x + 3) = 12$$
$$3(18) - 2(18 + 3) \stackrel{?}{=} 12$$
$$3(18) - 2(21) \stackrel{?}{=} 12$$
$$54 - 42 \stackrel{?}{=} 12$$
$$12 = 12 \qquad \textit{True}$$

Since we obtained a true statement, 18 is a solution.

▶ **Now Try Exercise 17**

EXAMPLE 3 ▶ Determine whether $-\dfrac{3}{2}$ is a solution to the following equation.

$$3(n + 3) = 6 + n$$

Solution   In this equation n is the variable. Substitute $-\dfrac{3}{2}$ for each n in the equation.

Check:

$$n = -\frac{3}{2}$$
$$3(n + 3) = 6 + n$$
$$3\left(-\frac{3}{2} + 3\right) \stackrel{?}{=} 6 + \left(-\frac{3}{2}\right)$$
$$3\left(-\frac{3}{2} + \frac{6}{2}\right) \stackrel{?}{=} \frac{12}{2} - \frac{3}{2}$$
$$3\left(\frac{3}{2}\right) \stackrel{?}{=} \frac{9}{2}$$
$$\frac{9}{2} = \frac{9}{2} \qquad \textit{True}$$

Thus, $-\dfrac{3}{2}$ is a solution.

▶ **Now Try Exercise 23**

USING YOUR CALCULATOR Checking Solutions

Calculators can be used to check solutions to equations. For example, to check whether $\dfrac{-10}{3}$ is a solution to the equation $2x + 3 = 5(x + 3) - 2$, we perform the following steps.

1. Substitute $\dfrac{-10}{3}$ for each x as shown below.

$$2x + 3 = 5(x + 3) - 2$$

$$2\left(\dfrac{-10}{3}\right) + 3 \stackrel{?}{=} 5\left(\dfrac{-10}{3} + 3\right) - 2$$

2. Evaluate each side of the equation separately using your calculator. If you obtain the same value on both sides, your solution checks.

Scientific Calculator

 To evaluate the left side of the equation, $2\left(\dfrac{-10}{3}\right) + 3$, press the following keys:

$$2 \boxed{\times} \boxed{(} 10 \boxed{+/-} \boxed{\div} 3 \boxed{)} \boxed{+} 3 \boxed{=} -3.6666667$$

To evaluate the right side of the equation, $5\left(\dfrac{-10}{3} + 3\right) - 2$, press the following keys:

$$5 \boxed{\times} \boxed{(} 10 \boxed{+/-} \boxed{\div} 3 \boxed{+} 3 \boxed{)} \boxed{-} 2 \boxed{=} -3.6666667$$

Since both sides give the same value, the solution checks. Note that because calculators differ in their electronics, sometimes the last digit of a calculation will differ.

Graphing Calculator

Left side of equation: $2 \boxed{(} \boxed{(-)} 10 \boxed{\div} 3 \boxed{)} \boxed{+} 3 \boxed{\text{ENTER}} -3.666666667$

Right side of the equation: $5 \boxed{(} \boxed{(-)} 10 \boxed{\div} 3 \boxed{+} 3 \boxed{)} \boxed{-} 2 \boxed{\text{ENTER}} -3.666666667$

Since both sides give the same value, the solution checks.

3 Identify Equivalent Equations

FIGURE 2.1

Now that we know how to check a solution to an equation we will discuss solving equations. Complete procedures for solving equations will be given shortly. For now, you need to understand that **to solve an equation, it is necessary to get the variable alone on one side of the equal sign. That is, we want to get an equation of the form $x =$ some number (or $1x =$ some number). When we get an equation in this form, we say that we isolate the variable**. To isolate the variable, we make use of two properties: the addition and multiplication properties of equality. Look first at **Figure 2.1**.

Think of an equation as a balanced statement whose left side is balanced by its right side. When solving an equation, we must make sure that the equation remains balanced at all times. That is, both sides must always remain equal. **We ensure that an equation always remains equal by doing the same thing to both sides of the equation.** For example, if we add a number to the left side of the equation, we must add exactly the same number to the right side. If we multiply the right side of the equation by some number, we must multiply the left side by the same number.

When we add the same number to both sides of an equation or multiply both sides of an equation by the same nonzero number, we do not change the solution to the equation, just the form of the equation. Two or more equations with the same solution are called **equivalent equations**. The equations $2x - 4 = 2$, $2x = 6$, and $x = 3$ are equivalent, since the solution to each is 3.

Check: $x = 3$

$$2x - 4 = 2 \qquad\qquad 2x = 6 \qquad\qquad x = 3$$
$$2(3) - 4 \overset{?}{=} 2 \qquad\qquad 2(3) \overset{?}{=} 6 \qquad\qquad 3 = 3 \quad \textcolor{green}{\textit{True}}$$
$$6 - 4 \overset{?}{=} 2 \qquad\qquad 6 = 6 \quad \textcolor{green}{\textit{True}}$$
$$2 = 2 \quad \textcolor{green}{\textit{True}}$$

When solving an equation, we use the addition and multiplication properties to express a given equation as simpler equivalent equations until we obtain the solution.

4   Use the Addition Property to Solve Equations

Now we are ready to define the **addition property of equality**.

> ### Addition Property of Equality
> If $a = b$, then $a + c = b + c$ for any real numbers $a, b,$ and c.

This property means that the same number can be added to both sides of an equation without changing the solution. **The addition property is used to solve equations of the form $x + a = b$.** To isolate the variable x in equations of this form, add the opposite or additive inverse of a, $-a$, to both sides of the equation.

To isolate the variable when solving equations of the form $x + a = b$, **we use the addition property to eliminate the number on the same side of the equal sign as the variable**. Study the following examples carefully.

TEACHING TIP
Point out that the addition property of equality is used to make an equivalent equation. When used intelligently, it can be used to solve an equation. Have students use the property on $x + 3 = 10$ and $x - 4 = 5$ to
a) make an equivalent equation which does not give the solution.
b) make the equivalent equation which gives the solution.

Equation	To Solve, Use the Addition Property to Eliminate the Number
$x - 4 = -3$	-4
$x + 5 = 9$	5
$-3 = k + 7$	7
$-5 = x - 4$	-4
$-6.25 = y + 12.78$	12.78

Now let's work some examples.

EXAMPLE 4 ▶ Solve the equation $x - 4 = -3$.

Solution   To isolate the variable, x, we must eliminate the -4 from the left side of the equation. To do this we add 4, the opposite of -4, to *both sides* of the equation.

$$x - 4 = -3$$
$$x - 4 + 4 = -3 + 4 \qquad \textcolor{magenta}{\textit{Add 4 to both sides.}}$$
$$x + 0 = 1$$
$$x = 1$$

INSTRUCTOR EXAMPLE
Solve the equation $a - 8 = -12$.
Ans.: $a = -4$

Note how the process helps to isolate x.

Check:

$$x - 4 = -3$$
$$1 - 4 \overset{?}{=} -3$$
$$-3 = -3 \quad \textcolor{green}{\textit{True}}$$

▶ **Now Try Exercise 29**

In Example 5, we will not show the check. Space limitations prevent us from showing all checks. However, *you should check all of your answers.*

EXAMPLE 5 ▶ Solve the equation $x + 5 = 9$.

Solution To solve this equation, we must isolate the variable, x. Therefore, we must eliminate the 5 from the left side of the equation. To do this, we add -5, the opposite of 5, to *both sides* of the equation.

$$x + 5 = 9$$
$$x + 5 + (-5) = 9 + (-5) \qquad \text{\textit{Add} -5 \textit{to both sides.}}$$
$$x + 0 = 4$$
$$x = 4$$

▶ **Now Try Exercise 31**

In Example 5, we added -5 to both sides of the equation. From Section 1.7 we know that $5 + (-5) = 5 - 5$. Thus, we can see that adding a negative 5 to both sides of the equation is equivalent to subtracting a 5 from both sides of the equation. According to the addition property, the same number may be *added* to both sides of an equation. **Since subtraction is defined in terms of addition, the addition property also allows us to *subtract* the same number from both sides of the equation.** Thus, Example 5 could have also been worked as follows:

$$x + 5 = 9$$
$$x + 5 - 5 = 9 - 5 \qquad \text{\textit{Subtract 5 from both sides.}}$$
$$x + 0 = 4$$
$$x = 4$$

In this text, unless there is a specific reason to do otherwise, rather than adding a negative number to both sides of the equation, we will subtract a number from both sides of the equation.

EXAMPLE 6 ▶ Solve the equation $-3 = k + 7$.

Solution We must isolate the variable, k, which is on the right side of the equal sign.

$$-3 = k + 7$$
$$-3 - 7 = k + 7 - 7 \qquad \text{\textit{Subtract 7 from both sides.}}$$
$$-10 = k + 0$$
$$-10 = k$$

Check:
$$-3 = k + 7$$
$$-3 \stackrel{?}{=} -10 + 7$$
$$-3 = -3 \qquad \text{\textit{True}}$$

▶ **Now Try Exercise 27**

Helpful Hint

Remember that our goal in solving an equation is to get the variable alone on one side of the equation. To do this, we add or subtract **the number on the same side of the equation as the variable** to or from both sides of the equation.

Equation	Must Eliminate	Number to Add (or Subtract) to (or from) Both Sides of the Equation	Correct Results	Solution
$x - 5 = 8$	-5	add 5	$x - 5 + 5 = 8 + 5$	$x = 13$
$x - 3 = -12$	-3	add 3	$x - 3 + 3 = -12 + 3$	$x = -9$
$2 = x - 7$	-7	add 7	$2 + 7 = x - 7 + 7$	$9 = x$ or $x = 9$
$x + 12 = -5$	$+12$	subtract 12	$x + 12 - 12 = -5 - 12$	$x = -17$
$6 = x + 4$	$+4$	subtract 4	$6 - 4 = x + 4 - 4$	$2 = x$ or $x = 2$
$13 = x + 9$	$+9$	subtract 9	$13 - 9 = x + 9 - 9$	$4 = x$ or $x = 4$

Notice that under the *Correct Results* column, when the equation is simplified by combining terms, the x will become isolated because the sum of a number and its opposite is 0, and $x + 0$ equals x.

EXAMPLE 7 ▶ Solve the equation $-5 = x - 4$.

Solution The variable, x, is on the right side of the equation. To isolate the x, we must eliminate the -4 from the right side of the equation. This can be accomplished by adding 4 to both sides of the equation.

$$-5 = x - 4$$
$$-5 + 4 = x - 4 + 4 \qquad \textit{Add 4 to both sides.}$$
$$-1 = x + 0$$
$$-1 = x$$

Thus, the solution is -1.

▶ **Now Try Exercise 37**

EXAMPLE 8 ▶ Solve the equation $-6.25 = y + 12.78$.

Solution The variable, y, is on the right side of the equation. Subtract 12.78 from both sides of the equation to isolate the variable.

$$-6.25 = y + 12.78$$
$$-6.25 - 12.78 = y + 12.78 - 12.78 \qquad \textit{Subtract 12.78 from both sides.}$$
$$-19.03 = y + 0$$
$$-19.03 = y$$

Thus, the solution is -19.03.

▶ **Now Try Exercise 67**

Avoiding Common Errors

When solving an equation, our goal is to isolate the variable on one side of the equal sign. Consider the equation $x + 3 = -4$. How do we solve it?

CORRECT	INCORRECT
Remove the 3 from the left side of the equation.	Remove the -4 from the right side of the equation.

CORRECT
$$x + 3 = -4$$
$$x + 3 - 3 = -4 - 3$$
$$x = -7$$
Variable is now isolated.

INCORRECT
$$x + 3 = -4$$
$$x + 3 + 4 = -4 + 4$$
$$x + 7 = 0$$
*Variable is **not** isolated.*

Remember, use the addition property to *remove the number that is on the same side of the equal sign as the variable.*

---

5 Solve Equations by Doing Some Steps Mentally

Consider the following two problems.

a)
$$x - 5 = 12$$
$$x - 5 + 5 = 12 + 5$$
$$x + 0 = 12 + 5$$
$$x = 17$$

b)
$$15 = x + 3$$
$$15 - 3 = x + 3 - 3$$
$$15 - 3 = x + 0$$
$$12 = x$$

Note how the number on the same side of the equal sign as the variable is transferred to the opposite side of the equal sign when the addition property is used. Also note that the sign of the number changes when transferred from one side of the equal sign to the other.

When you feel comfortable using the addition property of equality, you may wish to do some of the steps mentally to reduce some of the written work. For example, the preceding two problems may be shortened as follows:

Shortened Form

a)
$$x - 5 = 12$$
$$x - 5 + 5 = 12 + 5 \quad \longleftarrow \text{Do this step mentally.}$$
$$x = 12 + 5$$
$$x = 17$$

$$x - 5 = 12$$
$$x = 12 + 5$$
$$x = 17$$

Shortened Form

b)
$$15 = x + 3$$
$$15 - 3 = x + 3 - 3 \quad \longleftarrow \text{Do this step mentally.}$$
$$15 - 3 = x$$
$$12 = x$$

$$15 = x + 3$$
$$15 - 3 = x$$
$$12 = x$$

1. a statement that shows two algebraic expressions are equal   **2. a)** the number(s) that make the equation a true statement
b) to find the solutions to an equation   **3.** Substitute the value in the equation. Then determine if it results in a true statement
4. Answers will vary.   **5.** two or more equations with the same solution   **6. a)** get the variable by itself on one side of the equation
9. One example is $x + 2 = 1$.   **10.** Subtraction is defined in terms of addition.   **11.** all have the same solution, 1

EXERCISE SET 2.2

 MathXL®   MyMathLab

Concept/Writing Exercises

1. What is an equation?

2. a) What is meant by the "solution to an equation"?
   b) What does it mean to "solve an equation"?

3. Explain how the solution to an equation may be checked.

4. Explain the addition property of equality.

5. What are equivalent equations?

6. To solve an equation we "isolate the variable."
   a) Explain what this means.
   b) Explain how to isolate the variable in the equations discussed in this section.   Answers will vary.

7. When solving the equation $6 = x + 2$, would you subtract 6 from both sides of the equation or subtract 2 from both sides of the equation? Explain.   Subtract 2.

8. When solving the equation $x - 4 = 6$, would you add 4 to both sides of the equation or subtract 6 from both sides of the equation? Explain.   Add 4.

9. Give an example of a linear equation in one variable.

10. Explain why the addition property allows us to subtract the same quantity from both sides of an equation.

11. Explain why the following three equations are equivalent.
$$2x + 3 = 5, \qquad 2x = 2, \qquad x = 1$$

12. To solve the equation $x - \square = \triangle$ for x, do we add $\square$ to both sides of the equation or do we subtract $\triangle$ from both sides of the equation? Explain.   Add $\square$.

Practice the Skills

13. Is $x = 2$ a solution of $4x - 3 = 5$?   yes

14. Is $x = -6$ a solution of $2x + 1 = x - 5$?   yes

15. Is $x = -3$ a solution of $2x - 5 = 5(x + 2)$?   no

16. Is $x = 1$ a solution of $2(x - 3) = -3(x + 1)$?   no

17. Is $p = -15$ a solution of $2p - 5(p + 7) = 10$?   yes

18. Is $k = -2$ a solution of $5k - 6(k - 1) = 8$?   yes

19. Is $x = 3.4$ a solution of $3(x + 2) - 3(x - 1) = 9$?   yes

20. Is $x = \dfrac{3}{4}$ a solution of $x + 5 = 5x + 2$?   yes

21. Is $x = \dfrac{1}{2}$ a solution of $4x - 4 = 2x - 2$?   no

22. Is $x = \dfrac{1}{3}$ a solution of $7x + 3 = 2x + 5$?   no

23. Is $x = \dfrac{11}{2}$ a solution of $3(x + 2) = 5(x - 1)$?   yes

24. Is $h = 3$ a solution of $-(h - 5) - (h - 6) = 3h - 4$?   yes

Solve each equation and check your solution.

25. $x + 2 = 7$ 5

26. $x - 4 = 13$ 17

27. $-6 = x + 1$ −7

28. $-5 = x + 4$ −9

29. $x - 4 = -8$ −4

30. $x - 16 = -12$ 4

31. $x + 9 = 52$ 43

32. $x + 8 = 17$ 9

33. $-6 + w = 9$ 15

34. $3 = 7 + t$ −4

35. $27 = x + 16$ 11

36. $50 = x - 25$ 75

37. $-18 = x - 14$ −4

38. $-4 = x - 3$ −1

39. $9 + x = 4$ −5

40. $x + 29 = -29$ −58

41. $4 + x = -9$ −13

42. $9 = x - 3$ 12

43. $7 + r = -23$ −30

44. $a - 5 = -9$ −4

45. $8 = 8 + v$ 0
46. $9 + x = 12$ 3
47. $7 + x = -50$ −57
48. $-17 = 8 + x$ −25
49. $12 = 16 + x$ −4
50. $62 = z - 15$ 77
51. $15 + x = -5$ −20
52. $-20 = 4 + x$ −24
53. $-15 + x = -15$ 0
54. $8 = 8 + x$ 0
55. $5 = x - 12$ 17
56. $-12 = 20 + c$ −32
57. $-50 = x - 24$ −26
58. $-29 + x = -15$ 14
59. $43 = 15 + p$ 28
60. $-25 = 74 + x$ −99
61. $40.2 + x = -5.9$ −46.1
62. $-27.23 + x = 9.77$ 37
63. $-37 + x = 9.5$ 46.5
64. $7.2 + x = 7.2$ 0
65. $x - 8.77 = -17$ −8.23
66. $6.1 + x = 10.2$ 4.1
67. $9.32 = x + 3.75$ 5.57
68. $-5.62 = y + 11.39$ −17.01

Problem Solving

69. Do you think the equation $x + 1 = x + 2$ has a real number as a solution? Explain. (We will discuss equations like this in Section 2.5.) no

70. Do you think the equation $x + 4 = x + 4$ has more than one real number as a solution? If so, how many solutions does it have? Explain. (We will discuss equations like this in Section 2.5.) yes, infinite number

Challenge Problems

We can solve equations that contain unknown symbols. Solve each equation for the symbol indicated by adding (or subtracting) a symbol to (or from) both sides of the equation. Explain each answer. (Remember that to solve the equation you want to isolate the symbol you are solving for on one side of the equation.)

71. $x - \triangle = \square$, for x $x = \square + \triangle$

72. $\square + \odot = \triangle$, for $\odot$ $\odot = \triangle - \square$

73. $\odot = \square + \triangle$, for $\square$ $\square = \odot - \triangle$

74. $\square = \triangle + \odot$, for $\odot$ $\odot = \square - \triangle$

Group Activity

Discuss and answer Exercise 75 as a group.

75. Consider the equation $2(x + 3) = 2x + 6$.

  a) Group member 1: Determine whether 4 is a solution to the equation. yes

  b) Group member 2: Determine whether −2 is a solution to the equation. yes

  c) Group member 3: Determine whether 0.3 is a solution to the equation. yes

  d) Each group member: Select a number not used in parts **a)**–**c)** and determine whether that number is a solution to the equation. yes

  e) As a group, write what you think is the solution to the equation $2(x + 3) = 2x + 6$ and write a paragraph explaining your answer. all real numbers

Cumulative Review Exercises

[1.6] *Add.*

76. $-\dfrac{7}{15} + \dfrac{5}{6}$ $\dfrac{11}{30}$

77. $-\dfrac{11}{12} + \left(-\dfrac{3}{8}\right)$ $-\dfrac{31}{24}$

[2.1] *Simplify.*

78. $4x + 3(x - 2) - 5x - 7$ $2x - 13$

79. $-(2t + 4) + 3(4t - 5) - 3t$ $7t - 19$

2.3 The Multiplication Property of Equality

1   Identify reciprocals.

2   Use the multiplication property to solve equations.

3   Solve equations of the form $-x = a$.

4   Do some steps mentally when solving equations.

1   Identify Reciprocals

In Section 1.10, we introduced the **reciprocal** (or multiplative inverse) of a number. Recall that two numbers are reciprocals of each other when their product is 1. Some examples of numbers and their reciprocals follow.

Number	Reciprocal	Product
2	$\dfrac{1}{2}$	$(2)\left(\dfrac{1}{2}\right) = 1$
$-\dfrac{3}{5}$	$-\dfrac{5}{3}$	$\left(-\dfrac{3}{5}\right)\left(-\dfrac{5}{3}\right) = 1$
-1	-1	$(-1)(-1) = 1$

The reciprocal of a positive number is a positive number and the reciprocal of a negative number is a negative number. Note that 0 has no reciprocal. Why?

In general, if a represents any nonzero number, its reciprocal is $\dfrac{1}{a}$. For example, the reciprocal of 3 is $\dfrac{1}{3}$ and the reciprocal of -2 is $\dfrac{1}{-2}$ or $-\dfrac{1}{2}$. The reciprocal of $-\dfrac{3}{5}$ is $\dfrac{1}{-\dfrac{3}{5}}$, which can be written as $1 \div \left(-\dfrac{3}{5}\right)$. Simplifying, we get $\left(\dfrac{1}{1}\right)\left(-\dfrac{5}{3}\right) = -\dfrac{5}{3}$.

Thus, the reciprocal of $-\dfrac{3}{5}$ is $-\dfrac{5}{3}$.

2 Use the Multiplication Property to Solve Equations

In Section 2.2, we used the addition property of equality to solve equations of the form $x + a = b$, where a and b represent real numbers. In this section, we use the multiplication property of equality to solve equations of the form $ax = b$, where a and b represent real numbers.

It is important that you recognize the difference between equations like $x + 2 = 8$ and $2x = 8$. In $x + 2 = 8$, the 2 is a *term* that is being added to x, so we use the addition property to solve the equation. In $2x = 8$, the 2 is a *factor* of $2x$. The 2 is the coefficient multiplying the x, so we use the multiplication property to solve the equation. The multiplication property of equality is used to solve linear equations where the coefficient of the x-term is a number other than 1.

Now we present the *multiplication property of equality*.

> **Multiplication Property of Equality**
>
> If $a = b$, then $a \cdot c = b \cdot c$ for any real numbers a, b, and c.

TEACHING TIP
Point out that the multiplication property of equality is used to make an equivalent equation. When used intelligently, it can be used to solve an equation. Then have students use the property on $4x = 12$ and $\frac{1}{3}x = 12$ to

a) make an equivalent equation which does not give the solution.
b) make the equivalent equation which gives the solution.

The multiplication property means that both sides of an equation can be multiplied by the same nonzero number without changing the solution. **The multiplication property can be used to solve equations of the form $ax = b$.** We can isolate the variable in equations of this form by multiplying both sides of the equation by the reciprocal of a, which is $\dfrac{1}{a}$. Doing so makes the numerical coefficient of the variable, x, become 1, which can be omitted when we write the variable.

Equation	To Solve, Use the Multiplication Property to Change
$4x = 9$	$4x$ to $1x$
$-5x = 20$	$-5x$ to $1x$
$15 = \dfrac{1}{2}x$	$\dfrac{1}{2}x$ to $1x$
$7 = -9x$	$-9x$ to $1x$

Now let's work some examples.

EXAMPLE 1 ▶ Solve the equation $9x = 63$.

Solution To isolate the variable, x, we must change the $9x$ on the left side of the equal sign to $1x$. To do this, we multiply both sides of the equation by the reciprocal of 9, which is $\dfrac{1}{9}$.

INSTRUCTOR EXAMPLE
Solve the equation $5b = 65$.
Ans.: $b = 13$

$$9x = 63$$

$$\frac{1}{9} \cdot 9x = \frac{1}{9} \cdot 63 \qquad \textit{Multiply both sides by } \tfrac{1}{9}.$$

$$\frac{1}{\cancel{9}} \cdot \cancel{9}x = \frac{1}{\cancel{9}} \cdot \overset{7}{\cancel{63}} \qquad \textit{Divide out the common factors.}$$

$$1x = 7$$

$$x = 7$$

▶ **Now Try Exercise 9**

Notice in Example 1 that $1x$ is replaced by x in the last step. Usually we do this step mentally.

EXAMPLE 2 ▶ Solve the equation $\dfrac{x}{2} = 4$.

Solution   Since dividing by 2 is the same as multiplying by $\dfrac{1}{2}$, the equation $\dfrac{x}{2} = 4$ is the same as $\dfrac{1}{2}x = 4$. We will therefore multiply both sides of the equation by the reciprocal of $\dfrac{1}{2}$, which is 2.

INSTRUCTOR EXAMPLE
Solve the equation $\dfrac{r}{4} = 7$.

Ans.: $r = 28$

$$\frac{x}{2} = 4$$

$$\overset{1}{2}\left(\frac{x}{\underset{1}{\cancel{2}}}\right) = 2 \cdot 4 \qquad \textit{Multiply both sides by 2.}$$

$$x = 2 \cdot 4$$

$$x = 8$$

▶ **Now Try Exercise 11**

EXAMPLE 3 ▶ Solve the equation $\dfrac{2}{3}x = 6$.

Solution   The reciprocal of $\dfrac{2}{3}$ is $\dfrac{3}{2}$. We multiply both sides of the equation by $\dfrac{3}{2}$.

INSTRUCTOR EXAMPLE
Solve the equation $\dfrac{3}{4}x = 9$.

Ans.: $x = 12$

$$\frac{2}{3}x = 6$$

$$\frac{3}{2} \cdot \frac{2}{3}x = \frac{3}{2} \cdot 6 \qquad \textit{Multiply both sides by } \frac{3}{2}.$$

$$1x = 9$$

$$x = 9$$

We will show a check of this solution.

Check:
$$\frac{2}{3}x = 6$$

$$\frac{2}{3}(9) \overset{?}{=} 6$$

$$6 = 6 \qquad \textit{True}$$

▶ **Now Try Exercise 49**

In Example 1, we multiplied both sides of the equation $9x = 63$ by $\dfrac{1}{9}$ to isolate the variable. We could have also isolated the variable by dividing both sides of the equation by 9, as follows:

$$9x = 63$$

$$\frac{\overset{1}{\cancel{9}}x}{\underset{1}{\cancel{9}}} = \frac{\overset{7}{\cancel{63}}}{\underset{1}{\cancel{9}}} \qquad \textit{Divide both sides by 9.}$$

$$x = 7$$

We can do this because dividing by 9 is equivalent to multiplying by $\dfrac{1}{9}$. **Since division can be defined in terms of multiplication** $\left(\dfrac{a}{b} \textbf{ means } a \cdot \dfrac{1}{b}\right)$**, the multiplication property also allows us to divide both sides of an equation by the same nonzero number.** This process is illustrated in Examples 4 through 6.

EXAMPLE 4 ▶ Solve the equation $8w = 3$.

Solution   In this equation, w is the variable. To solve the equation we divide both sides of the equation by 8.

$$8w = 3$$

$$\frac{8w}{8} = \frac{3}{8} \qquad \textit{\textcolor{magenta}{Divide both sides by 8.}}$$

$$w = \frac{3}{8}$$

▶ **Now Try Exercise 33**

EXAMPLE 5 ▶ Solve the equation $-15 = -3z$.

Solution   In this equation, the variable, z, is on the right side of the equal sign. To isolate z, we divide both sides of the equation by -3.

$$-15 = -3z$$

$$\frac{-15}{-3} = \frac{-3z}{-3} \qquad \textit{\textcolor{magenta}{Divide both sides by -3.}}$$

$$5 = z$$

▶ **Now Try Exercise 21**

EXAMPLE 6 ▶ Solve the equation $0.24x = 1.20$.

Solution   We begin by dividing both sides of the equation by 0.24 to isolate the variable x.

$$0.24x = 1.20$$

$$\frac{0.24x}{0.24} = \frac{1.20}{0.24} \qquad \textit{\textcolor{magenta}{Divide both sides by 0.24.}}$$

$$1x = 5$$

$$x = 5$$

▶ **Now Try Exercise 35**

Working problems involving decimal numbers on a calculator will probably save you time.

Helpful Hint

When solving an equation of the form $ax = b$, we can isolate the variable by

1. multiplying both sides of the equation by the reciprocal of a, $\dfrac{1}{a}$, as was done in Examples 1, 2, and 3, or

2. dividing both sides of the equation by a, as was done in Examples 4, 5, and 6.

Either method may be used to isolate the variable. However, if the equation contains a fraction, or fractions, you will arrive at a solution more quickly by multiplying by the reciprocal of a. This is illustrated in Examples 7 and 8.

EXAMPLE 7 ▶ Solve the equation $-2x = \dfrac{3}{5}$.

Solution   Since this equation contains a fraction, we will isolate the variable by multiplying both sides of the equation by $-\dfrac{1}{2}$, which is the reciprocal of -2.

$$-2x = \frac{3}{5}$$

$$\left(-\frac{1}{2}\right)(-2x) = \left(-\frac{1}{2}\right)\left(\frac{3}{5}\right) \qquad \textit{Multiply both sides by } -\frac{1}{2}.$$

$$1x = \left(-\frac{1}{2}\right)\left(\frac{3}{5}\right)$$

$$x = -\frac{3}{10}$$

▶ **Now Try Exercise 39**

INSTRUCTOR EXAMPLE

Solve the equation $-4x = \dfrac{5}{8}$.

Ans.: $x = -\dfrac{5}{32}$

In Example 7, if you wished to solve the equation by dividing both sides of the equation by -2, you would have to divide the fraction $\dfrac{3}{5}$ by -2.

EXAMPLE 8 ▶ Solve the equation $-6 = -\dfrac{3}{5}x$.

Solution   Since this equation contains a fraction, we will isolate the variable by multiplying both sides by the reciprocal of $-\dfrac{3}{5}$, which is $-\dfrac{5}{3}$.

$$-6 = -\frac{3}{5}x$$

$$\left(-\frac{5}{3}\right)(-6) = \left(-\frac{5}{3}\right)\left(-\frac{3}{5}x\right) \qquad \textit{Multiply both sides by } -\frac{5}{3}.$$

$$10 = 1x$$

$$10 = x$$

▶ **Now Try Exercise 57**

INSTRUCTOR EXAMPLE

Solve the equation $-7 = -\dfrac{2}{5}x$.

Ans.: $x = \dfrac{35}{2}$

In Example 8, the equation was written as $-6 = -\dfrac{3}{5}x$. This equation is equivalent to the equations $-6 = \dfrac{-3}{5}x$ and $-6 = \dfrac{3}{-5}x$. Can you explain why? All three equations have the same solution, 10.

3 Solve Equations of the Form $-x = a$

When solving an equation, we may obtain an equation like $-x = 7$. This is not a solution since $-x = 7$ means $-1x = 7$. The solution to an equation is of the form $x =$ some number. When an equation is of the form $-x = 7$, we can solve for x by multiplying both sides of the equation by -1, as illustrated in the following example.

EXAMPLE 9 ▶ Solve the equation $-x = 7$.

Solution $-x = 7$ means that $-1x = 7$. We are solving for x, not $-x$. We can multiply both sides of the equation by -1 to isolate x on the left side of the equation.

$$-x = 7$$

$$-1x = 7$$

$$(-1)(-1x) = (-1)(7) \qquad \textit{Multiply both sides by } -1.$$

$$1x = -7$$

$$x = -7$$

INSTRUCTOR EXAMPLE

Solve the equation $-y = 10$.
Ans.: $y = -10$

Check:

$$-x = 7$$

$$-(-7) \overset{?}{=} 7$$

$$7 = 7 \qquad \textit{True}$$

Thus, the solution is -7.

▶ **Now Try Exercise 23**

Example 9 may also be solved by dividing both sides of the equation by -1. Try this now and see that you get the same solution. Whenever we have the opposite (or negative) of a variable equal to a quantity, as in Example 9, we can solve for the variable by multiplying (or dividing) both sides of the equation by -1.

EXAMPLE 10 ▶ Solve the equation $-x = -5$.

Solution
$$-x = -5$$
$$-1x = -5$$
$$(-1)(-1x) = (-1)(-5) \quad \textit{Multiply both sides by } -1.$$
$$1x = 5$$
$$x = 5$$

▶ **Now Try Exercise 25**

Helpful Hint

For any real number a, if $-x = a$, then $x = -a$.

Examples

$$-x = 7 \qquad\qquad -x = -2$$
$$x = -7 \qquad\qquad x = -(-2)$$
$$x = 2$$

4 Do Some Steps Mentally When Solving Equations

When you feel comfortable using the multiplication property, you may wish to do some of the steps mentally to reduce some of the written work. Now we present two examples worked out in detail, along with their shortened form.

EXAMPLE 11 ▶ Solve the equation $-3x = -21$.

Solution

SHORTENED FORM

$$-3x = -21$$
$$\frac{-3x}{-3} = \frac{-21}{-3} \quad \longleftarrow \boxed{\text{Do this step mentally.}}$$
$$x = \frac{-21}{-3}$$
$$x = 7$$

$$-3x = -21$$
$$x = \frac{-21}{-3}$$
$$x = 7$$

▶ **Now Try Exercise 61**

EXAMPLE 12 ▶ Solve the equation $\frac{1}{5}x = 20$.

Solution

SHORTENED FORM

$$\frac{1}{5}x = 20$$
$$5\left(\frac{1}{5}x\right) = 5(20) \quad \longleftarrow \boxed{\text{Do this step mentally.}}$$
$$x = 5(20)$$
$$x = 100$$

$$\frac{1}{5}x = 20$$
$$x = 5(20)$$
$$x = 100$$

▶ **Now Try Exercise 63**

In Section 2.2, we discussed the addition property and in this section we discussed the multiplication property. It is important that you understand the difference between the two. The following Helpful Hint should be studied carefully.

Helpful Hint

The **addition property** is used to solve equations of the form $x + a = b$. The *addition property* is used when a number is *added to or subtracted from* a variable.

$$x + 3 = -6 \qquad\qquad x - 5 = -2$$
$$x + 3 \;-3 = -6\; -3 \qquad\qquad x - 5 \;+5 = -2\; +5$$
$$x = -9 \qquad\qquad x = 3$$

The **multiplication property** is used to solve equations of the form $ax = b$. It is used when a variable is *multiplied* or *divided by* a number.

$$3x = 6 \qquad \frac{x}{2} = 4 \qquad \frac{2}{5}x = 12$$

$$\frac{3x}{3} = \frac{6}{3} \qquad 2\left(\frac{x}{2}\right) = 2(4) \qquad \left(\frac{5}{2}\right)\left(\frac{2}{5}x\right) = \left(\frac{5}{2}\right)(12)$$

$$x = 2 \qquad x = 8 \qquad x = 30$$

1. Answers will vary.   **2.** Division is defined in terms of multiplication.

EXERCISE SET 2.3

MathXL®   MyMathLab

Concept/Writing Exercises

1. Explain the multiplication property of equality.

2. Explain why the multiplication property allows us to divide both sides of an equation by a nonzero quantity.

3. a) If $-x = a$, where a represents any real number, what does x equal? $-a$

    b) If $-x = 5$, what is x? -5

    c) If $-x = -5$, what is x? 5

4. When solving the equation $-2x = 5$, would you divide both sides of the equation by -2 or by 5? Explain.   Divide by -2.

5. When solving the equation $3x = 5$, would you divide both sides of the equation by 3 or by 5? Explain.   Divide by 3.

6. When solving the equation $4 = \dfrac{x}{3}$, what would you do to isolate the variable? Explain.   Multiply both sides by 3.

7. When solving the equation $\dfrac{x}{2} = 3$, what would you do to isolate the variable? Explain.   Multiply both sides by 2.

8. When solving the equation $ax = b$ for x, would you divide both sides of the equation by a or b? Explain.   By a, to isolate the variable x.

Practice the Skills

Solve each equation and check your solution.

9. $4x = 12$ 3

10. $5x = 50$ 10

11. $\dfrac{x}{3} = 7$ 21

12. $\dfrac{y}{5} = 3$ 15

13. $-4x = 12$ -3

14. $8 = 16y$ $\dfrac{1}{2}$

15. $\dfrac{x}{4} = -2$ -8

16. $\dfrac{x}{3} = -3$ -9

17. $\dfrac{x}{5} = 1$ 5

18. $-7x = 49$ -7

19. $-27n = 81$ -3

20. $\dfrac{x}{8} = -3$ -24

21. $-7 = 3r$ $-\dfrac{7}{3}$

22. $16 = -4y$ -4

23. $-x = 13$ -13

24. $-x = 9$ -9

25. $-x = -8$ 8

26. $-x = -15$ 15

27. $-\dfrac{w}{3} = -13$ 39

28. $-4 = \dfrac{c}{7}$ -28

29. $4 = -12x$ $-\dfrac{1}{3}$

30. $12y = -15$ $-\dfrac{5}{4}$

31. $-\dfrac{x}{3} = -2$ 6

32. $-\dfrac{a}{8} = -7$ 56

33. $43t = 26$ $\dfrac{26}{43}$

34. $-24x = -18$ $\dfrac{3}{4}$

35. $-4.2x = -8.4$ 2

36. $-3.88 = 1.94y$ -2

37. $3x = \dfrac{3}{5}$ $\dfrac{1}{5}$

38. $7x = -7$ -1

39. $5x = -\dfrac{3}{8}$ $-\dfrac{3}{40}$

40. $-2b = -\dfrac{4}{5}$ $\dfrac{2}{5}$

41. $15 = -\dfrac{x}{4}$ -60

42. $\dfrac{c}{9} = 0$ 0

43. $-\dfrac{b}{4} = -60$ 240

44. $-x = -\dfrac{5}{9}$ $\dfrac{5}{9}$

45. $\dfrac{x}{5} = -7$ -35

46. $-3r = 0$ 0

47. $5 = \dfrac{x}{4}$ 20

48. $-3 = \dfrac{x}{-5}$ 15

49. $\dfrac{3}{5}d = -30$ -50

50. $\dfrac{2}{7}x = 7$ $\dfrac{49}{2}$

51. $\dfrac{y}{-2} = 0$ 0

52. $-6x = \dfrac{5}{2}$ $-\dfrac{5}{12}$

53. $\dfrac{-7}{8}w = 0$ 0

54. $-x = \dfrac{5}{8}$ $-\dfrac{5}{8}$

55. $\dfrac{1}{5}x = 4.5$ 22.5

56. $-\dfrac{1}{4}x = \dfrac{3}{4}$ -3

57. $-4 = -\dfrac{2}{3}z$ 6

58. $-9 = \dfrac{-5}{3}n$ $\dfrac{27}{5}$

59. $-1.4x = 28.28$ -20.2

60. $-0.42x = -2.142$ 5.1

Solve each equation by doing some steps mentally. Check your solution.

61. $-8x = -56$ 7

62. $-9x = -45$ 5

63. $\dfrac{2}{3}x = 6$ 9

64. $\dfrac{1}{3}x = 15$ 45

Problem Solving

65. a) Explain the difference between $5 + x = 10$ and $5x = 10$.   Answers will vary.
  b) Solve $5 + x = 10$. $x = 5$
  c) Solve $5x = 10$. $x = 2$

66. a) Explain the difference between $3 + x = 6$ and $3x = 6$.
  b) Solve $3 + x = 6$. $x = 3$
  c) Solve $3x = 6$. $x = 2$

67. Consider the equation $\dfrac{2}{3}x = 4$. This equation could be solved by multiplying both sides of the equation by $\dfrac{3}{2}$, the reciprocal of $\dfrac{2}{3}$, or by dividing both sides of the equation by $\dfrac{2}{3}$. Which method do you feel would be easier? Explain your answer. Find the solution to the equation.   multiply by $\dfrac{3}{2}$; 6

68. Consider the equation $4x = \dfrac{3}{5}$. Would it be easier to solve this equation by dividing both sides of the equation by 4 or by multiplying both sides of the equation by $\dfrac{1}{4}$, the reciprocal of 4? Explain your answer. Find the solution to the problem.

69. Consider the equation $\dfrac{3}{7}x = \dfrac{4}{5}$. Would it be easier to solve this equation by dividing both sides of the equation by $\dfrac{3}{7}$ or by multiplying both sides of the equation by $\dfrac{7}{3}$, the reciprocal of $\dfrac{3}{7}$? Explain your answer. Find the solution to the equation.   multiply by $\dfrac{7}{3}$; $\dfrac{28}{15}$

66. a) Answers will vary.   **68.** multiply by $\dfrac{1}{4}$; $\dfrac{3}{20}$

Challenge Problems

70. Consider the equation $\square \odot = \triangle$.
  a) To solve for $\odot$, what symbol do we need to isolate? $\odot$
  b) How would you isolate the symbol you specified in part **a)**?   Divide both sides by $\square$.
  c) Solve the equation for $\odot$. $\odot = \dfrac{\triangle}{\square}$

71. Consider the equation $\odot = \triangle \boxdot$.
  a) To solve for $\boxdot$, what symbol do we need to isolate? $\boxdot$
  b) How would you isolate the symbol you specified in part **a)**?   Divide both sides by $\triangle$.

  c) Solve the equation for $\boxdot$. $\boxdot = \dfrac{\odot}{\triangle}$

72. Consider the equation $\# = \dfrac{\odot}{\triangle}$.
  a) To solve for $\odot$, what symbol do we need to isolate? $\odot$
  b) How would you isolate the symbol you specified in part **a)**?   Multiply both sides by $\triangle$.
  c) Solve the equation for $\odot$. $\odot = \#\triangle$

Cumulative Review Exercises

[1.7] **73.** Subtract -4 from -8. -4

[1.8] **74.** Evaluate $(-3)(-2)(5)(-1)$. -30

[1.9] **75.** Evaluate $4^2 - 2^3 \cdot 6 \div 3 + 6$.   6

[1.10] **76.** Name the property illustrated.
  $2 + (4 + y) = (2 + 4) + y$ associative, addition

[2.2] **77.** Solve the equation $-48 = x + 9$. -57

2.4 Solving Linear Equations with a Variable on Only One Side of the Equation

1 Solve linear equations with a variable on only one side of the equal sign.

2 Solve equations containing decimal numbers or fractions.

1 Solve Linear Equations with a Variable on Only One Side of the Equal Sign

In this section, we discuss how to solve linear equations using *both* the addition and multiplication properties of equality when a variable appears on only one side of the equal sign. In Section 2.5, we will discuss how to solve linear equations using both properties when a variable appears on both sides of the equal sign.

The general procedure we use to solve equations is to "isolate the variable." That is, get the variable alone on one side of the equal sign.

No one method is the "best" to solve all linear equations. But the following general procedure can be used to solve linear equations when the variable appears on only one side of the equation.

To Solve Linear Equations with a Variable on Only One Side of the Equal Sign

1. If the equation contains fractions, multiply **both** sides of the equation by the least common denominator (LCD). This will eliminate the fractions from the equation.

2. Use the distributive property to remove parentheses.

3. Combine like terms on the same side of the equal sign.

4. Use the addition property to obtain an equation with the term containing the variable on one side of the equal sign and a constant on the other side. This will result in an equation of the form $ax = b$.

5. Use the multiplication property to isolate the variable. This will give a solution of the form $x = \dfrac{b}{a}\left(\text{or } 1x = \dfrac{b}{a}\right)$.

6. Check the solution in the original equation.

When solving an equation, you should always check your solution, as is indicated in step 6. To conserve space, we will not show all checks.

When solving an equation, remember that our goal is to isolate the variable on one side of the equation.

Consider the equation $2x + 4 = 10$ which contains no fractions or parentheses, and no like terms on the same side of the equal sign. Therefore, we start with step 4, using the addition property. Remember that the addition property allows us to add (or subtract) the same quantity to (or from) both sides of an equation without changing its solution. Here we subtract 4 from both sides of the equation to get the $2x$ by itself on one side of the equal sign.

Equation

$2x + 4 = 10$

$2x + 4\ \boxed{-\ 4} = 10\ \boxed{-\ 4}$ *Addition property*

$2x + 0 = 6$

or $2x = 6$ *x-term is now isolated*

Notice how the term containing the variable, $2x$, is now by itself on one side of the equal sign. We can now say that we have *isolated the term containing the variable* or have *isolated the variable term*. Now we use the multiplication property, step 5, to isolate the variable, x. Remember that the multiplication property allows us to multiply or divide both sides of the equation by the same nonzero number without changing its solution. Here we divide both sides of the equation by 2, the coefficient of the term containing the variable, to obtain the solution, 3.

$2x = 6$

$\dfrac{\overset{1}{\cancel{2}}x}{\underset{1}{\cancel{2}}} = \dfrac{\overset{3}{\cancel{6}}}{\underset{1}{\cancel{2}}}$ *Multiplication property*

$1x = 3$

$x = 3$ *x is now isolated*

The solution to the equation $2x + 4 = 10$ is 3. Now let's work some examples.

EXAMPLE 1 ▶ Solve the equation $5x - 7 = 13$.

Solution   We will follow the procedure outlined for solving equations. Since the equation contains no fractions nor parentheses, and since there are no like terms to be combined, we start with step 4.

$$5x - 7 = 13$$

Step 4 $5x - 7 \boxed{+ 7} = 13 \boxed{+ 7}$ *Add 7 to both sides.*

$$5x = 20$$

Step 5 $\dfrac{5x}{\boxed{5}} = \dfrac{20}{\boxed{5}}$ *Divide both sides by 5.*

$$x = 4$$

Step 6   Check: $5x - 7 = 13$

$$5(4) - 7 \overset{?}{=} 13$$
$$20 - 7 \overset{?}{=} 13$$
$$13 = 13 \qquad \text{True}$$

Since the check is true, the solution is 4. Note that after completing step 4, we obtain $5x = 20$, which is an equation of the form $ax = b$. After completing step 5, we obtain the answer in the form $x =$ some real number.

▶ **Now Try Exercise 15**

Helpful Hint

When solving an equation that does not contain fractions, **the addition property (step 4) is to be used before the multiplication property (step 5)**. If you use the multiplication property before the addition property, it is still possible to obtain the correct answer. However, you will usually have to do more work, and you may end up working with fractions. What would happen if you tried to solve Example 1 using the multiplication property before the addition property?

EXAMPLE 2 ▶ Solve the equation $-2r - 6 = -3$.

Solution

$$-2r - 6 = -3$$

Step 4 $-2r - 6 \boxed{+ 6} = -3 \boxed{+ 6}$ *Add 6 to both sides.*

$$-2r = 3$$

Step 5 $\dfrac{-2r}{\boxed{-2}} = \dfrac{3}{\boxed{-2}}$ *Divide both sides by -2.*

$$r = -\dfrac{3}{2}$$

Step 6   Check: $-2r - 6 = -3$

$$-2\left(-\dfrac{3}{2}\right) - 6 \overset{?}{=} -3$$
$$3 - 6 \overset{?}{=} -3$$
$$-3 = -3 \qquad \text{True}$$

The solution is $-\dfrac{3}{2}$.

▶ **Now Try Exercise 23**

Note that checks are always made with the *original* equation. In some of the following examples, the check will be omitted to save space. You should check all of your answers.

EXAMPLE 3 ▶ Solve the equation $16 = 4x + 6 - 2x$.

Solution   Again we must isolate the variable, x. Since the right side of the equation has two like terms containing the variable, x, we will first combine these like terms.

$$16 = 4x + 6 - 2x$$

Step 3 $\qquad\qquad 16 = 2x + 6 \qquad$ *Like terms were combined.*

Step 4 $\qquad 16 - 6 = 2x + 6 - 6 \qquad$ *Subtract 6 from both sides.*

$$10 = 2x$$

Step 5 $\qquad\qquad \dfrac{10}{2} = \dfrac{2x}{2} \qquad$ *Divide both sides by 2.*

$$5 = x$$

▶ **Now Try Exercise 37**

The preceding solution can be condensed as follows.

$$16 = 4x + 6 - 2x$$
$$16 = 2x + 6 \qquad \textit{Like terms were combined.}$$
$$10 = 2x \qquad \textit{6 was subtracted from both sides.}$$
$$5 = x \qquad \textit{Both sides were divided by 2.}$$

EXAMPLE 4 ▶ Solve the equation $5x - 2(x + 4) = 3$.

Solution

$$5x - 2(x + 4) = 3$$

Step 2 $\qquad 5x - 2x - 8 = 3 \qquad$ *Distributive property was used.*

Step 3 $\qquad\qquad 3x - 8 = 3 \qquad$ *Like terms were combined.*

Step 4 $\qquad 3x - 8 + 8 = 3 + 8 \qquad$ *Add 8 to both sides.*

$$3x = 11$$

Step 5 $\qquad\qquad \dfrac{3x}{3} = \dfrac{11}{3} \qquad$ *Divide both sides by 3.*

$$x = \dfrac{11}{3}$$

▶ **Now Try Exercise 65**

The solution to Example 4 can be condensed as follows:

$$5x - 2(x + 4) = 3$$
$$5x - 2x - 8 = 3 \qquad \textit{Distributive property was used.}$$
$$3x - 8 = 3 \qquad \textit{Like terms were combined.}$$
$$3x = 11 \qquad \textit{8 was added to both sides.}$$
$$x = \dfrac{11}{3} \qquad \textit{Both sides were divided by 3.}$$

EXAMPLE 5 ▶ Solve the equation $3p - (2p + 5) = 7$.

Solution $\qquad 3p - (2p + 5) = 7$

$$3p - 2p - 5 = 7 \qquad \textit{Distributive property was used.}$$
$$p - 5 = 7 \qquad \textit{Like terms were combined.}$$
$$p = 12 \qquad \textit{5 was added to both sides.}$$

▶ **Now Try Exercise 69**

2 Solve Equations Containing Decimal Numbers or Fractions

In Chapter 3, we will be solving many equations that contain decimal numbers. To solve such equations, we may follow the same procedure as outlined earlier. Example 6 illustrates two methods to solve an equation that contains decimal numbers.

EXAMPLE 6 ▶ Solve the equation $x + 1.24 - 0.07x = 4.96$.

Solution   We will work this example using two methods. In method 1, we work with decimal numbers throughout the solving process. In method 2, we multiply both sides of the equation by a power of 10 to change the decimal numbers to whole numbers.

Method 1

$$x + 1.24 - 0.07x = 4.96$$

$$0.93x + 1.24 = 4.96 \qquad \text{\textit{Like terms were combined,}} \ 1x - 0.07x = 0.93x.$$

$$0.93x + 1.24 - 1.24 = 4.96 - 1.24 \qquad \text{\textit{Subtract 1.24 from both sides.}}$$

$$0.93x = 3.72$$

$$\frac{0.93x}{0.93} = \frac{3.72}{0.93} \qquad \text{\textit{Divide both sides by 0.93.}}$$

$$x = 4$$

Method 2 Some students prefer to eliminate the decimal numbers from the equation by multiplying both sides of the equation by 10 if the decimal numbers are given in tenths, by 100 if the decimal numbers are given in hundredths, and so on. In Example 6, since the decimal numbers are in hundredths, you can eliminate the decimals from the equation by multiplying both sides of the equation by 100. This alternate method would give the following.

$$x + 1.24 - 0.07x = 4.96$$

$$100(x + 1.24 - 0.07x) = 100(4.96) \qquad \text{\textit{Multiply both sides of equation by 100.}}$$

$$100(x) + 100(1.24) - 100(0.07x) = 496 \qquad \text{\textit{Distributive property was used.}}$$

$$100x + 124 - 7x = 496$$

$$93x + 124 = 496 \qquad \text{\textit{Like terms were combined.}}$$

$$93x = 372 \qquad \text{\textit{124 was subtracted from both sides.}}$$

$$x = 4 \qquad \text{\textit{Both sides were divided by 93.}}$$

Study both methods provided to see which method you prefer.

▶ **Now Try Exercise 41**

Now let's look at solving equations that contain fractions. There will be various times throughout the course when we will need to solve equations containing fractions. Often, the first step in solving equations containing fractions is to multiply both sides of the equation by the LCD to eliminate the fractions from the equations. Examples 7–9 illustrate this procedure. Example 7 will contain the expression $\frac{1}{5}(x + 1)$, Since the $\frac{1}{5}$ is multiplied by $(x + 1)$, the expression $\frac{1}{5}(x + 1)$ is a single term whose factors are $\frac{1}{5}$ and $(x + 1)$. When multiplying a term by a constant or variable, we multiply only one of the factors of the term by the number or variable. Therefore, for example,

$$5\left[\frac{1}{5}(x + 1)\right] = \cancel{5}\left(\frac{1}{\cancel{5}}\right)(x + 1) = 1(x + 1) = x + 1$$

EXAMPLE 7 ▶ Solve $\frac{1}{5}(x + 1) = 1$.

Solution The LCD of the fraction is 5. We will begin by multiplying both sides of the equation by the LCD. This step will eliminate fractions from the equation.

$$\frac{1}{5}(x + 1) = 1$$

Step 1 $$5\left[\frac{1}{5}(x + 1)\right] = 5 \cdot 1 \qquad \textcolor{red}{\textit{Multiply both sides by the LCD, 5.}}$$

$$\cancel{5}\left(\frac{1}{\cancel{5}}\right)(x + 1) = 5$$

$$x + 1 = 5$$

Step 4 $$x = 4 \qquad \textcolor{red}{\textit{1 was subtracted from both sides.}}$$

Step 6   Check: $$\frac{1}{5}(x + 1) = 1$$

$$\frac{1}{5}(4 + 1) \stackrel{?}{=} 1$$

$$\frac{1}{\cancel{5}}(\cancel{5}) \stackrel{?}{=} 1$$

$$1 = 1 \qquad \textit{True}$$

The solution is 4.

▶ **Now Try Exercise 45**

Example 7 could also be written as $\dfrac{x + 1}{5} = 1$. To solve this equation, we would begin by multiplying both sides of the equation by the LCD, 5, as follows.

$$\frac{x + 1}{5} = 1$$

$$5\left(\frac{x + 1}{5}\right) = 5 \cdot 1$$

$$x + 1 = 5$$

$$x = 4$$

EXAMPLE 8 ▶ Solve the equation $\dfrac{d}{2} + 3d = 14$.

Solution Step 1 tells us to multiply both sides of the equation by the LCD, 2. This step will eliminate fractions from the equation.

Step 1 $$2\left(\frac{d}{2} + 3d\right) = 2 \cdot 14 \qquad \textcolor{red}{\textit{Multiply both sides by the LCD, 2.}}$$

Step 2 $$\cancel{2}\left(\frac{d}{\cancel{2}}\right) + 2 \cdot 3d = 2 \cdot 14 \qquad \textcolor{red}{\textit{Distributive property}}$$

$$d + 6d = 28$$

Step 3 $$7d = 28 \qquad \textcolor{red}{\textit{Like terms were combined.}}$$

Step 5 $$d = 4 \qquad \textcolor{red}{\textit{Both sides were divided by 7.}}$$

Step 6   Check: $$\frac{d}{2} + 3d = 14$$

$$\frac{4}{2} + 3(4) \stackrel{?}{=} 14$$

$$2 + 12 \stackrel{?}{=} 14$$

$$14 = 14 \qquad \textit{True}$$

▶ **Now Try Exercise 89**

EXAMPLE 9 ▶ Solve the equation $\frac{1}{5}x - \frac{3}{8}x = \frac{1}{10}$.

Solution The LCD of 5, 8, and 10 is 40. Multiply both sides of the equation by 40 to eliminate fractions from the equation.

INSTRUCTOR EXAMPLE
Solve the equation $\frac{1}{5}x - \frac{2}{7}x = \frac{1}{6}$.

Ans.: $x = -\frac{35}{18}$

$$\frac{1}{5}x - \frac{3}{8}x = \frac{1}{10}$$

Step 1 $40\left(\frac{1}{5}x - \frac{3}{8}x\right) = 40\left(\frac{1}{10}\right)$ *Multiply both sides by the LCD, 40.*

Step 2 $40\left(\frac{1}{5}x\right) - 40\left(\frac{3}{8}x\right) = 40\left(\frac{1}{10}\right)$ *Distributive property*

$$8x - 15x = 4$$

Step 3 $-7x = 4$ *Like terms were combined.*

Step 5 $x = -\frac{4}{7}$ *Both sides were divided by −7.*

Step 6   Check: $\frac{1}{5}x - \frac{3}{8}x = \frac{1}{10}$

$$\frac{1}{5}\left(-\frac{4}{7}\right) - \frac{3}{8}\left(-\frac{4}{7}\right) \overset{?}{=} \frac{1}{10}$$ *Substitute $-\frac{4}{7}$ for each x.*

$$-\frac{4}{35} + \frac{3}{14} \overset{?}{=} \frac{1}{10}$$ *Divide out common factors, then multiply fractions.*

$$-\frac{8}{70} + \frac{15}{70} \overset{?}{=} \frac{7}{70}$$ *Write each fraction with the LCD, 70.*

$$\frac{7}{70} = \frac{7}{70}$$ *True*

▶ **Now Try Exercise 99**

Helpful Hint

In Example 9, we multiplied both sides of the equation by the LCD, 40. When solving equations containing fractions, multiplying both sides of the equation by *any* common denominator will eventually lead to the correct answer (if you don't make a mistake), but you may have to work with larger numbers. In Example 9, if you multiplied both sides of the equation by 80, 120, or 160, for example, you would eventually obtain the answer $-\frac{4}{7}$. When solving equations containing fractions, you should multiply both sides of the equation by the LCD. But if you mistakenly multiply both sides of the equation by a different common denominator to clear fractions, you will still obtain the correct answer. To show that other common denominators may be used, solve Example 9 now by multiplying both sides of the equation by the common denominator 80 instead of the LCD, 40.

When checking solutions to equations that contain fractions, you may sometimes want to perform the check using a calculator. When checking a solution using a calculator, work with each side of the equation separately. Below we show the steps used to evaluate the left side of the equation in Example 9 for $x = -\frac{4}{7}$ using a scientific calculator.*

$$\frac{1}{5}x - \frac{3}{8}x = \frac{1}{10}$$

$$\frac{1}{5}\left(-\frac{4}{7}\right) - \frac{3}{8}\left(-\frac{4}{7}\right) = \frac{1}{10}$$

Evaluate the left side of the equation.

$$1 \boxed{\div} 5 \boxed{\times} 4 \boxed{+/-} \boxed{\div} 7 \boxed{-} 3 \boxed{\div} 8 \boxed{\times} 4 \boxed{+/-} \boxed{\div} 7 \boxed{=} \; 0.1.$$

Since the right side of the equation, $\frac{1}{10} = 0.1$, the answer checks.

---

*Keystrokes may differ on some scientific calculators. Read the instruction manual for your calculator.

Helpful Hint

Some of the most commonly used terms in algebra are "evaluate," "simplify," "solve," and "check." Make sure you understand what each term means and when each term is used.

Evaluate: To *evaluate an expression* means to find its numerical value.

Evaluate $16 \div 2^2 + 36 \div 4$

$$= 16 \div 4 + 36 \div 4$$
$$= 4 + 36 \div 4$$
$$= 4 + 9$$
$$= 13$$

Evaluate $-x^2 + 3x - 2$ when $x = 4$

$$= -4^2 + 3(4) - 2$$
$$= -16 + 3(4) - 2$$
$$= -16 + 12 - 2$$
$$= -4 - 2$$
$$= -6$$

Simplify: To *simplify an expression* means to perform the operations and combine like terms.

Simplify $3(x - 2) - 4(2x + 3)$

$$3(x - 2) - 4(2x + 3) = 3x - 6 - 8x - 12$$
$$= -5x - 18$$

Note that when you simplify an expression containing variables you do not generally end up with just a numerical value unless all the variable terms happen to add to zero.

Solve: To *solve an equation* means to find the value or the values of the variable that make the equation a true statement.

Solve $2x + 3(x + 1) = 18$

$$2x + 3x + 3 = 18$$
$$5x + 3 = 18$$
$$5x = 15$$
$$x = 3$$

Check: To *check the proposed solution to an equation*, substitute the value in the original equation. If this substitution results in a true statement, then the answer checks. For example, to check the solution to the equation just solved, we substitute 3 for x in the original equation.

Check $2x + 3(x + 1) = 18$

$$2(3) + 3(3 + 1) \stackrel{?}{=} 18$$
$$2(3) + 3(4) \stackrel{?}{=} 18$$
$$6 + 12 \stackrel{?}{=} 18$$
$$18 = 18 \qquad \textit{True}$$

Since we obtained a true statement, the 3 checks.

It is important to realize that expressions may be evaluated or simplified (depending on the type of problem) and equations are solved and then checked.

EXERCISE SET 2.4

Concept/Writing Exercises

11. a) Answers will vary.   **12.** Multiply both sides of the equation by the LCD.

1. Does the equation $x + 3 = 2x + 5$ contain a variable on only one side of the equation? Explain. no

2. Does the equation $2x - 4 = 3$ contain a variable on only one side of the equation? Explain. yes

3. If $1x = \dfrac{1}{3}$, what does x equal? $x = \dfrac{1}{3}$

4. If $1x = -\dfrac{3}{5}$, what does x equal? $x = -\dfrac{3}{5}$

5. If $-x = \dfrac{1}{2}$ what does x equal? $x = -\dfrac{1}{2}$

6. If $-x = \dfrac{7}{8}$, what does x equal? $x = -\dfrac{7}{8}$

7. If $-x = -\dfrac{4}{9}$, what does x equal? $x = \dfrac{4}{9}$

8. If $-x = -\dfrac{3}{5}$, what does x equal? $x = \dfrac{3}{5}$

9. Do you evaluate or solve an expression? Explain. evaluate

10. Do you evaluate or solve an equation? Explain. solve

11. a) Write the general procedure for solving an equation where the variable appears on only one side of the equal sign.

  b) Refer to page 120 to see whether you omitted any steps.

12. When solving equations that contain fractions, what is the first step in the process of solving the equation?

13. a) Explain, in a step-by-step manner, how to solve the equation $2(3x + 4) = -4$. Answers will vary.

  b) Solve the equation by following the steps you listed in part **a)**. -2

14. a) Explain, step-by-step, how to solve the equation $4x - 2(x + 3) = 4$. Answers will vary.

  b) Solve the equation by following the steps you listed in part **a)**. 5

Practice the Skills

Solve each equation. You may wish to use a calculator to solve equations containing decimal numbers.

15. $5x - 6 = 19$ 5

16. $2x - 4 = 8$ 6

17. $-4w - 5 = 11$ -4

18. $-4x + 6 = 20$ $-\dfrac{7}{2}$

19. $3x + 6 = 12$ 2

20. $6 - 3x = 18$ -4

21. $5x - 2 = 10$ $\dfrac{12}{5}$

22. $-2t + 9 = 21$ -6

23. $-5k - 4 = -19$ 3

24. $-4x - 7 = -6$ $-\dfrac{1}{4}$

25. $12 - x = 9$ 3

26. $-3x - 3 = -12$ 3

27. $8 + 3x = 19$ $\dfrac{11}{3}$

28. $-2x + 7 = -10$ $\dfrac{17}{2}$

29. $16x + 5 = -14$ $-\dfrac{19}{16}$

30. $19 = 25 + 4x$ $-\dfrac{3}{2}$

31. $-4.2 = 3x + 25.8$ -10

32. $-24 + 16x = -24$ 0

33. $7r - 16 = -2$ 2

34. $-2w + 4 = -8$ 6

35. $60 = -5s + 9$ $-\dfrac{51}{5}$

36. $15 = 7x + 1$ 2

37. $14 = 5x + 8 - 3x$ 3

38. $15 = 6x - 3 + 3x$ 2

39. $2.3x - 9.34 = 6.3$ 6.8

40. $x + 0.05x = 21$ 20

41. $0.91y + 2.25 - 0.01y = 5.85$ 4

42. $0.15 = 0.05x - 1.35 - 0.20x$ -10

43. $28.8 = x + 1.40x$ 12

44. $8.40 = 2.45x - 1.05x$ 6

45. $\dfrac{1}{7}(x + 6) = 4$ 22

46. $\dfrac{m - 6}{5} = 2$ 16

47. $\dfrac{d + 3}{7} = 9$ 60

48. $\dfrac{1}{5}(x + 2) = -3$ -17

49. $\dfrac{1}{3}(t - 5) = -6$ -13

50. $\dfrac{2}{3}(n - 3) = 8$ 15

51. $\dfrac{3}{4}(x - 5) = -12$ -11

52. $\dfrac{1}{4} = \dfrac{z + 1}{4}$ 0

53. $\dfrac{x + 4}{7} = \dfrac{3}{7}$ -1

54. $\dfrac{4x + 5}{6} = \dfrac{7}{2}$ 4

55. $\dfrac{3}{4} = \dfrac{4m - 5}{6}$ $\dfrac{19}{8}$

56. $\dfrac{5}{6} = \dfrac{5t - 4}{2}$ $\dfrac{17}{15}$

57. $4(n + 2) = 8$ 0

58. $3(x - 2) = 12$ 6

59. $-2(x - 3) = 26$ -10

60. $5(3 - x) = 15$ 0

61. $-4 = -(x + 5)$ -1

62. $-3(2 - 3x) = 9$ $\dfrac{5}{3}$

63. $12 = 4(x - 3)$ 6

64. $-2(x + 8) - 5 = 1$ -11

65. $2x - 3(x + 5) = 6$ -21

66. $5(3x + 1) - 12x = -2$ $-\dfrac{7}{3}$

67. $-3r - 4(r + 2) = 11$ $-\dfrac{19}{7}$

68. $9 = -2(a - 3)$ $-\dfrac{3}{2}$

69. $x - 3(2x + 3) = 11$ -4

70. $3y - (y + 5) = 9$ 7

71. $5x + 3x - 4x - 7 = 9$ 4

72. $4(x + 2) = 13$ $\dfrac{5}{4}$

73. $0.7(x - 3) = 1.4$ 5

74. $21 + (c - 9) = 24$ 12

75. $2.5(4q - 3) = 0.5$ 0.8

76. $0.1(2.4x + 5) = 1.7$ 5

77. $3 - 2(x + 3) + 2 = 1$ -1

78. $2(3x - 4) - 4x = 12$ 10

79. $1 + (x + 3) + 6x = 6$ $\dfrac{2}{7}$

80. $5x - 2x + 7x = -81$ -8.1

81. $4.85 - 6.4x + 1.11 = 22.6$ -2.6 **82.** $5.76 - 4.24x - 1.9x = 27.864$ -3.6 **83.** $7 = 8 - 5(m + 3)$ $-\dfrac{14}{5}$

84. $4 = \dfrac{3t + 1}{7}$ 9 **85.** $10 = \dfrac{2s + 4}{5}$ 23 **86.** $12 = \dfrac{4d - 1}{3}$ $\dfrac{37}{4}$

87. $x + \dfrac{2}{3} = \dfrac{3}{5}$ $-\dfrac{1}{15}$ **88.** $n - \dfrac{1}{4} = \dfrac{1}{2}$ $\dfrac{3}{4}$ **89.** $\dfrac{r}{3} + 2r = 7$ 3

90. $\dfrac{x}{4} - 6x = 23$ -4 **91.** $\dfrac{3}{7} = \dfrac{3t}{4} + 1$ $-\dfrac{16}{21}$ **92.** $\dfrac{5}{8} = \dfrac{5t}{6} + 2$ $-\dfrac{33}{20}$

93. $\dfrac{1}{2}r + \dfrac{1}{5}r = 7$ 10 **94.** $\dfrac{x}{3} - \dfrac{3x}{4} = \dfrac{1}{12}$ $-\dfrac{1}{5}$ **95.** $\dfrac{2}{8} + \dfrac{3}{4} = \dfrac{w}{5}$ 5

96. $\dfrac{x}{4} - \dfrac{x}{6} = \dfrac{1}{4}$ 3 **97.** $\dfrac{1}{2}x + 4 = \dfrac{1}{6}$ $-\dfrac{23}{3}$ **98.** $\dfrac{4}{5} + n = \dfrac{1}{3}$ $-\dfrac{7}{15}$

99. $\dfrac{4}{5}s - \dfrac{3}{4}s = \dfrac{1}{10}$ 2 **100.** $\dfrac{1}{3}x - \dfrac{3}{4}x = \dfrac{1}{5}$ $-\dfrac{12}{25}$ **101.** $\dfrac{4}{9} = \dfrac{1}{3}(n - 7)$ $\dfrac{25}{3}$

102. $-\dfrac{3}{8} = \dfrac{1}{8} - \dfrac{2x}{7}$ $\dfrac{7}{4}$ **103.** $-\dfrac{3}{5} = -\dfrac{1}{9} - \dfrac{3}{4}x$ $\dfrac{88}{135}$ **104.** $-\dfrac{3}{5} = -\dfrac{1}{6} - \dfrac{5}{4}m$ $\dfrac{26}{75}$

Problem Solving

105. a) Explain why it is easier to solve the equation $3x + 2 = 11$ by first subtracting 2 from both sides of the equation rather than by first dividing both sides of the equation by 3.   You will not have to work with fractions.

   b) Solve the equation. 3

106. a) Explain why it is easier to solve the equation $5x - 3 = 12$ by first adding 3 to both sides of the equation rather than by first dividing both sides of the equation by 5.   You will not have to work with fractions.

   b) Solve the equation. 3

Challenge Problems

For exercises 107–109, solve the equation.

107. $3(x - 2) - (x + 5) - 2(3 - 2x) = 18$ $\dfrac{35}{6}$

108. $-6 = -(x - 5) - 3(5 + 2x) - 4(2x - 4)$ $\dfrac{4}{5}$

109. $4[3 - 2(x + 4)] - (x + 3) = 13$ -4

110. Solve the equation $\square \odot - \triangledown = @$ for $\odot$. $\odot = \dfrac{@ + \triangledown}{\square}$

Group Activity

In Chapter 3, we will discuss procedures for writing application problems as equations. Let's look at an application now.

   Birthday Party John Logan purchased 2 large chocolate bars and a birthday card. The birthday card cost \$3. The total cost was \$9. What was the price of a single chocolate bar?

This problem can be represented by the equation $2x + 3 = 9$, which can be used to solve the problem. Solving the equation we find that x, the price of a single chocolate bar, is \$3.

*For Exercises 111 and 112, each group member should do parts **a)** and **b)**. Then do part **c)** as a group.*

   a) *Obtain an equation that can be used to solve the problem.*

   b) *Solve the equation and answer the question.*

   c) *Compare and check each other's work.*

111. Stationery Eduardo Verner purchased three boxes of stationery. He also purchased wrapping paper and thank-you cards. If the wrapping paper and thank-you cards together cost \$6, and the total he paid was \$42, find the cost of a box of stationery.   **a)** $3x + 6 = 42$ **b)** \$12

112. Candies Mahandi Ison purchased three rolls of peppermint candies and the local newspaper. The newspaper cost 50 cents. He paid \$2.75 in all. What did a roll of candies cost?   **a)** $3x + 0.5 = 2.75$ **b)** \$0.75

Cumulative Review Exercises

[1.4] **113.** True or false: Every real number is a rational number.   F

[1.9] **114.** Evaluate $[5(2 - 6) + 3(8 \div 4)^2]^2$. 64

[2.2] **115.** To solve an equation, what do you need to do to the variable?   Isolate the variable on one side of the equation.

[2.3] **116.** To solve the equation $7 = -4x$, would you add 4 to both sides of the equation or divide both sides of the equation by -4? Explain your answer.   Divide both sides by -4.

Mid-Chapter Test: 2.1–2.4

To find out how well you understand the chapter material to this point, take this brief test. The answers, and the section where the material was initially discussed, are given in the back of the book. Review any questions that you answered incorrectly.

In Exercises 1 and 2, combine like terms.

1. $5x - 9y - 12 + 4y - 7x + 6$ $-2x - 5y - 6$

2. $\dfrac{2}{5}x - 8 - \dfrac{3}{4}x + \dfrac{1}{2}$ $-\dfrac{7}{20}x - \dfrac{15}{2}$

In Exercises 3 and 4, use the distributive property to remove parentheses.

3. $-4(2a - 3b + 6)$ $-8a + 12b - 24$

4. $1.6(2.1x - 3.4y - 5.2)$ $3.36x - 5.44y - 8.32$

5. Simplify $5(t - 3) - 3(t + 7) - 2$. $2t - 38$

6. Is $x = 2$ a solution of $3(x - 4) = -2(x + 1)$?   yes

7. Is $p = \dfrac{2}{5}$ a solution of $7p - 3 = 2p - 5$?   no

In Exercises 8–10, solve each equation and check your solution.

8. $x - 5 = -9$ -4

9. $12 + x = -4$ -16

10. $-16 = 7 + y$ -23

11. When solving the equation $\dfrac{x}{4} = 5$, what would you do to isolate the variable? Explain.   Multiply both sides by 4.

In Exercises 12–15, solve each equation and check your solution.

12. $6 = 12y$ $\dfrac{1}{2}$

13. $\dfrac{x}{8} = 3$ 24

14. $-\dfrac{x}{5} = -2$ 10

15. $-x = \dfrac{3}{7}$ $-\dfrac{3}{7}$

In Exercises 16–20, solve each equation.

16. $6x - 3 = 12$ $\dfrac{5}{2}$

17. $-4 = -2w - 7$ $-\dfrac{3}{2}$

18. $\dfrac{3}{4} = \dfrac{4n - 1}{6}$ $\dfrac{11}{8}$

19. $-5(x + 4) - 7 = 3$ -6

20. $8 - 9(y + 4) + 6 = -2$ $-\dfrac{20}{9}$

2.5 Solving Linear Equations with the Variable on Both Sides of the Equation

1. Solve equations with the variable on both sides of the equal sign.

2. Solve equations containing decimal numbers or fractions.

3. Identify identities and contradictions.

1 Solve Equations with the Variable on Both Sides of the Equal Sign

The equation $4x + 6 = 2x + 4$ contains the variable, x, on both sides of the equal sign. To solve equations of this type, we must use the appropriate properties to rewrite the equation with all terms containing the variable on only one side of the equal sign and all terms not containing the variable on the other side of the equal sign. Following is a general procedure, similar to the one outlined in Section 2.4, that can be used to solve linear equations with the variable on both sides of the equal sign. The steps in the procedure are only guidelines to use. For example, there may be times when you may choose to use the distributive property, step 2, before multiplying both sides of the equation by the LCD, step 1. We will illustrate this in Examples 8 and 9.

To Solve Linear Equations with the Variable on Both Sides of the Equal Sign

1. If the equation contains fractions, multiply **both** sides of the equation by the least common denominator. This will eliminate fractions from the equation.

2. Use the distributive property to remove parentheses.

3. Combine like terms on the same side of the equal sign.

4. Use the addition property to rewrite the equation with all terms containing the variable on one side of the equal sign and all terms not containing the variable on the other side of the equal sign. It may be necessary to use the addition property twice to accomplish this goal. You will eventually get an equation of the form $ax = b$.

5. Use the multiplication property to isolate the variable. This will give a solution of the form $x = $ some number.

6. Check the solution in the original equation.

The steps listed on page 129 are basically the same as the steps listed in the boxed procedure on page 120, except that in step 4 you may need to use the addition property more than once to obtain an equation of the form $ax = b$.

Remember that our goal in solving an equation is to isolate the variable, that is, to get the variable alone on one side of the equation.

Consider the equation $3x + 4 = x + 12$ which contains no fractions or parentheses, and no like terms on the same side of the equal sign. Therefore, we start with step 4, the addition property. We will use the addition property twice in order to obtain an equation where the variable appears on only one side of the equal sign. We begin by subtracting x from both sides of the equation to get all the terms containing the variable on the left side of the equation. This will give the following:

TEACHING TIP
Point out that once the x is subtracted from both sides of the equation the resulting equation is just like those we solved in the previous section.

Equation

$$3x + 4 = x + 12$$
$$3x - x + 4 = x - x + 12 \quad \text{Addition property}$$
$$\text{or} \quad 2x + 4 = 12 \quad \text{Variable appears only on left side of equal sign.}$$

Notice that the variable, x, now appears on only one side of the equation. However, $+4$ still appears on the same side of the equal sign as the $2x$. We use the addition property a second time to get the term containing the variable by itself on one side of the equation. Subtracting 4 from both sides of the equation gives $2x = 8$, which is an equation of the form $ax = b$.

Equation

$$2x + 4 = 12$$
$$2x + 4 - 4 = 12 - 4 \quad \text{Addition property}$$
$$2x = 8 \quad \text{x-term is now isolated.}$$

The x-term, $2x$, is now by itself on one side of the equation. Therefore, we have isolated the x-term on the left side of the equation. We can now use the multiplication property, step 5, to isolate the variable and solve the equation for x. We divide both sides of the equation by 2 to isolate the variable and solve the equation.

$$2x = 8$$
$$\frac{2x}{2} = \frac{8}{2} \quad \text{Multiplication property}$$
$$x = 4 \quad \text{x is now isolated.}$$

The solution to the equation is 4.

EXAMPLE 1 ▶ Solve the equation $4x + 6 = 2x + 4$.

Solution We start by getting all the terms with the variable on one side of the equal sign and all terms without the variable on the other side. The terms with the variable may be collected on either side of the equal sign. Many methods can be used to get the terms with the variable by themselves on one side of the equal sign. We will illustrate two. In method 1, we will collect all terms with the variable on the left side of the equation. In method 2, we will collect all terms with the variable on the right side of the equation. In both methods, we will follow the steps given in the box on page 129. Since this equation does not contain fractions or parentheses, and there are no like terms on the same side of the equal sign, we begin with step 4.

INSTRUCTOR EXAMPLE
Solve the equation
$4x - 10 = 5x - 15$.
Ans.: $x = 5$

Method 1: Isolate the variable term on the left.

$$4x + 6 = 2x + 4$$
Step 4 $$4x - 2x + 6 = 2x - 2x + 4 \quad \text{Subtract 2x from both sides.}$$
$$2x + 6 = 4$$

Step 4 $\qquad$ $2x + 6 \boxed{-6} = 4 \boxed{-6}$ $\qquad$ *Subtract 6 from both sides.*

$$2x = -2$$

Step 5 $\qquad$ $\dfrac{2x}{2} = \dfrac{-2}{2}$ $\qquad$ *Divide both sides by 2.*

$$x = -1$$

Method 2: Isolate the variable term on the right.

$$4x + 6 = 2x + 4$$

Step 4 $\qquad$ $4x \boxed{-4x} + 6 = 2x \boxed{-4x} + 4$ $\qquad$ *Subtract 4x from both sides.*

$$6 = -2x + 4$$

Step 4 $\qquad$ $6 \boxed{-4} = -2x + 4 \boxed{-4}$ $\qquad$ *Subtract 4 from both sides.*

$$2 = -2x$$

Step 5 $\qquad$ $\dfrac{2}{-2} = \dfrac{-2x}{-2}$ $\qquad$ *Divide both sides by −2.*

$$-1 = x$$

The same answer is obtained whether we collect the terms with the variable on the left or right side. However, we need to divide both sides of the equation by a negative number in method 2.

Step 6   Check: $\qquad\qquad 4x + 6 = 2x + 4$

$$4(-1) + 6 \stackrel{?}{=} 2(-1) + 4$$

$$-4 + 6 \stackrel{?}{=} -2 + 4$$

$$2 = 2 \qquad \textit{True}$$

Since the check is true, the solution is −1.

▶ **Now Try Exercise 19**

TEACHING TIP
Since there is more than one way to arrive at the correct answer, you may wish to suggest that students choose a style to use when solving equations. Some wish to solve so the variable is isolated on the left side of the equations. Others may wish to avoid dividing by a negative number so the variable is isolated on whichever side has a larger quantity of the variable. You may wish to indicate which method you prefer.

EXAMPLE 2 ▶ Solve the equation $2x - 3 - 5x = 13 + 4x - 2$.

Solution   We will choose to collect the terms containing the variable on the right side of the equation in order to create a positive coefficient of x. Since there are like terms *on the same side of the equal sign*, we will begin by combining these like terms.

$$2x - 3 - 5x = 13 + 4x - 2$$

INSTRUCTOR EXAMPLE
Solve the equation
$4x + 2 - 6x = 28 + 8x + 4$.
Ans.: $x = -3$

Step 3 $\qquad$ $-3x - 3 = 4x + 11$ $\qquad$ *Like terms were combined.*

Step 4 $\qquad$ $-3x \boxed{+3x} - 3 = 4x \boxed{+3x} + 11$ $\qquad$ *Add 3x to both sides.*

$$-3 = 7x + 11$$

Step 4 $\qquad$ $-3 \boxed{-11} = 7x + 11 \boxed{-11}$ $\qquad$ *Subtract 11 from both sides.*

$$-14 = 7x$$

Step 5 $\qquad$ $\dfrac{-14}{7} = \dfrac{7x}{7}$ $\qquad$ *Divide both sides by 7.*

$$-2 = x$$

Step 6   Check: $\qquad\quad 2x - 3 - 5x = 13 + 4x - 2$

$$2(-2) - 3 - 5(-2) \stackrel{?}{=} 13 + 4(-2) - 2$$

$$-4 - 3 + 10 \stackrel{?}{=} 13 - 8 - 2$$

$$-7 + 10 \stackrel{?}{=} 5 - 2$$

$$3 = 3 \qquad \textit{True}$$

Since the check is true, the solution is −2.

▶ **Now Try Exercise 29**

The solution to Example 2 could be condensed as follows:

$$2x - 3 - 5x = 13 + 4x - 2$$

$$-3x - 3 = 4x + 11 \qquad \text{\textcolor{red}{Like terms were combined.}}$$

$$-3 = 7x + 11 \qquad \text{\textcolor{red}{3x was added to both sides.}}$$

$$-14 = 7x \qquad \text{\textcolor{red}{11 was subtracted from both sides.}}$$

$$-2 = x \qquad \text{\textcolor{red}{Both sides were divided by 7.}}$$

We solved Example 2 by moving the terms containing the variable to the right side of the equation. Now rework the problem by moving the terms containing the variable to the left side of the equation. You should obtain the same answer.

EXAMPLE 3 ▶ Solve the equation $2(p + 3) = -3p + 10$.

Solution

$$2(p + 3) = -3p + 10$$

Step 2 $\qquad 2p + 6 = -3p + 10 \qquad$ *Distributive property was used.*

Step 4 $\qquad 2p + 3p + 6 = -3p + 3p + 10 \qquad$ *Add 3p to both sides.*

$$5p + 6 = 10$$

Step 4 $\qquad 5p + 6 - 6 = 10 - 6 \qquad$ *Subtract 6 from both sides.*

$$5p = 4$$

Step 5 $\qquad \dfrac{5p}{5} = \dfrac{4}{5} \qquad$ *Divide both sides by 5.*

$$p = \dfrac{4}{5}$$

The solution is $\dfrac{4}{5}$.

▶ **Now Try Exercise 27**

INSTRUCTOR EXAMPLE
Solve the equation
$3(p + 2) = 5p - 19$.
Ans.: $p = \dfrac{25}{2}$

The solution to Example 3 could be condensed as follows:

$$2(p + 3) = -3p + 10$$

$$2p + 6 = -3p + 10 \qquad \text{\textcolor{red}{Distributive property was used.}}$$

$$5p + 6 = 10 \qquad \text{\textcolor{red}{3p was added to both sides.}}$$

$$5p = 4 \qquad \text{\textcolor{red}{6 was subtracted from both sides.}}$$

$$p = \dfrac{4}{5} \qquad \text{\textcolor{red}{Both sides were divided by 5.}}$$

Helpful Hint

After the distributive property was used in Example 3, we obtained the equation $2p + 6 = -3p + 10$. Then we had to decide whether to collect terms with the variable on the left or the right side of the equal sign. If we wish the sum of the terms containing a variable to be positive, we use the addition property to eliminate the variable term with the *smaller* numerical coefficient from one side of the equation. Since -3 is smaller than 2, we added $3p$ to both sides of the equation. This eliminated $-3p$ from the right side of the equation and resulted in the sum of the variable terms on the left side of the equation, $5p$, being positive.

EXAMPLE 4 ▶ Solve the equation $2(x - 5) + 3 = 3x + 9$.

Solution $\qquad\qquad 2(x - 5) + 3 = 3x + 9$

Step 2 $\qquad 2x - 10 + 3 = 3x + 9 \qquad$ *Distributive property was used.*

Step 3 $\qquad 2x - 7 = 3x + 9 \qquad$ *Like terms were combined.*

Step 4 $\qquad\qquad -7 = x + 9 \qquad$ *2x was subtracted from both sides.*

Step 4 $\qquad\qquad -16 = x \qquad$ *9 was subtracted from both sides.*

INSTRUCTOR EXAMPLE
Solve the equation
$3(x - 7) + 2 = 4x + 4$.
Ans.: $x = -23$

The solution is -16.

▶ **Now Try Exercise 35**

EXAMPLE 5 ▶ Solve the equation $7 - 2x + 5x = -2(-3x + 4)$.

Solution

$$7 - 2x + 5x = -2(-3x + 4)$$

Step 2	$7 - 2x + 5x = 6x - 8$	*Distributive property was used.*
Step 3	$7 + 3x = 6x - 8$	*Like terms were combined.*
Step 4	$7 = 3x - 8$	*3x was subtracted from both sides.*
Step 4	$15 = 3x$	*8 was added to both sides.*
Step 5	$5 = x$	*Both sides were divided by 3.*

The solution is 5.

▶ **Now Try Exercise 63**

2   Solve Equations Containing Decimal Numbers or Fractions

Now we will solve an equation that contains decimal numbers. As explained in the previous section, equations containing decimal numbers may be solved by a number of different procedures. We will illustrate two procedures for solving Example 6.

EXAMPLE 6 ▶ Solve the equation $5.74x + 5.42 = 2.24x - 9.28$.

Solution

Method 1 We first notice that there are no like terms on the same side of the equal sign that can be combined. We will elect to collect the terms containing the variable on the left side of the equation.

$$5.74x + 5.42 = 2.24x - 9.28$$

Step 4 $5.74x - 2.24x + 5.42 = 2.24x - 2.24x - 9.28$ *Subtract 2.24x from both sides.*

$$3.50x + 5.42 = -9.28$$

Step 4 $3.50x + 5.42 - 5.42 = -9.28 - 5.42$ *Subtract 5.42 from both sides.*

$$3.50x = -14.70$$

Step 5 $\dfrac{3.50x}{3.50} = \dfrac{-14.70}{3.50}$ *Divide both sides by 3.50.*

$$x = -4.20$$

The solution is -4.20.

Method 2 In the previous section, we introduced a procedure to eliminate decimal numbers from equations. If the equation contains decimals given in tenths, multiply both sides of the equation by 10. If the equation contains decimals given in hundredths, multiply both sides of the equation by 100, and so on. Since the given equation has numbers given in hundredths, we will multiply both sides of the equation by 100.

$$5.74x + 5.42 = 2.24x - 9.28$$

$100(5.74x + 5.42) = 100(2.24x - 9.28)$ *Multiply both sides by 100.*

$100(5.74x) + 100(5.42) = 100(2.24x) - 100(9.28)$ *Distributive property*

$$574x + 542 = 224x - 928$$

Step 4 $574x + 542 - 542 = 224x - 928 - 542$ *Subtract 542 from both sides.*

$$574x = 224x - 1470$$

Step 4 $574x - 224x = 224x - 224x - 1470$ *Subtract 224x from both sides.*

$$350x = -1470$$

Step 5 $\dfrac{350x}{350} = \dfrac{-1470}{350}$ *Divide both sides by 350.*

$$x = -4.20$$

Notice we obtain the same answer using either method. You may use either method to solve equations of this type.

▶ **Now Try Exercise 25**

Now let's solve some equations that contain fractions.

EXAMPLE 7 ▶ Solve the equation $\frac{1}{2}a = \frac{3}{4}a + \frac{1}{5}$.

Solution

Step 1   In this equation we are solving for a. The least common denominator is 20. Begin by multiplying both sides of the equation by the LCD.

$$\frac{1}{2}a = \frac{3}{4}a + \frac{1}{5}$$

Step 2 $\boxed{20}\left(\frac{1}{2}a\right) = \boxed{20}\left(\frac{3}{4}a + \frac{1}{5}\right)$ *Multiply both sides by the LCD, 20.*

Step 3 $10a = \overset{5}{\cancel{20}}\left(\frac{3}{\cancel{4}}a\right) + \overset{4}{\cancel{20}}\left(\frac{1}{\cancel{5}}\right)$ *Distributive property*

$$10a = 15a + 4$$

Step 4 $-5a = 4$ *15a was subtracted from both sides.*

Step 5 $a = -\frac{4}{5}$ *Both sides were divided by −5.*

Step 6   Check: $\frac{1}{2}a = \frac{3}{4}a + \frac{1}{5}$

$$\frac{1}{2}\left(-\frac{4}{5}\right) \overset{?}{=} \frac{3}{4}\left(-\frac{4}{5}\right) + \frac{1}{5}$$

$$-\frac{2}{5} \overset{?}{=} -\frac{3}{5} + \frac{1}{5}$$

$$-\frac{2}{5} = -\frac{2}{5} \qquad \textit{True}$$

The solution is $-\frac{4}{5}$.

▶ **Now Try Exercise 43**

Helpful Hint

The equation in Example 7, $\frac{1}{2}a = \frac{3}{4}a + \frac{1}{5}$ could have been written as $\frac{a}{2} = \frac{3a}{4} + \frac{1}{5}$ because $\frac{1}{2}a$ is the same as $\frac{a}{2}$, and $\frac{3}{4}a$ is the same as $\frac{3a}{4}$. You would solve the equation $\frac{a}{2} = \frac{3a}{4} + \frac{1}{5}$ the same way you solved the equation in Example 7.

You would begin by multiplying both sides of the equation by the LCD, 20.

EXAMPLE 8 ▶ Solve the equation $\frac{x}{4} + 3 = 2(x - 2)$.

Solution   We will begin by multiplying both sides of the equation by the LCD, 4.

$$\frac{x}{4} + 3 = 2(x - 2)$$

$$\boxed{4}\left(\frac{x}{4} + 3\right) = \boxed{4}[2(x - 2)]$$ *Multiply both sides by the LCD, 4.*

$$4\left(\frac{x}{4}\right) + 4(3) = 4[2(x - 2)] \qquad \text{\textit{\textcolor{red}{Distributive property (used on left)}}}$$

$$x + 12 = 8(x - 2)$$

$$x + 12 = 8x - 16 \qquad \text{\textit{\textcolor{red}{Distributive property (used on right)}}}$$

$$12 = 7x - 16 \qquad \text{\textit{\textcolor{red}{x was subtracted from both sides.}}}$$

$$28 = 7x \qquad \text{\textit{\textcolor{red}{16 was added to both sides.}}}$$

$$4 = x \qquad \text{\textit{\textcolor{red}{Both sides were divided by 7.}}}$$

A check will show that 4 is the solution.

▶ **Now Try Exercise 61**

Helpful Hint

Notice the equation in Example 8 had *two terms* on the left side of the equal sign, $\frac{x}{4}$ and 3.

The equation had only *one term* on the right side of the equal sign, $2(x - 2)$. Therefore, after we multiplied both sides of the equation by 4, the next step was to use the distributive property on the left side of the equation.

In Example 8, we began the solution by multiplying both sides of the equation by the LCD. In Example 9, we will solve the same equation, but this time we will begin by using the distributive property.

EXAMPLE 9 ▶ Solve the equation in Example 8, $\frac{x}{4} + 3 = 2(x - 2)$, by first using the distributive property.

Solution   Begin by using the distributive property.

$$\frac{x}{4} + 3 = 2(x - 2)$$

$$\frac{x}{4} + 3 = 2x - 4 \qquad \text{\textit{\textcolor{red}{Distributive property}}}$$

$$4\left(\frac{x}{4} + 3\right) = 4(2x - 4) \qquad \text{\textit{\textcolor{red}{Multiply both sides by the LCD, 4.}}}$$

$$4\left(\frac{x}{4}\right) + 4(3) = 4(2x) - 4(4) \qquad \text{\textit{\textcolor{red}{Distributive property (used on left and right)}}}$$

$$x + 12 = 8x - 16$$

$$12 = 7x - 16 \qquad \text{\textit{\textcolor{red}{x was subtracted from both sides.}}}$$

$$28 = 7x \qquad \text{\textit{\textcolor{red}{16 was added to both sides.}}}$$

$$4 = x \qquad \text{\textit{\textcolor{red}{Both sides were divided by 7.}}}$$

The solution is 4.

▶ **Now Try Exercise 65**

Notice that we obtained the same answer in Examples 8 and 9. You may work problems of this type using either procedure unless your instructor asks you to work problems of this type using a specific method.

EXAMPLE 10 ▶ Solve the equation $\frac{1}{2}(2x + 3) = \frac{2}{3}(x - 6) + 4$.

Notice that this equation contains one term on the left side of the equal sign and two terms on the right side of the equal sign.

Solution   We will work this problem by first using the distributive property.

$$\frac{1}{2}(2x + 3) = \frac{2}{3}(x - 6) + 4$$

$$\frac{1}{2}(2x) + \frac{1}{2}(3) = \frac{2}{3}(x) - \frac{2}{3}(\overset{2}{6}) + 4 \qquad \textit{Distributive property (used on left and right)}$$

$$x + \frac{3}{2} = \frac{2}{3}x - 4 + 4$$

$$x + \frac{3}{2} = \frac{2}{3}x \qquad \textit{Like terms were combined.}$$

$$6\left(x + \frac{3}{2}\right) = 6\left(\frac{2}{3}x\right) \qquad \textit{Multiply both sides by the LCD, 6.}$$

$$6x + 6\left(\frac{3}{2}\right) = 6\left(\frac{2}{3}x\right) \qquad \textit{Using the distributive property}$$

$$6x + \overset{3}{6}\left(\frac{3}{2}\right) = \overset{2}{6}\left(\frac{2}{3}x\right)$$

$$6x + 9 = 4x$$

$$2x + 9 = 0 \qquad \textit{4x was subtracted from both sides.}$$

$$2x = -9 \qquad \textit{9 was subtracted from both sides.}$$

$$x = -\frac{9}{2} \qquad \textit{Both sides were divided by 2.}$$

Check: Substitute $-\dfrac{9}{2}$ for each x in the equation.

$$\frac{1}{2}(2x + 3) = \frac{2}{3}(x - 6) + 4$$

$$\frac{1}{2}\left[2\left(-\frac{9}{2}\right) + 3\right] \overset{?}{=} \frac{2}{3}\left(-\frac{9}{2} - 6\right) + 4$$

$$\frac{1}{2}(-9 + 3) \overset{?}{=} \frac{2}{3}\left(-\frac{9}{2} - \frac{12}{2}\right) + 4$$

$$\frac{1}{2}(-6) \overset{?}{=} \frac{2}{3}\left(-\frac{21}{2}\right) + 4$$

$$-3 \overset{?}{=} -7 + 4$$

$$-3 = -3 \qquad \textit{True}$$

The solution is $-\dfrac{9}{2}$.

▶ **Now Try Exercise 75**

In Example 10, we began by using the distributive property. We could have also begun by multiplying both sides of the equation by the LCD, 6, before using the distributive property. Work Example 10 again now by first multiplying both sides of the equation by the LCD, 6. You should obtain the same answer, $x = -\dfrac{9}{2}$.

Example 10 could have also been written as $\dfrac{2x+3}{2} = \dfrac{2(x-6)}{3} + 4$. If you were given the equation in this form, you could begin by using the distributive property on $2(x-6)$ or you could begin by multiplying both sides of the equation by the LCD, 6. Because this is just another way of writing the equation in Example 10, the answer would be $-\dfrac{9}{2}$.

We will discuss solving equations containing fractions in more detail later in the book.

3 Identify Identities and Contradictions

Thus far all the equations we have solved have had a single value for a solution. Equations of this type are called **conditional equations**, for they are only true under specific conditions. Some equations, as in Example 11, are true for infinitely many values of x. Equations that are true for infinitely many values of x are called **identities**. A third type of equation, as in Example 12, has no solution and is called a **contradiction**.

EXAMPLE 11 ▶ Solve the equation $5x - 5 - 2x = 3(x-2) + 1$.

Solution

$$5x - 5 - 2x = 3(x-2) + 1$$
$$5x - 5 - 2x = 3x - 6 + 1 \qquad \textit{Distributive property was used.}$$
$$3x - 5 = 3x - 5 \qquad \textit{Like terms were combined.}$$

Since the same expression appears on both sides of the equal sign, the statement is true for infinitely many values of x. If we continue to solve this equation further, we might obtain

$$3x - 5 = 3x - 5$$
$$3x = 3x \qquad \textit{5 was added to both sides.}$$
$$0 = 0 \qquad \textit{3x was subtracted from both sides.}$$

NOTE: The solution process could have been stopped at $3x - 5 = 3x - 5$. Since one side is identical to the other side, the equation is true for infinitely many values of x. *The solution to this equation is all real numbers.* **When solving an equation like the equation in Example 11, that is always true, write your answer as "all real numbers."**

▶ **Now Try Exercise 47**

EXAMPLE 12 ▶ Solve the equation $-2x + 5 + 3x = 5x - 4x + 7$.

Solution

$$-2x + 5 + 3x = 5x - 4x + 7$$
$$x + 5 = x + 7 \qquad \textit{Like terms were combined.}$$
$$x - x + 5 = x - x + 7 \qquad \textit{Subtract x from both sides.}$$
$$5 = 7 \qquad \textit{False}$$

NOTE: When solving an equation, if you obtain an obviously false statement, as in this example, the equation has *no solution*. No value of x will make the equation a true statement. **When solving an equation like the equation in Example 12, that is never true, write your answer as "no solution."** An answer left blank may be marked wrong.

▶ **Now Try Exercise 31**

Helpful Hint

Some students start solving equations correctly but do not complete the solution. Sometimes they are not sure that what they are doing is correct and they give up for lack of confidence. You must have confidence in yourself. As long as you follow the procedure on page 129, you should obtain the correct solution even if it takes quite a few steps. Remember two important things: (1) your goal is to isolate the variable, and (2) whatever you do to one side of the equation you must also do to the other side. That is, you must treat both sides of the equation equally.

EXERCISE SET 2.5

Concept/Writing Exercises   **2.** an equation that is true only under specific conditions

1. a) Write the general procedure for solving an equation that does not contain fractions where the variable appears on both sides of the equation.   Answers will vary.

    b) Refer to page 129 to see whether you omitted any steps.

2. What is a conditional equation?

3. a) What is an identity?

    b) What is the solution to the equation $3x + 5 = 3x + 5$?

4. When solving an equation, how will you know if the equation is an identity?

5. Explain why the equation $x + 5 = x + 5$ must be an identity.   Both sides are identical.

6. a) What is a contradiction?   an equation that has no solution

    b) What is the solution to a contradiction?   no solution

7. When solving an equation, how will you know if the equation has no solution?   will obtain a false statement

8. Explain why the equation $x + 5 = x + 4$ must be a contradiction.   Subtract x from both sides; $5 \neq 4$.

9. a) Explain, step-by-step, how to solve the equation $4x + 3(x + 2) = 5x - 10$.   Answers will vary.

    b) Solve the equation by following the steps you listed in part **a)**. -8

10. a) Explain, step-by-step, how to solve the equation $4(x + 3) = 6(x - 5)$.   Answers will vary.

    b) Solve the equation by following the steps you listed in part **a)**.   21

3. a) an equation that is true for infinitely many values of the variable   **b)** all real numbers
4. The same expression will appear on both sides of the equation.

Practice the Skills

Solve each equation.

11. $3x = -2x + 15$ 3

12. $x + 4 = 2x - 7$ 11

13. $-4x + 10 = 6x$ 1

14. $3a = 4a + 8$ -8

15. $5x + 3 = 6$ $\dfrac{3}{5}$

16. $-6x = 2x + 16$ -2

17. $21 - 6p = 3p - 2p$ 3

18. $8 - 3x = 4x + 50$ -6

19. $2x - 4 = 3x - 6$ 2

20. $5x + 7 = 3x + 5$ -1

21. $6 - 2y = 9 - 8y + 6y$ no solution

22. $-4 + 2y = 2y - 6 + y$ 2

23. $124.8 - 9.4x = 4.8x + 32.5$ 6.5

24. $9 - 0.5x = 4.5x + 8.5$ 0.1

25. $0.62x - 0.65 = 9.75 - 2.63x$ 3.2

26. $8.71 - 2.44x = 11.02 - 5.74x$ 0.7

27. $5x + 3 = 2(x + 6)$ 3

28. $x - 14 = 3(x + 2)$ -10

29. $4y - 2 - 8y = 19 + 5y - 3$ -2

30. $3x - 5 + 9x = 2 + 4x + 9$ 2

31. $2(x - 2) = 4x - 6 - 2x$ no solution

32. $4r = 10 - 2(r - 4)$ 3

33. $-(w + 2) = -6w + 32$ $\dfrac{34}{5}$

34. $7(-3m + 5) = 3(10 - 6m)$ $\dfrac{5}{3}$

35. $-3(2t - 5) + 5 = 3t + 13$ $\dfrac{7}{9}$

36. $4(x - 3) + 2 = 2x + 8$ 9

37. $\dfrac{a}{5} = \dfrac{a - 3}{2}$ 5

38. $\dfrac{b}{16} = \dfrac{b - 6}{4}$ 8

39. $\dfrac{n}{10} = 9 - \dfrac{n}{5}$ 30

40. $6 - \dfrac{x}{4} = \dfrac{x}{8}$ 16

41. $\dfrac{5}{2} - \dfrac{x}{3} = 3x$ $\dfrac{3}{4}$

42. $\dfrac{x}{4} - 3 = -2x$ $\dfrac{4}{3}$

43. $\dfrac{5}{8} + \dfrac{1}{4}a = \dfrac{1}{2}a$ $\dfrac{5}{2}$

44. $\dfrac{3}{4}x + \dfrac{1}{2} = \dfrac{1}{2}x$ -2

45. $0.1(x + 10) = 0.3x - 4$ 25

46. $5(3.2x - 3) = 2(x - 4)$ $\dfrac{1}{2}$

47. $2(x + 4) = 4x + 3 - 2x + 5$ all real numbers

48. $3(y - 1) + 9 = 8y + 6 - 5y$ all real numbers

49. $5(3n + 3) = 2(5n - 4) + 6n$ 23

50. $-4(-3z - 5) = -(10z + 8) - 2z$ $-\dfrac{7}{6}$

51. $-(3 - p) = -(2p + 3)$ 0

52. $12 - 2x - 3(x + 2) = 4x + 6 - x$ 0

53. $-(x + 4) + 5 = 4x + 1 - 5x$ all real numbers

54. $18x + 3(4x - 9) = -6x + 81$ 3

55. $35(2x - 1) = 7(x + 4) + 3x$ $\dfrac{21}{20}$

56. $10(x - 10) + 5 = 5(2x - 20)$ no solution

57. $0.4(x + 0.7) = 0.6(x - 4.2)$ 14

58. $0.5(6x - 8) = 1.4(x - 5) - 0.2$ -2

59. $\dfrac{3}{5}x - 2 = x + \dfrac{1}{3}$ $-\dfrac{35}{6}$

60. $\dfrac{3}{5}x + 4 = \dfrac{1}{5}x + 5$ $\dfrac{5}{2}$

61. $\dfrac{y}{5} + 2 = 3(y - 4)$ 5

62. $2(x - 4) = \dfrac{x}{5} + 10$ 10

63. $12 - 3x + 7x = -2(-5x + 6)$ 4

64. $-2x - 3 - x = -3(-2x + 7)$ 2

65. $3(x - 6) - 4(3x + 1) = x - 22$ 0

66. $-2(-3x + 5) + 6 = 4(x - 2)$ -2

67. $5 + 2x = 6(x + 1) - 5(x - 3)$ 16

68. $4 - (6x + 6) = -(-2x + 10)$ 1

69. $7 - (-y - 5) = 2(y + 3) - 6(y + 1)$ $-\dfrac{12}{5}$

70. $12 - 6x + 3(2x + 3) = 2x + 5$ 8

71. $\dfrac{3}{5}(x - 6) = \dfrac{2}{3}(3x - 5)$ $-\dfrac{4}{21}$

72. $\dfrac{1}{2}(2d + 4) = \dfrac{1}{3}(4d - 4)$ 10

73. $\dfrac{3(2r-5)}{5} = \dfrac{3r-6}{4}$ $\dfrac{10}{3}$

74. $\dfrac{3(x-4)}{4} = \dfrac{5(2x-3)}{3}$ $\dfrac{24}{31}$

75. $\dfrac{2}{7}(5x+4) = \dfrac{1}{2}(3x-4)+1$ 30

76. $\dfrac{5}{12}(x+2) = \dfrac{2}{3}(2x+1)+\dfrac{1}{6}$ 0

77. $\dfrac{a-5}{2} = \dfrac{3a}{4}+\dfrac{a-25}{6}$ 4

78. $\dfrac{a-7}{3} = \dfrac{a+5}{2}-\dfrac{7a-1}{6}$ 5

79. a) Answers will vary, one example is $x + x + 1 = x + 2$.
80. a) Answers will vary, one example is $x + 2 = x + x + 1$.
81. a) Answers will vary, one example is $x + x + 1 = 2x + 1$.
82. a) Answers will vary, one example is $2x + 1 = x + x + 1$.

Problem Solving

79. a) Construct a *conditional equation* containing three terms on the left side of the equal sign and two terms on the right side of the equal sign.

  b) Explain how you know your answer to part **a)** is a conditional equation.   has a single solution

  c) Solve the equation.   For the example given in **a)**, $x = 1$.

80. a) Construct a *conditional equation* containing two terms on the left side of the equal sign and three terms on the right side of the equal sign.

  b) Explain how you know your answer to part **a)** is a conditional equation.   has a single solution

  c) Solve the equation.   For the example given in **a)**, $x = 1$.

81. a) Construct an *identity* containing three terms on the left side of the equal sign and two terms on the right side of the equal sign.

  b) Explain how you know your answer to part **a)** is an identity.   When simplified, both sides are the same.

  c) What is the solution to the equation?   all real numbers

82. a) Construct an *identity* containing two terms on the left side of the equal sign and three terms on the right side of the equal sign.

  b) Explain how you know your answer to part **a)** is an identity.   When simplified, both sides are the same.

  c) What is the solution to the equation?   all real numbers

83. a) Construct a *contradiction* containing three terms on the left side of the equal sign and two terms on the right side of the equal sign.

  b) Explain how you know your answer to part **a)** is a contradiction.   When simplified, you obtain a false statement.

  c) What is the solution to the equation?   no solution

84. a) Construct a *contradiction* containing three terms on the left side of the equal sign and four terms on the right side of the equal sign.

  b) Explain how you know your answer to part **a)** is a contradiction.   When simplified, you obtain a false statement.

  c) What is the solution to the equation?   no solution

83. a) Answers will vary, one example is $x + x + 1 = 2x + 2$.
84. a) Answers will vary, one example is $x + x + 2 = x + x + 2 + 1$.

Challenge Problems

85. Solve the equation $5❋ - 1 = 4❋ + 5❋$ for $❋$. $❋ = -\dfrac{1}{4}$

86. Solve the equation $2\triangle - 4 = 3\triangle + 5 - \triangle$ for $\triangle$.   no solution

87. Solve the equation $3☺ - 5 = 2☺ - 5 + ☺$ for $☺$.

88. Solve $-2(x + 3) + 5x = 3(4 - 2x) - (x + 2)$. $\dfrac{8}{5}$

89. Solve $4 - [5 - 3(x + 2)] = x - 3$. -4

87. all real numbers

Group Activity

Discuss and answer Exercise 90 as a group. In the next chapter, we will be discussing procedures for writing application problems as equations. Let's get some practice now.

90. Chocolate Bars Consider the following word problem. Mary Kay purchased two large chocolate bars. The total cost of the two chocolate bars was equal to the cost of one chocolate bar plus $6. Find the cost of one chocolate bar.

  a) Each group member: Represent this problem as an equation with the variable x. $2x = x + 6$

  b) Each group member: Solve the equation you determined in part **a)**. $6

  c) As a group, check your equation and your answer to make sure that it makes sense.

Cumulative Review Exercises

[1.5] **91.** Evaluate

  a) $|4|$ 4   **b)** $|-7|$ 7   **c)** $|0|$.   0

[1.9] **92.** Evaluate $\left(\dfrac{2}{3}\right)^5$ on your calculator. ≈ 0.131687243

[2.1] **93.** Explain the difference between factors and terms.

94. Simplify $2(x - 3) + 4x - (4 - x)$. $7x - 10$

[2.4] **95.** Solve $2(x - 3) + 4x - (4 - x) = 0$. $\dfrac{10}{7}$

96. Solve $(x + 4) - (4x - 3) = 16$. -3

93. Factors are expressions that are multiplied. Terms are expressions that are added.

2.6 Formulas

1 Use the simple interest formula and the distance formula.

2 Use geometric formulas.

3 Solve for a variable in a formula.

A **formula** is an equation commonly used to express a specific relationship mathematically. For example, the formula for the area of a rectangle is

$$\text{area} = \text{length} \cdot \text{width} \quad \text{or} \quad A = lw$$

To **evaluate a formula**, substitute the appropriate numerical values for the variables and perform the indicated operations.

1 Use the Simple Interest Formula and the Distance Formula

A formula commonly used in banking is the **simple interest formula**.

TEACHING TIP
Point out that the units for *r* and *t* are related. When *r* is given as the annual interest rate, *t* is given in years.

> ### Simple Interest Formula
> $$\text{interest} = \text{principal} \cdot \text{rate} \cdot \text{time} \quad \text{or} \quad i = prt$$

This formula is used to determine the simple interest, i, earned on some savings accounts, or the simple interest an individual must pay on certain loans. In the simple interest formula $i = prt$, p is the principal (the amount invested or borrowed), r is the interest rate in decimal form, and t is the amount of time of the investment or loan.

EXAMPLE 1 ▶ **Auto Loan** To buy a car, Mary Beth Orrange borrowed $10,000 from a bank for 3 years. The bank charged 5% simple annual interest for the loan. How much interest will Mary Beth owe the bank?

Solution   **Understand and Translate**   Since the bank charged simple interest, we use the simple interest formula to solve the problem. We are given that the rate, r, is 5%, or 0.05 in decimal form. The principal, p, is $10,000 and the time, t, is 3 years. We substitute these values in the simple interest formula and solve for the interest, i.

INSTRUCTOR EXAMPLE
How much simple interest will be owed on a $12,000 4-year loan at 6% simple interest?
Ans.: $2880

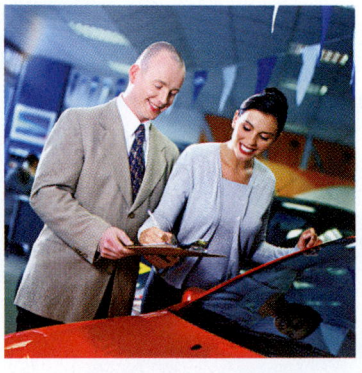

$$i = prt$$

Carry Out
$$i = 10,000(0.05)(3)$$

$$i = 1500$$

Check   There are various ways to check this problem. First ask yourself "Is the answer realistic?" $1500 is a realistic answer. The interest on $10,000 for 1 year at 5% is $500. Therefore for 3 years, an interest of $1500 is correct.

Answer   Mary Beth will pay $1500 interest. After 3 years, when she repays the loan, she will pay the principal, $10,000, plus the interest, $1500 for a total of $11,500.

▶ **Now Try Exercise 89**

EXAMPLE 2 ▶ **Savings Account** John Starmack invests $4000 in a savings account that earns simple interest for 2 years. If the interest earned from the account is $500, find the rate.

Solution   **Understand and Translate**   We use the simple interest formula, $i = prt$. We are given the principal, p, the time, t, and the interest, i. We are asked to find the rate, r. We substitute the given values in the simple interest formula and solve the resulting equation for r.

$$i = prt$$
$$500 = 4000(r)(2)$$

Carry Out

$$500 = 8000r$$
$$\frac{500}{8000} = \frac{8000r}{8000}$$
$$0.0625 = r$$

Check and Answer   The simple interest rate of 0.0625 or 6.25% per year is realistic. If we substitute $p = \$4000$, $r = 0.0625$ and $t = 2$, we obtain the interest, $i = \$500$. Thus, the answer checks. The simple interest rate is 6.25%.

▶ **Now Try Exercise 91**

We will use the simple interest formula again in Section 3.4.
    Another important formula is the distance formula.

Distance Formula

distance = rate · time   or $d = r \cdot t$

Example 3 illustrates the use of the distance formula.

EXAMPLE 3 ▶ **Auto Race**   At a NASCAR auto race, Dale Earnhart, Jr., completed the race in 3.2 hours at an average speed of 156.25 miles per hour. Determine the distance of the race.

Solution   **Understand and Translate**   We are given the rate, 156.25 miles per hour, and the time is 3.2 hours. We are asked to find the distance.

$$\text{distance} = \text{rate} \cdot \text{time}$$

Carry Out

$$= (156.25)(3.2) = 500$$

Answer   Thus, the distance of the race was 500 miles.

▶ **Now Try Exercise 95**

Let's look at the units in Example 3. The rate is given in miles per hour and the time is given in hours. If we analyze the units (a process called *dimensional analysis*), we see that the answer is given in miles.

$$\text{distance} = \text{rate} \cdot \text{time}$$
$$= \frac{\text{miles}}{\text{hour}} \cdot \text{hour}$$
$$= \text{miles}$$

We will use the distance formula again in Section 3.4.
    Now we will discuss geometric formulas that will be used throughout the book.

2 Use Geometric Formulas

The **perimeter**, P, is the sum of the lengths of the sides of a figure. Perimeters are measured in the same common unit as the sides. For example, perimeter may be measured in centimeters, inches, or feet. The **area**, A, is the total surface within the figure's boundaries. Areas are measured in square units. For example, area may be measured in square centimeters, square inches, or square feet. **Table 2.1** on page 142 gives the formulas for finding the areas and perimeters of triangles and quadrilaterals. **Quadrilateral** is a general name for a four-sided figure.
    In **Table 2.1**, the letter h is used to represent the *height* of the figure. In the figure of the trapezoid, the sides b and d are called the *bases* of the trapezoid. In the triangle, the side labeled b is called the *base* of the triangle.

TABLE 2.1	Formulas for Areas and Perimeters of Quadrilaterals and Triangles*		
Figure	**Sketch**	**Area**	**Perimeter**
Square	s	$A = s^2$	$P = 4s$
Rectangle	w l	$A = lw$	$P = 2l + 2w$
Parallelogram	h w l	$A = lh$	$P = 2l + 2w$
Trapezoid	b a h c d	$A = \frac{1}{2}h(b + d)$	$P = a + b + c + d$
Triangle	a h c b	$A = \frac{1}{2}bh$	$P = a + b + c$

FIGURE 2.2

EXAMPLE 4 ▶ **Building an Exercise Area** Dr. Alex Taurke, a veterinarian, decides to fence in a large rectangular area in the yard behind his office for exercising dogs that are boarded overnight. The part of the yard to be fenced in will be 40 feet long and 23 feet wide (see **Fig. 2.2**).

a) How much fencing is needed?

b) How large, in square feet, will the fenced in area be?

Solution

a) Understand To find the amount of fencing required, we need to find the perimeter of the rectangular area to be fenced in. To find the perimeter, P, substitute 40 for the length, l, and 23 for the width, w, in the perimeter formula, $P = 2l + 2w$.

$$P = 2l + 2w$$

Carry Out $\qquad P = 2(40) + 2(23) = 80 + 46 = 126$

Check and Answer By looking at **Figure 2.2**, we can see that a perimeter of 126 feet is a reasonable answer. Thus, 126 feet of fencing will be needed to fence in the area for the dogs to exercise.

b) To find the fenced in area, substitute 40 for the length and 23 for the width in the formula for the area of a rectangle. Both the length and width are measured in feet. Since we are multiplying an amount measured in feet by a second amount measured in feet, the answer will be in square feet (or ft^2).

$$A = lw$$

$$= 40(23) = 920 \text{ square feet (or } 920 \text{ ft}^2)$$

Based upon the data given, an area of 920 ft^2 is reasonable. The area to be fenced in will be 920 square feet.

▶ **Now Try Exercise 97**

*See Appendix C for additional information on geometry and geometric figures.

EXAMPLE 5 ▶ **Panoramic Photo** Heather Hunter enlarges rectangular panoramic photos, like the one shown below. One of her enlarged panoramic photos has a perimeter of 116 inches and a length of 40 inches. Find the width of the photo.

Solution   Understand and Translate   The perimeter, P, is 116 inches and the length, l, is 40 inches. Substitute these values into the formula for the perimeter of a rectangle and solve for the width, w.

$$P = 2l + 2w$$
$$116 = 2(40) + 2w$$

Carry Out

$$116 = 80 + 2w$$
$$116 - 80 = 80 - 80 + 2w \qquad \textit{Subtract 80 from both sides.}$$
$$36 = 2w$$
$$\frac{36}{2} = \frac{2w}{2} \qquad \textit{Divide both sides by 2.}$$
$$18 = w$$

Check and Answer   By considering what you know about panoramic photos, and comparing their length and width, you should realize that the dimensions of a length of 40 inches and a width of 18 inches is reasonable. The answer is, the width of the photo is 18 inches.

▶ **Now Try Exercise 25**

EXAMPLE 6 ▶ **Sailboat** A small sailboat has a triangular sail that has an area of 30 square feet and a base of 5 feet (see **Fig. 2.3**). Determine the height of the sail.

Solution   Understand and Translate   We use the formula for the area of a triangle given in **Table 2.1**.

$$A = \frac{1}{2}bh$$
$$30 = \frac{1}{2}(5)h$$

Carry Out

$$2 \cdot 30 = 2 \cdot \frac{1}{2}(5)h \qquad \textit{Multiply both sides by 2.}$$
$$60 = 5h$$
$$\frac{60}{5} = \frac{5h}{5} \qquad \textit{Divide both sides by 5.}$$
$$12 = h$$

FIGURE 2.3

Check and Answer   The height of the triangle is 12 feet. By looking at **Figure 2.3**, and by your knowledge of sailboat sails, you may realize that a sail 12 feet tall and 5 feet wide at the base is reasonable. Thus, the height of the sail is 12 feet.

▶ **Now Try Exercise 99**

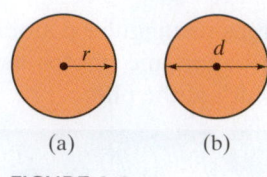

(a)   (b)

FIGURE 2.4

Another figure that we see and use daily is the circle. The **circumference**, C, is the length (or perimeter) of the curve that forms a circle. The **radius**, r, is the line segment from the center of the circle to any point on the circle (**Fig. 2.4a**). The **diameter** of a circle is a line segment through the center whose endpoints both lie on the circle (**Fig. 2.4b**). *Note that the length of the diameter is twice the length of the radius.*

The formulas for both the area and the circumference of a circle are given in **Table 2.2**.

TEACHING TIP
Have students write a formula for circumference based on diameter.

TABLE 2.2	Formulas for Circles	
Circle	**Area**	**Circumference**
	$A = \pi r^2$	$C = 2\pi r$

The value of **pi**, symbolized by the Greek lowercase letter π, is an irrational number which cannot be exactly expressed as a decimal number or a numerical fraction. Pi is *approximately* 3.14.

USING YOUR CALCULATOR

Scientific and graphing calculators have a key for finding the value of π. If you press the $\boxed{\pi}$ key, your calculator may display 3.1415927. This is only an approximation of π. If you own a scientific or graphing calculator, use the $\boxed{\pi}$ key when evaluating expressions containing π. If your calculator does not have a $\boxed{\pi}$ key, use 3.14 to approximate it. *When evaluating an expression containing π, we will use the $\boxed{\pi}$ key on a calculator to obtain the answer.* The final answer displayed in the text or answer section may therefore be slightly different (and more accurate) than yours if you use 3.14 for π.

EXAMPLE 7 ▶ **Pizza** A Pizza Hut large pizza has a diameter of 14 inches. Determine the area and circumference of the pizza.

INSTRUCTOR EXAMPLE
Find the area and circumference of a pizza with a 10-in. diameter.
Ans.: ≈78.5 in.², ≈31.4 in.

Solution   The radius is half its diameter, so $r = \dfrac{14}{2} = 7$ inches.

$A = \pi r^2$ $C = 2\pi r$

$A = \pi (7)^2$ $C = 2\pi (7)$

$A = \pi (49)$ $C \approx 43.98$ inches

$A \approx 153.94$ square inches

To obtain our answers 153.94 and 43.98, we used the $\boxed{\pi}$ key on a calculator and rounded our final answer to the nearest hundredth. If you do not have a calculator with a $\boxed{\pi}$ key and use 3.14 for π, your answer for the area would be 153.86.

▶ **Now Try Exercise 101**

Table 2.3 on page 145 gives formulas for finding the volume of certain **three-dimensional figures**. **Volume** may be considered the space occupied by a figure, and it is measured in cubic units, such as cubic centimeters or cubic feet.

EXAMPLE 8 ▶ **Spaceship Earth** The inside of Spaceship Earth at Epcot Center in Disney World, Florida, is a sphere with a diameter of 165 feet (see photo). Determine the volume of Spaceship Earth.

Solution   **Understand and Translate**   **Table 2.3** gives the formula for the volume of a sphere. The formula involves the radius. Since the diameter is 165 feet, its radius is $\dfrac{165}{2} = 82.5$ feet.

$$V = \frac{4}{3}\pi r^3$$

Carry Out $V = \frac{4}{3}\pi(82.5)^3 = \frac{4}{3}\pi(561,515.625) \approx 2,352,071.15$

Check and Answer The volume inside the sphere is very large, 2,352,071.15 cubic feet. Since a rollercoaster-type ride is inside the sphere, the volume must be very large, and so the answer is reasonable.

▶ **Now Try Exercise 109**

TABLE 2.3   Formulas for Volumes of Three-Dimensional Figures

Figure	Sketch	Volume
Rectangular solid		$V = lwh$
Right circular cylinder		$V = \pi r^2 h$
Right circular cone		$V = \frac{1}{3}\pi r^2 h$
Sphere		$V = \frac{4}{3}\pi r^3$

3 Solve for a Variable in a Formula

Often in this course and in other mathematics and science courses, you will be given an equation or formula solved for one variable and have to solve it for a different variable. We will now learn how to do this. This material will reinforce what you learned about solving equations earlier in this chapter. We will use the procedures learned here to solve problems in many other sections of the text.

To solve for a variable in a formula, treat each of the quantities, except the one for which you are solving, as if they were constants. Then solve for the desired variable by isolating it on one side of the equation.

EXAMPLE 9 ▶ **Distance Formula** Solve the distance formula $d = rt$ for t.

Solution We must get t all by itself on one side of the equal sign. Since t is multiplied by r, we divide both sides of the equation by r to isolate the t.

$$d = rt$$

$$\frac{d}{r} = \frac{rt}{r} \qquad \text{\textcolor{red}{Divide both sides by r.}}$$

$$\frac{d}{r} = t$$

Therefore, $t = \dfrac{d}{r}$.

Now Try Exercise 45

EXAMPLE 10 ▶ Perimeter of Rectangle The formula for the perimeter of a rectangle is $P = 2l + 2w$. Solve this formula for the length, l.

Solution   We must get l all by itself on one side of the equation. We begin by removing the $2w$ from the right side of the equation to isolate the term containing the l.

$$P = 2l + 2w$$

$$P - 2w = 2l + 2w - 2w \qquad \text{Subtract } 2w \text{ from both sides.}$$

$$P - 2w = 2l$$

$$\frac{P - 2w}{2} = \frac{2l}{2} \qquad \text{Divide both sides by 2.}$$

$$\frac{P - 2w}{2} = l \quad \left(\text{or} \quad l = \frac{P}{2} - w \right)$$

▶ **Now Try Exercise 53**

Some formulas contain fractions. When a formula contains a fraction, we can eliminate the fraction by multiplying both sides of the equation by the least common denominator, as illustrated in Example 11. We use the multiplication property of equality, as explained in Section 2.3.

EXAMPLE 11 ▶ The formula for the area of a triangle is $A = \dfrac{1}{2}bh$. Solve this formula for h.

Solution   We begin by multiplying both sides of the equation by the LCD, 2, to eliminate the fraction. We then isolate the variable h.

$$A = \frac{1}{2}bh$$

$$2 \cdot A = 2 \cdot \frac{1}{2}bh \qquad \text{Multiply both sides by 2.}$$

$$2A = bh$$

$$\frac{2A}{b} = \frac{bh}{b} \qquad \text{Divide both sides by } b.$$

$$\frac{2A}{b} = h$$

Thus, $h = \dfrac{2A}{b}$.

▶ **Now Try Exercise 51**

Write Equations in $y = mx + b$ Form

When discussing graphing later in this book, we will need to solve many equations for the variable y, and write the equation in the form $y = mx + b$, where m and b represent real numbers. Examples of equations in this form are $y = 2x + 4$, $y = -\dfrac{1}{2}x - 3$, and $y = \dfrac{4}{5}x + \dfrac{1}{3}$. The procedure to write equations in $y = mx + b$ form is illustrated in Examples 12 and 13.

EXAMPLE 12 ▶ Solve the equation $6x + 3y = 12$ for y. Write the answer in $y = mx + b$ form.

Solution   Begin by isolating the term containing the variable y.

Write the equation $12x - 4y = 20$ in
$y = mx + b$ form.
Ans.: $y = 3x - 5$

$$6x + 3y = 12$$

$$6x - 6x + 3y = 12 - 6x \qquad \textit{Subtract 6x from both sides.}$$

$$3y = 12 - 6x$$

$$\frac{3y}{3} = \frac{12 - 6x}{3} \qquad \textit{Divide both sides by 3.}$$

$$y = \frac{12 - 6x}{3}$$

$$y = \frac{12}{3} - \frac{6x}{3} \qquad \textit{Write as two fractions.}$$

$$y = 4 - 2x$$

$$y = -2x + 4$$

▶ **Now Try Exercise 67**

Helpful Hint

Notice that in Example 12, when we obtained $y = \dfrac{12 - 6x}{3}$, we had solved the equation for y since the y was isolated on one side of the equation. When we wrote the answer as $y = -2x + 4$, we wrote the equation in $y = mx + b$ form.

EXAMPLE 13 ▶ Solve the equation $y - \dfrac{1}{3} = \dfrac{1}{4}(x - 6)$ for y. Write the answer in $y = mx + b$ form.

Write the equation
$y - \dfrac{1}{2} = \dfrac{1}{3}(x - 3)$ in $y = mx + b$
form.
Ans.: $y = \dfrac{1}{3}x - \dfrac{1}{2}$

Solution Multiply both sides of the equation by the LCD, 12.

$$y - \frac{1}{3} = \frac{1}{4}(x - 6)$$

$$12\left(y - \frac{1}{3}\right) = 12 \cdot \frac{1}{4}(x - 6) \qquad \textit{Multiply both sides by 12.}$$

$$12y - 4 = 3(x - 6) \qquad \textit{Distributive property used on left}$$

$$12y - 4 = 3x - 18 \qquad \textit{Distributive property used on right}$$

$$12y = 3x - 14 \qquad \textit{Add 4 to both sides}$$

$$y = \frac{3x - 14}{12} \qquad \textit{Divided both sides by 12.}$$

$$y = \frac{3x}{12} - \frac{14}{12} \qquad \textit{Write as two fractions.}$$

$$y = \frac{1}{4}x - \frac{7}{6}$$

▶ **Now Try Exercise 79**

In Example 13, you may wish to use the distributive property on the right side of the equation before multiplying both sides of the equation by the LCD, 12. Try working the example using this method now to see which procedure you prefer.

EXERCISE SET 2.6

MathXL®   MyMathLab

Concept/Writing Exercises

1. an equation used to express a relationship mathematically
2. to substitute values and perform the indicated operations

1. What is a formula?

2. What does it mean to *evaluate a formula*?

3. Write the simple interest formula, then indicate what each letter in the formula represents. $i = prt$

4. What is a quadrilateral? a four-sided figure

5. Write the distance formula, then indicate what each letter in the formula represents. $d = rt$

6. What is the relationship between the radius and the diameter of a circle? The radius is one-half the diameter.

7. Is π equal to 3.14? Explain your answer.   no
8. a) What is the perimeter of a figure?
   b) What is the area of a figure?

9. By using any formula for area, explain why area is measured in square units.
10. By using any formula for volume, explain why volume is measured in cubic units.   When you multiply the same unit three times, you get a cubic unit.

8. a) the sum of the lengths of the sides of the figure   **b)** the total surface within the figure's boundaries   **9.** When you multiply a unit by the same unit, you get a square unit.

Practice the Skills

Use the formula to find the value of the variable indicated. Use a calculator to save time and where necessary, round your answer to the nearest hundredth.

11. $d = rt$ (distance formula); find d when $r = 60$ and $t = 4$.   240
12. $P = 4s$ (perimeter of a square); find P when $s = 6$.   24
13. $A = lw$ (area of a rectangle); find A when $l = 12$ and $w = 8$.   96
14. $A = s^2$ (area of a square); find A when $s = 7$.   49
15. $i = prt$ (simple interest formula); find i when $p = 2000$, $r = 0.06$, and $t = 3$.   360
16. $c = 2.54i$ (to change inches to centimeters); find c when $i = 12$.   30.48
17. $P = 2l + 2w$ (perimeter of a rectangle); find P when $l = 8$ and $w = 5$.   26
18. $f = 1.47m$ (to change speed from mph to ft/sec); find f when $m = 60$.   88.2
19. $A = \pi r^2$ (area of a circle); find A when $r = 5$.   78.54
20. $A = \dfrac{m + n}{2}$ (mean of two values); find A when $m = 16$ and $n = 56$.   36
21. $A = \dfrac{a + b + c}{3}$ (mean of three values); find A when $a = 72, b = 81$, and $c = 93$.   82

22. $p = i^2 r$ (formula for finding electrical power); find r when $p = 2000$ and $i = 4$.   125
23. $z = \dfrac{x - m}{s}$ (statistics formula for finding the z-score); find z when $x = 100, m = 80$, and $s = 10$.   2
24. $A = \dfrac{1}{2}bh$ (area of a triangle); find b when $A = 30$ and $h = 10$ 6
25. $P = 2l + 2w$ (perimeter of a rectangle); find l when $P = 28$ and $w = 6$.   8
26. $A = P(1 + rt)$ (banking formula to find the amount in an account); find r when $A = 1050, t = 1$, and $P = 1000$.   0.05
27. $V = \pi r^2 h$ (volume of a cylinder); find h when $V = 678.24$ and $r = 6$.   6.00
28. $V = \dfrac{4}{3}\pi r^3$ (volume of a sphere); find V when $r = 8$.   2144.66
29. $B = \dfrac{703w}{h^2}$ (for finding body mass index); find w when $B = 24$ and $h = 61$.   127.03
30. $S = C + rC$ (for determining selling price when an item is marked up); find S when $C = 160$ and $r = 0.12$ (or 12%).   179.2

In Exercises 31–36, use **Tables 2.1, 2.2,** *and* **2.3** *to find the formula for the area or volume of the figure. Then determine either the area or volume.*

31. 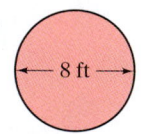 ≈ 50.27 ft^2

8 ft

32.   12 in.^{2}

4 in.

6 in.

33.   16.5 ft^2

4 ft

3 ft

7 ft

34.   60 ft^3

5 ft

4 ft

3 ft

35. ≈ 452.39 cm^3

4 cm

9 cm

36. ≈ 134.04 m^3

8 m

4 m

In Exercises 37 and 38, use the formula $C = \dfrac{5}{9}(F - 32)$ to find the Celsius temperature (C) equivalent to the given Fahrenheit temperature (F).

37. $F = 50°$ $C = 10°$

38. $F = 86°$ $C = 30°$

In Exercises 39 and 40, use the formula $F = \dfrac{9}{5}C + 32$, to find the Fahrenheit temperature (F) equivalent to the given Celsius temperature (C).

39. $C = 25°$ $F = 77°$

40. $C = 10°$ $F = 50°$

In Exercises 41–44, find the missing quantity. Use the ideal gas law, $P = KT/V$, where P is pressure, T is temperature, V is volume, and K is a constant.

41. $T = 20, K = 2, V = 1$ $P = 40$
43. $T = 30, P = 3, K = 0.5$ $V = 5$

42. $P = 80, T = 100, V = 5$ $K = 4$
44. $P = 100, K = 2, V = 6$ $T = 300$

In Exercises 45–66, solve for the indicated variable.

45. $A = lw$, for w $w = A/l$

46. $P = 4s$, for s $s = P/4$

47. $d = rt$, for t $t = d/r$

48. $C = \pi d$, for d $d = C/\pi$

49. $i = prt$, for t $t = i/(pr)$

50. $V = lwh$, for l $l = V/(wh)$

51. $A = \dfrac{1}{2}bh$, for b $b = 2A/h$

52. $E = IR$, for I $I = E/R$

53. $P = 2l + 2w$, for w $w = (P - 2l)/2$

54. $PV = KT$, for T $T = PV/K$

55. $3 - 2r = n$, for r $r = (-n + 3)/2$

56. $4m + 5n = 25$, for n $n = (-4m + 25)/5$

57. $y = mx + b$, for b $b = y - mx$

58. $y = mx + b$, for x $x = (y - b)/m$

59. $d = a + b + c$, for b $b = d - a - c$

60. $ax + by = c$, for y $y = (-ax + c)/b$

61. $ax + by + c = 0$, for y

62. $V = \pi r^2 h$, for h $h = V/(\pi r^2)$

63. $V = \dfrac{1}{3}\pi r^2 h$, for h $h = 3V/(\pi r^2)$

64. $A = \dfrac{m + 2d}{3}$, for d $d = \dfrac{3A - m}{2}$

65. $A = \dfrac{m + d}{2}$, for m $m = 2A - d$

66. $L = \dfrac{c + 2d}{4}$, for d $d = \dfrac{4L - c}{2}$

61. $y = (-ax - c)/b$

In Exercises 67–82, solve each equation for y. Write the answer in y = mx + b form. See Examples 12 and 13.

67. $2x + y = 5$ $y = -2x + 5$

68. $6x + 2y = -12$ $y = -3x - 6$

69. $-3x + 3y = -15$ $y = x - 5$

70. $-2y + 4x = -8$ $y = 2x + 4$

71. $4x = 6y - 8$ $y = \dfrac{2}{3}x + \dfrac{4}{3}$

72. $15 = 3y - x$ $y = \dfrac{1}{3}x + 5$

73. $5y = -10 + 3x$ $y = \dfrac{3}{5}x - 2$

74. $-2y = -3x - 18$ $y = \dfrac{3}{2}x + 9$

75. $-6y = 15 - 3x$ $y = \dfrac{1}{2}x - \dfrac{5}{2}$

76. $-12 = -2x - 3y$ $y = -\dfrac{2}{3}x + 4$

77. $-8 = -x - 2y$ $y = -\dfrac{1}{2}x + 4$

78. $4x + 3y = 20$ $y = -\dfrac{4}{3}x + \dfrac{20}{3}$

79. $y + 3 = -\dfrac{1}{3}(x - 4)$ $y = -\dfrac{1}{3}x - \dfrac{5}{3}$

80. $y - 3 = \dfrac{2}{3}(x + 4)$ $y = \dfrac{2}{3}x + \dfrac{17}{3}$

81. $y - \dfrac{1}{5} = 2\left(x + \dfrac{1}{3}\right)$ $y = 2x + \dfrac{13}{15}$

82. $y + 5 = \dfrac{3}{4}\left(x + \dfrac{1}{2}\right)$ $y = \dfrac{3}{4}x - \dfrac{37}{8}$

Problem Solving   **83.** stays the same   **89.** $1440

83. When using the distance formula, what happens to the distance if the rate is doubled and the time is halved? Explain.

84. When using the simple interest formula, what happens to the simple interest if both the principal and rate are doubled but the time is halved? Explain.   doubles

85. Consider the formula for the area of a square, $A = s^2$. If the length of the side of a square, s, is doubled, what is the change in its area? Explain.   4 times as large

86. Consider the formula for the volume of a cube, $V = s^3$. If the length of the side of a cube, s, is doubled, what is the change in its volume? Explain.   8 times as large

87. Which would have the greater area, a square whose side has a length of s inches, or a circle whose diameter has a length of s inches? Explain, using a sketch.   square

88. Which would have the greater area, a square whose diagonal has a length of s inches, or a circle whose diameter has a length of s inches? Explain, using a sketch.   circle

In Exercises 89–92, use the simple interest formula.

89. **Auto Loan** Thang Tran decided to borrow $6000 from Citibank to help pay for a car. His loan was for 3 years at a simple interest rate of 8%. How much interest will Thang pay?

90. **Simple Interest Loan** Holly Broesamle lent her brother $4000 for a period of 2 years. At the end of the 2 years, her brother repaid the $4000 plus $640 interest. What simple interest rate did her brother pay?   8%

91. **Savings Account** Mary Seitz invested a certain amount of money in a savings account paying 3% simple interest per year. When she withdrew her money at the end of 3 years, she received $450 in interest. How much money did Mary place in the savings account? $5000

92. **Savings Account** Peter Ostroushko put $6000 in a savings account earning $3\dfrac{1}{2}\%$ simple interest per year. When he withdrew his money, he received $840 in interest. How long had he left his money in the account?   4 yr

In Exercises 93–96, use the distance formula.

93. **Average Speed** On her way from Omaha, Nebraska, to Kansas City, Kansas, Peg Hovde traveled 150 miles in 3 hours. What was her average speed?   50 mph

94. **Walk** Lisa Feintech went for a walk where she walked at an average speed of 3.4 miles per hour for 2 hours. How far did she walk?   6.8 mi

95. **Fastest Car** The fastest speed recorded on land was about 763.2 miles per hour by a jet powered car called ThrustSSC. If, during the speed trial, the car traveled for 0.01 hour, how far had the car traveled?   7.632 mi

The ThrustSSC

96. **Fastest Plane** The fastest aircraft is the Lockheed SR-71 Blackbird. If, during the trial run, the plane covered a distance of 660 miles in 0.3 hours, determine the plane's average speed.   2200 mph

Use the formulas given in **Tables 2.1, 2.2,** *and* **2.3** *to work Exercises 97–110.*

97. DVD Player A portable DVD player has a screen with a length of 8 inches and a width (or height) of 6 inches. Determine the area of the screen.   48 in.²

98. Television A plasma television has a screen with a length of 34.9 inches and a width (or height) of 19.6 inches. Determine the perimeter of the screen.   109 in.

99. Yield Sign A yield traffic sign is triangular with a base of 36 inches and a height of 31 inches. Find the area of the sign.   558 in.²

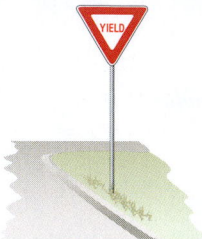

100. Fencing Milt McGowen has a rectangular lot that measures 100 feet by 60 feet. If Milt wants to fence in his lot, how much fencing will he need?   320 ft

101. Swimming Pool A circular above-ground swimming pool has a diameter of 24 feet. Determine the circumference of the pool.   ≈75.40 ft

102. Living Room Table A round living room table top has a diameter of 3 feet. Find the area of the table top.   ≈7.07 ft²

103. Kite Below we show a kite. Determine the area of the kite.   3 ft²

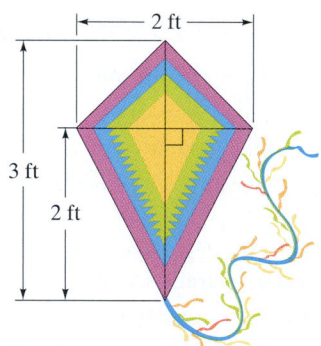

104. Suitcase A suitcase measures 26 inches long by 19.5 inches wide and 11 inches deep. Determine the volume of the suitcase.   5577 in.³

105. Trapezoidal Sign Canter Martin made a sign to display at a baseball game. The sign was in the shape of a trapezoid. Its bases are 4 feet and 3 feet, and its height is 2 feet. Find the area of the sign.   7 ft²

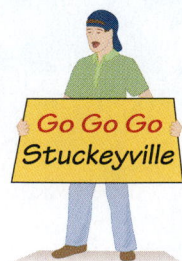

106. Jacuzzi The inside of a circular jacuzzi is 8 feet in diameter. If the water inside the jacuzzi is 3 feet deep, determine, in cubic feet, the volume of water in the jacuzzi.   ≈150.80 ft³

107. Banyan Tree The largest banyan tree in the continental United States is at the Edison House in Fort Myers, Florida. The circumference of the aerial roots of the tree is 390 feet. Find the *diameter* of the aerial roots to the nearest tenth of a foot.   ≈124.1 ft

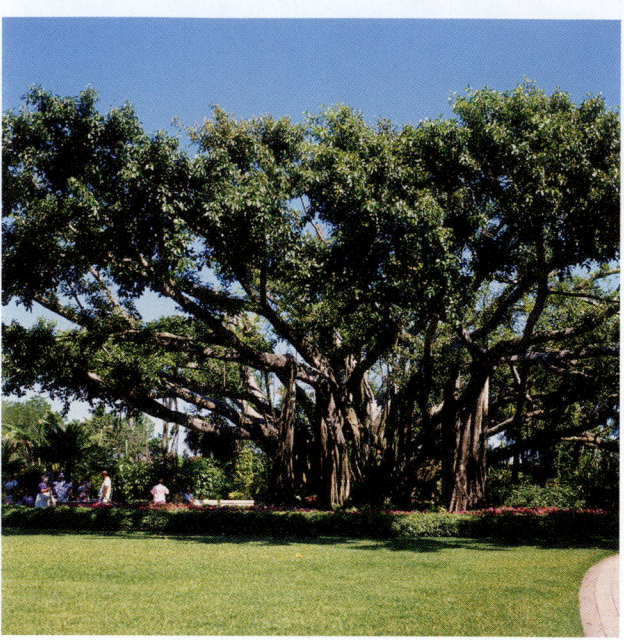

108. Amphitheater The seats in an amphitheater are inside a trapezoidal area as shown in the figure.

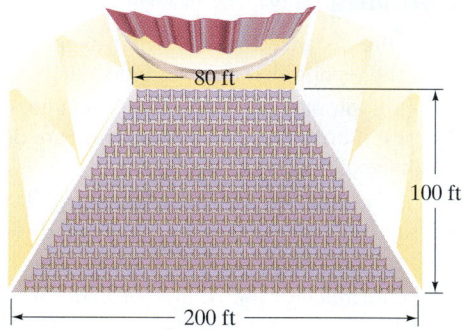

The bases of the trapezoidal area are 80 feet and 200 feet, and the height is 100 feet. Find the area of the floor occupied by seats.   14,000 ft²

109. Basketball Find the volume of a basketball if its diameter is 9 inches.   ≈381.7 in.³

110. Oil Drum Roberto Sanchez has an empty oil drum that he uses for storage. The oil drum is 4 feet high and has a diameter of 24 inches. Find the volume of the drum in cubic feet.   12.57 ft³

111. Body Mass Index A person's body mass index (BMI) is found by multiplying a person's weight, w, in pounds by 703, then dividing this product by the square of the person's height, h, in inches.

a) Write a formula to find the BMI. $B = \dfrac{703w}{h^2}$

b) Brandy Belmont is 5 feet 3 inches tall and weighs 135 pounds. Find her BMI.   ≈23.91

112. Body Mass Index Refer to Exercise 111. Mario Guzza's weight is 162 pounds, and he is 5 feet 7 inches tall. Find his BMI.   ≈25.37

Challenge Problems

113. Cereal Box A cereal box is to be made by folding the cardboard along the dashed lines as shown in the figure on the right.

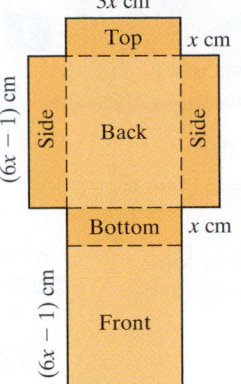

a) Using the formula

$$\text{volume} = \text{length} \cdot \text{width} \cdot \text{height}$$

write an equation for the volume of the box. $V = 18x^3 - 3x^2$

b) Find the volume of the box when $x = 7$ cm.   6027 cm³

c) Write an equation for the surface area of the box.
$S = 54x^2 - 8x$

d) Find the surface area when $x = 7$ cm.   2590 cm²

Group Activity

114. Square Face on Cube Consider the following photo. The front of the figure is a square with a smaller black square painted on the center of the larger square. Suppose the length of one side of the larger square is A, and length of one side of the smaller (the black square) is B. Also the thickness of the block is C.

a) Group member one: Determine an expression for the surface area of the black square. B^2

b) Group member two: Determine an expression for the surface area of the larger square (which includes the smaller square). A^2

c) Group member three: Determine the surface area of the larger square minus the black square (the purple area shown). $A^2 - B^2$

d) As a group, write an expression for the volume of the entire solid block. A^2C

e) As a group, determine the volume of the entire solid block if its length is 1.5 feet and its width is 0.8 feet.
1.8 ft³

Cumulative Review Exercises

[1.7] 115. Evaluate $-\dfrac{4}{15} + \dfrac{2}{5}$. $\dfrac{2}{15}$

116. Evaluate $-6 + 7 - 4 - 3$. -6

[1.9] 117. Evaluate. $[4(12 \div 2^2 - 3)^2]^2$.   0

[2.4] 118. Solve the equation $\dfrac{r}{2} + 2r = 20$.   8

2.7 Ratios and Proportions

1 Understand ratios.

2 Solve proportions using cross-multiplication.

3 Solve applications.

4 Use proportions to change units.

5 Use proportions to solve problems involving similar figures.

The Incredibles

1 Understand Ratios

A **ratio** is a quotient of two quantities. Ratios provide a way to compare two numbers or quantities. The ratio of the number a to the number b may be written

$$a \text{ to } b, \quad a:b, \quad \text{or} \quad \frac{a}{b}$$

where a and b are called the **terms of the ratio**. Notice that the symbol : can be used to indicate a ratio.

EXAMPLE 1 ▶ **Favorite Movies** Several children in sixth grade were asked to name their favorite movie of 2004. The results are indicated on the graph in **Figure 2.5**.

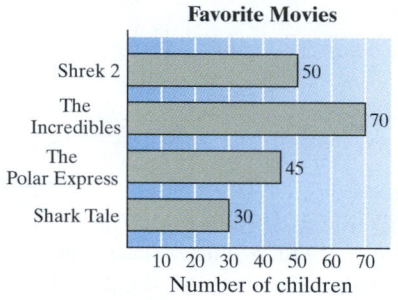

Favorite Movies

FIGURE 2.5

a) Find the ratio of the number of children who selected *The Incredibles* to those who selected *The Polar Express*. Then write the ratio in lowest terms.

b) Find the ratio of the number of children who selected *Shrek 2* to the total number in the survey.

Solution   We will use our five-step problem-solving procedure.

a) Understand and Translate   The ratio we are seeking is

Number who selected *The Incredibles* : Number who selected *The Polar Express*

Carry Out   We substitute the appropriate values into the ratio. This gives

$$70:45$$

To write the ratio in *lowest terms*, we simplify by dividing each number in the ratio by 5, the greatest number that divides both terms in the ratio. This gives

$$14:9$$

Check and Answer   Our division is correct. The ratio is $14:9$.

b) We use the same procedure as in part **a)**. Fifty children selected *Shrek 2*. There were $50 + 70 + 45 + 30$ or 195 children surveyed. Thus, the ratio is $50:195$, which simplifies to

$$10:39$$

▶ **Now Try Exercise 33**

The answer in Example 1, part **a)** could have also been written $\frac{14}{9}$ or 14 to 9.

The answer in part **b)** could have also been written $\frac{10}{39}$ or 10 to 39.

EXAMPLE 2 ▸ **Cholesterol Level** There are two types of cholesterol: low-density lipoprotein, (LDL—considered the harmful type of cholesterol) and high-density lipoprotein (HDL—considered the healthful type of cholesterol). Some doctors recommend that the ratio of low- to high-density cholesterol be less than or equal to 4:1. Mr. Suarez's cholesterol test showed that his low-density cholesterol measured 167 milligrams per deciliter, and his high-density cholesterol measured 40 milligrams per deciliter. Is Mr. Suarez's ratio of low- to high-density cholesterol less than or equal to the recommended 4:1 ratio?

Solution　**Understand**　We need to determine if Mr. Suarez's low- to high-density cholesterol is less than or equal to 4:1.

Translate　Mr. Suarez's low- to high-density cholesterol is 167:40. To make the second term equal to 1, we divide both terms in the ratio by the second term, 40.

Carry Out
$$\frac{167}{40} : \frac{40}{40}$$

or 4.175 : 1

Check and Answer　Our division is correct. Therefore, Mr. Suarez's ratio is not less than or equal to the desired 4 : 1 ratio.

　　　　　　　　　　　　　　　　　　　　　　　　▸ Now Try Exercise 87

EXAMPLE 3 ▸ **Gas–Oil Mixture** Some power equipment, such as chainsaws and blowers, use a gas–oil mixture to run the engine. The instructions on a particular chainsaw indicate that 5 gallons of gasoline should be mixed with 40 ounces of special oil to obtain the proper gas–oil mixture. Find the ratio of gasoline to oil in the proper mixture.

Solution　**Understand**　To express these quantities in a ratio, both quantities must be in the same units. We can either convert 5 gallons to ounces or 40 ounces to gallons.

Translate　Let's change 5 gallons to ounces. Since there are 128 ounces in 1 gallon, 5 gallons of gas equals 5(128) or 640 ounces. The ratio we are seeking is

　　　　　　　　　　ounces of gasoline : ounces of oil

Carry Out　　　　　　　　　　640 : 40

　　　　　　　　　　or 16 : 1　　　*Divide both terms by 40 to simplify.*

Check and Answer　Our simplification is correct. The correct ratio of gas to oil for this chainsaw is 16:1.

　　　　　　　　　　　　　　　　　　　　　　　　▸ Now Try Exercise 23

Driving gear　60 teeth
8 teeth
Driven gear

FIGURE 2.6

EXAMPLE 4 ▸ **Gear Ratio** The *gear ratio* of two gears is defined as

$$\text{gear ratio} = \frac{\text{number of teeth on the driving gear}}{\text{number of teeth on the driven gear}}$$

Find the gear ratio of the gears shown in **Figure 2.6**.

Solution　**Understand and Translate**　To find the gear ratio we need to substitute the appropriate values.

Carry Out　　gear ratio $= \dfrac{\text{number of teeth on driving gear}}{\text{number of teeth on driven gear}} = \dfrac{60}{8} = \dfrac{15}{2}$

Thus, the gear ratio is 15:2. Gear ratios are generally given as some quantity to 1. If we divide both terms of the ratio by the second term, we will obtain a ratio of some number to 1. Dividing both 15 and 2 by 2 gives a gear ratio of 7.5:1.

Check and Answer　The gear ratio is 7.5:1. This means that as the driving gear goes around once the driven gear goes around 7.5 times. (A typical first gear ratio on a passenger car may be 3.545:1.)

　　　　　　　　　　　　　　　　　　　　　　　　▸ Now Try Exercise 27

2 Solve Proportions Using Cross-Multiplication

A **proportion** is a special type of equation. It is a statement of equality between two ratios. One way of denoting a proportion is $a:b = c:d$, which is read "a is to b as c is to d." In this text we write proportions as

$$\frac{a}{b} = \frac{c}{d}$$

The a and d are referred to as the **extremes**, and the b and c are referred to as the **means** of the proportion. In Sections 2.4 and 2.5, we solved equations containing fractions by multiplying both sides of the equation by the LCD to eliminate fractions. For example, for the proportion

$$\frac{x}{3} = \frac{35}{15}$$

$$15\left(\frac{x}{3}\right) = 15\left(\frac{35}{15}\right) \qquad \textit{Multiply both sides by the LCD, 15.}$$

$$5x = 35$$

$$x = 7$$

Another method that can be used to solve proportions is **cross-multiplication**. This process of cross-multiplication gives the same results as multiplying both sides of the equation by the LCD. However, many students prefer to use cross-multiplication because they do not have to determine the LCD of the fractions, and then multiply both sides of the equation by the LCD.

Cross-Multiplication

$$\text{If } \frac{a}{b} = \frac{c}{d}, \text{ then } ad = bc.$$

Note that *the product of the extremes is equal to the product of the means.*

If any three of the four quantities of a proportion are known, the fourth quantity can easily be found.

INSTRUCTOR EXAMPLE
Solve $\frac{x}{4} = \frac{42}{28}$ for x by cross-multiplying.

Ans.: $x = 6$

EXAMPLE 5 ▶ Solve $\dfrac{x}{3} = \dfrac{35}{15}$ for x by cross-multiplying.

Solution

$$\frac{x}{3} = \frac{35}{15}$$

$$x \cdot 15 = 3 \cdot 35$$

$$15x = 105$$

$$x = \frac{105}{15} = 7$$

Check:

$$\frac{x}{3} = \frac{35}{15}$$

$$\frac{7}{3} \overset{?}{=} \frac{35}{15}$$

$$\frac{7}{3} = \frac{7}{3} \qquad \textit{True}$$

▶ **Now Try Exercise 37**

Before we introduced cross-multiplication, we solved the proportion $\dfrac{x}{3} = \dfrac{35}{15}$ by multiplying both sides of the equation by 15. In Example 5, we solved the same proportion using cross-multiplication. Notice we obtained the same solution, 7, in each case. When you solve an equation using cross-multiplication, you are in effect multiplying both sides of the equation by the product of the two denominators, and then dividing out the common factors. However, this process is not shown.

INSTRUCTOR EXAMPLE

Solve $\dfrac{-9}{10} = \dfrac{90}{x}$ for x by cross-multiplying.

Ans.: $x = -100$

EXAMPLE 6 ▶ Solve $\dfrac{-8}{3} = \dfrac{64}{x}$ for x by cross-multiplying.

Solution

$$\frac{-8}{3} = \frac{64}{x}$$

$$-8 \cdot x = 3 \cdot 64$$

$$-8x = 192$$

$$\frac{-8x}{-8} = \frac{192}{-8}$$

$$x = -24$$

Check:

$$\frac{-8}{3} = \frac{64}{x}$$

$$\frac{-8}{3} \overset{?}{=} \frac{64}{-24}$$

$$\frac{-8}{3} \overset{?}{=} \frac{8}{-3}$$

$$\frac{-8}{3} = \frac{-8}{3} \quad \textit{True}$$

▶ **Now Try Exercise 41**

3 Solve Applications

Often, practical problems can be solved using proportions. To solve such problems, use the five-step problem-solving procedure we have been using throughout the book. Below we give that procedure with more specific directions for translating problems into proportions.

<table>
<tr><td>

To Solve Problems Using Proportions

1. Understand the problem.
2. Translate the problem into mathematical language.
   a) First, represent the unknown quantity by a variable (a letter).
   b) Second, set up the proportion by listing the given ratio on the left side of the equal sign, and the unknown and the other given quantity on the right side of the equal sign. When setting up the right side of the proportion, the same respective quantities should occupy the same respective positions on the left and the right. For example, an acceptable proportion might be

   Given ratio $\left\{ \dfrac{\text{miles}}{\text{hour}} = \dfrac{\text{miles}}{\text{hour}} \right.$

3. Carry out the mathematical calculations necessary to solve the problem.
   a. Once the proportion is correctly written, drop the units and cross-multiply.
   b. Solve the resulting equation.
4. Check the answer obtained in step 3.
5. Make sure you have answered the question.

</td></tr>
</table>

Note that the two ratios* used in a proportion must have the same units. For example, if one ratio is given in miles/hour and the second ratio is given in feet/hour, one of the ratios must be changed before setting up the proportion.

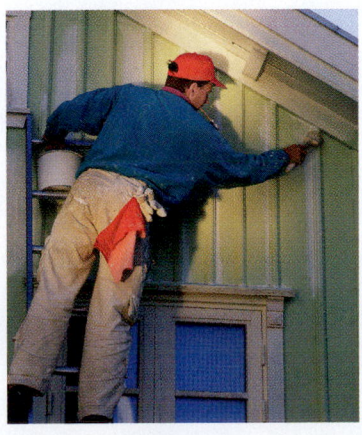

EXAMPLE 7 ▶ **Painting** A gallon of paint will cover an area of 575 square feet.

a) How many gallons of paint are needed to cover a house with a surface area of 6525 square feet?

b) If a gallon of paint costs $24.99, what will it cost (before tax) to paint the house?

Solution

a) Understand   The given ratio is 1 gallon per 575 square feet. The unknown quantity is the number of gallons necessary to cover 6525 square feet.

---

* Strictly speaking, a quotient of two quantities with different units, such as $\dfrac{6 \ miles}{1 \ hour}$, is called a *rate.* However, few books make the distinction between ratios and rates when discussing proportions.

Translate   Let x = number of gallons.

$$\text{Given ratio}\begin{cases}\dfrac{1 \text{ gallon}}{575 \text{ square feet}} = \dfrac{x \text{ gallons}}{6525 \text{ square feet}} \leftarrow \text{\textit{Unknown}} \\ \phantom{\dfrac{1 \text{ gallon}}{575 \text{ square feet}}} \leftarrow \text{\textit{Given quantity}}\end{cases}$$

Note how the amount, in gallons, and the area, in square feet, are given in the same relative positions.

Carry Out

$$\frac{1}{575} = \frac{x}{6525}$$

$$1(6525) = 575x \qquad \textit{Cross-multiply.}$$

$$6525 = 575x \qquad \textit{Solve.}$$

$$\frac{6525}{575} = x$$

$$11.3 \approx x$$

Check   Using a calculator, we determine that both ratios in the proportion, $\dfrac{1}{575}$ and $\dfrac{11.3}{6525}$, have approximately the same value of 0.00173. Thus, the answer of about 11.3 gallons checks.

Answer   The amount of paint needed to cover an area of 6525 square feet is about 11.3 gallons.

b) Assuming the painter only buys full gallons of paint, he will need to buy 12 gallons in order to paint the house. Since each gallon costs $24.99, the cost (before tax) to paint the house is found by multiplication.

$$12 \times 24.99 = \$299.88$$

The cost (before tax) to paint the house is $299.88.

▶ **Now Try Exercise 61**

EXAMPLE 8 ▶ **Charity Luncheon** Each year in Tampa, Florida, the New York Yankees host a charity luncheon, with the proceeds going to support the Tampa Boys and Girls Clubs. At the luncheon, the guests meet and get autographs from members of the team. If a particular player signs, on the average, 33 autographs in 4 minutes, how much time must be allowed for him to sign 350 autographs?

Solution   The unknown quantity is the time needed for the player to sign 350 autographs. We are given that, on the average, he signs 33 autographs in 4 minutes. We will use this given ratio in setting up our proportion.

Translate   We will let x represent the time to sign 350 autographs.

$$\text{Given ratio}\begin{cases}\dfrac{33 \text{ autographs}}{4 \text{ minutes}} = \dfrac{350 \text{ autographs}}{x \text{ minutes}}\end{cases}$$

Carry Out

$$\frac{33}{4} = \frac{350}{x}$$

$$33x = 4(350)$$

$$33x = 1400$$

$$x = \frac{1400}{33} \approx 42.4$$

Check and Answer   Using a calculator, we can determine that both ratios in the proportion, $\dfrac{33}{4}$ and $\dfrac{350}{42.4}$, have approximately the same value of 8.25. Thus, about 42.4 minutes would be needed for the player to sign the 350 autographs.

▶ **Now Try Exercise 55**

EXAMPLE 9 ▸ **Drug Dosage** A doctor asks a nurse to give a patient 250 milligrams of the drug simethicone. The drug is available only in a solution whose concentration is 40 milligrams of simethicone per 0.6 milliliter of solution. How many milliliters of solution should the nurse give the patient?

Solution Understand and Translate   We can set up the proportion using the medication on hand as the given ratio and the number of milliliters needed to be given as the unknown.

$$\text{Given ratio (medication on hand)} \left\{ \frac{40 \text{ milligrams}}{0.6 \text{ milliliter}} = \frac{250 \text{ milligrams}}{x \text{ milliliters}} \right. \begin{matrix} \longleftarrow \text{Desired medication} \\ \longleftarrow \text{Unknown} \end{matrix}$$

Carry Out

$$\frac{40}{0.6} = \frac{250}{x}$$

$$40x = 0.6(250) \qquad \textit{Cross-multiply.}$$

$$40x = 150 \qquad \textit{Solve.}$$

$$x = \frac{150}{40} = 3.75$$

Check and Answer   The nurse should administer 3.75 milliliters of the simethicone solution.

▸ **Now Try Exercise 69**

Helpful Hint

When you are setting up a proportion, it does not matter which unit in the given ratio is in the numerator and which is in the denominator as long as the units in the other ratio are *in the same relative position*. For example,

$$\frac{60 \text{ miles}}{1.5 \text{ hours}} = \frac{x \text{ miles}}{4.2 \text{ hours}} \quad \text{and} \quad \frac{1.5 \text{ hours}}{60 \text{ miles}} = \frac{4.2 \text{ hours}}{x \text{ miles}}$$

will both give the same answer of 168 (try it and see). When setting up the proportion, set it up so that it makes the most sense to you. Notice that when setting up a proportion containing different units, the same units should not be multiplied by themselves during cross multiplication.

Correct	Incorrect
$\dfrac{\text{miles}}{\text{hour}} = \dfrac{\text{miles}}{\text{hour}}$	$\dfrac{\text{miles}}{\text{hour}} \quad \dfrac{\text{hour}}{\text{miles}}$

4 Use Proportions to Change Units

Proportions can also be used to convert from one quantity to another. For example, you can use a proportion to convert a measurement in feet to a measurement in meters, or to convert from pounds to kilograms. The following examples illustrate converting units.

EXAMPLE 10 ▸ **Kilometers to Miles** There are approximately 1.6 kilometers in 1 mile. What is the distance, in miles, of 78 kilometers?

Solution Understand and Translate   We know that 1 mile ≈ 1.6 kilometers. We use this known fact in one ratio of our proportion. In the second ratio, we set the quantities with the same units in the same respective positions. The unknown quantity is the number of miles, which we will call x.

$$\text{Known ratio} \left\{ \frac{1 \text{ mile}}{1.6 \text{ kilometers}} = \frac{x \text{ miles}}{78 \text{ kilometers}} \right.$$

Note that both numerators contain the same units, and both denominators contain the same units.

INSTRUCTOR EXAMPLE
A nurse must administer 220 mg of a drug to a patient. The drug is only available in a solution whose concentration is 50 mg of the drug per 0.9 ml of solution. How many ml of solution should the nurse administer?
Ans.: 3.96 ml

INSTRUCTOR EXAMPLE
There are 1760 yards in a mile. What is the distance, in miles, of 7920 yards?
Ans.: 4.5 mi

Carry Out   Now drop the units and solve for x by cross-multiplying.

$$\frac{1}{1.6} = \frac{x}{78}$$

$$1(78) = 1.6x \qquad \textit{Cross-multiply.}$$

$$78 = 1.6x \qquad \textit{Solve.}$$

$$\frac{78}{1.6} = \frac{1.6x}{1.6}$$

$$48.75 = x$$

Check and Answer   Thus, 78 kilometers equals about 48.75 miles.

▸ **Now Try Exercise 75**

EXAMPLE 11 ▸ **Exchanging Currency** When people travel to a foreign country they often need to exchange currency. Donna Boccio visited Cancun, Mexico. She stopped by a local bank and was told that $1 U.S. could be exchanged for 10.96 pesos.

 a) How many pesos would she get if she exchanged $150 U.S.?

 b) Later that same day, Donna went to the city market where she purchased a ceramic figurine. The price she negotiated for the figurine was 245 pesos. Using the exchange rate given, determine the cost of the figurine in U.S. dollars.

Solution

 a) Understand We are told that $1 U.S. can be exchanged for 10.96 Mexican pesos. We use this known fact for one ratio in our proportion. In the second ratio, we set the quantities with same units in the same respective positions.

Translate The unknown quantity is the number of pesos, which we shall call x.

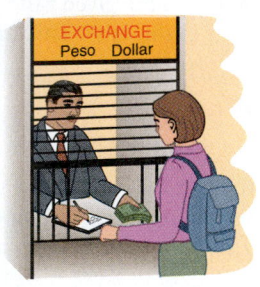

$$\textit{Given ratio} \left\{ \frac{\$1 \text{ U.S.}}{10.96 \text{ pesos}} = \frac{\$150 \text{ U.S.}}{x \text{ pesos}} \right.$$

Note that both numerators contain U.S. dollars and both denominators contain pesos.

Carry Out
$$\frac{1}{10.96} = \frac{150}{x}$$

$$1x = 10.96(150)$$

$$x = 1644$$

Check and Answer   Thus, $150 U.S. could be exchanged for 1644 Mexican pesos.

 b) Understand and Translate We use the same given ratio that we used in part **a)**. Now we must find the equivalent in U.S. dollars of 245 Mexican pesos. Let's call the equivalent U.S. dollars x.

$$\textit{Given ratio} \left\{ \frac{\$1 \text{ U.S.}}{10.96 \text{ pesos}} = \frac{\$x \text{ U.S.}}{245 \text{ pesos}} \right.$$

Carry Out
$$\frac{1}{10.96} = \frac{x}{245}$$

$$1(245) = 10.96x$$

$$245 = 10.96x$$

$$22.35 \approx x$$

Check and Answer   The cost of the figurine in U.S. dollars is $22.35.

▸ **Now Try Exercise 85**

INSTRUCTOR EXAMPLE

At a bank, $123.70 Canadian can be exchanged for $100 U.S. How much will a person receive in U.S. dollars if they convert $700 Canadian?

Ans.: $565.89

Helpful Hint

Some of the problems we have just worked using proportions could have been done without using proportions. However, when working problems of this type, students often have difficulty in deciding whether to multiply or divide to obtain the correct answer. By setting up a proportion, you may be better able to understand the problem and have more success in obtaining the correct answer.

5 Use Proportions to Solve Problems Involving Similar Figures

Proportions can also be used to solve problems in geometry and trigonometry. The following examples illustrate how proportions may be used to solve problems involving **similar figures**. Two figures are said to be similar when their corresponding angles are equal and their corresponding sides are in proportion. Two similar figures will have the same shape.

5 in.

2 in.
12 in.
x

EXAMPLE 12 ▶ The figures to the left are similar. Find the length of the side indicated by the x.

Solution We set up a proportion of corresponding sides to find the length of side x.

5 inches and 12 inches are corresponding sides of similar figures. →

2 inches and x are corresponding sides of similar figures. →

Lengths from smaller figure   Lengths from larger figure

$$\frac{5}{2} = \frac{12}{x}$$

$$5x = 24$$

$$x = \frac{24}{5} = 4.8$$

Thus, the side indicated by x is 4.8 inches in length.

▶ **Now Try Exercise 51**

Note in Example 12 that the proportion could have also been set up as

$$\frac{5}{12} = \frac{2}{x}$$

because one pair of corresponding sides is in the numerators and another pair is in the denominators.

EXAMPLE 13 ▶ Triangles ABC and $AB'C'$ are similar triangles. Find the length of side AB'.

Solution We set up a proportion of corresponding sides to find the length of side AB'. We will let x represent the length of side AB'. One proportion we can use is

$$\frac{\text{length of } AB}{\text{length of } BC} = \frac{\text{length of } AB'}{\text{length of } B'C'}$$

Now we insert the proper values and solve for the variable, x.

$$\frac{15}{9} = \frac{x}{7.2}$$

$$(15)(7.2) = 9x$$

$$108 = 9x$$

$$12 = x$$

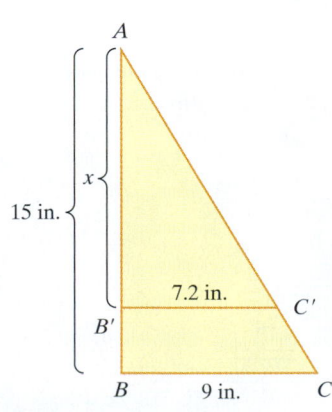

Thus, the length of side AB' is 12 inches.

▶ **Now Try Exercise 53**

EXERCISE SET 2.7

MathXL®   MyMathLab

Concept/Writing Exercises

5. need a given ratio and one of the two parts of a second ratio
6. corresponding angles equal and corresponding sides in proportion

1. What is a ratio?   a quotient of two quantities

2. In the ratio $a:b$, what are the a and b called?   terms

3. List three ways to write the ratio of c to d. c to $d, c:d, \dfrac{c}{d}$

4. What is a proportion?   a statement of equality between two ratios

5. As you have learned, proportions can be used to solve a wide variety of problems. What information is needed for a problem to be set up and solved using a proportion?

6. What are similar figures?

7. Must similar figures have the same shape? Explain.   yes

8. Must similar figures be the same size? Explain.   no

In Exercises 9–12, is the proportion set up correctly? Explain.

9. $\dfrac{\text{gal}}{\text{min}} = \dfrac{\text{gal}}{\text{min}}$ yes

10. $\dfrac{\text{mi}}{\text{hr}} = \dfrac{\text{mi}}{\text{hr}}$ yes

11. $\dfrac{\text{ft}}{\text{sec}} = \dfrac{\text{sec}}{\text{ft}}$ no

12. $\dfrac{\text{tax}}{\text{cost}} = \dfrac{\text{cost}}{\text{tax}}$ no

Practice the Skills

The results of a mathematics examination are 6 A's, 4 B's, 9 C's, 3 D's, and 2 F's. Write the following ratios in lowest terms.

13. A's to C's   2:3

14. F's to total grades   1:12

15. D's to A's   1:2

16. Grades better than C to total grades   5:12

17. Total grades to D's   8:1

18. Grades better than C to grades less than C   2:1

Determine the following ratios. Write each ratio in lowest terms.

19. 7 gallons to 4 gallons   7:4

20. 50 dollars to 60 dollars   5:6

21. 5 ounces to 15 ounces   1:3

22. 18 liters to 24 liters   3:4

23. 3 hours to 30 minutes   6:1

24. 6 feet to 4 yards   1:2

25. 7 dimes to 12 nickels   7:6

26. 26 ounces to 4 pounds   13:32

In Exercises 27 and 28, find the gear ratio. Write the ratio as some quantity to 1. (See Example 4.)

27. Driving gear, 40 teeth; driven gear, 5 teeth   8:1

28. Driving gear, 30 teeth; driven gear, 8 teeth   15:4 or 3.75:1

In Exercises 29–32, **a)** *Determine the indicated ratio, and* **b)** *write the ratio as some quantity to 1.*

29. **American Consumers** According to a report issued by the U.S. Department of Agriculture's Economic Research Service, each year the average American consumer drinks approximately 50 gallons of soft drinks compared to 26 gallons of coffee, 23 gallons of milk, and less than 10 gallons of fruit juices. What is the ratio of the number of gallons of soft drinks consumed to the number of gallons of milk consumed?   **a)** 50:23   **b)** ≈2.17:1

30. **Mail Letter** In January 2006, the cost to mail a one-ounce letter was 39 cents and the cost to mail a two-ounce letter was 63 cents. What is the ratio of the cost to mail a one-ounce letter to the cost to mail a two-ounce letter?   **a)** 39:63 or 13:21   **b)** ≈0.62:1

31. **Minimum Wage** The United States minimum wage in 1985 was $3.35 per hour, and the United States minimum wage in 2005 was $5.15 per hour. What is the ratio of the U.S. minimum wage in 2005 to the U.S. minimum wage in 1985?   **a)** 5.15:3.35 or 1.03:0.67   **b)** ≈1.54:1

32. **Population** The United States population in 1990 was about 249 million, and the population in 2006 was about 299 million. What is the ratio of the U.S. population in 2006 to the U.S. population in 1990?   **a)** 299:249   **b)** ≈1.20:1

Exercises 33–36 show graphs. For each exercise, find the indicated ratio.

33. **Traveling the Toll Roads**   **33. a)** 19.2:2.2 or 9.6:1.1

   a) Determine the ratio of the toll rate on the Delaware Turnpike to the toll rate on the Garden State Parkway.

   b) Determine the ratio of the toll rate on the Massachusetts Turnpike (Boston ext.) to the toll rate on the New York State Thruway (Current).   6.7:3.1

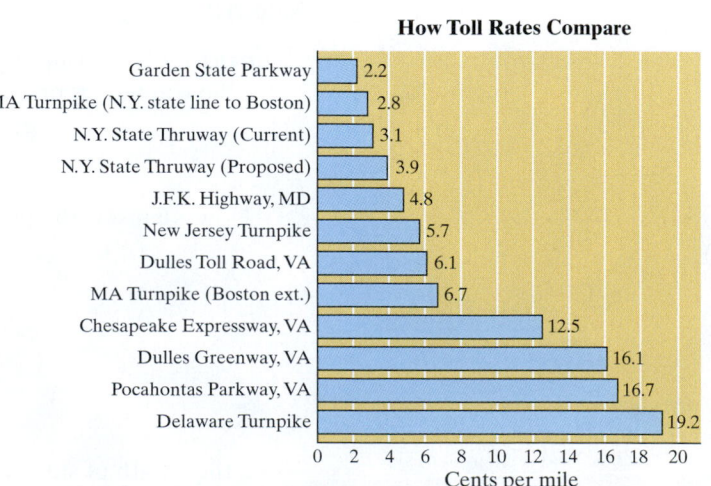

How Toll Rates Compare

	Cents per mile
Garden State Parkway	2.2
MA Turnpike (N.Y. state line to Boston)	2.8
N.Y. State Thruway (Current)	3.1
N.Y. State Thruway (Proposed)	3.9
J.F.K. Highway, MD	4.8
New Jersey Turnpike	5.7
Dulles Toll Road, VA	6.1
MA Turnpike (Boston ext.)	6.7
Chesapeake Expressway, VA	12.5
Dulles Greenway, VA	16.1
Pocahontas Parkway, VA	16.7
Delaware Turnpike	19.2

Source: Rochester Democrat & Chronicle, April, 2005

34. Number of Passports Processed

a) Estimate the ratio of passports processed in the United States in 1996 to those processed in the United States in 2004. $5.6:8.8$ or $0.7:1.1$

b) Estimate the ratio of passports processed in the United States in 2002 to those processed in the United States in 1997. $7.0:6.3$ or $1.0:0.9$

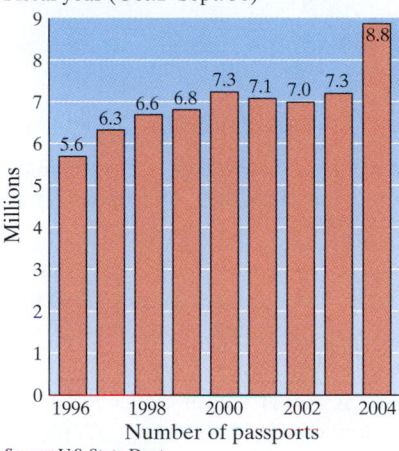

Passports Processed in the United States
Fiscal year (Oct.1–Sept. 30)

Source: U.S. State Dept.

Favorite Doughnut Flavors

Source: The Heller Research Group

35. Favorite Doughnut

See figure at the top of the next column.

a) Determine the ratio of people whose favorite doughnut is glazed to people whose favorite doughnut is filled. $40:32$ or $5:4$

b) Determine the ratio of people whose favorite doughnut is frosted to people whose favorite doughnut is plain. $15:11$

36. Commuting to Work

a) Determine the ratio of workers who drove alone to work to those who carpooled to work. $78:10$ or $39:5$

b) Determine the ratio of workers who walked to work to those who worked at home. $2:4$ or $1:2$

Commuting to Work, 2003

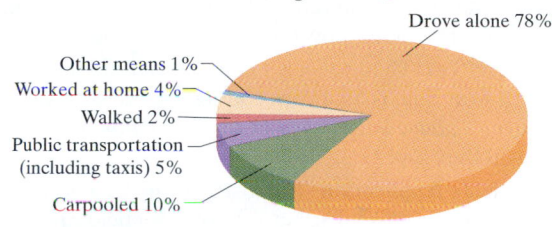

Source: www.factfinder.census.gov

Solve each proportion for the variable by cross-multiplying.

37. $\dfrac{x}{3} = \dfrac{20}{5}$ 12

38. $\dfrac{x}{8} = \dfrac{24}{48}$ 4

39. $\dfrac{5}{3} = \dfrac{75}{a}$ 45

40. $\dfrac{x}{3} = \dfrac{90}{30}$ 9

41. $\dfrac{-7}{3} = \dfrac{21}{p}$ -9

42. $\dfrac{-12}{13} = \dfrac{36}{x}$ -39

43. $\dfrac{15}{45} = \dfrac{x}{-6}$ -2

44. $\dfrac{y}{6} = \dfrac{7}{42}$ 1

45. $\dfrac{3}{z} = \dfrac{-1.5}{27}$ -54

46. $\dfrac{3}{12} = \dfrac{-1.4}{z}$ -5.6

47. $\dfrac{9}{12} = \dfrac{x}{8}$ 6

48. $\dfrac{2}{20} = \dfrac{x}{200}$ 20

The following figures are similar. For each pair, find the length of the side indicated by x.

49.   32 in.

3 in.   8 in.

12 in.   x

50. 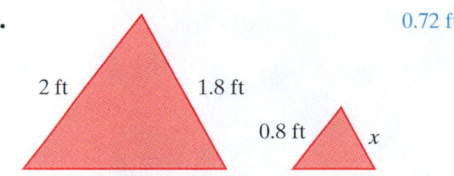 0.72 ft

2 ft   1.8 ft   0.8 ft   x

51.   15.75 in.

x   9 in.   7 in.   4 in.

52.   11.2 ft

5 ft   7 ft   8 ft   x

53.

19.5 in.

16 in.
26 in.
12 in.

x

54.

5.6 in.

14 in.
20 in.

x

8 in.

Problem Solving

In Exercises 55–74, write a proportion that can be used to solve the problem. Then solve the equation to obtain the answer.

55. Washing Clothes A bottle of liquid Tide contains 100 fluid ounces. If one wash load requires 4 ounces of the detergent, how many washes can be done with one bottle of Tide?   25 loads

56. Laying Cable A telephone cable crew is laying cable at a rate of 42 feet an hour. How long will it take them to lay 252 feet of cable?   6 hr

57. Truck Mileage A 2004 Chevy S-10 pickup truck with a 4.3-liter engine is rated to get 19 miles per gallon (highway driving). How far can it travel on 14.2 gallons of gas?   269.8 mi

58. Purchasing Stock If 2 shares of stock can be purchased for $38.25, how many shares can be purchased for $344.25?   18 shares

59. Model Train A model train set is in a ratio of 1 : 20. That is, one foot of the model represents 20 feet of the original train. If a caboose is 30 feet long, how long should the model be?   1.5 ft

60. Property Tax The property tax in the city of Hendersonville, North Carolina, is $9.475 per $1000 of assessed value. If the Estever's house is assessed at $145,000, how much property tax will they owe? $1373.88

61. Insecticide Application The instructions on a bottle of liquid insecticide say "use 3 teaspoons of insecticide per gallon of water." If your sprayer has an 8-gallon capacity, how much insecticide should be used to fill the sprayer?   24 tsp

62. Spreading Fertilizer If a 40-pound bag of fertilizer covers 5000 square feet, how many pounds of fertilizer are needed to cover an area of 26,000 square feet?   208 lb

63. Blue Heron The photograph shows a blue heron. If the blue heron, that measures 3.5 inches in the photo is actually 3.75 feet tall, approximately how long is its beak if it measures 0.4 inch in the photo?   ≈0.43 ft

64. Maps On a map, 0.5 inch represents 22 miles. What will be the length on a map that corresponds to a distance of 55 miles?   1.25 in.

65. Onion Soup A recipe for 6 servings of French onion soup requires $1\frac{1}{2}$ cups of thinly sliced onions. If the recipe were to be made for 15 servings, how many cups of onions would be needed?   3.75 cups

66. John Grisham Novel Karen Estes is currently reading a John Grisham novel. If she reads 72 pages in 1.3 hours, how long will it take her to read the entire 656-page novel?   ≈11.84 hours

67. Wall Street Bull Suppose the famous bull by the New York Stock Exchange (see photo below) is a replica of a real bull in a ratio of 2.95 to 1. That is, the metal bull is 2.95 times greater than the regular bull. If the length of the Wall Street bull is 28 feet long, approximately how long is the bull that served as its model?   ≈9.49 ft

68. Flood When they returned home from vacation, the Duncans had a foot of water in their basement. They contacted their fire department, which sent equipment to pump out the water. After the pump had been on for 30 minutes, 3 inches of water had been removed. How long, from the time they

started pumping, will it take to remove all the water from the basement?   2 hr

69. Drug Dosage A nurse must administer 220 micrograms of atropine sulfate. The drug is available in solution form. The concentration of the atropine sulfate solution is 400 micrograms per milliliter. How many milliliters should be given?   0.55 ml

70. Dosage by Body Surface A doctor asks a nurse to administer 0.7 gram of meprobamate per square meter of body surface. The patient's body surface is 0.6 square meter. How much meprobamate should be given?   0.42 g

71. Reading a Novel Mary read 40 pages of a novel in 30 minutes. If she continues reading at the same rate, how long will it take her to read the entire 760-page book?   570 min or 9 hr 30 min

72. Swimming Laps Jason Abbott swims 3 laps in 2.3 minutes. Approximately how long will it take him to swim 30 laps if he continues to swim at the same rate?   23 min

73. Prader-Willi Syndrome It is estimated that each year in the United States about 1 in every 12,000 (1 : 12,000) people is born with a genetic disorder called Prader-Willi syndrome. If there were approximately 4,063,000 births in the United States in 2005, approximately how may children were born with Prader-Willi syndrome?   ≈339 children

74. Scrapbooking Penelope Penna completed 4 scrapbook pages in 20.5 minutes. Approximately how long will it take her to complete 36 scrapbook pages if she continues to complete the scrapbook at the same rate?
184.5 min or 3 hr 4 min 30 sec

In Exercises 75–86, use a proportion to make the conversion. Round your answers to two decimal places.

75. Convert 78 inches to feet.   6.5 ft

76. Convert 22,704 feet to miles (5280 feet = 1 mile).   4.3 mi

77. Convert 26.1 square feet to square yards (9 square feet = 1 square yard).   2.9 sq yd

78. Convert 146.4 ounces to pounds.   9.15 lb

79. Newborn One inch equals 2.54 centimeters. Find the length of a newborn, in inches, if it measures 50.8 centimeters.   20 in.

80. Distance One mile equals approximately 1.6 kilometers. Find the distance, in kilometers, from San Diego, California, to San Francisco, California—a distance of 520 miles.   832 km

San Francisco, California

81. Home Run Record Barry Bonds, who plays for the San Francisco Giant's baseball team, holds the record for the most home runs, 73, in a 162 game season. In the first 50 games of a season, how many home runs would a player need to hit to be on schedule to break Bonds' record?   ≈23

82. Topsoil A 40 pound bag of topsoil covers 12 square feet (one inch deep). How many pounds of the top soil are needed to cover 350 square feet (one inch deep)?   ≈1166.67 lb

83. Interest on Savings Jim Chao invests a certain amount of money in a savings account. If he earned $110.52 in 180 days, how much interest would he earn in 500 days assuming the interest rate stays the same? $307

84. Gold If gold is selling for $408 per 480 grains (a troy ounce), what is the cost per grain? $0.85

85. Mexican Pesos Suppose that the exchange rate from U.S. dollars to Mexican pesos is $1 per 10.567 pesos. How many pesos would Elizabeth Averbeck receive if she exchanged $200 U.S.?   2113.4 pesos

86. Currency Exchange When Mike Weatherbee visited the United States from Canada, he exchanged $13.50 Canadian for $10 U.S.. If he exchanges his remaining $600 Canadian for U.S. dollars, how much more in dollars will he receive? $444.44

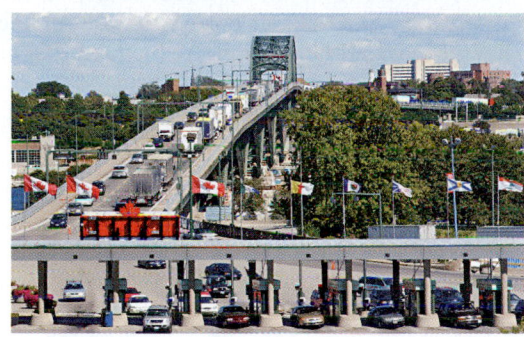

The Peace Bridge Connecting the United States and Canada

87. Cholesterol Mrs. Ruff's low-density cholesterol level is 127 milligrams per deciliter (mg/dL). Her high-density cholesterol level is 60 mg/dL. Is Mrs. Ruff's ratio of low-to high-density cholesterol level less than or equal to the 4 : 1 recommended level? (See Example 2.)   Yes, her ratio is 2.12 : 1.

88. Cholesterol

a) Another ratio used by some doctors when measuring cholesterol level is the ratio of total cholesterol to high-density cholesterol.* Is this ratio increased or decreased if the total cholesterol remains the same but the high-density level is increased? Explain.   decreased

b) Doctors recommend that the ratio of total cholesterol to high-density cholesterol be less than or equal to 4.5 : 1. If Mike's total cholesterol is 220 mg/dL and his high-density cholesterol is 50 mg/dL, is his ratio less than or equal to 4.5 : 1? Explain.   Yes, his ratio is 4.4 : 1.

89. For the proportion $\frac{a}{b} = \frac{c}{d}$, if a increases while b and d stay the same, what must happen to c? Explain.   must increase

90. For the proportion $\frac{a}{b} = \frac{c}{d}$, if a and c remain the same while d decreases, what must happen to b? Explain.   must decrease

---

*Total cholesterol includes both low- and high-density cholesterol, plus other types of cholesterol.

Challenge Problems

92. $\frac{1}{6}$ tsp salt, $\frac{1}{3}$ cup flour,1 cup sugar, $\frac{2}{3}$ tsp nutmeg, $1\frac{1}{3}$ tbsp butter, $\frac{2}{3}$ tsp cinnamon

91. Wear on Tires A new Goodyear tire has a tread of about 0.34 inch. After 5000 miles the tread is about 0.31 inch. If the legal minimum amount of tread for a tire is 0.06 inch, how many more miles will the tires last? (Assume no problems with the car or tires and that the tires wear at an even rate.)   ≈41,667 mi

92. Apple Pie The recipe for the filling for an apple pie calls for

12 cups sliced apples $\frac{1}{4}$ teaspoon salt

$\frac{1}{2}$ cup flour $1\frac{1}{2}$ cups sugar

1 teaspoon nutmeg   2 tablespoons butter or margarine

1 teaspoon cinnamon

Determine the amount of each of the other ingredients that should be used if only 8 cups of apples are available.

93. Insulin Insulin comes in 10-cubic-centimeter (cc) vials labeled in the number of units of insulin per cubic centimeter. Thus, a vial labeled U40 means there are 40 units of insulin per cubic centimeter of fluid. If a patient needs 25 units of insulin, how many cubic centimeters of fluid should be drawn up into a syringe from the U40 vial?   0.625 cc

Group Activity

Discuss and answer Exercises 94 and 95 as a group.

94. a) Each group member: Find the ratio of your height to your arm span (finger tips to finger tips) when your arms are extended horizontally outward. You will need help from your group in getting these measurements.

b) If a box were to be drawn about your body with your arms extended, would the box be a square or a rectangle? If a rectangle, would the longer length be your arm span or your height measurement? Explain.

c) Compare these results with other members of your group.

d) What one ratio would you use to report the height to arm span for your group as a whole? Explain.

95. A special ratio in mathematics is called the *golden ratio*. Do research in a history of mathematics book or on the Internet, and as a group write a paper that explains what the golden ratio is and why it is important.

Cumulative Review Exercises

[1.10] *Name each illustrated property.*

96. $x + 3 = 3 + x$ commutative, addition

97. $3(xy) = (3x)y$ associative, multiplication

98. $2(x - 3) = 2x - 6$ distributive property

[2.5] **99.** Solve $3(4x - 3) = 6(2x + 1) - 15$ all real numbers

[2.6] **100.** Solve $y = mx + b$ for m. $m = (y - b)/x$

2.8 Inequalities in One Variable

1 Solve linear inequalities.

2 Solve linear inequalities that have all real numbers as their solution, or have no solution.

1 Solve Linear Inequalities

The is-greater-than symbol, $>$, and is-less-than symbol, $<$, were introduced in Section 1.5. The symbol $\geq$ means is greater than or equal to and $\leq$ means is less than or equal to. A mathematical statement containing one or more of these symbols is called an **inequality**. The direction of the symbol is sometimes called the **sense** or **order of the inequality**.

Examples of Inequalities in One Variable

$$x + 3 < 5 \qquad x + 4 \geq 2x - 6 \qquad 4 > -x + 3$$

To solve an inequality, we must get the variable by itself on one side of the inequality symbol. To do this, we make use of properties very similar to those used to solve equations. Here are four properties used to solve inequalities. Later in this section, we will introduce two additional properties.

Properties Used to Solve Inequalities

For real numbers, $a, b,$ and c:

1. If $a > b$, then $a + c > b + c$.

2. If $a > b$, then $a - c > b - c$.

3. If $a > b$ **and** $c > 0$, then $ac > bc$.

4. If $a > b$ **and** $c > 0$, then $\dfrac{a}{c} > \dfrac{b}{c}$.

Property 1 says the same number may be added to both sides of an inequality. Property 2 says the same number may be subtracted from both sides of an inequality. Property 3 says the same *positive* number may be used to multiply both sides of an inequality. Property 4 says the same *positive* number may be used to divide both sides of an inequality. When any of these four properties is used, *the direction of the inequality symbol does not change.*

EXAMPLE 1 ▶ Solve the inequality $x - 5 > -2$, and graph the solution on a number line.

Solution   To solve this inequality, we need to isolate the variable, x. Therefore, we must eliminate the -5 from the left side of the inequality. To do this, we add 5 to both sides of the inequality.

$$x - 5 > -2$$
$$x - 5 + 5 > -2 + 5 \qquad \textit{Add 5 to both sides.}$$
$$x > 3$$

The solution is all real numbers greater than 3. We can illustrate the solution on a number line by placing an open circle at 3 on a number line and drawing an arrow to the right (**Fig. 2.7**).

FIGURE 2.7

    The open circle at the 3 indicates that the 3 is *not* part of the solution. The arrow going to the right indicates that all the values greater than 3 are solutions to the inequality.

▶ **Now Try Exercise 13**

EXAMPLE 2 ▶ Solve the inequality $2x + 6 \le -2$, and graph the solution on a number line.

Solution   To isolate the variable, we must eliminate the $+6$ from the left side of the inequality. We do this by subtracting 6 from both sides of the inequality.

$$2x + 6 \le -2$$
$$2x + 6 - 6 \le -2 - 6 \qquad \textit{Subtract 6 from both sides.}$$
$$2x \le -8$$
$$\frac{2x}{2} \le \frac{-8}{2} \qquad \textit{Divide both sides by 2.}$$
$$x \le -4$$

The solution is all real numbers less than or equal to -4. We can illustrate the solution on a number line by placing a closed, or darkened, circle at -4 and drawing an arrow to the left (**Fig. 2.8.**)

    The darkened circle at -4 indicates that -4 *is* a part of the solution. The arrow going to the left indicates that all the values less than -4 are also solutions to the inequality.

▶ **Now Try Exercise 21**

FIGURE 2.8

    Notice in properties 3 and 4 that we specified that $c > 0$. What happens when an inequality is multiplied or divided by a negative number? Examples 3 and 4 illustrate that **when an inequality is multiplied or divided by a negative number, the direction of the inequality symbol changes.**

EXAMPLE 3 ▶

a) Multiply both sides of the inequality $8 > -4$ by -2.
b) Divide both sides of the inequality $8 > -4$ by -2.

Solution

a)
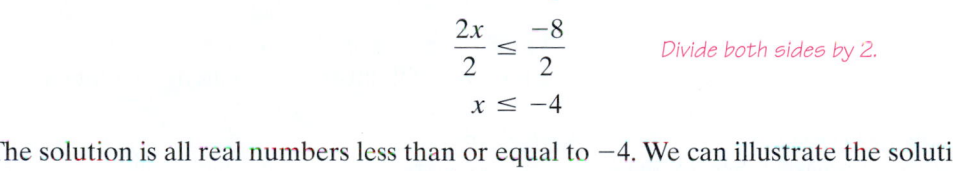
$$8 > -4$$
$$-2(8) < -2(-4) \qquad \textit{Change the direction of the inequality symbol.}$$
$$-16 < 8$$

TEACHING TIP
Stress that the change of direction of
the inequality symbol occurs in the
step where you multiply by a negative
number (not the step where you simplify the multiplication).

b)
$$8 > -4$$

$$\frac{8}{-2} < \frac{-4}{-2}$$ *Change the direction of the inequality symbol.*

$$-4 < 2$$

▶ **Now Try Exercise 9**

Now we state two additional properties, used when an inequality is multiplied or divided by a negative number.

> ### Additional Properties Used to Solve Inequalities
>
> **5.** If $a > b$ **and** $c < 0$, then $ac < bc$.
>
> **6.** If $a > b$ **and** $c < 0$, then $\dfrac{a}{c} < \dfrac{b}{c}$.

INSTRUCTOR EXAMPLE
Solve the inequality $-4x < 12$, and
graph the solution on a number line.
Ans.: $x > -3$,

EXAMPLE 4 ▶ Solve the inequality $-2x < 8$, and graph the solution on a number line.

Solution To isolate the variable, we must eliminate the -2 on the left side of the inequality. To do this, we can divide both sides of the inequality by -2. When we do this, however, we must remember to *change the direction* of the inequality symbol.

$$-2x < 8$$

$$\frac{-2x}{-2} > \frac{8}{-2}$$ *Divide both sides by -2, and change the direction of the inequality symbol.*

$$x > -4$$

The solution is all real numbers greater than -4. The solution is graphed on a number line in **Figure 2.9**.

▶ **Now Try Exercise 19**

FIGURE 2.9

EXAMPLE 5 ▶ Solve the inequality $4 \geq -5 - x$, and graph the solution on a number line. We will illustrate two methods that can be used to solve this inequality.

INSTRUCTOR EXAMPLE
Solve the inequality $7 > -9 - x$, and
graph the solution on a number line.
Ans.: $x > -16$,

Solution

Method 1:

$$4 \geq -5 - x$$

$$4 + 5 \geq -5 + 5 - x$$ *Add 5 to both sides.*

$$9 \geq -x$$

$$-1(9) \leq -1(-x)$$ *Multiply both sides by -1, and change the direction of the inequality symbol.*

$$-9 \leq x$$

The inequality $-9 \leq x$ can also be written $x \geq -9$.

TEACHING TIP
Suggest that students adopt the style
of always giving their solution to an
inequality with the variable on the
left side.

Method 2:

$$4 \geq -5 - x$$

$$4 + x \geq -5 - x + x$$ *Add x to both sides.*

$$4 + x \geq -5$$

$$4 - 4 + x \geq -5 - 4$$ *Subtract 4 from both sides.*

$$x \geq -9$$

FIGURE 2.10

The solution is graphed on a number line in **Figure 2.10**. Other methods could also be used to solve this problem.

▶ **Now Try Exercise 17**

Notice in Example 5, Method 1, we wrote $-9 \le x$ as $x \ge -9$. Although the solution $-9 \le x$ is correct, it is customary to write the solution to an inequality with the variable on the left. One reason we write the variable on the left is that it often makes it easier to graph the solution on the number line. How would you graph $-3 > x$? How would you graph $-5 \le x$? If you rewrite these inequalities with the variable on the left side, the answer becomes clearer.

$$-3 > x \quad \text{means} \quad x < -3$$
$$-5 \le x \quad \text{means} \quad x \ge -5$$

Notice that you can change an answer from an is-greater-than statement to an is-less-than statement or from an is-less-than statement to an is-greater-than statement. When you change the answer from one form to the other, remember that the inequality symbol must point to the letter or number to which it was pointing originally.

Helpful Hint

$a > x$ means $x < a$ *Note that both inequality symbols point to x.*

$a < x$ means $x > a$ *Note that both inequality symbols point to a.*

Examples

$-3 > x$ means $x < -3$

$-5 \le x$ means $x \ge -5$

Now let's solve inequalities where the variable appears on both sides of the inequality symbol. To solve these inequalities, we use the same basic procedure that we used to solve equations. However, we must remember that whenever we multiply or divide both sides of an inequality by a negative number, we must change the direction of the inequality symbol.

EXAMPLE 6 ▶ Solve the inequality $-5p + 9 < -2p + 6$, and graph the solution on a number line.

Solution   This inequality uses the variable, p. The variable used does not affect the procedure for solving the inequality.

$$-5p + 9 < -2p + 6$$

$$-5p + 5p + 9 < -2p + 5p + 6 \qquad \textit{Add 5p to both sides.}$$

$$9 < 3p + 6$$

$$9 - 6 < 3p + 6 - 6 \qquad \textit{Subtract 6 from both sides.}$$

$$3 < 3p$$

$$\frac{3}{3} < \frac{3p}{3} \qquad \textit{Divide both sides by 3.}$$

$$1 < p$$

$$\text{or} \quad p > 1$$

FIGURE 2.11

The solution is graphed in **Figure 2.11**.

▶ **Now Try Exercise 33**

EXAMPLE 7 ▶ Solve the inequality $\frac{1}{2}x + 3 \le -\frac{1}{3}x + 7$, and graph the solution on a number line.

Solution   Since the inequality contains fractions, we begin by multiplying both sides of the inequality by the LCD, 6, to eliminate the fractions.

$$\frac{1}{2}x + 3 \le -\frac{1}{3}x + 7$$

$$6\left(\frac{1}{2}x + 3\right) \le 6\left(-\frac{1}{3}x + 7\right) \qquad \textit{Multiply both sides by the LCD, 6.}$$

$$3x + 18 \le -2x + 42 \qquad \textit{Distributive property}$$

$$5x + 18 \le 42 \qquad \textit{2x was added to both sides.}$$

$$5x \le 24 \qquad \textit{18 was subtracted from both sides.}$$

$$x \le \frac{24}{5} \qquad \textit{Both sides were divided by 5.}$$

The solution is graphed in **Figure 2.12**.

▶ **Now Try Exercise 53**

2 Solve Linear Inequalities That Have All Real Numbers as Their Solution, or Have No Solution

In Examples 8 and 9, we illustrate two special types of inequalities. Example 8 is an inequality that is true for all real numbers, and Example 9 is an inequality that is never true for any real number.

EXAMPLE 8 ▶ Solve the inequality $2(x + 3) \le 5x - 3x + 8$, and graph the solution on a number line.

Solution

$$2(x + 3) \le 5x - 3x + 8$$

$$2x + 6 \le 5x - 3x + 8 \qquad \textit{Distributive property was used.}$$

$$2x + 6 \le 2x + 8 \qquad \textit{Like terms were combined.}$$

$$2x - 2x + 6 \le 2x - 2x + 8 \qquad \textit{Subtract 2x from both sides.}$$

$$6 \le 8$$

Since 6 is always less than or equal to 8, the solution is **all real numbers** (**Fig. 2.13**).

▶ **Now Try Exercise 37**

EXAMPLE 9 ▶ Solve the inequality $4(x + 1) > x + 5 + 3x$, and graph the solution on a number line.

Solution

$$4(x + 1) > x + 5 + 3x$$

$$4x + 4 > x + 5 + 3x \qquad \textit{Distributive property was used.}$$

$$4x + 4 > 4x + 5 \qquad \textit{Like terms were combined.}$$

$$4x - 4x + 4 > 4x - 4x + 5 \qquad \textit{Subtract 4x from both sides.}$$

$$4 > 5$$

Since 4 is never greater than 5, the answer is **no solution** (**Fig. 2.14**). There is no real number that makes the statement true.

▶ **Now Try Exercise 43**

Chapter 2 Summary

IMPORTANT FACTS AND CONCEPTS	EXAMPLES

Section 2.1

The **terms** of an expression are the parts that are added.

$2x^2 - 3xy + 5$ has 3 terms: $2x^2$, $-3xy$, and 5.

The numerical part of a term is called its **numerical coefficient**.

The numerical coefficient of $\dfrac{3x}{4}$ is $\dfrac{3}{4}$.

A **constant** is a term that is a number without a variable.

In $3x^2 + 2x - 7$, the -7 is a constant.

Like terms have the same variables with the same exponents.

$7x$ and x; $6y^2$ and $2y^2$; $3(x + 4)$ and $-8(x + 4)$

To Combine Like Terms

1. Determine which terms are like terms.
2. Add or subtract the coefficients of the like terms.
3. Multiply the number found in step 2 by the common variable(s).

$$-3x^2 + 4y - 7x^2 + 6 - y - 9$$
$$= -3x^2 - 7x^2 + 4y - y + 6 - 9$$
$$= -10x^2 + 3y - 3$$

Distributive Property

For any real numbers a, b, and c,

$$a(b + c) = ab + ac$$

$$-5(3r - 6) = -15r + 30$$

To Simplify an Expression

1. Use the distributive property to remove any parentheses.
2. Combine like terms.

$$2(3c - 1) - 5(c + 4) - 6$$
$$= 6c - 2 - 5c - 20 - 6$$
$$= c - 28$$

When two or more expressions are multiplied, each expression is a **factor** of the product.

Since $7 \cdot 8 = 56$, the 7 and the 8 are factors of 56.

Section 2.2

A **linear equation** in one variable is an equation that can be written in the form

$$ax + b = c$$

where a, b, and c are real numbers and $a \neq 0$.

$$9x - 2 = 16$$

The **solution to an equation** is the number or numbers that when substituted for the variable or variables make the equation a true statement.

The solution to $2x + 3 = 9$ is 3.

The solution to an equation may be **checked** by substituting the value that is believed to be the solution for the variable in the original equation.

To check whether -2 is the solution to $-7x + 1 = 15$:
$$-7x + 1 = 15$$
$$-7(-2) + 1 \stackrel{?}{=} 15$$
$$14 + 1 \stackrel{?}{=} 15$$
$$15 = 15 \quad \textit{True}$$

Thus, -2 is the solution.

IMPORTANT FACTS AND CONCEPTS	EXAMPLES

Section 2.2 (continued)

Two or more equations with the same solution are called **equivalent equations**.	$-4x = 12, 2x - 3 = -9$, and $x = -3$ are equivalent equations
Addition Property of Equality If $a = b$, then $a + c = b + c$ for any real numbers $a, b,$ and c.	Solve the equation $x - 9 = -2$. $$x - 9 = -2$$ $$x - 9 \boxed{+ 9} = -2 \boxed{+ 9}$$ $$x = 7$$

Section 2.3

Two numbers are **reciprocals** of each other when their product is 1.	3 and $\dfrac{1}{3}$ are reciprocals since $3 \cdot \dfrac{1}{3} = 1$.
Multiplication Property of Equality If $a = b$, then $a \cdot c = b \cdot c$ for any real numbers $a, b,$ and c.	Solve the equation $\dfrac{3}{7}x = 6$. $$\dfrac{3}{7}x = 6$$ $$\boxed{\dfrac{7}{3}} \cdot \dfrac{3}{7}x = \boxed{\dfrac{7}{3}} \cdot 6$$ $$x = 14$$

Section 2.4

To Solve Linear Equations with a Variable on Only One Side of the Equal Sign 1. If the equation contains fractions, multiply **both** sides of the equation by the least common denominator (LCD). 2. Use the distributive property to remove parentheses. 3. Combine like terms on the same side of the equal sign. 4. Use the addition property to obtain an equation with the term containing the variable on one side of the equal sign and a constant on the other side. 5. Use the multiplication property to isolate the variable. 6. Check the solution in the original equation.	Solve the equation $3(x - 5) - 6x = -2$. $$3(x - 5) - 6x = -2$$ $$3x - 15 - 6x = -2$$ $$-3x - 15 = -2$$ $$-3x - 15 \boxed{+ 15} = -2 \boxed{+ 15}$$ $$-3x = 13$$ $$\dfrac{-3x}{-3} = \dfrac{13}{-3}$$ $$x = -\dfrac{13}{3}$$ A check will show that $-\dfrac{13}{3}$ is the solution.

Section 2.5

To Solve Linear Equations with the Variable on Both Sides of the Equal Sign 1. If the equation contains fractions, multiply **both** sides of the equation by the LCD. 2. Use the distributive property to remove parentheses. 3. Combine like terms on the same side of the equal sign. 4. Use the addition property to rewrite the equation with all terms containing the variable on one side of the equal sign and all terms not containing the variable on the other side of the equal sign. 5. Use the multiplication property to isolate the variable. 6. Check the solution in the original equation.	Solve the equation $9 - 3x - 2(x + 5) = 4x + 7 - x$. $$9 - 3x - 2(x + 5) = 4x + 7 - x$$ $$9 - 3x - 2x - 10 = 4x + 7 - x$$ $$-5x - 1 = 3x + 7$$ $$-5x \boxed{+ 5x} - 1 = 3x \boxed{+ 5x} + 7$$ $$-1 = 8x + 7$$ $$-1 \boxed{- 7} = 8x + 7 \boxed{- 7}$$ $$-8 = 8x$$ $$\dfrac{-8}{\boxed{8}} = \dfrac{8x}{\boxed{8}}$$ $$-1 = x$$ A check will show that -1 is the solution.

IMPORTANT FACTS AND CONCEPTS	EXAMPLES

Section 2.5 (continued)

A **conditional equation** is an equation that has a single value for a solution.	$3x - 2 = 8$ is a conditional equation since its solution is $\frac{10}{3}$.
An **identity** is an equation that is true for infinitely many values of the variable.	$-4(x + 3) = -5x - 12 + x$ is an identity because the equation is true for any real number.
A **contradiction** is an equation that has no solution.	$-9x + 7 + 6x = -5x + 1 + 2x$ is a contradiction because the equation is never true and has no solution.

Section 2.6

Simple Interest Formula

$$\text{interest} = \text{principal} \cdot \text{rate} \cdot \text{time} \quad \text{or} \quad i = prt$$

Determine the interest earned on a $5000 investment at 3% simple interest for 2 years.

$$i = prt$$
$$i = 5000(0.03)(2)$$
$$i = \$300$$

Distance Formula

$$\text{distance} = \text{rate} \cdot \text{time} \quad \text{or} \quad d = r \cdot t$$

Timothy John completed a snowmobile race in 2.4 hours at an average speed of 75 miles per hour. Determine the distance of the race.

$$d = rt$$
$$d = (75)(2.4)$$
$$d = 180 \text{ miles}$$

Area is the total surface within the figure's boundaries. Areas are measured in square units.

Perimeter is the sum of the lengths of the sides of a figure. Perimeters are measured in the same common unit as the sides.

Perimeter and area formulas can be found in **Table 2.1** on page 142.

Determine the perimeter and area of the following trapezoid.

$$P = a + b + c + d$$
$$P = 5 + 6 + 10.4 + 18.6$$
$$P = 40 \text{ ft}$$

$$A = \frac{1}{2}h(b + d)$$

$$A = \frac{1}{2}(4)(6 + 18.6)$$

$$A = 49.2 \text{ ft}^2$$

The **circumference** of a circle is the length (or perimeter) of the curve that forms a circle.

Circle formulas can be found in **Table 2.2** on page 144.

Determine the area and circumference of the following circle.

$$A = \pi r^2$$
$$A = \pi(4)^2$$
$$A = \pi(16)$$
$$A \approx 50.27 \text{ cm}^2$$
$$C = 2\pi r$$
$$C = 2\pi(4)$$
$$C = 8\pi$$
$$C \approx 25.13 \text{ cm}$$

IMPORTANT FACTS AND CONCEPTS	EXAMPLES

Section 2.6 (continued)

Volume may be considered the space occupied by a figure. Volume is measured is cubic units.

Volume formulas can be found in **Table 2.3** on page 145.

Determine the volume of the following figure.

7 m

3 m

$$V = \frac{1}{3}\pi r^2 h$$

$$V = \frac{1}{3}\pi (3)^2 (7)$$

$$V = \frac{1}{3}\pi (9)(7)$$

$$V = 21\pi$$

$$V \approx 65.97 \text{ m}^3$$

To **solve for a variable in a formula**, treat each of the quantities, except the one for which you are solving, as if they were constants. Then solve for the desired variable by isolating it on one side of the equation.

Solve $V = lwh$, for h.

$$V = lwh$$

$$\frac{V}{lw} = \frac{lwh}{lw}$$

$$\frac{V}{lw} = h$$

Section 2.7

A **ratio** is a quotient of two quantities.

$$3 \text{ to } 5, \quad 3:5, \quad \frac{3}{5}$$

A **proportion** is a statement of equality between two ratios. In the proportion $\frac{a}{b} = \frac{c}{d}$, the a and d are called the **extremes**, and the b and c are called the **means** of the proportion.

$$\frac{7}{10} = \frac{21}{30}$$

7 and 30 are the extremes. 10 and 21 are the means.

Cross-Multiplication

$$\text{If } \frac{a}{b} = \frac{c}{d}, \text{ then } ad = bc.$$

Solve $\frac{-9}{2} = \frac{126}{x}$ for x by cross-multiplying.

$$\frac{-9}{2} = \frac{126}{x}$$

$$-9 \cdot x = 2 \cdot 126$$

$$-9x = 252$$

$$\frac{-9x}{-9} = \frac{252}{-9}$$

$$x = -28$$

IMPORTANT FACTS AND CONCEPTS	EXAMPLES

Section 2.7 (continued)

To Solve Problems Using Proportions

1. Understand the problem.

2. Translate the problem into mathematical language.

3. Carry out the mathematical calculations necessary to solve the problem.

4. Check the answer obtained in step 3.

5. Make sure you have answered the question.

See page 155 for more details on proportions.

Melanie Jo can type 40 words per minute. If she types for 20.5 minutes, how many words will she type?

$$\frac{40 \text{ words}}{1 \text{ minute}} = \frac{x \text{ words}}{20.5 \text{ minutes}}$$

$$40(20.5) = 1(x)$$

$$820 = x$$

Melanie Jo will type 820 words.

Similar figures are figures whose corresponding angles are equal and whose corresponding sides are in proportion.

These two figures are similar.

12 in.

21.6 in.

5 in.

9 in.

Section 2.8

An **inequality** is a mathematical statement containing one or more of the following symbols: $>, <, \geq, \leq$.

$$x + 7 \leq 3x - 5$$

Properties Used to Solve Inequalities

For real numbers, a, b, and c:

1. If $a > b$, then $a + c > b + c$.

2. If $a > b$, then $a - c > b - c$.

3. If $a > b$ **and** $c > 0$, then $ac > bc$.

4. If $a > b$ **and** $c > 0$, then $\dfrac{a}{c} > \dfrac{b}{c}$.

5. If $a > b$ **and** $c < 0$, then $ac < bc$.

6. If $a > b$ **and** $c < 0$, then $\dfrac{a}{c} < \dfrac{b}{c}$.

1. If $x - 5 > 3$, then $x - 5 + 5 > 3 + 5$.

2. If $x + 4 \geq -9$, then $x + 4 - 4 \geq -9 - 4$.

3. If $\dfrac{1}{3}x > 2$, then $\left(\dfrac{1}{3}x\right)(3) > 2(3)$.

4. If $6x > 12$, then $\dfrac{6x}{6} > \dfrac{12}{6}$.

5. If $-\dfrac{1}{4}x > 8$, then $\left(-\dfrac{1}{4}x\right)(-4) < 8(-4)$.

6. If $-7x \geq 35$, then $\dfrac{-7x}{-7} \leq \dfrac{35}{-7}$.

Chapter 2 Review Exercises

[2.1] *Use the distributive property to simplify.*

1. $3(x + 4)$ $3x + 12$

2. $5(x - 2)$ $5x - 10$

3. $-2(x + 4)$ $-2x - 8$

4. $-(x + 2)$ $-x - 2$

5. $-(m + 3)$ $-m - 3$

6. $-4(4 - x)$ $-16 + 4x$

7. $5(5 - p)$ $25 - 5p$

8. $6(4x - 5)$ $24x - 30$

9. $-5(5x - 5)$ $-25x + 25$

10. $4(-x + 3)$ $-4x + 12$

11. $\dfrac{1}{2}(2x + 4)$ $x + 2$

12. $-\dfrac{1}{3}(3 + 6y)$ $-1 - 2y$

13. $-(x + 2y - z)$ $-x - 2y + z$

14. $-3(2a - 5b + 7)$ $-6a + 15b - 21$

[2.1] *Simplify.*

15. $7x - 3x$ $4x$

16. $5 - 3y + 3$ $-3y + 8$

17. $1 + 3x + 2x$ $5x + 1$

18. $-2x - x + 3y$ $-3x + 3y$

19. $4m + 2n + 4m + 6n$ $8m + 8n$

20. $9x + 3y + 2$ $9x + 3y + 2$

21. $6x - 2x + 3y + 6$ $4x + 3y + 6$

22. $x + 8x - 9x + 3$ 3

23. $-4x^2 - 8x^2 + 3$ $-12x^2 + 3$

24. $-2(3a^2 - 4) + 6a^2 - 8$ 0

25. $2x + 3(x + 4) - 5$ $5x + 7$

26. $-4 + 2(3 - 2b) + b$ $-3b + 2$

27. $6 - (-7x + 6) - 7x$ 0

28. $2(2x + 5) - 10 - 4$ $4x - 4$

29. $-6(4 - 3x) - 18 + 4x$ $22x - 42$

30. $4y - 3(x + y) + 6x^2$ $6x^2 - 3x + y$

31. $\dfrac{1}{4}d + 2 - \dfrac{3}{5}d + 5$ $-\dfrac{7}{20}d + 7$

32. $3 - (x - y) + (x - y)$ 3

33. $\dfrac{5}{6}x - \dfrac{1}{3}(2x - 6)$ $\dfrac{1}{6}x + 2$

34. $\dfrac{2}{3} - \dfrac{1}{4}n - \dfrac{1}{3}(n + 2)$ $-\dfrac{7}{12}n$

[2.2–2.5] *Solve.*

35. $-3x = -3$ 1

36. $x + 6 = -7$ -13

37. $x - 4 = 7$ 11

38. $\dfrac{x}{3} = -9$ -27

39. $5x + 1 = 12$ $\dfrac{11}{5}$

40. $14 = 3 + 2x$ $\dfrac{11}{2}$

41. $4c + 3 = -21$ -6

42. $9 - 2a = 15$ -3

43. $-x = -12$ 12

44. $3(x - 2) = 6$ 4

45. $-12 = 3(2x - 8)$ 2

46. $4(6 + 2x) = 0$ -3

47. $-6n + 2n + 6 = 0$ $\dfrac{3}{2}$

48. $-3 = 3w - (4w + 6)$ -3

49. $6 - (2n + 3) - 4n = 6$ $-\dfrac{1}{2}$

50. $4x + 6 - 7x + 9 = 18$ -1

51. $5 + 3(x - 1) = 3(x + 1) - 1$

52. $8.4r - 6.3 = 6.3 + 2.1r$ 2

53. $19.6 - 21.3t = 80.1 - 9.2t$ -5

54. $0.35(c - 5) = 0.45(c + 4)$ -35.5

55. $0.2(x + 6) = -0.3(2x - 1)$ -1.125

56. $-2.3(x - 8) = 3.7(x + 4)$ 0.6

57. $\dfrac{p}{3} + 2 = \dfrac{1}{4}$ $-\dfrac{21}{4}$

58. $\dfrac{d}{6} + \dfrac{1}{7} = 2$ $\dfrac{78}{7}$

59. $\dfrac{3}{5}(r - 6) = 3r$ $-\dfrac{3}{2}$

60. $\dfrac{2}{3}w = \dfrac{1}{7}(w - 2)$ $-\dfrac{6}{11}$

61. $8x - 5 = -4x + 19$ 2

62. $-(w + 2) = 2(3w - 6)$ $\dfrac{10}{7}$

63. $2x + 6 = 3x + 9 - 3$ 0

64. $-5a + 3 = 2a + 10$ -1

65. $5p - 2 = -2(-3p + 6)$ 10

66. $3x - 12x = 24 - 9x$ no solution

67. $4(2x - 3) + 4 = 8x - 8$ all real numbers

68. $4 - c - 2(4 - 3c) = 3(c - 4)$ -4

69. $2(x + 7) = 6x + 9 - 4x$ no solution

70. $-5(3 - 4x) = -6 + 20x - 9$

71. $4(x - 3) - (x + 5) = 0$ $\dfrac{17}{3}$

72. $-2(4 - x) = 6(x + 2) + 3x$ $-\dfrac{20}{7}$

73. $\dfrac{x + 3}{2} = \dfrac{x}{2}$ no solution

74. $\dfrac{x}{6} = \dfrac{x - 4}{2}$ 6

75. $\dfrac{1}{5}(3s + 4) = \dfrac{1}{3}(2s - 8)$ 52

76. $\dfrac{2(2t - 4)}{5} = \dfrac{3t + 6}{4} - \dfrac{3}{2}$ 32

77. $\dfrac{2}{5}(2 - x) = \dfrac{1}{6}(-2x + 2)$ 7

78. $\dfrac{x}{4} + \dfrac{x}{6} = \dfrac{1}{2}(x + 3)$ -18

51. all real numbers   **70.** all real numbers

[2.6] *Use the formula to find the value of the variable indicated.*

79. $y = mx + b$ (slope-intercept form of a line); find m when $y = 7$, $x = 2$, and $b = 1$. 3

80. $A = \dfrac{1}{2}h(b + d)$ (area of a trapezoid); find A when $h = 12$, $b = 3$, and $d = 5$. 48

Determine the area or volume of the figure.

81. 12 cm^2

82. $\approx 33.51 \text{ in.}^3$

Solve for the indicated variable.

83. $P = 2l + 2w$, for l $l = (P - 2w)/2$

84. $y - y_1 = m(x - x_1)$, for m $m = \dfrac{y - y_1}{x - x_1}$

85. $-x + 3y = 2$, for y $y = \dfrac{1}{3}x + \dfrac{2}{3}$

86. Spring Break Yong Wolfer traveled to Florida for spring break at an average speed of 61.7 miles per hour for 5 hours. How for did he travel?   308.5 mi

87. Flower Garden Chrishawn Miller has a rectangular flower garden that measures 20 feet by 12 feet. What is the area of Chrishawn's flower garden?   240 ft²

88. Tuna Fish Find the volume of a tuna fish can if its diameter is 4 inches and its height is 2 inches.   ≈25.13 in.³

[2.7] *Determine the following ratios. Write each ratio in lowest terms.*

89. 12 feet to 20 feet   3:5

90. 80 ounces to 12 pounds   5:12

91. 4 minutes:40 seconds   6:1

Solve each proportion.

92. $\frac{x}{4} = \frac{8}{16}$ 2

93. $\frac{5}{20} = \frac{x}{80}$ 20

94. $\frac{3}{x} = \frac{15}{45}$ 9

95. $\frac{20}{45} = \frac{15}{x}$ $\frac{135}{4}$

96. $\frac{6}{5} = \frac{-12}{x}$ −10

97. $\frac{b}{6} = \frac{8}{-3}$ −16

98. $\frac{-7}{9} = \frac{-12}{y}$ $\frac{108}{7}$

99. $\frac{x}{-15} = \frac{30}{-5}$ 90

The following pairs of figures are similar. For each pair, find the length of the side indicated by x.

100.

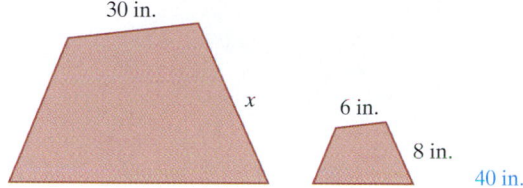

30 in.   x   6 in.   8 in.   40 in.

101.

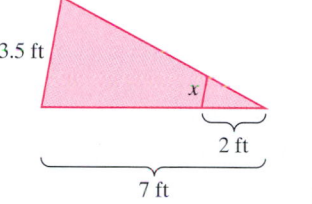

3.5 ft   x   2 ft   7 ft   1 ft

[2.8] *Solve each inequality, and graph the solution on a number line.*

102. $3x + 4 \geq 10$ $x \geq 2$,

103. $-4a - 6 > 4a - 14$ $a < 1$,

104. $5 - 3r \leq 2r + 15$ $r \geq -2$,

105. $2(x + 4) \leq 2x - 5$ no solution,

106. $2(x + 3) > 6x - 4x + 4$ all real numbers,

107. $x + 6 > 9x + 30$ $x < -3$,

108. $x - 8 \leq -3x + 9$ $x \leq \frac{17}{4}$,

109. $-(x + 2) < -2(-2x + 5)$ $x > \frac{8}{5}$,

110. $\frac{x}{2} < \frac{2}{3}(x + 3)$ $x > -12$,

111. $\frac{3}{10}(t - 2) \leq \frac{3}{4}(4 + 2t)$ $t \geq -3$,

[2.7] *Set up a proportion and solve each problem.*

112. Boat Trip A boat travels 40 miles in 1.8 hours. If it travels at the same rate, how long will it take for it to travel 140 miles?   6.3 hr

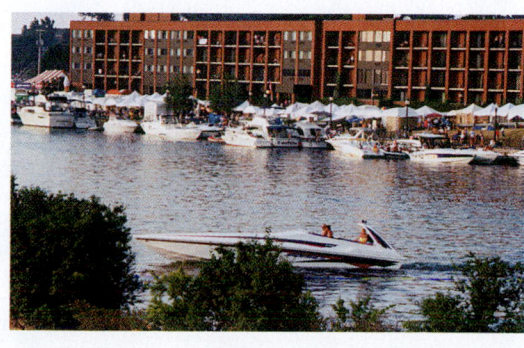

113. Washing Dishes If Adam Kloza can wash 12 dishes in 3.5 minutes, how many dishes can he wash in 21 minutes?   72 dishes

114. Copy Machine If a copy machine can copy 20 pages per minute, how many pages can be copied in 22 minutes?   440 pages

115. Map Scale If the scale of a map is 1 inch to 60 miles, what distance on the map represents 380 miles? $6\frac{1}{3}$ in.

116. Model Car Bryce Winston builds a model car to a scale of 1 inch to 1.5 feet. If the completed model is 10.5 inches, what is the size of the actual car?   15.75 ft

117. Money Exchange Suppose that one U.S. dollar can be exchanged for 9.165 Mexican pesos, find the value of 1 peso in terms of U.S. dollars.   ≈$0.109

118. Ketchup If a machine can fill and cap 80 bottles of ketchup in 50 seconds, how many bottles of ketchup can it fill and cap in 2 minutes?   192 bottles

Chapter 2 Practice Test

*To find out how well you understand the chapter material, take this practice test. The answers, and the section where the material was initially discussed, are given in the back of the book. Each problem is also fully worked out on the **Chapter Test Prep Video CD**. Review any questions that you answered incorrectly.*

Use the distributive property to simplify.

1. $-3(4 - 2x)$ $6x - 12$

2. $-(x + 3y - 4)$ $-x - 3y + 4$

Simplify.

3. $5x - 8x + 4$ $-3x + 4$

4. $4 + 2x - 3x + 6$ $-x + 10$

5. $-y - x - 4x - 6$ $-5x - y - 6$

6. $a - 2b + 6a - 6b - 3$ $7a - 8b - 3$

7. $2x^2 + 3 + 2(3x - 2)$ $2x^2 + 6x - 1$

Solve exercises 8–16.

8. $2.4x - 3.9 = 3.3$ 3

9. $\dfrac{5}{6}(x - 2) = x - 3$ 8

10. $2x - 3(-2x + 4) = -13 + x$ $-\dfrac{1}{7}$

11. $3x - 4 - x = 2(x + 5)$ no solution

12. $-3(2x + 3) = -2(3x + 1) - 7$ all real numbers

13. $ax + by + c = 0$, for x $x = \dfrac{-by - c}{a}$

14. $-6x + 5y = -2$, for y $y = \dfrac{6}{5}x - \dfrac{2}{5}$

15. $\dfrac{1}{7}(2x - 5) = \dfrac{3}{8}x - \dfrac{5}{7}$ 0

16. $\dfrac{9}{x} = \dfrac{3}{-15}$ -45

17. What do we call an equation that has

a) exactly one solution,   conditional equation

b) no solution,   contradiction

c) all real numbers as its solution?   identity

21. all real numbers, [number line with arrows, 0]

Solve Exercises 18–21, and graph the solution on a number line.

18. $2x - 4 < 4x + 10$ $x > -7$, [number line, open circle at −7]

19. $3(x + 4) \geq 5x - 12$ $x \leq 12$, [number line, closed circle at 12]

20. $4(x + 3) + 2x < 6x - 3$ no solution, [number line, 0]

21. $-(x - 2) - 3x = 4(1 - x) - 2$

22. The following figures are similar. Find the length of side x. $\dfrac{32}{3} = 10\dfrac{2}{3}$ ft

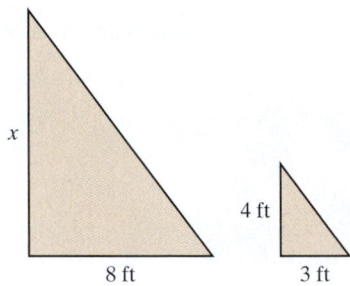

x 4 ft

8 ft   3 ft

23. **Simple Interest Loan** Laura Hoye lent her sister $2000 for a period of 1 year. At the end of 1 year, her sister repaid the $2000 plus $80 interest. What simple interest rate did her sister pay?   4%

24. **Peanut Butter Pie** A peanut butter pie has a diameter of 9 inches. Determine the circumference of the pie.   ≈28.27 in.

25. **Travel Time** While traveling, you notice that you traveled 25 miles in 35 minutes. If your speed does not change, how long will it take you to travel 125 miles?   175 min or 2 hr 55 min

Cumulative Review Test

Take the following test and check your answers with those given in the back of the book. Review any questions that you answered incorrectly. The section where the material was covered is indicated after the answer.

1. Multiply $\dfrac{52}{15} \cdot \dfrac{10}{13}$ $\dfrac{8}{3}$

2. Divide $\dfrac{5}{24} \div \dfrac{2}{9}$ $\dfrac{15}{16}$

3. Insert $<$, $>$, or $=$ in the shaded area to make a true statement: $|-2|$ ⬛ 1. $>$

4. Evaluate $-5 - (-4) + 12 - 8$. 3

5. Subtract -6 from -7. -1

6. Evaluate $20 - 6 \div 3 \cdot 2$. 16

7. Evaluate $3[6 - (4 - 3^2)] - 30$. 3

8. Evaluate $-2x^2 - 6x + 8$ when $x = -2$. 12

9. Name the illustrated property.   distributive property
$$-5(x - 3y - 4z) = -5x + 15y + 20z$$

Simplify.

10. $8x + 2y + 4x - y$ $12x + y$

11. $9 - \dfrac{2}{3}x + 16 + \dfrac{3}{4}x$ $\dfrac{1}{12}x + 25$

Solve.

12. $7x + 3 = -4$ -1

13. $4(x - 2) = 5(x - 1) + 3x + 2$ $-\dfrac{5}{4}$

14. $\dfrac{3}{4}n - \dfrac{1}{5} = \dfrac{2}{3}n$ $\dfrac{12}{5}$

15. $A = \dfrac{a + b + c}{3}$, for b $b = 3A - a - c$

16. $\dfrac{40}{30} = \dfrac{3}{x}$ $\dfrac{9}{4}$ or 2.25

Solve, and graph the solution on a number line.

17. $x - 3 > 7$ $x > 10$, [number line, open circle at 10]

18. $2x - 7 \leq 3x + 5$ $x \geq -12$, [number line, closed circle at −12]

19. **Trampoline** A circular trampoline has a diameter of 22 feet. Determine the area of the trampoline.   ≈380.13 ft²

20. **Earnings** If Samuel earns $10.50 after working for 2 hours mowing a lawn, how much does he earn after 8 hours? $42

3 Applications of Algebra

WE OFTEN PURCHASE items that need to be delivered to our homes or apartments. When this occurs there may be a delivery charge, and certain other charges. In Example 5 on page 198 we set up and solve an equation dealing with a delivery charge and the purchase of sod for the lawn.

3.1 Changing Application Problems into Equations

1 Translate phrases into mathematical expressions.

2 Express the relationship between two related quantities.

3 Write expressions involving multiplication.

4 Translate applications into equations.

1 Translate Phrases into Mathematical Expressions

Helpful Hint *Study Tip*

It is important that you prepare for this chapter carefully. Make sure you read the book and work the examples carefully. *Attend class every day, and most of all, work all the exercises assigned to you.*

As you read through the examples in the rest of the chapter, think about how they can be expanded to other, similar problems. For example, in Example 1a) we will state that the distance, d, increased by 10 miles, can be represented by $d + 10$. You can generalize this to other, similar problems. For example, a weight, w, increased by 15 pounds, can be represented as $w + 15$.

One practical advantage of knowing algebra is that you can use it to solve everyday problems involving mathematics. For algebra to be useful in solving everyday problems, you must first be able to *translate application problems into mathematical language*. One purpose of this section is to help you take an application problem, also referred to as a *word* or *verbal problem*, and write it as a mathematical equation.

Often the most difficult part of solving an application problem is translating it into an equation. Before you can translate a problem into an equation, you must understand the meaning of certain words and phrases and how they are expressed mathematically. **Table 3.1** is a list of selected words and phrases and the operations they imply. We used the variable x. However, any variable could have been used.

TEACHING TIP
There is some overlap in setting up equations in Sections 3.1 and 3.2. This was done to give students more practice with this important material.

TABLE 3.1

Word or Phrase	Operation	Statement	Algebraic Form
Added to	Addition	8 *added to* a number	$x + 8$
More than		6 *more than* a number	$x + 6$
Increased by		A number *increased by* 3	$x + 3$
The sum of		*The sum of* a number and 4	$x + 4$
Subtracted from	Subtraction	6 *subtracted from* a number	$x - 6$
Less than		2 *less than* a number	$x - 2$
Decreased by		A number *decreased by* 5	$x - 5$
The difference between		The *difference between* a number and 9	$x - 9$
Multiplied by	Multiplication	A number *multiplied by* 6	$6x$
The product of		*The product of* 4 and a number	$4x$
Twice a number, 3 times a number, etc.		*Twice a number*	$2x$
Of, when used with a percent or fraction		20% *of* a number	$0.20x$
Divided by	Division	A number *divided by* 8	$\dfrac{x}{8}$
The quotient of		*The quotient of* a number and 6	$\dfrac{x}{6}$

Often a statement contains more than one operation. The following chart provides some examples of this.

TEACHING TIP
Point out that "a number decreased by 5" is not the same as "5 decreased by a number." Use a specific number to illustrate the difference between the two expressions.

Statement	Algebraic Form
Four more than twice a number	$\underbrace{2x}_{\text{Twice a number}} + 4$
Five less than 3 times a number	$\underbrace{3x}_{\text{Three times a number}} - 5$
Three times the sum of a number and 8	$3\underbrace{(x + 8)}_{\text{The sum of a number and 8}}$
Twice the difference between a number and 4	$2\underbrace{(x - 4)}_{\text{The difference between a number and 4}}$

> ### Avoiding Common Errors
>
> Subtraction is not commutative. That is, $a - b \neq b - a$. Therefore, you must be very careful when writing expressions involving subtraction. Study the following examples.
>
> 5 less than 3 times a number
>
> | CORRECT | INCORRECT |
> |---------|-----------|
> | $3x - 5$ | ~~$5 - 3x$~~ |
>
> 5 subtracted from 3 times a number
>
> | CORRECT | INCORRECT |
> |---------|-----------|
> | $3x - 5$ | ~~$5 - 3x$~~ |
>
> the difference between $3x$ and 5
>
> | CORRECT | INCORRECT |
> |---------|-----------|
> | $3x - 5$ | ~~$5 - 3x$~~ |

To give you more practice with the mathematical terms, we will also convert some algebraic expressions into statements. Often an algebraic expression can be written in several different ways. Following is a list of some of the possible statements that can be used to represent the given algebraic expression.

TEACHING TIP
Point out the importance of a comma. Three times a number, decreased by 4 is written as $3x - 4$. But, three times a number decreased by 4 is written as $3(x - 4)$.

Algebraic	Statements
$2x + 3$	Three more than twice a number The sum of twice a number and 3 Twice a number, increased by 3 Three added to twice a number
$3x - 4$	Four less than 3 times a number Three times a number, decreased by 4 The difference between 3 times a number and 4 Four subtracted from 3 times a number

INSTRUCTOR EXAMPLE
Express the statement "five inches less than twice the height, h" as an algebraic expression.
Ans.: $2h - 5$

EXAMPLE 1 ▶ Express each statement as an algebraic expression.

a) The distance, d, increased by 10 miles

b) Six times the height, h

c) Eight less than twice the area, a

d) Four pounds more than 5 times the weight, w

Solution

a) $d + 10$ **b)** $6h$ **c)** $2a - 8$ **d)** $5w + 4$

▶ **Now Try Exercise 13**

2 Express the Relationship between Two Related Quantities

Sometimes in a problem, two numbers are related to each other in a certain way. We often represent the simplest, or most basic, number that needs to be expressed as a variable, and the other as an expression containing that variable. Some examples follow.

Statement	One Number	Second Number
Two numbers differ by 5	x	$x + 5$
Mike's age now and Mike's age in 8 years	x	$x + 8$
One number is 6 times the other number	x	$6x$
One number is 12% less than the other	x	$x - 0.12x$

x $25 − x
Kendra   Phil

FIGURE 3.1

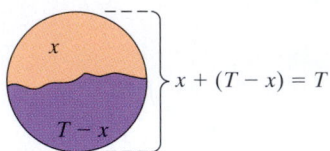

$x + (T − x) = T$

FIGURE 3.2

Note that often more than one pair of expressions can be used to represent the two numbers. For example, "two numbers differ by 5" can also be expressed as x and $x − 5$.

Now let's consider when one quantity is divided into two parts. For example, suppose $25 is divided between Kendra and Phil. If Kendra gets $10, how much does Phil get? Phil will get $25 − $10 or $15. If Kendra gets $12, then Phil will get $25 − $12 or $13. In general, if we let x represent the amount Kendra gets, then Phil will get $25 − x. Note that the sum of x and $25 − x$ is 25 (see **Fig. 3.1**).

In general, if T represents the total amount to be divided into two parts, then if one part is called x, the other part will be $T − x$. In **Figure 3.2**, if T represents the total area of the circle and x is the area of one part of the circle, then the area of the remaining part must be $T − x$.

There are many sections in this book where you will need to read a word problem and write an expression or equation to represent the word problem. The first thing you will need to do to write an expression or equation is to determine what quantity to let the variable represent. For example, if x is the variable, you will need to write "let $x =$." When doing so, in general, if one quantity is given in terms of another quantity, we let the variable represent the basic (or the original quantity) on which the second quantity is based. For example, suppose we are given that "Paul is 6 years older than George." Since Paul's age is given in terms of George's age, we let the variable represent George's age. Thus, we would write "let $x =$ George's age."

In Example 2, we give you some practice in identifying the item to call x when reading a word problem.

EXAMPLE 2 ▶ For each part, determine what to let $x =$.

a) Mary weighs 15 pounds more than Sue.

b) The length of a rectangle is 4 inches more than twice its width.

c) Joe earns $56.20 less than Larry.

d) The theater sold 525 tickets, some were adult and some were children's tickets.

Solution   In general, when writing expressions to represent word problems, if a quantity A is expressed in terms of a quantity B, then we let $x =$ quantity B.

a) Since Mary's weight is expressed in terms of Sue's weight, we let $x =$ Sue's weight.

b) Since the length of a rectangle is expressed in terms of its width, we let $x =$ width of the rectangle.

c) Since the amount Joe earns is expressed in terms of what Larry earns, we let $x =$ amount Larry makes.

d) Here, since neither quantity of adult tickets nor children's tickets is expressed in terms of the other's quantity, we can let $x =$ number of adult tickets sold or let $x =$ number of children's tickets sold. If we let $x =$ number of adult tickets sold, then $525 − x$ will equal the number of children's tickets sold. If we let $x =$ number of children's tickets sold, then $525 − x$ will equal the number of adult tickets sold.

▶ **Now Try Exercise 37**

In Example 2 we let x represent the variable. Although x is often used as the variable, other letters may be used. For example, consider the statement "Paul is 6 years older than George." If we choose to use the letter g as the variable, then we would write "let $g =$ George's age." The variable selected is just a matter of choice. If for example, the question discusses time, we may let the variable be t. If the question discusses the cost of an item, we may let the variable be c, and so on.

In Example 3, you will select the variable to use to represent quantities.

EXAMPLE 3 ▶ For each relationship, select a variable to represent one quantity and state what that variable represents. Then express the second quantity in terms of the variable selected.

a) The Dukes scored 12 points more than the Chiefs.

b) An adult robin is 4.3 times the weight of a baby robin.

c) Bill and Mary share $75.

d) Kim has 7 more than 5 times the amount Sylvia has.

e) The length of a rectangle is 3 feet less than 4 times its width.

Solution   To express the relationships, we must first decide which quantity we will let the variable represent. To give you practice with variables other than x, we will select different letters to represent the variable. We will select variables that relate to the expression given.

a) Since the number of points scored by the Dukes is expressed in terms of the number of points scored by the Chiefs, we will select to use the variable c.

$$\text{Let } c = \text{number of points scored by the Chiefs.}$$
$$\text{Then } c + 12 = \text{number of points scored by the Dukes.}$$

It is important that you realize that any other letter could have been selected for the variable. Suppose you used p since we are discussing points scored. Then you would have

$$\text{Let } p = \text{number of points scored by the Chiefs.}$$
$$\text{Then } p + 12 = \text{number of points scored by the Dukes.}$$

There is no "correct" variable to use; it is just a matter of preference. In the answers in the back of the book, if we listed two related quantities as c and $c + 12$, and you wrote the two related quantities as p and $p + 12$, you would still be correct.

b) The weight of an adult robin is given in terms of the weight of a baby robin.

$$\text{Let } w = \text{weight of a baby robin.}$$
$$\text{Then } 4.3w = \text{weight of an adult robin.}$$

c) We are not told how much of the $75 each person receives. In this case we can let the variable represent the amount either person receives. We will let a represent the amount Bill receives.

$$\text{Let } a = \text{amount Bill receives.}$$
$$\text{Then } 75 - a = \text{amount Mary receives.}$$

d) The amount Kim has is given in terms of the amount Sylvia has.

$$\text{Let } s = \text{amount Sylvia has.}$$
$$\text{Then } 5s + 7 = \text{amount Kim has.}$$

e) The length of the rectangle is given in terms of the width of the rectangle.

$$\text{Let } w = \text{width of the rectangle.}$$
$$\text{Then } 4w - 3 = \text{length of the rectangle.}$$

▶ **Now Try Exercise 47**

3 Write Expressions Involving Multiplication

Consider the statement "the cost of 3 items at $5 each." How would you represent this quantity using mathematical symbols? You would probably reason that the cost would be 3 times $5 and write $3 \cdot 5$ or $3(5)$.

Now consider the statement "the cost of x items at $5 each." How would you represent this statement using mathematical symbols? If you use the same reasoning, you might write $x \cdot 5$ or $x(5)$. Another way to write this product is $5x$. Thus, the cost of x items at $5 each could be represented as $5x$.

Finally, consider the statement "the cost of x items at y dollars each." Following the reasoning used in the previous two illustrations, you might write $x \cdot y$ or $x(y)$. Since these products can be written as xy, the cost of x items at y dollars each can be represented as xy.

EXAMPLE 4 ▶ Write each statement as an algebraic expression.

a) The cost of purchasing x pens at \$2 each

b) A 5% commission on x dollars in sales

c) The dollar amount earned in h hours if a person earns \$6.50 per hour

d) The number of cents in q quarters

e) The number of ounces in x pounds

Solution

a) We can reason like this: One pen would cost $1(2)$ dollars, two pens would cost $2(2)$ dollars, three pens $3(2)$ dollars, four pens $4(2)$ dollars, and so on. Continuing this reasoning process, we can see that x pens would cost $x(2)$ or $2x$ dollars.

b) A 5% commission on \$1 sales would be $0.05(1)$, on \$2 sales $0.05(2)$, on \$3 sales $0.05(3)$, on \$4 sales $0.05(4)$, and so on. Therefore, the commission on sales of x dollars would be $0.05(x)$ or $0.05x$.

   Note: If you need a review on changing a percent to a decimal number, review Appendix A.

c) In one hour the person would earn $1(\$6.50)$. In two hours the person would earn $2(\$6.50)$, and in h hours the person would earn $h(\$6.50)$ or $\$6.50h$.

d) We know that each quarter is worth 25 cents. Thus, one quarter is $1(25)$ cents. Two quarters is $2(25)$ cents, and so on. Therefore, q quarters is $q(25)$ cents or $25q$ cents.

e) Each pound is equal to 16 ounces. Using the same reasoning as in part **d)**, we see that x pounds is $16x$ ounces.

▶ **Now Try Exercise 71**

EXAMPLE 5 ▶ **Truck Rental** Maria Mears rented a truck for 1 day. She paid a daily fee of \$38 and a mileage fee of 25 cents per mile. Write an expression that represents her total cost when she drives x miles.

Solution   Maria's total cost consists of two parts, the daily fee and the mileage fee. Notice the daily fee is given in terms of dollars, and the mileage fee is given in cents. When writing an expression to represent the total cost, we want the units to be the same. Therefore, we will use a mileage fee of \$0.25 per mile, which is equal to 25 cents per mile.

$$\text{Let } x = \text{number of miles driven.}$$

$$\text{Then } 0.25x = \text{cost of driving } x \text{ miles}$$

$$\overbrace{\underset{38 \quad + \quad 0.25x}{\text{daily fee } + \text{ mileage fee}}}^{\text{total cost}}$$

Thus, the expression that represents Maria's total cost is $38 + 0.25x$.

▶ **Now Try Exercise 75**

EXAMPLE 6 ▶ **Write a Sum or Difference** In a bus the number of males was 3 more than twice the number of females. Write an expression for

a) the sum of the number of males and females

b) the difference between the number of males and females

c) the difference between the number of females and males

Solution   Since the number of males is expressed in terms of the number of females, we let the variable represent the number of females. We will choose x to represent the variable.

Let x = number of females.

Then $2x + 3$ = number of males

a) The expression for the sum of the number of males and females is

$$\underbrace{(2x + 3)}_{\substack{\text{number} \\ \text{of males}}} + \underbrace{x}_{\substack{\text{number} \\ \text{of females}}}$$

b) The expression for the difference between the number of males and females is

$$\underbrace{(2x + 3)}_{\substack{\text{number} \\ \text{of males}}} - \underbrace{x}_{\substack{\text{number} \\ \text{of females}}}$$

c) The expression for the difference between the number of females and males is

$$\underbrace{x}_{\substack{\text{number} \\ \text{of females}}} - \underbrace{(2x + 3)}_{\substack{\text{number} \\ \text{of males}}}$$

Notice that parentheses are needed around the $2x + 3$ since both terms $2x$ and 3 are being subtracted.

▶ **Now Try Exercise 87**

Helpful Hint

This Helpful Hint will discuss the use of parentheses when writing the sum or difference of quantities.

Sum: When writing the sum of two quantities, parentheses may be used to help in the understanding of the problem, but they are not necessary.

Examples	Answers
Find the sum of x and $2x - 3$.	$x + (2x - 3)$ or $x + 2x - 3$
Find the sum of $3c - 4$ and $c + 5$.	$(3c - 4) + (c + 5)$ or $3c - 4 + c + 5$

Difference: When writing the difference of two quantities, when only *a single term* is being subtracted, parentheses may be used in the understanding of the problem, but they are not necessary.

Examples	Answers
Subtract r from $3r - 2$.	$(3r - 2) - r$ or $3r - 2 - r$
Find the difference between $2s + 6$ and s.	$(2s + 6) - s$ or $2s + 6 - s$

When writing the difference of two quantities, *when two or more terms are being subtracted, parentheses **must** be placed around all the terms being subtracted*, since all the terms are being subtracted and not just the first term.

Examples	Answers
Subtract $x + 2$ from $3x$.	$3x - (x + 2)$
Subtract $3t - 4$ from $5t$.	$5t - (3t - 4)$
Subtract $r - 5$ from $2r + 3$.	$(2r + 3) - (r - 5)$ or $2r + 3 - (r - 5)$
Find the difference between 6 and $m + 3$.	$6 - (m + 3)$
Find the difference between $4n - 9$ and $2n - 3$.	$(4n - 9) - (2n - 3)$ or $4n - 9 - (2n - 3)$

Expressions Involving Percent

Example 7 involves percent. Before we leave this section, let's discuss expressions that involve percent further. Since percents are used so often, you must have a clear understanding of how to write expressions involving percent. Whenever we perform a calculation involving percent, we change the percent to a decimal number or a fraction first.

When shopping we may see a "25% off" sign. We assume that this means 25% of the *original cost*, even though this is not stated. If we let c represent the original cost, then 25% of the original cost would be represented as $0.25c$. Twenty-five percent off the original cost means the original cost, c, decreased by 25% of the original cost. Twenty five percent off the original cost would be represented as $c - 0.25c$.

25% off the original cost

$$c - 0.25c$$

Original cost ——— decreased by ——— 25% of the original cost

Now let's work an example involving percent.

INSTRUCTOR EXAMPLE
Express the statement "the profit, p, decreased by 15%" as an algebraic expression.
Ans.: $p - 0.15p$

EXAMPLE 7 ▶ Write each statement as an algebraic expression.

a) The cost of a pair of boots c, increased by 6%

b) The population in the town of Brooksville, p, decreased by 12%

Solution

a) The question asks for the cost increased by 6%. We assume that this means the cost increased by 6% of the original cost. Therefore, the answer is $c + 0.06c$.

b) Using the same reasoning as in part **a)**, the answer is $p - 0.12p$.

TEACHING TIP
Have students use the distributive property to rewrite $c + 0.06c$.

▶ **Now Try Exercise 79**

Avoiding Common Errors

In Example 7**a)** we asked you to represent a cost, c, increased by 6%. Note, the answer is $c + 0.06c$. Often, students write the answer to this question as $c + 0.06$. It is important to realize that a percent of a quantity must always be a percent multiplied by some number or letter. Some phrases involving the word percent and the correct and incorrect interpretations follow.

PHRASE	CORRECT	INCORRECT
A $7\frac{1}{2}$% sales tax on c dollars	$0.075c$	~~0.075~~
The cost, c, increased by a $7\frac{1}{2}$% sales tax	$c + 0.075c$	~~$c + 0.075$~~
The cost, c, reduced by 25%	$c - 0.25c$	~~$c - 0.25$~~

---

4 Translate Applications into Equations

Now we will explain how to write application problems as equations. The word *is* in an application problem often means *is equal to* and is represented by an equal sign. Some examples of statements written as equations follow.

Statement	Equation
Six times a number *is* 42.	$6x = 42$
Five more than twice a number *is* 4.	$2x + 5 = 4$
A number decreased by 4 *is* 3 more than twice the number.	$x - 4 = 2x + 3$
The sum of a number and the number increased by 4 *is* 60.	$x + (x + 4) = 60$
Twice the difference of a number and 3 *is* the sum of the number and 20.	$2(x - 3) = x + 20$
A number increased by 15% *is* 120.	$x + 0.15x = 120$
Six less than three times a number *is* one-fourth the number.	$3x - 6 = \dfrac{1}{4}x$

Now let's translate some equations into statements. Some examples of equations written as statements follow. We will write only two statements for each equation, but remember there are other ways these equations can be written.

Equation	Statements
$3x - 4 = 4x + 3$	Four less than 3 times a number *is* 3 more than 4 times the number.
	Three times a number, decreased by 4 *is* 4 times the number, increased by 3.
$3(x - 2) = 6x - 4$	Three times the difference between a number and 2 *is* 4 less than 6 times the number.
	The product of 3 and the difference between a number and 2 *is* 6 times the number, decreased by 4.

Now let's work some examples where we write equations.

INSTRUCTOR EXAMPLE
Write the following as an equation.
"The cost for *p* pens at $2.20 per pen is $25."
Ans.: $2.20p = 25$

EXAMPLE 8 ▶ **Translate Words into Equations** Write each problem as an equation.

a) The population in the town of Rush is increasing by 500 people per year. The increase in population in *t* years *is* 2500.

b) The number of cents in *d* dimes *is* 120.

c) The cost of *x* gallons of gasoline at $3.20 per gallon *is* $35.20.

Solution

a) In one year the population increases by 1(500). In two years the population increases by 2(500), and in *t* years the increase in population is *t*(500) or 500*t*. Since the increase in population in *t* years *is* 2500, the equation is $500t = 2500$.

b) The number of cents in 1 dime is 1(10). The number of cents in 2 dimes is 2(10), and the number of cents in *d* dimes is *d*(10) or 10*d*. Since the number of cents in *d* dimes *is* 120, the equation is $10d = 120$.

c) Using similar reasoning as in parts **a)** and **b)**, the equation is $3.20x = 35.20$.

▶ **Now Try Exercise 109**

Helpful Hint

In a written expression certain other words may be used in place of *is* to represent the equal sign. Some of these are *will be*, *was*, *yields*, and *gives*. For example,

"When 4 is added to a number, the sum *will be* 20" can be expressed as $x + 4 = 20$.

"Six subtracted from a number *was* $\dfrac{1}{2}$ the number" can be expressed as $x - 6 = \dfrac{1}{2}x$.

"A rental car cost $25 per day. The cost for renting the car for *x* days *was* $150" can be expressed as $25x = 150$.

EXAMPLE 9 ▶ **Translate Words into an Equation** Write the problem as an equation.

One number is 4 less than twice the other. Their sum is 14.

Solution   First, we express the two numbers in terms of the variable. We will use the variable x to represent one of the numbers.

$$\text{Let } x = \text{one number.}$$
$$\text{Then } 2x - 4 = \text{second number.}$$

Now we write the equation using the information given.

$$\text{first number} + \text{second number} = 14$$
$$x + (2x - 4) = 14$$

▶ **Now Try Exercise 99**

Helpful Hint

If you examine Example 9, the word *is* is used twice, once in each sentence. However, only one equal sign appears in the equation. When the word *is* appears more than once, generally one *is* is being used to express the relationship between the numbers, and the other *is* will represent the equal sign in the equation. When you come across this situation, read the question carefully to determine which *is* will represent the equal sign in the equation.

In Example 10 we will use the term *consecutive even integers*. **Consecutive integers** are integers that differ by 1 unit. For example, the integers 6 and 7 are consecutive integers. Two consecutive integers may be represented as x and $x + 1$. **Consecutive even integers** are even integers that differ by 2 units. For example, 6 and 8 are consecutive even integers. **Consecutive odd integers** also differ by 2 units. For example, 7 and 9 are consecutive odd integers. Two consecutive even integers or two consecutive odd integers may be represented as x and $x + 2$, where x is always the smaller of the integers and $x + 2$ is always the larger of the integers.

EXAMPLE 10 ▶ **Consecutive Even Integers** Write the problem as an equation.

For two consecutive even integers, the sum of the smaller and 3 times the larger is 22.

Solution   First, we express the two consecutive even integers in terms of the variable.

$$\text{Let } x = \text{smaller consecutive even integer.}$$
$$\text{Then } x + 2 = \text{larger consecutive even integer.}$$

Now we write the equation using the information given.

$$\text{smaller} + 3 \text{ times the larger} = 22$$
$$x + 3(x + 2) = 22$$

▶ **Now Try Exercise 107**

EXAMPLE 11 ▶ **Translate Words into an Equation** Write the problem as an equation.

One train travels 3 miles more than twice the distance another train travels. The total distance traveled by both trains is 800 miles.

Solution   First express the distance traveled by each train in terms of the variable.

$$\text{Let } x = \text{distance traveled by one train.}$$
$$\text{Then } 2x + 3 = \text{distance traveled by second train.}$$

Now write the equation using the information given.

$$\text{distance of train 1} + \text{distance of train 2} = \text{total distance}$$
$$x + (2x + 3) = 800$$

▶ **Now Try Exercise 121**

INSTRUCTOR EXAMPLE
Write the following as an equation.

Mary has $1 more than four times the amount of money John has. The difference in the amount of money is $17.

Ans.: $(4x + 1) - x = 17$

EXAMPLE 12 ▸ **Translate Words into an Equation** Write the problem as an equation.

Lori Soushon is 4 years older than 3 times the age of her son Ron. The difference in Lori's age and Ron's age is 26 years.

Solution Since Lori's age is given in terms of Ron's age, we will let the variable represent Ron's age.

$$\text{Let } x = \text{Ron's age.}$$

$$\text{Then } 3x + 4 = \text{Lori's age.}$$

We are told that the difference in Lori's age and Ron's age is 26 years. The word *difference* indicates subtraction. Since Lori is older than Ron, we must subtract Ron's age from Lori's age to get a positive number.

$$\text{Lori's age} - \text{Ron's age} = 26$$

$$(3x + 4) - x = 26$$

▸ **Now Try Exercise 117**

Example 13 will involve percent. Make sure you understand the example.

INSTRUCTOR EXAMPLE
Translate the following into an equation.

Ursula's GPA increased by 8.2%. Her new GPA is 3.4.

Ans.: $x + 0.082x = 3.4$

EXAMPLE 13 ▸ **Translate Words into an Equation.** Write the problem as an equation.

The 2007 property tax for Danielle's house was 3.9% greater than her property tax in 2006. Her property tax in 2007 was $4008.

Solution In this example, we will choose to use the variable t, for tax. Since the 2007 property tax is based upon the 2006 property tax, we will let the variable represent the 2006 property tax.

$$\text{Let } t = 2006 \text{ property tax.}$$

$$\text{Then } t + 0.039t = 2007 \text{ property tax.}$$

this represents the 3.9% increase

Since Danielle's 2007 property tax *was* $4008, the equation we write is $t + 0.039t = 4008$.

▸ **Now Try Exercise 123**

Helpful Hint

It is important that you understand this section and work all your assigned homework problems. You will use the material learned in this section in the next three sections, and throughout the book.

In the examples in this section, we used different letters to represent the variable. Often the letter x is used to represent the variable, but other letters might be used. For example, when discussing an expression or equation involving distance, you may use x to represent the distance, or you may choose to use d, or another variable to represent the distance. Thus to represent the expression "the distance increased by 20 miles," you may write $x + 20$ or $d + 20$. Both are correct.

If your teacher, or the exercise, does not indicate which letter to use to represent the variable, you may select the letter you wish to use. If the answer appendix has an answer as $d + 20$ and your answer is $x + 20$, your answer would be correct, if x and d represent the same quantity.

EXERCISE SET 3.1

MathXL®   MyMathLab

Concept/Writing Exercises

1. Give four phrases that indicate the operation of addition.

2. Give four phrases that indicate the operation of subtraction.

3. Give four phrases that indicate the operation of multiplication.

4. Give four phrases that indicate the operation of division.

5. Explain why $c + 0.25$ *does not* represent the cost of an item increased by 25 percent.   need $0.25c$

6. Explain why $c - 0.10$ *does not* represent the cost of an item decreased by 10 percent.   need $0.10c$

1. added to, more than, increased by, sum

2. subtracted from, less than, decreased by, difference between

7. A 25-foot length of rope is cut into two pieces. If one of the pieces has length x, what is the length of the other piece?

8. A 42-foot length of board is cut into two pieces. If one of the pieces has length y, what is the length of the other piece?

9. Give at least four words or phrases that may be used to indicate the use of an equal sign.

10. Consider the statement "Juan is 3 years older than twice Paul's age." Is Juan's age expressed in terms of Paul's age or is Paul's age expressed in terms of Juan's age. Explain.
Juan's age is expressed in terms of Paul's age.

Practice the Skills

3. multiplied by, product of, twice, three times.   **4.** divided by, quotient of, one-half, one-third.

7. $25 - x$ **8.** $42 - y$ **9.** is, was, will be, yields, gives

In Exercises 11–30, express the statement as an algebraic expression. See Example 1.

11. The height, h, increased by 4 inches $h + 4$

12. The weight, w, increased by 20 pounds $w + 20$

13. The age, a, decreased by 5 years $a - 5$

14. The time, t, decreased by 3 hours $t - 3$

15. Five times the height, h $5h$

16. Seven times the length, l $7l$

17. Twice the distance, d $2d$

18. Three times the rate, r $3r$

19. One-half the age, a $\frac{1}{2}a$

20. One-third the weight, w $\frac{1}{3}w$

21. Five subtracted from r $r - 5$

22. Nine subtracted from p $p - 9$

23. m subtracted from 8 $8 - m$

24. n subtracted from 4 $4 - n$

25. Eight pounds more than twice the weight, w $2w + 8$

26. Six inches more than 3 times the height, h $3h + 6$

27. Four years less than 5 times the age, a $5a - 4$

28. One mile more than $\frac{1}{2}$ the distance, d $\frac{1}{2}d + 1$

29. One-third the weight, w, decreased by 7 pounds $\frac{1}{3}w - 7$

30. One-fifth the height, h, increased by 2 feet $\frac{1}{5}h + 2$

32. $x =$ width   **34.** $x =$ Natasha's speed   **35.** $x =$ number of medals Finland won   **36.** $x =$ distance to Tennessee   **39.** $x =$ Teri's grade

40. $x =$ Nick's salary   **41.** $x =$ amount Kristen receives or $x =$ amount Yvonne receives

In Exercises 31–44, determine what $x =$. See Example 2.

42. $x =$ number of red marbles or $x =$ number of blue marbles

31. Paul is 4 inches taller than Sonya. $x =$ Sonya's height

32. The length of a rectangle is 5 inches greater than its width.

33. The length of Tortuga Beach is 60 feet shorter than the length of Jones Beach. $x =$ length of Jones Beach

34. Wilma ran 4 miles per hour faster than Natasha.

35. The United States won 3 times the number of medals that Finland won.

36. The distance to Georgia is $\frac{1}{2}$ the distance to Tennessee.

37. The Cadillac costs $200 more than twice the cost of the Chevy. $x =$ cost of the Chevy

38. Noah received 25 more votes than 3 times the number of votes that Tawnya received. $x =$ number of votes Tawnya received

39. June's grade was 2 points less than twice Teri's grade.

40. Alberto's salary was $2000 greater than 4 times Nick's salary.

41. $60 divided between Kristen and Yvonne.

42. Drawka has 25 marbles. They are either red or blue marbles.

43. Together Don and Angela weigh 270 pounds.

44. Together Oliver and Dalane have 1053 clients.

43. $x =$ Don's weight or $x =$ Angela's weight   **44.** $x =$ number of clients Oliver has or $x =$ number of clients Dalane has

45. let $c =$ cost of chair, then $3c =$ cost of table   **46.** let $a =$ area of Alfredo's house, then $a + 810 =$ area of Joan's house

In Exercises 45–56, select a variable to represent one quantity and state what that variable represents. Express the second quantity in terms of the variable selected. See Example 3. Note that the variable you select may be different than the variable used in the answers in the back of the book.

45. The table costs 3 times as much as the chair.

46. Joan's house is 810 square feet larger than Alfredo's house.

47. The area of the living room is 20 square feet greater than twice the area of the kitchen.

48. The amount in Darla's savings account is $250 less than 4 times the amount in Carmen's savings account.

49. The length of the rectangle is 2 inches less than 5 times the width.

47. let $a =$ area of the kitchen, then $2a + 20 =$ area of the living room

48. let $a =$ amount in Carmen's savings account, then $4a - 250 =$ amount in Darla's savings account

49. let $w =$ width of rectangle, then $5w - 2 =$ length of rectangle

50. let x = amount Evita receives, then $600 - x$ = amount Brian receives, or let x = amount Brian receives, then $600 - x$ = amount Evita receives

50. A total of $600 is to be divided between Evita and Brian.

51. A total of 38 medals were won by Sweden and Brazil.

52. A movie theatre sold a total of 220 more adult tickets than children tickets.

53. Mike's age is 2 years more than $\frac{1}{2}$ George's age.

54. The book *Golden Angels* sold 4 copies less than 5 times the amount the book *Flycatcher* sold.

55. Jan and Edward used two different treadmills for exercise. The total distance walked between them was 6.4 miles.

56. On a 540-mile trip Cheng and Elsie shared the driving.

51. let w = number of medals won by Sweden, then $38 - w$ = number of medals won by Brazil, or let w = number of medals won by Brazil, then $38 - w$ = number of medals won by Sweden

52. let n = number of children tickets, then $n + 220$ = number of adult tickets

53. let g = George's age, then $\frac{1}{2}g + 2$ = Mike's age

54. let f = number of copies *Flycatcher* sold, then $5f - 4$ = number of copies *Golden Angels* sold

55. let m = number of miles Jan walked, then $6.4 - m$ = number of miles Edward walked or let m = number of miles Edward walked, then $6.4 - m$ = number of miles Jan walked   **56.** let m = number of miles Cheng drove, then $540 - m$ = number of miles Elsie drove, or let m = number of miles Elsie drove, then $540 - m$ = number of miles Cheng drove

In Exercises 57–84, write the indicated expression. See Examples 3–7.

57. Age Dan Graber is n years old now. Write an expression that represents his age in 8 years. $n + 8$

58. Speed-Reading John Debruzzi used to read p words per minute. After taking a speed-reading course, his speed increased by 60 words per minute. Write an expression that represents his new reading speed. $p + 60$

59. Motorcycle Melissa Blum is selling her motorcycle. She was asking x dollars for the motorcycle but has cut the price in half. Write an expression that represents the new price. $\frac{x}{2}$

60. Age Cathy Bennett's son is one-third as old as Cathy, c. Write an expression for her son's age. $\frac{1}{3}c$

61. Age Gayle Krzemien's age is one less than twice Mary Lou Baker's age, a. Write an expression for Gayle's age. $2a - 1$

62. Calories The calories in a serving of mixed nuts is 280 calories less than twice the number of calories in a serving of cashew nuts, c. Write an expression for the number of calories in a serving of mixed nuts. $2c - 280$

63. Temperature The average daily temperature in Jacksonville, Florida in July is 30° less than twice its average daily temperature in January, t. Write an expression for the average daily temperature in July. $2t - 30$

64. Population In 2005, the population of China was 20 million more than 1.2 times the population of India, p. Write an expression for the population of China. $2p - 2.3$

65. Weight Anika Angel weighed p pounds at birth. At age 6 months her weight was 2.3 pounds less than twice her birth weight. Write an expression for Anika's weight at age 6 months. $1.2p + 20$

66. Population Increase The city of Clarkville has a population of 4000. If the population increases by 300 people per year, write an expression that represents the population after n years. $4000 + 300n$

67. Profits Monica and Julia share in the profits of a toy store. If the total profit is $80,000 and m is the amount Monica receives, write an expression for the amount Julia receives. $80,000 - m$

68. Charity Event A total of 83 men and women attended a charity event. If the number of men who attended is m, write an expression for the number of women who attended. $83 - m$

69. Home Runs In professional baseball, as of this writing the all-time home run-leader is Hank Aaron, and Babe Ruth is second. Hank Aaron had 673 less than twice the number of home runs Babe Ruth had, r. Write an expression for the number of home runs Hank Aaron had. $2r - 673$

70. Life Expectancy In 2005, the country with the highest average life expectancy was Japan, and the country with the lowest average life expectancy was Botswana. The average life expectancy in Japan was 3.2 years greater than twice that in Botswana, b. Write an expression for the average life expectancy in Japan. (*Source:* Population Connection). $2b + 3.2$

71. Money Carolyn Curley found that she had x dimes in her handbag. Write an expression that represents this quantity of money in cents. $10x$

72. Weight Jason Mahar's weight is *w* pounds. Write an expression that represents his weight in ounces. $16w$

73. Money Susan Grady has *d* dollars in her purse. Write an expression that represents this quantity of money in cents. $100d$

74. Soil A total of six hundred pounds of soil is put onto two trucks. If *a* pounds of soil is placed onto one truck, write an expression for the amount of soil placed onto the other truck. $600 - a$

75. Truck Rental Bob Melina rented a truck for a trip. He paid a daily fee of $45 and a mileage fee of 40 cents a mile. Write an expression that represents his total cost when he travels *x* miles in one day. $45 + 0.40x$

76. Soil Delivery Mary Vachon had top soil delivered to her house. The total cost included a delivery charge of $48 plus $60 per cubic yard of soil. Write an expression for the total cost if Mary has *x* cubic yards of soil delivered. $48 + 60x$

77. Sales Increase Barry Cogan is a sales representative for a medical supply company. His 2006 sales increased by 20% over his 2005 sales, *s*. Write an expression for his 2006 sales. $s + 0.20s$

78. Salary Increase Charles Idion, an engineer, had a salary increase of 15% over last year's salary, *s*. Write an expression for this year's salary. $s + 0.15s$

79. Electricity Use Jean Olson's electricity use in 2006 decreased by 12% from her 2005 electricity use, *e*. Write an expression for her 2006 electricity use. $e - 0.12e$

80. Shirt Sale At a 25% off everything sale, Bill Winchief purchased a new shirt. If *c* represents the original cost, write an expression for the sale price of the shirt. $c - 0.25c$

81. Car Cost The cost of a new car purchased in Collier County included a 7% sales tax. If *c* represents the cost of the car before tax, write an expression for the total cost, including the sales tax. $c + 0.07c$

82. Film The number of rolls of film sold in 2005 was 43.9% fewer than the number of rolls sold in 2000. Write an expression for the number of rolls sold in 2005 if *r* represents the number of rolls sold in 2000. (*Source:* Photo Marketing Association) $r - 0.439r$

83. Median Age In 2005, the state with the greatest median age was Maine and the state with the lowest was Utah. The median age in Utah was 31.3% less than that of Maine. If *m* represents the median age in Maine, write an expression for the median age in Utah. (*Source:* U.S. Census Bureau) $m - 0.313m$

84. Growing Las Vegas Las Vegas, Nevada, according to the U.S. Census Bureau, had the greatest population growth from 2003 to 2004 of any major city in the United States. Its population in 2004 was 4.1% greater than its population in 2003. If *p* represents Las Vegas's population in 2003, write an expression for its 2004 population. $p + 0.041p$

Las Vegas at Night

In Exercises 85–98, write the indicated expression. You will need to select the variable to use. Note that the variable you use may be different than the variable used in the answer section. See Example 6.

85. Weight Jennifer's weight is 15 pounds more than Frieda's weight. Write an expression for the sum of their weights. $f + (f + 15)$

86. Length The Chestnut-mandibled toucan is 3 inches longer than the keel-billed toucan (shown). Write an expression for the sum of their lengths. $k + (k + 3)$

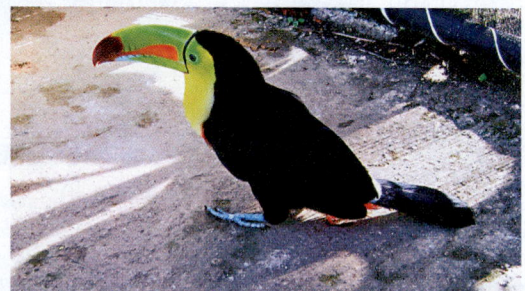

87. Height Armando is taller than his son Luis. Armando is 1 inch less than twice Luis's height. Write an expression for the *difference* in Armando's and Luis's height. $(2l - 1) - l$

88. Profits A company's profits in 2005 were $100 less than the company's profits in 2006. Write an expression for the *difference* in the 2006 and 2005 profits. $p - (p - 100)$

89. Numbers The smaller of two numbers is 40 less than 3 times the larger number. Write an expression for the smaller number *subtracted from* the larger number. $n - (3n - 40)$

90. Numbers The smaller of two numbers is 16 less than twice the larger number. Write an expression for the smaller number *subtracted* from the larger number. $l - (2l - 16)$

91. Weight Jill's four-year-old child weighs 3 pounds less than twice the weight of her two-year-old child. Write an expression for the sum of their weights. $w + (2w - 3)$

92. Assessed Value The assessed value of Glen Sandifer's house is $200 more than twice that of Olga Thompson's house. Write an expression for the sum of the assessed values. $a + (2a + 200)$

93. $r + (479r + 462)$ **94.** $(2s - 6) - s$

93. Land Area The largest state in area is Alaska and the smallest is Rhode Island. The area of Alaska is 462 square miles more than 479 times the area of Rhode Island. Write an expression for the sum of the areas of the two states.

94. Black Bear The number of black bear sightings in 2006 in Ocala National Forest was 6 less than twice the number of sightings in 2005. Write an expression for the number of 2005 sightings subtracted from the number of 2006 sightings.

95. Stocks The price of Apple Computer stock is 6% greater than the cost of National Bank stock. Write an expression for the sum of the prices of National Bank and Apple Computer stocks. $n + (n + 0.06n)$

96. Car Cost The cost of a 2006 Chevrolet Corvette increased by 1.2% over the cost of the 2005 Corvette. Write an expression for the sum of the costs of a 2005 and a 2006 Corvette. $c + (c + 0.012c)$

97. Bank Assets The 2006 assets in Third National Bank were 2.3% lower then their 2005 assets. Write an expression for the 2006 assets subtracted from the 2005 assets. $a - (a - 0.023a)$

98. Spam The number of pieces of spam (or junk mail) that Laura Hoye received in 2006 was 12% less than the number she received in 2005. Write an expression for the difference between the number of pieces of spam she received in 2005 and 2006. $s - (s - 0.12s)$

In Exercises 99–130, write an equation to represent the problem. See Examples 8–13.

99. Two Numbers One number is 4 times another. The sum of the two numbers is 20. $x + 4x = 20$

100. Age Marie is 6 years older than Denise. The sum of their ages is 48. $x + (x + 6) = 48$

101. Consecutive Integers The sum of two consecutive integers is 41. $x + (x + 1) = 41$

102. Even Integers The product of two consecutive even integers is 74. $x(x + 2) = 74$

103. Numbers Twice a number, decreased by 8 is 12.

104. Consecutive Integers For two consecutive integers, the sum of the smaller and twice the larger is 29. $x + 2(x + 1) = 29$

105. Numbers One-fifth of the sum of a number and 10 is 150.

106. Numbers One-third of the sum of a number and 12 is 5.

107. Even Integers For two consecutive even integers, the sum of the smaller and twice the larger is 22. $x + 2(x + 2) = 22$

108. Odd Integers For two consecutive odd integers, the sum of 3 times the smaller and the larger is 14. $3x + (x + 2) = 14$

109. Earnings John Jones earns $12.50 per hour. If he works h hours his earnings will be $150. $12.50h = 150$

110. Employees The T. W. Wilson company plans to increase its number of employees by 20 per year. The increase in the number of employees in t years will be 120. $20t = 120$

111. Top Soil Abe Mantell purchased x bags of top soil at a cost of $2.99 a bag. The total he paid was $17.94. $2.99x = 17.94$

112. Plants Mark Ernsthausen purchased p plants at a nursery for $5.99 each. The total he paid was $65.89. $5.99p = 65.89$

113. Quarters The number of cents in q quarters is 175.

114. Seconds The number of seconds in m minutes is 480.

115. Age Darta Aguilar is 1 year older than twice Julie Chesser's age. The sum of their ages is 52. $a + (2a + 1) = 52$

116. Horses Marc Campbell owns more horses than Selina Jones owns. The number of horses that Marc owns is 3 less than five times the number that Selina owns. The difference in the number of horses owned by Marc and Selina is 5. $(5s - 3) - s = 5$

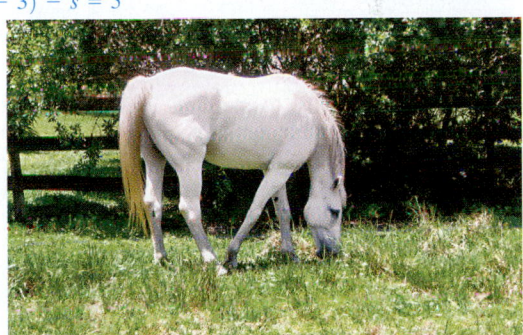

117. Baseball Cards Jakob Meyer owns 300 more than twice the number of baseball cards that Saul Gonzales owns. The difference in the number of cards that Jakob and Saul own is 420. $(2s + 300) - s = 420$

118. Jogging David Ostrow jogs 5 times as far as Jennifer Freer. The total distance traveled by both people is 8 miles.

119. Amtrak An Amtrak train travels 4 miles less than twice the distance traveled by a Southern Pacific train. The total distance traveled by both trains is 890 miles.

120. Wagon Ride On a wagon ride the number of girls was 6 less than twice the number of boys. The total number of boys and girls on the wagon was 18. $b + (2b - 6) = 18$

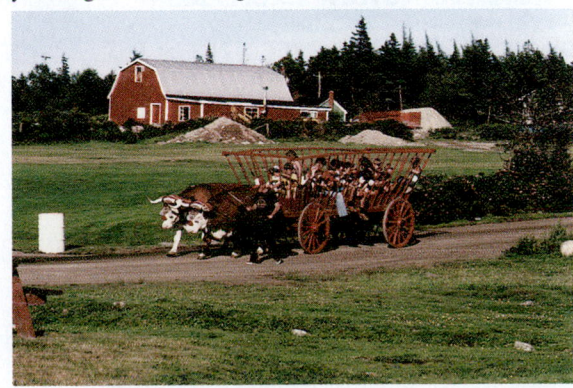

103. $2x - 8 = 12$ **105.** $\frac{1}{5}(x + 10) = 150$ **106.** $\frac{1}{3}(x + 12) = 5$ **113.** $25q = 175$ **114.** $60m = 480$ **118.** $f + 5f = 8$ **119.** $s + (2s - 4) = 890$

121. Distance Walked Donna Douglas walked 2 miles less than 3 times as far as Malik Oamar walked. Together they walked a total of 12.6 miles. $m + (3m - 2) = 12.6$

122. Distance Lilia Orlova rollerbladed 4 miles less than twice the distance she ran. The total distance she traveled was 15 miles. $r + (2r - 4) = 15$

123. Viper The cost of a new Dodge Viper increased by 2.3% over last year's price. The new price is $89,600.

124. Income Dan Tadeo's 2006 income was 4.6% greater than his 2005 income. His income in 2006 was $56,900.

125. Population The population of the town of Tom's Valley decreased by 1.9%. The population after the decrease was 12,087. $p - 0.019p = 12,087$

126. Video Cassette At the Better Buy Warehouse, Anne Long purchased a video cassette recorder that was reduced by 10% for $208. $c - 0.10c = 208$

127. New Car Carlotta Diaz bought a new car. The cost of the car plus a 7% sales tax was $32,600. $c + 0.07c = 32,600$

128. Sport Coat David Gillespie purchased a sport coat at a 25% off sale. He paid $195 for the sport coat.

123. $c + 0.023c = 89,600$ **124.** $d + 0.046d = 56,900$ **128.** $c - 0.25c = 195$ **129.** $c + 0.15c = 42.50$

129. Cost of Meal Beth Rechsteiner ate at a steakhouse. The cost of the meal plus a 15% tip was $42.50.

130. Railroad In a narrow gauge railway, the distance between the tracks is about 64% of the distance between the tracks in a standard gauge railroad. The difference in the distances between the tracks in the two types of railroads is about 1.67 feet. $s - 0.64s = 1.67$

Challenge Problem

131. Time

a) Write an algebraic expression for the number of seconds in d days, h hours, m minutes, and s seconds.
$86,400d + 3600h + 60m + s$

b) Use the expression found in part **a)** to determine the number of seconds in 4 days, 6 hours, 15 minutes, and 25 seconds. $368,125$ sec

Group Activity

Exercises 132 and 133 will help prepare you for the next section, where we set up and solve application problems. Discuss and work each exercise as a group. For each exercise, write down the quantity you are being asked to find and represent this quantity with a variable. Then write an equation containing your variable that can be used to solve the problem. Do not solve the equation.

132. Water Usage An average bath uses 30 gallons of water and an average shower uses 6 gallons of water per minute. How long a shower would result in the same water usage as a bath? $30 = 6t$

133. Salary Plans An employee has a choice of two salary plans. Plan A provides a weekly salary of $200 plus a 5% commission on the employee's sales. Plan B provides a weekly salary of $100 plus an 8% commission on the employee's sales. What must be the weekly sales for the two plans to give the same weekly salary? $200 + 0.05s = 100 + 0.08s$

Cumulative Review Exercises

[1.9] 134. Evaluate $3[(4 - 16) \div 2] + 5^2 - 3$. 4

[2.6] 135. $P = 2l + 2w$; find l when $P = 40$ and $w = 5$. 15

136. Solve $3x - 2y = 6$ for y. $y = \dfrac{3x - 6}{2}$ or $y = \dfrac{3}{2}x - 3$

[2.7] 137. Solve the proportion $\dfrac{3.6}{x} = \dfrac{10}{7}$. 2.52

[2.8] 138. Solve the inequality $2x - 4 > 3$ and graph the solution on a number line. $x > \dfrac{7}{2}$,

3.2 Solving Application Problems

1 Use the Problem-Solving Procedure

Many types of application problems can be solved using algebra. In this section we introduce several types. In Sections 3.3 and 3.4 we introduce additional types of applications. They are also presented in many other sections and exercise sets throughout the book. Your instructor may not have time to cover all the applications given in this book. If not, you may still wish to spend some time on your own reading those problems just to get a feel for the types of applications presented.

To be prepared for this section, you must understand the material presented in Section 3.1. The best way to learn how to set up an application or word problem is to practice. The more problems you study and attempt, the easier it will become to solve them.

The general problem-solving procedure given in Section 1.2 can be used to solve all types of verbal problems. Below, we present the **five-step problem-solving procedure** again so you can easily refer to it. We have included some additional information under steps 1 and 2, since in this section we are going to emphasize translating application problems into equations.

> **Problem-Solving Procedure for Solving Applications**
>
> 1. **Understand the problem.**   Identify the quantity or quantities you are being asked to find.
> 2. **Translate the problem into mathematical language (express the problem as an equation).**
>   a) Choose a variable to represent one quantity, *and write down exactly what it represents*. Represent any other quantity to be found in terms of this variable.
>   b) Using the information from step a), write an equation that represents the application.
> 3. **Carry out the mathematical calculations (solve the equation).**
> 4. **Check the answer (using the** *original* **application).**
> 5. **Answer the question asked.**

TEACHING TIP
Point out that when solving word problems, you must answer the question asked.

Sometimes we will combine two steps in the problem-solving procedure when it helps to clarify the explanation. We may not show the check of a problem to save space. Even if we do not show a check, you should check the problem yourself and make sure your answer is reasonable and makes sense.

Let's now set up and solve some application problems using this procedure.

2 Set Up and Solve Number Application Problems

The examples presented under this objective involve information and data but do not contain percents. When we work the examples we will follow the five-step problem-solving procedure.

INSTRUCTOR EXAMPLE
Four subtracted from three times a number is 11. Find the number.
Ans.: 5

EXAMPLE 1 ▶ An Unknown Number Two subtracted from 4 times a number is 10. Find the number.

Solution **Understand** To solve this problem, we need to express the statement given as an equation. We are asked to find the unknown number. We use the information learned in the previous section to write the equation.

Translate Let x = the unknown number. Now write the equation.

$$\underbrace{\text{2 subtracted from 4 times a number}} \quad \overset{\text{is}}{\underset{\downarrow}{}} \quad \overset{10}{\underset{\downarrow}{}}$$
$$4x - 2 \quad = \quad 10$$

Carry Out
$$4x = 12$$
$$x = 3$$

Check   Substitute 3 for the number in the original problem, two subtracted from 4 times a number is 10.

$$4(3) - 2 \overset{?}{=} 10$$
$$10 = 10 \qquad \textit{True}$$

Answer   Since the solution checks, the unknown number is 3.

▸ **Now Try Exercise 3**

INSTRUCTOR EXAMPLE
The difference of two numbers is 16. Find the two numbers if the larger number is 2 less than 4 times the smaller number.
Ans.: 6, 22

EXAMPLE 2 ▸ **Number Problem** The sum of two numbers is 26. Find the two numbers if the larger number is 2 less than three times the smaller number.

Solution   **Understand**   This problem involves finding two numbers. When finding two numbers, if a second number is expressed in terms of a first number, we generally let the variable represent the first number. Then we represent the second number as an expression containing the variable used for the first number. In this example, we are given that "the larger number is 2 less than three times the smaller number." Notice that the larger number is expressed in terms of the smaller number. Therefore, we will let the variable represent the smaller number.

Translate   Let x = smaller number.

Then $3x - 2$ = larger number.

The sum of the two numbers is 26. Therefore, we write the equation

smaller number + larger number = 26
$$x + (3x - 2) = 26$$

Carry Out   Now we solve the equation.

$$4x - 2 = 26$$
$$4x = 28$$
$$x = 7$$

The smaller number is 7. Now we find the larger number.

$$\text{larger number} = 3x - 2$$
$$= 3(7) - 2 \qquad \textit{Substitute 7 for x.}$$
$$= 19$$

The larger number is 19.

Check   The sum of the two numbers is 26.

$$7 + 19 \overset{?}{=} 26$$
$$26 = 26 \qquad \textit{True}$$

Answer   The two numbers are 7 and 19.

▸ **Now Try Exercise 9**

Helpful Hint

When reading a word problem, ask yourself, "How many answers are required?" In Example 2, the question asked for the two numbers. The answer is 7 and 19. It is important that you read the question and identify what you are being asked to find. If the question had asked "Find the *smaller* of the two numbers if the larger number is 2 less than three times the smaller number," then the answer would have been only the 7. If the question had asked to find the *larger* of the two numbers, then the answer would have been only 19. *Make sure you answer the question asked in the problem.*

EXAMPLE 3 ▶ 2006 Winter Olympics In the 2006 Winter Olympics in Torino, Italy, Germany won the most medals and the United States won the second greatest number of medals. Germany won 21 less than twice the number of medals won by the United States. If the difference between the number of medals won by Germany and the United States was 4, determine the number of medals won by Germany.

Solution Understand   The word *difference* in the problem indicates that this problem will involve subtraction. We are asked to find the number of medals won by Germany. Since the number of medals won by Germany is given in terms of the number of medals won by the United States, we will let the variable represent the number of medals won by the United States. We will use the variable w.

Translate   Let w = medals won by United States.

Then $2w - 21$ = medals won by Germany.

Now we write the equation using the given information. In real-life problems, in order to get a positive answer, the smaller amount will always be subtracted from the larger amount. Since the difference in medals between Germany and the United States is 4, we write the following equation.

$$\underbrace{\text{number of medals won by Germany}}_{2w - 21} - \underbrace{\text{number of medals won by United States.}}_{w} = 4$$

Carry Out $2w - 21 - w = 4$

$w - 21 = 4$

$w = 25$

Check and Answer   The answer is not 25. Remember w represents the number of medals won by the United States. We are asked to find the number of medals won by Germany. The number of medals won by Germany is $2w - 21$ or $2(25) - 21 = 50 - 21$ or 29. Notice the difference in the number of medals won by Germany and the United States is $29 - 25$ or 4, so the answer checks.

▶ Now Try Exercise 23

EXAMPLE 4 ▶ Bicycles The Chain Wheel Drive Bicycle Company presently manufactures 800 bicycles a month. Each month after this month the company plans to increase production by 150 bicycles a month until its monthly production reaches 1700 bicycles. How long will it take the company to reach its production goal?

Solution Understand   We are asked to find the *number of months* that it will take for the company's production to reach 1700 bicycles a month. Next month its production will increase by 150 bicycles. In two months, its production will increase by $2(150)$ over the present month's production. In n months, its production will increase by $n(150)$ or $150n$. We will use this information when we write the equation to solve the problem.

Translate   Let n = number of months.

Then $150n$ = increase in production over n months.

$$(\text{present production}) + \left(\begin{array}{c}\text{increased production}\\\text{over } n \text{ months}\end{array}\right) = \text{future production}$$

$$800 + 150n = 1700$$

Carry Out $150n = 900$

$$n = \frac{900}{150}$$

$$n = 6 \text{ months}$$

Check and Answer   As a check, let's list the number of bicycles produced this month and for the next 6 months.

Presently	Next month	Month 2	Month 3	Month 4	Month 5	Month 6
↓	↓	↓	↓	↓	↓	↓
800	950	1100	1250	1400	1550	1700

Thus, in 6 months the company will produce 1700 bicycles per month.

▶ **Now Try Exercise 19**

3 Set Up and Solve Application Problems Involving Money

When setting up an equation that involves money, you must make sure that all the monetary units entered into the equation are the same, either all dollars or all cents. When given problems to convert to equations, some information might be given in dollars and other information might be given in cents. When this happens, we generally convert the amount given in cents to an equivalent amount of dollars. For example, when renting a truck the cost may be $30 a day plus 20 cents a mile. When writing the equation, we would write the 20 cents a mile as $0.20 a mile. The cost of traveling x miles at 20 cents a mile would be written $0.20x.

Now let's work some examples.

INSTRUCTOR EXAMPLE:
A truck rental costs $42 a day plus 24 cents a mile. If the total cost for a 1-day rental is $63.60, how many miles were driven?
Ans.: 90 mi

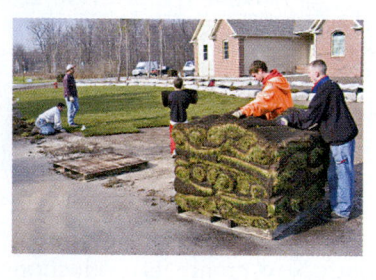

EXAMPLE 5 ▶ **Grub Problem**   Part of Kim Martello's lawn was destroyed by grubs. She decided to purchase new sod (or grass) to lay down. The cost of the sod is 45 cents per square foot plus a delivery charge of $59. If the total cost of delivery plus the sod was $284, how many square feet of sod was delivered?

Solution   **Understand**   The total cost consists of two parts, a variable cost of 45 cents per square foot of sod, plus a fixed delivery charge of $59. We need to determine the number of square feet of sod that will result in a total cost of $284. Since the fixed cost is given in dollars, we write the variable cost, or the cost of the sod, in dollars also.

Translate

Let x = number of square feet of sod.

Then $0.45x$ = cost of x square feet of sod.

sod cost + delivery cost = total cost

$$0.45x + 59 = 284$$

Carry Out

$$0.45x = 225 \qquad \textit{59 was subtracted from both sides.}$$

$$\frac{0.45x}{0.45} = \frac{225}{0.45}$$

$$x = 500$$

Check   The cost of 500 square feet of sod at 45 cents a square foot is $500(0.45) = \$225$. Adding the $225 to the delivery cost of $59 gives $284, so the answer checks.

Answer   Five hundred square feet of sod was delivered.

▶ **Now Try Exercise 31**

INSTRUCTOR EXAMPLE
The cost of having a load of rubbish picked up by Waste Management is $49 plus 30 cents per pound of rubbish. The cost of having rubbish picked up by Sun City Disposal is $89 plus 10 cents per pound of rubbish. How many pounds of rubbish would need to be picked up to make the cost of both pickups the same?
Ans.: 200 lb.

EXAMPLE 6 ▶ **Photo Printer**   Elsie Newman is going to purchase a photo printer to print pictures from her digital camera. She is considering a Hewlett-Packard (HP) printer and a Lexmark™ printer. The HP printer costs $419 and the cost for the ink and paper is 14 cents per photo printed. The Lexmark printer costs $299 and the cost for the ink and paper is 18 cents per photo. How many photos would need to be printed for the total cost of the printers, ink, and paper to be the same?

Solution **Understand** The Hewlett-Packard printer has a greater initial cost ($419 versus $299); however, its cost per photo printed is less (14 cents versus 18 cents). We are asked to find the number of photos printed so that the total cost of the two printers will be the same.

Translate

$$\text{Let } n = \text{number of photos.}$$

$$\text{Then } 0.14n = \text{cost for printing } n \text{ photos with the HP printer}$$

$$\text{and } 0.18n = \text{cost for printing } n \text{ photos with the Lexmark printer.}$$

$$\text{total cost of HP printer} = \text{total cost of Lexmark printer}$$

$$\begin{pmatrix} \text{initial} \\ \text{cost} \end{pmatrix} + \begin{pmatrix} \text{cost} \\ \text{for } n \text{ photos} \end{pmatrix} = \begin{pmatrix} \text{initial} \\ \text{cost} \end{pmatrix} + \begin{pmatrix} \text{cost} \\ \text{for } n \text{ photos} \end{pmatrix}$$

$$419 + 0.14n = 299 + 0.18n$$

Carry Out
$$120 + 0.14n = 0.18n \qquad \textit{299 was subtracted from both sides.}$$

$$120 = 0.04n \qquad \textit{0.14n was subtracted from both sides.}$$

$$\frac{120}{0.04} = \frac{0.04n}{0.04}$$

$$3000 = n$$

Check and Answer The total cost would be the same when 3000 photos were printed. We will leave the check of this answer for you.

▶ **Now Try Exercise 35**

4   Set Up and Solve Applications Concerning Percent

Now we'll look at some application problems that involve percent. Remember that a percent is always a percent of something. Thus if the cost of an item, c, is increased by 8%, we would represent the new cost as $c + 0.08c$, and not $c + 0.08$. See the Avoiding Common Errors box on page 186.

EXAMPLE 7 ▶ **Water Bike Rental** At a beachfront hotel, the cost for a water bike rental is $30 per half hour, which includes a $7\frac{1}{2}$% sales tax. Find the cost of the rental before tax.

Solution **Understand** We are asked to find the cost of the water bike rental before tax. The cost of the rental before tax plus the tax on the water bike must equal $30.

Translate
$$\text{Let } x = \text{cost of the rental before tax.}$$

$$\text{Then } 0.075x = \text{tax on the rental.}$$

$$\text{(cost of the water bike rental before tax)} + \text{(tax on the rental)} = 30$$

$$x + 0.075x = 30$$

Carry Out
$$1.075x = 30$$

$$x = \frac{30}{1.075}$$

$$x \approx 27.91$$

Check and Answer A check will show that if the cost of the rental is $27.91, the cost of the rental including a $7\frac{1}{2}$% tax is about $30.

▶ **Now Try Exercise 43**

EXAMPLE 8 ▶ **Caloric Intake** According to the Centers for Disease Control and Prevention, from 1971 to 2005 the average caloric intake for men in the United States increased by 8% to 2646 calories. Determine the average caloric intake for men in 1971.

Solution Understand We can represent the 2005 caloric intake in terms of the 1971 caloric intake. Therefore, we will select a variable to represent the 1971 caloric intake and represent the 2005 caloric intake in terms of the variable selected. The 2005 caloric intake must be 8% greater than the 1971 caloric intake.

Translate   Let c = the 1971 caloric intake.

Then $c + 0.08c$ = the 2005 caloric intake.

Since the 2005 caloric intake is 2646, we set up the following equation.

2005 caloric intake is 2646

$$c + 0.08c = 2646$$

Carry Out $$1.08c = 2646$$

$$c = \frac{2646}{1.08}$$

$$c = 2450$$

Check and Answer Since c represents the 1971 caloric intake, and it is less than the 2005 caloric intake, our answer is reasonable. The 1971 caloric intake for men was 2450 calories.

▶ **Now Try Exercise 45**

EXAMPLE 9 ▶ **Salary Plans** Jeanne Pirie recently graduated from college and has accepted a position selling medical supplies and equipment. During her first year, she is given a choice of salary plans. Plan 1 is a $450 weekly base salary plus a 3% commission of weekly sales. Plan 2 is a straight 10% commission of weekly sales. What weekly sales, in dollars, would result in Jeanne receiving the same salary from both plans?

Solution Understand We are asked to find the *dollar sales* that will result in Jeanne receiving the same total salary from both plans. To solve this problem, we write expressions to represent the salary from each of the plans. We then obtain the desired equation by setting the salaries from the two plans equal to one another.

Translate   Let x = dollar sales.

Then $0.03x$ = commission from plan 1 sales

and $0.10x$ = commission from plan 2 sales.

salary from plan 1 = salary from plan 2

base salary + 3% commission = 10% commission

$$450 + 0.03x = 0.10x$$

Carry Out $$450 = 0.07x$$

or $$0.07x = 450$$

$$\frac{0.07x}{0.07} = \frac{450}{0.07}$$

$$x \approx 6428.57$$

Check We will leave it up to you to show that sales of $6428.57 result in Jeanne receiving the same weekly salary from both plans.

Answer Jeanne's weekly salary will be the same from both plans if she sells $6428.57 worth of medical supplies and equipment.

▶ **Now Try Exercise 55**

Helpful Hint

Here are some suggestions if you find you are having some difficulty with application problems.

1. **Instructor**—Make an appointment to see your instructor. Make sure you have read the material in the book and attempted all the homework problems. Go with specific questions for your instructor.

2. **Video CDs**—Find out if the video CDs that accompany this book are available at your college. If so, view the videos that go with this chapter. Using the pause control, you can watch the videos at your own pace.

3. **Tutoring**—If your college learning center offers free tutoring, as many colleges do, you may wish to take advantage of tutoring.

4. **Study Group**—Form a study group with classmates. Exchange phone numbers and e-mail addresses. You may be able to help one another.

5. **Student's Solutions Manual**—If you get stuck on an exercise you may want to use the Student's Solutions Manual to help you understand a problem. Do not use the Solutions Manual in place of working the exercises. In general, the Solutions Manual should be used only to check your work.

6. **MyMathLab**—MyMathLab provides free-response exercises correlated to the text that are algorithmically generated for unlimited practice and mastery. In addition, online tools such as video lectures, animations, and a multimedia textbook are available to help you understand the material. Check with your instructor to determine if MyMathLab is available.

7. **Math XL®**—MathXL is a powerful online homework, tutorial, and assessment system correlated specifically to this text. You can take chapter tests in MathXL and receive a personalized study plan based on your test results. The study plan links directly to tutorial exercises for the objectives you need to study or retest. Check with your instructor to determine if MathXL is available.

8. **Prentice Hall Mathematics Tutor**—Once the program has been initiated by your instructor, you can get individual tutoring by phone, fax, or e-mail.

It is important that you keep trying! Remember, the more you practice, the better you will become at solving application problems.

EXERCISE SET 3.2
MathXL®   MyMathLab

Concept/Writing Exercises

1. Outline the five-step problem-solving procedure we use.
Answers will vary.

2. If you are having difficulty with some of the material in this section, list some of the things you may be able to do to help you. See the Helpful Hint above. Answers will vary.

Practice the Skills/Problem Solving

Exercises 3–28 involve finding a number or numbers. Review Examples 1–4, then set up an equation that can be used to solve the problem. Solve the equation and **answer the question asked.** *Use a calculator where you feel it is appropriate.*

3. Unknown Number Three subtracted from 4 times a number is 17. Find the number. 5

4. Unknown Number Five subtracted from 6 times a number is 13. Find the number. 3

5. Consecutive Integers The sum of two consecutive integers is 87. Find the numbers. 43, 44

6. Consecutive Integers The sum of two consecutive integers is 113. Find the numbers. 56, 57

7. Odd Integers The sum of two consecutive odd integers is 96. Find the numbers. 47, 49

8. Even Integers The sum of two consecutive even integers is 146. Find the numbers. 72, 74

9. Sum of Numbers One number is 3 more than twice a second number. Their sum is 27. Find the numbers. 8, 19

10. Sum of Numbers One number is 5 less than 3 times a second number. Their sum is 43. Find the numbers. 12, 31

11. Difference of Numbers The larger of two numbers is 4 less than five times the smaller. When the smaller number is subtracted from the larger, the difference is 4. Find the two numbers. 2, 6

12. Sum of Numbers One number is 2 less than 3 times a second number. Their sum is 26. Find the numbers. 7, 19

13. Difference of Numbers The larger of two integers is 8 less than twice the smaller. When the smaller number is subtracted from the larger, the difference is 17. Find the two numbers. 25, 42

14. Facing Pages The sum of the two facing page numbers in an open book is 145. What are the page numbers? 72, 73

15. Grandma's Gifts Grandma gave some baseball cards to Richey and some to Erin. She gave 3 times the amount to Erin as she did to Richey. If the total amount she gave to both of them was 260 cards, how many cards did she give to Richey?   65 cards

16. Ski Shop The Alpine Valley Ski Shop sold 6 times as many downhill skis as cross-country skis. Determine the number of pairs of cross-country skis sold if the difference in the number of pairs of downhill and cross-country skis sold is 1800.   360 pairs

17. Animal Art Joseph Murray built a horse for display at a baseball stadium. It took him 1.4 hours more than twice the number of hours to attach the baseball gloves to the horse than to build the horse. If the total time it took him to build the horse and attach the gloves was 32.6 hours, how long did it take to attach the gloves?   22.2 hr

The author, Allen R. Angel, is shown in this photo.

18. Candle Shop A candle shop makes 60 candles per week. It plans to increase the number of candles it makes by 8 per week until it reaches a production of 132 candles per week. How many weeks will it take for the shop to reach its production schedule?   9 weeks

19. Collecting Frogs Mary Shapiro collects ceramic and stuffed frogs. She presently has 422 frogs. She wishes to add 6 a week to her collection until her collection reaches a total of 500 frogs. How long will it take Mary's frog collection to reach 500 frogs?   13 weeks

20. Population The town of Dover currently has a population of 6500. If its population is increasing at a rate of 1200 people per year, how long will it take for the population to reach 20,600?   11.75 yr

21. Circuit Boards The FGN Company produces circuit boards. It now has 4600 employees nationwide. It wishes to reduce the number of employees by 250 per year through retirements, until its total employment is 2200. How long will this take?   9.6 yr

22. Computers The CTN Corporation has a supply of 3600 computers. It wishes to ship 120 computers each week until its supply drops to 2000. How long will this take?   ≈13.3 weeks

23. Tornados According to The Weather Channel, the greatest number of tornados in the United States occurs in June and the fewest number occurs in December. The average number of tornados in June is 16 less than 11 times the average number of tornados in December. If the difference between the average number of tornados in June and December is 204, determine the average number of tornados in December and June.   Dec: 22, June: 226

24. Watching TV According to the Kaiser Family Foundation, in the United States, the amount of time per day spent by 8–18-year-olds watching television is 16 minutes more than 5 times the number of minutes they spend reading. If the total amount of time per day reading and watching television is 274 minutes, determine the number of minutes spent watching television.   231 min

25. Housekeepers The average hourly wage paid to hotel housekeepers in New York City is $1.46 more than twice the average wage paid to hotel housekeepers in New Orleans. Determine the average hourly wage paid to housekeepers in New York City if the difference in their average hourly wages is $8.10. $14.74

26. Albums According to *Wikipedia*, the best-selling album in 2005 was Mariah Carey's *The Emancipation of Mimi*. The best-selling album in 2004 was the album *Confession* by Usher. *Confession* sold 0.94 million copies less than twice the amount *The Emancipation of Mimi* sold. The sum of these two albums was 13.97 million copies. Determine the sales of both albums.   *Emancipation*: 4.97 million; *Confession*: 9.00 million

27. Cost to Produce Shirt According to the World Trade Organization, in 2005 the cost to produce a shirt in Northern China was less than in any other area. The cost (in U.S. dollars) to produce a shirt in Mexico is 16 cents less than 3 times the amount to produce a shirt in Northern China. The cost to produce one shirt in each country totals $3.28. Determine the cost to produce a shirt in Northern China and in Mexico.   Northern China: $0.86; Mexico: $2.42

28. Oil Use According to the International Energy Agency, the demand for oil in the United States is far greater than in any other country. In 2004, the United States used an average of 1.6 million gallons of oil per day more than 3 times that used by China, the second greatest user. The total used by both countries in one day was 26.8 million gallons. Determine the number of gallons of oil used in one day in the United States in 2004.   20.5 million gal

*Exercises 29–42 involve money. Read Examples 5–6, then set up an equation that can be used to solve the problem. Solve the equation and **answer the question asked**.*

29. Gasoline Luvia Rivera has only $48 to purchase gasoline. If gasoline costs $3.20 per gallon, determine how many gallons of gasoline Luvia can purchase. 15 gal

30. Truck Rental Carol Battle rents a truck for one day and pays $50 per day plus 30 cents a mile. How far can Carol drive in one day if she has only $92? 140 mi

31. Copy Machine Yamil Bernz purchased a copy machine for $2100 and a one-year maintenance protection plan that costs 2 cents per copy made. If he spends a total of $2462 in a year, which includes the cost of the machine and the copies made, determine the number of copies he made. 18,100 copies

32. Gym Membership At Goldies Gym there is a one-time membership fee of $300 plus dues of $40 per month. If Carlos Manieri has spent a total of $700 for Goldies Gym, how long has he been a member? 10 months

33. Television Miles Potier's Time Warner cable bill costs $72.68 per month plus $3.95 for each On Demand movie he watches that month. If his cable bill for December was $96.38, determine the number of On Demand movies he watched in December. 6 movies

34. Hardwood Floors Ruth Zasada is having hardwood floors installed in her living room. The cost for the material is $2840 plus an installation charge of $1.90 per square foot. If the total cost for the material plus installation is $5120, determine the area of her living room. 1200 sq ft

35. Truck Rental Howard Sporn is considering two companies from which to rent a truck. American Truck Rental charges $20 per day and 25 cents a mile. SavMor Truck Rental charges $35 a day and 15 cents a mile. How far would Howard need to drive in one day for the both companies to have the same total cost? 150 mi

36. Washing Machines Scott Montgomery is considering two washing machines, a Kenmore® and a Neptune®. The Neptune costs $454 while the Kenmore costs $362. The energy guides indicate that the Kenmore will cost an estimated $84 per year to operate and the Neptune will cost an estimated $38 per year to operate. How long will it be before the total cost is the same for both washing machines? 2 yr

37. Salaries Brooke Mills is being recruited by a number of high-tech companies. Data Technology Corporation has offered her an annual salary of $40,000 per year plus a $2400 increase per year. Nuteck has offered her an annual salary of $49,600 per year plus a $800 increase per year. In how many years will the salaries from the companies be the same? 6 yr

38. Racquet Club The Coastline Racquet Club has two payment plans for its members. Plan 1 has a monthly fee of $20 plus $8 per hour for court time. Plan 2 has no monthly fee, but court time is $16.25 per hour. If court time is rented in 1-hour intervals, how many hours would you have to play per month so that plan 1 becomes a better buy? 3 hr (more than 2.42)

39. Printers Hector Hanna will purchase one of two laser printers, a Hewlett-Packard (HP) or a Lexmark®. The HP costs $499 and the Lexmark costs $419. Suppose, because of the price of the ink cartridges, the cost of printing a page on the HP is $0.06 per page and the cost of printing a page on the Lexmark is $0.08 per page. How many pages would need to be printed for the two printers to have the same total cost? 4000 pages

40. Satellite or Cable Sean Stewart is deciding whether to select a satellite receiver or cable for his television programming. The satellite receiver costs $298.90 and the monthly charge is $68.70. With cable there is no initial cost to purchase equipment, but the monthly charge for comparable channels is $74.80. After how many months will the the total cost of the two systems be equal? 49 months

41. Newsletter Neil Simpson had a professional organization newsletter printed and sent out to all the members. The total cost included a $600 printing cost plus a 39 cents mailing cost for each envelope. If the total cost was $1380, determine how many newsletters were mailed. 2000 newsletters

42. Patio Resurfacing Elizabeth Chu is having her patio resurfaced using cement pavers. She is considering two companies for the job. A & E Pavers charge $1500 for the pavers plus $40 per hour for labor to install the pavers. The Jerilyn Fairman Company charges $1800 for the pavers plus $25 per hour to install the pavers. How many hours of labor would result in the same total cost with both companies? 20 hr

*Exercises 43–64 involve percents. Read Examples 7–9, then set up an equation that can be used to solve the problem. Solve the equation and **answer the questions asked**.*

43. Airfare The airfare for a flight from Amarillo, Texas, to New Orleans cost $280, which includes a 7% sales tax. What is the cost of the flight before tax? $261.68

44. New Car Yoliette Fournier purchased a new car. The cost of the car, including a 7.5% sales tax was $24,600. What was the cost of the car before tax? $22,883.72

45. Salary Increase Zhen Tong just received a job offer that will pay him 30% more than his present job does. If the salary at his new job will be $30,200, determine his present salary. $23,230.77

46. New Headquarters Tarrach and Associates plan on increasing the size of its headquarters by 20%. If its new headquarters is to be 14,200 square feet, determine the size of its present headquarters. ≈11,833.33 sq ft

47. Oysters The number of bushels of oysters harvested in Chesapeake Bay has been consistently decreasing. There has been a 93% decrease in the number of bushels of oysters harvested in 2004 from the number harvested in 2001. If in 2004, about 26 thousand bushels of oysters were harvested, determine the number of bushels of oysters harvested in 2001. (*Source:* Maryland Department of Natural Resources) ≈371 thousand bushels

48. Retirement Income Ray and Mary Burnham have decided to retire. They estimate their annual income after retirement will be reduced by 15% from their pre-retirement income. If they estimate their retirement income to be $42,000, determine their pre-retirement income. $49,411.76

49. Autographs A tennis star was hired to sign autographs at a convention. She was paid $3000 plus 3% of all admission fees collected at the door. The total amount she received for the day was $3750. Find the total amount collected at the door. $25,000

50. Sale At a 1-day 20% off sale, Jane Demsky purchased a hat for $25.99. What is the regular price of the hat? $32.49

51. Wage Cut A manufacturing plant is running at a deficit. To avoid layoffs, the workers agree on a temporary wage cut of 2%. If the average salary in the plant after the wage cut is $38,600, what was the average salary before the wage cut? $39,387.76

52. Teachers During the 2006 contract negotiations, the city school board approved a 5% pay increase for its teachers effective in 2007. If Dana Frick, a first-grade teacher, projects his 2007 annual salary to be $46,400, what is his present salary? ≈$44,190.48

53. Earnings and Education The U.S. Census Bureau reported that in 2005, graduates with an associate's degree earned an average of 24.6% less than graduates with a bachelor's degree. If, in 2005, the average graduate with an associate's degree earned $37,600, determine the average salary of a graduate with a bachelor's degree. $49,867

54. Sales Volume Mona Fabricant receives a weekly salary of $350. She also receives a 6% commission on the total sales she makes. What must her sales be in a week, if she is to make a total of $710? $6000

55. Salary Plans Vince McAdams, a salesman, is given a choice of two salary plans. Plan 1 is a weekly salary of $600 plus 2% commission of sales. Plan 2 is a straight commission of 10% of sales. How much in sales must Vince make in a week for both plans to result in the same salary? $7500

56. Area The Johnson Performing Arts Center has increased in size. The area of the new building is 42% larger than the area of the original building. If the area of the new building is 56,000 square feet, determine the area of the original building. ≈39,436.62 sq ft

57. Book The number of pages in the third edition of a book was 4% less than the number of pages in the second edition. If the number of pages in the third edition is 480, determine the number of pages in the second edition. 500 pages

58. Financial Planning Belen Poltorade, a financial planner, is offering her customers two financial plans for managing their assets. With plan 1 she charges a planning fee of $1000 plus 1% of the assets she will manage for the customers. With plan 2 she charges a planning fee of $500 plus 2% of the assets she will manage. How much in customer assets would result in both plans having the same total fees? $50,000

59. Salary Plans Becky Schwartz, a saleswoman, is offered two salary plans. Plan 1 is $400 per week salary plus a 2% commission of sales. Plan 2 is a $250 per week salary plus a 16% commission of sales. How much would Becky need to make in sales for the salary to be the same from both plans? $1071.43

60. Art Show Bill Rush wants to rent a building for a week to show his artwork and has been offered two rental plans. Plan 1 is a rental fee of $500 plus 3% of the dollar sales he makes. Plan 2 is $100 plus 15% of the dollar sales he makes. What dollar sales would result in both plans having the same total cost? $3333.33

61. Eating Out After Linda Kodama is seated in a restaurant, she realizes that she has only $30. From this $30 she must pay a 7% tax and she wishes to leave a 15% tip on the price of the meal before tax. What is the maximum price for a meal that she can afford to pay? $24.59

62. Membership Fees The Holiday Health Club has reduced its annual membership fee by 10%. In addition, if you sign up on a Monday, the Club will take an additional $20 off the already reduced price. If Jorge Sanchez purchases a year's membership on a Monday and pays $250, what is the regular membership fee? $300

63. Estate Phil Dodge left an estate valued at $140,000. In his will, he specified that his wife will get 25% more of his estate than his daughter. How much will his wife receive? $77,777.78

64. Charitable Giving Charles Ford made a $200,000 cash contribution to two charities, the American Red Cross and the United Way. The amount received by the American Red Cross was 30% greater than the amount received by the United Way. How much did the United Way receive? $86,956.52

Challenge Problems

65. Average Value To find the *average* of a set of values, you find the sum of the values and divide the sum by the number of values.

a) If Paul Lavenski's first three test grades are 74, 88, and 76, write an equation that can be used to find the grade that Paul must get on his fourth exam to have an 80 average. $80 = \dfrac{74 + 88 + 76 + x}{4}$

b) Solve the equation from part **a)** and determine the grade Paul must receive.   82

66. Driver Education A driver education course costs $45 but saves those under age twenty-five 10% of their annual insurance premiums until they reach age twenty-five. Scott Day has just turned 18, and his insurance costs $600 per year.

a) How long will it take for the amount saved from insurance to equal the price of the course?   0.75 yr or 9 mo

b) Including the cost of the course, when Scott turns 25, how much will he have saved? $375

Cumulative Review Exercises

[1.9]   **67.** Evaluate $4[(4 - 6) \div 2] + 3^2 - 1$.   4

[1.10] **68.** Name the following property: $3x + 4 = 4 + 3x$.
Commutative property of addition

[2.6]   **69.** Solve the formula $A = \dfrac{1}{2}bh$ for h. $h = \dfrac{2A}{b}$

[2.7]   **70.** Solve the proportion $\dfrac{4.5}{6} = \dfrac{9}{x}$.   12

Mid-Chapter Test: 3.1–3.2

5. 50n   8. x = length of poison dart frog   9. let p = distance Pedro traveled, then
4p + 6 = distance Mary traveled   18. Betty: 196 clients, Anita: 404 clients

To find out how well you understand the chapter material to this point, take this brief test. The answers and the section where the material was initially discussed are given in the back of the book. Review any questions you answered incorrectly.

In Exercises 1–6, express each statement as an algebraic expression.

1. Six times the weight, w   6w

2. Five inches more than 3 times the height, h   3h + 5

3. Represent the cost, c, increased by 20%, as a mathematical expression.   c + 0.20c

4. Dennis Donahue rents a truck for $40 per day plus 25 cents per mile, m. Write an expression for the total cost of the rental for one day.   40 + 0.25m

5. Write an expression for the number of cents in n half-dollars.

6. Twenty-five dollars is divided between Amy Keyser and Sherry Norris. If Amy gets x dollars, how much will Sherry get?   25 − x

7. Explain why the cost, c, of an item at a 25% off sale is not c − 25. Write the correct algebraic expression for the cost of an item at a 25% off sale.   c − 0.25c

8. In the statement, determine what x =.

    A Gaudy Leaf Frog is 2 centimeters longer than 3 times the length of a Poison Dart Frog (see photos).

Gaudy Leaf Frog

Poison Dart Frog

9. Select a variable to represent one quantity and state what that variable represents. Express the second quantity in terms of the variable selected.

    The distance Mary traveled is 6 miles more than 4 times the distance Pedro traveled.

10. The value of a car in 2005 was 18% less than its value in 2006. Write an expression for the difference in the value of the car from 2006 to 2005.   v − (v − 0.18v)

In Exercises 11 and 12, write the problem as an equation. Do not solve.

11. The population of Cedar Oaks increased by 12%. The population after the increase was 38,619.   p + 0.12p = 38,619

12. For two consecutive odd integers, the sum of the smaller and 3 times the larger is 26.   x + 3(x + 2) = 26

In Exercises 13–20, write an equation that can be used to solve the problem. Solve the equation and answer the question asked.

13. **Consecutive Integers** The sum of two consecutive integers is 93. Find the numbers.   46, 47

14. **Numbers** The larger of two integers is one less than 3 times the smaller. When the smaller number is subtracted from the larger, the difference is 7. Find the numbers.   4, 11

15. **Candy** A candy manufacturer presently produces 240 boxes of candy a day and wants to increase production by 20 boxes per day until it produces 600 boxes of candy per day. How many days will it take for production to reach 600 boxes per day?   18 days

16. **Tennis** Kristina Schmid is considering joining one of two tennis clubs. At Dale's Tennis Club the monthly fee is $90, and court time is $4 per hour. At Abel's Tennis Club the monthly fee is $30, but court time is $8 per hour. How many hours in a month would Kristina need to play for the total cost to be the same with both clubs?   15 hr

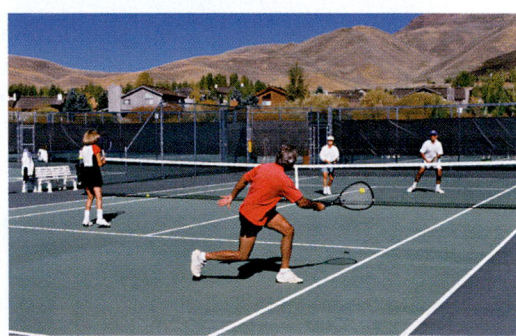

17. **Television** The cost of a television plus a 7% sales tax is $749. Find the cost of the television before tax. $700

18. **Clients** Anita and Betty together have a total of 600 clients. If Anita has 12 more than twice the number of clients Betty has, determine the number of clients each person has.

19. **Truck Rental** A truck cost $36 a day plus 18 cents a mile to rent. If the total cost for a one-day rental is $45.36, how many miles were driven?   52 mi

20. **Salary Plans** A salesman is offered two salary plans. Plan 1 is $200 per week plus 8% commission of the dollar sales he makes. Plan 2 is $300 per week plus 6% of the dollar sales he makes. How much in sales must the salesman make in a week for the two plans to have the same total salary? $5000

3.3 Geometric Problems

1 Solve geometric problems.

1 Solve Geometric Problems

This section serves two purposes. One is to reinforce the geometric formulas introduced in Section 2.6. The second is to reinforce procedures for setting up and solving verbal problems discussed in Sections 3.1 and 3.2. The more practice you have at setting up and solving the verbal problems, the better you will become at solving them.

EXAMPLE 1 ▶ **Sandbox** Mrs. Christine O'Connor is planning to build a sandbox for her daughter. She has 30 feet of lumber with which to build the perimeter: What should be the dimensions of the rectangular sandbox if the length is to be 3 feet longer than the width (**Fig. 3.3**)?

Solution Understand We are asked to find the dimensions of the sandbox that Christine plans to build. Since the amount of lumber that will be used to make the frame is 30 feet, the perimeter is 30 feet. Since the length is given in terms of the width, we will let the variable represent the width. Then we can express the length in terms of the variable selected for the width. To solve this problem, we use the formula for the perimeter of a rectangle, $P = 2l + 2w$, where $P = 30$ feet.

FIGURE 3.3

Translate   Let w = width of the sandbox.

Then $w + 3$ = length of the sandbox.

$$P = 2l + 2w$$
$$30 = 2(w + 3) + 2w$$

Carry Out $30 = 2w + 6 + 2w$
$$30 = 4w + 6$$
$$24 = 4w$$
$$6 = w$$

The width is 6 feet. Since the length is 3 feet longer than the width, the length is $6 + 3 = 9$ feet.

Check   We will check the solution by substituting the appropriate values in the perimeter formula.

$$P = 2l + 2w$$
$$30 \overset{?}{=} 2(9) + 2(6)$$
$$30 = 30 \qquad \text{True}$$

Answer   The width of the sandbox will be 6 feet and the length will be 9 feet.

▶ **Now Try Exercise 23**

EXAMPLE 2 ▶ **Corner Lot** A triangle that contains two sides of equal length is called an **isosceles triangle**. In isosceles triangles, the angles opposite the two sides of equal length have equal measures. Mr. and Mrs. Harmon Katz have a corner lot that is in the shape of an isosceles triangle. Two angles of their triangular lot are the same and the third angle is 30° greater than the other two. Find the measure of all three angles (see **Fig. 3.4**).

Solution Understand To solve this problem, you must know that the sum of the angles of any triangle measures 180°. We are asked to find the measure of each of the three angles, where the two smaller angles have the same measure. We will let the variable represent the measure of the smaller angles, and then we will express the larger angle in terms of the variable selected for the smaller angles.

FIGURE 3.4

Translate   Let x = the measure of each smaller angle.

Then $x + 30$ = the measure of the larger angle.

$$\text{sum of the 3 angles} = 180$$
$$x + x + (x + 30) = 180$$

Carry Out
$$3x + 30 = 180$$
$$3x = 150$$
$$x = \frac{150}{3} = 50$$

The two smaller angles are each 50°. The larger angle is $x + 30°$ or $50° + 30° = 80°$.

Check and Answer   Since $50° + 50° + 80° = 180°$, the answer checks. The two smaller angles are each 50° and the larger angle is 80°.

▶ **Now Try Exercise 11**

Recall from Section 2.6 that a quadrilateral is a four-sided figure. Quadrilaterals include squares, rectangles, parallelograms, and trapezoids. The sum of the measures of the angles of any quadrilateral is 360°. We will use this information in Example 3.

FIGURE 3.5

EXAMPLE 3 ▶ **Water Trough** Sarah Fuqua owns horses and uses a water trough whose ends are trapezoids. The measure of the two bottom angles of the trapezoid are the same, and the measure of the two top angles are the same. The bottom angles measure 15° less than twice the measure of the top angles. Find the measure of each angle.

Solution   Understand   To help visualize the problem, we draw a picture of the trapezoid, as in **Figure 3.5**. We use the fact that the sum of the measures of the four angles of a quadrilateral is 360°.

Translate   Let x = the measure of each of the two smaller angles.

Then $2x - 15$ = the measure of each of the two larger angles.

$$\left(\begin{array}{c} \text{measure of the} \\ \text{two smaller angles} \end{array} \right) + \left(\begin{array}{c} \text{measure of the} \\ \text{two larger angles} \end{array} \right) = 360$$

$$x + x + (2x - 15) + (2x - 15) = 360$$

Carry Out
$$x + x + 2x - 15 + 2x - 15 = 360$$
$$6x - 30 = 360$$
$$6x = 390$$
$$x = 65$$

Each smaller angle is 65°. Each larger angle is $2x - 15 = 2(65) - 15 = 115°$.

Check and Answer   Since $65° + 65° + 115° + 115° = 360°$, the answer checks. Each smaller angle is 65° and each larger angle is 115°.

▶ **Now Try Exercise 27**

FIGURE 3.6

EXAMPLE 4 ▶ **Fenced-In Area** Ronald Yates recently started an ostrich farm. He is separating the ostriches by fencing in three equal rectangular areas, as shown in **Figure 3.6**. The length of the fenced-in area, l, is to be 30 feet greater than the width and the total amount of fencing available is 660 feet. Find the length and width of the fenced-in area.

Solution   Understand   The fencing consists of four pieces of fence of length w, and two pieces of fence of length l.

Translate   Let w = width of fenced-in area.

Then $w + 30$ = length of fenced-in area.

$$\left(\begin{array}{c} \text{4 pieces of fence} \\ \text{of length } w \end{array} \right) + \left(\begin{array}{c} \text{2 pieces of fence} \\ \text{of length } w + 30 \end{array} \right) = 660$$

$$4w + 2(w + 30) = 660$$

Carry Out
$$4w + 2w + 60 = 660$$
$$6w + 60 = 660$$
$$6w = 600$$
$$w = 100$$

Since the width is 100 feet, the length is $w + 30$ or $100 + 30$ or 130 feet.

Check and Answer Since $4(100) + 2(130) = 660$, the answer checks. The width of the ostrich farm is 100 feet and the length is 130 feet.

▸ **Now Try Exercise 37**

EXERCISE SET 3.3

MathXL®   MyMathLab

Concept/Writing Exercises

2. area increases ninefold   **4.** circumference is tripled   **6.** volume is 27 times as great   **9.** 180°

1. In the equation $A = l \cdot w$, what happens to the area if the length is doubled and the width is halved? Explain your answer.   The area remains the same.

2. In the equation $A = s^2$, what happens to the area if the length of a side, s, is tripled? Explain your answer.

3. In the equation $V = l \cdot w \cdot h$, what happens to the volume if the length, width, and height are all doubled? Explain your answer.   volume is 8 times as great

4. In the equation $C = 2\pi r$, what happens to the circumference if the radius is tripled? Explain your answer.

5. In the equation $A = \pi r^2$, what happens to the area if the radius is tripled? Explain your answer.   area is 9 times as great

6. In the equation $V = \frac{4}{3}\pi r^3$, what happens to the volume if the radius is tripled? Explain your answer.

7. What is an isosceles triangle?   a triangle with two equal sides

8. What is a quadrilateral?   a four-sided figure

9. What is the sum of the measures of the angles of a triangle?

10. What is the sum of the measures of the angles of a quadrilateral?   360°

Practice the Skills/Problem Solving

*Solve the following geometric problems.**

11. Isosceles Triangle In an isosceles triangle, one angle is 42° greater than the other two equal angles. Find the measure of all three angles. See Example 2.   46°, 46°, 88°

12. Triangular Building This building in New York City, referred to as the Flatiron Building, is in the shape of an isosceles triangle. If the shortest side of the building is 50 feet shorter than the two longer sides, and the perimeter around the building is 196 feet, determine the length of the three sides of the building.   82 feet, 82 feet, 32 feet

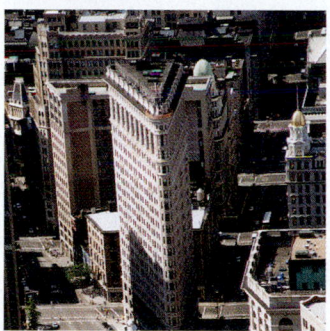

13. A Special Triangle An **equilateral triangle** is a triangle that has three sides of the same length. The perimeter of an equilateral triangle is 34.5 inches. Find the length of each side.   11.5 in.

14. Equilateral Triangle The perimeter of an equilateral triangle is 48.6 centimeters. Find the length of each side. See Exercise 13.   16.2 cm

15. Complementary Angles Two angles are **complementary angles** if the sum of their measures is 90°. Angle A and angle B are complementary angles, and angle A is 21° more than twice angle B. Find the measures of angle A and angle B. $A = 67°, B = 23°$

Complementary Angles

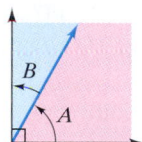

16. Complementary Angles Angles A and B are complementary angles, and angle B is 14° less than angle A. Find the measures of angle A and angle B. See Exercise 15. $A = 52°, B = 38°$

17. Supplementary Angles Two angles are **supplementary angles** if the sum of their measures is 180°. Angle A and angle B are supplementary angles, and angle B is 8° less than three times angle A. Find the measures of angle A and angle B. $A = 47°, B = 133°$

Supplementary Angles

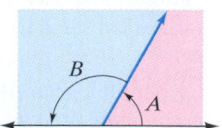

18. Supplementary Angles Angles A and B are supplementary angles and angle A is 2° more than 4 times angle B. Find the measures of angle A and angle B. See Exercise 17. $A = 144.4°, B = 35.6°$

---

*See Appendix C for more material on geometry.

19. Vertical Angles When two lines cross, the opposite angles are called **vertical angles**. Vertical angles have equal measures. Determine the measures of the vertical angles indicated in the following figure. 88°

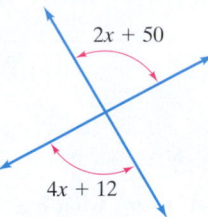

$2x + 50$

$4x + 12$

20. Vertical Angles A pair of vertical angles is indicated in the following figure. Determine the measure of the vertical angles indicated. See Exercise 19. 65°

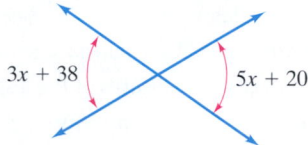

$3x + 38$ $5x + 20$

21. Unknown Angles One angle of a triangle is 10° greater than the smallest angle, and the third angle is 30° less than twice the smallest angle. Find the measures of the three angles. 50°, 60°, 70°

22. Unknown Angles One angle of a triangle is 20° larger than the smallest angle, and the third angle is 6 times as large as the smallest angle. Find the measures of the three angles. 20°, 40°, 120°

23. Dimensions of Rectangle The length of a rectangle is 6 feet more than its width. What are the dimensions of the rectangle if the perimeter is 44 feet? $l = 14$ ft, $w = 8$ ft

24. Dimensions of Rectangle The perimeter of a rectangle is 120 feet. Find the length and width of the rectangle if the length is twice the width. $l = 40$ ft, $w = 20$ ft

25. Tennis Court The length of a regulation tennis court is 6 feet greater than twice its width. The perimeter of the court is 228 feet. Find the length and width of the court. $l = 78$ ft, $w = 36$ ft

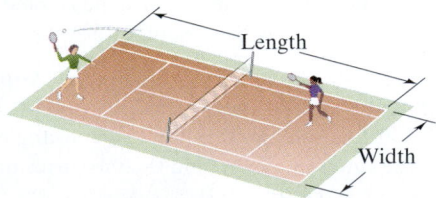

Length

Width

26. Patio Rikki Blair is building a rectangular patio. The perimeter of the patio is to be 96 feet. Determine the dimensions of the patio if the length is to be 6 feet less than twice the width. 18 ft by 30 ft

27. Parallelogram In a parallelogram the opposite angles have the same measures. Each of the two larger angles in a parallelogram is 20° less than 3 times the smaller angles. Find the measure of each angle. smaller angles, 50°; larger angles, 130°

$3x - 20$

$3x - 20$

x

x

Smaller angle

Larger angle

28. Parallelogram The two smaller angles of a parallelogram have equal measures, and the two larger angles each measure 27° less than twice each smaller angle. Find the measure of each angle. smaller angles, 69°; larger angles, 111°

29. Rhombus A rhombus is a parallelogram with four equal sides. Each of the two larger angles of a rhombus is 5 times as large as the two smaller angles. Find the measure of each of the four angles. 30°, 30°, 150°, 150°

$5x$ $5x$ x x

Smaller angle

Larger angle

30. Rhombus Each of the two larger angles of a rhombus are 20° less than four times the two smaller angles. Find the measure of each of the four angles. 40°, 40°, 140°, 140°

31. Quadrilateral The measure of one angle of a quadrilateral is 10° greater than the smallest angle; the third angle is 14° greater than twice the smallest angle; and the fourth angle is 21° greater than the smallest angle. Find the measures of the four angles of the quadrilateral. 63°, 73°, 140°, 84°

32. Quadrilateral The measure of one angle of a quadrilateral is twice the smallest angle; the third angle is 20° greater than the smallest angle; and the fourth angle is 20° less than twice the smallest angle. Find the measures of the four angles of the quadrilateral. 60°, 120°, 80°, 100°

33. Building a Bookcase A bookcase is to have four shelves, including the top, as shown. The height of the bookcase is to be 3 feet more than the width. Find the width and height of the bookcase if only 30 feet of lumber is available. $w = 4$ ft; $h = 7$ ft

Shelf 1

Shelf 2

Shelf 3

Shelf 4

$x + 3$

x

34. Bookcase A bookcase is to have four shelves as shown. The height of the bookcase is to be 2 feet more than the width, and only 20 feet of lumber is available. What should be the width and height of the bookcase? $w = 2\frac{2}{3}$ ft, $h = 4\frac{2}{3}$ ft

1

2

3

4

35. Bookcase What should be the width and height of the bookcase in Exercise 34 if the height is to be twice the width? $w = 2.5$ ft, $h = 5$ ft

36. Storage Shelves Carlotta plans to build storage shelves as shown. She has only 45 feet of lumber for the entire unit and wishes the width to be 3 times the height. Find the width and height of the unit. $w = 9$ ft, $h = 3$ ft

37. Fenced-In Area A rectangular area is to be fenced in along a straight river bank as illustrated. The length of the fenced-in area is to be 5 feet greater than the width, and the total amount of fencing to be used is 71 feet. Find the width and length of the fenced-in area. $w = 11$ ft, $l = 16$ ft

38. Gardening Trina Zimmerman is placing a border around and within a garden where she intends to plant flowers (see the figure). She has 60 feet of bordering, and the length of the garden is to be 2 feet greater than the width. Find the length and width of the garden. The red shows the location of all the bordering in the figure. $l = 12$ ft, $w = 10$ ft

40. a)

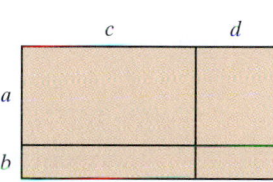

Challenge Problems

39. One way to express the area of the figure on the right is $(a + b)(c + d)$. Can you determine another expression, using the area of the four rectangles, to represent the area of the figure? $ac + ad + bc + bd$

Group Activity

Discuss and answer Exercise 40 as a group.

40. Consider the four pieces shown. Two are squares and two are rectangles.

a) Individually, rearrange and place the four pieces together to form one square.

b) The area of the square you constructed is $(a + b)^2$. Write another expression for the area of the square by adding the four individual areas. $a^2 + 2ab + b^2$

c) Compare your answers. If each member of the group did not get the same answers to parts **a)** and **b)**, work together to determine the correct answer.

d) Answer the following question as a group. If b is twice the length of a, and the perimeter of the square you created is 54 inches, find the length of a and b. $a = 4.5$ in., $b = 9$ in.

e) Use the values of a and b found in part **d)** to find the area of the square you created. 182.25 in.^{2}

f) Use the values of a and b found in part **d)** to find the areas of the four individual pieces that make up the large square. 20.25 in.^{2}, 40.50 in.^{2}, 40.50 in.^{2}, 81.00 in.^{2}

g) Does the sum of the areas of the four pieces found in part **f)** equal the area of the large square found in part **e)**? Is this what you expected? Explain. yes

Cumulative Review Exercises

Insert either $>$, $<$, or $=$ in each shaded area to make the statement true.

[1.5] **41.** $-|-6|$ ▨ $|-4|$ $<$

42. $|-3|$ ▨ $-|3|$ $>$

[1.7] **43.** Evaluate $-8 - (-2) + (-4)$. -10

[2.1] **44.** Simplify $-7y + x - 3(x - 2) + 2y$. $-2x - 5y + 6$

[2.6] **45.** Solve $6x + 3y = 9$ for y. $y = -2x + 3$

3.4 Motion, Money, and Mixture Problems

We now discuss three additional types of applications: motion, money, and mixture problems. These problems are grouped in the same section because, as you will learn shortly, you use the same general multiplication procedure to solve them. We begin by discussing motion problems.

1 Solve Motion Problems Involving Two Rates

A **motion problem** is one in which an object is moving at a specific rate for a specific period of time. A car traveling at a constant speed or a person walking at a constant speed may be considered motion problems. Motion problems are often solved using the distance formula, distance = rate × time, that was given in Section 2.6. In this section, we will discuss motion problems that involve *two rates*, such as two trains traveling at different speeds. In these problems, we generally begin by letting the variable represent one of the unknown quantities, and then we represent the second unknown quantity in terms of the first unknown quantity. For example, suppose that one train travels 20 miles per hour faster than another train. We might let r represent the rate of the slower train and $r + 20$ represent the rate of the faster train.

To solve problems of this type that use the distance formula and involve two different rates, we can construct a table, like the following one, to organize the information. The formula at the top of the table shows how the distance in the last column is calculated.

Rate × Time = Distance

Item	Rate	Time	Distance
Item 1			distance 1
Item 2			distance 2

Depending upon the information given in the problem, we generally add the two distances, or subtract the smaller distance from the larger, or set the two distances equal to each other. We can set up one of two types of equations, as indicated below, to solve the problem.

$$\text{distance 1} + \text{distance 2} = \text{total distance}$$
$$\text{distance 1} - \text{distance 2} = \text{difference in distance}$$
$$(\text{or distance 2} - \text{distance 1} = \text{difference in distance})$$

Examples 1 and 2 illustrate the procedure used.

EXAMPLE 1 ▶ **Camping Trip** Maryanne and Paul Justinger and their son Danny are on a canoe trip on the Erie Canal. Danny is in one canoe and Paul and Maryanne are in a second canoe. Both canoes start at the same time from the same point and travel in the same direction. The parents paddle their canoe at 2 miles per hour and their son paddles his canoe at 4 miles per hour. In how many hours will the two canoes be 5 miles apart?

Solution   Understand and Translate   We are asked to find the time it takes for the canoes to become separated by 5 miles. We will construct a table to aid us in setting up the problem.

Let t = time when canoes are 5 miles apart.

We draw a sketch to help visualize the problem (**Fig. 3.7**). When the two canoes are 5 miles apart, each has traveled for the same number of hours, t.

Canoe	Rate	Time	Distance
Parents	2	t	$2t$
Son	4	t	$4t$

Rate: 2 mph   Rate: 4 mph

|← 5 miles →|

FIGURE 3.7

Since the canoes are traveling in the same direction, the distance between them is found by subtracting the distance traveled by the slower canoe from the distance traveled by the faster canoe.

$$\left(\begin{array}{c}\text{distance traveled}\\\text{by faster canoe}\end{array}\right) - \left(\begin{array}{c}\text{distance traveled}\\\text{by slower canoe}\end{array}\right) = 5 \text{ miles}$$

Carry Out

$$4t - 2t = 5$$
$$2t = 5$$
$$t = 2.5$$

Answer   After 2.5 hours the two canoes will be 5 miles apart.

▶ **Now Try Exercise 1**

EXAMPLE 2 ▶ **Paving Roads**   Two highway paving crews are 20 miles apart working toward each other. One crew paves 0.4 mile of road per day more than the other crew, and the two crews meet after 10 days. Find the rate at which each crew paves the road.

Solution   **Understand and Translate**   We are asked to find the two rates. We are told that both crews work for 10 days.

$$\text{Let } r = \text{rate of slower crew.}$$
$$\text{Then } r + 0.4 = \text{rate of faster crew.}$$

We make a sketch (**Fig. 3.8**) and set up a table of values.

Rate: r Rate: $r + 0.4$

20 miles covered in 10 days

FIGURE 3.8

Crew	Rate	Time	Distance
Slower	r	10	$10r$
Faster	$r + 0.4$	10	$10(r + 0.4)$

The total distance covered by both crews is 20 miles. Since the crews are moving in opposite directions, the distance between them is found by adding the two distances.

$$\left(\begin{array}{c}\text{distance covered}\\\text{by slower crew}\end{array}\right) + \left(\begin{array}{c}\text{distance covered}\\\text{by faster crew}\end{array}\right) = 20 \text{ miles}$$

Carry Out

$$10r + 10(r + 0.4) = 20$$
$$10r + 10r + 4 = 20$$
$$20r + 4 = 20$$
$$20r = 16$$
$$\frac{20r}{20} = \frac{16}{20}$$
$$r = 0.8$$

Answer   The slower crew paves 0.8 mile of road per day and the faster crew paves $r + 0.4$ or $0.8 + 0.4 = 1.2$ miles of road per day.

▶ **Now Try Exercise 17**

Helpful Hint

Notice in Example 1 that the canoes are traveling in the *same direction* and the solution involves *subtracting* the smaller distance from the larger distance. In Example 2, the crews are traveling in the *opposite directions* and the solution involves *addition*. In general, when working with two different moving items, if the items are moving in the same direction, the solution will involve subtracting the smaller distance from the larger distance. If the items are moving in opposite directions, the solution will involve adding the distances together.

2 Solve Money Problems

Now we will work some examples that involve *two items*, where each is assigned a specific amount of money. We place these examples here because they are solved using a procedure very similar to the procedure used to solve motion problems with two rates. One type of money problem involves simple interest. The simple interest formula, interest = principal · rate · time, was discussed in Section 2.6. In Example 3, we use the simple interest formula, where two different principals are involved.

When working with interest problems involving two amounts, we often let the variable represent one amount of money, then we represent the second amount in terms of the variable. For example, if we know the total amount invested in two simple interest accounts is $20,000, we might let x represent the amount in one account, then $20,000 - x$ would be the amount invested in the other account. When solving an interest problem involving two amounts, we can use a table, as illustrated below, just as we did when working with motion problems.

Principal × Rate × Time = Interest

Account	Principal	Rate	Time	Interest
Account 1				interest 1
Account 2				interest 2

After determining the interest columns on the right, we generally use one of the following formulas, depending on the question, to determine the answer.

$$\text{interest 1} + \text{interest 2} = \text{total interest}$$
$$\text{interest 1} - \text{interest 2} = \text{difference in interest}$$
$$(\text{or interest 2} - \text{interest 1} = \text{difference in interest})$$
$$\text{interest 1} = \text{interest 2}$$

Do you see the similarities with the motion problems? Now let's work an example.

EXAMPLE 3 ▶ Investments Carmine DeSanto has $15,000 to invest. He is considering two investments. One is a loan he can make to another party that pays him 8% simple interest for a year. A second investment is a 1-year certificate of deposit that pays 5%. Carmine decides that he wants to place some money in each investment, and he wants to earn a total of $1125 interest in 1 year from the two investments. How much money should Carmine put in each investment?

Solution **Understand and Translate** We use the simple interest formula, interest = principal · rate · time, to solve this problem.

$$\text{Let } x = \text{amount to be invested at 5\%.}$$
$$\text{Then } 15,000 - x = \text{amount to be invested at 8\%.}$$

Account	Principal	Rate	Time	Interest
CD	x	0.05	1	$0.05x$
Loan	$15,000 - x$	0.08	1	$0.08(15,000 - x)$

Since the sum of the interest from the two investments is $1125, we write the equation

$$\left(\begin{array}{c}\text{interest from} \\ \text{5\% CD}\end{array}\right) + \left(\begin{array}{c}\text{interest from} \\ \text{8\% investment}\end{array}\right) = \text{total interest}$$

$$0.05x + 0.08(15,000 - x) = 1125$$

Carry Out
$$0.05x + 0.08(15,000) - 0.08(x) = 1125$$
$$0.05x + 1200 - 0.08x = 1125$$
$$-0.03x + 1200 = 1125$$
$$-0.03x = -75$$
$$x = \frac{-75}{-0.03} = 2500$$

Check and Answer Thus, $2500 should be invested at 5% interest. The amount to be invested at 8% is

$$15,000 - x = 15,000 - 2500 = 12,500$$

The total amount invested is $2500 + $12,500 = $15,000, which checks with the information given.

▶ **Now Try Exercise 25**

In Example 3, we let x represent the amount invested at 5%. If we had let x represent the amount invested at 8%, the answer would not have changed. Rework Example 3 now, letting x represent the amount invested at 8%.

In other types of problems involving two amounts of money, we generally set up similar tables, as illustrated in the next example.

EXAMPLE 4 ▶ **Rocking Chairs** Johnson's Patio Furniture Store sells two types of rocking chairs. The single-person rocking chair sells for $130 each and the two-person rocking chair sells for $240 each. On a given day 10 rocking chairs were sold for a total of $1740. Determine the number of single-person and the number of two-person rocking chairs that were sold.

Solution **Understand and Translate** We are asked to find the number of each type of rocking chair sold.

Let x = number of single-person rocking chairs sold.

Then $10 - x$ = number of two-person rocking chairs sold.

The income received from the sale of the single-person rocking chairs is found by multiplying the number of single-person rocking chairs sold by the cost of a single-person rocking chair. The income received from the sale of the two-person rocking chairs is found by multiplying the number of two-person rocking chairs sold by the cost of a two-person rocking chair.

$$\begin{pmatrix} \text{Number of} \\ \text{Rocking chairs} \end{pmatrix} \times \begin{pmatrix} \text{Cost of} \\ \text{Rocking chairs} \end{pmatrix} = \begin{pmatrix} \text{Income from} \\ \text{Rocking chairs} \end{pmatrix}$$

Rocking Chair	Number of Rocking Chairs	Cost	Income from Rocking Chairs
Single	x	130	$130x$
Double	$10 - x$	240	$240(10 - x)$

$$\begin{pmatrix} \text{income from} \\ \text{single-person} \\ \text{rocking chairs} \end{pmatrix} + \begin{pmatrix} \text{income from} \\ \text{two-person} \\ \text{rocking chairs} \end{pmatrix} = \text{total income}$$

$$130x + 240(10 - x) = 1740$$

Carry Out
$$130x + 2400 - 240x = 1740$$
$$-110x + 2400 = 1740$$
$$-110x = -660$$
$$x = \frac{-660}{-110} = 6$$

Check and Answer Six single-person rocking chairs and $10 - 6$ or 4 two-person rocking chairs were sold.

Check
$$\text{income from 6 single-person rocking chairs} = 780$$
$$\text{income from 4 two-person rocking chairs} = \underline{960}$$
$$\text{total} = 1740 \quad \textit{True}$$

▶ **Now Try Exercise 35**

INSTRUCTOR EXAMPLE
Twelve paintings were sold for a total of $400. Some were sold at $20 each while others were sold at $52 each. How many paintings were sold at each price?
Ans.: 7 at $20, 5 at $52

3 Solve Mixture Problems

Now we will work some mixture problems. Any problem in which two or more quantities are combined to produce a different quantity or a single quantity is separated into two or more different quantities may be considered a **mixture problem**. Mixture problems are familiar to everyone, as we can see in the everyday examples that follow.

Mixture problems in this section will generally be one of two types. In one type, we will mix two solids, as illustrated in **Figure 3.9a**, and be concerned about the value or cost of the mixture. In the second type, we will mix two liquids or solutions, as illustrated in **Figure 3.9b**, and be concerned about the content or strength of the mixture.

Type 1
Mixing solids together

Type 2
Mixing liquids, or solutions, together

(a) Concerned about the value or the cost of the mixture

(b) Concerned about the content or the strength of the mixture

FIGURE 3.9

As we did with motion problems involving two rates and money problems, we will use a table to help analyze mixture problems.

When we construct a table for mixture problems, our table will generally have three rows instead of two as with motion and money problems. One row will be for each of the two individual items being mixed, and the third row will be for the mixture of the two items.

Type 1—Mixing Solids

When working with mixture problems involving solids, we often let the variable represent one unknown quantity, and then we represent a second unknown quantity in terms of the first unknown quantity. For example, if we know the total weight of a mixture of two items is 10 pounds, and one of the items in the mixture weighs x pounds, then the weight of the other item in the mixture will be $10 - x$ pounds.

When working with mixture problems involving solids, we generally use the fact that the value (or cost) of one part of the mixture plus the value (or cost) of the second part of the mixture is equal to the total value (or total cost) of the mixture.

When we are combining two solid items and are interested in the *value* of the mixture, the following table, or a variation of it, is often used.

Quantity × Price (per unit) = Value of Item

Item	Quantity	Price	Value of Item
item 1			value of item 1
item 2			value of item 2
mixture			value of mixture

When we use this table, we generally use the following formula to solve the problem.

value of item 1 + value of item 2 = value of mixture

Now let's look at a mixture problem where we discuss the value or cost of the mixture.

EXAMPLE 5 ▶ **Grass Seed** Scott's® Family grass seed sells for $2.65 per pound, and Scott's Spot Filler grass seed sells for $2.30 per pound. How many pounds of each should be mixed to get a 10-pound mixture that sells for $2.40 per pound?

Solution **a) Understand and Translate** We are asked to find the number of pounds of each type of grass seed.

Let x = number of pounds of Family grass seed.

Then $10 - x$ = number of pounds of Spot Filler grass seed.

We make a sketch of the situation (**Fig. 3.10**), then construct a table.

FIGURE 3.10

The cost or value of the seeds is found by multiplying the number of pounds by the price per pound.

Type of Seeds	Number of Pounds	Cost per Pound	Cost of Seeds
Family	x	2.65	$2.65x$
Spot Filler	$10 - x$	2.30	$2.30(10 - x)$
Mixture	10	2.40	$2.40(10)$

$$\left(\begin{array}{c} \text{cost of} \\ \text{Family Seed} \end{array}\right) + \left(\begin{array}{c} \text{cost of Spot} \\ \text{Filler Seed} \end{array}\right) = \text{cost of mixture}$$

$$2.65x + 2.30(10 - x) = 2.40(10)$$

Carry Out
$$2.65x + 23.0 - 2.30x = 24.0$$
$$0.35x + 23.0 = 24.0$$
$$0.35x = 1.00$$
$$x \approx 2.86$$

Answer Thus, about 2.86 pounds of the Family grass seed must be mixed with $10 - x$ or $10 - 2.86 = 7.14$ pounds of the Spot Filler grass seeds to make a mixture that sells for $2.40 a pound.

▶ **Now Try Exercise 39**

Now we will first discuss the second type of mixture problem, involving mixing solutions.

Type 2—Mixing Solutions

When solving mixture problems involving solutions, we often let the variable represent one unknown quantity, and then we represent a second unknown quantity in terms of the first unknown quantity. For example, if we know that when two solutions are mixed they make a total of 8 liters, we may represent the number of liters of one of the solutions as x and the number of liters of the second solution as $8 - x$. Note that when we add x and $8 - x$ we get 8, the total amount.

We generally solve mixture problems involving solutions by using the fact that the amount of one part of the mixture plus the amount of the second part of the mixture is equal to the total amount of the mixture.

When working with solutions, we use the formula, *amount of substance in the solution = quantity of solution × strength of solution (in percent)*. When we are mixing two quantities and are interested in the *composition* of the mixture, we generally use the following table or a variation of the table.

Quantity × Strength (in percent) = Amount of Substance

Solution	Quantity	Strength	Amount of Substance
Solution 1			amount of substance in solution 1
Solution 2			amount of substance in solution 2
Mixture			amount of substance in mixture

When using this table, we generally use the following formula to solve the problem.

$$\begin{pmatrix} \text{amount of substance} \\ \text{in solution 1} \end{pmatrix} + \begin{pmatrix} \text{amount of substance} \\ \text{in solution 2} \end{pmatrix} = \begin{pmatrix} \text{amount of substance} \\ \text{in mixture} \end{pmatrix}$$

Let us now look at an example of a mixture problem where two solutions are combined.

EXAMPLE 6 ▶ Mixing Acid Solutions Mr. Dave Lumsford needs a 10% acetic acid solution for a chemistry experiment. After checking the store room, he finds that there are only 5% and 20% acetic acid solutions available. Mr. Lumsford decides to make the 10% solution by combining the 5% and 20% solutions. How many liters of the 5% solution must he add to 8 liters of the 20% solution to get a solution that is 10% acetic acid?

Solution   Understand and Translate   We are asked to find the number of liters of the 5% acetic acid solution to mix with 8 liters of the 20% acetic acid solution.

Let x = number of liters of 5% acetic acid solution.

Let's draw a sketch of the problem (**Fig. 3.11**).

FIGURE 3.11

The amount of acid in a given solution is found by multiplying the number of liters by the percent strength.

Solution	Liters	Strength	Amount of Acetic Acid
5%	x	0.05	$0.05x$
20%	8	0.20	$0.20(8)$
Mixture	$x + 8$	0.10	$0.10(x + 8)$

TEACHING TIP
Have students work in pairs to write a
motion problem and a mixture problem. Then have them give their problems to another pair of students to
solve.

$$\left(\begin{array}{c}\text{amount of acid}\\\text{in 5\% solution}\end{array}\right) + \left(\begin{array}{c}\text{amount of acid}\\\text{in 20\% solution}\end{array}\right) = \left(\begin{array}{c}\text{amount of acid}\\\text{in 10\% mixture}\end{array}\right)$$

$$0.05x + 0.20(8) = 0.10(x + 8)$$

Carry Out
$$0.05x + 1.6 = 0.10x + 0.8$$
$$0.05x + 0.8 = 0.10x$$
$$0.8 = 0.05x$$
$$\frac{0.8}{0.05} = x$$
$$16 = x$$

Answer   Sixteen liters of 5% acetic acid solution must be added to the 8 liters of 20% acetic acid solution to get a 10% acetic acid solution. The total number of liters that will be obtained is 16 + 8 or 24.

▶ **Now Try Exercise 47**

INSTRUCTOR EXAMPLE
How much of 16% and 30% potassi-
um iodine solutions must be mixed to
get 20 ounces of 25% sodium iodine
solution?
Ans.: ≈7.14 ounce of 16% and
≈12.86 oz of 30%.

EXAMPLE 7 ▶ Nicole Pappas, a medical researcher, has 40% and 5% solutions of phenobarbital. How much of each solution must she mix to get 0.6 liter of a 20% phenobarbital solution?

Solution   **Understand and Translate**   We are asked to find how much of the 40% and 5% phenobarbital solutions must be mixed to get 0.6 liter of a 20% solution. We can choose to let x be the amount of either the 40% or the 5% solution. We will choose as follows:

Let x = number of liters of the 40% solution.

Then $0.6 - x$ = number of liters of the 5% solution.

Remember from Section 3.1 that if a total of 0.6 liter is divided in two, if one part is x, the other part is $0.6 - x$.

Let's draw a sketch of the problem (**Fig. 3.12**).

FIGURE 3.12

The amount of phenobarbital in a given solution is found by multiplying the number of liters by the percent strength.

Solution	Liters	Strength	Amount of Phenobarbital
40%	x	0.40	$0.40x$
5%	$0.6 - x$	0.05	$0.05(0.6 - x)$
Mixture	0.6	0.20	$0.6(0.20)$

$$\left(\begin{array}{c}\text{amount of phenobarbital}\\\text{in 40\% solution}\end{array}\right) + \left(\begin{array}{c}\text{amount of phenobarbital}\\\text{in 5\% solution}\end{array}\right) = \left(\begin{array}{c}\text{amount of phenobarbital}\\\text{in mixture}\end{array}\right)$$

$$0.40x + 0.05(0.6 - x) = (0.6)(0.20)$$

Carry Out

$$0.40x + 0.03 - 0.05x = 0.12$$
$$0.35x + 0.03 = 0.12$$
$$0.35x = 0.09$$
$$x \approx 0.26$$

Answer   Since the answer was less than 0.6 liter, the answer is reasonable. About 0.26 liter of the 40% solution must be mixed with about $0.6 - x = 0.60 - 0.26 = 0.34$ liter of the 5% solution to get 0.6 liter of the 20% mixture.

▶ **Now Try Exercise 55**

In Example 7, we chose to let x = number of liters of the 40% solution. We could have selected to let x = number of liters of the 5% solution. Then $0.6 - x$ would be the number of liters of the 40% solution. Had you worked the problem out like this, you would have found that x was approximately 0.34 liter. Try reworking Example 7 now letting x = number of liters of the 5% solution.

EXAMPLE 8 ▶ An orange punch contains 4% orange juice. If 5 ounces of water is added to 8 ounces of the punch, determine the percent of orange juice in the mixture.

Solution   **Understand and Translate**   We are asked to find the percent of orange juice in the mixture.

Let x = percent of orange juice in the mixture.

We will again set up a table.

Solution	Ounces	Percent of Juice	Amount of Juice
Punch	8	0.04	8(0.04)
Water	5	0.00	5(0.00)
Mixture	13	x	$13x$

$$\left(\begin{array}{c} \text{amount of juice} \\ \text{in punch} \end{array} \right) + \left(\begin{array}{c} \text{amount of juice} \\ \text{in water} \end{array} \right) = \left(\begin{array}{c} \text{amount of juice} \\ \text{in mixture} \end{array} \right)$$

$$8(0.04) + 5(0.00) = 13x$$

Carry Out

$$0.32 + 0.00 = 13x$$
$$0.32 = 13x$$
$$0.025 \approx x$$

Answer   Therefore, the percent of juice in the mixture is about 2.5%.

▶ **Now Try Exercise 51**

EXERCISE SET 3.4

Practice the Skills/Problem Solving

In Exercises 1–58, set up an equation that can be used to solve each problem. Solve the equation, and answer the question. Use a calculator when you feel it is appropriate.

In Exercises 1–24, solve the motion problem. See Examples 1 and 2.

1. Ferries Two high-speed ferries leave at the same time from Ft. Myers, Florida, going to Key West, Florida. The first ferry, the *Cat*, travels at 34 miles per hour. The second ferry, the *Bird*, travels at 28 miles per hour. In how many hours will the two ferries be 6 miles apart?   1 hr

2. Trains Two trains in New York City start at the same station going in the same direction on sets of parallel tracks. The local train stops often and averages 18.4 miles per hour. The express train stops less frequently and averages 30.2 miles per hour. In how many hours will the two trains be 5.9 miles apart?   0.5 hr

3. Horseback Riding Two friends, Jodi Cotton and Abe Mantell, go horseback riding on the same trail in the same direction. Jodi's horse travels at 8 miles per hour while Abe's horse travels at a slower pace. After 2 hours they are 4 miles apart. Find the speed at which Abe's horse is traveling. 6 mph

4. Camel Riding In the Outback in Australia, Betty Sue Adams and Carl Minieri go camel riding in the same direction along the same path. Betty Sue's camel travels at 6 miles per hour while Carl's camel travels at a slower pace. After 3 hours they are 2.4 miles apart. Find the speed of Carl's camel. 5.2 mph.

5. Airplanes A Jet Blue airplane leaves Chicago for New York at the same time a Southwest airplane leaves New York for Chicago. The distance from Chicago to New York is 821 miles. If the Jet Blue plane travels at 560 miles per hour and the Southwest plane travels at 580 miles per hour, how long into their flights will the two planes pass each other? ≈0.72 hr

6. Walking Barb Dansky and Sandy Spears are at opposite ends of a shopping mall 4780.4 feet apart walking toward each other. If Barb walks 1.5 feet per second and Sandy walks 2.2 feet per second, how long will it be before they meet? 1292 sec or ≈21.53 min

7. Walkie-Talkies Willie and Shanna Johnston have walkie-talkies that have a range of 16.8 miles. Willie and Shanna start at the same point and walk in opposite directions. If Willie walks 3 miles per hour and Shanna walks 4 miles per hour, how long will it take before they are out of range? 2.4 hr

8. Blue Angels At a Navy Blue Angel air show two F/A-18 Hornet jets travel toward each other, both at a speed of 1000 miles per hour. After they pass each other, if they were to keep flying at the same speed in opposite directions, how long would it take for them to be 500 miles apart? 0.25 hr or 15 min

9. Product Testing The Goodyear Tire Company is testing new tires by placing them on a machine that can simulate the tires riding on a road. First, the machine runs the tires for 7.2 hours at 60 miles per hour. Then the tires are run for 6.8 hours at a different speed. After this 14-hour period, the machine indicates that the tires have traveled the equivalent of 908 miles. Find the second speed to which the machine was set. 70 mph

10. Ski Lifts To get to the top of Whistler Mountain, people must use two different ski lifts. The first lift travels 4 miles per hour for 0.2 hours. The second lift travels for 0.3 hours to reach the top of the mountain. If the total distance traveled up the mountain is 1.2 miles, find the average speed of the second ski lift. ≈1.33 mph

11. Earthquakes Earthquakes generate circular p-waves and s-waves, which travel outward (see the figure). Suppose the p-waves have a velocity of 3.6 miles per second and the s-waves have a velocity of 1.8 miles per second. How long after the earthquake will p-waves and s-waves be 80 miles apart? ≈44.4 sec

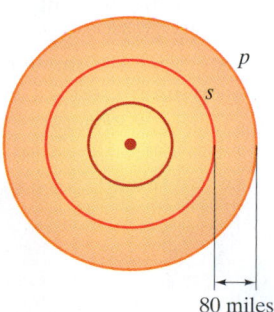

12. Navigating O'Hare Airport Sadie Bragg and Jose Cruz are in Chicago's O'Hare airport walking between terminals. Sadie walks on the moving walkway (like a flat escalator moving along the floor). Her speed (relative to the ground) is 220 feet per minute. Jose starts walking at the same time and walks alongside the walkway at a speed of 100 feet per minute. How long have they been walking when Sadie is 600 feet ahead of Jose? 5 min

13. Disabled Boat Two Coast Guard cutters are 225 miles apart traveling toward each other, one from the east and the other from the west, searching for a disabled boat. The eastbound cutter travels 5 miles per hour faster than the westbound cutter. If the two cutters pass each other after 3 hours, find the average speed of each cutter.   35 mph, 40 mph

14. Snowplowing Two snowplowing crews are clearing snow from a 2.56-mile runway at an airport. Crew A starts at one end of the runway and crew B starts at the other end. They start cleaning at the same time and they work toward each other. Crew A clears the runway at a speed of 0.4 miles per hour faster than crew B. If they meet 0.5 hours after they start, find the average speed of each snowplow.   2.36 mph, 2.76 mph

15. Round Trip Samia Metwali walks for a time at 4 miles per hour, then slows down and walks at 3.2 miles per hour. The total distance she walked was 6 miles. If she walked for 0.5 hour more at 3.2 miles per hour than she did at 4 miles per hour, determine the time Samia walked at 4 miles per hour.   ≈0.61 hr

16. Visit to Grandchild Chuck Neumann drove from his house in Auburn Hills, Michigan, to visit his grandchild in Pasadena, Texas, a distance of 1343 miles. Part of the way he drove at 60 miles per hour and part of the way he drove at 70 miles per hour. If he drove for 0.5 hour more at 60 miles per hour than he did at 70 miles per hour, determine the time Chuck drove at 60 miles per hour.   ≈10.6 hr

17. Paving Road Two crews are laying blacktop on a road. They start at the same time at opposite ends of a 12-mile road and work toward one another. One crew lays blacktop at an average rate of 0.75 mile a day faster than the other crew. If the two crews meet after 3.2 days, find the rate of each crew.   1.5 mi/day, 2.25 mi/day

18. Beach Clean-Up On Earth Day, two groups of people clean a 7-mile stretch of Myrtle Beach. Auturo's group and Jane's group start at the same time at opposite ends of the beach and walk toward each other. Auturo's group is traveling at a rate of 0.5 mile per hour faster than Jane's group, and they meet in 2 hours. Find the speed of each group.

19. Sailing Two sailboats are 9.8 miles apart and sailing toward each other. The larger boat, the *Pythagoras*, sails 4 miles per hour faster than the smaller boat, the *Apollo*. The two boats pass each other after 0.7 hour. Find the speed of each boat.   *Apollo*, 5 mph; *Pythagoras*, 9 mph

20. Exercising Dien and Phuong Vu belong to a health club and exercise together regularly. They start running on two treadmills at the same time. Dien's machine is set for 6

miles per hour and Phuong's machine is set for 4 miles per hour. When they finish, they compare the distances and find that together they have run a total of 11 miles. How long had they run?   1.1 hr

21. Traffic Jam Betty Truitt drives for a number of hours at 70 miles per hour. When traffic slows, she drives at 50 miles per hour. She travels at 50 miles per hour for 0.5 hour longer than she traveled at 70 miles per hour. The difference in the distance traveled at 50 mph and 70 mph is 5 miles. Determine how long Betty traveled at 50 miles per hour.   1.5 hr

22. Salt Mine The ore at a mine must travel on two different conveyer belts to be loaded onto a train. The second conveyer belt travels at a rate of 0.6 foot per second faster than the first conveyer belt. The ore travels 180 seconds on the first belt and 160 seconds on the second belt. If the total distance traveled by the ore is 1116 feet, determine the speed of the second belt.   3.6 ft/sec

23. Ironman Triathlon A triathlon consists of three parts: swimming, cycling, and running. Participants in the Ironman Triathlon in Hawaii must swim, cycle, and run certain distances. The 2005 woman's winner was Switzerland's Natascha Badmann. She swam at an average of 2.31 miles per hour for 1.04 hours then cycled at an average of 23.00 miles per hour for 4.87 hours. Finally, she ran at an average of 8.45 miles per hour for about 3.10 hours.

a) Estimate the distance that Natascha swam.   2.4 mi

b) Estimate the distance that Natascha cycled.   112.0 mi

c) Estimate the distance that Natascha ran.   26.2 mi

d) Estimate the total distance covered during the triathlon.   140.6 mi

e) Estimate the winning time of the triathlon.*   9.01 hr

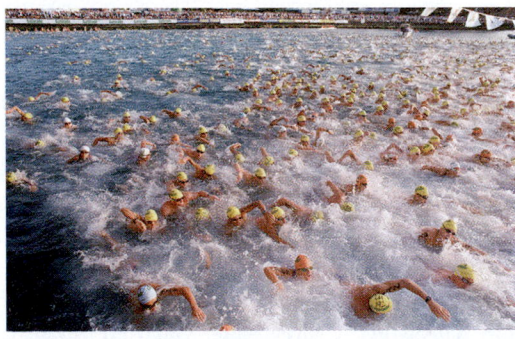

24. Ironman Triathlon Refer to Exercise 23, about the Ironman Triathlon. The 2005 men's winner of the Ironman was Faris Al-Sultan of Germany. He swam at an average speed of 2.89 miles per hour for 0.83 hour, then cycled at an average speed of 25.4 miles per hour for 4.40 hours, then ran at an average speed of 8.98 miles per hour for 2.92 hours. Answer parts a)–e) of the question in Exercise 23.   **a)** 2.40 mi **b)** 112.0 mi   **c)** 26.20 mi   **d)** 140.6 mi   **e)** 8.15 hr

18. Jane's, 1.5 mph; Auturo's, 2 mph

---

*The actual distances are: swim, 2.4 mi; cycle, 112 mi; run 26 mi, 385 yd.

In Exercises 25–38, solve the money problems. See Examples 3 and 4.

25. Simple Interest Paul and Donna Petrie invested $12,000, part at 5% simple interest and the rest at 7% simple interest for a period of 1 year. How much did they invest at each rate if their total annual interest from both investments was $800? (Use interest = principal·rate·time.)

26. Simple Interest Jerry Correa invested $7000, part at 8% simple interest and the rest at 5% simple interest for a period of 1 year. If he received a total annual interest of $476 from both investments, how much did he invest at each rate? $4200 at 8%, $2800 at 5%

27. Simple Interest Aleksandra Tomich invested $6000, part at 6% simple interest and part at 4% simple interest for a period of 1 year. How much did she invest at each rate if each account earned the same interest? $2400 at 6%, $3600 at 4%

28. Simple Interest Susan Foreman invested $12,500, part at 7% simple interest and part at 6% simple interest for a period of 1 year. How much was invested at each rate if each account earned the same interest? $5769.23 at 7%, $6730.77 at 6%

29. Simple Interest Míng Wang invested $10,000, part at 4% and part at 5% simple interest for a period of 1 year. How much was invested in each account if the interest earned in the 5% account was $320 greater than the interest earned in the 4% account? $2000 at 4%, $8000 at 5%

30. Simple Interest Sharon Sledge invested $20,000, part at 5% and part at 7% simple interest for a period of 1 year. How much was invested in each account if the interest earned in the 7% account was $440 greater than the interest earned in the 5% account? $12,000 at 7%, $8000 at 5%

31. Rate Increase Patricia Burgess knows that at some point during the calendar year her basic monthly telephone rate increased from $17.10 to $18.40. If she paid a total of $207.80 for basic telephone service for the calendar year, in what month did the rate increase take effect?   November

32. Cable TV Violet Kokola knows that her subscription rate for the basic tier of cable television increased from $18.20 to $19.50 at some point during the calendar year. She paid a total of $230.10 for the year to the cable company. Determine the month of the rate increase.

33. Wages Mihály Sarett holds two part-time jobs. One job, at Home Depot, pays $6.50 an hour and the second job, at a veterinary clinic, pays $7.00 per hour. Last week Mihály worked a total of 18 hours and earned $122.00. How many hours did Mihály work at each job?   8 hr at Home Depot, 10 hr at clinic

34. Rock and Roll Hall of Fame At the Rock and Roll Hall of Fame in Cleveland, Ohio, adult admission is $20 and children admission is $11. During one day, a total of 1551 adult and children admissions were collected, and $24,441 in admission fees were collected. How many children admissions were collected?   731 Children

35. Baseball Hall of Fame At the Baseball Hall of Fame in Cooperstown, New York, adult admission is $14.50 and children admission is $5.00. During one day, a total of 2100 adult and children admissions were collected, and $21,900 in admission fees was collected. How many adult admissions were collected?   1200 Adults

36. Ticket Sales At a movie theater an evening show cost $7.50 and a matinee cost $4.75. On one day there was one matinee and one evening showing of *Superman Returns*. On that day a total of 310 adult tickets were sold, which resulted in ticket sales of $2022.50. How many adults went to the matinee and how many went to the evening show?   evening, 200; matinee, 110

37. Stock Purchase Suppose Nike stock is selling at $78 a share and Kellogg stock is selling at $33 a share. Mike Moussa has a maximum of $10,000 to invest. He wishes to purchase five times as many shares of Kellogg as of Nike. Only whole shares of stock can be purchased.
   a) How many shares of each will he purchase?
   b) How much money will be left over? $37

38. Stock Purchase Suppose Wal-Mart stock is selling at $59 a share and Mattel stock is selling at $28 a share. Amy Waller has a maximum of $6000 to invest. She wishes to purchase four times as many shares of Wal-Mart as of Mattel. Only whole shares of stock can be purchased.
   a) How many shares of each will she purchase?
   b) How much money will be left over? $192

25. $10,000 at 7%, $2000 at 5%   **32.** She paid 3 months at lower rate, so increase occurred in April.   **37. a)** 41 shares Nike, 205 shares Kellogg
38. a) 22 shares Mattel, 88 shares Wal-Mart   **40.** 2.86 lb Family; 7.14 lb Spot Filler   **41.** $160: 6 cu yd, $120: 2 cu yd

In Exercises 39–58 solve the mixture problem. See Examples 5–8.

39. Nut Shop Jean Valjean owns a nut shop where walnuts cost $6.80 per pound and almonds cost $6.40 per pound. Jean gets an order that specifically requests a 30-pound mixture of walnuts and almonds that will cost $6.65 per pound. How many pounds of each type of nut should Jean mix to get the desired mixture?   11.25 lb almonds, 18.75 lb walnuts

40. Grass Seed Scott's® Family grass seed sells for $2.45 per pound and Scott's Spot Filler grass seed sells for $2.10 per pound. How many pounds of each should be mixed to get a 10-pound mixture that sells for $2.20 per pound?

41. Top Soil Strained top soil sells for $160 per cubic yard and unstrained top soil sells for $120 per cubic yard. How many cubic yards of each should be mixed to make 8 cubic yards of a mixture that sells for $150 per cubic yard?

42. Bird Food At Agway Gardens, bird food is sold in bulk. In one barrel are sunflower seeds that sell for $1.80 per pound. In a second barrel is cracked corn that sells for $1.40 per pound. If a mixture is made by taking 2.5 pounds of the sunflower seeds and 1 pound of the cracked corn, what should the mixture cost per pound? $1.69 per lb

43. Bulk Candies A grocery store sells certain candies in bulk. The Good and Plenty cost $2.49 per pound and Sweet Treats cost $2.89 per pound. If Jane Strange takes 3 scoops of Good and Plenty and mixes it with 5 scoops of Sweet Treats, how much per pound should the mixture sell for? Assume each scoop contained the same weight of candy. $2.74 per lb

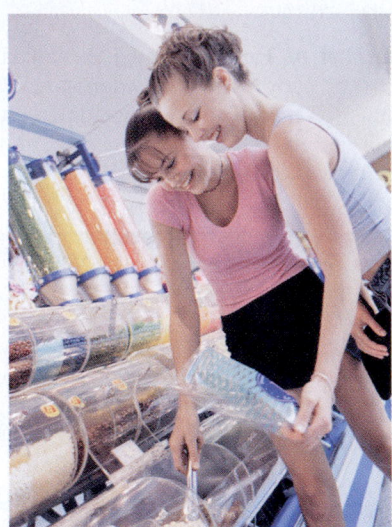

44. Starbucks Ruth Cordeff runs a coffee house where chocolate almond coffee beans sell for $7.00 per pound and hazelnut coffee beans sell for $6.10 per pound. A customer asks Ruth to make a 6-pound mixture using the two kinds of beans. How many pounds of each should be used if the mixture is to cost $6.40 per pound?   2 lb chocolate almond; 4 lb hazelnut

45. Beef Wellington To make beef Wellington, Chef Ramon uses a marinade that is a blend of two red wines. He mixes 5 liters of a wine that is 12% alcohol by volume with 2 liters of a wine that is 9% alcohol by volume. Determine the alcohol content of the mixture.   ≈11.1%

46. Pharmacy Susan Staples, a pharmacist, has a 60% solution of sodium iodite. She also has a 25% solution of the same drug. She gets a prescription calling for a 40% solution of the drug. How much of each solution should she mix to make 0.5 liter of the 40% solution?   ≈0.21 L 60%; ≈0.29 L 25%

47. Sulfuric Acid In chemistry class, Todd Corbin has 1 liter of a 20% sulfuric acid solution. How much of a 12% sulfuric acid solution must he mix with the 1 liter of 20% solution to make a 15% sulfuric acid solution? $1\frac{2}{3}$ L

48. Paint Nick Pappas has two cans of white paint, one with a 2% yellow pigment and the other with a 5% yellow pigment. Nick wants to mix the two paints to get paint with a 4% yellow pigment. How much of the 5% yellow pigment paint should be mixed with 0.4 gallon of the 2% yellow pigment paint to get the desired paint?   0.8 gal

49. Mouthwash The label on the Listerine® Cool Mint Antiseptic mouthwash says that it is 21.6% alcohol by volume. The label on the Scope Original Mint mouthwash says that it is 15.0% alcohol by volume. If Hans mixes 6 ounces of the Listerine with 4 ounces of the Scope, what is the percent alcohol content of the mixture?   18.96%

50. Clorox Clorox® bleach is 5.25% sodium hypochlorite. The instructions on the Clorox bottle say to add 1 cup of Clorox to 4 cups (a quart) of water. Find the percent of sodium hypochlorite in the mixture.   1.05%

51. Orange Juice Mary Ann Terwilliger has made 6 quarts of an orange juice punch for a party. The punch contains 12% orange juice. She feels that she may need more punch, but she has no more orange juice so she adds $\frac{1}{2}$ quart of water to the punch. Find the percent of orange juice in the new mixture.   ≈11.1%

52. Insecticide The active ingredient in one type of Ortho® insect spray is 50% malathion. The instructions on the bottle says to add 1 fluid ounce to a gallon (128 fluid ounces) of water. What percent of malathion will be in the mixture?   ≈0.39%

53. Hawaiian Punch The label on a 12-ounce can of frozen concentrate Hawaiian Punch® indicates that when the can of concentrate is mixed with 3 cans (36 ounces) of cold water, the resulting mixture is 10% juice. Find the percent of pure juice in the concentrate.   40% pure juice

54. Salt Concentration Suppose the dolphins at Sea World must be kept in salt water with an 0.8% salt content. After a week of warm weather, the salt content has increased to 0.9% due to water evaporation. How much water with 0% salt content must be added to 50,000 gallons of the 0.9% salt water to lower the salt concentration to 0.8%?   6250 gal

55. Bleach Clorox® bleach is 5.25% sodium hypochlorite and swimming pool shock treatment is 10.5% sodium hypochlorite. How much of each item must be mixed to get 6 cups of a mixture that is 7.2% sodium hypochlorite?

56. Antifreeze Prestone® antifreeze contains 12% ethylene glycose, and Xeres® antifreeze contains 9% ethylene glycose. How much of each type antifreeze should be mixed to get 10 quarts of a mixture that is 10% ethylene glycose?

57. Alcohol Solution How many pints of a 12% isotrophic alcohol solution should Jenny Crawford mix with 15 pints of a 5% isotrophic alcohol solution to get a mixture that is 8% isotrophic alcohol?   11.25 pints

58. Plant Food Miracle-Gro® All Purpose liquid plant food has 12% nitrogen. Miracle-Gro Quick Start liquid plant food has 4% nitrogen. If 2 cups of the All Purpose plant food are mixed with 3 cups of the Quick Start plant food, determine the percent of nitrogen in the mixture.   7.2%

55. ≈3.77 cups Clorox, ≈2.23 cups shock treatment   **56.** $3\frac{1}{3}$ qt Prestone, $6\frac{2}{3}$ qt Xeres

Challenge Problems

59. Fat Albert The home base of the Navy's Blue Angels is in Pensacola, Florida. The Angels spend winters in El Centro, California. Assume they fly at about 900 miles per hour when they fly from Pensacola to El Centro in their F/A-18 Hornets. On every trip, their C-130 transport (affectionately called Fat Albert) leaves before them, carrying supplies and support personnel. The C-130 generally travels at about 370 miles per hour. On a trip from Pensacola to El Centro, how long before the Hornets leave should Fat Albert leave if it is to arrive 3 hours before the Hornets? The flying distance between Pensacola and El Centro is 1720 miles. ≈5.74 hr

Group Activity

Discuss and answer Exercises 60 and 61 as a group.

60. Race Horse According to the *Guinness Book of World Records*, the fastest race horse speed recorded was by a horse called Big Racket on February 5, 1945, in Mexico City, Mexico. Big Racket ran a $\frac{3}{4}$-mile race in 62.41 seconds. Find Big Racket's speed in miles per hour. Round your answer to the nearest hundredth. 43.26 mph

61. Garage Door Opener An automatic garage door opener is designed to begin to open when a car is 100 feet from the garage. At what rate will the garage door have to open if it is to raise 6 feet by the time a car traveling at 4 miles per hour reaches it? (1 mile per hour≈1.47 feet per second.) ≈0.35 ft/sec

Cumulative Review Exercises

[1.3] **62. a)** Divide $2\frac{3}{4} \div 1\frac{5}{8}$. $\frac{22}{13}$ or $1\frac{9}{13}$

  b) Add $2\frac{3}{4} + 1\frac{5}{8}$. $\frac{35}{8}$ or $4\frac{3}{8}$

[2.5] **63.** Solve the equation $6(x - 3) = 4x - 18 + 2x$. all real numbers

[2.7] **64.** Solve the proportion $\frac{6}{x} = \frac{72}{9}$. $\frac{3}{4}$ or 0.75

[2.8] **65.** Solve the inequality $3x - 4 \leq -4x + 3(x - 1)$. $x \leq \frac{1}{4}$

Chapter 3 Summary

IMPORTANT FACTS AND CONCEPTS	EXAMPLES
Section 3.1	
a subtracted from b means $b - a$.	3 subtracted from $5x$ is $5x - 3$.
The difference between a and b means $a - b$.	The difference between 3 and $5x$ is $3 - 5x$.
If T represents the total amount to be divided in two parts, and if x represents one of the parts, then $T - x$ represents the other part.	If $800 is divided between Jay and Rose and if Rose gets x dollars, then Jay gets $800 - x$ dollars.
A percent is always a percent of some number.	An 8% sales tax on r dollars is $0.08r$. The cost of an item c increased by 5% is $c + 0.05c$.
When writing equations, the words *is, was, will be, yields, gives,* often mean =.	"Two less than 5 times a number *is* the number increased by 3" can be expressed as $5x - 2 = x + 3$.
Consecutive integers, such as 23 and 24, differ by 1 unit.	x and $x + 1$ represent consecutive integers.
Consecutive even integers, such as 24 and 26, differ by 2 units.	x and $x + 2$ represent consecutive even integers.
Consecutive odd integers, such as 23 and 25, differ by 2 units.	x and $x + 2$ represent consecutive odd integers.

IMPORTANT FACTS AND CONCEPTS	EXAMPLES

Section 3.2

Problem-Solving Procedure

1. Understand the problem.
2. Translate the problem into mathematical language.
3. Carry out the mathematical calculation.
4. Check the answer.
5. Answer the question asked.

(See page 195 for more detailed information.)

Three subtracted from 4 times a number is 17. Find the number.

Solution **Understand** We need to express the information given as an equation. We are asked to find the unknown number.

Translate Let x = the unknown number, then we can write the equation

$$4x - 3 = 17$$

Carry out
$$4x = 20$$
$$x = 5$$

Check Substitute 5 for the unknown number
$$4(5) - 3 = 17$$
$$17 = 17, \text{ true}$$

Answer The unknown number is 5.

If you are having difficulty with this section, seek help.

See Helpful Hint on page 201 for possible sources for help.

Section 3.3

An **isosceles triangle** has two sides of the same length. The angles opposite the sides of equal length have equal measures.

Two angles of an isosceles triangle are each 30° greater than the smallest angle. Find the measures of the three angles.

Solution   Let x = the smallest angle.

Then $x + 30$ = the measure of each larger angle.
$$x + (x + 30) + (x + 30) = 180$$
$$3x + 60 = 180$$
$$3x = 120$$
$$x = 40$$

The smallest angle is 40°, and the two larger angles are 40° + 30° or 70°. Note that 40° + 70° + 70° = 180°, so the answer checks.

Section 3.4

A **motion problem** can involve two rates.

Peter and Paul go walking. They start at the same point at the same time and walk in the same direction. Peter walks at 4 mph and Paul walks at 3.5 mph. In how many hours will they be 1 mile apart?

Solution Let t = time when they are 1 mile apart.
$$4t - 3.5t = 1$$
$$0.5t = 1$$
$$t = 2$$
In 2 hours they will be 1 mile apart.

A **money problem** can involve two rates of interest or two different costs.

John sold 12 paintings in one day. Some sold at $80 and the others sold at $125. If he collected a total of $1275, how many of each type did he sell?

Solution   Let x = number of $80 paintings.

Then $12 - x$ = number of $125 paintings.
$$80x + 125(12 - x) = 1275$$
$$80x + 1500 - 125x = 1275$$
$$-45x + 1500 = 1275$$
$$-45x = -225$$
$$x = 5$$

Five $80 paintings and $12 - 5$ or 7 $125 paintings were sold.

IMPORTANT FACTS AND CONCEPTS	EXAMPLES

Section 3.4 (continued)

A **mixture problem** may involve mixing different strengths or different types of solutions, or mixing solid items, such as nuts.

How many liters of an 8% acetic acid solution must be mixed with 6 liters of a 15% acetic acid solution to get a 10% acetic acid solution?

Solution   Let x = number of liters of the 8% solution.

$$0.08x + 0.15(6) = 0.10(x + 6)$$
$$0.08x + 0.9 = 0.10x + 0.6$$
$$0.9 = 0.02x + 0.6$$
$$0.3 = 0.02x$$
$$15 = x$$

Fifteen liters of the 8% solution must be mixed with the 6 liters of the 15% solution.

Chapter 3 Review Exercises

[3.1]

1. **Age** Charles's age is 7 more than 3 times Norman's age, n. Write an expression for Charles's age. $3n + 7$

2. **Gasoline** The cost of a gallon of gasoline in California is 1.2 times the cost of a gallon of gasoline in Georgia, g. Write an expression for the cost of a gallon of gasoline in California. $1.2g$

3. **Dress** Write an expression for the cost of a dress, d, reduced by 25%. $d - 0.25d$

4. **Pounds** Write an expression for the number of ounces in y pounds. $16y$

5. **Money** Two hundred dollars is divided between Jishing Wang and Norma Agras. If Jishing gets x dollars, write an expression for the amount Norma gets. $200 - x$

6. **Age** Mario is 6 years older than seven times Dino's age. Select a variable to represent one quantity and state what the variable represents. Express the second quantity in terms of the variable selected.   let d = Dino's age, then $7d + 6$ = Mario's age

7. **Robberies** The number of robberies in 2006 was 12% less than the number of robberies in 2005. Write an expression for the difference in the number of robberies between 2005 and 2006. $c - (c - 0.12c)$

8. **Numbers** The smaller of two numbers is 24 less than 3 times the larger. When the smaller is subtracted from the larger, the difference is 8. Write an equation to represent this information. Do not solve the equation. $n - (3n - 24) = 8$

[3.2] *In Exercises 9–18, set up an equation that can be used to solve the problem. Solve the equation and answer the question.*

9. **Numbers** One number is 8 more than the other. Find the two numbers if their sum is 74.   33 and 41

10. **Consecutive Integers** The sum of two consecutive integers is 237. Find the two integers.   118 and 119

11. **Numbers** The larger of two integers is 3 more than 5 times the smaller integer. Find the two numbers if the smaller subtracted from the larger is 31.   38 and 7

12. **New Car** Shaana recently purchased a new car. What was the cost of the car before tax if the total cost including a 7% tax was $23,260? $21,738.32

13. **Bagels** A bakery currently ships 520 bagels per month to various outlets. They wish to increase the shipment of bagels by 20 per month until reaching a shipment level of 900 bagels. How long will this take?   19 months

14. **Salary Comparison** Irene Doo, a salesperson, receives a salary of $600 per week plus a 3% commission on all sales she makes. Her company is planning on changing her salary to $500 per week, plus an 8% commission on all sales she makes. What weekly dollar sales would she have to make for the total salaries from each plan to be the same? $2000

15. **Sales Price** During a going-out-of-business sale, all prices were reduced by 20%. If, during the sale Kathy Golladay purchased a camcorder for $495, what was the original price of the camcorder? $618.75

16. **Landscaping** Two Brothers Nursery charges $400 for a tree and $45 per hour to plant the tree. ABC Nursery charges $200 for the same size tree and $65 per hour to plant the tree. How many hours for planting would result in the total price for both landscapers being the same?   10 hr

17. House Price According to the National Association of Realtors, the median sale price for single-family homes increased 11.7% from June 2003 to January 2005. If the median price was $191,000 in 2005, find the median price in 2003. ≈$171,000

18. Tax Refund According to the Internal Revenue Service, the average refund in 2004 was $282 less than 4 times the 1980 annual refund. If the average annual refund in 2004 was $2454, find the average annual refund in 1980. $684

[3.3] Solve each problem.

19. Unknown Angles One angle of a triangle measures 10° greater than the smallest angle, and the third angle measures 10° less than twice the smallest angle. Find the measures of the three angles. 45°, 55°, 80°

20. Unknown Angles One angle of a trapezoid measures 10° greater than the smallest angle; a third angle measures five times the smallest angle; and the fourth angle measures 20° greater than four times the smallest angle. Find the measure of the four angles. 30°, 40°, 150°, 140°

21. Garden Steve Rodi has a rectangular garden whose length is 4 feet longer than its width. The perimeter of the garden is 70 feet. Find the width and length of the garden. $w = 15.5$ ft, $l = 19.5$ ft

22. Designing a House The figure shows plans for a rectangular basement of a house. The dots represents poles in the ground and the lines represent string that has been attached to the poles. The length of the basement is to be 30 feet greater than the width. If a total of 310 feet of string was used to mark off the rooms, find the width and length of the basement. $w = 50$ ft, $l = 80$ ft

23. Rhombus The two larger angles of a rhombus are each 3 times the measure of the two smaller angles. Find the measure of each angle. 45°, 45°, 135°, 135°

24. Bookcase Wade Ellis is building a bookcase with 4 shelves. The length of the bookcase is to be twice the height, as illustrated. If only 20 feet of lumber is available, what should be the length and height of the bookcase? height: 2 ft, length: 4 ft

[3.4] Solve each problem.

25. Jogging Two joggers follow the same route. Harold Lowe jogs at 8 kilometers per hour and Susan Karney Fackert at 6 kilometers per hour. If they leave at the same time, how long will it take for them to be 4 kilometers apart? 2 hr

26. Trains Leaving Two trains going in opposite directions leave from the same station on parallel tracks. One train travels at 50 miles per hour and the other at 60 miles per hour. How long will it take for the trains to be 440 miles apart? 4 hr

27. Pittsburgh Incline The Duquesne Incline in Pittsburgh, Pennsylvania, is shown below. The two cars start at the same time at opposite ends of the incline and travel toward each other at the same speed. The length of the incline is 400 feet and the time it takes for the cars to be at the halfway point is about 22.73 seconds. Determine, in feet per second, the speed the cars travel. ≈8.8 ft/sec

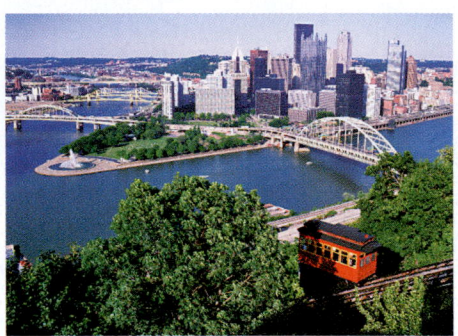

28. Savings Accounts Tatiana wishes to place part of $12,000 into a savings account earning 8% simple interest and part into a savings account earning $7\frac{1}{4}$% simple interest. How much should she invest in each if she wishes to earn $900 in interest for the year? $4000 at 8%, $8000 at $7\frac{1}{4}$%

29. Savings Accounts Aimee Tait invests $4000 into two savings accounts. One account pays 3% simple interest and the other account pays 3.5% simple interest. If the interest earned in the account paying 3.5% simple interest is $94.50 more than the interest earned in the 3% account, how much was invested in each account? $700 at 3%, $3300 at 3.5%

30. Holiday Punch Marcie Waderman is having a holiday party at her house. She made 2 gallons of a punch solution that contains 2% alcohol. How much pure punch must Marcie add to the punch to reduce the alcohol level to 1.5%? ≈0.67 gal

31. Wind Chimes Alan Carmell makes and then sells wind chimes. He makes two types, a smaller one that sells for $8 and a larger one that sells for $20. At an arts and crafts show he sells a total of 30 units, and his total receipts were $492. How many of each type of chime did he sell? small: 9, larger: 21

32. Acid Solution Bruce Kennan, a chemist, wishes to make 2 liters of an 8% acid solution by mixing a 10% acid solution and a 5% acid solution. How many liters of each should he use? 1.2 L of 10%, 0.8 L of 5%

[3.2–3.4] *Solve each problem.*

33. **Numbers** The sum of two consecutive odd integers is 208. Find the two integers.   103 and 105

34. **Television** What is the cost of a television before tax if the total cost, including a 6% tax, is $477? $450

35. **Medical Supplies** Mr. Chang sells medical supplies. He receives a weekly salary of $300 plus a 5% commission on the sales he makes. If Mr. Chang earned $900 last week, what were his sales in dollars? $12,000

36. **Triangle** One angle of a triangle is 8° greater than the smallest angle. The third angle is 4° greater than twice the smallest angle. Find the measure of the three angles of the triangle.

37. **Increase Staff** The Darchelle Leggett Company plans to increase its number of employees by 25 per year. If the company now has 427 employees, how long will it take before they have 627 employees?   8 years

38. **Parallelogram** The two larger angles of a parallelogram each measure 40° greater than the two smaller angles. Find the measure of the four angles.   70°, 70°, 110°, 110°

39. **Copy Centers** Copy King charges a monthly fee of $20 plus 4 cents per copy. King Kopie charges a monthly fee of $25 plus 3 cents a copy. How many copies made in a month would result in both companies charging the same amount?

40. **Swimming** Rita Gonzales and Jim Ham are going swimming in Putnam Lake. They start swimming in the same direction at the same time. Rita swims at 1 mph and Jim swims at a slower pace. After 0.5 hour they are 0.2 mile apart. Find the speed that Jim is swimming.   0.6 mph

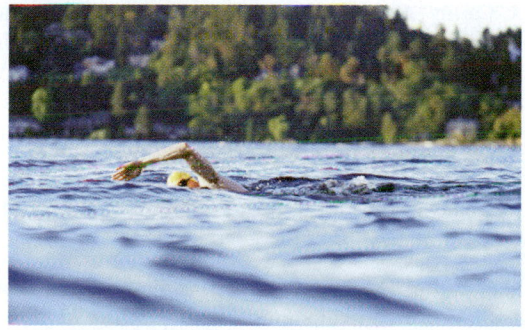

41. **Butcher** A butcher combined ground beef that cost $3.50 per pound with ground beef that cost $4.10 per pound. How many pounds of each were used to make 80 pounds of a mixture that sells for $3.65 per pound?   60 lb of $3.50, 20 lb of $4.10

42. **Speed Traveled** Two brothers who are 230 miles apart start driving toward each other at the same time. The younger brother travels 5 miles per hour faster than the older brother, and the brothers meet after 2 hours. Find the speed traveled by each brother.   older brother, 55 mph; younger brother, 60 mph

43. **Acid Solution** How many liters of a 30% acid solution must be mixed with 2 liters of a 12% acid solution to obtain a 15% acid solution?   0.4 L

44. **Fencing** Kathy Tomaino is partitioning a rectangular yard using fencing, as shown below. If the length is 1.5 times the width and if only 96 feet of fencing is available, find the length and width of the partitioned area.   *w*: 16 ft, *l*: 24 ft

45. **Acid Solution** Six liters of a 3% sulfuric acid solution is mixed with an 8% sulfuric acid solution. If the mixture is a 4% sulfuric acid solution, determine how many liters of the 8% sulfuric acid solution were used in the mixture.   1.5 L

36. 42°, 50°, 88°   **39.** 500 copies

Chapter 3 Practice Test

 To find out how well you understand the chapter material, take this practice test. The answers, and the section where the material was initially discussed, are given in the back of the book. Each problem is also fully worked out on the **Chapter Test Prep Video CD**. *Review any questions that you answered incorrectly.*

1. **Money** Five hundred dollars was divided between Boris and Monique. If Monique received *n* dollars, write an expression for the amount Boris received.   500 − *n*

2. **Restaurants** The money Sally Sestini earned was $6000 more than twice what William Rowley earned. Write an expression for what Sally earned.   2*w* + 6000

3. Write an expression for the number of seconds in *t* minutes.   60*t*

4. **Season Tickets** The cost of a season ticket for the Dallas Cowboys football games increased by 6% from the previous years cost, *c*. Write an expression for the cost of a season ticket for this year.   *c* + 0.06*c*

In Exercises 5–6, select a variable to represent one quantity and state what it represents. Express the second quantity in terms of the variable selected.

5. **Tic Tacs** The number of packages of peppermint flavored Tic Tacs® sold was 105 packages less than 7 times the number of packages of orange flavored Tic Tacs sold

6. **Men and Women** At a play there were 600 men and women.

7. **Numbers** The larger of two numbers is 1 less than twice the smaller number. Write an expression for the smaller number subtracted from the larger number $(2n - 1) - n$

8. **Liquid Tide** The number of fluid ounces in a large bottle of Tide® is 18 fluid ounces more than the amount in a smaller bottle. Write an expression for the sum of the amounts in a small and large bottle. $n + (n + 18)$

9. **Nuts** The cost of a can of Planters® Deluxe Nuts is 84% greater than the cost of a can of Planters Peanuts. Write an expression for the difference in cost between the Deluxe Nuts and the Peanuts. $(c + 0.84c) - c$

In Exercises 10–25, set up an equation that can be used to solve the problem. Solve the problem and answer the question asked.

10. **Integers** The sum of two integers is 158. Find the two integers if the larger is 10 less than twice the smaller.   56 and 102

11. **Consecutive Odd Integers** For two consecutive odd integers, the sum of the smaller and 4 times the larger is 33. Find the integers.   5 and 7

12. **Numbers** One number is 12 less than 5 times the other. Find the two numbers if their sum is 42.   9 and 33

13. **Lawn Furniture** Dona Bishop purchased a set of lawn furniture. The cost of the furniture, including a 6% tax, was $2650. Find the cost of the furniture before tax. $2500

14. **Eating Out** Mark Sullivan has only $40. He wishes to leave a 15% tip. Find the price of the most expensive meal that he can order. $34.78

15. **Business Venture** Julie Burgmeier receives twice the profit in a business venture than Peter Ancona does. If the profit for the year was $120,000, how much will each receive?

16. **Snowplowing** William Echols is going to hire a snow plowing service. Elizabeth Suco charges an annual fee of $80, plus $5 each time she plows. Jon Wilkins charges an annual fee of $50, plus $10 each time he plows. How many times would the snow need to be plowed for the cost of both plans to be the same?   6 times

17. **Laser Printers** A Delta laser printer cost $499. The cost of printing each page of text is 1 cent. A TexMar laser printer cost $350. The cost of printing each page is 3 cents. How many pages would need to be printed for the total cost of both printers to be the same?   7450 pages

18. **Triangle** A triangle has a perimeter of 75 inches. Find the three sides if one side is 15 inches larger than the smallest side, and the third side is twice the smallest side.   15 in., 30 in., 30 in.

19. **American Flag** Carlos Mendoze's American flag has a perimeter of 28 feet. Find the dimensions of the flag if the length is 4 feet less than twice its width.   width: 6 ft, length: 8 ft

20. **Trapezoid** The two larger angles of a trapezoid measure 3° more than twice the two smaller angles. Determine the four angles of the trapezoid.   59°, 59°, 121°, 121°

21. **Laying Cable** Ellis and Harlene Matza are digging a shallow 67.2-foot-long trench to lay electrical cable to a new outdoor light fixture they just installed. They start digging at the same time at opposite ends of where the trench is to go, and dig toward each other. Ellis digs at a rate of 0.2 foot per minute faster than Harlene, and they meet after 84 minutes. Find the speed that each digs.   Harlene: 0.3 ft/min; Ellis: 0.5 ft/min

22. **Running** Alice and Bonnie start running at the same time from the same point and run in the same direction. Alice runs at 8 mph while Bonnie runs at a slower pace. After 2 hours they are 4 miles apart. Determine the speed at which Bonnie is running.   6 mph

23. **Bulk Candy** A candy shop sells candy in bulk. In one bin is Jelly Belly candy, which sells for $2.20 per pound, and in a second bin is Kits, which sells for $2.75 per pound. How much of each type should be mixed to obtain a 3 pound mixture, which sells for $2.40 per pound?   Jelly Belly: ≈1.91 lb, Kits: ≈1.09 lb

24. **Salt Solution** How many liters of 20% salt solution must be added to 60 liters of 40% salt solution to get a solution that is 35% salt?   20 L

25. **Acid Solution** A chemist wishes to make 3 liters of a 6% acid solution by mixing an 8% acid solution and a 5% acid solution. How many liters of each should she mix?

5. let n = number of packages of orange, then $7n - 105$ = number of packages of peppermint
6. let x = number of men, then $600 - x$ = number of woman, or let x = number of woman, then $600 - x$ = number of men
15. Peter: $40,000, Julie: $80,000
25. 1 L of 8%, 2 L of 5%

Cumulative Review Test

Take the following test and check your answers with those given in the back of the book. Review any questions that you answered incorrectly. The section where the material was covered is indicated after the answer.   **6. c)** quotient of two integers, denominator not 0

1. **Social Security** The following circle graph shows what the typical retiree receives in social security, as a percent of their total income.

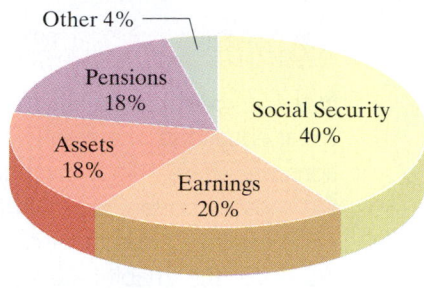

Where Social Security Recipients Get Their Income

Source: Newsweek

If Emily receives \$40,000 per year, and her income is typical of all social security recipients, how much is she receiving in social security?   \$16,000

2. **Engineers** The following graph appeared in the Febuary 2, 2006 issue of *USA Today*. The article said that by 2010 about 90% of the world's scientists and engineers will live in Asia.

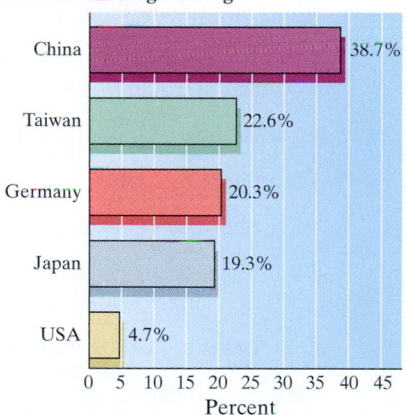

Percentage of Undergraduate Degrees Awarded in Engineering

Country	Percent
China	38.7%
Taiwan	22.6%
Germany	20.3%
Japan	19.3%
USA	4.7%

Source: National Science Foundation
(2000, latest data available)

a) What is the percentage difference in the Engineering degrees awarded in China and the United States?   34%

b) If 1.3 million undergraduate degrees were awarded in the United States in 2006, how many were Engineering degrees?   ≈0.06 million or ≈60,000

3. **Carbon Dioxide Levels** David Warner, an environmentalist, was checking the level of carbon dioxide in the air. On five readings, he got the results indicated in the table above on the right.

Test	Carbon Dioxide (parts per million)
1	5
2	6
3	8
4	12
5	5

a) Find the mean level of carbon dioxide detected.   7.2 ppm

b) Find the median level of carbon dioxide detected.   6 ppm

4. Evaluate $\dfrac{5}{12} \div \dfrac{3}{4}$. $\dfrac{5}{9}$

5. How much larger is $\dfrac{2}{3}$ inch than $\dfrac{1}{8}$ inch? $\dfrac{13}{24}$ in.

6. **a)** List the set of natural numbers. $\{1, 2, 3, 4, \dots\}$

b) List the set of whole numbers. $\{0, 1, 2, 3, \dots\}$

c) What is a rational number?

7. **a)** Evaluate $|-4|$.   4

b) Which is greater, $|-5|$ or $|-3|$? Explain. $|-5|$

8. Evaluate $2 - 6^2 \div 2 \cdot 2$. -34

9. Simplify $4(2x - 3) - 2(3x + 5) - 6$. $2x - 28$

In Exercises 10–12, solve the equation.

10. $5x - 6 = x + 14$ 5

11. $6r = 2(r + 3) - (r + 5)$ $\dfrac{1}{5}$

12. $2(x + 5) = 3(2x - 4) - 4x$ no solution

13. If $A = \pi r^2$, find A when $r = 6$.   ≈113.10

14. Consider the equation $4x + 8y = 16$.

a) Solve the equation for y and write the equation in $y = mx + b$ form. $y = -\dfrac{1}{2}x + 2$

b) Find y when $x = -4$.   4

15. Solve the formula $P = 2l + 2w$ for w. $w = \dfrac{P - 2l}{2}$

16. **Gas Needed** If Lisa Shough's car can travel 50 miles on 2 gallons of gasoline, how many gallons of gas will it need to travel 225 miles?   9 gal

17. Solve the inequality $3x - 4 \le -1$ and graph the solution on a number line. $x \le 1$,

18. **Calling Plan** Lori Sypher is considering two cellular telephone plans. Plan A has a monthly charge of \$19.95 plus 35 cents per minute. Plan B has a monthly charge of \$29.95 plus 10 cents per minute. How long would Lori need to talk in a month for the two plans to have the same total cost?   40 min

19. **Sum of Numbers** The sum of two numbers is 29. Find the two numbers if the larger is 11 greater than twice the smaller.   6, 23

20. **Quadrilateral** One angle of a quadrilateral measures 5° larger than the smallest angle; the third angle measures 50° larger than the smallest angle; and the fourth angle measures 25° greater than 4 times the smallest angle. Find the measure of each angle of the quadrilateral.   40°, 45°, 90°, 185°

Graphing Linear Equations

4

WE SEE GRAPHS daily. They are very important in both mathematics and in everyday living. Graphs are used to display information. For example, in Exercise 77 on page 250, we use a graph to illustrate the total cost of renting a truck under various conditions.

4.1 The Cartesian Coordinate System and Linear Equations in Two Variables

1 Plot points in the Cartesian coordinate system.

2 Determine whether an ordered pair is a solution to a linear equation.

René Descartes

1 Plot Points in the Cartesian Coordinate System

Many algebraic relationships are easier to understand if we can see a picture of them. A **graph** shows the relationship between two variables in an equation. In this chapter we discuss several procedures that can be used to draw graphs using the **Cartesian (or rectangular) coordinate system**. The Cartesian coordinate system is named for its developer, the French mathematician and philosopher René Descartes (1596–1650).

The Cartesian coordinate system provides a means of locating and identifying points just as the coordinates on a map help us find cities and other locations. Consider the map of the Great Smoky Mountains (see **Fig. 4.1**). Can you find Cades Cove on the map? If we tell you that it is in grid A3, you can probably find it much more quickly and easily.

FIGURE 4.1

The Cartesian coordinate system is a grid system, like that of a map, except that it is formed by two axes (or number lines) drawn perpendicular to each other. The two intersecting axes form four **quadrants**, numbered I through IV in **Figure 4.2**.

The horizontal axis is called the **x-axis**. The vertical axis is called the **y-axis**. The point of intersection of the two axes is called the **origin**. At the origin the value of x is 0 and the value of y is 0. Starting from the origin and moving to the right along the x-axis, the numbers increase (**Fig. 4.3**). Starting from the origin and moving to the left, the numbers decrease. Starting from the origin and moving up the y-axis, the numbers increase. Starting from the origin and moving down, the numbers decrease.

FIGURE 4.2

FIGURE 4.3

FIGURE 4.4

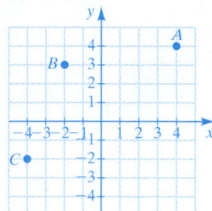

To locate a point, it is necessary to know both the value of x and the value of y, or the **coordinates**, of the point. When the x- and y-coordinates of a point are placed in parentheses, *with the x-coordinate listed first*, we have an **ordered pair**. In the ordered pair $(3, 5)$ the x-coordinate is 3 and the y-coordinate is 5. The point corresponding to the ordered pair $(3, 5)$ is plotted in **Figure 4.4**. The phrase "the point corresponding to the ordered pair $(3, 5)$" is often abbreviated "the point $(3, 5)$." For example, if we write "the point $(-1, 2)$," it means "the point corresponding to the ordered pair $(-1, 2)$."

EXAMPLE 1 ▶ Plot (or mark) each point on the same axes.

a) $A(5, 3)$ **b)** $B(2, 4)$ **c)** $C(-3, 1)$

d) $D(4, 0)$ **e)** $E(-2, -5)$ **f)** $F(0, -3)$

g) $G(0, 2)$ **h)** $H\left(6, -\dfrac{9}{2}\right)$ **i)** $I\left(-\dfrac{3}{2}, -\dfrac{5}{2}\right)$

Solution   The first number in each ordered pair is the x-coordinate and the second number is the y-coordinate. The points are plotted in **Figure 4.5**.

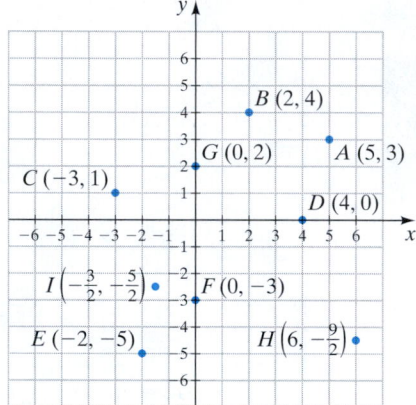

FIGURE 4.5

Note that when the x-coordinate is 0, as in Example 1 **f)** and 1 **g)**, the point is on the y-axis. When the y-coordinate is 0, as in Example 1 **d)**, the point is on the x-axis.

▶ **Now Try Exercise 29**

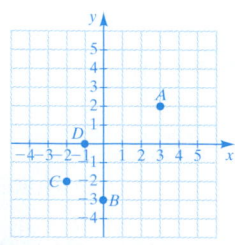
EXAMPLE 2 ▶ List the ordered pairs for each point shown in **Figure 4.6**.

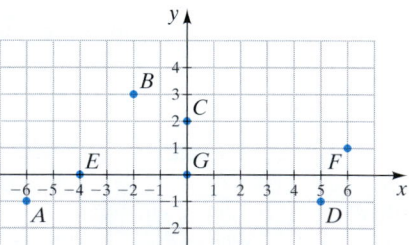

FIGURE 4.6

Solution   Remember to give the x-value first in the ordered pair.

Point	Ordered Pair
A	$(-6, -1)$
B	$(-2, 3)$
C	$(0, 2)$
D	$(5, -1)$
E	$(-4, 0)$
F	$(6, 1)$
G	$(0, 0)$

▶ **Now Try Exercise 27**

2 Determine Whether an Ordered Pair Is a Solution to a Linear Equation

In Section 4.2 we will learn to graph linear equations in two variables. Below we explain how to identify a linear equation in two variables.

> ### Linear Equations in Two Variables
>
> A **linear equation in two variables** is an equation that can be put in the form
>
> $$ax + by = c$$
>
> where $a, b,$ and c are real numbers.

TEACHING TIP
Point out that the adjective *straight* is not needed to describe lines. All lines are straight. It is used to emphasize the shape of the graph.

The graphs of equations of the form $ax + by = c$ are straight lines. For this reason such equations are called linear. Linear equations may be written in various forms, as we will show later. A linear equation in the form $ax + by = c$ is said to be in **standard form**.

Examples of Linear Equations

$$4x - 3y = 12$$
$$y = 5x + 3$$
$$x - 3y + 4 = 0$$

Note in the examples that only the equation $4x - 3y = 12$ is in standard form. However, the bottom two equations can be written in standard form, as follows:

$y = 5x + 3$	$x - 3y + 4 = 0$
$-5x + y = 3$	$x - 3y = -4$

Most of the equations we have discussed thus far have contained only one variable. Exceptions to this include formulas used in application sections. Consider the linear equation in *one* variable, $2x + 3 = 5$. What is its solution?

$$2x + 3 = 5$$
$$2x = 2$$
$$x = 1$$

This equation has only one solution, 1.

Check
$$2x + 3 = 5$$
$$2(1) + 3 \stackrel{?}{=} 5$$
$$5 = 5 \quad \textit{True}$$

Now consider the linear equation in *two* variables, $y = x + 1$. What is the solution? Since the equation contains two variables, its solutions must contain two numbers, one for each variable. One pair of numbers that satisfies this equation is $x = 1$ and $y = 2$. To see that this is true, we substitute both values into the equation and see that the equation checks.

Check
$$y = x + 1$$
$$2 \stackrel{?}{=} 1 + 1$$
$$2 = 2 \quad \textit{True}$$

We write this answer as an ordered pair by writing the x- and y-values within parentheses separated by a comma. Remember that the x-value is always listed first because the form of an ordered pair is (x, y). Therefore, one possible solution to this equation is the ordered pair $(1, 2)$. The equation $y = x + 1$ has other possible solutions. Below we show three other solutions and their checks.

	Solution	Solution	Solution
	$x = 2, y = 3$	$x = -3, y = -2$	$x = -\frac{1}{3}, y = \frac{2}{3}$
Check	$y = x + 1$	$y = x + 1$	$y = x + 1$
	$3 \overset{?}{=} 2 + 1$	$-2 \overset{?}{=} -3 + 1$	$\frac{2}{3} \overset{?}{=} -\frac{1}{3} + 1$
	$3 = 3$ *True*	$-2 = -2$ *True*	$\frac{2}{3} = \frac{2}{3}$ *True*

Solution Written as an Ordered Pair

$(2, 3)$ $(-3, -2)$ $\left(-\frac{1}{3}, \frac{2}{3}\right)$

TEACHING TIP
After discussing several solutions to the equation $y = x + 1$, ask, Is there a relationship between the x- and y-values? Point out that the equation concisely describes this relationship.

How many possible solutions does the equation $y = x + 1$ have? The equation $y = x + 1$ has an unlimited or *infinite number* of possible solutions. Since it is not possible to list all the specific solutions, the solutions are illustrated with a graph.

Graph of an Equation

A **graph** of an equation in two variables is an illustration of a set of points whose coordinates satisfy the equation.

Figure 4.7a shows the points $(2, 3)$, $(-3, -2)$, and $\left(-\frac{1}{3}, \frac{2}{3}\right)$ plotted in the Cartesian coordinate system. **Figure 4.7b** shows a straight line drawn through the three points. Arrowheads are placed at the ends of the line to show that the line continues in both directions. Every point on this line will satisfy the equation $y = x + 1$, so this graph illustrates all the solutions of $y = x + 1$. The ordered pair $(1, 2)$, which is on the line, also satisfies the equation.

In **Figure 4.7b**, what do you notice about the points $(2, 3)$, $(1, 2)$, $\left(-\frac{1}{3}, \frac{2}{3}\right)$, and $(-3, -2)$? You probably noticed that they are in a straight line. A set of points that are in a straight line are said to be **collinear**. *In Section 4.2 when you graph linear equations by plotting points, the points you plot should all be collinear.*

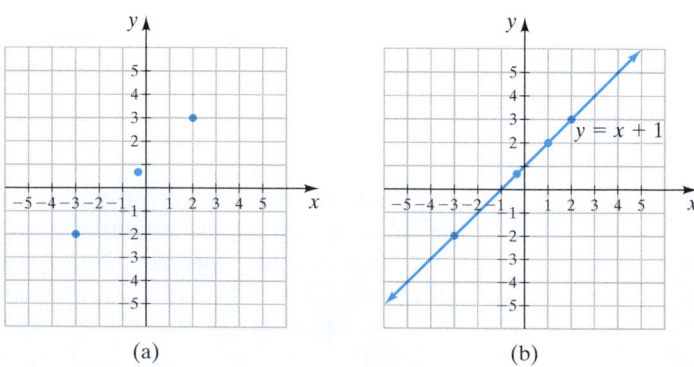

FIGURE 4.7   (a)   (b)

EXAMPLE 3 ▶ Determine whether the three points appear to be collinear.

a) $(2, 7), (0, 3)$, and $(-2, -1)$

b) $(0, 5), \left(\frac{5}{2}, 0\right)$, and $(5, -5)$

c) $(-2, -5), (0, 1)$, and $(6, 8)$

Solution We plot the points to determine whether they appear to be collinear. The solution is shown in **Figure 4.8**.

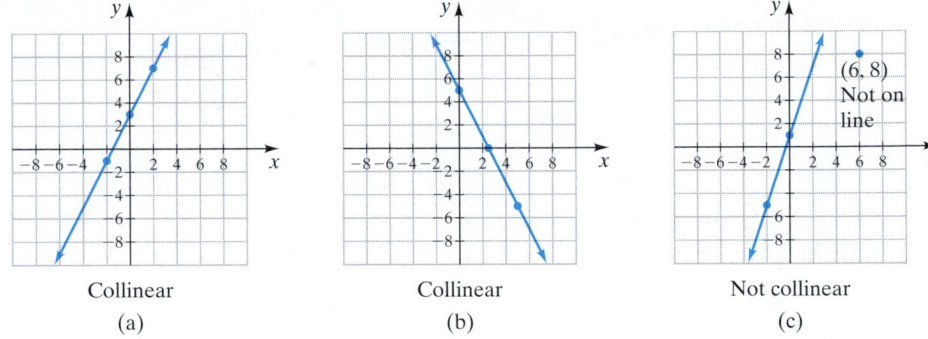

Collinear	Collinear	Not collinear
(a)	(b)	(c)

FIGURE 4.8

▶ **Now Try Exercise 33**

To graph an equation, you will need to determine ordered pairs that satisfy the equation and then plot the points.

How many points do you need to graph a linear equation? As mentioned earlier, *the graph of every linear equation of the form ax + by = c will be a straight line.* Since only two points are needed to draw a straight line, only two points are needed to graph a linear equation. However, it is always a good idea to plot at least three points. See the Helpful Hint that follows.

Helpful Hint

Only two points are needed to graph a linear equation because the graph of every linear equation is a straight line. However, if you graph a linear equation using only two points and you have made an error in determining or plotting one of those points, your graph will be wrong and you will not know it. In **Figures 4.9a** and **b** we plot only two points to show that if only one of the two points plotted is incorrect, the graph will be wrong. In both **Figures 4.9a** and **b** we use the ordered pair $(-2, -2)$. However, in **Figure 4.9a** the second point is $(1, 2)$, while in **Figure 4.9b** the second point is $(2, 1)$. Notice how the two graphs differ.

If you use at least three points to plot your graph, as in **Figure 4.7b** on page 236, and they appear to be collinear, you probably have not made a mistake.

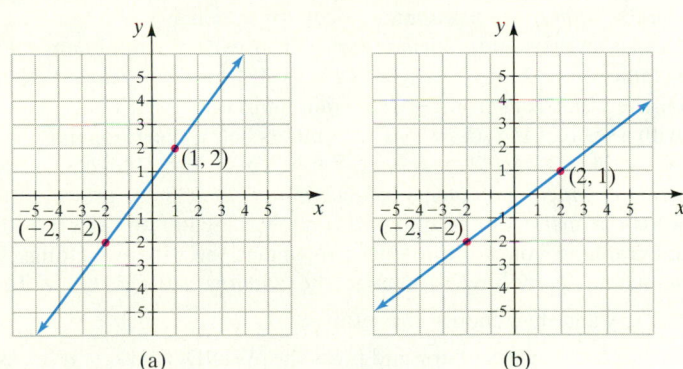

FIGURE 4.9   (a)   (b)

EXAMPLE 4 ▶

a) Determine which of the following ordered pairs satisfy the equation $2x + y = 4$.

$$(2, 0), (0, 4), (3, 1), (-1, 6)$$

b) Plot all the points that satisfy the equation on the same axes and draw a straight line through the points.

c) What does this straight line represent?

Solution

a) We substitute values for x and y into the equation $2x + y = 4$ and determine whether they check.

Check

$(2, 0)$

$2x + y = 4$

$2(2) + 0 \stackrel{?}{=} 4$

$4 = 4$ *True*

$(0, 4)$

$2x + y = 4$

$2(0) + 4 \stackrel{?}{=} 4$

$4 = 4$ *True*

$(3, 1)$

$2x + y = 4$

$2(3) + 1 \stackrel{?}{=} 4$

$7 = 4$ *False*

$(-1, 6)$

$2x + y = 4$

$2(-1) + 6 \stackrel{?}{=} 4$

$4 = 4$ *True*

The ordered pairs $(2, 0)$, $(0, 4)$, and $(-1, 6)$ satisfy the equation. The ordered pair $(3, 1)$ does not satisfy the equation.

b) **Figure 4.10** shows the three points that satisfy the equation. A straight line drawn through the three points shows that they appear to be collinear.

c) The straight line represents all solutions of $2x + y = 4$. The coordinates of every point on this line satisfy the equation $2x + y = 4$.

▸ **Now Try Exercise 37**

FIGURE 4.10

USING YOUR GRAPHING CALCULATOR

Some of you may have graphing calculators. In this chapter we will give a number of Using Your Graphing Calculator boxes with some information on using your calculator. Because the instructions will be general, you may need to refer to your calculator manual for more specific instructions. The keystrokes you will use will depend on the brand and model of your calculator. In this book all graphing calculator windows displayed will be from TI-83 Plus or TI-84 Plus graphing calculator. Both calculators display the same window. In using Using Your Graphing Calculator boxes throughout the book, we will sometimes indicate that the keystrokes and windows shown are for a TI-84 Plus graphing calculator. The same keystrokes and windows will also apply to the TI-83 Plus graphing calculator even though we may not indicate this in the boxes.

A primary use of a graphing calculator is to graph equations. A graphing calculator *window* is the rectangular screen in which a graph is displayed. **Figure 4.11** shows a calculator window with labels added. **Figure 4.12** shows the meaning of the information given in **Figure 4.11**. These are the *standard window settings* for a graphing calculator screen.

The x-axis on the standard window goes from -10 (the minimum value of x, Xmin) to 10 (the maximum value of x, Xmax) with a scale of 1. Therefore, each tick mark represents 1 unit (Xscl = 1). The y-axis goes from -10 (the minimum value of y, Ymin) to 10 (the maximum value of y, Ymax) with a scale of 1 (Yscl = 1). The numbers below the graph in **Figure 4.11** indicate, in order, the window settings: Xmin, Xmax, Xscl, Ymin, Ymax, Yscl. *When no settings are shown below a graph, always assume the standard window setting is used.* Since the window is rectangular, the distance between tick marks on the standard window is greater on the x-axis than on the y-axis.

When graphing, you will often need to change the window settings. Read your graphing calculator manual to learn how to change the window settings. On a TI-84 Plus you press the WINDOW key and then change the settings.

Now, turn on your calculator and press the WINDOW key. If necessary, adjust the window so that it looks like the window in **Figure 4.12**. Use the (–) key, if necessary, to make negative numbers. (You can also obtain the standard window settings on a TI-84 Plus by pressing the ZOOM key and then pressing option 6, ZStandard.) Next press the GRAPH key. Your screen should resemble the screen in **Figure 4.11** (without the labels that were added). Now press the WINDOW key again. Then use the appropriate keys to change the window setting so it is the same as that shown in **Figure 4.13** on page 239.

Now press the GRAPH key again. You should get the screen shown in **Figure 4.14** on page 239. In **Figure 4.14**, the x-axis starts at 0 and goes to 50, and each tick mark represents 5 units (represented by the first 3 numbers under the window). The y-axis starts at 0 and goes to 100, and each tick mark represents 10 units (represented by the last 3 numbers under the window).

$-10, 10, 1, -10, 10, 1$

FIGURE 4.11

```
WINDOW
 Xmin=-10
 Xmax=10
 Xscl=1
 Ymin=-10
 Ymax=10
 Yscl=1
 Xres=1
```

FIGURE 4.12

(continued on the next page)

FIGURE 4.13

0, 50, 5, 0, 100, 10

FIGURE 4.14

EXERCISES

For Exercises 1 and 2, set your window to the values shown.
Then use the GRAPH *key to shown the axes formed.*

1. Xmin = −20, Xmax = 40, Xscl = 5,
   Ymin = −10, Ymax = 60, Yscl = 10

2. Xmin = −200, Xmax = 400, Xscl = 100,
   Ymin = −500, Ymax = 1000, Yscl = 200   **1.** and **2.** See graphing answer section.

3. Consider the screen in **Figure 4.15**. The numbers under the window have been omitted.
   If Xmin = −300 and Xmax = 400, find Xscl. Explain how you determined your answer.   40

4. In **Figure 4.15**, if Ymin = −200 and Ymax = 1000, find Yscl. Explain how you determined
   your answer.   100

FIGURE 4.15

1. the *x*-coordinate   2. rectangular coordinate system   4. the point of intersection of the two axes   5. Axis is singular, axes is plural.   6. Place the point directly above the −2 on the x-axis and directly to the left of 4 on the y-axis.   7. an illustration of a set of points whose coordinates satisfy the equation   10. a straight line   12. They lie in a straight line.

EXERCISE SET 4.1

Math XL   MyMathLab
MathXL®   MyMathLab

Concept/Writing Exercises

1. In an ordered pair, which coordinate is always listed first?

2. What is another name for the Cartesian coordinate system?

3. a) Is the *horizontal axis* the *x*- or *y*-axis in the Cartesian coordinate system?   *x*-axis

   b) Is the *vertical axis* the *x*- or *y*-axis?   *y*-axis

4. What is the *origin* in the Cartesian coordinate system?

5. We can refer to the *x-axis* and we can refer to the *y-axis*. We can also refer to the *x*- and *y-axes*. Explain when we use the word *axis* and when we use the word *axes*.

6. Explain how to plot the point (−2, 4) in the Cartesian coordinate system.

7. What does the graph of a linear equation illustrate?

8. Why are arrowheads added to the ends of graphs of linear equations?   to show that the line extends in both directions

9. a) How many points are needed to graph a linear equation?   two

   b) Why is it always a good idea to use three or more points when graphing a linear equation?   to catch errors

10. What will the graph of a linear equation look like?

11. What is the standard form of a linear equation? $ax + by = c$

12. When graphing linear equations, the points that are plotted should all be *collinear*. Explain what this means.

13. In the Cartesian coordinate system there are four quadrants. Draw the *x*- and *y*-axes and mark the four quadrants, I through IV, on your axes.   See graphing answer section.

14. How many solutions does a linear equation in two variables have?   an infinite number

Practice the Skills

Indicate the quadrant in which each of the points belongs.

15. (−4, 3)   II

16. (−3, 1)   II

17. (5, −6)   IV

18. (2, −3)   IV

19. (8, 5)   I

20. (4, 30)   I

21. (−17, −87)   III

22. (63, 47)   I

23. (−124, −132)   III

24. (75, 200)   I

25. (−8, 42)   II

26. (76, −92)   IV

27. List the ordered pairs corresponding to each point.

$A(3, 1)$

$B(−3, 0)$

$C(1, −3)$

$D(−2, −3)$

$E(0, 3)$

$F\left(\frac{3}{2}, −1\right)$

28. List the ordered pairs corresponding to each point.

$A(8, 5)$

$B(4, 0)$

$C(6, −15)$

$D(−4, 20)$

$E(0, −20)$

$F(−6, −5)$

$G(−5, 10)$

Plot each point on the same axes.

29. $A(3, 2), B(-4, 1), C(0, -3), D(-2, 0), E(-3, -4), F\left(-4, -\dfrac{5}{2}\right)$

30. $A(-3, -1), B(2, 0), C(3, 2), D\left(\dfrac{1}{2}, -4\right), E(-4, 2), F(0, 5)$

31. $A(4, 0), B(-1, 3), C(2, 4), D(0, -2), E(-3, -3), F(2, -3)$

32. $A(-3, 4), B(2, 3), C(0, 3), D(-1, 0), E(-2, -2), F(2, -4)$

34. (4, 1) not on line   **35.** (−5, −3) not on line   **36.** (3, 5) not on line
29.–32. See graphing answer section.

Plot the following points. Then determine whether they appear to be collinear.

33. $A(1, -1), B(5, 3), C(-3, -5), D(0, -2), E(2, 0)$ yes

34. $A(1, -2), B(0, -5), C(4, 1), D(-1, -8), E\left(\dfrac{1}{2}, -\dfrac{7}{2}\right)$

35. $A(1, 5), B\left(-\dfrac{1}{2}, \dfrac{1}{2}\right), C(0, 2), D(-5, -3), E(-2, -4)$

36. $A(1, -1), B(3, 5), C(0, -3), D(-2, -7), E(2, 1)$

In Exercises 37–42, **a)** *determine which of the four ordered pairs does not satisfy the given equation.* **b)** *Plot all the points that satisfy the equation on the same axes and draw a straight line through the points.*   **37.–42. b)** See graphing answer section.

37. $y = x + 2$,   **a)** $(2, 4)$ not **c)**   **b)** $(-2, 0)$ **c)** $(-1, 5)$ **d)** $(0, 2)$

38. $2x + y = -4$,   **a)** $(-2, 0)$ not **b)**   **b)** $(2, 3)$ **c)** $(0, -4)$ **d)** $(-1, -2)$

39. $3x - 2y = 6$,   **a)** $(4, 0)$ not **a)**   **b)** $(2, 0)$ **c)** $\left(\dfrac{2}{3}, -2\right)$ **d)** $\left(\dfrac{4}{3}, -1\right)$

40. $4x - 3y = 0$,   **a)** $(3, 4)$ not **d)**   **b)** $(-3, -4)$ **c)** $(0, 0)$ **d)** $(2, 5)$

41. $\dfrac{1}{2}x + 4y = 4$,   **a)** $(-2, 3)$ not **a)**   **b)** $\left(2, \dfrac{3}{4}\right)$ **c)** $(0, 1)$ **d)** $\left(-4, \dfrac{3}{2}\right)$

42. $y = \dfrac{1}{2}x + 2$,   **a)** $(0, 2)$ not **b)**   **b)** $(-4, 3)$ **c)** $(-2, 1)$ **d)** $(4, 4)$

Problem Solving

Consider the linear equation $y = 3x - 4$. *In Exercises 43–46, find the value of y that makes the given ordered pair a solution to the equation.*

43. $(2, y)$ 2   **44.** $(-1, y)$ −7   **45.** $(0, y)$ −4   **46.** $(3, y)$ 5

Consider the linear equation $2x + 3y = 12$. *In Exercises 47–50, find the value of x that makes the given ordered pair a solution to the equation.*

47. $(x, 2)$ 3   **48.** $(x, 4)$ 0   **49.** $\left(x, \dfrac{11}{3}\right)$ $\dfrac{1}{2}$ **50.** $\left(x, \dfrac{22}{3}\right)$ −5

51. What is the value of y at the point where a straight line crosses the x-axis? Explain.   0

52. What is the value of x at the point where a straight line crosses the y-axis? Explain.   0

53. **Longitude and Latitude** Another type of coordinate system that is used to identify a location or position on earth's surface involves *latitude* and *longitude*. On a globe, the longitudinal lines are lines that go from top to bottom; on a world map they go up and down. The latitudinal lines go around the globe, or left to right on a world map. The locations of Hurricane Georges and Tropical Storm Hermine are indicated on the map on the right.

    a) Estimate the latitude and longitude of Hurricane Georges.   lat., 16°N; long., 56°W

    b) Estimate the latitude and longitude of Tropical Storm Hermine.   lat., 29°N; long., 90.5°W

    c) Estimate the latitude and longitude of the city of Miami.   lat., 26°N; long., 80.5°W

    d) Use either a map or a globe to estimate the latitude and longitude of your college.   Answers will vary.

Source: National Weather Service

Group Activity

*In Section 4.2 we discuss how to find ordered pairs to plot when graphing linear equations. Let's see if you can draw some graphs now. Individually work parts **a)** through **c)** in Exercises 54–56.*

a) *Select any three values for x and find the corresponding values of y.*

b) *Plot the points (they should appear to be collinear).*

c) *Draw the graph.*

d) *As a group, compare your answers. You should all have the same lines.*

54. $y = x$ See graphing answer section.   **55.** $y = 2x$ See graphing answer section.   **56.** $y = -2x$ See graphing answer section.

Cumulative Review Exercises

58. a linear equation that has only one solution   **60.** $C = 6\pi \approx 18.84$ in. $A = 9\pi \approx 28.27$ in^2.

61. $y = \dfrac{2x - 6}{5} = \dfrac{2}{5}x - \dfrac{6}{5}$

[2.2] **57.** Give the general form of a linear equation in one variable. an equation of the form $ax + b = c$

[2.6] **60.** Find the circumference and area of the circle shown below.

[2.5] **58.** What is a conditional equation in one variable?

3 in.

59. Solve $-2(-3x + 5) + 6 = 4(x - 2)$. -2

61. Solve the equation $2x - 5y = 6$ for y.

4.2 Graphing Linear Equations

1 **Graph linear equations by plotting points.**

2 **Graph linear equations of the form $ax + by = 0$.**

3 **Graph linear equations using the x- and y-intercepts.**

4 **Graph horizontal and vertical lines.**

5 **Study applications of graphs.**

In Section 4.1 we explained the Cartesian coordinate system, how to plot points, and how to recognize linear equations in two variables. Now we are ready to graph linear equations. *In this section we discuss two methods that can be used to graph linear equations: (1) graphing by plotting points and (2) graphing using the x- and y-intercepts.*

1 Graph Linear Equations by Plotting Points

Graphing by plotting points is the most versatile method of graphing because we can also use it to graph second- and higher-degree equations. In Chapter 10, we will graph quadratic equations, which are second-degree equations, by plotting points.

> **To Graph Linear Equations by Plotting Points**
>
> **1.** Solve the linear equation for the variable y. That is, get the variable y by itself on the left side of the equal sign.
>
> **2.** Select a value for the variable x. Substitute this value in the equation for x and find the corresponding value of y. Record the ordered pair (x, y).
>
> **3.** Repeat step 2 with two different values of x. This will give you two additional ordered pairs.
>
> **4.** Plot the three ordered pairs. The three points should appear to be collinear. If they do not, recheck your work for mistakes.
>
> **5.** With a straightedge, draw a straight line through the three points. Draw arrowheads on each end of the line to show that the line continues indefinitely in both directions.

In step 1 you are asked to solve the equation for y. Although it is not necessary to do this to graph the equation, it can provide insight as to which values to select for the variable in step 2. If you have forgotten how to solve the equation for y, review Section 2.6. When selecting values in step 2, you should select integer values of x that result in integer values of y if possible. Also, you should select values of x that are small enough so that the ordered pairs obtained can be plotted on the axes. Since y is often easy to find when $x = 0$, 0 is always a good value to select for x.

EXAMPLE 1 ▶ Graph $y = 3x + 6$.

Solution First we determine that this is a linear equation. Its graph must therefore be a straight line. The equation is already solved for y. We select three values for x, substitute them in the equation, and find the corresponding values for y. We will arbitrarily select the values $-2, 0,$ and 1 for x. The calculations that follow show that when $x = -2$, $y = 0$, when $x = 0$, $y = 6$, and when $x = 1$, $y = 9$.

x	$y = 3x + 6$	Ordered Pair
-2	$y = 3(-2) + 6 = 0$	$(-2, 0)$
0	$y = 3(0) + 6 = 6$	$(0, 6)$
1	$y = 3(1) + 6 = 9$	$(1, 9)$

x	y
-2	0
0	6
1	9

It is convenient to list the x- and y-values in a table. Then we plot the three ordered pairs on the same axes (**Fig. 4.16**).

Since the three points appear to be collinear, the graph appears correct. Connect the three points with a straight line and place arrowheads at the ends of the line to show that the line continues infinitely in both directions.

▶ **Now Try Exercise 25**

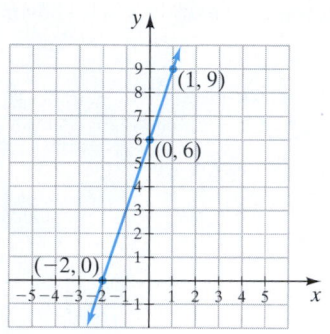

FIGURE 4.16

To graph the equation $y = 3x + 6$, we arbitrarily used the three values $x = -2, x = 0,$ and $x = 1$. We could have selected three entirely different values and obtained exactly the same graph. When selecting values to substitute for x, use values that make the equation easy to evaluate.

The graph drawn in Example 1 represents the set of *all* ordered pairs that satisfy the equation $y = 3x + 6$. If we select any point on this line, the ordered pair represented by that point will be a solution to the equation $y = 3x + 6$. Similarly, any solution to the equation will be represented by a point on the line. Let's select some points on the line, say, $(-1, 3)$ and $(-3, -3)$, and verify that they are solutions to the equation (**Fig. 4.17**).

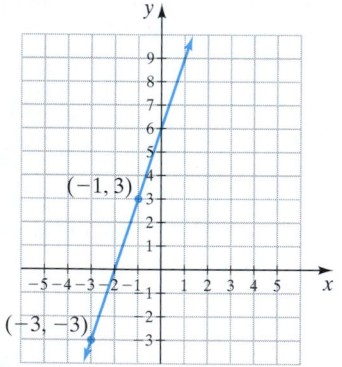

FIGURE 4.17

Check $(-1, 3)$

$y = 3x + 6$

$3 \stackrel{?}{=} 3(-1) + 6$

$3 \stackrel{?}{=} -3 + 6$

$3 = 3$ *True*

Check $(-3, -3)$

$y = 3x + 6$

$-3 \stackrel{?}{=} 3(-3) + 6$

$-3 \stackrel{?}{=} -9 + 6$

$-3 = -3$ *True*

Remember, a graph of an equation is an illustration of the set of points whose coordinates satisfy the equation.

EXAMPLE 2 ▶ Graph $3y = 5x - 6$.

Solution We begin by solving the equation for y. This will help us in selecting values to use for x. To solve the equation for y, we divide both sides of the equation by 3.

$$3y = 5x - 6$$

$$y = \frac{5x - 6}{3}$$

$$y = \frac{5x}{3} - \frac{6}{3}$$

$$y = \frac{5}{3}x - 2$$

Now we can see that if we select values for x that are multiples of the denominator, 3, the values we obtain for y will be integers. Let's select the values $-3, 0,$ and 3 for x.

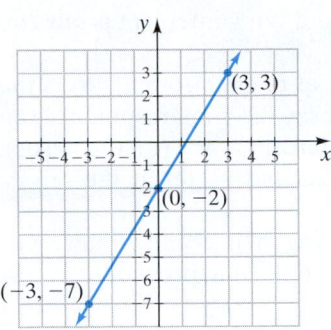

FIGURE 4.18

$$y = \frac{5}{3}x - 2$$

Let $x = -3$. $y = \frac{5}{3}(-3) - 2 = -5 - 2 = -7$

Let $x = 0$. $y = \frac{5}{3}(0) - 2 = -2$

Let $x = 3$. $y = \frac{5}{3}(3) - 2 = 5 - 2 = 3$

x	y
-3	-7
0	-2
3	3

Finally, we plot the points and draw the straight line (**Figure 4.18**).

▶ **Now Try Exercise 31**

2 Graph Linear Equations of the Form *ax* + *by* = 0

In Example 3 we graph an equation of the form $ax + by = 0$, which is a linear equation whose constant is 0.

INSTRUCTOR EXAMPLE
Graph $2x + 3y = 0$.

Ans.:

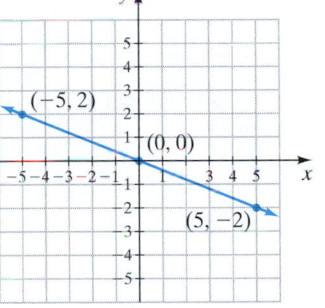

FIGURE 4.19

EXAMPLE 3 ▶ Graph $2x + 5y = 0$.

Solution   We begin by solving the equation for y.

$$2x + 5y = 0$$
$$5y = -2x$$
$$y = -\frac{2x}{5} \quad \text{or} \quad y = -\frac{2}{5}x$$

Now we select values for x and find the corresponding values of y. Which values shall we select for x? Notice that the coefficient of the x-term is a fraction, with the denominator 5. If we select values for x that are multiples of the denominator, such as $\ldots, -15, -10, -5, 0, 5, 10, 15, \ldots$, the 5 in the denominator will divide out. This will give us integer values for y. We will arbitrarily select the values $x = -5$, $x = 0$, and $x = 5$.

$$y = -\frac{2}{5}x$$

Let $x = -5$. $y = \left(-\frac{2}{5}\right)(-5) = 2$

Let $x = 0$. $y = \left(-\frac{2}{5}\right)(0) = 0$

Let $x = 5$. $y = -\frac{2}{5}(5) = -2$

x	y
-5	2
0	0
5	-2

Now we plot the points and draw the graph **(Fig. 4.19)**.

▶ **Now Try Exercise 37**

The graph in Example 3 passes through the origin. The graph of every linear equation with a constant of 0 (equations of the form $ax + by = 0$) will pass through the origin.

3 Graph Linear Equations Using the *x*- and *y*-Intercepts

Now we discuss graphing linear equations using the x- and y-intercepts. The **x-intercept** is the point at which a graph crosses the x-axis and the **y-intercept** is the point at which the graph crosses the y-axis. Consider the graph in **Figure 4.20**, which is the graph we drew in Example 1. Note that the graph crosses the x-axis at -2. Therefore, $(-2, 0)$ is the x-intercept. Since the graph crosses the x-axis at -2, we might say the x-intercept is

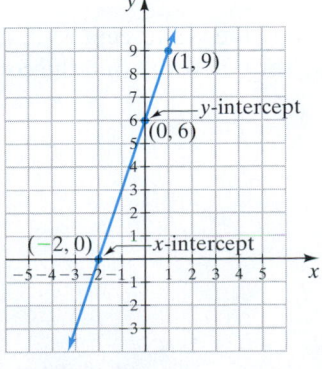

FIGURE 4.20

at −2 (on the *x*-axis). In general, the *x*-intercept is (*x*, 0), and the *x*-intercept is *at x* (on the *x*-axis).

Note that the graph in **Figure 4.20** crosses the *y*-axis at 6. Therefore, (0, 6) is the *y*-intercept. Since the graph crosses the *y*-axis at 6, we might say the *y*-intercept is *at* 6 (on the *y*-axis). In general, the *y*-intercept is (0, *y*), and the *y*-intercept is *at y* (on the *y*-axis).

Note that the graph in **Figure 4.19** crosses both the *x*- and *y*-axes at the origin. Thus, both the *x*- and *y*-intercepts of this graph are (0, 0).

It is often convenient to graph linear equations by finding their *x*- and *y*-intercepts. To graph an equation using the *x*- and *y*-intercepts, use the following procedure.

To Graph Linear Equations Using the *x*- and *y*-Intercepts

1. Find the *y*-intercept by setting *x* in the given equation equal to 0 and finding the corresponding value of *y*.

2. Find the *x*-intercept by setting *y* in the given equation equal to 0 and finding the corresponding value of *x*.

3. Determine a check point by selecting a nonzero value for *x* and finding the corresponding value of *y*.

4. Plot the *y*-intercept (where the graph crosses the *y*-axis), the *x*-intercept (where the graph crosses the *x*-axis), and the check point. The three points should appear to be collinear. If not, recheck your work.

5. Using a straightedge, draw a straight line through the three points. Draw an arrowhead at both ends of the line to show that the line continues indefinitely in both directions.

TEACHING TIP
Ask students, "Why is it convenient to graph $3x - 5y = 30$ using *x*- and *y*-intercepts rather than plotting other points?"

Helpful Hint

Since only two points are needed to determine a straight line, it is not absolutely necessary to determine and plot the check point in step 3. However, if you use only the *x*- and *y*-intercepts to draw your graph and one of those points is wrong, your graph will be incorrect and you will not know it. It is always a good idea to use three points when graphing a linear equation.

INSTRUCTOR EXAMPLE
Graph $4y = 8x + 4$ using *x*- and *y*-intercepts.

Ans.:

EXAMPLE 4 ▸ Graph $3y = 6x + 12$ using the *x*- and *y*-intercepts.

Solution To find the *y*-intercept (where the graph crosses the *y*-axis), set $x = 0$ and find the corresponding value of *y*.

$$3y = 6x + 12$$
$$3y = 6(0) + 12$$
$$3y = 0 + 12$$
$$3y = 12$$
$$y = \frac{12}{3} = 4$$

The graph crosses the *y*-axis at 4. The ordered pair representing the *y*-intercept is (0, 4). To find the *x*-intercept (where the graph crosses the *x*-axis), set $y = 0$ and find the corresponding value of *x*.

$$3y = 6x + 12$$
$$3(0) = 6x + 12$$
$$0 = 6x + 12$$
$$-12 = 6x$$
$$\frac{-12}{6} = x$$
$$-2 = x$$

The graph crosses the x-axis at -2. The ordered pair representing the x-intercept is $(-2, 0)$. Now plot the intercepts (**Fig. 4.21**).

Before graphing the equation, select a nonzero value for x, find the corresponding value of y, and make sure that it is collinear with the x- and y-intercepts. This third point is the check point.

$$\text{Let } x = 2.$$
$$3y = 6x + 12$$
$$3y = 6(2) + 12$$
$$3y = 12 + 12$$
$$3y = 24$$
$$y = \frac{24}{3} = 8$$

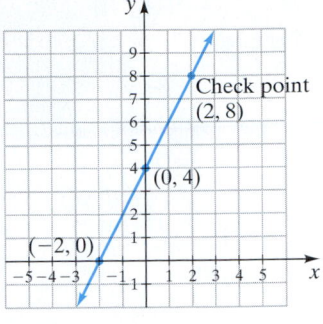

FIGURE 4.21

Plot the check point $(2, 8)$. Since the three points appear to be collinear, draw the straight line through all three points.

▶ **Now Try Exercise 55**

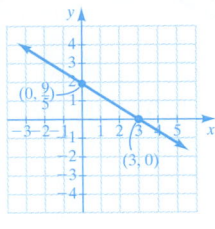
EXAMPLE 5 ▶ Graph $2x + 5y = 12$ using the x- and y-intercepts.

Solution

Find y-intercept	Find x-intercept	Check Point
Let $x = 0$.	Let $y = 0$.	Let $x = 1$.
$2x + 5y = 12$	$2x + 5y = 12$	$2x + 5y = 12$
$2(0) + 5y = 12$	$2x + 5(0) = 12$	$2(1) + 5y = 12$
$0 + 5y = 12$	$2x + 0 = 12$	$2 + 5y = 12$
$5y = 12$	$2x = 12$	$5y = 10$
$y = \dfrac{12}{5}$	$x = 6$	$y = 2$

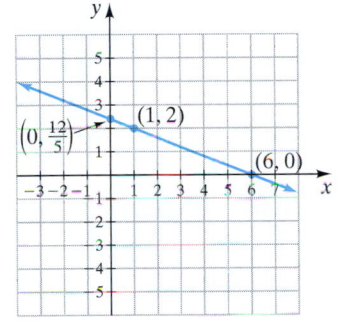

FIGURE 4.22

The three ordered pairs are $\left(0, \dfrac{12}{5}\right)$, $(6, 0)$, and $(1, 2)$.

The three points appear to be collinear. Draw a straight line through all three points (**Fig. 4.22**).

▶ **Now Try Exercise 45**

EXAMPLE 6 ▶ Graph $y = 20x + 60$.

Solution

Find y-Intercept	Find x-Intercept	Check Point
Let $x = 0$.	Let $y = 0$.	Let $x = 3$.
$y = 20x + 60$	$y = 20x + 60$	$y = 20x + 60$
$y = 20(0) + 60$	$0 = 20x + 60$	$y = 20(3) + 60$
$y = 60$	$-60 = 20x$	$y = 60 + 60$
	$-3 = x$	$y = 120$

The three ordered pairs are $(0, 60)$, $(-3, 0)$, and $(3, 120)$. Since the values of y are large, we let each interval on the y-axis be 15 units rather than 1 (**Fig. 4.23**). Sometimes you will have to use different scales on the x- and y-axes, as illustrated, to accommodate the graph. Now we plot the points and draw the graph.

▶ **Now Try Exercise 59**

FIGURE 4.23

When selecting the scales for your axes, you should realize that different scales will result in the same equation having a different appearance. Consider the graphs shown in **Figure 4.24**. Both graphs represent the same equation, $y = x$. In **Figure 4.24a** both the x- and y-axes have the same scale. In **Figure 4.24b**, the x- and y-axes do not have the same scale. Both graphs are correct in that each represents the graph of $y = x$. The difference in appearance is due to the difference in scales on the x-axis. When possible, keep the scales on the x- and y-axes the same, as in **Figure 4.24a**.

    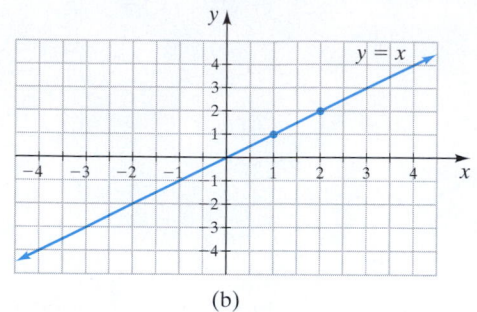

FIGURE 4.24   (a)   (b)

USING YOUR GRAPHING CALCULATOR

To graph an equation on a graphing calculator, use the following steps.

1. Solve the equation for y, if necessary.

2. Press the $\boxed{Y =}$ key and enter the equation.

3. Press the $\boxed{GRAPH}$ key (to see the graph). You may need to adjust the window, as explained in the Using Your Graphing Calculator box on page 238.

When we solve the equation $2y = 4x - 12$ for y we obtain $y = 2x - 6$. If you press $\boxed{Y =}$ and enter $2x - 6$ as Y_1, and then press $\boxed{GRAPH}$ you should get the graph shown in **Figure 4.25**.

If you do not get the graph in **Figure 4.25**, press $\boxed{WINDOW}$ and determine whether you have the standard window $-10, 10, 1, -10, 10, 1$. If not, change to the standard window and press the $\boxed{GRAPH}$ key again.

It is possible to graph two or more equations on your graphing calculator. If, for example, you wanted to graph both $y = 2x - 6$ and $y = -3x + 4$ on the same screen, you would begin by pressing the $\boxed{Y =}$ key. Then you would let $Y_1 = 2x - 6$ and $Y_2 = -3x + 4$. After you enter both equations and press the $\boxed{GRAPH}$ key, both equations will be graphed. Try graphing both equations on your graphing calculator now.

EXERCISES

Graph each equation on your graphing calculator.

1. $y = 3x - 5$ 2. $y = -2x + 6$

3. $2x - 3y = 6$ 4. $5x + 10y = 20$ See graphing answer section.

FIGURE 4.25

---

4 Graph Horizontal and Vertical Lines

When a linear equation contains only one variable, its graph will be either a horizontal or a vertical line, as is explained in Examples 7 and 8.

EXAMPLE 7 ▶ Graph $y = 3$.

Solution This equation can be written as $y = 3 + 0x$. Thus, for any value of x selected, y will be 3. The graph of $y = 3$ is illustrated in **Figure 4.26**.

FIGURE 4.26

▶ **Now Try Exercise 23**

The graph of an equation of the form $y = b$ is a **horizontal line** *whose y-intercept is* $(0, b)$.

EXAMPLE 8 ▶ Graph $x = -2$.

Solution This equation can be written as $x = -2 + 0y$. Thus, for any value of y selected, x will have a value of -2. The graph of $x = -2$ is illustrated in **Figure 4.27**.

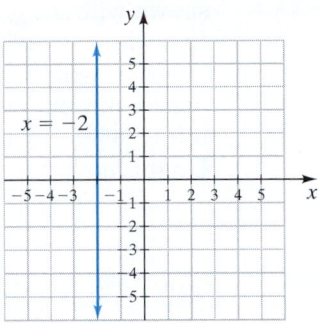

FIGURE 4.27   ▶ Now Try Exercise 21

The graph of an equation of the form $x = a$ is a **vertical line** *whose x-intercept is $(a, 0)$.*

5 Study Applications of Graphs

Before we leave this section, let's look at an application of graphing. We will see additional applications of graphing linear equations in Sections 4.4 and 4.5.

EXAMPLE 9 ▶ **Weekly Salary** Carol Bradley recently graduated from college. She accepted a position as a sales manager trainee at a furniture store where she is paid a weekly salary plus a commission on her sales. She will receive a salary of $300 per week plus a 7% commission on all her sales, s.

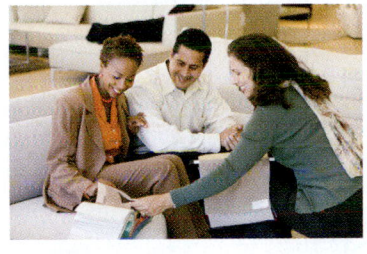

a) Write an equation for the salary Carol will receive, R, in terms of the sales, s.

b) Graph the salary for sales of $0 up to and including $20,000.

c) From the graph, estimate Carol's salary if her weekly sales are $15,000.

d) From the graph, estimate the sales needed for Carol to earn a weekly salary of $900.

Solution

a) Since s is the amount of sales, a 7% commission on s dollars in sales is $0.07s$.

$$\text{salary received} = \$300 + \text{commission}$$
$$R = 300 + 0.07s$$

b) We select three values for s and find the corresponding values of R.

$R = 300 + 0.07s$		s	R
Let $s = 0$.	$R = 300 + 0.07(0) = 300$	0	300
Let $s = 10,000$.	$R = 300 + 0.07(10,000) = 1000$	10,000	1000
Let $s = 20,000$.	$R = 300 + 0.07(20,000) = 1700$	20,000	1700

The graph is illustrated in **Figure 4.28**. Notice that since we only graph the equation for values of s from $0 to $20,000, we do not place arrowheads on the ends of the graph.

c) To determine Carol's weekly salary on sales of $15,000, locate $25,000 on the sales axis. Then draw a vertical line up to where it intersects the graph, the *red* line in **Figure 4.28**. Now draw a horizontal line across to the salary axis. Since the horizontal line crosses the salary axis at about $1350, weekly sales of $15,000 would result in a weekly salary of about $1350. We can

FIGURE 4.28

find the exact salary by substituting 15,000 for s in the equation $R = 300 + 0.07s$ and finding the value of R. Do this now.

d) To find the sales needed for Carol to earn a weekly salary of $900, we find $900 on the salary axis. We then draw a horizontal line from that point to the graph, as shown with the *green* line in **Figure 4.28** on page 247. We then draw a vertical line from the point of intersection of the graph to the sales axis. This value on the sales axis represents the sales needed for Carol to earn $900. Thus, sales of about $8600 per week would result in a salary of $900. We can find an exact answer by substituting 900 for R in the equation $R = 300 + 0.07s$ and solving the equation for s. Do this now.

▶ **Now Try Exercise 75**

USING YOUR GRAPHING CALCULATOR

Before we leave this section, let's spend more time discussing the graphing calculator. In the previous Using Your Graphing Calculator, we graphed $y = 2x - 6$. The graph of $y = 2x - 6$ is shown again using the standard window in **Figure 4.29**. After obtaining the graph, if you press the $\boxed{\text{TRACE}}$ key, you may (depending on your calculator) obtain the graph in **Figure 4.30**.

Notice that the cursor, the blinking box in **Figure 4.30**, is on the y-intercept, that is, where $x = 0$ and $y = -6$. By pressing the left or the right arrow keys, you can move the cursor. The corresponding values of x and y change with the position of the cursor. You can magnify the part of the graph by the cursor by using the $\boxed{\text{ZOOM}}$ key. Read your calculator manual to learn how to use the ZOOM feature and the various ZOOM options available.

Another important key on many graphing calculators is the TABLE feature. On the TI-84 Plus when you press $\boxed{2^{\text{nd}}}$ $\boxed{\text{GRAPH}}$ to get the TABLE feature, you may get the display shown in **Figure 4.31**.

If your display does not show the screen in **Figure 4.31**, use your up and down arrows until you get the screen shown. The table gives x-values and corresponding y-values for the graph. Notice from the table that when $x = 3$, $y = 0$ (the x-intercept) and when $x = 0$, $y = -6$ (the y-intercept).

You can change the table features by pressing $\boxed{\text{TBLSET}}$ (press $\boxed{2^{\text{nd}}}$ $\boxed{\text{WINDOW}}$ on the TI-84 Plus). For example, if you want the table to give values of x in tenths, you could change ΔTbl to 0.1 instead of the standard 1 unit.

FIGURE 4.29

FIGURE 4.30

EXERCISES

Use the TABLE feature of your calculator to find the x- and y-intercepts of the graphs of the following equations. In Exercises 3 and 4, you will need to set the table to tenths.

1. $y = 4x - 8$ (2, 0), (0, −8)

2. $y = -2x - 6$ (−3, 0), (0, −6)

3. $4x - 5y = 10$ (2.5, 0), (0, −2)

4. $2y = 6x - 9$ (1.5, 0), (0, −4.5)

FIGURE 4.31

1. x-intercept: substitute 0 for y and find corresponding value of x; y-intercept: substitute 0 for x and find corresponding value of y

3. a horizontal line   **4.** a vertical line

EXERCISE SET 4.2

 MathXL®

 MyMathLab

Concept/Writing Exercises

1. Explain how to find the x- and y-intercepts of a line.

2. How many points are needed to graph a straight line? How many points should be used? Why?   2, 3

3. What will the graph of $y = b$ look like for any real number b?

4. What will the graph of $x = a$ look like for any real number a?

5. In Example 9c and 9d, we made an estimate. Why is it sometimes not possible to obtain an exact answer from a graph?   You may not be able to read exact answers from a graph.

6. In Example 9 does the salary, R, depend on the sales, s, or do the sales depend on the salary? Explain.   salary depends on sales

7. Will the equation $2x - 4y = 0$ go through the origin? Explain.   yes

8. Write an equation, other than the ones given in this section, whose graph will go through the origin. Explain how you determined your answer.   Answers will vary.

Practice the Skills

Find the missing coordinate if the ordered pair is to be a solution to the equation $3x + y = 9$.

9. $(3, ?)$ 0

10. $(-4, ?)$ 21

11. $(?, -6)$ 5

12. $(?, -9)$ 6

13. $(?, 0)$ 3

14. $\left(\dfrac{3}{2}, ? \right)$ $\dfrac{9}{2}$

Find the missing coordinate in the given solutions for $3x - 2y = 8$.

15. $(4, ?)$ 2

16. $(0, ?)$ -4

17. $(?, 0)$ $\dfrac{8}{3}$

18. $\left(?, -\dfrac{5}{2} \right)$ 1

19. $(-2, ?)$ -7

20. $(?, 5)$ 6

Graph each equation.

21. $x = -3$

22. $x = \dfrac{3}{2}$

23. $y = 4$

24. $y = -\dfrac{5}{3}$

Graph by plotting points. Plot at least three points for each graph.

21.-64. See graphing answer section.

25. $y = 3x - 1$

26. $y = -x + 3$

27. $y = 4x - 2$

28. $y = x - 4$

29. $x + 2y = 6$

30. $-3x + 3y = 6$

31. $3x - 2y = 4$

32. $3x - 2y = 6$

33. $4x + 3y = -9$

34. $6y - 12x = 18$

35. $6x + 5y = 30$

36. $2x + 3y = -6$

37. $-4x + 5y = 0$

38. $3x + 2y = 0$

39. $y = -20x + 60$

40. $2y - 100x = 50$

41. $y = \dfrac{4}{3}x$

42. $y = -\dfrac{3}{5}x$

43. $y = \dfrac{1}{2}x + 4$

44. $y = -\dfrac{2}{5}x + 2$

Graph using the x- and y-intercepts.

45. $y = 3x + 3$

46. $y = -3x + 6$

47. $y = -4x + 2$

48. $y = -2x + 5$

49. $y = 4x + 16$

50. $y = -5x + 4$

51. $4y + 6x = 24$

52. $4x = 3y - 9$

53. $\dfrac{1}{2}x + 2y = 4$

54. $x + \dfrac{1}{2}y = 2$

55. $12x - 24y = 48$

56. $25x + 50y = 100$

57. $8y = 6x - 12$

58. $6y = -4x + 12$

59. $y = 15x + 45$

60. $y = -10x + 30$

61. $\dfrac{1}{3}x + \dfrac{1}{4}y = 12$

62. $\dfrac{1}{4}x - \dfrac{2}{3}y = 60$

63. $\dfrac{1}{2}x = \dfrac{2}{5}y - 80$

64. $\dfrac{2}{3}y = \dfrac{5}{4}x + 120$

Write the equation represented by the given graph.

65.

$x = -2$

66.

$x = \dfrac{5}{2}$

67.

$y = 6$

68.

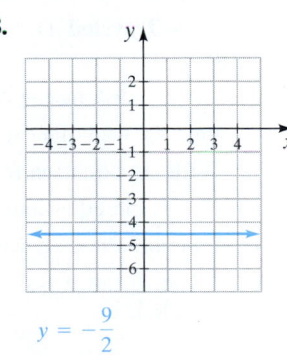

$y = -\dfrac{9}{2}$

Problem Solving

69. What is the value of a if the graph of $ax + 3y = 10$ is to have an x-intercept of $(2, 0)$?   5

70. What is the value of a if the graph of $ax + 7y = 6$ is to have an x-intercept of $(3, 0)$?   2

71. What is the value of b if the graph of $3x + by = 14$ is to have a y-intercept of $(0, 7)$?   2

72. What is the value of b if the graph of $4x + by = 15$ is to have a y-intercept of $(0, -3)$? -5

The bar graphs in Exercises 73 and 74 display information. State whether the graph displays a linear relationship. Explain your answer.

73.

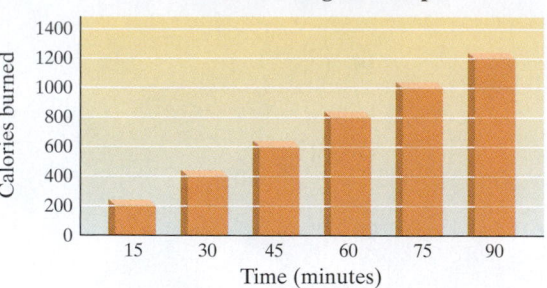

Calories Burned by Average 150–Pound Person Walking at 4.5 mph

74.

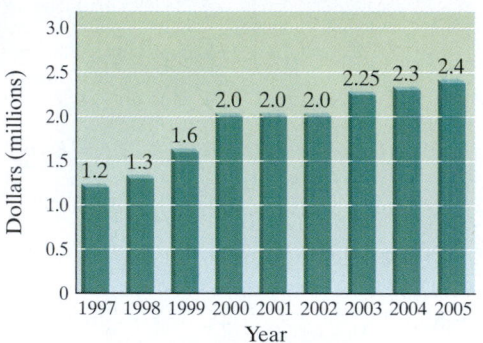

Price of a 30-Second Super Bowl Ad

Source: NFL Research, St. Petersburg Times Research

Review Example 9 before working Exercises 75–80.

75. Telephone Calls Ken Judd's telephone plan consists of a monthly fee of $15 plus 10 cents per minute for long-distance calls made.

a) Write an equation for the total monthly cost, C, when n minutes are used for long-distance calls. $C = 0.10n + 15$

b) Graph the equation for up to and including 100 minutes of long-distance calls made.   See graphing answer section.

c) Estimate the total monthly cost if 40 minutes of long-distance calls are made. $19

d) If the totally monthly bill is $25, estimate the number of minutes used for long-distance calls.   100 min

76. Distance Traveled Distance traveled is calculated using the formula,

$$\text{distance} = \text{rate} \cdot \text{time or } d = rt.$$

Assume the rate of a car is a constant 30 miles per hour.

a) Write an equation for the distance, d, in terms of time, t.

b) Graph the equation for times of 0 to 20 hours inclusive.

c) Estimate the distance traveled in 12 hours.   360 mi

d) If the distance traveled is 150 miles, estimate the time traveled.   5 hr

77. Truck Rental Lynn Brown needs a large truck to move some furniture. She found that the cost C, of renting a truck is $40 per day plus $1 per mile, m.

a) Write an equation for the cost in terms of the miles driven. $C = m + 40$

b) Graph the equation for values up to and including 100 miles.   See graphing answer section.

c) Estimate the cost of driving 60 miles in one day. $100

d) Estimate the miles driven if the cost for one day is $70.

78. Simple Interest Simple interest is calculated by the simple interest formula,

$$\text{interest} = \text{principal} \cdot \text{rate} \cdot \text{time or } I = prt.$$

Suppose the principal is $10,000 and the rate is 5%.

a) Write an equation for simple interest in terms of time.

b) Graph the equation for times of 0 to 20 years inclusive.

c) What is the simple interest for 10 years? $5000

d) If the simple interest is $500, find the length of time.   1 yr

79. Video Store Profit The weekly profit, P of a video rental store can be approximated by the formula $P = 1.5n - 200$, where n is the number of videos rented weekly.

a) Draw a graph of profit in terms of video rentals for up to and including 1000 tapes.   See graphing answer section.

b) Estimate the weekly profit if 500 videos are rented. $550

c) Estimate the number of videos rented if the week's profit is $1000.   800 Videos

80. Playing Tennis The cost, C, of playing tennis in the Downtown Tennis Club includes an annual $200 membership fee plus $10 per hour, h, of court time.

a) Write an equation for the annual cost of playing tennis at the Downtown Tennis Club in terms of hours played.

b) Graph the equation for up to and including 300 hours.

c) Estimate the cost for playing 50 hours in a year. $700

d) If the annual cost for playing tennis was $1700, estimate how many hours of tennis were played.   150 hr

76. a) $d = 30t$ **b)** See graphing answer section.   **77. d)** 30 mi   **78. a)** $I = 500t$ **b)** See graphing answer section.
80. a) $C = 10h + 200$ **b)** See graphing answer section.

Determine the coefficients to be placed in the shaded areas so that the graph of the equation will be a line with the x- and y-intercepts specified. Explain how you determined your answer.

81. ▢$x +$ ▢$y = 6$; x-intercept at 2; y-intercept at 3   3, 2

82. ▢$x +$ ▢$y = 18$; x-intercept at −3, y-intercept at 6   −6, 3

83. ▢$x -$ ▢$y = -12$; x-intercept at −2, y-intercept at 3   6, 4

84. ▢$x -$ ▢$y = 30$; x-intercept at −10, y-intercept at −15   −3, 2

Challenge Problems

85. a) See graphing answer section.   b) (2, 3)

85. Consider the following equations: $y = 2x - 1$, $y = -x + 5$.

   a) Carefully graph both equations on the same axes.

   b) Determine the point of intersection of the two graphs.

   c) Substitute the values for x and y at the point of intersection into each of the two equations and determine whether the point of intersection satisfies each equation.   yes

   d) Do you believe there are any other ordered pairs that satisfy both equations? Explain your answer. (We will study equations like these, called systems of equations, in Chapter 5.)   no

86. In Chapter 10 we will be graphing quadratic equations. The graphs of quadratic equations are *not* straight lines. Graph the quadratic equation $y = x^2 - 4$ by selecting values for x and find the corresponding values of y, then plot the points. Make sure you plot a sufficient number of points to get an accurate graph.   See graphing answer section.

Group Activity

Discuss and answer Exercise 87 as a group.

87. a)–d) See graphing answer section.   e) They appear to be parallel lines.

87. Let's study the graphs of the equations $y = 2x + 4$, $y = 2x + 2$, and $y = 2x - 2$ to see how they are similar and how they differ. Each group member should start with the same axes.

   a) Group member 1: Graph $y = 2x + 4$.

   b) Group member 2: Graph $y = 2x + 2$.

   c) Group member 3: Graph $y = 2x - 2$.

   d) Now transfer all three graphs onto the same axes. (You can use one of the group members' graphs or you can construct new axes.)

   e) Explain what you notice about the three graphs.

   f) Explain what you notice about the y-intercepts.
The constant is the y-intercept.

Cumulative Review Exercises

[1.9] **88.** Evaluate $2[6 - (4 - 5)] \div 2 - 8^2$. -57

89. Evaluate $\dfrac{-3^2 \cdot 4 \div 2}{\sqrt{9} - 2^2}$.   18

[2.7] **90. House Cleaning** According to the instructions on a bottle of concentrated household cleaner, 8 ounces of the cleaner should be mixed with 3 gallons of water. If your bucket holds only 2.5 gallons of water, how much cleaner should you use?   6.67 oz

[3.2] **91. Integers** The larger of two integers is 1 more than 3 times the smaller. If the sum of the two integers is 37, find the two integers.   9, 28

4.3 Slope of a Line

1. Find the slope of a line.

2. Recognize positive and negative slopes.

3. Examine the slopes of horizontal and vertical lines.

4. Examine the slopes of parallel and perpendicular lines.

1 Find the Slope of a Line

In this section we discuss the *slope* of a line. In the following Helpful Hint we discuss similarities between slope as commonly used and the slope of a line.

Helpful Hint *Slope*

We often come across slopes in everyday life. A highway (or a ramp) may have a grade (or slope) of 8%. A roof may have a pitch (or slope) of $\dfrac{6}{15}$. The slope is a measure of steepness which can be determined by dividing the vertical change, called the *rise*, by the horizontal change, called the *run*.

(continued on the next page)

Suppose a road has an 8% grade. Since $8\% = \dfrac{8}{100}$, this means the road drops (or rises) 8 feet for each 100 feet of horizontal length. A roof pitch of $\dfrac{6}{15}$ means the roof drops 6 feet for each 15 feet of horizontal length.

When we find the slope of a line we are also finding a ratio of the vertical change to the horizontal change. The major difference is that when we find the slope of a non-horizontal, non-vertical line, the slope can be a positive number or a negative number, as will be explained shortly.

The *slope of a line* is a measure of the *steepness* of the line. The slope of a line is an important concept in many areas of mathematics. A knowledge of slope is helpful in understanding linear equations. We now define the slope of a line.

Slope of a Line

The **slope of a line** is a ratio of the vertical change to the horizontal change between any two selected points on the line.

As an example, consider the line that goes through the two points $(3, 6)$ and $(1, 2)$. (see **Fig. 4.32a**).

If we draw a line parallel to the *x*-axis through the point $(1, 2)$ and a line parallel to the *y*-axis through the point $(3, 6)$, the two lines intersect at $(3, 2)$, see **Figure 4.32b**. From the figure, we can determine the slope of the line. The vertical change (along the *y*-axis) is $6 - 2$, or 4 units. The horizontal change (along the *x*-axis) is $3 - 1$, or 2 units.

$$\text{slope} = \frac{\text{vertical change}}{\text{horizontal change}} = \frac{4}{2} = 2$$

TEACHING TIP
Draw three lines, one with a steep slope, one with a shallow slope, and one with a slope of zero. Have students label the lines as steep, shallow, or horizontal and explain their answer. Then point out that mathematics allows us to quantify the steepness of a line.

(a)

(b)

FIGURE 4.32

FIGURE 4.33

Thus, the slope of the line through these two points is 2. By examining the line connecting these two points, we can see that as the graph moves up 2 units on the *y*-axis it moves to the right 1 unit on the *x*-axis (**Fig. 4.33**).

Now we present the procedure to find the slope of a line between any two points (x_1, y_1) and (x_2, y_2). Consider **Figure 4.34**.

The vertical change can be found by subtracting y_1 from y_2. The horizontal change can be found by subtracting x_1 from x_2.

FIGURE 4.34

Slope of a Line through the Points (x_1, y_1) and (x_2, y_2)

$$\text{slope} = \frac{\text{change in } y \ (\text{vertical change})}{\text{change in } x \ (\text{horizontal change})} = \frac{y_2 - y_1}{x_2 - x_1}$$

It makes no difference which two points are selected when finding the slope of a line. It also makes no difference which point you label (x_1, y_1) or (x_2, y_2). The Greek capital letter delta, Δ, is often used to represent the words the change in. So, Δy is read, the change in y, and Δx is read, the change in x. Thus, the slope, which is symbolized by the letter m, is indicated as

$$m = \frac{\Delta y}{\Delta x} = \frac{y_2 - y_1}{x_2 - x_1}$$

INSTRUCTOR EXAMPLE
Find the slope of the line through $(-2, 1)$ and $(3, 4)$.

Ans.: $\dfrac{3}{5}$

EXAMPLE 1 ▶ Find the slope of the line through the points $(-6, 1)$ and $(3, 5)$.

Solution We will designate $(-6, 1)$ as (x_1, y_1) and $(3, 5)$ as (x_2, y_2).

$$m = \frac{y_2 - y_1}{x_2 - x_1}$$

$$= \frac{5 - 1}{3 - (-6)}$$

$$= \frac{5 - 1}{3 + 6} = \frac{4}{9}$$

Thus, the slope is $\dfrac{4}{9}$.

If we had designated $(3, 5)$ as (x_1, y_1) and $(-6, 1)$ as (x_2, y_2), we would have obtained the same results.

$$m = \frac{y_2 - y_1}{x_2 - x_1}$$

$$= \frac{1 - 5}{-6 - 3} = \frac{-4}{-9} = \frac{4}{9}$$

▶ **Now Try Exercise 13**

> ## Avoiding Common Errors
>
> Students sometimes subtract the x's and y's in the slope formula in the wrong order. For instance, using the problem in Example 1:
>
> $$m = \frac{y_2 - y_1}{x_1 - x_2} = \frac{5 - 1}{-6 - 3} = \frac{5 - 1}{-6 - 3} = \frac{4}{-9} = -\frac{4}{9}$$
>
> Notice that subtracting in this incorrect order results in a negative slope, when the actual slope of the line is positive. The same sign error will occur each time subtraction is done incorrectly in this manner.

2 Recognize Positive and Negative Slopes

TEACHING TIP
Point out that you read the slope of a graph from left to right just as you read a book.

A straight line for which the value of y increases as x increases has a **positive slope**; see **Figure 4.35a**. A line with a positive slope rises as it moves from left to right. A straight line for which the value of y decreases as x increases has a **negative slope**; see **Figure 4.35b**. A line with a negative slope falls as it moves from left to right.

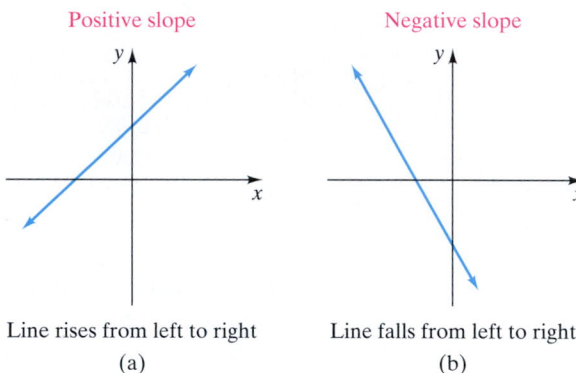

FIGURE 4.35

Positive slope — Line rises from left to right (a)

Negative slope — Line falls from left to right (b)

FIGURE 4.36

EXAMPLE 2 ▶ Consider the line in **Figure 4.36**.

a) Determine the slope of the line by observing the vertical change and horizontal change between the points $(1, 5)$ and $(0, 2)$ on the graph.

b) Calculate the slope of the line using the two given points.

Solution

a) The first thing you should notice is that the slope is positive since the line rises from left to right. Now determine the vertical change between the two points. The vertical change is $+3$ units. Next determine the horizontal change between the two points. The horizontal change is $+1$ unit. Since the slope is the ratio of the vertical change to the horizontal change between any two points, and since the slope is positive, the slope of the line is $\frac{3}{1}$ or 3.

INSTRUCTOR EXAMPLE 2
Repeat Examples 2 **a)** and **b)** for the points $(1, 0)$ and $(3, 4)$ shown in the following graph.

Ans.: a) 2 b) 2

b) We can use any two points on the line to determine its slope. Since we are given the ordered pairs $(1, 5)$ and $(0, 2)$, we will use them.

Let (x_2, y_2) be $(1, 5)$. Let (x_1, y_1) be $(0, 2)$.

$$m = \frac{y_2 - y_1}{x_2 - x_1} = \frac{5 - 2}{1 - 0} = \frac{3}{1} = 3$$

Note that the slope obtained in part **b)** agrees with the slope obtained in part **a)**. If we had designated $(1, 5)$ as (x_1, y_1) and $(0, 2)$ as (x_2, y_2), the slope would not have changed. Try it and see that you will still obtain a slope of 3.

▶ **Now Try Exercise 25**

EXAMPLE 3 ▶ Find the slope of the line in **Figure 4.37** using the vertical change and horizontal change between the two points shown.

Solution   Since the graph falls from left to right, you should realize that the line has a negative slope. The vertical change between the two given points is -3 units since it is decreasing. The horizontal change between the two given points is 4 units since it is increasing. Since the ratio of the vertical change to the horizontal change is -3 units to 4 units, the slope of this line is $\dfrac{-3}{4}$ or $-\dfrac{3}{4}$.

FIGURE 4.37

▶ **Now Try Exercise 29**

Using the two points shown in **Figure 4.37** and the definition of slope, calculate the slope of the line in Example 3. You should obtain the same answer.

EXAMPLE 4 ▶ **Poverty Rate in the United States** The poverty rate in the United States fell in the years from 1993 to 2000. In the years from 2000 to 2003, the poverty rate increased. The poverty rate fell almost linearly from 1993 to 1996 and from 1996 to 2000. It increased almost linearly from 2000 to 2003.

The graph in **Figure 4.38** closely approximates the poverty rates over these 11 years.

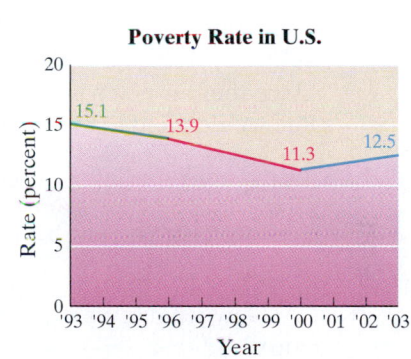

FIGURE 4.38   *Source*: U.S. Census Bureau, *USA Today* (5/11/05)

a) Use the points (1996, 13.9) and (2000, 11.3), to determine the slope of the red line segment.

b) Use the points (2000, 11.3) and (2003, 12.5), to determine the slope of the blue line segment.

Solution:

a) To determine the slope of the red line segment, divide the change in poverty rates, on the vertical axis, by the change in years, on the horizontal axis. We will use $(2000, 11.3)$ as (x_2, y_2) and $(1996, 13.9)$ as (x_1, y_1).

$$m = \frac{y_2 - y_1}{x_2 - x_1} = \frac{\text{poverty rate in 2000} - \text{poverty rate in 1996}}{2000 - 1996}$$

$$= \frac{11.3 - 13.9}{4} = \frac{-2.6}{4} \times \frac{10}{10} = \frac{-26}{40} = -\frac{13}{20}$$

Thus the slope of the red line segment is $-\dfrac{13}{20}$.

b) To find the slope of the blue line segment, we will use $(2003, 12.5)$ as (x_2, y_2) and $(2000, 11.3)$ as (x_1, y_1).

$$m = \frac{y_2 - y_1}{x_2 - x_1} = \frac{\text{poverty rate in 2003} - \text{poverty rate in 2000}}{2003 - 2000}$$

$$= \frac{12.5 - 11.3}{3} = \frac{1.2}{3} \times \frac{10}{10} = \frac{12}{30} = \frac{2}{5}$$

Thus the slope of the blue line segment is $\frac{2}{5}$.

▶ **Now Try Exercise 71**

In Example 4, observe that the slope of the red line segment is a negative number since the poverty rates were decreasing for the years from 1996 to 2000. The slope of the blue line segment is a positive number since the poverty rates were increasing for the years from 2000 to 2003.

3 Examine the Slopes of Horizontal and Vertical Lines

Now we consider the slope of horizontal and vertical lines.

Consider the graph of $y = 5$ (**Fig. 4.39**). What is its slope?

The graph is parallel to the x-axis and goes through the points $(2, 5)$ and $(6, 5)$. Arbitrarily select $(6, 5)$ as (x_2, y_2) and $(2, 5)$ as (x_1, y_1). Then the slope of the line is

$$m = \frac{y_2 - y_1}{x_2 - x_1} = \frac{5 - 5}{6 - 2} = \frac{0}{4} = 0$$

Since there is no change in y, this line has a slope of 0. Note that *any* two points on the line would yield the same slope, 0.

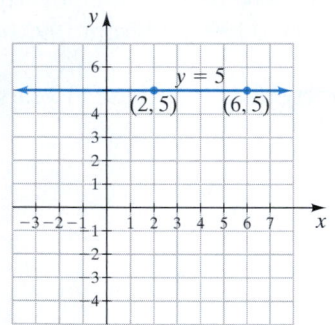

FIGURE 4.39

> ### Slope of a Horizontal Line
> Every horizontal line has a slope of 0.

Now we discuss vertical lines. Consider the graph of $x = 2$ (**Fig. 4.40**). What is its slope?

The graph is parallel to the y-axis and goes through the points $(2, 1)$ and $(2, 4)$. Arbitrarily select $(2, 4)$ as (x_2, y_2) and $(2, 1)$ as (x_1, y_1). Then the slope of the line is

$$m = \frac{y_2 - y_1}{x_2 - x_1} = \frac{4 - 1}{2 - 2} = \frac{3}{0}$$

We learned in Section 1.8 that $\frac{3}{0}$ is undefined. Thus, we say that the slope of this line is undefined.

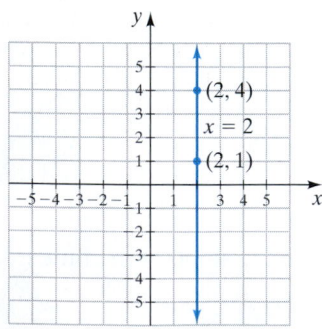

FIGURE 4.40

> ### Slope of a Vertical Line
> The slope of any vertical line is undefined.

4 Examine the Slopes of Parallel and Perpendicular Lines

Two lines are **parallel** when they do not intersect, no matter how far they are extended. **Figure 4.41** on page 257 illustrates two parallel lines.

If we compute the slope of line 1 using the given points, we obtain a slope of 3. If we compute the slope of line 2, we obtain a slope of 3. (You should compute the slopes of both lines now to verify this.) Notice both lines have the same slopes. Any two non-vertical lines that have the same slope are parallel lines.

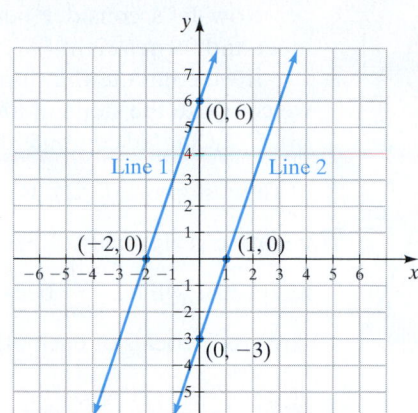

FIGURE 4.41

Parallel Lines

Two nonvertical lines with the same slope and different y-intercepts are parallel lines. Any two vertical lines are parallel to each other.

EXAMPLE 5 ▶

a) Draw a line with a slope of $\frac{1}{2}$ through the point $(2, 3)$.

b) On the same set of axes, draw a line with a slope of $\frac{1}{2}$ through the point $(-1, -3)$.

c) Are the two lines in part a) and b) parallel? Explain.

INSTRUCTOR EXAMPLE 5

a) Draw two lines with a slope of 1; one through $(1, 3)$ and the other through $(-2, -5)$.

b) Are the two lines parallel?

Ans.:

a)

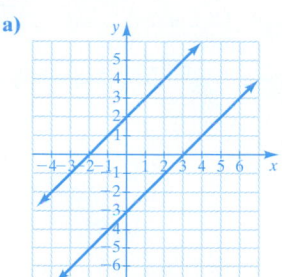

b) Yes

Solution

a) Place a dot at $(2, 3)$. Because the slope is a positive $\frac{1}{2}$, from the point $(2, 3)$ move *up* 1 unit and to the *right* 2 units to get a second point. Draw a line through the two points; see the blue line in **Figure 4.42**.

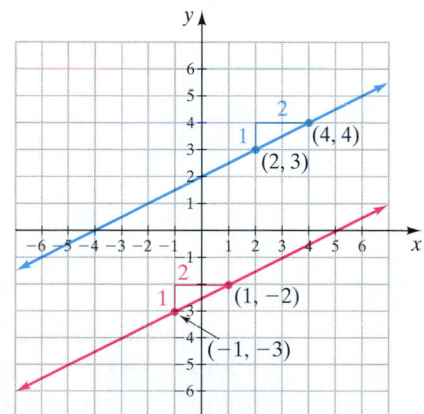

FIGURE 4.42

b) Place a dot at $(-1, -3)$. From the point $(-1, -3)$ move up 1 unit and to the right 2 units to get a second point. Draw a line through the two points; see the red line in **Figure 4.42**.

c) The lines appear to be parallel on the graph. Since both lines have the same slope, $\frac{1}{2}$, they are parallel lines.

▶ **Now Try Exercise 73**

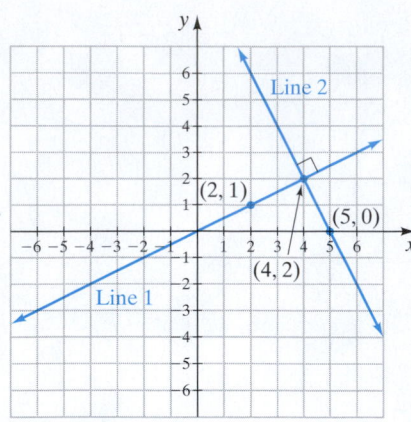

FIGURE 4.43

a) Draw a line with a slope of 2 through the point $(1, -1)$.

b) Draw another line with a slope of $-\dfrac{1}{2}$ through the point $(-2, 4)$.

c) Are the two lines perpendicular?

Ans.:

c) yes

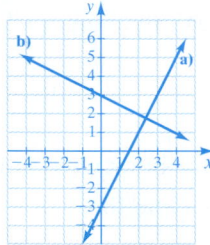

Now let's consider perpendicular lines. Two lines are **perpendicular** when they meet and form a right (90°) angle. **Figure 4.43** illustrates two perpendicular lines.

If we compute the slope of line 1 using the given points, we obtain a slope of $\dfrac{1}{2}$. If we compute the slope of line 2 using the given points, we obtain a slope of -2.

(You should compute the slopes of both lines now to verify this.) Notice the product of their slopes, $\dfrac{1}{2}(-2)$, is -1. Any two numbers whose product is -1 are said to be **negative reciprocals** of each other. In general, if m represents a number, its negative reciprocal will be $-\dfrac{1}{m}$ because $m\left(-\dfrac{1}{m}\right) = -1$. Any two lines with slopes that are negative reciprocals of each other are perpendicular lines.

> ### Perpendicular Lines
> Two lines whose slopes are negative reciprocals of each other are perpendicular lines. Any vertical line is perpendicular to any horizontal line.

EXAMPLE 6 ▶

a) Draw a line with a slope of -3 through the point $(2, 3)$.

b) On the same set of axes, draw a line with a slope of $\dfrac{1}{3}$ through the point $(-1, -3)$.

c) Are the two lines in parts **a)** and **b)** perpendicular? Explain.

Solution

a) Place a dot at $(2, 3)$. A slope of -3 means $\dfrac{-3}{1}$. Because the slope is *negative*, from the point $(2, 3)$ move *down* 3 units and to the *right* 1 unit to get a second point. Draw a line through the two points; see the blue line in **Figure 4.44**.

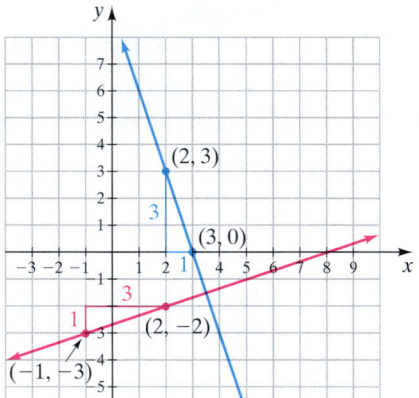

FIGURE 4.44

b) Place a dot at $(-1, -3)$. Because the slope is a *positive* $\dfrac{1}{3}$, from this point move *up* 1 unit and to the *right* 3 units. Draw a line through the two points; see the red line in **Figure 4.44**.

c) The lines appear to be perpendicular on the graph. To determine if they are perpendicular, multiply the slopes of the two lines together. If their product is -1, then the slopes are negative reciprocals, and the lines are perpendicular.

$$\text{Slope of line 1 (or } m_1) = -3, \text{ slope of line 2 (or } m_2) = \frac{1}{3}$$

$$m_1 \cdot m_2 = (-3)\left(\frac{1}{3}\right) = -1$$

Since the slopes are negative reciprocals, the two lines are perpendicular.

▶ **Now Try Exercise 75**

INSTRUCTOR EXAMPLE
Repeat Example 7 using the
following slopes.

a) $m_1 = \dfrac{2}{3}, m_2 = -\dfrac{3}{2}$

b) $m_1 = \dfrac{4}{7}, m_2 = \dfrac{4}{7}$

c) $m_1 = \dfrac{1}{3}, m_2 = 3$

Ans.:
a) perpendicular
b) parallel
c) neither

EXAMPLE 7 ▶ If m_1 represents the slope of line 1 and m_2 represents the slope of line 2, determine if line 1 and line 2 are parallel, perpendicular or neither.

a) $m_1 = \dfrac{5}{6}, m_2 = \dfrac{5}{6}$ b) $m_1 = \dfrac{2}{5}, m_2 = 4$ c) $m_1 = \dfrac{3}{5}, m_2 = -\dfrac{5}{3}$

Solution

a) Since the slopes are the same, both $\dfrac{5}{6}$, the lines are parallel.

b) Since the slopes are not the same, the lines are not parallel. Since $m_1 \cdot m_2 = \left(\dfrac{2}{5}\right)(4) \neq -1$, the slopes are not negative reciprocals and the lines are not perpendicular. Thus the answer is neither.

c) Since the slopes are not the same, the lines are not parallel. Since $m_1 \cdot m_2 = \dfrac{3}{5}\left(-\dfrac{5}{3}\right) = -1$, the slopes are negative reciprocals and the lines are perpendicular.

▶ **Now Try Exercise 53**

1. the ratio of the vertical change to the horizontal change between any two points on a line 2. Calculate the ratio of the vertical to horizontal change between any two points. 3. rises from left to right 4. falls from left to right 5. positive: lines rise from left to right; negative: lines fall from left to right 7. No, since we cannot divide by 0, the slope is undefined.

EXERCISE SET 4.3   *Math XL*   **MyMathLab**
MathXL®   MyMathLab

Concept/Writing Exercises

1. Explain what is meant by the slope of a line.
2. Explain how to find the slope of a line.
3. Describe the appearance of a line that has a positive slope.
4. Describe the appearance of a line that has a negative slope.
5. Explain how to tell by observation whether a line has a positive slope or negative slope.
6. What is the slope of any horizontal line? Explain your answer. 0, there is no vertical change.

7. Do vertical lines have a slope? Explain.
8. What letter is used to represent the slope? m
9. If two non-vertical lines are parallel, what do we know about the slopes of the two lines? They are the same.
10. If two non-vertical lines are perpendicular, what do we know about the slopes of the two lines?
Their slopes are negative reciprocals.

Practice the Skills

Using the slope formula, find the slope of the line through the given points.

11. $(4, 1)$ and $(6, 5)$ 2
12. $(9, -2)$ and $(7, -4)$ 1
13. $(8, 0)$ and $(4, -2)$ $\dfrac{1}{2}$
14. $(-4, 2)$ and $(6, 5)$ $\dfrac{3}{10}$

15. $\left(9, \dfrac{1}{2}\right)$ and $\left(-3, \dfrac{1}{2}\right)$ 0
16. $(-8, 6)$ and $(-2, 6)$ 0
17. $(5, -6)$ and $(8, -3)$ 1
18. $(9, 3)$ and $(5, -6)$ $\dfrac{9}{4}$

19. $(6, 4)$ and $(6, 2)$ undefined
20. $(-7, 8)$ and $(3, -1)$ $-\dfrac{9}{10}$
 21. $(6, 0)$ and $(-2, 3)$ $-\dfrac{3}{8}$
22. $(-2, 3)$ and $(-2, -5)$

23. $\left(0, \dfrac{5}{2}\right)$ and $\left(-\dfrac{3}{4}, 2\right)$ $\dfrac{2}{3}$
24. $(-1, 8)$ and $\left(\dfrac{1}{3}, -1\right)$ $-\dfrac{27}{4}$
22. undefined

By observing the vertical and horizontal change of the line between the two points indicated, determine the slope of each line.

25.

$m = 2$

26.

$m = \dfrac{3}{5}$

27.

$m = -2$

28.

$$m = -\frac{2}{5}$$

29.

$$m = -\frac{4}{7}$$

30.

$$m = -\frac{4}{3}$$

31.

$$m = \frac{7}{4}$$

32.

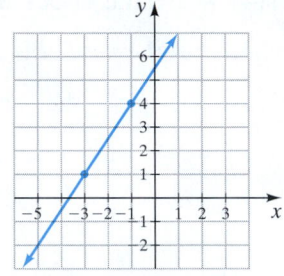

$$m = \frac{3}{2}$$

33.

$$m = 0$$

34.

$$m = 0$$

35.

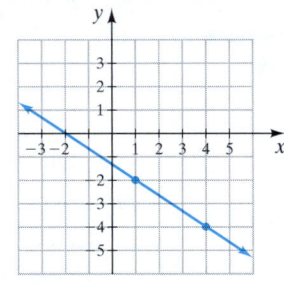

$$m = -\frac{2}{3}$$

36.

$$m = -\frac{3}{4}$$

37.

undefined

38.

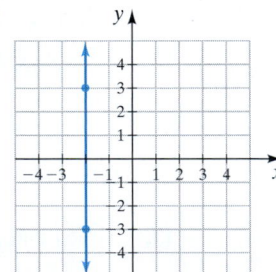

undefined

In Exercises 39–48, graph the line with the given slope that goes through the given point.   **39.–48.**   See graphing answer section.

39. Through $(3, -1)$ with $m = 2$.

40. Through $(-1, -2)$ with $m = -2$

41. Through $(0, -2)$ with $m = \frac{1}{2}$

42. Through $(0, 2)$ with $m = -\frac{1}{2}$

43. Through $(0, 0)$ with $m = -\frac{1}{3}$

44. Through $(-3, 4)$ with $m = -\frac{2}{3}$

45. Through $(-3, 2)$ with $m = 0$

46. Through $(-1, 3)$ with $m = 0$

47. Through $(2, -2)$ with slope undefined

48. Through $(-1, 5)$ with slope undefined

In Exercises 49–64, m_1 represents the slope of line 1, and m_2 represents the slope of the distinct line, line 2. Indicate whether line 1 and line 2 are parallel, perpendicular, or neither.

49. $m_1 = 3, m_2 = 3$ Parallel

50. $m_1 = \frac{1}{2}, m_2 = -6$ Neither

51. $m_1 = \frac{1}{4}, m_2 = -4$ Perpendicular

52. $m_1 = -1, m_2 = -1$ Parallel

53. $m_1 = \frac{2}{3}, m_2 = -\frac{3}{2}$ Perpendicular

54. $m_1 = 7, m_2 = -7$ Neither

55. $m_1 = 6, m_2 = \dfrac{2}{3}$ Neither   **56.** $m_1 = -\dfrac{1}{3}, m_2 = -3$ Neither   **57.** $m_1 = \dfrac{1}{4}, m_2 = 4$ Neither

58. $m_1 = 6, m_2 = -\dfrac{1}{6}$ Perpendicular   **59.** $m_1 = 0, m_2 = 0$ Parallel   **60.** $m_1 = 0, m_2 = -\dfrac{2}{5}$ Neither

61. m_1 is undefined, m_2 is undefined   Parallel   **62.** $m_1 = 0, m_2$ is undefined   Perpendicular

63. m_1 is undefined, $m_2 = 0$ Perpendicular   **64.** $m_1 = 5, m_2 = -5$ Neither

65. The slope of a given line is 3. If a line is to be drawn parallel to the given line, what will be its slope?   3

66. The slope of a given line is -2. If a line is to be drawn parallel to the given line, what will be its slope? -2

67. The slope of a given line is -4. If a line is to be drawn perpendicular to the given line, what will be its slope? $\dfrac{1}{4}$

68. The slope of a given line is 5. If a line is to be drawn perpendicular to the given line, what will be its slope? $-\dfrac{1}{5}$

Problem Solving

In Exercises 69 and 70, determine which line (the first or second) has the greater slope. Explain your answer. Notice that the scales on the x- and y-axes are different.

69.

first

70.

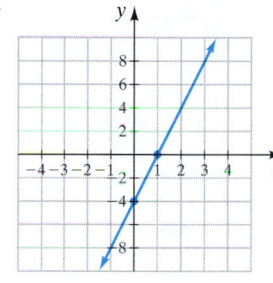

second

In Exercises 71 and 72, find the slope of the line segments indicated in **a)** *red and* **b)** *blue.*

71.

Temperature at Noon on Inaugural Day in Washington D.C.

Warmest 55°   51°
45°
22°
Coldest 7°

Degrees (F)

37 41 45 49 53 57 61 65 69 73 77 81 85 89 93 97 01 05
Year

Franklin Roosevelt, Harry S. Truman, Dwight Eisenhower, John F. Kennedy, Lyndon Johnson, Richard Nixon, Jimmy Carter, Ronald Reagan, George Bush, Bill Clinton, George W. Bush

Source: USA Today, www.msn.com, plus additional research.

72.

Stopping Distance on Wet Pavement for Midsize Car

(80, 618)
(70, 475)
(65, 410)
(75, 545)
(60, 280)

Stopping distance (feet)

60   65   70   75   80
Speed (miles per hour)

Source: Automobile Association of America

71. a) $-\dfrac{23}{4}$ **b)** 11   **72. a)** 26   **b)** 14.6

73. A given line goes through the points $(2, 6)$ and $(4, -2)$. If a line is to be drawn parallel to the given line, what will be its slope? -4

74. A given line goes through the points $(-2, 5)$ and $(4, 7)$. If a line is to be drawn parallel to the given line, what will be its slope? $\dfrac{1}{3}$

75. A given line goes through the points $(1, -7)$ and $(2, 1)$. If a line is to be drawn perpendicular to the given line, what will be its slope? $-\dfrac{1}{8}$

76. A given line goes through the points $(-3, 0)$ and $(-2, 3)$. If a line is to be drawn perpendicular to the given line, what will be its slope? $-\dfrac{1}{3}$

Challenge Problems

77. Find the slope of the line through the points $\left(\frac{1}{2}, -\frac{3}{8}\right)$ and $\left(-\frac{4}{9}, -\frac{7}{2}\right)$. $\frac{225}{68}$

78. If one point on a line is $(6, -4)$ and the slope of the line is $-\frac{5}{3}$, identify another point on the line. $(3, 1)$

79. A quadrilateral (a four-sided figure) has four vertices (the points where the sides meet). Vertex A is at $(0, 1)$, vertex B is at $(6, 2)$, vertex C is at $(5, 4)$, and vertex D is at $(1, -1)$.

   a) Graph the quadrilateral in the Cartesian coordinate system.   See graphing answer section.

   b) Find the slopes of sides AC, CB, DB, and AD.

   c) Do you think this figure is a parallelogram? Explain.   yes

80. Population The following graph shows the world's population estimated to the year 2016.

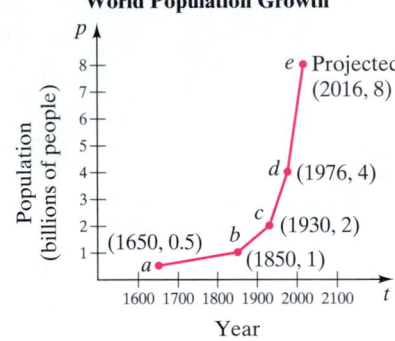

World Population Growth

a) Find the slope of the line segment between each pair of points, that is, ab, bc, and so on. Remember, the second coordinate is in billions. Thus, for example, 0.5 billion is actually 500,000,000.

b) Would you say that this graph represents a linear equation? Explain.   no

81. Consider the graph below.

a) Determine the slope of each of the three solid blue lines.

b) Determine the average of the three slopes found in part a).

c) Determine the slope of the red dashed line from A to D.

d) Determine whether the slope of the red dashed line from A to D is the same as the (mean) average of the slopes of the three solid blue lines.   yes

e) Explain what this example illustrates.   Answers will vary.

79. b) $AC, m = \frac{3}{5}$; $CB, m = -2$; $DB, m = \frac{3}{5}$; $AD, m = -2$ **80. a)** $ab, m = 2{,}500{,}000$; $bc, m = 12{,}500{,}000$; $cd, m \approx 43{,}478{,}261$; $de, m = 100{,}000{,}000$

81. a) $AB, m = 4$; $BC, m = -2$; $CD, m = 4$ **b)** $[4 + (-2) + 4]/3 = 2$ **c)** $AD, m = 2$

Group Activity

Discuss and answer Exercise 82 as a group, according to the instructions.

82. The slope of a hill and the slope of a line both measure steepness. However, there are several important differences.

   a) As a group, explain how you think the slope of a hill is determined.   Answers will vary.

   b) Is the slope of a line, graphed in the Cartesian coordinate system, measured in any specific unit?
   slope of line, no units

   c) Is the slope of a hill measured in any specific unit?
   slope of hill, degrees

Cumulative Review Exercises

[1.9]   **83.** Evaluate $4x^2 + 9x + \frac{x}{3}$ when $x = 0$.   0

[2.3]   **84. a)** If $-x = -\frac{5}{2}$, what is the value of x? $\frac{5}{2}$

   b) If $8x = 0$, what is the value of x?   0

[2.4]   **85.** Solve $\frac{2}{3}x + \frac{1}{7}x = 4$. $\frac{84}{17}$

[2.6]   **86.** Solve the equation $d = a + b + c$ for c. $c = d - a - b$

[4.2]   **87.** Find the x- and y-intercepts for the line whose equation is $5x - 3y = 30$.
   x-intercept: $(6, 0)$; y-intercept: $(0, -10)$

Mid-Chapter Test: 4.1–4.3

To find out how well you understand the chapter material to this point, take this brief test. The answers, and the section where the material was initially discussed, are given in the back of the book. Review any questions that you answered incorrectly.

1. In which quadrant does the point $(3, -4)$ belong?   IV

2. Plot the points $A(2, 6)$, $B(-3, 1)$, $C(-5, -2)$, $D(0, -4)$, $E(4, -7)$ on the same axes.   See graphing answer section.

3. Determine which of the three ordered pairs does not satisfy the equation $\frac{1}{3}x + y = -2$.   b)

   a) $(3, -3)$ **b)** $(0, 2)$ **c)** $(-6, 0)$

4. Find the value of y that makes the ordered pair $(-1, y)$ a solution to the linear equation $y = 5x + 1$. -4

5. Find the value of x that makes the ordered pair $(x, 2)$ a solution to the equation $3x - 4y = 1$.   3

6. What does the graph of an equation illustrate?

Graph each equation.

7. $x = \frac{5}{2}$ See graphing answer section.

8. $y = -2$ See graphing answer section.

Graph by plotting points.

9. $y = 3x + 1$ See graphing answer section.

10. $y = -\frac{1}{2}x + 4$ See graphing answer section.

Graph using the x- and y-intercepts.

11. $3x - 4y = 12$ See graphing answer section.

12. $\frac{1}{2}x + \frac{1}{5}y = 10$ See graphing answer section.

Find the slope of the line through each pair of points.

13. $(-1, 5)$ and $(6, 3)$ $-\frac{2}{7}$ 14. $(4, 2)$ and $(7, 2)$ 0

15. $(-3, 0)$ and $(-3, 5)$ Undefined

6. A graph of an equation in two variables is an illustration of a set of points whose coordinates satisfy the equation.

Graph the line with the given slope that goes through the given point.

16. Through $(-2, 3)$ with $m = -\frac{1}{2}$.   See graphing answer section.

17. Through $(4, 1)$ with $m = \frac{3}{5}$.   See graphing answer section.

Indicate whether the lines with the following slopes are parallel, perpendicular, or neither.

18. $m_1 = 5$ and $m_2 = \frac{1}{5}$ Neither

19. $m_1 = \frac{6}{7}$ and $m_2 = -\frac{7}{6}$ Perpendicular

20. **Interest** The following graph illustrates the interest obtaind when \$1000 is invested for 1 year of various interest rates from 0% to 10%. Determine the slope of the line in the graph.   10

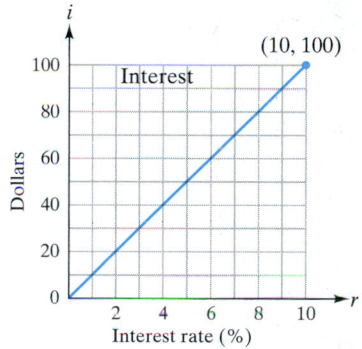

4.4 Slope-Intercept and Point-Slope Forms of a Linear Equation

1 Write a linear equation in slope-intercept form.

2 Graph a linear equation using the slope and y-intercept.

3 Use the slope-intercept form to determine the equation of a line.

4 Use the point-slope form to determine the equation of a line.

5 Compare the three methods of graphing linear equations.

In Section 4.1 we introduced the *standard form* of a linear equation, $ax + by = c$. In this section we introduce two more forms, the slope-intercept form and the point-slope form. We begin our discussion with the slope-intercept form.

1 Write a Linear Equation in Slope-Intercept Form

A very important form of a linear equation is the **slope-intercept form, $y = mx + b$** (recall that we briefly discussed the $y = mx + b$ form in Section 2.6). The graph of an equation of the form $y = mx + b$ will always be a straight line with a **slope of m** and a **y-intercept $(0, b)$**. For example, the graph of the equation $y = 3x - 4$ will be a straight line with a slope of 3 and a y-intercept $(0, -4)$. The graph of $y = -2x + 5$ will be a straight line with a slope of -2 and a y-intercept $(0, 5)$.

Slope-Intercept Form of a Linear Equation

$$y = mx + b$$

where m is the slope, and $(0, b)$ is the y-intercept of the line.

slope   where the graph crosses the y-axis

$$y = mx + b$$

Equations in Slope-Intercept Form	Slope	y-Intercept
$y = 4x - 6$	4	$(0, -6)$
$y = \dfrac{1}{2}x + \dfrac{3}{2}$	$\dfrac{1}{2}$	$\left(0, \dfrac{3}{2}\right)$
$y = -5x + 3$	-5	$(0, 3)$

Writing an Equation in Slope-Intercept Form

To write a linear equation in slope-intercept form, solve the equation for y.

Once the equation is solved for y, the numerical coefficient of the x-term will be the slope, and the constant term will give the y-intercept.

EXAMPLE 1 ▶ Write the equation $-3x + 4y = 8$ in slope-intercept form. State the slope and y-intercept.

Solution To write this equation in slope-intercept form, we solve the equation for y.

$$-3x + 4y = 8$$
$$4y = 3x + 8$$
$$y = \frac{3x + 8}{4}$$
$$y = \frac{3}{4}x + \frac{8}{4}$$
$$y = \frac{3}{4}x + 2$$

The slope is $\dfrac{3}{4}$, and the y-intercept is $(0, 2)$.

▶ **Now Try Exercise 11**

EXAMPLE 2 ▶ Determine whether the two equations represent lines that are parallel, perpendicular, or neither.

a. $2x + y = 9$
$\quad 2y = -4x + 5$

b. $3x - 2y = 7$
$\quad 6y + 4x = -6$

Solution We learned in Section 4.3 that two lines that have the same slope are parallel lines, and two lines whose slopes are negative reciprocals are perpendicular lines. We can determine the slope of each line by solving each equation for y. The coefficient of the x term will be the slope.

a) $2x + y = 9$

$$y = -2x + 9$$

$$2y = -4x + 5$$
$$y = \frac{-4x + 5}{2}$$
$$y = -2x + \frac{5}{2}$$

Since both equations have the same slope, -2, the equations represent lines that are parallel. Notice the equations represent two different lines because their y-intercepts are different.

INSTRUCTOR EXAMPLE

Write the equation $2x + 4y = 8$ in slope-intercept form. State the slope and y-intercept.

Ans.: $y = -\dfrac{1}{2}x + 2$, $m = -\dfrac{1}{2}$, $(0, 2)$

INSTRUCTOR EXAMPLE

Determine whether the two lines are parallel, perpendicular, or neither.

a) $3x + y = 5$
$\quad 2y = -6x + 9$

b) $5x - 4y = 8$
$\quad 4x + 5y = 10$

Ans.:

a) parallel   **b)** perpendicular

b) $3x - 2y = 7$

$$-2y = -3x + 7$$

$$y = \frac{-3x + 7}{-2}$$

$$y = \boxed{\frac{3}{2}}x - \frac{7}{2}$$

$6y + 4x = -6$

$$6y = -4x - 6$$

$$y = \frac{-4x - 6}{6}$$

$$y = \boxed{-\frac{2}{3}}x - 1$$

The slope of one line is $\frac{3}{2}$ and the slope of the other line is $-\frac{2}{3}$. Multiplying the slopes we obtain $\left(\frac{3}{2}\right)\left(-\frac{2}{3}\right) = -1$. Since the product is -1, the slopes are negative reciprocals. Therefore the equations represent lines that are perpendicular.

▶ **Now Try Exercise 39**

2 Graph a Linear Equation Using the Slope and y-Intercept

In Section 4.2 we discussed two methods of graphing a linear equation. They were (1) by plotting points and (2) using the x- and y-intercepts. Now we present a third method. This method makes use of the slope and the y-intercept. Remember that when we solve an equation for y we put the equation in slope-intercept form. Once it is in this form, we can determine the slope and y-intercept of the graph from the equation.

We graph equations using the slope and y-intercept in a manner very similar to the way we worked Examples 5 and 6 in Section 4.3. However, when graphing using the slope-intercept form, our starting point is always the y-intercept. After you determine the y-intercept, a second point can be obtained by moving up and to the right if the slope is positive, or down and to the right if the slope is negative.

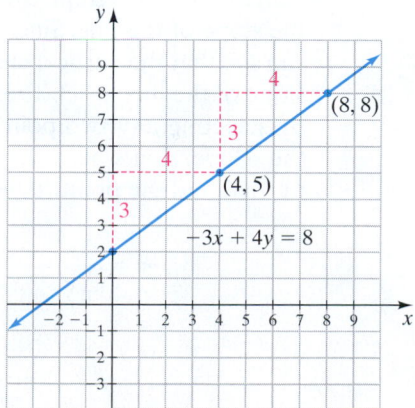

EXAMPLE 3 ▶ Write the equation $-3x + 4y = 8$ in slope-intercept form; then use the slope and y-intercept to graph $-3x + 4y = 8$.

Solution In Example 1 we solved $-3x + 4y = 8$ for y. We found that

$$y = \frac{3}{4}x + 2$$

The slope of the line is $\frac{3}{4}$ and the y-intercept is $(0, 2)$. We mark the first point, the y-intercept at 2 on the y-axis (**Fig. 4.45**). Now we use the slope $\frac{3}{4}$, to find a second point. Since the slope is positive, we move 3 units up and 4 units to the right to find the second point. A second point will be at $(4, 5)$. We can continue this process to obtain a third point at $(8, 8)$. Now we draw a straight line through the three points. Notice that the line has a positive slope, which is what we expected.

FIGURE 4.45

▶ **Now Try Exercise 19**

INSTRUCTOR EXAMPLE
Graph $-2x + 5y = 10$ using the
slope and y-intercept.

Ans.:

EXAMPLE 4 ▶ Graph $5x + 3y = 12$ by using the slope and y-intercept.

Solution   Solve the equation for y.

$$5x + 3y = 12$$

$$3y = -5x + 12$$

$$y = \frac{-5x + 12}{3}$$

$$= -\frac{5}{3}x + 4$$

Thus, the slope is $-\frac{5}{3}$ and the y-intercept is $(0, 4)$. Begin by marking a point at 4 on the y-axis (**Fig. 4.46**). Then move 5 units down and 3 units to the right to determine the next point. Move down and to the right because the slope is negative and a line with a negative slope must fall as it goes from left to right. You can follow this procedure again to obtain a third point. Finally, draw the straight line between the plotted points.

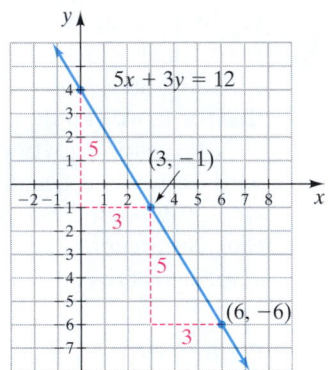

FIGURE 4.46

▶ **Now Try Exercise 21**

3 Use the Slope-Intercept Form to Determine the Equation of a Line

Now that we know how to use the slope-intercept form of a line, we can use it to write the equation of a given line. To do so, we need to determine the slope, m, and y-intercept of the line. Once we determine these values we can write the equation in slope-intercept form, $y = mx + b$. For example, if we determine the slope of a line is -4 and the y-intercept is at 6, the equation of the line is $y = -4x + 6$.

INSTRUCTOR EXAMPLE
Determine the equation of the line.

Ans.: $y = 2x - 5$

EXAMPLE 5 ▶ Determine the equation of the line shown in **Figure 4.47**.

Solution   The graph shows that the y-intercept is at -5. Now we need to determine the slope of the line. Since the graph falls from left to right, it has a negative slope. We can see that the vertical change is 3 units for each horizontal change of 1 unit. Thus, the slope of the line is -3. The slope can also be determined by selecting any two points on the line and calculating the slope. Let's use the point $(-2, 1)$ to represent (x_2, y_2) and the point $(0, -5)$ to represent (x_1, y_1).

$$m = \frac{\Delta y}{\Delta x} = \frac{y_2 - y_1}{x_2 - x_1}$$

$$= \frac{1 - (-5)}{-2 - 0}$$

$$= \frac{1 + 5}{-2} = \frac{6}{-2} = -3$$

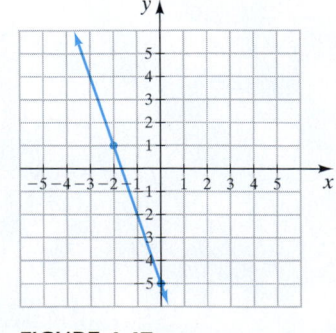

FIGURE 4.47

Again we obtain a slope of -3, Substituting -3 for m and -5 for b into the slope-intercept form of a line gives us the equation of the line in **Figure 4.47** on page 266, which is $y = -3x - 5$.

▶ **Now Try Exercise 29**

Now let's look at an application of graphing.

EXAMPLE 6 ▶ **Artistic Vases** Kris, a pottery artist, makes ceramic vases that he sells at art shows. His business has a fixed monthly cost (booth rental, advertising, cell phone, etc.) and a variable cost per vase made (cost of materials, cost of labor, cost for kiln use, etc.). The total monthly cost for making x vases is illustrated in the graph in **Figure 4.48**.

FIGURE 4.48

a) Find the equation of the total monthly cost when x vases are made.

b) Use the equation found in part **a)** to find the total monthly cost if 30 vases are made.

c) Use the graph in **Figure 4.48** to see whether your answer in part **b)** appears correct.

Solution **a) Understand and Translate** Notice that the vertical axis is cost, C, and not y. The letters or names used on the axes do not change the way we solve the problem. We will use slope-intercept form to write the equation of the line. However, since y is replaced by C, we will use $C = mx + b$, in which b is where the graph crosses the vertical or C-axis. We first note that the graph crosses the vertical axis at 200. Thus, b is 200. Now we need to find the slope of the line. Let's use the point $(0, 200)$ as (x_1, y_1) and $(50, 1450)$ as (x_2, y_2).

Carry Out

$$m = \frac{y_2 - y_1}{x_2 - x_1}$$

$$= \frac{1450 - 200}{50 - 0} = \frac{1250}{50} = 25$$

Answer The slope is 25. The equation in slope-intercept form is

$$C = mx + b$$
$$= 25x + 200$$

b) To find the monthly cost when 30 vases are sold, we substitute 30 for x.

$$C = 25x + 200$$
$$= 25(30) + 200$$
$$= 750 + 200 = 950$$

The monthly cost when 30 vases are made is $950.

c) If we draw a vertical line up from 30 on the x-axis (the red line), we see that the corresponding cost is about $950. Thus, our answer in part **b)** appears correct.

▶ **Now Try Exercise 65**

INSTRUCTOR EXAMPLE 6

Repeat Example 6 a)-c) for the following graph.

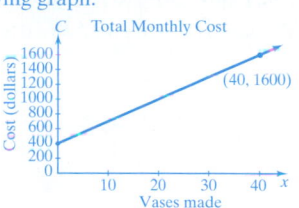

Ans.: a) $C = 30x + 400$
b) $1300
c) appears correct

4 Use the Point-Slope Form to Determine the Equation of a Line

Thus far, we have discussed the standard form of a linear equation, $ax + by = c$, and the slope-intercept form of a linear equation, $y = mx + b$. Now we will discuss another form, called the *point-slope form*.

When the slope of a line and a point on the line are known, we can use the point-slope form to determine the equation of the line. The **point-slope form** can be obtained by beginning with the slope between any selected point (x, y) and a fixed point (x_1, y_1) on a line.

$$m = \frac{y - y_1}{x - x_1} \quad \text{or} \quad \frac{m}{1} = \frac{y - y_1}{x - x_1}$$

Now cross-multiply to obtain

$$m(x - x_1) = y - y_1 \quad \text{or} \quad y - y_1 = m(x - x_1)$$

> ### Point-Slope Form of a Linear Equation
> $$y - y_1 = m(x - x_1)$$
> where m is the slope of the line and (x_1, y_1) is a point on the line.

INSTRUCTOR EXAMPLE
Write an equation, in slope-intercept form, of a line that goes through the point $(-1, 4)$ and has a slope of 3.
Ans.: $y = 3x + 7$

EXAMPLE 7 ▶ Write an equation, in slope-intercept form, of the line that goes through the point $(4, 2)$ and has a slope of 5.

Solution   Since we are given a point on the line and the slope of the line, we begin by writing the equation in point-slope form. The slope m is 5. The point on the line is $(4, 2)$; we will use this point for (x_1, y_1) in the formula. We substitute 5 for m, 4 for x_1, and 2 for y_1 in the point-slope form of a linear equation.

$$y - y_1 = m(x - x_1)$$
$$y - 2 = 5(x - 4) \qquad \textit{Equation in point-slope form}$$
$$y - 2 = 5x - 20 \qquad \textit{Distributive property}$$
$$y = 5x - 18 \qquad \textit{Equation in slope-intercept form}$$

The graph of $y = 5x - 18$ has a slope of 5 and passes through the point $(4, 2)$.

▶ **Now Try Exercise 51**

The answer to Example 7 was given in slope-intercept form. If we were asked to give the answer in standard form, two acceptable answers would be $-5x + y = -18$ or $5x - y = 18$. Your instructor may specify the form in which the equation is to be given.

In Example 8, we will work an example very similar to Example 7. However, in the solution to Example 8, the equation will contain a fraction. We solved some equations that contained fractions in Chapter 2. Recall that to simplify an equation that contains a fraction, we multiply both sides of the equation by the denominator of the fraction.

INSTRUCTOR EXAMPLE
Write an equation, in slope-intercept form, of a line that goes through the point $(8, -2)$ and has a slope of $\frac{3}{4}$.
Ans.: $y = \frac{3}{4}x - 8$

EXAMPLE 8 ▶ Write an equation, in slope-intercept form, of the line that goes through the point $(6, -2)$ and has a slope of $\frac{2}{3}$.

Solution   We will begin with the point-slope form of a line, where m is $\frac{2}{3}$, 6 is x_1, and -2 is y_1.

$$y - y_1 = m(x - x_1)$$

$$y - (-2) = \frac{2}{3}(x - 6) \qquad \textcolor{red}{\textit{Equation in point-slope form}}$$

$$y + 2 = \frac{2}{3}(x - 6)$$

$$3(y + 2) = 3 \cdot \frac{2}{3}(x - 6) \qquad \textcolor{red}{\textit{Multiply both sides by 3.}}$$

$$3y + 6 = 2(x - 6) \qquad \textcolor{red}{\textit{Distributive property}}$$

$$3y + 6 = 2x - 12 \qquad \textcolor{red}{\textit{Distributive property}}$$

$$3y = 2x - 18 \qquad \textcolor{red}{\textit{Subtract 6 from both sides.}}$$

$$y = \frac{2x - 18}{3} \qquad \textcolor{red}{\textit{Divide both sides by 3.}}$$

$$y = \frac{2}{3}x - 6 \qquad \textcolor{red}{\textit{Equation in slope-intercept form}}$$

▶ **Now Try Exercise 53**

Helpful Hint

We have discussed three forms of a linear equation. We summarize the three forms below. It is important that you memorize these forms.

Standard Form	Examples
$ax + by = c$	$2x - 3y = 8$
	$-5x + y = -2$

Slope-Intercept Form	Examples
$y = mx + b$	$y = 2x - 5$
m is the slope, $(0, b)$ is the y-intercept	$y = -\frac{3}{2}x + 2$

Point-Slope Form	Examples
$y - y_1 = m(x - x_1)$	$y - 3 = 2(x + 4)$
m is the slope, (x_1, y_1) is a point on the line	$y + 5 = -4(x - 1)$

We now discuss how to use the point-slope form to determine the equation of a line when two points on the line are known.

EXAMPLE 9 ▶ Find an equation of the line through the points $(-1, 3)$ and $(-5, 1)$. Write the equation in slope-intercept form.

Solution   To use the point-slope form, we must first find the slope of the line through the two points. To determine the slope, let's designate $(-1, 3)$ as (x_1, y_1) and $(-5, 1)$ as (x_2, y_2).

$$m = \frac{y_2 - y_1}{x_2 - x_1} = \frac{1 - 3}{-5 - (-1)} = \frac{1 - 3}{-5 + 1} = \frac{-2}{-4} = \frac{1}{2}$$

The slope is $\frac{1}{2}$. We can use either point (one at a time) in determining the equation of the line. This example will be worked out using both points to show that the solutions obtained are identical.

Using the point $(-1, 3)$ as (x_1, y_1),

$$y - y_1 = m(x - x_1)$$

$$y - 3 = \frac{1}{2}[x - (-1)]$$

$$y - 3 = \frac{1}{2}(x + 1)$$

$$2 \cdot (y - 3) = 2 \cdot \frac{1}{2}(x + 1) \qquad \text{\textit{Multiply both sides by the LCD, 2.}}$$

$$2y - 6 = x + 1$$

$$2y = x + 7$$

$$y = \frac{x + 7}{2} \quad \text{or} \quad y = \frac{1}{2}x + \frac{7}{2}$$

Using the point $(-5, 1)$ as (x_1, y_1),

$$y - y_1 = m(x - x)$$

$$y - 1 = \frac{1}{2}[x - (-5)]$$

$$y - 1 = \frac{1}{2}(x + 5)$$

$$2 \cdot (y - 1) = 2 \cdot \frac{1}{2}(x + 5) \qquad \text{\textit{Multiply both sides by the LCD, 2.}}$$

$$2y - 2 = x + 5$$

$$2y = x + 7$$

$$y = \frac{x + 7}{2} \quad \text{or} \quad y = \frac{1}{2}x + \frac{7}{2}$$

Note that the equations for the line are identical.

▶ **Now Try Exercise 57**

Helpful Hint

In the exercise set at the end of this section, you will be asked to write a linear equation in slope-intercept form. Even though you will eventually write the equation in slope-intercept form, you may need to start your work with the point-slope form. Below we indicate the initial form to use to solve the problem.

Begin with the **slope-intercept form** if you know

The slope of the line and the y-intercept

Begin with the **point-slope form** if you know

a)   The slope of the line and a point on the line, or

b)   Two points on the line (first find the slope, then use the point-slope form)

5 Compare the Three Methods of Graphing Linear Equations

We have discussed three methods to graph a linear equation: (1) plotting points, (2) using the x- and y-intercepts, and (3) using the slope and y-intercept. In Example 10 we graph an equation using all three methods. No single method is always the easiest to use. If the equation is given in slope-intercept form, $y = mx + b$, then graphing by plotting points or by using the slope and y-intercept might be easier. If the equation is given in standard form, $ax + by = c$, then graphing using the intercepts might be easier. Unless your teacher specifies that you should graph by a specific method, you may use the method with which you feel most comfortable. Graphing by plotting points is the most versatile method since it can also be used to graph equations that are not straight lines.

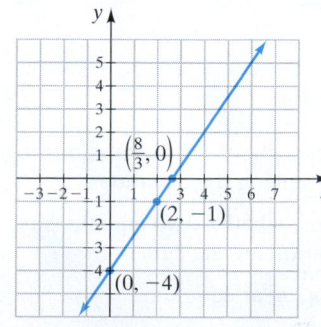

EXAMPLE 10 ▶ Graph $3x - 2y = 8$

  a) by plotting points;

  b) using the x- and y-intercepts;

  c) using the slope and y-intercept.

Solution　For parts **a)** and **c)** we will write the equation in slope-intercept form.

$$3x - 2y = 8$$

$$-2y = -3x + 8$$

$$y = \frac{-3x + 8}{-2} = \frac{3}{2}x - 4$$

  a) **Plotting Points** To find ordered pairs to plot, we substitute values for x and find the corresponding values of y. Three ordered pairs are indicated in the following table. Next we plot the ordered pairs and draw the graph (**Fig. 4.49**).

$$y = \frac{3}{2}x - 4$$

x	y
0	-4
2	-1
4	2

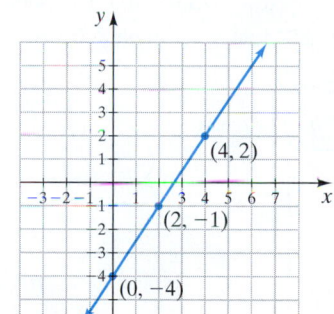

FIGURE 4.49

  b) **Intercepts** We find the x- and y-intercepts and a check point. Then we plot the points and draw the graph (**Fig. 4.50**).

$$3x - 2y = 8$$

x-Intercept	y-Intercept	Check Point
Let $y = 0$.	Let $x = 0$.	Let $x = 2$.
$3x - 2y = 8$	$3x - 2y = 8$	$3x - 2y = 8$
$3x - 2(0) = 8$	$3(0) - 2y = 8$	$3(2) - 2y = 8$
$3x = 8$	$-2y = 8$	$6 - 2y = 8$
$x = \dfrac{8}{3}$	$y = -4$	$-2y = 2$
		$y = -1$

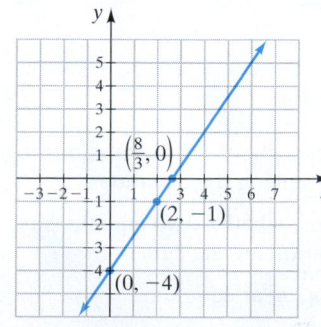

FIGURE 4.50

The three ordered pairs are $\left(\dfrac{8}{3}, 0\right)$, $(0, -4)$, and $(2, -1)$.

FIGURE 4.51

c) Slope and *y*-intercept The *y*-intercept is $(0, -4)$; therefore, we place a point at -4 on the *y*-axis. Since the slope is $\dfrac{3}{2}$, we obtain a second point by moving 3 units up and 2 units to the right. The graph is illustrated in **Figure 4.51**.

Notice that we get the same line by all three methods.

▸ **Now Try Exercise 27**

USING YOUR GRAPHING CALCULATOR

In Example 10, we graphed the equation $y = \dfrac{3}{2}x - 4$. Let's see what the graph of $y = \dfrac{3}{2}x - 4$ looks like on a graphing calculator using three different window settings. **Figure 4.52** shows the graph of $y = \dfrac{3}{2}x - 4$ using the *standard window setting*.

To obtain the standard window, press the $\boxed{\text{ZOOM}}$ key and then choose option 6, ZStandard. Notice that in the standard window setting, the units on the *y*-axis are not as long as the units on the *x*-axis.

In **Figure 4.53**, we illustrate the graph of $y = \dfrac{3}{2}x - 4$ using the *square window setting*. To obtain the square window setting, press the $\boxed{\text{ZOOM}}$ key and then choose option 5, ZSquare. This setting makes the units on both axes the same size. This allows the line to be displayed at the correct orientation to the axes.

In **Figure 4.54**, we illustrate the graph using the *decimal window setting*. To obtain the decimal window setting, press the $\boxed{\text{ZOOM}}$ key and then choose option 4, ZDecimal. The decimal window setting also makes the units the same on both axes, but sets the increment from one pixel (dot) to the next at 0.1 on both axes.

STANDARD WINDOW SETTING
($\boxed{\text{ZOOM}}$: OPTION 6)

$-10, 10, 1, -10, 10, 1$

FIGURE 4.52

SQUARE WINDOW SETTING
($\boxed{\text{ZOOM}}$: OPTION 5)

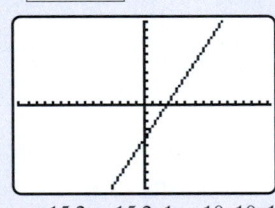

$\approx -15.2, \approx 15.2, 1, -10, 10, 1$

FIGURE 4.53

DECIMAL WINDOW SETTING
($\boxed{\text{ZOOM}}$: OPTION 4)

$-4.7, 4.7, 1, -3.1, 3.1, 1$

FIGURE 4.54

EXERCISES

Graph each equation using the a) standard window, b) square window, and c) decimal window settings.

1. $y = 4x - 6$

2. $y = -\dfrac{1}{5}x + 4$ See graphing answer section.

1. $y = mx + b$ **5.** If the slopes are the same and the *y*-intercepts are different, the lines are parallel.   **6.** slopes are same and *y*-intercepts are same
7. $y - y_1 = m(x - x_1)$

EXERCISE SET 4.4

Concept/Writing Exercises

1. Give the slope-intercept form of a linear equation.

2. When you are given an equation in a form other than slope-intercept form, how can you change it to slope-intercept form?   Solve the equation for *y*.

3. What is the equation of a line, in slope-intercept form, if the slope is 3 and the *y*-intercept is at -5? $y = 3x - 5$

4. What is the equation of a line, in slope-intercept form, if the slope is -3 and the *y*-intercept is at 5? $y = -3x + 5$

5. Explain how you can determine whether two equations represent parallel lines without graphing the equations.

6. Explain how you can determine whether two equations represent the same line without graphing the equations.

7. Give the point-slope form of a linear equation.

8. Assume the slope of a line is 2 and the line goes through the origin. Write the equation of the line in point-slope form. $y - 0 = 2(x - 0)$

Practice the Skills

Determine the slope and y-intercept of the line represented by the given equation.

9. $y = 2x - 6$ $2, (0, -6)$ **10.** $y = -3x + 17$ $-3, (0, 17)$ **11.** $4x - 3y = 21$ $\frac{4}{3}, (0, -7)$ **12.** $7x = 5y + 25$ $\frac{7}{5}, (0, -5)$

Determine the slope and y-intercept of the line represented by each equation. Graph the line using the slope and y-intercept.

13. $y = x - 3$ $1, (0, -3)$ **14.** $y = -x + 5$ $-1, (0, 5)$ **15.** $y = 3x + 2$ $3, (0, 2)$ **16.** $3x + y = 4$ $-3, (0, 4)$

17. $y = 2x$ $2, (0, 0)$ **18.** $y = -4x$ $-4, (0, 0)$ **19.** $-2x + y = -3$ $2, (0, -3)$ **20.** $3x + 3y = 9$ $-1, (0, 3)$

21. $5x - 2y = 10$ $\frac{5}{2}, (0, -5)$ **22.** $-x + 2y = 8$ $\frac{1}{2}, (0, 4)$ **23.** $6x + 12y = 18$ $-\frac{1}{2}, \left(0, \frac{3}{2}\right)$**24.** $16y = 8x + 32$ $\frac{1}{2}, (0, 2)$

25. $-6x + 2y - 8 = 0$ $3, (0, 4)$ **26.** $4x = 6y + 9$ $\frac{2}{3}, \left(0, -\frac{3}{2}\right)$ **27.** $3x = 2y - 4$ $\frac{3}{2}, (0, 2)$ **28.** $20x = 80y + 40$ $\frac{1}{4}, \left(0, -\frac{1}{2}\right)$

13.–28. See graphing answer section.

Determine the equation of each line.

29.

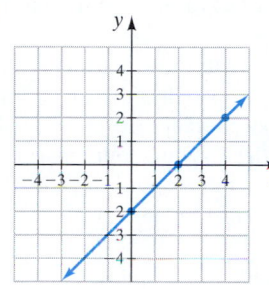

$y = x - 2$

30.

$y = 2x$

 31.

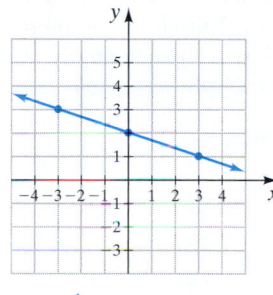

$y = -\frac{1}{3}x + 2$

32.

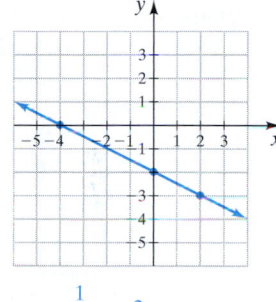

$y = -\frac{1}{2}x - 2$

33.

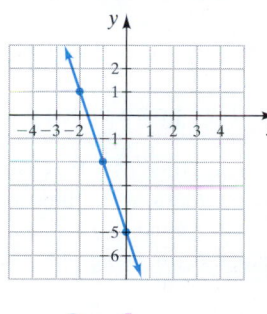

$y = -3x - 5$

34.

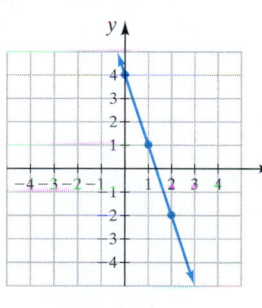

$y = -3x + 4$

35.

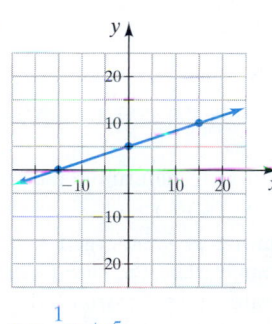

$y = \frac{1}{3}x + 5$

36.

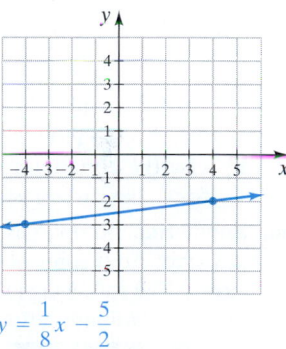

$y = \frac{1}{8}x - \frac{5}{2}$

Determine whether each pair of lines are parallel, perpendicular, or neither.

37. $y = 4x + 6$
    $y = 4x - 1$ parallel

38. $2x + 3y = 1$
    $y = -\frac{2}{3}x + 3$ parallel

39. $4x + 2y = 7$
    $4x = 8y + 12$ perpendicular

40. $3x - 5y = 7$
    $5y + 3x = 4$ neither

 41. $3x + 5y = 9$
    $6x = -10y + 9$ parallel

42. $8x + 2y = 10$
    $x - 7 = 4y$ perpendicular

43. $y = \frac{1}{2}x - 2$
    $2y = 6x + 9$ neither

44. $3y - 4 = -5x$
    $y = -\frac{5}{3}x - 3$ parallel

45. $5y = 2x + 9$
    $-10x = 4y + 11$ perpendicular

46. $3x - 9y = 21$
    $-3x + 9y = 27$ parallel

47. $3x + 7y = 21$
    $7x + 3y = 21$ neither

48. $5x - 6y = 18$
    $-6x + 5y = 10$ neither

Problem Solving

66. a) $y = -10t - 300$ 67. a) slope-intercept form

Write the equation of each line, with the given properties, in slope-intercept form.

49. Slope = 3, through $(0, 2)$ $y = 3x + 2$

50. Slope = 2, through $(4, 3)$ $y = 2x - 5$

51. Slope = -3, through $(-4, 5)$ $y = -3x - 7$

52. Slope = -3, through $(2, 0)$ $y = -3x + 6$

53. Slope = $\dfrac{1}{2}$, through $(-1, -3)$ $y = \dfrac{1}{2}x - \dfrac{5}{2}$

54. Slope = $-\dfrac{2}{3}$, through $(4, -5)$ $y = -\dfrac{2}{3}x - \dfrac{7}{3}$

55. Slope = $\dfrac{2}{3}$, y-intercept is $(0, 6)$ $y = \dfrac{2}{3}x + 6$

56. Slope = $\dfrac{1}{9}$, y-intercept is $\left(0, -\dfrac{2}{5}\right)$ $y = \dfrac{1}{9}x - \dfrac{2}{5}$

57. Through $(-4, -2)$ and $(-2, 4)$ $y = 3x + 10$

58. Through $(7, 4)$ and $(6, 3)$ $y = x - 3$

59. Through $(-6, 9)$ and $(8, -12)$ $y = -\dfrac{3}{2}x$

60. Through $(3, 0)$ and $(-3, 5)$ $y = -\dfrac{5}{6}x + \dfrac{5}{2}$

61. Through $(10, 3)$ and $(0, -2)$ $y = \dfrac{1}{2}x - 2$

62. Through $(-6, -2)$ and $(5, -3)$ $y = -\dfrac{1}{11}x - \dfrac{28}{11}$

63. Slope = 7.4, y-intercept is $(0, -4.5)$ $y = 7.4x - 4.5$

64. Slope = $-\dfrac{7}{8}$, y-intercept is $\left(0, -\dfrac{3}{10}\right)$ $y = -\dfrac{7}{8}x - \dfrac{3}{10}$

65. Weight Loss Clinic Stacy Best owns a weight loss clinic. She charges her clients a one-time membership fee. She also charges per pound of weight lost. Therefore, the more successful she is at helping clients lose weight, the more income she will receive. The following graph shows a client's cost for losing weight.

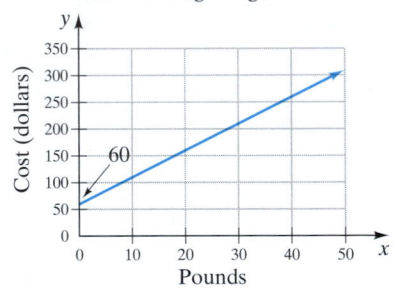

Cost of Losing Weight

a) Find the equation that represents the cost for a client who loses x pounds. $y = 5x + 60$

b) Use the equation found in part **a)** to determine the cost for a client who loses 30 pounds. $210

66. Submarine Submerges A submarine is submerged below sea level. Tom Johnson, the captain, orders the ship to dive slowly. The following graph illustrates the submarine's depth at a time t minutes after the submarine begins to dive.

Submarine's Depth

a) Find the equation that represents the depth at time t.

b) Use the equation found in part **a)** to find the submarine's depth after 30 minutes. -600 ft

67. Suppose that you were asked to write the equation of a line with the properties given below. Which form of a linear equation—standard form, slope-intercept form, or point-slope form—would you start with? Explain your answer.

a) The slope of the line and the y-intercept of the line

b) The slope and a point on the line   point-slope form

c) Two points on the line   point-slope form

68. Consider the two equations $20x - 30y = 50$ and $-20x + 30y = 40$.

a) When these equations are graphed, will the two lines have the same slope? Explain how you determined your answer.   yes

b) When these two equations are graphed, will they be parallel lines?   yes

69. Assume the slope of a line is 2 and two points on the line are $(-5, -4)$ and $(3, 12)$.

a) If you use $(-5, -4)$ as (x_1, y_1) and then $(3, 12)$ as (x_1, y_1) will the appearance of the two equations be the same in point-slope form? Explain.   no

b) Find the equation, in point-slope form, using $(-5, -4)$ as (x_1, y_1). $y + 4 = 2(x + 5)$

c) Find the equation, in point-slope form, using $(3, 12)$ as (x_1, y_1). $y - 12 = 2(x - 3)$

d) Write the equation obtained in part **b)** in slope-intercept form. $y = 2x + 6$

e) Write the equation obtained in part **c)** in slope-intercept form. $y = 2x + 6$

f) Are the equations obtained in parts **d)** and **e)** the same? If not, explain why.   yes

70. Assume the slope of a line is -3 and two points on the line are $(-1, 8)$ and $(2, -1)$.

a) If you use $(-1, 8)$ as (x_1, y_1) and then $(2, -1)$ as (x_1, y_1) will the appearance of the two equations be the same in point-slope form? Explain.   no

b) Find the equation, in point-slope form, using $(-1, 8)$ as (x_1, y_1). $y - 8 = -3(x + 1)$

c) Find the equation, in point-slope form, using $(2, -1)$ as (x_1, y_1). $y + 1 = -3(x - 2)$

d) Write the equation obtained in part **b)** in slope-intercept form. $y = -3x + 5$

e) Write the equation obtained in part **c)** in slope-intercept form. $y = -3x + 5$

f) Are the equations obtained in parts **d)** and **e)** the same? If not, explain why.   yes

Challenge Problems

71. Unit Conversions The following graph shows the approximate relationship between speed in miles per hour and feet per second.

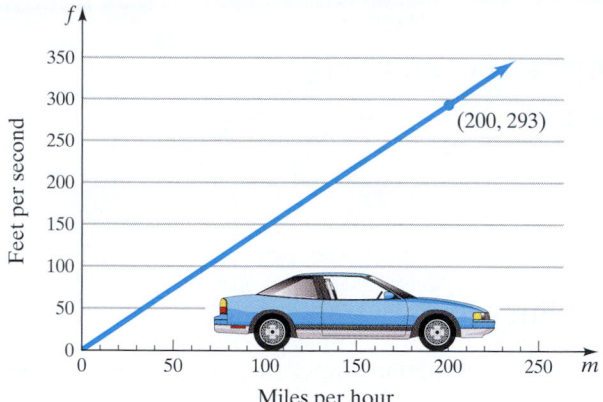

a) Determine the slope of the line.   1.465

b) Determine the equation of the line. $f = 1.465m$

c) At the 2006 Daytona 500, Jimmie Johnson, the winner, had an average speed of 142.7 miles per hour. (See photo). Use the equation you obtained in part **b)** to determine the speed in feet per second.   ≈209.06 ft/sec

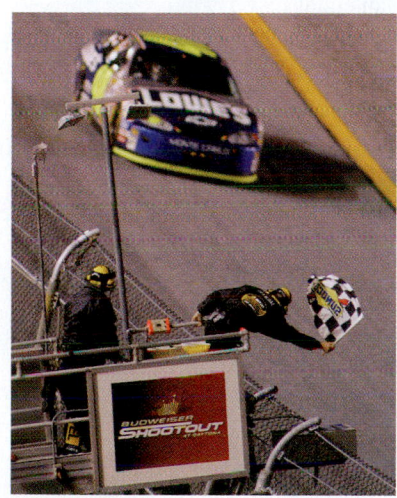

d) Use the graph to estimate a speed of 100 miles per hour in feet per second.   150 ft/sec

e) Use the graph to estimate a speed of 80 feet per second in miles per hour.   55 mph

72. Temperature The following graph shows the relationship between Fahrenheit temperature and Celsius temperature.

a) Determine the slope of the line. $\dfrac{9}{5}$

b) Determine the equation of the line in slope-intercept form.

c) Use the equation (or formula) you obtained in part **b)** to find the Fahrenheit temperature when the Celsius temperature is 20°.   68°F

d) Use the graph to estimate the Celsius temperature when the Fahrenheit temperature is 100°.   ≈ 38°C

e) Estimate the Celsius temperature that corresponds to a Fahrenheit temperature of 0°.   ≈ −18°C

73. Determine the equation of the line with y-intercept at 5 that is parallel to the line whose equation is $2x + y = 6$. Explain how you determined your answer. $y = -2x + 5$

74. Will a line through the points $(60, 30)$ and $(20, 90)$ be parallel to the line with x-intercept at 2 and y-intercept at 3? Explain how you determined your answer.   yes

75. Write an equation of the line parallel to the graph of $3x - 4y = 6$ that passes through the point $(-8, -1)$.

76. Determine the equation of the straight line that intersects the greatest number of shaded points on the following graph.

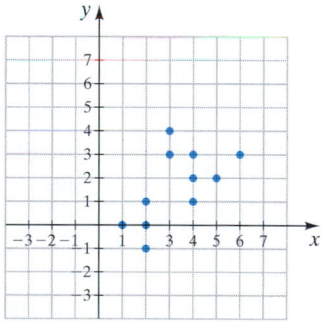

72. b) $F = \dfrac{9}{5}C + 32$ 75. $y = \dfrac{3}{4}x + 5$ 76. $y = x - 3$

Group Activity

Discuss and answer Exercise 77 as a group, according to the instructions.

77. Consider the equation $-3x + 2y = 4$.

a) Group member 1: Explain how to graph this equation by plotting points. Then graph the equation by plotting points.

b) Group member 2: Explain how to graph this equation using the intercepts. Then graph the equation using the intercepts.

c) Group member 3: Explain how to graph this equation using the slope and y-intercept. Then graph the equation using the slope and y-intercept.

d) As a group, compare your graphs. Did you all obtain the same graph? If not, determine why.   See graphing answer section.

Cumulative Review Exercises

[1.5] **78.** Insert either $>$, $<$, or $=$ in the shaded area to make the statement true: $|-4|$ ▨ $|-9|$. $<$

[1.8] *Indicate whether each statement is true or false.*

79. The product of two negative numbers is always a positive number.   T

80. The sum of two negative numbers is always a negative number.   T

81. The difference of two negative numbers is always a negative number.   F

82. The quotient of two negative numbers is always a negative number.   F

[1.9] **83.** Evaluate 4^3.   64

[2.6] **84.** Solve $i = prt$ for r. $r = \dfrac{i}{pt}$

4.5 Graphing Linear Inequalities

1 Graph linear inequalities in two variables.

1 Graph Linear Inequalities in Two Variables

A **linear inequality** occurs when the equal sign in a linear equation is replaced with an inequality sign.

Examples of Linear Inequalities in Two Variables

$$3x + 2y > 4 \qquad\qquad -x + 3y < -2$$
$$-x + 4y \geq 3 \qquad\qquad 4x - y \leq 4$$

TEACHING TIP
Point out that the line divides the co-ordinate plane into two regions: one region above the line and one region below the line.

> ### To Graph a Linear Inequality in Two Variables
>
> **1.** Replace the inequality symbol with an equal sign.
>
> **2.** Draw the graph of the equation in step 1. If the original inequality contained the symbol $\geq$ or $\leq$, draw the graph using a solid line. If the original inequality contained the symbol $>$ or $<$, draw the graph using a dashed line.
>
> **3.** Select any point not on the line and determine whether this point is a solution to the original inequality. If the selected point is a solution, shade the region on the side of the line containing this point. If the selected point does not satisfy the inequality, shade the region on the side of the line not containing this point.

INSTRUCTOR EXAMPLE
Graph the inequality $y < x - 1$.

Ans.:

EXAMPLE 1 ▶ Graph the inequality $y < 2x - 4$.

Solution   First we graph the equation $y = 2x - 4$ (**Fig. 4.55**). Since the original inequality contains an is-less-than sign, $<$, we use a dashed line when drawing the graph. The dashed line indicates that the points on this line are not solutions to the inequality $y < 2x - 4$.

Next we select a point not on the line and determine whether this point satisfies the inequality. Often the easiest point to use is the origin, $(0, 0)$. In the check we will use the symbol $\overset{?}{<}$ until we determine whether the statement is true or false.

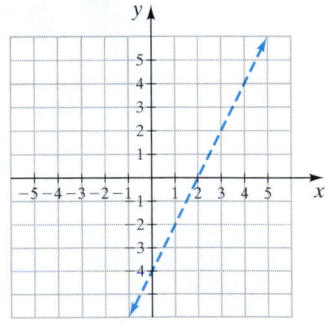

FIGURE 4.55

$$y < 2x - 4$$

Checkpoint

$$0 \overset{?}{<} 2(0) - 4$$

$$0 \overset{?}{<} 0 - 4$$

$$0 < -4 \qquad \textit{False}$$

Since 0 is not less than -4, the point $(0, 0)$ does not satisfy the inequality. The solution will therefore be all the points on the opposite side of the line from the point $(0, 0)$. We shade this region (**Fig. 4.56**).

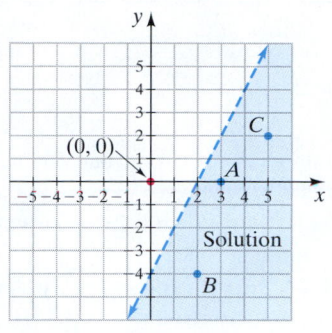

FIGURE 4.56

Every point in the shaded region satisfies the given inequality. Let's check a few selected points A, B, and C.

Point A	Point B	Point C
$(3, 0)$	$(2, -4)$	$(5, 2)$
$y < 2x - 4$	$y < 2x - 4$	$y < 2x - 4$
$0 \overset{?}{<} 2(3) - 4$	$-4 \overset{?}{<} 2(2) - 4$	$2 \overset{?}{<} 2(5) - 4$
$0 < 2$ *True*	$-4 < 0$ *True*	$2 < 6$ *True*

All points in the shaded region in **Figure 4.56** satisfy the inequality $y < 2x - 4$. The points in the unshaded region to the left of the dashed line would satisfy the inequality $y > 2x - 4$. The points on the line itself would satisfy the equation $y = 2x - 4$.

▸ **Now Try Exercise 11**

EXAMPLE 2 ▸ Graph the inequality $y \geq -\dfrac{1}{2}x$.

Solution Graph the equation $y = -\dfrac{1}{2}x$. Since the inequality symbol is $\geq$, we use a solid line to indicate that the points on the line are solutions to the inequality (**Fig. 4.57**). Since the point $(0, 0)$ is on the line, we cannot select it as our test point. Let's select the point $(3, 1)$.

$$y \geq -\frac{1}{2}x$$

Checkpoint
$$1 \overset{?}{\geq} -\frac{1}{2}(3)$$

$$1 \geq -\frac{3}{2} \qquad \textit{True}$$

Since the ordered pair $(3, 1)$ satisfies the inequality, every point on the same side of the line as $(3, 1)$ will also satisfy the inequality $y \geq -\dfrac{1}{2}x$. We shade this region (**Fig. 4.58**).

Every point in the shaded region as well as every point on the line satisfies the inequality.

FIGURE 4.57

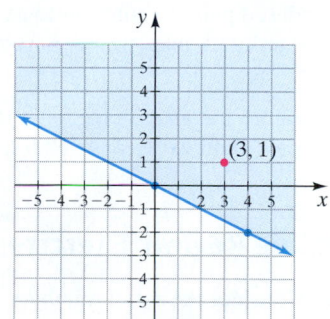

FIGURE 4.58

▸ **Now Try Exercise 9**

In some of the exercises you may need to solve the inequality for y before graphing. For example, to graph $-2x + y < -4$ you would solve the inequality for y to obtain $y < 2x - 4$. Then you would graph the inequality $y < 2x - 4$. Note that $y < 2x - 4$ was graphed in **Figure 4.56**.

TEACHING TIP
After discussing Example 2, ask, "What inequality describes the unshaded region?"

INSTRUCTOR EXAMPLE

Graph the inequality $y \geq -\dfrac{1}{3}x$.

Ans.:

TEACHING TIP
Have students graph $3x - y > 6$. Be sure they remember to change the inequality when multiplying or dividing by a negative number.

EXERCISE SET 4.5

MathXL®   MyMathLab

Concept/Writing Exercises

1. When graphing inequalities that contain either $\leq$ or $\geq$, explain why the points on the line will be solutions to the inequality.   Points on the line satisfy the $=$ part of the inequality.

2. When graphing inequalities that contain either $<$ or $>$, explain why the points on the line will not be solutions to the

inequality.   Points on line satisfy equation ($=$) but not any inequality that is strictly greater than or less than.

3. How do the graphs of $2x + 3y > 6$ and $2x + 3y < 6$ differ?   shading on opposite sides of the line

4. How do the graphs of $4x - 3y < 6$ and $4x - 3y \leq 6$ differ?   first graph, dashed line; second, solid line

Practice the Skills

Graph each inequality.   **5–24.** See graphing answer section.

5. $y > -3$

6. $y < \dfrac{7}{2}$

7. $x \geq \dfrac{3}{2}$

8. $x < -1$

9. $y \leq 3x$

10. $y > -2x$

11. $y < x - 4$

12. $y < 2x + 1$

13. $y < -3x + 4$

14. $y \geq 2x - 3$

15. $y \geq \dfrac{1}{2}x - 4$

16. $y > -\dfrac{x}{2} + 2$

17. $y > \dfrac{1}{2}x - 2$

18. $y > \dfrac{1}{3}x + 1$

19. $3x - 2 < y$

20. $y - 5 \leq -3x$

21. $2x + y \leq 3$

22. $x + y > -2$

23. $3y > 2x - 3$

24. $4x - 2y \leq 6$

Problem Solving

25. Determine whether $(4, 2)$ is a solution to each inequality.
  a) $2x + 4y < 16$ no
  b) $2x + 4y > 16$ no
  c) $2x + 4y \geq 16$ yes
  d) $2x + 4y \leq 16$ yes

26. Determine whether $(-3, 7)$ is a solution to each inequality.
  a) $-2x + 3y < 9$ no
  b) $-2x + 3y > 9$ yes
  c) $-2x + 3y \geq 9$ yes
  d) $-2x + 3y \leq 9$ no

27. If an ordered pair is not a solution to the inequality $ax + by < c$, must the ordered pair be a solution to $ax + by > c$? Explain.   no

28. If an ordered pair is not a solution to the inequality $ax + by \leq c$, must the ordered pair be a solution to $ax + by > c$? Explain.   yes

29. If an ordered pair is a solution to $ax + by > c$, is it possible for the ordered pair to be a solution to $ax + by \leq c$? Explain.   no

30. Is it possible for an ordered pair to be a solution to both $ax + by < c$ and $ax + by > c$? Explain.   no

31. Determine whether the given phrase means: less than, less than or equal to, greater than, or greater than or equal to.
  a) no more than   less than or equal to
  b) no less than   greater than or equal to
  c) at most   less than or equal to
  d) at least   greater than or equal to

32. Consider the two inequalities $2x + 1 > 5$ and $2x + y > 5$.
  a) How many variables does the inequality $2x + 1 > 5$ contain?   1
  b) How many variables does the inequality $2x + y > 5$ contain?   2
  c) What is the solution to $2x + 1 > 5$? Indicate the solution on a number line. $x > 2$;
  d) Graph $2x + y > 5$.   See graphing answers section.

33. Which of the following inequalities have the same graphs? Explain how you determined your answer.
  a) $2x - y > 4$
  b) $-2x + y < -4$
  c) $y < 2x - 4$
  d) $-2y + 4x < -8$

  a), b), and **c)**

Cumulative Review Exercises

[1.4]   **34.** Consider the set of numbers

$$\left\{ 2, -5, 0, \sqrt{7}, \frac{2}{5}, -6.3, \sqrt{3}, -\frac{23}{34} \right\}$$

List those that are
  a) natural numbers;   2
  b) whole numbers;   2, 0
  c) rational numbers;
  d) irrational numbers; $\sqrt{7}, \sqrt{3}$
  e) real numbers.

[2.5]   **35.** Solve $3(x - 2) + 4x = 5x - 2$.   2

[3.2]   **36. Taxi Ride** The cost of a taxi ride is $2.75 for the first mile and $1.95 for each additional mile or part thereof. Find the maximum distance Alexis Nagle can ride in the taxi if he has only $29.   14 mi

[4.4]   **37.** Determine the slope and y-intercept of the line represented by the equation $3x - 4y = 20$.

34. c) $2, -5, 0, \frac{2}{5}, -6.3, -\frac{23}{34}$ **e)** $2, -5, 0, \sqrt{7}, \frac{2}{5}, -6.3, \sqrt{3}, -\frac{23}{34}$ **37.** slope: $\frac{3}{4}$; y-intercept; $(0, -5)$

4.6 Functions

1 Find the domain and range of a relation.

2 Recognize functions.

3 Evaluate functions.

4 Graph linear functions.

In this section we introduce relations and functions. As you will learn shortly, a function is a special type of relation. Functions are a common thread in mathematics courses from algebra through calculus. In this section we give an informal introduction to relations and functions.

1 Find the Domain and Range of a Relation

First we will discuss **relations**.

> **Relation**
>
> A **relation** is any set of ordered pairs.

Since a relation is *any* set of points, *every graph will represent a relation.*

TEACHING TIP
You may want to describe relations in terms of nonnumeric relations such as (x, y), where x's biological daughter is y or (x, y) where x's biological mother is y.

Examples of Relations

$$\{(2, 5), (4, 6), (5, 9), (7, 12)\}$$
$$\{(1, 2), (2, 2), (3, 2), (4, 2)\}$$
$$\{(3, 2), (3, 3), (3, 4), (3, 5), (3, 6)\}$$

In the ordered pair (x, y), the x and y are called the **components of the ordered pair**. The **domain** of a relation is the set of *first components* in the set of ordered pairs. For example,

Relation	Domain
$\{(2, 5), (4, 6), (5, 9), (7, 12)\}$	$\{2, 4, 5, 7\}$
$\{(1, 2), (2, 2), (3, 2), (4, 2)\}$	$\{1, 2, 3, 4\}$
$\{(3, 2), (3, 3), (3, 4), (3, 5), (3, 6)\}$	$\{3\}$

The **range** of a relation is the set of *second components* in the set of ordered pairs. For example,

Relation	Range
$\{(2, 5), (4, 6), (5, 9), (7, 12)\}$	$\{5, 6, 9, 12\}$
$\{(1, 2), (2, 2), (3, 2), (4, 2)\}$	$\{2\}$
$\{(3, 2), (3, 3), (3, 4), (3, 5), (3, 6)\}$	$\{2, 3, 4, 5, 6\}$

In relations, the sets can contain elements other than numbers. For example,

Relation

$$\{(\text{Carol, Seat 1}), (\text{Mary, Seat 2}), (\text{John, Seat 3}), (\text{Olonso, Seat 4})\}$$

Domain

$$\{\text{Carol, Mary, John, Olonso}\}$$

Range

$$\{\text{Seat 1, Seat 2, Seat 3, Seat 4}\}$$

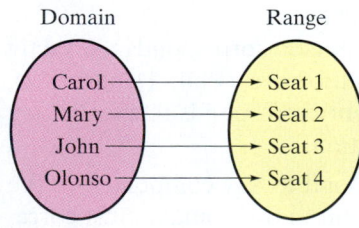

Domain   Range

FIGURE 4.59

Figure 4.59 illustrates the relation between the person and the seat number.

2 Recognize Functions

Now we are ready to discuss functions. Consider the relation shown in **Figure 4.59**. Notice that each member in the domain corresponds with exactly one member of the range. That is, each person is assigned to exactly one seat. This is an example of a **function**.

> ### Function
>
> A **function** is a set of ordered pairs in which each first component corresponds to exactly one second component.

Since a function is a special type of relation, our discussion of domain and range applies to functions. In the definition of a function, the set of first components represents the domain of the function and the set of second components represents the range of the function.

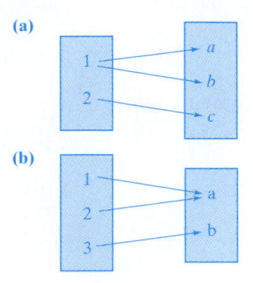
EXAMPLE 1 ▶ Consider the relations in **Figures 4.60a)** through **d)**. Which relations are functions?

(a)

(b)

(c)

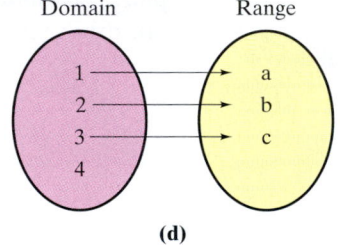

(d)

FIGURE 4.60

Solution

a) If we wished, we could represent the information given in the figure as the following set of ordered pairs: {(1, $0.20), (2, $0.40), (3, $0.60), (4, $0.80)}. Notice that each first component corresponds to exactly one second component. Therefore, this relation is a function.

b) If we look at **Figure 4.60b**, we can see that Todd does *not* correspond to exactly one car. If we were to list the set of ordered pairs to represent this relation, the set would contain the ordered pairs (Todd, Dodge) and (Todd, Toyota). Therefore, each first component does not correspond to exactly one second component and this relation is not a function.

c) Although both Maria and Gwen share a table, each person corresponds to exactly one table. If we listed the ordered pairs we would have (Phil, 1), (José, 2), (Maria, 3), (Gwen, 3). Note that each *first* component corresponds to exactly one second component. Therefore, this relation is a function.

d) Since the number 4 in the domain does not correspond to any component in the range, this relation is not a function. *Every* component in the domain must correspond to exactly one component in the range for the relation to be a function.

▶ **Now Try Exercise 19**

The functions given in Example 1**a)** and 1**c)** were determined by looking at correspondences in figures. Most functions have an infinite number of ordered pairs and are usually defined with an equation (or rule) that tells how to obtain the second component when you are given the first component. In Example 2, we determine a function from the information provided.

EXAMPLE 2 ▸ **Cost of Apples** Assume each apple costs $0.30. Write a function to determine the cost, c, when n apples are purchased.

Solution   When one apple is purchased, the cost is $0.30. When two apples are purchased, the cost is $2(\$0.30)$, and when n apples are purchased, the cost is $n(\$0.30)$ or $\$0.30n$. The function $c = 0.30n$ will give the cost, c, in dollars, when n apples are purchased. Note that for any value of n, there is exactly one value of c.

▸ **Now Try Exercise 51**

EXAMPLE 3 ▸ Determine whether the following sets of ordered pairs are functions.

  a) $\{(4, 5), (3, 2), (-2, -3), (2, 5), (1, 6)\}$

  b) $\{(4, 5), (3, 2), (-2, -3), (4, 1), (5, -2)\}$

Solution

  a) Since each first component corresponds with exactly one second component, this set of ordered pairs is a function.

  b) The ordered pairs $(4, 5)$ and $(4, 1)$ contain the same first component. Therefore, each first component does not correspond to exactly one second component, and this set of ordered pairs is not a function.

▸ **Now Try Exercise 13**

In **Figures 4.61a** and **4.61b** we plot the ordered pairs from Example 3a) and 3b), respectively.

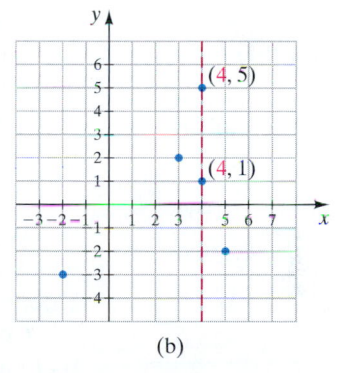

           (a)   (b)

          First set of ordered pairs,   Second set of ordered pairs,

FIGURE 4.61   Function   Not a function

Consider **Figure 4.61a**. If a vertical line is drawn through each point, no vertical line intersects more than one point. This indicates that no two ordered pairs have the same first (or x) coordinate and that each value of x in the domain corresponds to exactly one value of y in the range. Therefore, this set of points represents a function.

    Now look at **Figure 4.61b**. If a vertical line is drawn through each point, one vertical line passes through two points. The dashed red vertical line intersects both $(4, 5)$ and $(4, 1)$. Each element in the domain *does not* correspond to exactly one element in the range. The number 4 in the domain corresponds to two numbers, 5 and 1, in the range. Therefore, this set of ordered pairs does *not* represent a function.

    To determine whether a graph represents a function, we can use the **vertical line test** just described.

> ### Vertical Line Test
>
> If a vertical line can be drawn through any part of a graph and the vertical line intersects another part of the graph, then each value of x does not correspond to exactly one value of y and the graph does not represent a function.
>
> If a vertical line cannot be drawn to intersect the graph at more than one point, each value of x corresponds to exactly one value of y and the graph represents a function.

EXAMPLE 4 ▶ Use the vertical line test to determine which graphs represent functions.

a) b) c)

Solution

a) b) c)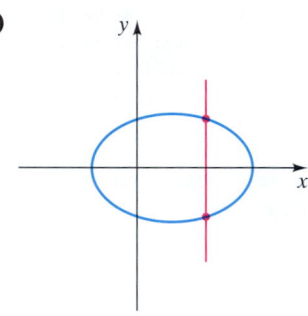

The graphs in parts **a)** and **b)** represent functions since it is not possible to draw a vertical line that intersects the graph at more than one point. The graph in part **c)** does not represent a function since a vertical line can be drawn to intersect the graph at more than one point.

▶ **Now Try Exercise 31**

We see functions all around us. Consider the information provided in **Table 4.1**, which may apply to some salespeople. This table of values is a function because each amount of sales corresponds to exactly one income.

Consider the graph shown in **Figure 4.62**. This graph represents a function. Notice that each year corresponds to a unique number of people employed in the securities industry. Both graphs in **Figure 4.63** represent functions. Each graph passes the vertical line test.

TABLE 4.1 Monthly Income

Sales (dollars)	Income (dollars)
0	$1500
$5000	$1800
$10,000	$2100
$15,000	$2400
$20,000	$2700
$25,000	$3000

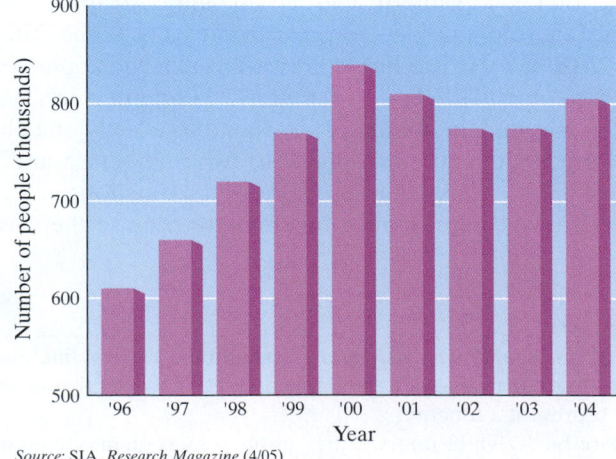

FIGURE 4.62

FIGURE 4.63

3 Evaluate Functions

When a function is represented by an equation, it is often convenient to use **function notation**, $f(x)$. If we were to graph $y = x + 2$, we would see that it is a function because its graph passes the vertical line test. The value of y in the equation or function depends on the value of x. Therefore, we say that y is a function of x, and we can write $y = f(x)$. The notation $y = f(x)$ is used to show that y is a function of the variable x. If we wish, we can write

$$y = f(x) = x + 2 \quad \text{or simply} \quad f(x) = x + 2$$

The notation $f(x)$ is read "f of x" *and does not mean f times x*.

To evaluate a function for a specific value of x, we substitute that value for x everywhere the x appears in the function. For example, to evaluate the function $f(x) = x + 2$ at $x = 1$, we do the following:

$$f(x) = x + 2$$
$$f(1) = 1 + 2 = 3$$

Thus, when x is 1, $f(x)$ or y is 3.

When $x = 4$, $f(x)$ or $y = 6$, as illustrated below.

$$y = f(x) = x + 2$$
$$y = f(4) = 4 + 2 = 6$$

The notation $f(1)$ is read "f of 1" and $f(4)$ is read "f of 4."

INSTRUCTOR EXAMPLE
Let $f(x) = x^2 - x + 2$.
Find **a)** $f(-1)$ and **b)** $f(3)$.
c) If $x = 4$, determine the value of y.
Ans.: a) 4 **b)** 8 **c)** 14

EXAMPLE 5 ▶ For the function $f(x) = x^2 + 4x - 9$, find **a)** $f(3)$ and **b)** $f(-6)$. **c)** If $x = -1$, determine the value of y.

Solution

a) Substitute 3 for each x in the function, and then evaluate.

$$f(x) = x^2 + 4x - 9$$
$$f(3) = 3^2 + 4(3) - 9$$
$$= 9 + 12 - 9 = 12$$

TEACHING TIP
Point out that $f(1)$ is a shorthand for "Evaluate the expression that the function equals for $x = 1$."

b)
$$f(x) = x^2 + 4x - 9$$
$$f(-6) = (-6)^2 + 4(-6) - 9$$
$$= 36 - 24 - 9 = 3$$

c) Since $y = f(x)$, we evaluate $f(x)$ at -1.

$$f(x) = x^2 + 4x - 9$$
$$f(-1) = (-1)^2 + 4(-1) - 9$$
$$= 1 - 4 - 9 = -12$$

Thus, when $x = -1$, $y = -12$.

▶ **Now Try Exercise 39**

4 Graph Linear Functions

The graphs of all equations of the form $y = ax + b$ will be straight lines that are functions. Therefore, we may refer to equations of the form $y = ax + b$ as **linear functions**. Equations of the form $f(x) = ax + b$ are also linear functions since $f(x)$ is the same as y. We may graph linear functions as shown in Example 6.

EXAMPLE 6 ▶ Graph $f(x) = 2x + 4$.

Solution Since $f(x)$ is the same as y, write $y = f(x) = 2x + 4$. Select values for x and find the corresponding values for y or $f(x)$.

$$y = f(x) = 2x + 4$$

Let $x = -3$.	$y = f(-3) = 2(-3) + 4 = -2$
Let $x = 0$.	$y = f(0) = 2(0) + 4 = 4$
Let $x = 1$.	$y = f(1) = 2(1) + 4 = 6$

x	y
-3	-2
0	4
1	6

Now plot the points and draw the graph of the function (**Fig. 4.64**).

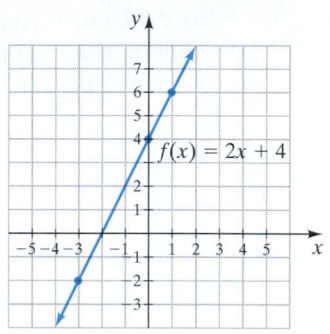

FIGURE 4.64

▶ **Now Try Exercise 45**

EXAMPLE 7 ▶ **Ice Skating Rink** The weekly profit, p, of an ice skating rink is a function of the number of skaters per week, n. The function approximating the profit is $p = f(n) = 8n - 600$, where $0 \le n \le 400$.

a) Construct a graph showing the relationship between the number of skaters and the weekly profit.

b) Estimate the profit if there are 200 skaters in a given week.

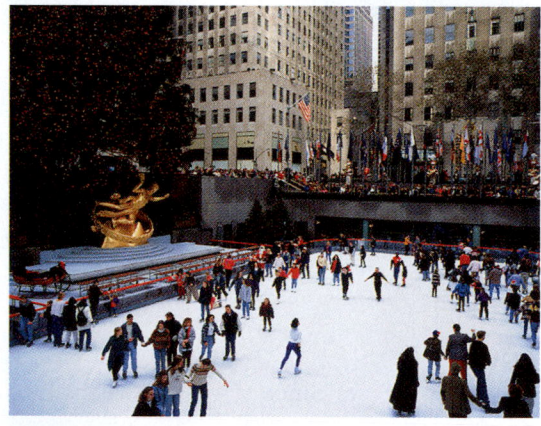

Rockefeller Plaza, New York City

Solution

a) Select values for n, and find the corresponding values for p. Then draw the graph (**Fig. 4.65**). Notice there are no arrowheads on the line because the function is defined only for values of n between 0 and 400 inclusive.

$$p = f(n) = 8n - 600$$

Let $n = 0$.	$p = f(0) = 8(0) - 600 = -600$
Let $n = 100$.	$p = f(100) = 8(100) - 600 = 200$
Let $n = 400$.	$p = f(400) = 8(400) - 600 = 2600$

n	p
0	-600
100	200
400	2600

FIGURE 4.65

b) Using the red dashed line on the graph, we can see that if there are 200 skaters the weekly profit is $1000.

▶ **Now Try Exercise 59**

EXERCISE SET 4.6

MathXL®   MyMathLab

Concept/Writing Exercises

1. What is a relation?   any set of ordered pairs
2. Is every graph in the Cartesian coordinate system a relation? Explain.   yes
3. What is a function?
4. Is every graph in the Cartesian coordinate system a function? Explain.   no
5. a) What is the domain of a relation or function?
   b) What is the range of a relation or function?
6. a) Is every relation a function?   no
   b) Is every function a relation? Explain your answer.   yes
7. If two distinct ordered pairs in a relation have the same first coordinate, can the relation be a function? Explain.   no
8. In a function is it necessary for each value of y in the range to correspond to exactly one value of x in the domain? Explain.

3. a set of ordered pairs in which each first component corresponds to exactly one second component   5. a) the set of first components in the set of ordered pairs   b) the set of second components in the set of ordered pairs   8. no

Practice the Skills

Determine which of the relations are also functions. Give the domain and range of each relation or function.

9. $\{(5, 4), (2, 2), (3, 5), (1, 3), (4, 1)\}$
   function, D: $\{1, 2, 3, 4, 5\}$, R: $\{1, 2, 3, 4, 5\}$

10. $\{(2, 0), (4, 9), (3, 2), (2, 5), (5, 1)\}$
    relation, D: $\{2, 3, 4, 5\}$, R: $\{0, 1, 2, 9\}$

11. $\{(5, 5), (3, 0), (3, 2), (1, 4), (2, 4), (7, -2)\}$
    relation, D: $\{1, 2, 3, 5, 7\}$, R: $\{-2, 0, 2, 4, 5\}$

12. $\{(-2, 1), (1, -3), (3, 4), (4, 5), (-2, 0)\}$
    relation, D: $\{-2, 1, 3, 4\}$, R: $\{-3, 0, 1, 4, 5\}$

13. $\{(5, 0), (4, -4), (0, -1), (3, 2), (1, 1)\}$
    function, D: $\{0, 1, 3, 4, 5\}$, R: $\{-4, -1, 0, 1, 2\}$

14. $\{(-6, 3), (-3, 4), (0, 3), (5, 2), (3, 5), (2, 3)\}$
    function, D: $\{-6, -3, 0, 2, 3, 5\}$, R: $\{2, 3, 4, 5\}$

15. $\{(3, 0), (0, -3), (1, 5), (1, 0), (1, 2)\}$
    relation, D: $\{0, 1, 3\}$, R: $\{-3, 0, 2, 5\}$

16. $\{(4, 5), (3, -7), (4, -9), (3, -3)\}$
    relation, D: $\{3, 4\}$, R: $\{-9, -7, -3, 5\}$

17. $\{(0, 3), (1, 3), (2, 3), (3, 3), (4, 3)\}$
    function, D: $\{0, 1, 2, 3, 4\}$, R: $\{3\}$

18. $\{(3, 5), (2, 4), (1, 0), (0, 1), (-1, 4)\}$
    function, D: $\{-1, 0, 1, 2, 3\}$, R: $\{0, 1, 4, 5\}$

In the figures in Exercises 19–22, the domain and range of a relation are illustrated. **a)** *Construct a set of ordered pairs that represent the relation.* **b)** *Determine whether the relation is a function. Explain your answer.*

19.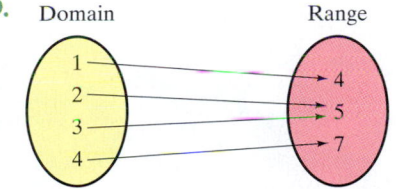

a) $\{(1, 4), (2, 5), (3, 5), (4, 7)\}$
b) function

20.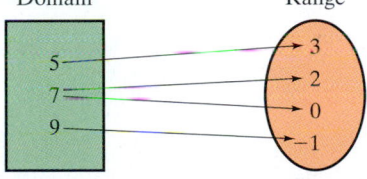

a) $\{(5, 3), (7, 2), (7, 0), (9, -1)\}$
b) not a function

21.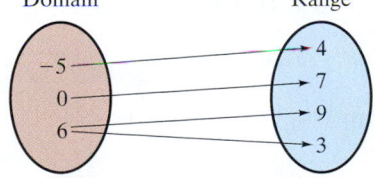

a) $\{(-5, 4), (0, 7), (6, 9), (6, 3)\}$ b) not a function

22.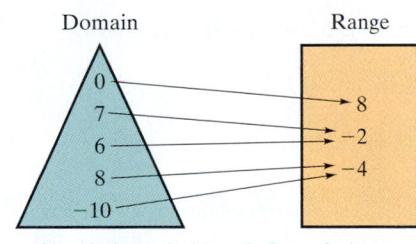

a) $\{(0, 8), (7, -2), (6, -2), (8, -4), (-10, -4)\}$ b) function

Use the vertical line test to determine whether each relation is also a function.

23.

function

24.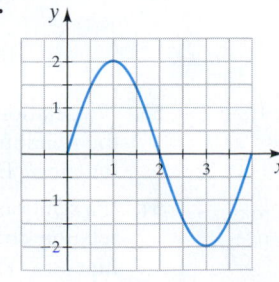

function

25.

not a function

26.

not a function

27.

function

28.

function

29.

function

30.

function

31.

not a function

32.

not a function

33.

function

34.

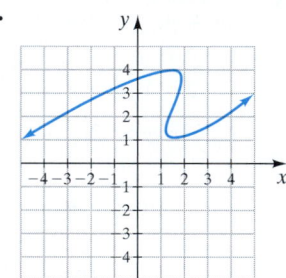

not a function

Evaluate each function at the indicated values.

35. $f(x) = 4x + 2$; find **a)** $f(3)$, **b)** $f(-1)$ **a)** 14 **b)** -2

36. $f(x) = -4x + 7$; find **a)** $f(0)$, **b)** $f(4)$,   **a)** 7 **b)** -9

37. $f(x) = x^2 - 5$; find **a)** $f(6)$, **b)** $f(-3)$ **a)** 31 **b)** 4

38. $f(x) = 2x^2 + 3x - 4$; find **a)** $f(2)$, **b)** $f(-3)$ **a)** 10 **b)** 5

39. $f(x) = 3x^2 - x + 4$; find **a)** $f(0)$, **b)** $f(1)$ **a)** 4 **b)** 6

40. $f(x) = \frac{1}{2}x - 4$; find **a)** $f(10)$, **b)** $f(-8)$ **a)** 1 **b)** -8

41. $f(x) = \frac{x + 4}{2}$; find **a)** $f(2)$, **b)** $f(12)$ **a)** 3 **b)** 8

42. $f(x) = \frac{1}{2}x^2 + 6$; find **a)** $f(4)$, **b)** $f(-6)$ **a)** 14 **b)** 24

Graph each function.   **43.–50.**   See graphing answer section.

43. $f(x) = x + 3$

44. $f(x) = -x + 4$

45. $f(x) = 2x - 1$

46. $f(x) = 4x + 2$

47. $f(x) = -2x + 4$

48. $f(x) = -x + 5$

49. $f(x) = -\frac{1}{2}x + 2$

50. $f(x) = -4x$

Problem Solving

51. Cost of Oranges Oranges cost $0.35 each. Write a function to determine the cost, c, when n oranges are purchased. $c = 0.35n$

52. Cost of Shirts Shirts cost $19.95 each. Write a function to determine the cost, c, when n shirts are purchased. $c = 19.95n$

53. If a relation consists of six ordered pairs and the domain of the relation consists of five values of x, can the relation be a function? Explain.   No, each x cannot have a unique value of y.

54. If a relation consists of six ordered pairs and the range of the relation consists of five values of y, can the relation be a function? Explain.   Yes, each x may have a unique value of y.

In exercises 55–56, are the graphs functions? Explain.

55. yes

Hybrid Cars Registered in the U.S.

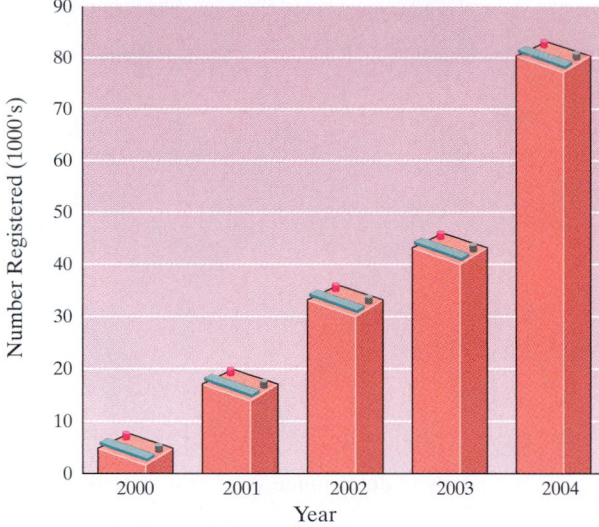

Source: R.L. Polk & Co.

56. yes

Social Security

Source: Social Security Administration   * Projections for 2010 and beyond

57. Babysitting Jacci Cavanaugh gets paid $8 per hour for babysitting. Her weekly income, I, from babysitting can be represented using the function $I = 8h$, where h is the number of hours she babysits.

a) Draw a graph of the function for times up to and including 60 hours. See graphing answer section.

b) Estimate her weekly income from babysitting if she babysits for 20 hours per week. $160

58. Bike Riding Rachel Falk and Tony Mathias go bike riding together. If they ride at a constant rate of 8 miles per hour, the distance they travel, d, can be found by the function $d = 8t$, where t is time in hours.

a) Draw a graph of the function for times up to and including 6 hours. See graphing answer section.

b) Estimate the distance they will travel if they ride for 4 hours. 32 mi

59. Selling a House The Ferraras are selling their house. The cost they will pay to the realtor is 6% of the selling price of the house, p. They expect to have $2000 in other selling costs. Therefore, the total cost, C, to the Ferreras for selling their house can be represented by the function

$$C = 2000 + 0.06p$$

a) Draw a graph of the function for selling prices from $0 up to and including $200,000. See graphing answer section.

b) Estimate the total cost if the selling price is $150,000. $11,000

60. Vacationing Frank Duomo plans to take a vacation in the San Diego/Los Angeles area. He determines that the cost, C, of the vacation can be estimated using the function $C = 350n + 400$, where n is the number of days spent in the area.

a) Draw a graph of the function for up to and including 10 days. See graphing answer section.

b) Estimate the cost of a 5-day vacation in the area. $ 2150

Grauman's Chinese Theatre, Hollywood

61. Photo Printer A photo printer costs $120. The cost per picture printed, n, is 40 cents each. Therefore, the total cost, C, of the printer plus the photos printed is $C = 120 + 0.40n$.

a) Draw a graph showing the total cost for up to and including 500 photos. See graphing answer section.

b) If 300 photos are printed, estimate the total cost. $240

62. Auto Registration A state's auto registration fee, f, is $20 plus $15 per 1000 pounds of the vehicle's gross weight. The registration fee is a function of the vehicle's weight, $f = 20 + 0.015w$, where w is the weight of the vehicle in pounds.

a) Draw a graph of the function for vehicle weights up to and including 10,000 pounds. See graphing answer section.

b) Estimate the registration fee of a vehicle whose gross weight is 6000 pounds. $110

63. Singing Sensation A new singing group, Three Forks and a Spoon, signs a recording contract with the Smash Record label. The contract provides a signing bonus of $10,000, plus an 8% royalty on the sales, s, of the group's new record, *There's Mud in Your Eye!* The group's income, i, is a function of its sales, $i = 10,000 + 0.08s$.

a) Draw a graph of the function for sales of up to and including $100,000. See graphing answer section.

b) Estimate the group's income if its sales are $20,000. $11,600

64. Electric Bill A monthly electric bill, m, in dollars, consists of a $20 monthly fee plus $0.07 per kilowatt-hour, k, of electricity used. The amount of the bill is a function of the kilowatt-hours used, $m = 20 + 0.07k$.

a) Draw a graph for up to and including 3000 kilowatt-hours of electricity used in a month. See graphing answer section.

b) Estimate the bill if 2100 kilowatt-hours of electricity are used. $167

Consider the following graphs. Recall from Section 2.8 that an open circle at the end of a line segment means that the endpoint is not included in the answer. A solid circle at the end of a line segment indicates that the endpoint is included in the answer. Determine whether the following graphs are functions. Explain your answer.

65.   yes

66.   no

67.   no

68.   yes

Challenge Problems

69. $f(x) = \dfrac{1}{2}x^2 - 3x + 5$; find

    a) $f\left(\dfrac{1}{2}\right)$, $\dfrac{29}{8}$

    b) $f\left(\dfrac{2}{3}\right)$, $\dfrac{29}{9}$

    c) $f(0.4)$ 3.88

70. $f(x) = x^2 + 2x - 4$; find

    a) $f(1)$, -1

    b) $f(2)$, 4

    c) $f(a)$. $a^2 + 2a - 4$

    Explain how you determined your answer to part **c)**.

Group Activity

Discuss and answer Exercises 71 and 72 as a group.

71. Submit three real-life examples (different from those already given) of a quantity that is a function of another. Write each as a function, and indicate what each variable represents.   Answer will vary.

72. Postage In January 2006, the cost of mailing a first class letter was 39 cents for the first ounce and 24 cents for each additional ounce. A graph showing the cost of mailing a letter first class is pictured below.

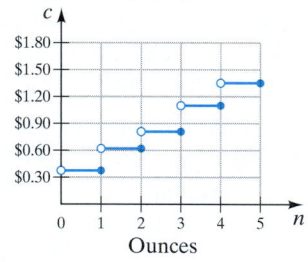

Ounces

a) Does this graph represent a function? Explain your answer.   Yes, each n has a unique value of c.

b) From the graph, estimate the cost of mailing a 4-ounce package first class. $1.10

c) Determine the exact cost of mailing a 4-ounce package first class. $1.11

d) From the graph, estimate the cost of mailing a 3.6-ounce package first class. $1.10

e) Determine the exact cost of mailing a 3.6-ounce package first class. $1.11

Cumulative Review Exercises

[1.3]   **73.** Evaluate $\dfrac{4}{9} - \dfrac{3}{7}$. $\dfrac{1}{63}$

[1.10]   **74.** Name each illustrated property.

    a) $2 + 5 = 5 + 2$ commutative property of addition

    b) $(x + 2) + 3 = x + (2 + 3)$

    c) $2(x + 7) = 2x + 2 \cdot 7$ distributive property

[2.5]   **75.** Solve $2x - 3(x + 2) = 8$. -14

[4.1]   **76.** What is a graph?   An illustration of a set of points whose coordinates satisfy an equation.

74. b) associative property of addition

Chapter 4 Summary

IMPORTANT FACTS AND CONCEPTS	EXAMPLES

Section 4.1

The **Cartesian coordinate system** is formed by two axes drawn perpendicular to each other. The point of intersection is called the **origin**. The horizontal axis is called the **x-axis**. The vertical axis is called the **y-axis**. **Ordered pairs** are of the form (x, y).

Cartesian coordinate system

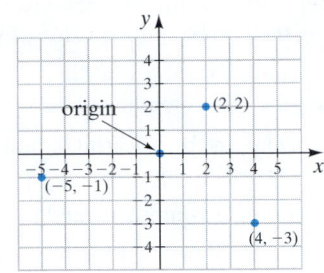

A **linear equation in two variables** is an equation that can be put in the form

$$ax + by = c$$

where a, b, and c are real numbers. This form is also called the **standard form** for a linear equation.

$$3x + 7y = 2, \quad -2x - y = 9$$

A **graph** of an equation in two variables is an illustration of a set of points whose coordinates satisfy the equation.
Points that lie in a straight line are **collinear**.

Every point on the graph satisfies the equation $y = 2x - 1$.

The points on the graph are collinear and the graph is a straight line.

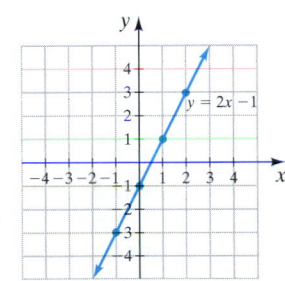

Section 4.2

To Graph Linear Equations by Plotting Points

1. Solve the linear equation for the variable y.
2. Select a value for the variable x. Substitute this value in the equation for x and find the corresponding value of y. Record the ordered pair (x, y).
3. Repeat step 2 with two different values of x.
4. Plot the three ordered pairs.
5. Draw a straight line through the three points. Draw arrowheads on each end of the line to show that the line continues indefinitely in both directions.

Graph $y = -x + 2$.

Table

x	y
-1	3
0	2
2	0

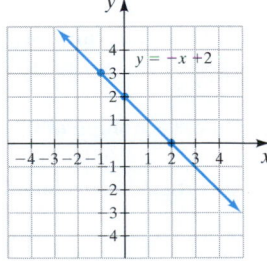

The **x-intercept** is the point where the graph crosses the x-axis.
The **y-intercept** is the point where the graph crosses the y-axis.

On the graph above, the x-intercept is $(2, 0)$ and the y-intercept is $(0, 2)$.

IMPORTANT FACTS AND CONCEPTS	EXAMPLES

Section 4.2 (continued)

To Graph Linear Equations using the x- and y-Intercepts

1. Find the y-intercept by setting x in the given equation equal to 0 and finding the corresponding value of y.

2. Find the x-intercept by setting y in the given equation equal to 0 and finding the corresponding value of x.

3. Determine a checkpoint by selecting a nonzero value for x and finding the corresponding value of y.

4. Plot the y-intercept, the x-intercept, and the checkpoint.

5. Draw a straight line through the three points. Draw an arrowhead at both ends of the line.

Graph $4x + 2y = 8$ using the x- and y-intercepts.

Let $x = 0$:
$$4(0) + 2y = 8$$
$$2y = 8$$
$$y = 4.$$
y-intercept: $(0, 4)$

Let $y = 0$:
$$4x + 2(0) = 8$$
$$4x = 8$$
$$x = 2$$
x-intercept: $(2, 0)$

Checkpoint: $(1, 2)$

Horizontal Line

The graph of an equation of the form $y = b$ is a horizontal line whose y-intercept is $(0, b)$.

Vertical Line

The graph of an equation of the form $x = a$ is a vertical line whose x-intercept is $(a, 0)$.

Graph $y = 2$.

Graph $x = -4$.

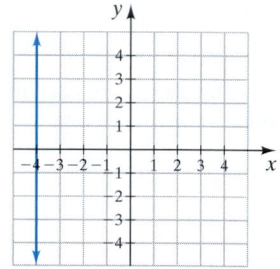

Section 4.3

The **slope of a line** is a ratio of the vertical change to the horizontal change between any two selected points on the line. The slope of a line through the points (x_1, y_1) and (x_2, y_2) is

$$\text{slope} = \frac{\text{change in } y \text{ (vertical change)}}{\text{change in } x \text{ (horizontal change)}} = \frac{y_2 - y_1}{x_2 - x_1}$$

The slope of the line through $(-1, 3)$ and $(5, 7)$ is

$$m = \frac{7 - 3}{5 - (-1)} = \frac{4}{6} = \frac{2}{3}$$

A straight line where the value of y increases as x increases has a **positive slope**.

A straight line where the value of y decreases as x increases has a **negative slope**.

A horizontal line has a **slope of 0**.

The slope of a vertical line is **undefined**.

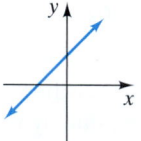

Positive slope
(rises to right)

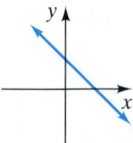

Negative slope
(falls to right)

Slope is 0.
(horizontal line)

Slope is undefined.
(vertical line)

IMPORTANT FACTS AND CONCEPTS	EXAMPLES

Section 4.3 (continued)

Two nonvertical lines with the same slope and different y-intercepts are **parallel lines**. Any two vertical lines are parallel to each other.	The graphs of the equations $y = 2x + 3$ and $y = 2x + 4$ are parallel lines since the graphs have the same slope, 2, and different y-intercepts.
Two lines whose slopes are negative reciprocals of each other are **perpendicular lines**. Any vertical line is perpendicular to any horizontal line.	The graphs of the equations $y = 2x + 4$ and $y = -\dfrac{1}{2}x + 3$ are perpendicular lines since the slopes of the graphs are negative reciprocals of each other.

Section 4.4

Slope-Intercept Form of a Linear Equation $$y = mx + b$$ where m is the slope, and $(0, b)$ is the y-intercept of the line.	The graph of $y = 3x - 4$ has a slope of 3 and a y-intercept of $(0, -4)$. The equation of a line with a slope of $-\dfrac{1}{2}$ and a y-intercept of $(0, 6)$ is $y = -\dfrac{1}{2}x + 6$.
To graph $ax + by = c$, write the equation in slope-intercept form by solving the equation for y. Then use the slope and y-intercept to sketch the graph.	$2x + 4y = 8$ written in slope-intercept form is $y = -\dfrac{1}{2}x + 2$. The slope is $-\dfrac{1}{2}$ and the y-intercept is $(0, 2)$. 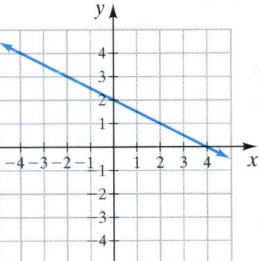
Point-Slope Form of a Linear Equation $$y - y_1 = m(x - x_1)$$ where m is the slope of the line and (x_1, y_1) is a point on the line.	The graph of $y - 7 = \dfrac{5}{6}(x - 3)$ has a slope of $\dfrac{5}{6}$ and contains the point $(3, 7)$.

Section 4.5

A **linear inequality** occurs when the equal sign in a linear equation is replaced with an inequality sign.	$4x - 3y > 1, \quad -x + 2y \le 7$

IMPORTANT FACTS AND CONCEPTS	EXAMPLES

Section 4.5 (continued)

To Graph a Linear Inequality in Two Variables

1. Replace the inequality symbol with an equal sign.

2. Draw the graph of the equation in step 1. If the original inequality symbol is $\geq$ or $\leq$, draw a solid line. If the original inequality symbol is $>$ or $<$, draw a dashed line.

3. Select any point not on the line and determine whether this point is a solution to the original inequality. If the selected point is a solution, shade the region on the side of the line containing this point. If the selected point does not satisfy the inequality, shade the region on the side of the line not containing this point.

Graph $y \leq x + 3$.

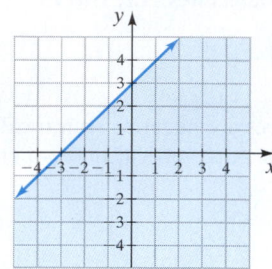

Section 4.6

A **relation** is any set of ordered pairs.

A **function** is a set of ordered pairs in which each first component corresponds to exactly one second component. The **domain** of a relation or function is the set of first components in the set of ordered pairs. The **range** of a relation or function is the set of second components in the set of ordered pairs.

Relation

$$\{(-1, 1), (3, 2), (3, 5), (0, 4)\}$$

Function

$$\{(1, 2), (2, -1), (6, 5), (0, 3)\}$$
Domain: $\{0, 1, 2, 6\}$,   Range: $\{-1, 2, 3, 5\}$

Vertical Line Test

If a vertical line can be drawn through any part of a graph and the vertical line intersects another part of the graph, the graph does not represent a function.
If a vertical line cannot be drawn to intersect the graph at more than one point, the graph represents a function.

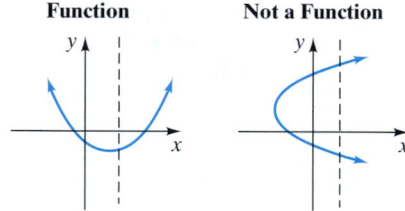

Function   **Not a Function**

When a function is represented by an equation, we can use function notation, $f(x)$.

Given the function $f(x)$, to compute $f(a)$, replace x by a.

$y = ax + b$ is a linear equation.
$f(x) = ax + b$ is a linear function.

The function $y = 3x^2 - x + 7$ can be written as
$f(x) = 3x^2 - x + 7$.

If $f(x) = 3x^2 - x + 7$, then
$f(-1) = 3(-1)^2 - (-1) + 7 = 11$.

Earlier we graphed the equation $y = -\dfrac{1}{2}x + 2$.

Both $y = -\dfrac{1}{2}x + 2$ and $f(x) = -\dfrac{1}{2}x + 2$ have the same graph since y can be replaced by $f(x)$.

Chapter 4 Review Exercises

[4.1]

1. Plot each ordered pair on the same axes.

   a) $A(5, 3)$ b) $B(0, 6)$ c) $C\left(5, \dfrac{1}{2}\right)$

   d) $D(-4, 3)$ e) $E(-6, -1)$ f) $F(-2, 0)$

   See graphing answer section.

2. Determine whether the following points are collinear.

   $(0, -4), (6, 8), (-2, 0), (4, 5)$ no

3. Which of the following ordered pairs satisfy the equation $2x + 3y = 9$?

   a) $\left(5, -\dfrac{1}{3}\right)$ b) $(3, 1)$

   c) $(-2, 4)$ d) $\left(2, \dfrac{5}{3}\right)$

   a), b), d)

[4.2]

4. Find the missing coordinate in the following solutions to $3x - 2y = 8$.

   a) $(2, ?)$ -1
   b) $(0, ?)$ -4
   c) $(?, 5)$ 6
   d) $(?, 0)$ $\dfrac{8}{3}$

Graph each equation using the method of your choice.   **5.–14.** See graphing answer section.

5. $y = 4$
6. $x = 2$
7. $y = 3x$
8. $y = 2x - 1$

9. $y = -2x + 5$
10. $2y + x = 8$
11. $-2x + 3y = 6$
12. $5x + 2y + 10 = 0$

13. $5x + 10y = 20$
14. $\dfrac{2}{3}x = \dfrac{1}{4}y + 20$

[4.3] *Find the slope of the line through the given points.*

15. $(6, -4)$ and $(1, 5)$ $-\dfrac{9}{5}$
16. $(-4, -6)$ and $(8, -7)$ $-\dfrac{1}{12}$
17. $(-2, -3)$ and $(-4, 1)$ -2

18. What is the slope of a horizontal line?   0
19. What is the slope of a vertical line?   undefined

 20. Define the slope of a straight line.   the ratio of the vertical change to the horizontal change between any two points on a line

Find the slope of each line.

21.

-2

22.

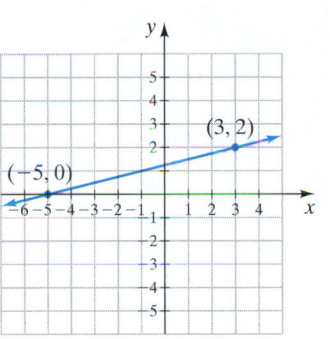

$\dfrac{1}{4}$

Assume that line 1 and line 2 are distinct lines. If m_1 represents the slope of line 1 and m_2 represents the slope of line 2, determine if line 1 and line 2 are parallel, perpendicular, or neither.

23. $m_1 = \dfrac{7}{8}, m_2 = -\dfrac{7}{8}$ neither

24. $m_1 = -3, m_2 = \dfrac{1}{3}$ perpendicular

25. The following graph shows the number of manatee deaths in Florida. Find the slope of the line segment in

   a) red,   214

   b) blue. -49

Manatee Deaths in Florida

Source: Florida Fish and Wildlife Conservation Commission,
www.floridamarine.com

[4.4] *Determine the slope and y-intercept of the graph of each equation.*

26. $6x + 7y = 21$ $-\dfrac{6}{7}, (0, 3)$

27. $2x + 7 = 0$ slope is undefined, no y-intercept

28. $4y + 12 = 0$ $0, (0, -3)$

Write the equation of each line.

29.

$y = 3x - 3$

30.

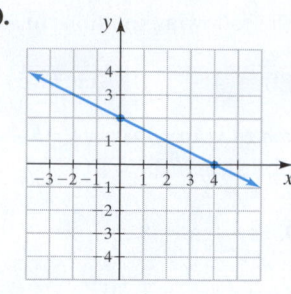

$y = -\dfrac{1}{2}x + 2$

Determine whether each pair of lines is parallel, perpendicular, or neither.

31. $y = 2x - 7$

   $6y = 12x + 18$ parallel

32. $2x - 3y = 15$

   $3x + 2y = 12$ perpendicular

Find the equation of each line with the given properties.

33. Slope $= 3$ through $(2, 7)$ $y = 3x + 1$

34. Slope $= -\dfrac{2}{3}$, through $(3, 2)$ $y = -\dfrac{2}{3}x + 4$

35. Slope $= 0$, through $(6, 2)$ $y = 2$

36. Slope is undefined, through $(4, 1)$ $x = 4$

37. Through $(-2, 4)$ and $(0, -3)$ $y = -\dfrac{7}{2}x - 3$

38. Through $(-5, -2)$ and $(-5, 3)$ $x = -5$

[4.5] *Graph each inequality.*   **39.–44.** See graphing answer section,

39. $y \geq 1$

40. $x < 4$

41. $y < 3x$

42. $y > 2x + 1$

43. $-6x + y \geq 5$

44. $3y + 6 \leq x$

[4.6] *Determine which of the following relations are also functions. Give the domain and range of each.*

45. $\{(3, 2), (4, -3), (1, 5), (2, -1), (6, 4)\}$
   function, D: $\{1, 2, 3, 4, 6\}$, R: $\{-3, -1, 2, 4, 5\}$

46. $\{(3, 1), (4, 2), (4, 5), (6, 1), (7, 0)\}$
   not a function. D: $\{3, 4, 6, 7\}$, R: $\{0, 1, 2, 5\}$

47. $\{(3, 1), (4, 1), (5, 1), (6, 2), (3, -3)\}$
   not a function, D: $\{3, 4, 5, 6\}$, R: $\{-3, 1, 2\}$

48. $\{(5, -2), (3, -2), (4, -2), (9, -2), (-2, -2)\}$
   function, D: $\{-2, 3, 4, 5, 9\}$, R: $\{-2\}$

In Exercises 49 and 50, the domain and range of a relation are illustrated. ***a)*** *Construct a set of ordered pairs that represent the relation.*
b) *Determine whether the relation is a function. Explain your answer.*

49.

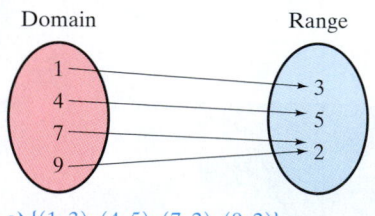

   a) $\{(1, 3), (4, 5), (7, 2), (9, 2)\}$
   b) function

50.

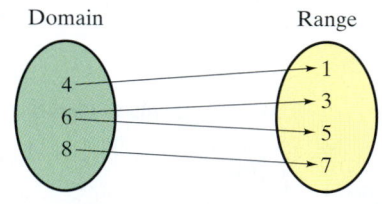

   a) $\{(4, 1), (6, 3), (6, 5), (8, 7)\}$
   b) not a function

In Exercises 51–54, ***a)*** *indicate the domain and range of the relation, and* ***b)*** *indicate if the relation is a function. If it is not a function, explain why.*

51.

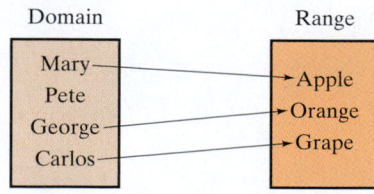

   a) D: {Mary, Pete, George, Carlos}, R: {Apple, Orange, Grape}
   b) not a function

52.

Domain	Range
Sarah	Seat 1
Jacob	Seat 2
Kristen	Seat 3
Erin	Seat 4

   a) D: {Sarah, Jacob, Kristen, Erin}, R: {Seat 1, Seat 2, Seat 3, Seat 4}
   b) not a function

53.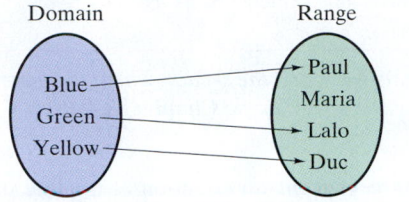

Domain   Range

a) D: {Blue, Green, Yellow}, R: {Paul, Maria, Lalo, Duc}
b) function

54.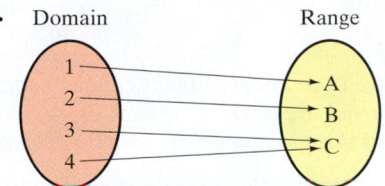

Domain   Range

a) D: {1, 2, 3, 4}, R: {A, B, C}
b) function

Use the vertical line test to determine whether the relation is also a function.

55.

function

56.

function

57.

not a function

58.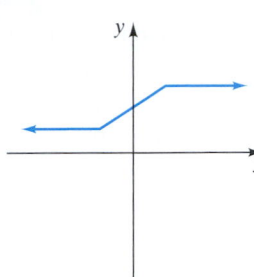

function

Evaluate each function at the indicated values.

59. $f(x) = 6x - 1$; find
a) $f(1)$, 5
b) $f(-5)$ −31

60. $f(x) = -4x - 7$; find
a) $f(-4)$, 9
b) $f(8)$ −39

61. $f(x) = \dfrac{1}{3}x - 5$; find
a) $f(3)$, −4
b) $f(-9)$ −8

62. $f(x) = 2x^2 - 4x + 6$; find
a) $f(3)$, 12
b) $f(-5)$ 76

Determine whether the following graphs are functions. Explain your answer.

63.   yes

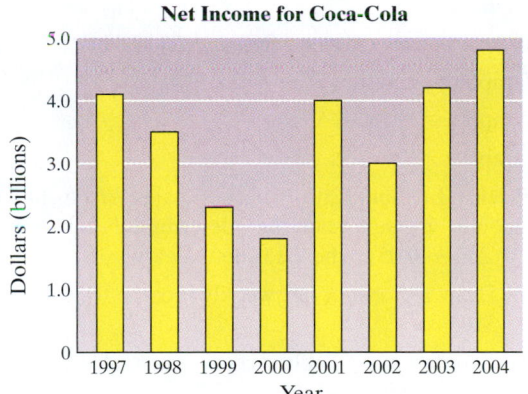

Net Income for Coca-Cola

Source: Coca-Cola, *The Wall Street Journal (4/19/2005)*

64.   yes

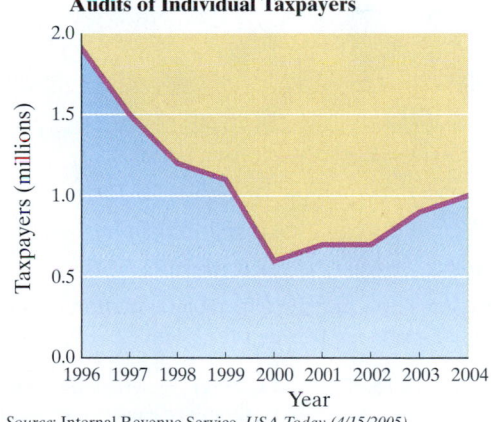

**Internal Revenue Service
Audits of Individual Taxpayers**

Source: Internal Revenue Service, *USA Today (4/15/2005)*

Graph the following functions.

65. $f(x) = 3x - 5$ See graphing answer section.

66. $f(x) = -2x + 3$ See graphing answer section.

67. Stock Purchase A discount stock broker charges $25 plus 3 cents per share of stock bought or sold. A customer's cost, c, in dollars, is a function of the number of shares, n, bought or sold, $c = 25 + 0.03n$.

a) Draw a graph illustrating a customer's cost for up to and including 10,000 shares of stock. See graphing answer section.

b) Estimate the cost if 4000 shares of a stock are purchased.
   $145

68. Dollar Store The monthly profit, p, of an Everything for a Dollar store can be estimated by the function $p = 4x - 1600$, where x represents the number of items sold.

a) Draw a graph of the function for up to and including 1000 items sold. See graphing answer section.

b) Estimate the profit if 500 items are sold. $400

Chapter 4 Practice Test

1. an illustration of a set of points that satisfy an equation   **3. a)** $ax + by = c$
b) $y = mx + b$ **c)** $y - y_1 = m(x - x_1)$

*To find out how well you understand the chapter material, take this practice test. The answers, and the section where the material was initially discussed, are given in the back of the book. Each problem is also fully worked out on the **Chapter Test Prep Video CD.** Review any questions that you answered incorrectly.*

1. What is a graph?

2. In which quadrants do the following points lie?

    a) $(3, -5)$ IV

    b) $\left(-2, \dfrac{1}{2}\right)$ II

3. a) What is the standard form of a linear equation?

    b) What is the slope-intercept form of a linear equation?

    c) What is the point-slope form of a linear equation?

4. Which of the following ordered pairs satisfy the equation $3y = 5x - 9$?

    a) $(4, 2)$

    b) $\left(\dfrac{9}{5}, 0\right)$

    c) $(-1, -10)$

    d) $(0, -3)$ **b)** and **d)**

5. Find the slope of the line through the points $(-2, 5)$ and $(4, -3)$. $-\dfrac{4}{3}$

6. Find the slope and y-intercept of $4x - 9y = 15$. $\dfrac{4}{9}; \left(0, -\dfrac{5}{3}\right)$

7. Write an equation of the graph in the accompanying figure. $y = -x - 1$

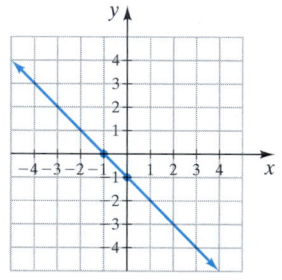

8. Graph $x = -4$.

9. Graph $y = 2$.

10. Graph $y = 3x - 2$ by plotting points.

11. a) Solve the equation $3x - 6y = 12$ for y. $y = \dfrac{1}{2}x - 2$

    b) Graph the equation by plotting points.

12. Graph $3x + 5y = 15$ using the intercepts.

13. Write, in slope-intercept form, an equation of the line with a slope of 4 passing through the point $(2, -5)$. $y = 4x - 13$

14. Write, in slope-intercept form, an equation of the line passing through the points $(3, -1)$ and $(-4, 2)$. $y = -\dfrac{3}{7}x + \dfrac{2}{7}$

15. Determine whether the following equations represent parallel lines. Explain how you determined your answer.

$$2y = 3x - 6 \quad \text{and} \quad y - \dfrac{3}{2}x = -5$$

16. Graph $y = 3x - 4$ using the slope and y-intercept.

17. Graph $4x - 2y = 6$ using the slope and y-intercept.

18. Define a function.

19. a) Determine whether the following relation is a function. Explain your answer.

$$\{(1, 2), (3, -4), (5, 3), (3, 0), (6, 5)\}$$

    b) Give the domain and range of the relation or function.

20. Determine whether the following graphs are functions. Explain how you determined your answer.

    a)

    b)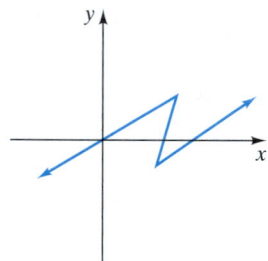

    function   not a function

21. If $f(x) = 2x^2 + 3x + 1$ find **a)** $f(2)$ and **b)** $f(-3)$.   **a)** 15 **b)** 10

22. Graph the function $f(x) = 2x - 4$.

23. Graph $y \geq -3x + 5$.

24. Graph $y < 4x - 2$.

25. Weekly Income Kate Moore, a salesperson, has a weekly income, i, that can be determined by the function $i = 200 + 0.05s$, where s is her weekly sales.

    a) Draw a graph of her weekly income for sales from $0 to $10,000.

    b) Estimate her weekly income if her sales are $5000. $450

8.–10., 11. b), 12., 16.–17., 22.–24., 25. a) See graphing answer section.   **15.** Yes, same slopes but different y-intercepts   **18.** A set of ordered pairs in which each first component corresponds to exactly one second component.   **19. a)** not a function   **b)** D: $\{1, 3, 5, 6\}$, R: $\{-4, 0, 2, 3, 5\}$

Cumulative Review Test

Take the following test and check your answers with those given in the back of the book. Review any questions that you answered incorrectly. The section where the material was covered is indicated after the answer.

1. Write the set of

    a) natural numbers. $\{1, 2, 3, \ldots\}$

    b) whole numbers. $\{0, 1, 2, 3, \ldots\}$

2. Evaluate $4 - 9 - (-10) + 13$.   18

3. Evaluate $(8 \div 4)^3 + 9^2 \div 3$.   35

4. Evaluate $(10 \div 5 \cdot 5 + 5 - 5)^2$.   100

5. Name each indicated property.

    a) $3(x + 2) = 3x + 3 \cdot 2$ distributive property

    b) $a + b = b + a$ commutative property of addition

6. Solve $2x + 5 = 3(x - 5)$.   20

7. Solve $3(x - 1) - (x + 4) = 2x - 7$ all real numbers

8. Solve the inequality $2x - 14 > 5x + 1$. Graph the solution on a number line. $x < -5$; ◄————○——►
                                       -5

9. Chicken Soup At Tsong Hsu's Grocery Store, 3 cans of chicken soup sell for \$1.50. Find the cost of 8 cans.   \$4.00

10. Solve $v = lwh$ for w. $w = \dfrac{v}{lh}$

11. Numbers Eleven increased by twice a number is 19. Find the number.   4

12. Rectangle The length of a rectangle is 3 more than twice the width. Find the length and width of the rectangle if its perimeter is 36 feet. $w = 5$ ft, $l = 13$ ft

13. Running Two runners start at the same point and run in opposite directions. One runs at 6 mph and the other runs at 8 mph. In how many hours will they be 28 miles apart?   2 hr

14. Give three ordered pairs that satisfy the equation $2x + 4y = 8$.

15. Graph $y = 3x - 5$ by plotting points.

14. Answers will vary.   **15.–17., 19.** See graphing answer section.

16. Graph $6x - 3y = -12$ using the intercepts.

17. Graph $y = \dfrac{2}{3}x - 3$ using the slope and y-intercept.

18. Write the equation, in point-slope form, of the line with a slope of 3 passing through the point $(5, 2)$. $y - 2 = 3(x - 5)$

19. Graph the inequality $y \leq 2x - 3$.

20. Determine whether the following relations are functions. Explain your answer.

a)

no

b) $\{(-4, 1), (5, 3), (7, 3), (-2, 0)\}$ yes

Systems of Linear Equations

5

ALMOST DAILY we make financial decisions. Often an understanding of systems of equations is helpful in making such decisions. For instance, in Exercise 21 on page 332, we use a system of equations to decide which carpet store to select for purchasing and installing new carpet. As you read through this chapter, you will see many real-life applications of systems of equations.

5.1 Solving Systems of Equations Graphically

1 Determine if an ordered pair is a solution to a system of equations.

2 Determine if a system of equations is consistent, inconsistent, or dependent.

3 Solve a system of equations graphically.

1 Determine If an Ordered Pair Is a Solution to a System of Equations.

When we seek a common solution to two or more linear equations, the equations are called a **system of linear equations**. An example of a system of linear equations follows:

$$\left.\begin{array}{l}(1)\ y = x + 5 \\ (2)\ y = 2x + 4\end{array}\right\} \quad \textit{System of linear equations}$$

The **solution to a system of equations** is the ordered pair or pairs that satisfy all equations in the system. The solution to the system above is $(1, 6)$.

TEACHING TIP
Point out that the solution to a system of equations is an ordered pair.

Check

In Equation (1)	In Equation (2)
$(1, 6)$	$(1, 6)$
$y = x + 5$	$y = 2x + 4$
$6 \overset{?}{=} 1 + 5$	$6 \overset{?}{=} 2(1) + 4$
$6 = 6$ *True*	$6 = 6$ *True*

Because the ordered pair $(1, 6)$ satisfies *both* equations, it is a solution to the system of equations. Notice that the ordered pair $(3, 8)$ satisfies the first equation but does not satisfy the second equation.

Check

In Equation (1)	In Equation (2)
$(3, 8)$	$(3, 8)$
$y = x + 5$	$y = 2x + 4$
$8 \overset{?}{=} 3 + 5$	$8 \overset{?}{=} 2(3) + 4$
$8 = 8$ *True*	$8 = 10$ *False*

Since the ordered pair $(3, 8)$ does not satisfy *both* equations, it is *not* a solution to the system of equations.

INSTRUCTOR EXAMPLE
Determine which of the following ordered pairs satisfies the system of equations.
$$y = 3x - 2$$
$$5x - 2y = 2$$
a) $(2, 4)$ **b)** $(3, 3)$
Ans.:
a) yes   **b)** no

EXAMPLE 1 ▶ Determine which of the following ordered pairs satisfy the system of equations.

$$y = 2x - 8$$
$$2x + y = 4$$

a) $(1, -6)$ **b)** $(3, -2)$

Solution

a) Substitute 1 for x and -6 for y in each equation.

$y = 2x - 8$	$2x + y = 4$
$-6 \overset{?}{=} 2(1) - 8$	$2(1) + (-6) \overset{?}{=} 4$
$-6 \overset{?}{=} 2 - 8$	$2 - 6 \overset{?}{=} 4$
$-6 \overset{?}{=} -6$ *True*	$-4 = 4$ *False*

Since $(1, -6)$ does not satisfy both equations, it is not a solution to the system of equations.

b) Substitute 3 for x and -2 for y in each equation.

$$y = 2x - 8 \qquad\qquad\qquad 2x + y = 4$$
$$-2 \overset{?}{=} 2(3) - 8 \qquad\qquad 2(3) + (-2) \overset{?}{=} 4$$
$$-2 \overset{?}{=} 6 - 8 \qquad\qquad\qquad 6 - 2 \overset{?}{=} 4$$
$$-2 = -2 \quad \textit{True} \qquad\qquad\qquad 4 = 4 \quad \textit{True}$$

Since $(3, -2)$ satisfies both equations, it is a solution to the system of linear equations.

▸ **Now Try Exercise 13**

In this chapter we discuss three methods for finding the solution to a system of equations: the *graphical method*, the *substitution method*, and the *addition method*. In this section we discuss the graphical method.

2 Determine If a System of Equations Is Consistent, Inconsistent, or Dependent

The **solution to a system of linear equations** is the ordered pair (or pairs) common to all lines in the system when the lines are graphed. When two lines are graphed, three situations are possible, as illustrated in **Figure 5.1**.

In **Figure 5.1a**, lines 1 and 2 are not parallel lines. They intersect at exactly one point. This system of equations has *exactly one solution*. This is an example of a **consistent system of equations**. A consistent system of equations is a system of equations that has a solution.

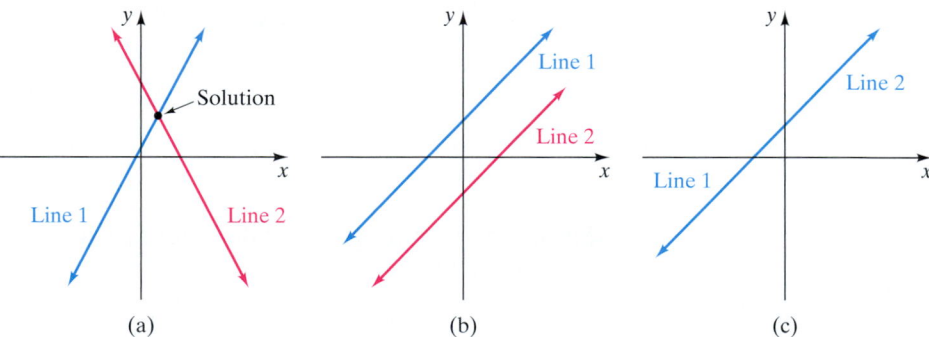

FIGURE 5.1   (a)   (b)   (c)

In **Figure 5.1b**, lines 1 and 2 are two different parallel lines. The lines do not intersect, and this system of equations has *no solution*. This is an example of an **inconsistent system of equations**. An inconsistent system of equations is a system of equations that has no solution.

In **Figure 5.1c**, lines 1 and 2 are actually the same line. In this case, every point on the line satisfies both equations and is a solution to the system of equations. This system has *an infinite number of solutions*. This is an example of a **dependent system of equations**. A dependent system of linear equations is a system of equations that has an infinite number of solutions. If a system of two linear equations is dependent, then both equations represent the same line. *Note that a dependent system is also a consistent system since it has a solution.*

We can determine if a system of linear equations is consistent, inconsistent, or dependent by writing each equation in slope-intercept form and comparing the slopes and y-intercepts. If the slopes of the lines are different (**Fig. 5.1a**), the system is consistent. If the slopes are the same but the y-intercepts are different (**Fig. 5.1b**), the system is inconsistent. If both the slopes and the y-intercepts are the same (**Fig. 5.1c**), the system is dependent.

TEACHING TIP
Emphasize to your students the importance of the information in this paragraph.

EXAMPLE 2 ▶ Determine whether the following system has exactly one solution, no solution, or an infinite number of solutions.

$$2x + 4y = -15$$
$$-8y = 4x - 12$$

Solution   Write each equation in slope-intercept form and then compare the slopes and the *y*-intercepts.

$$2x + 4y = -15 \qquad\qquad\qquad -8y = 4x - 12$$

$$4y = -2x - 15 \qquad\qquad\qquad y = \frac{4x - 12}{-8}$$

$$y = \frac{-2x - 15}{4} \qquad\qquad\qquad y = -\frac{4}{8}x + \frac{12}{8}$$

$$y = -\frac{2}{4}x - \frac{15}{4} \qquad\qquad\qquad y = -\frac{1}{2}x + \frac{3}{2}$$

$$y = -\frac{1}{2}x - \frac{15}{4}$$

Since the lines have the same slope, $-\dfrac{1}{2}$, and different *y*-intercepts, the lines are parallel. This system of equations is therefore inconsistent and has no solution.

▶ **Now Try Exercise 29**

3 Solve a System of Equations Graphically

Now we will see how to solve systems of equations graphically.

> **To Obtain the Solution to a System of Equations Graphically**
>
> Graph each equation and determine the point or points of intersection.

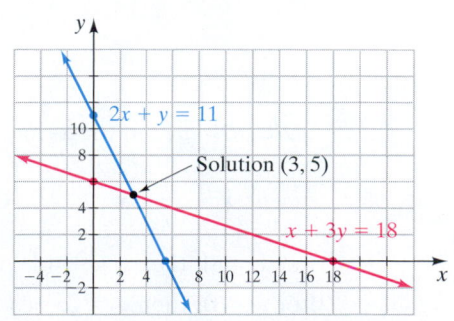

EXAMPLE 3 ▶ Solve the following system of equations graphically.

$$2x + y = 11$$
$$x + 3y = 18$$

Solution   Find the *x*- and *y*-intercepts of each graph; then draw the graphs.

$2x + y = 11$	Ordered Pair	$x + 3y = 18$	Ordered Pair
Let $x = 0$; then $y = 11$.	$(0, 11)$	Let $x = 0$; then $y = 6$.	$(0, 6)$
Let $y = 0$; then $x = \dfrac{11}{2}$.	$\left(\dfrac{11}{2}, 0\right)$	Let $y = 0$; then $x = 18$.	$(18, 0)$

The two graphs (**Fig. 5.2**) appear to intersect at the point $(3, 5)$. The point $(3, 5)$ may be the solution to the system of equations. To be sure, however, we must check to see that $(3, 5)$ satisfies *both* equations.

FIGURE 5.2

Check

$$2x + y = 11$$
$$2(3) + 5 \stackrel{?}{=} 11$$
$$11 = 11 \quad \textit{True}$$

$$x + 3y = 18$$
$$3 + 3(5) \stackrel{?}{=} 18$$
$$18 = 18 \quad \textit{True}$$

Since the ordered pair $(3, 5)$ checks in both equations, it is the solution to the system of equations. This system of equations is consistent.

▶ **Now Try Exercise 43**

INSTRUCTOR EXAMPLE
Solve the system of equations graphically.

$$y = -x + 4$$
$$2x + 2y = 0$$

Ans.:

EXAMPLE 4 ▶ Solve the following system of equations graphically.

$$2x + y = 3$$
$$4x + 2y = 12$$

Solution   Find the x- and y-intercepts of each graph; then draw the graphs.

$2x + y = 3$	Ordered Pair	$4x + 2y = 12$	Ordered Pair
Let $x = 0$; then $y = 3$.	$(0, 3)$	Let $x = 0$; then $y = 6$.	$(0, 6)$
Let $y = 0$; then $x = \dfrac{3}{2}$.	$\left(\dfrac{3}{2}, 0\right)$	Let $y = 0$; then $x = 3$.	$(3, 0)$

The two lines (**Fig. 5.3**) appear to be parallel.

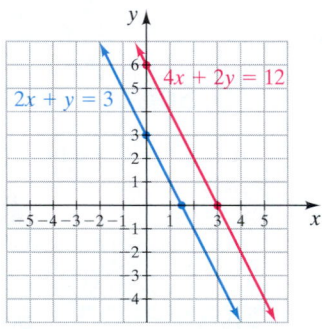

FIGURE 5.3

To show that the two lines are indeed parallel, write each equation in slope-intercept form.

$$2x + y = 3$$
$$y = -2x + 3$$

$$4x + 2y = 12$$
$$2y = -4x + 12$$
$$y = -2x + 6$$

Both equations have the same slope, -2, and different y-intercepts; thus the lines must be parallel. Since parallel lines do not intersect, this system of equations has no solution. This system of equations is inconsistent.

▶ **Now Try Exercise 55**

INSTRUCTOR EXAMPLE
Solve the system of equations graphically.

$$y = \frac{1}{2}x + 1$$
$$2y - x = 2$$

Ans.:

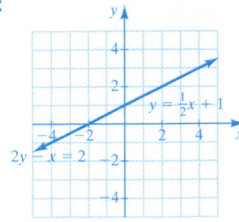

EXAMPLE 5 ▶ Solve the following system of equations graphically.

$$x - \frac{1}{2}y = 2$$
$$y = 2x - 4$$

Solution   Find the x- and y-intercepts of each graph; then draw the graphs.

$x - \dfrac{1}{2}y = 2$	Ordered Pair	$y = 2x - 4$	Ordered Pair
Let $x = 0$; then $y = -4$.	$(0, -4)$	Let $x = 0$; then $y = -4$.	$(0, -4)$
Let $y = 0$; then $x = 2$.	$(2, 0)$	Let $y = 0$; then $x = 2$.	$(2, 0)$

FIGURE 5.4

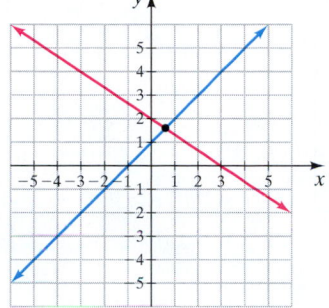

FIGURE 5.5

Because the lines have the same x- and y-intercepts, both equations represent the same line (**Fig. 5.4**). When the equations are written in slope-intercept form, it becomes clear that the equations are identical and the system is dependent.

$$x - \frac{1}{2}y = 2 \qquad y = 2x - 4$$

$$2\left(x - \frac{1}{2}y\right) = 2(2)$$

$$2x - y = 4$$

$$-y = -2x + 4$$

$$y = 2x - 4$$

The solution to this system of equations is all the points on the line.

▸ **Now Try Exercise 53**

When graphing a system of equations, the intersection of the lines is not always easy to read on the graph. For example, can you determine the solution to the system of equations shown in **Figure 5.5**? You may estimate the solution to be $\left(\frac{7}{10}, \frac{3}{2}\right)$ when it may actually be $\left(\frac{4}{5}, \frac{8}{5}\right)$. The accuracy of your answer will depend on how carefully you draw the graphs and on the scale of the graph paper used. In Section 5.2 we present an algebraic method that gives exact solutions to systems of equations.

USING YOUR GRAPHING CALCULATOR

A graphing calculator can be used to solve or check systems of equations. To solve a system of equations graphically, graph both equations as was explained in Chapter 4. The point or points of intersection of the graphs is the solution to the system of equations.

The first step in solving the system on a graphing calculator is to solve each equation for y. For example, consider the system of equations given in Example 3.

System of Equations	Equations Solved for y
$2x + y = 11$	$y = -2x + 11$
$x + 3y = 18$	$y = -\frac{1}{3}x + 6$

Let $Y_1 = -2x + 11$

$$Y_2 = -\frac{1}{3}x + 6.$$

Figure 5.6 shows the screen of a TI-84 Plus with these two equations graphed.

To find the intersection of the two graphs, you can use the $\boxed{\text{TRACE}}$ and $\boxed{\text{ZOOM}}$ keys or the TABLE feature as was explained earlier. **Figure 5.7** shows a table of values for equations Y_1 and Y_2. Notice when $x = 3$, Y_1 and Y_2 both have the same value, 5. Therefore both graphs intersect at $(3, 5)$, and $(3, 5)$ is the solution.

FIGURE 5.6

X	Y₁	Y₂
0	11	6
1	9	5.6667
2	7	5.3333
3	5	5
4	3	4.6667
5	1	4.3333
6	-1	4

X=3

FIGURE 5.7

(continued on the next page)

Some graphing calculators have a feature that displays the intersection of graphs by pressing a sequence of keys. For example, on the TI-84 Plus if you go to CALC (which stands for calculate) by pressing $\boxed{2^{\text{nd}}}$ $\boxed{\text{TRACE}}$, you get the screen shown in **Figure 5.8**. Now press $\boxed{5}$, intersect. Once the *intersect* feature has been selected, the calculator will display the graph and the question

FIRST CURVE?

At this time, move the cursor along the first curve until it is close to the point of intersection. Then press $\boxed{\text{ENTER}}$ The calculator now shows

SECOND CURVE?

and has the cursor on the second curve. If the cursor is not close to the point of intersection, move it along this curve until it is close to the intersection. Then press $\boxed{\text{ENTER}}$. The calculator now displays

GUESS?

Now press $\boxed{\text{ENTER}}$ and the point of intersection is displayed; see **Figure 5.9**. The point of intersection is (3, 5).

FIGURE 5.8

FIGURE 5.9

EXERCISES

Use your graphing calculator to find the solution to each system of equations. Round noninteger answers to the nearest tenth.

1. $x + 2y = -11$
$2x - y = -2$
$(-3, -4)$

2. $x - 3y = -13$
$-2x - 2y = 2$
$(-4, 3)$

3. $2x - y = 7.7$
$-x - 3y = 1.4$
$(3.1, -1.5)$

4. $3x + 2y = 7.8$
$-x + 3y = 15.0$
$(-0.6, 4.8)$

In the example that follows, we will work an application problem using two variables and illustrate the solution in the form of a graph. Although an answer may sometimes be easier to obtain using only one variable, a graph of the situation may help you to better visualize the total picture.

EXAMPLE 6 ▶ **Security Systems** Meghan O'Donnell plans to install a security system in her house. She has narrowed her choices to two security dealers: Moneywell and Doile. Moneywell's system costs $3580 to install and the monitoring fee is $20 per month. Doile's equivalent system costs only $2620 to install, but the monitoring fee is $32 per month.

a) Assuming that the monthly monitoring fees do not change, in how many months would the total cost of Moneywell's and Doile's systems be the same?

b) If both dealers guarantee not to raise monthly fees for 10 years, and if Meghan plans to use the system for 10 years, which system would be the least expensive?

Solution   **a) Understand and Translate**   We need to determine the number of months for which both systems will have the same total cost.

Let n = number of months

c = total cost of the security system over n months.

Now we can write an equation to represent the cost of each system using the two variables c and n.

This house is protected by Moneywell Security Systems

TEACHING TIP
Point out that students see problems like this often in their everyday lives. Have students bring in real-life problems like this that they come across.

Moneywell   **Doile**

$$\text{Total cost} = \begin{pmatrix} \text{initial} \\ \text{cost} \end{pmatrix} + \begin{pmatrix} \text{fees over} \\ n \text{ months} \end{pmatrix} \qquad \text{Total cost} = \begin{pmatrix} \text{initial} \\ \text{cost} \end{pmatrix} + \begin{pmatrix} \text{fees over} \\ n \text{ months} \end{pmatrix}$$

$$c = 3580 + 20n \qquad\qquad\qquad c = 2620 + 32n$$

Thus, our system of equations is

$$c = 3580 + 20n$$
$$c = 2620 + 32n$$

Carry Out   Now let's graph each equation. Following are tables of values.

$$c = 3580 + 20n$$

Let $n = 0.$ $c = 3580 + 20(0) = 3580$
Let $n = 100.$ $c = 3580 + 20(100) = 5580$
Let $n = 160.$ $c = 3580 + 20(160) = 6780$

n	c
0	3580
100	5580
160	6780

$$c = 2620 + 32n$$

Let $n = 0.$ $c = 2620 + 32(0) = 2620$
Let $n = 100.$ $c = 2620 + 32(100) = 5820$
Let $n = 160.$ $c = 2620 + 32(160) = 7740$

n	c
0	2620
100	5820
160	7740

Figure 5.10 shows the graphs of the equations.

FIGURE 5.10

Check and Answer   The graph (**Fig. 5.10**) shows that the total cost of the two security systems would be the same in 80 months.

b) Since 10 years is 120 months, we draw a dashed vertical line at $n = 120$ months and see where it intersects the two lines. Since at 120 months the Doile line is higher than the Moneywell line, the cost for the Doile system for 120 months is more than the cost of the Moneywell system. Therefore, the cost of the Moneywell system would be less expensive for 10 years.

▶ **Now Try Exercise 71**

We will discuss applications of systems of equations further in Section 5.4.

EXERCISE SET 5.1

1. the ordered pairs that satisfy all the equations in the system
2. b) has no solution   **c)** has an infinite number of solutions

Concept/Writing Exercises

1. What does the solution to a system of equations represent?

2. a) What is a consistent system of equations?   has a solution

    b) What is an inconsistent system of equations?

c) What is a dependent system of equations?

3. Explain how to determine without graphing if a system of linear equations has exactly one solution, no solution, or an infinite number of solutions.   compare their slopes and y-intercepts

4. When a dependent system of two linear equations is graphed, what will be the result?   a single line

5. Explain why it may be difficult to obtain an exact answer to a system of equations graphically.   The point of intersection can only be estimated.

6. Is a dependent system of equations a consistent system or an inconsistent system? Explain.   consistent

Practice the Skills

Determine which, if any, of the following ordered pairs satisfy each system of linear equations.

7. $y = 3x - 6$
$y = -3x$
  a) $(2, 0)$ **b)** $(0, 0)$ **c)** $(1, -3)$ c)

8. $y = -4x$
$y = -2x + 8$
  a) $(0, 8)$ **b)** $(-4, 16)$ **c)** $(3, -12)$ b)

9. $y = 2x - 3$
$y = x + 5$
  a) $(8, 13)$ **b)** $(4, 5)$ **c)** $(5, 7)$ a)

10. $x + 2y = 4$
$y = 3x - 5$
  a) $(0, 2)$ **b)** $(2, 1)$ **c)** $(4, 0)$ b)

11. $4x + y = 15$
$5x + y = 10$
  a) $(3, 3)$ **b)** $(2, 0)$ **c)** $(-1, 19)$ (none)

12. $y = 2x + 6$
$y = 2x - 1$
  a) $(0, 6)$ **b)** $(3, 5)$ **c)** $(-2, 0)$ (none)

13. $4x - 6y = 12$
$y = \dfrac{2}{3}x - 2$
  a) $(3, 0)$ **b)** $(9, 4)$ **c)** $(6, 1)$ a), b)

14. $y = -x + 5$
$2y = -2x + 10$
  a) $(6, -1)$ **b)** $(0, 5)$ **c)** $(-2, 3)$ a), b)

15. $3x - 4y = 8$
$2y = \dfrac{2}{3}x - 4$
  a) $(0, -2)$ **b)** $(1, -6)$ **c)** $\left(-\dfrac{1}{3}, -\dfrac{9}{4}\right)$ a)

16. $2x + 3y = 6$
$-x + \dfrac{5}{2} = \dfrac{1}{2}y$
  a) $\left(\dfrac{1}{2}, \dfrac{5}{3}\right)$ **b)** $\left(-2, \dfrac{10}{3}\right)$ **c)** $\left(\dfrac{9}{4}, \dfrac{1}{2}\right)$ c)

Identify each system of linear equations (lines are labeled 1 and 2) as consistent, inconsistent, or dependent. State whether the system has exactly one solution, no solution, or an infinite number of solutions.

17.

consistent—one solution

18.

consistent—one solution

19.

dependent—infinite number

20.

dependent—infinite number

21.

consistent—one solution

22.

consistent—one solution

23.

inconsistent—no solution

24.
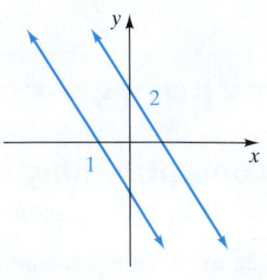
inconsistent—no solution

Express each equation in slope-intercept form. Without graphing the equations, state whether the system of equations has exactly one solution, no solution, or an infinite number of solutions.

25. $y = 2x - 1$
$3y = 5x - 6$ one solution

26. $x + y = 8$
$x - y = 8$ one solution

27. $2y = 3x + 3$
$y = \dfrac{3}{2}x - 2$ no solution

28. $y = \dfrac{1}{2}x + 3$
$2y = x + 6$ infinite number of solutions

29. $2x = y - 6$
$3x = 3y + 5$ one solution

30. $x + 3y = 6$
$4x + y = 4$ one solution

31. $3x + 5y = -7$
$-3x - 5y = -10$ no solution

32. $x - y = 2$
$2x - 2y = -6$ no solution

33. $x = 3y + 5$
$2x - 6y = 10$ infinite number of solutions

34. $x - y = 3$
$\dfrac{1}{2}x - 2y = -8$ one solution

35. $y = \dfrac{3}{2}x + \dfrac{1}{2}$
$3x - 2y = \dfrac{5}{2}$ no solution

36. $2y = \dfrac{7}{3}x - 9$
$4y = 8x + 9$ one solution

Determine the solution to each system of equations graphically. If the system is dependent or inconsistent, so state.

37. $y = x + 3$
$y = -x + 3$ $(0, 3)$

38. $y = 2x + 4$
$y = -3x - 6$ $(-2, 0)$

39. $y = 3x - 6$
$y = -x + 6$ $(3, 3)$

40. $y = 3x - 4$
$y = -x$ $(1, -1)$

41. $4x = 8$
$y = -3$ $(2, -3)$

42. $2x - y = 7$
$2y = 2x - 6$ $(4, 1)$

43. $x + y = 5$
$-x + y = 1$ $(2, 3)$

44. $-x + 2y = 7$
$2x - y = -2$ $(1, 4)$

45. $y = -\dfrac{1}{2}x + 4$
$x + 2y = 6$ inconsistent

46. $-x + 2y = 0$
$2x - y = -3$ $(-2, -1)$

47. $x + 2y = 8$
$5x + 2y = 0$ $(-2, 5)$

48. $3x + y = -6$
$2x = 1 + y$ $(-1, -3)$

49. $2x + 3y = 6$
$4x = -6y + 12$ dependent

50. $2x + 5y - 6 = 0$
$2x - 3y = 6$ $(3, 0)$

51. $y = 3$
$y = 2x - 3$ $(3, 3)$

52. $x = 5$
$y = 2x - 8$ $(5, 2)$

53. $x - 2y = 4$
$2x - 4y = 8$ dependent

54. $4x - y = 6$
$2y = 8x - 12$ dependent

55. $2x + y = -2$
$6x + 3y = 6$ inconsistent

56. $y = 2x - 1$
$2y = 4x + 5$ inconsistent

57. $4x - 3y = 6$
$2x + 4y = 14$ $(3, 2)$

58. $2x + 6y = 12$
$y = -\dfrac{1}{3}x + 2$ dependent

59. $2x - 3y = 0$
$x + 2y = 0$ $(0, 0)$

60. $4x = 4y - 12$
$-8x + 8y = 8$ inconsistent

61. and **62.** lines parallel; slopes same, y-intercepts different   **63.** an infinite number

Problem Solving

61. Given the system of equations $6x - 4y = 12$ and $12y = 18x - 24$, determine without graphing whether the graphs of the two equations will be parallel lines. Explain how you determined your answer.

62. Given the system of equations $4x - 8y = 12$ and $2x - 8 = 4y$, determine without graphing whether the graphs of the two equations will be parallel lines. Explain how you determined your answer.

63. If a system of linear equations has solutions $(4, 3)$ and $(6, 5)$, how many solutions does the system have? Explain.

64. If the slope of one line in a system of linear equations is 2 and the slope of the second line in the system is 3, how many solutions does the system have? Explain.   one

65. If two distinct lines are parallel, how many solutions does the system have? Explain.   none

66. If two different lines in a linear system of equations pass through the origin, must the solution to the system be $(0, 0)$? Explain.   yes

67. Consider the system $x = 5$ and $y = 3$. How many solutions does the system have? What is the solution?   one, $(5, 3)$

68. A system of linear equations has $(3, -1)$ as its solution. If one line in the system is vertical and the other line is horizontal, determine the equations in the system. $x = 3, y = -1$

In Exercises 69–72, find each solution by graphing the system of equations.

69. Furnace Repair Edith Hall's furnace is 10 years old and has a problem. The furnace repair man indicates that it will cost Edith $600 to repair her furnace. She can purchase a new, more efficient furnace for $1800. Her present furnace averages about $650 per year for energy cost and the new furnace would average about $450 per year.

    We can represent the total cost, *c*, of repair or replacement, plus energy cost over *n* years by the following system of equations.

(repair) $c = 600 + 650n$

(replacement) $c = 1800 + 450n$

Find the number of years for which the total cost of repair would equal the total cost of replacement.   6 yr

70. Security Systems Juan Varges is considering the two security systems discussed in Example 6. If Moneywell's system costs $4400 plus $15 per month and Doile's system costs $3400 plus $25 per month, after how many months would the total cost of the two systems be the same?   100 months or 8 yr 4 months

71. Boat Ride Rudy has visitors at his home and wants to take them out on a pontoon boat for a day. There are two pontoon boat rental agencies on the lake. Bob's Boat Rental charges $25 per hour for the boat rental, which includes all the gasoline used. Hopper's Rental charges $21 per hour plus a flat charge of $28 for the gasoline used. The equations that repre-

sent the total cost, *c*, follow. In the equations *h* represents the number of hours the boats are rented.

$$c = 25h$$
$$c = 21h + 28$$

Determine the number of hours the boats must be rented for the total cost to be the same.   7 hr

72. Landscaping The Evergreen Landscape Service charges a consultation fee of $200 plus $50 per hour for labor. The Out of Sight Landscape Service charges a consultation fee of $300 plus $40 per hour for labor. We can represent this situation with the system of equations

$$c = 200 + 50h$$
$$c = 300 + 40h$$

where *c* is the total cost and *h* is the number of hours of labor. Find the number of hours of labor for the two services to have the same total cost.   10 hr

Group Activity

Discuss and answer Exercises 73–78 as a group. Suppose that a system of three linear equations in two variables is graphed on the same axes. Find the maximum number of points where two or more of the lines can intersect if

73. the three lines have the same slope but different *y*-intercepts.   0

74. the three lines have the same slope and the same *y*-intercept.   infinite number

75. two lines have the same slope but different *y*-intercepts and the third line has a different slope.   2

76. the three lines have different slopes but the same *y*-intercept.   1

77. the three lines have different slopes but two have the same *y*-intercept.   3

78. the three lines have different slopes and different *y*-intercepts.   3

Cumulative Review Exercises

[2.1]   **79.** Simplify $7x - (x - 6) + 4(3 - x)$. $2x + 18$

[2.5]   **80.** Solve the equation $2(x + 3) - x = 5x + 2$.   1

[2.6]   **81.** If $A = p(1 + rt)$, find *r* when $A = 1000$, $t = 20$, and $p = 500$.   0.05

83. a) $(6, 0), (0, 4)$ **b)** See graphing answer section.

82. Solve the formula $A = \dfrac{1}{2}bh$ for *h*. $h = \dfrac{2A}{b}$

[4.2]   **83. a)** Find the *x*- and *y*-intercepts of $2x + 3y = 12$.

      b) Use the intercepts to graph the equation.

5.2 Solving Systems of Equations by Substitution

1 Solve systems of equations by substitution.

As we stated in Section 5.1, a graphic solution to a system of equations may be inaccurate since you may need to estimate the coordinates of the point of intersection. When an exact solution is necessary, the system should be solved algebraically, either by substitution or by addition of equations.

1 Solve Systems of Equations by Substitution

The procedure for solving a system of equations by **substitution** is illustrated in Example 1. The procedure for solving by addition is presented in Section 5.3. Regardless of which of the two algebraic techniques is used to solve a system of equations, our immediate goal remains the same, that is, *to obtain one equation containing only one unknown.*

EXAMPLE 1 ▸ Solve the following system of equations by substitution.

$$x + 3y = 18$$
$$2x + y = 11$$

Solution   Begin by solving for one of the variables in either of the equations. You may solve for any of the variables; however, if you solve for a variable with a numerical coefficient of 1 or -1, you may avoid working with fractions. In this system the x-term in $x + 3y = 18$ and the y-term in $2x + y = 11$; both have a numerical coefficient of 1.

Let's solve for x in $x + 3y = 18$.

$$x + 3y = 18$$
$$x = -3y + 18$$

Next, substitute $-3y + 18$ for x in the *other equation*, $2x + y = 11$, and solve for the remaining variable, y.

$$2x + y = 11$$
$$2(\overbrace{-3y + 18}) + y = 11$$
$$-6y + 36 + y = 11$$
$$-5y + 36 = 11$$
$$-5y = -25$$
$$y = 5$$

Substitution; this is now an equation in only one variable, y.

Finally, substitute $y = 5$ in the equation that is solved for x and find the value of x,

$$x = -3y + 18$$
$$x = -3(5) + 18$$
$$x = -15 + 18$$
$$x = 3$$

A check using $x = 3$ and $y = 5$ in both equations will show that the solution is the ordered pair $(3, 5)$.

▸ **Now Try Exercise 5**

The system of equations in Example 1 could also be solved by substitution by solving the equation $2x + y = 11$ for y. Do this now. You should obtain the same answer.

Note that the solution in Example 1 is identical to the graphical solution obtained in Example 3 of Section 5.1. Now we summarize the procedure for solving a system of equations by substitution.

> ### To Solve a System of Equations by Substitution
>
> 1. Solve for a variable in either equation. (If possible, solve for a variable with a numerical coefficient of 1 or -1 to avoid working with fractions.)
> 2. Substitute the expression found for the variable in step 1 into the other equation.
> 3. Solve the equation determined in step 2 to find the value of one variable.
> 4. Substitute the value found in step 3 into the equation obtained in step 1 to find the value of the other variable.
> 5. Check by substituting both values in both original equations.

EXAMPLE 2 ▸ Solve the following system of equations by substitution.

$$2x + y = 3$$
$$4x + 2y = 12$$

Solution   Solve for y in $2x + y = 3$.

$$2x + y = 3$$
$$y = -2x + 3$$

Now substitute the expression $-2x + 3$ for y in the *other equation*, $4x + 2y = 12$, and solve for x.

$$4x + 2y = 12$$

$$4x + 2(\overbrace{-2x + 3}) = 12 \qquad \text{\color{red}\textit{Substitution; this is now an equation in only one variable, x.}}$$

$$4x - 4x + 6 = 12$$

$$6 = 12 \qquad \text{\color{red}\textit{False}}$$

Since the statement $6 = 12$ is false, the system has no solution. Therefore, the graphs of the equations will be parallel lines and the system is inconsistent because it has no solution.

▶ **Now Try Exercise 17**

Note that the solution in Example 2 is identical to the graphical solution obtained in Example 4 of Section 5.1. **Figure 5.3** on page 302 shows the parallel lines.

EXAMPLE 3 ▶ Solve the following system of equations by substitution.

$$x - \frac{1}{2}y = 2$$

$$y = 2x - 4$$

Solution   The equation $y = 2x - 4$ is already solved for y. Substitute $2x - 4$ for y in the other equation, $x - \frac{1}{2}y = 2$, and solve for x.

$$x - \frac{1}{2}y = 2$$

$$x - \frac{1}{2}(\overbrace{2x - 4}) = 2$$

$$x - x + 2 = 2$$

$$2 = 2 \qquad \text{\color{green}\textit{True}}$$

Notice that the sum of the x terms is 0, and when simplified, x is no longer part of the equation. *Since the statement $2 = 2$ is true, this system has an infinite number of solutions. Therefore, the graphs of the equations represent the same line and the system is dependent.*

▶ **Now Try Exercise 9**

Note that the solution in Example 3 is identical to the solution obtained graphically in Example 5 of Section 5.1. **Figure 5.4** on page 303 shows that the graphs of both equations are the same line.

EXAMPLE 4 ▶ Solve the following system of equations by substitution.

$$3x + 6y = 9$$

$$2x - 3y = 6$$

Solution   None of the variables in either equation has a numerical coefficient of 1. However, since the numbers 3, 6, and 9 are all divisible by 3, if you solve the first equation for x, you will avoid having to work with fractions.

$$3x + 6y = 9$$

$$3x = -6y + 9$$

$$\frac{3x}{3} = \frac{-6y + 9}{3}$$

$$x = -\frac{6}{3}y + \frac{9}{3}$$

$$x = -2y + 3$$

Now substitute $-2y + 3$ for x in the other equation, $2x - 3y = 6$, and solve for the remaining variable, y.

$$2x - 3y = 6$$
$$2(\overbrace{-2y + 3}) - 3y = 6$$
$$-4y + 6 - 3y = 6$$
$$-7y + 6 = 6$$
$$-7y = 0$$
$$y = 0$$

Finally, solve for x by substituting $y = 0$ in the equation previously solved for x.

$$x = -2y + 3$$
$$x = -2(0) + 3 = 0 + 3 = 3$$

The solution is $(3, 0)$.

▶ **Now Try Exercise 23**

Helpful Hint

Remember that a solution to a system of linear equations must contain both an x- and a y-value. Don't solve the system for one of the variables and forget to solve for the other. Write the solution as an ordered pair.

EXAMPLE 5 ▶ Solve the following system of equations by substitution.

$$6x + 8y = 3$$
$$3x = 3y + 5$$

INSTRUCTOR EXAMPLE

Solve the system of equations by substitution.

$$4x - 8y = -7$$
$$3x + 5y = 3$$

Ans.: $\left(-\dfrac{1}{4}, \dfrac{3}{4}\right)$

Solution   We will elect to solve for x in the second equation.

$$3x = 3y + 5$$
$$x = \frac{3y + 5}{3}$$
$$x = y + \frac{5}{3}$$

Now substitute $y + \dfrac{5}{3}$ for x in the other equation.

$$6x + 8y = 3$$
$$6\left(\overbrace{y + \frac{5}{3}}\right) + 8y = 3$$
$$6y + 10 + 8y = 3$$
$$14y + 10 = 3$$
$$14y = -7$$
$$y = \frac{-7}{14} = -\frac{1}{2}$$

Finally, find the value of x.

$$x = y + \frac{5}{3}$$
$$x = -\frac{1}{2} + \frac{5}{3} = -\frac{3}{6} + \frac{10}{6} = \frac{7}{6}$$

The solution is the ordered pair $\left(\dfrac{7}{6}, -\dfrac{1}{2}\right)$.

▶ **Now Try Exercise 25**

EXAMPLE 6 ▶ **Mule Trip** In 2006 and 2007 a total of 2462 people took a mule trip to the bottom of the Grand Canyon. If the number who took the mule trip in 2007 was 372 more than the number who took the mule trip in 2006, determine the number of people who took the mule trip in 2006 and in 2007.

Solution **Understand and Translate** We are provided sufficient information to obtain two equations for our system of equations. Let $x =$ number of people who took the mule trip in 2006 and let $y =$ number of people who took the mule trip in 2007. Because the total for these two years was 2462, one equation is $x + y = 2462$. Since the number of people who took the trip in 2007 was 372 more than the number who took the trip in 2006, an equation that represents the number of people who took the trip in 2007 is $y = x + 372$. This is our second equation in the system of equations.

$$\text{System of equations} \begin{cases} x + y = 2462 \\ y = x + 372 \end{cases}$$

Carry Out Because the second equation, $y = x + 372$, is already solved for y, we will substitute $x + 372$ for y in the first equation.

$$x + y = 2462$$

$$x + \overbrace{x + 372} = 2462$$

$$2x + 372 = 2462$$

$$2x = 2090$$

$$x = 1045$$

Check and Answer The number of people who took the trip in 2006 was 1045. The number of people who took the trip in 2007 is therefore $x + 372 = 1045 + 372 = 1417$. Notice that $1045 + 1417 = 2462$.

▶ **Now Try Exercise 35**

INSTRUCTOR EXAMPLE
The perimeter of a rectangle is 100 meters. Find the length and width of the rectangle if the length is 10 meters greater than the width.
Ans.: *l*: 30 m, *w*: 20 m.

EXERCISE SET 5.2

Concept/Writing Exercises

1. When solving the system of equations

$$3x + 6y = 12$$
$$4x + 3y = 8$$

by substitution, which variable, in which equation, would you choose to solve for to make the solution easier? Explain your answer. The x in the first equation, both 6 and 12 are divisible by 3.

2. When solving the system of equations

$$4x + 2y = 8$$
$$3x - 9y = 8$$

by substitution, which variable, in which equation, would you choose to solve for to make the solution easier? Explain your answer. The y in the first equation, both 4 and 8 are divisible by 2.

3. When solving a system of linear equations by substitution, how will you know if the system is inconsistent?

4. When solving a system of linear equations by substitution, how will you know if the system is dependent?

3. You will obtain a false statement, such as $3 = 0$.

4. You will obtain a true statement, such as $2 = 2$.

Practice the Skills

Find the solution to each system of equations by substitution.

5. $x + 2y = 6$
   $2x - 3y = 5$ $(4, 1)$

6. $y = 2x + 7$
   $y = -x - 5$ $(-4, -1)$

7. $x + y = -2$
   $x - y = 0$ $(-1, -1)$

8. $x + 2y = 6$
   $4y = 12 - 2x$ infinite number of solutions

9. $3x + y = 3$
   $3x + y + 5 = 0$ no solution

10. $3x - y = 8$
    $6x - 2y = 10$ no solution

11. $x = 3$
$x + y + 5 = 0$ (3, −8)

12. $y = 2x + 4$
$y = -2$ (−3, −2)

13. $x = y + 1$
$4x + 2y = -14$ (−2, −3)

14. $2x + 3y = 7$
$6x - y = 1$ $\left(\frac{1}{2}, 2\right)$

15. $2x + y = 11$
$y = 3x - 4$ (3, 5)

16. $y = -2x + 7$
$x + 4y = 0$ (4, −1)

17. $y = \frac{1}{3}x - 2$
$x - 3y = 6$ infinite number of solutions

18. $x - \frac{1}{2}y = 7$
$y = 2x - 14$ infinite number of solutions

19. $2x + 5y = 9$
$6x - 2y = 10$ (2, 1)

20. $3x - 3y = 4$
$2x + 3y = 5$ $\left(\frac{9}{5}, \frac{7}{15}\right)$

21. $y = 2x - 13$
$-4x - 7 = 9y$ (5, −3)

22. $5x - 2y = -7$
$8 = y - 4x$ (−3, −4)

23. $4x - 5y = -4$
$3x = 2y - 3$ (−1, 0)

24. $2x - 3y = 9$
$5x + 2y = -6$ (0, −3)

25. $4x + 5y = -6$
$2x - \frac{10}{3}y = -4$ $\left(-\frac{12}{7}, \frac{6}{35}\right)$

26. $4x + y = 1$
$10x - 5y = -2$ $\left(\frac{1}{10}, \frac{3}{5}\right)$

27. $3x - 4y = 15$
$-6x + 8y = -14$ no solution

28. $\frac{1}{2}x + 2y = 5$
$3x - \frac{1}{2}y = 5$ (2, 2)

29. $4x - y = 1$
$10x + \frac{1}{2}y = 1$ $\left(\frac{1}{8}, -\frac{1}{2}\right)$

30. $-\frac{1}{5}x + \frac{3}{7}y = 2$
$\frac{3}{5}x - \frac{2}{7}y = 1$ (5, 7)

Problem Solving

34. $w = 5$ ft, $l = 25$ ft

31. Positive Integers The sum of two positive integers is 80. Find the integers if one number is 8 greater than the other.   36, 44

32. Positive Integers The difference of two positive integers is 44. Find the integers if the larger number is twice the smaller number.   88, 44

33. Rectangle The perimeter of a rectangle is 50 feet. Find the dimensions of the rectangle if the length is 9 feet greater than the width. $w = 8$ ft, $l = 17$ ft

34. Rectangle The perimeter of a rectangle is 60 feet. Find the dimensions of the rectangle if its length is 5 times its width.

35. Rodeo Attendance At a rodeo the total paid attendance was 2500. If the number of people who received a discount on the admission fee was 622 less than the number who did not, determine the number of paid attendees that paid the full fee.   1561 attendees

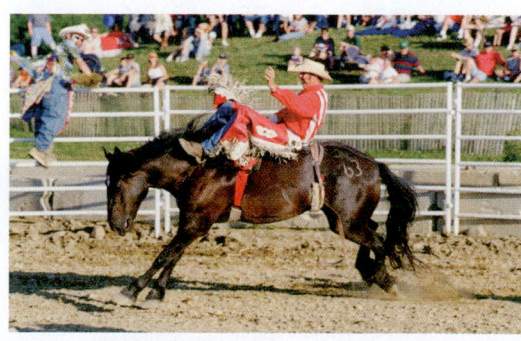

36. Wooden Horse To buy a statue of a wooden horse Billy and Jean combined their money. Together they had $530. If Jean had $130 more than Billy, how much money did each have?   Billy: $200, Jean: $330

37. Legal Settlement After a legal settlement, the client's portion of the award was three times as much money as the attorney's portion. If the total award was $40,000, how much did the client get? $30,000

38. Jelly Beans A candy store mixed green and red jelly beans in a barrel. The barrel contains 42 pounds of the mixture. If there are 3 times as many pounds of the green jelly beans as red jelly beans, find the number of pounds of green jelly beans and the number of pounds of red jelly beans in the barrel.   red: 10.5 lb, green: 31.5 lb

39. Refinancing Dona Boccio is considering refinancing her house. The cost of refinancing is a one-time charge of $1280. With her reduced mortgage rate, her monthly interest and principal payments would be $794 per month. Her total cost, c, for n months could be represented by $c = 1280 + 794n$. At her current rate her mortgage payments are $874 per month and the total cost for n months can be represented by $c = 874n$.

a) Determine the number of months for which both mortgage plans would have the same total cost.   16 months

b) If Dona plans to remain in her house for 12 years, should she refinance?   yes

40. Temperatures In Seattle the temperature is 86°F, but it is decreasing by 2 degrees per hour. The temperature, T, at time, t, in hours, is represented by $T = 86 - 2t$. In Spokane the temperature is 59°F, but it is increasing by 2.5 degrees per hour. The temperature, T, can be represented by $T = 59 + 2.5t$.

a) If the temperature continues decreasing and increasing at the same rate in these cities, how long will it be before both cities have the same temperature?   6 hr

b) When both cities have the same temperature, what will that temperature be?   74°F

Seattle, Washington

41. Traveling by Car Jean Woody's car is at the 80 mile marker on a highway. Roberta Kieronski's car is 15 miles behind Jean's car. Jean's car is traveling at 60 miles per hour. The mile marker that Jean's car will be at in t hours can be found by the equation $m = 80 + 60t$. Roberta's car is traveling at 72 miles per hour. The mile marker that Roberta's car will be at in t hours can be found by the equation $m = 65 + 72t$.

a) Determine the time it will take for Roberta's car to catch up with Jean's car.   1.25 hr

b) At which mile marker will they be when they meet?   155 mile marker

42. Computer Store Will Worthy's present salary consists of a fixed weekly salary of $300 plus a $20 bonus for each computer system he sells. His weekly salary can be represented by $s = 300 + 20n$, where n is the number of computer systems he sells. He is considering another position where his weekly salary would be $400 plus a $10 bonus for each computer system he sells. The other position's weekly salary can be represented by $s = 400 + 10n$. How many computer systems would Will need to sell in a week for his salary to be the same with both employers?   10 systems

Challenge Problems

Answer parts **a)** *through* **d)** *on your own.*

43. Heat Transfer In a laboratory during an experiment on heat transfer, a large metal ball is heated to a temperature of 180°F. This metal ball is then placed in a gallon of oil at a temperature of 20°F. Assume that when the ball is placed in the oil it loses temperature at the rate of 10 degrees per minute while the oil's temperature rises at a rate of 6 degrees per minute.

a) Write an equation that can be used to determine the ball's temperature t minutes after being placed in the oil.
$T = 180 - 10t$

b) Write an equation that can be used to determine the oil's temperature t minutes after the ball is placed in it. $T = 20 + 6t$

c) Determine how long it will take for the ball and oil to reach the same temperature.   10 min

d) When the ball and oil reach the same temperature, what will the temperature be?   80°F

Group Activity

Discuss and work Exercise 44 as a group.

44. In intermediate algebra you may solve systems containing three equations with three variables. As a group, solve the system of equations on the right. Your answer will be in the form of an **ordered triple** (x, y, z).

$$x = 4$$
$$2x - y = 6$$
$$-x + y + z = -3 \quad (4, 2, -1)$$

Cumulative Review Exercises

47. See graphing answer section.   **48.** slope: $\dfrac{3}{5}$; y-intercept: $(0, -5)$ **49.** $y = 2x + 4$

[2.6] **45. Willow Tree** The diameter of a willow tree grows about 1.2 inches per year. What is the approximate age of a willow tree whose diameter is 27.6 inches?   23 yr

[4.2] **46.** Find the missing coordinate in the given solution $(3, ?)$ for $4x + 5y = 22$.   2

47. Graph $4x - 8y = 16$ using the intercepts.

[4.4] **48.** Find the slope and y-intercept of the graph of the equation $3x - 5y = 25$.

49. Determine the equation of the following line.

5.3 Solving Systems of Equations by the Addition Method

1 Solve systems of equations by the addition method.

1 Solve Systems of Equations by the Addition Method

A third, and often the easiest, method of solving a system of equations is by the **addition (or elimination) method.** *The goal of this process is to obtain two equations whose sum will be an equation containing only one variable.* Always keep in mind that our immediate goal is to obtain one equation containing only one unknown.

In the addition method, we use the fact that if $a = b$ and $c = d$, then $a + c = b + d$. Suppose we have the following two equations.

$$x - 2y = 9$$
$$3x + 2y = 11$$

If we add the left sides of the two equations we obtain $4x$ because $-2y + 2y = 0$. If we add the right sides of the equations we get $9 + 11 = 20$. Thus, the sum of the equations is $4x = 20$, which is an equation in only one variable.

TEACHING TIP
Stress that the object of this process is to obtain two equations whose sum will be an equation containing only one variable.

$$\begin{array}{r} x - 2y = 9 \\ \underline{3x + 2y = 11} \\ 4x \quad\quad = 20 \end{array}$$

From the equation $4x = 20$, we determine that $x = 5$.

$$4x = 20$$
$$x = 5$$

We can now substitute 5 for x in either of the original equations to find y. We will substitute 5 for x in $x - 2y = 9$.

$$x - 2y = 9$$
$$5 - 2y = 9$$
$$-2y = 4$$
$$y = -2$$

The solution to the system is $(5, -2)$. This ordered pair will check in both equations. Check this solution now. Now let's work some examples.

EXAMPLE 1 ▶ Solve the following system of equations using the addition method.

$$x + y = 6$$
$$2x - y = 3$$

INSTRUCTOR EXAMPLE
Solve the system of equations using the addition method.

$$x + y = 7$$
$$4x - y = 3$$

Ans.: $(2, 5)$

Solution   Note that one equation contains $+y$ and the other contains $-y$. By adding the equations, we can eliminate the variable y and obtain one equation containing only one variable, x. When added, $+y$ and $-y$ sum to 0, and the variable y is eliminated.

$$\begin{array}{r} x + y = 6 \\ \underline{2x - y = 3} \\ 3x \quad\quad = 9 \end{array}$$

Now we solve for the remaining variable, x.

$$\frac{3x}{3} = \frac{9}{3}$$
$$x = 3$$

Finally, we solve for y by substituting $x = 3$ in either of the original equations.

TEACHING TIP
After discussing Example 1, you may want to ask students what the ordered pair $(3, 3)$ represents on the graph of the two equations.

$$x + y = 6$$
$$3 + y = 6$$
$$y = 3$$

The solution is $(3, 3)$.

We check the answer in *both* equations.

Check
$$x + y = 6 \qquad\qquad 2x - y = 3$$
$$3 + 3 \stackrel{?}{=} 6 \qquad\qquad 2(3) - 3 \stackrel{?}{=} 3$$
$$6 = 6 \quad \textit{True} \qquad\qquad 6 - 3 \stackrel{?}{=} 3$$
$$3 = 3 \quad \textit{True}$$

▶ **Now Try Exercise 7**

Now we summarize the procedure.

> ### To Solve a System of Equations Using the Addition (or Elimination) Method
>
> 1. If necessary, rewrite each equation so that the terms containing variables appear on the left side of the equal sign and any constants appear on the right side of the equal sign.
> 2. If necessary, multiply one or both equations by a constant(s) so that when the equations are added the resulting sum will contain only one variable.
> 3. Add the equations. This will result in a single equation containing only one variable.
> 4. Solve for the variable in the equation from step 3.
> 5. **a)** Substitute the value found in step 4 into either of the original equations. Solve that equation to find the value of the remaining variable.
>
>   or
>
>   **b)** Repeat steps 2–4 to eliminate the other variable.
> 6. Check the values obtained in all original equations.

In step 5 we give two methods for finding the second variable after the first variable has been found. Method a) is generally used if the value obtained for the first variable is an integer. Method b) is often preferred if the value obtained for the first variable is a fraction.

In step 2 it may be necessary to multiply one or both equations by a constant. For example, suppose we have the system of equations, labeled (*eq.* 1) and (*eq.* 2) as shown below.

$$3x + 2y = 6 \quad (eq.\,1)$$
$$x - y = 8 \quad (eq.\,2)$$

If we wish to multiply equation 2 by -3, we will indicate this process as follows.

$$3x + 2y = 6 \qquad\qquad\qquad\qquad 3x + 2y = 6$$
$$-3(x - y) = -3(8) \quad (eq.\,2) \quad \textit{Multiplied by} -3 \quad \text{or} \quad -3x + 3y = -24$$

After performing the multiplication we will generally work with the revised system of equations, like the system given on the right.

TEACHING TIP
Stress that when solving a system, *both sides* of the equation are to be multiplied by a given number.

EXAMPLE 2 ▶ Solve the following system of equations using the addition method.

$$x + 3y = 13 \quad (eq.\,1)$$
$$x + 4y = 18 \quad (eq.\,2)$$

Solution   The goal of the addition process is to obtain two equations whose sum will be an equation containing only one variable. If we add these two equations, none of the variables will be eliminated. However, if we multiply either equation by -1 and then add, the terms containing x will sum to 0, and we will accomplish our goal. We will multiply (*eq.* 1) by -1.

INSTRUCTOR EXAMPLE
Solve the system of equations using the addition method.

$$x + 2y = 2$$
$$x + 3y = 6$$

Ans.: $(-6, 4)$

$$-1(x + 3y) = -1 \cdot 13 \quad (eq.\,1) \quad \textit{Multiplied by} -1 \quad \text{or} \quad -x - 3y = -13$$
$$x + 4y = 18 \qquad\qquad (eq.\,2) \qquad\qquad\qquad\qquad x + 4y = 18$$

Remember that both sides of the equation must be multiplied by −1. This process changes the sign of each term in the equation being multiplied without changing the solution to the system of equations. Now add the two equations on the right on the bottom of the preceding page.

$$-x - 3y = -13$$
$$\underline{x + 4y = 18}$$
$$y = 5$$

Now we solve for x in either of the original equations.

$$x + 3y = 13$$
$$x + 3(5) = 13$$
$$x + 15 = 13$$
$$x = -2$$

A check will show that the solution is $(-2, 5)$.

▶ **Now Try Exercise 13**

EXAMPLE 3 ▶ Solve the following system of equations using the addition method.

$$2x + y = 11 \quad (eq.\,1)$$
$$x + 3y = 18 \quad (eq.\,2)$$

Solution   To eliminate the variable x, multiply $(eq.\,2)$ by -2 and add the two equations.

$$2x + y = 11 \quad (eq.\,1) \qquad\qquad 2x + y = 11$$
$$-2(x + 3y) = -2 \cdot 18 \quad (eq.\,2) \quad \text{Multiplied by } -2 \quad \text{or} \quad -2x - 6y = -36$$

Now add:

$$2x + y = 11$$
$$\underline{-2x - 6y = -36}$$
$$-5y = -25$$
$$y = 5$$

Solve for x.

$$2x + y = 11$$
$$2x + 5 = 11$$
$$2x = 6$$
$$x = 3$$

The solution is $(3, 5)$.

▶ **Now Try Exercise 23**

Note that the solution in Example 3 is the same as the solutions obtained graphically in Example 3 of Section 5.1 and by substitution in Example 1 of Section 5.2.

In Example 3, we could have multiplied the $(eq.\,1)$ by -3 to eliminate the variable y. At this time, rework Example 3 by eliminating the variable y to see that you get the same answer.

EXAMPLE 4 ▶ Solve the following system of equations using the addition method.

$$4x = -2y - 18$$
$$-5y = 2x + 10$$

Solution　Step 1 of the procedure indicates that we should rewrite each equation so that the terms containing variables appear on the left side of the equal sign and the constants appear on the right side of the equal sign. By adding $2y$ to both sides of the first equation and subtracting $2x$ from both sides of the second equation we obtain the following system of equations.

$$4x + 2y = -18 \qquad (eq.\,1)$$
$$-2x - 5y = 10 \qquad (eq.\,2)$$

We now continue to solve the system. To eliminate the variable, x, we can multiply $(eq.\,2)$ by 2 and then add.

$$4x + 2y = -18 \qquad (eq.\,1) \qquad\qquad 4x + 2y = -18$$
$$2(-2x - 5y) = 2 \cdot 10 \qquad (eq.\,2) \;\; \textit{Multiplied by 2} \quad \text{or} \quad -4x - 10y = 20$$

$$
\begin{array}{r}
4x + 2y = -18 \\
-4x - 10y = 20 \\
\hline
-8y = 2 \\
y = -\dfrac{1}{4}
\end{array}
$$

Solve for x.

$$4x + 2y = -18$$
$$4x + 2\left(-\frac{1}{4}\right) = -18$$
$$4x - \frac{1}{2} = -18$$
$$2\left(4x - \frac{1}{2}\right) = 2(-18) \qquad \textit{Multiply both sides by 2 to remove fractions.}$$
$$8x - 1 = -36$$
$$8x = -35$$
$$x = -\frac{35}{8}$$

The solution is $\left(-\dfrac{35}{8}, -\dfrac{1}{4}\right)$.

Check the solution $\left(-\dfrac{35}{8}, -\dfrac{1}{4}\right)$ in both equations.

Check

$$4x + 2y = -18 \qquad\qquad\qquad -2x - 5y = 10$$
$$4\left(-\frac{35}{8}\right) + 2\left(-\frac{1}{4}\right) \stackrel{?}{=} -18 \qquad -2\left(-\frac{35}{8}\right) - 5\left(-\frac{1}{4}\right) \stackrel{?}{=} 10$$
$$-\frac{35}{2} - \frac{1}{2} \stackrel{?}{=} -18 \qquad\qquad \frac{35}{4} + \frac{5}{4} \stackrel{?}{=} 10$$
$$-\frac{36}{2} \stackrel{?}{=} -18 \qquad\qquad\qquad \frac{40}{4} \stackrel{?}{=} 10$$
$$-18 = -18 \quad \textit{True} \qquad\qquad\qquad 10 = 10 \quad \textit{True}$$

▸ **Now Try Exercise 29**

Note that the solution to Example 4 contains fractions. You should not always expect to get integers as answers.

EXAMPLE 5 ▶ Solve the following system of equations using the addition method.

$$2x + 3y = 6 \qquad (eq. 1)$$
$$5x - 4y = -8 \qquad (eq. 2)$$

Solution   The variable x can be eliminated by multiplying ($eq. 1$) by -5 and ($eq. 2$) by 2 and then adding the equations.

$$-5(2x + 3y) = -5 \cdot 6 \qquad (eq. 1) \quad \text{Multiplied by } -5 \quad \text{or} \quad -10x - 15y = -30$$
$$2(5x - 4y) = 2 \cdot (-8) \quad (eq. 2) \quad \text{Multiplied by 2} \quad \text{or} \quad 10x - 8y = -16$$

$$\begin{array}{r} -10x - 15y = -30 \\ 10x - 8y = -16 \\ \hline -23y = -46 \\ y = 2 \end{array}$$

Solve for x.

$$2x + 3y = 6$$
$$2x + 3(2) = 6$$
$$2x + 6 = 6$$
$$2x = 0$$
$$x = 0$$

The solution is $(0, 2)$.

▶ **Now Try Exercise 19**

In Example 5, the same value could have been obtained for y by multiplying the ($eq. 1$) by 5 and ($eq. 2$) by -2 and then adding. Try it now and see. We could have also begun by eliminating the variable y by multiplying ($eq. 1$) by 4 and ($eq. 2$) by 3.

EXAMPLE 6 ▶ Solve the following system of equations using the addition method.

$$2x + y = 3 \qquad (eq. 1)$$
$$4x + 2y = 12 \qquad (eq. 2)$$

Solution   The variable y can be eliminated by multiplying ($eq. 1$) by -2 and then adding the two equations.

$$-2(2x + y) = -2 \cdot 3 \quad (eq. 1) \quad \text{Multiplied by } -2 \quad \text{or} \quad -4x - 2y = -6$$
$$4x + 2y = 12 \qquad\qquad (eq. 2) \qquad\qquad\qquad\qquad 4x + 2y = 12$$

$$\begin{array}{r} -4x - 2y = -6 \\ 4x + 2y = 12 \\ \hline 0 = 6 \quad \text{False} \end{array}$$

Don't panic when both variables drop out and you see an expression like $0 = 6$. Not all systems of equations have a solution. *Since $0 = 6$ is a false statement, this system has no solution*. The system is inconsistent. The graphs of the equations will be parallel lines.

▶ **Now Try Exercise 25**

Note that the solution in Example 6 is identical to the solutions obtained by graphing in Example 4 of Section 5.1 and by substitution in Example 2 of Section 5.2.

EXAMPLE 7 ▶ Solve the following system of equations using the addition method.

$$x - \frac{1}{2}y = 2$$
$$y = 2x - 4$$

Solution   First align the *x*- and *y*-terms on the left side of the equal sign by subtracting $2x$ from both sides of the second equation.

$$x - \frac{1}{2}y = 2 \qquad (eq. 1)$$
$$-2x + y = -4 \qquad (eq. 2)$$

Now proceed as in the previous examples. Begin by multiplying (*eq. 1*) by 2 to remove fractions from the equation.

$$2\left(x - \frac{1}{2}y\right) = 2 \cdot 2 \quad (eq. 1) \quad \textit{Multiplied by 2} \quad \text{or} \quad 2x - y = 4$$
$$-2x + y = -4 \qquad (eq. 2) \qquad\qquad\qquad\qquad -2x + y = -4$$

$$\begin{array}{r} 2x - y = \ \ 4 \\ -2x + y = -4 \\ \hline 0 = \ \ 0 \quad \textit{True} \end{array}$$

Again both variables have dropped out. Here we are left with $0 = 0$. **Since $0 = 0$ is a true statement, the system is dependent and has an infinite number of solutions.** When graphed, both equations will be the same line.

▶ **Now Try Exercise 21**

The solution in Example 7 is the same as the solutions obtained by graphing in Example 5 of Section 5.1 and by substitution in Example 3 of Section 5.2.

EXAMPLE 8 ▶ Solve the following system of equations using the addition method.

$$2x + 3y = 7 \qquad (eq. 1)$$
$$5x - 7y = -3 \qquad (eq. 2)$$

Solution   We can eliminate the variable *x* by multiplying (*eq. 1*) by -5 and (*eq. 2*) by 2.

$$-5(2x + 3y) = -5 \cdot 7 \quad (eq. 1) \quad \textit{Multiplied by } -5 \quad \text{or} \quad -10x - 15y = -35$$
$$2(5x - 7y) = 2(-3) \quad (eq. 2) \quad \textit{Multiplied by 2} \quad \text{or} \quad 10x - 14y = -6$$

$$\begin{array}{r} -10x - 15y = -35 \\ 10x - 14y = -6 \\ \hline -29y = -41 \end{array}$$

$$y = \frac{41}{29}$$

We can now find *x* by substituting $y = \frac{41}{29}$ into one of the original equations and solving for *x*. If you try this, you will see that although it can be done, the calculations are messy. An easier method of solving for *x* is to go back to the original equations and eliminate the variable *y*. We can do this by multiplying (*eq. 1*) by 7 and (*eq. 2*) by 3.

$$\boxed{7}\,(2x + 3y) = \boxed{7} \cdot 7 \qquad (eq.\,1) \quad \text{Multiplied by 7} \quad \text{or} \quad 14x + 21y = 49$$

$$\boxed{3}\,(5x - 7y) = \boxed{3}\,(-3) \qquad (eq.\,2) \quad \text{Multiplied by 3} \quad \text{or} \quad 15x - 21y = -9$$

$$
\begin{aligned}
14x + 21y &= 49 \\
15x - 21y &= -9 \\
\hline
29x \qquad\;\; &= 40 \\
x &= \frac{40}{29}
\end{aligned}
$$

The solution is $\left(\dfrac{40}{29}, \dfrac{41}{29}\right)$.

▶ **Now Try Exercise 33**

Helpful Hint

We have illustrated three methods for solving a system of linear equations: graphing, substitution, and addition. When you are given a system of equations, which method should you use to solve the system? When you need an exact solution, graphing should not be used. Of the two algebraic methods, the addition method may be easier to use if there are no numerical coefficients of 1 in the system. If one or more of the variables have a coefficient of 1, you can use either substitution or addition.

EXERCISE SET 5.3

 MathXL®   MyMathLab

1. multiply top equation by 2   2. multiply bottom equation by 2
3. You will obtain a false statement, such as 0 = 6.

Concept/Writing Exercises

✎ **1.** When solving the following system of equations by the addition method, what will your first step be in solving the system? Explain your answer. Do not solve the system.

$$-x + 3y = 4$$
$$2x + 5y = 2$$

✎ **2.** When solving the following system of equations by the addition method, what will your first step be in solving the system? Explain your answer. Do not solve the system.

$$2x + 4y = -8$$
$$3x - 2y = 10$$

✎ **3.** When solving a system of linear equations by the addition method, how will you know if the system is inconsistent?

✎ **4.** When solving a system of linear equations by the addition method, how will you know if the system is dependent? You will obtain a true statement, such as 0 = 0.

Practice the Skills

Solve each system of equations using the addition method.

5. $x + y = 6$
$\quad x - y = 4 \quad (5, 1)$

6. $x - y = 10$
$\quad x + y = 8 \quad (9, -1)$

7. $x + y = 9$
$\quad -x + y = 1 \quad (4, 5)$

8. $5x + y = 14$
$\quad 4x - y = 4 \quad (2, 4)$

9. $x + 2y = 21$
$\quad 2x - 2y = -6 \quad (5, 8)$

10. $x - y = 3$
$\quad x + y = -3 \quad (0, -3)$

11. $4x + y = 6$
$\quad -8x - 2y = 20 \quad \text{no solution}$

12. $x - y = 2$
$\quad 3x - 3y = 1 \quad \text{no solution}$

13. $-5x + y = 14$
$\quad -3x + y = -2 \quad (-8, -26)$

14. $6x + 3y = 30$
$\quad 2x + 3y = 18 \quad (3, 4)$

15. $2x + y = -6$
$\quad 2x - 2y = 3 \quad \left(-\dfrac{3}{2}, -3\right)$

16. $-4x + 3y = 0$
$\quad 7x - 6y = 3 \quad (-3, -4)$

17. $2y = 6x + 16$
$\quad y = -3x - 4 \quad (-2, 2)$

18. $2x - 3y = 4$
$\quad 2x + y = -4 \quad (-1, -2)$

19. $5x + 3y = 12$
$\quad 3x - 6y = 15 \quad (3, -1)$

20. $8x - 4y = 12$
$\quad 2x - 8y = 3 \quad \left(\dfrac{3}{2}, 0\right)$

21. $-2y = -4x + 12$
$\quad y = 2x - 6 \quad \text{infinite number of solutions}$

22. $4x - 2y = 12$
$\quad 4y = 8x - 24 \quad \text{infinite number of solutions.}$

23. $5x - 4y = -3$

$7y = 2x + 12$ $(1, 2)$

24. $2x + 3y = -3$

$-3x - 5y = 7$ $(6, -5)$

25. $5x - 4y = 1$

$-10x + 8y = -3$ no solution

26. $2x - 3y = 11$

$5y = 3x - 17$ $(4, -1)$

27. $5x - 6y = 0$

$3x + 4y = 0$ $(0, 0)$

28. $4x - 2y = -4$

$5x - 6y = -26$ $(2, 6)$

29. $-5x + 4y = -20$

$3x - 2y = 15$ $\left(10, \dfrac{15}{2}\right)$

30. $4x - 3y = -4$

$3x - 5y = 10$ $\left(-\dfrac{50}{11}, -\dfrac{52}{11}\right)$

31. $6x = 4y + 12$

$3y - 5x = -6$ $(-6, -12)$

32. $5x = 2y - 4$

$3x - 5y = 6$ $\left(-\dfrac{32}{19}, -\dfrac{42}{19}\right)$

33. $4x + 5y = 0$

$3x = 6y + 4$ $\left(\dfrac{20}{39}, -\dfrac{16}{39}\right)$

34. $4x - 3y = 8$

$-3x + 4y = 9$ $\left(\dfrac{59}{7}, \dfrac{60}{7}\right)$

35. $x - \dfrac{1}{2}y = 4$

$3x + y = 6$ $\left(\dfrac{14}{5}, -\dfrac{12}{5}\right)$

36. $2x - \dfrac{1}{3}y = 6$

$3x - \dfrac{5}{6}y = -13$ $(14, 66)$

37. $3x - y = 4$

$2x - \dfrac{2}{3}y = 8$ no solution

38. $-5x + 6y = -12$

$\dfrac{5}{3}x - 4 = 2y$ infinite number of solutions

Problem Solving

39. Sum of Numbers The sum of two numbers is 20. When the second number is subtracted from the first number, the difference is 8. Find the two numbers. 14, 6

40. Sum of Numbers The sum of two numbers is 46. When the first number is subtracted from the second number, the difference is 6. Find the two numbers. 20, 26

41. Sum of Numbers The sum of a number and twice a second number is 14. When the second number is subtracted from the first number the difference is 2. Find the two numbers. 6, 4

42. Sum of Numbers The sum of two numbers is 9. Twice the first number subtracted from three times the second number is 7. Find the two numbers. 4, 5

43. Rectangles When the length of a rectangle is x inches and the width is y inches, the perimeter is 18 inches. If the length is doubled and the width is tripled, the perimeter becomes 42 inches. Find the length and width of the original rectangle. $w = 3$ in., $l = 6$ in.

44. Perimeter of a Rectangle When the length of a rectangle is x inches and the width is y inches, the perimeter is 28 inches. If the length is doubled and the width is tripled, the perimeter becomes 66 inches. Find the length and width of the original rectangle. $w = 5$ in., $l = 9$ in.

45. Photograph A photograph has a perimeter of 36 inches. The difference between the photograph's length and width is 2 inches. Find the length and width of the photograph.

45. $w = 8$ in., $l = 10$ in. **47.** Answers will vary.

46. Rectangular Garden John has a large rectangular garden with a perimeter of 82 feet. The difference between the garden's length and width is 11 feet. Determine the length and width of his garden. $w = 15$ ft, $l = 26$ ft

47. Construct a system of two equations that has no solution. Explain how you know the system has no solution.

48. Construct a system of two equations that has an infinite number of solutions. Explain how you know the system has an infinite number of solutions. Answers will vary.

49. a) Solve the system of equations

$$4x + 2y = 1000$$
$$2x + 4y = 800 \qquad (200, 100)$$

b) If we divide all the terms in the top equation by 2 we get the following system:

$$2x + y = 500$$
$$2x + 4y = 800$$

How will the solution to this system compare to the solution in part **a)**? Explain and then check your explanation by solving this system. same solution

50. Suppose we divided all the terms in both equations given in Exercise 49 **a)** by 2, and then solved the system. How will the solution to this system compare to the solution in part **a)**? Explain and then check your explanation by solving each system. same solution

Challenge Problems

In Exercises 51 and 52, solve each system of equations using the addition method. (Hint: First remove all fractions by multiplying both sides of the equation by the LCD.)

51. $\dfrac{x + 2}{2} - \dfrac{y + 4}{3} = 4$

$\dfrac{x + y}{2} = \dfrac{1}{2} + \dfrac{x - y}{3}$ $(8, -1)$

52. $\dfrac{5}{2}x + 3y = \dfrac{9}{2} + y$

$\dfrac{1}{4}x - \dfrac{1}{2}y = 6x + 12$ $\left(-\dfrac{105}{41}, \dfrac{447}{82}\right)$

In intermediate algebra you may solve systems of three equations with three unknowns. Solve the following system.

53.

$$x + 2y - z = 2$$
$$2x - y + z = 3$$
$$3x + y + z = 8$$

Hint: Work with *one pair* of equations to get one equation in two unknowns. Then work with *a different pair* of the original equations to get another equation in the same two unknowns. Then solve the system of two equations in two unknowns. List your answer as an *ordered triple* of the form (x, y, z). $(1, 2, 3)$

Group Activity

Work parts **a)** *and* **b)** *of Exercise 54 on your own. Then discuss and work parts* **c)** *and* **d)** *as a group.*

54. a) Answers will vary.

54. How difficult is it to construct a system of linear equations that has a specific solution? It is really not too difficult to do. Consider:

$$2(3) + 4(5) = 26$$
$$4(3) - 7(5) = -23$$

The system of equations

$$2x + 4y = 26$$
$$4x - 7y = -23$$

has solution $(3, 5)$.

a) Using the information provided, determine another system of equations that has $(3, 5)$ as a solution.

b) Determine a system of linear equations that has $(2, 3)$ as a solution.   Answers will vary.

c) Compare your answer with the answers of the other members of your group.   Answers will vary.

d) As a group, determine the number of systems of equations that have $(2, 3)$ as a solution.   an infinite number

---

Cumulative Review Exercises

[1.9] **55.** Evaluate 5^3.   125

[2.5] **56.** Solve the equation $2(2x - 5) = 2x + 4$.   7

[2.8] **57.** Solve the inequality $2x - 4 < 4x - 2$ and graph the solution on a number line. $x > -1$;

[4.4] **58.** Write an equation, in slope-intercept form, of the line that passes through the point $(1, 5)$ and has a slope of 3. $y = 3x + 2$

[4.6] **59.** If $f(x) = 2x^2 - 4$, find $f(-3)$.   14

Mid-Chapter Test: 5.1–5.3

To find out how well you understand the chapter material to this point, take this brief test. The answers, and the section where the material was initially discussed, are given in the back of the book. Review any questions that you answered incorrectly.

Determine which of the following ordered pairs satisfy each system of equations.

1. $4x + 3y = -1$

$x - 2y = 8$

a) $(-1, 1)$ **b)** $(2, -3)$ **b)**

2. $6x - y = -2$

$7x + \dfrac{1}{2}y = 6$

a) $\left(\dfrac{1}{2}, 5\right)$ **b)** $\left(\dfrac{1}{3}, 4\right)$ **a)**

Without graphing, state whether the system of equations has exactly one solution, no solution, or an infinite number of solutions.

3. $2x + y = 8$

$3x - 4y = 1$ one solution

4. $\dfrac{1}{2}x - 3y = 5$

$-2x + 12y = -20$ infinite number of solutions

5. $y = \dfrac{3}{2}x + \dfrac{5}{2}$

$3x - 2y = 7$ no solution

Determine the solution to each system of equations graphically. If the system is dependent or inconsistent, so state.

6. $y = 2x + 1$

$y = -x + 4$ $(1, 3)$

7. $x = 5$

$y = -3$ $(5, -3)$

Solve each system of equations by substitution.

8. $3x + y = -2$

$2x - 3y = -16$ $(-2, 4)$

9. $x - 3y = 2$

$4x + 9y = 1$ $\left(1, -\dfrac{1}{3}\right)$

10. $3x - y = 5$

$x - \dfrac{1}{3}y = 2$ no solution

11. Rectangle The perimeter of a rectangle is 44 feet. Find the length and the width if the length is 8 feet greater than the width.   *l*: 15 ft; *w*: 7 ft

Solve each system of equations using the addition method.

12. $x + 3y = 1$

  $2x - 3y = 11$ $(4, -1)$

13. $4x + 3y = 4$

  $-8x + 5y = 14$ $\left(-\dfrac{1}{2}, 2\right)$

14. $5x - 2y = 1$

  $-10x + 4y = -2$ infinite number of solutions

15. In solving the system of equations

$$3x - 5y = -16$$
$$2x + 3y = 21,$$

Hugo Platt stated that the solution was $x = 3$. This is incorrect. Why? Explain your answer. Give the correct solution to the system.   must have two values, one for x and one for y: $(3, 5)$

5.4 Systems of Equations: Applications and Problem Solving

1 Use systems of equations to solve application problems.

FIGURE 5.11

FIGURE 5.12

1 ▸ Use Systems of Equations to Solve Application Problems

The method you use to solve a system of equations may depend on whether you wish to see "the entire picture" or are interested in finding the exact solution. If you are interested in the trend as the variable changes, you might decide to graph the equations. If you want only the solution—that is, the ordered pair common to both equations—you might use one of the two algebraic methods to find the common solution.

Many of the application problems solved in earlier chapters using only one variable can also be solved using two variables. In Example 1 we use **complementary angles**, which are two angles whose sum measures 90°. **Figure 5.11** illustrates complementary angles x and y.

EXAMPLE 1 ▸ **Building a Patio** Phil Mahler is building a rectangular patio out of cement (**Fig. 5.12**). When he measures the two angles formed by a diagonal he finds that angle x is 22° greater than angle y. Find the two angles.

Solution **Understand and Translate** A rectangle has 4 right (or 90°) angles. Angles x and y are therefore complementary, and the sum of angles x and y is 90°. Thus one equation in the system of equations is $x + y = 90$. Since angle x is 22° greater than angle y, the second equation is $x = y + 22$.

System of equations
$$\begin{cases} x + y = 90 \\ x = y + 22 \end{cases}$$

Carry Out Subtract y from each side of the second equation. Then use the addition method to solve.

$$\begin{array}{r} x + y = \ \ 90 \\ x - y = \ \ 22 \\ \hline 2x \ \ \ \ \ = 112 \\ x = \ \ 56 \end{array}$$

Now substitute 56 for x in the first equation and solve for y.

$$x + y = 90$$
$$56 + y = 90$$
$$y = 34$$

Check and Answer Angle x is 56° and angle y is 34°. Note that their sum is 90° and angle x is 22° greater than angle y.

▸ **Now Try Exercise 3**

Example 1 could also have been solved using the substitution method. Try solving the system now using substitution.

EXAMPLE 2 ▶ Greek Ruins In Paestum, Italy, there are both ancient Greek and ancient Roman ruins, including three ancient Greek temples built about 500 B.C. The perimeter of the rectangular Basilica, also called the Temple of Hera, shown in the photo, is 161.2 meters, and the length is 2.1 times its width. Determine the dimensions of the Basilica.

Solution Understand and Translate   The formula for the perimeter of a rectangle is $P = 2l + 2w$. We will use this formula to determine one equation in the system. The other equation comes from the fact that the length is 2.1 times the width. Let w = width of the Basilica and l = length of the Basilica. Since the perimeter is 161.2 meters, one equation is $161.2 = 2l + 2w$. Since the length is 2.1 times the width, the other equation is $l = 2.1w$.

System of equations
$$\begin{cases} 161.2 = 2l + 2w \\ l = 2.1w \end{cases}$$

Carry Out   We will solve this system by substitution. Since $l = 2.1w$, substitute $2.1w$ for l in the equation $161.2 = 2l + 2w$ to obtain

$$161.2 = 2l + 2w$$
$$161.2 = 2(2.1w) + 2w$$
$$161.2 = 4.2w + 2w$$
$$161.2 = 6.2w$$
$$26 = w$$

Check and Answer   The width is 26 meters. Since the length is 2.1 times the width, the length is 2.1(26) or 54.6 meters. Notice that the perimeter is 2(26) + 2(54.6) = 161.2 meters.

▶ **Now Try Exercise 7**

INSTRUCTOR EXAMPLE 2
Determine the dimensions of a rectangle having a perimeter of 92 meters and whose length is 6 meters greater than the width.
Ans.: l = 26 m, w = 20 m

EXAMPLE 3 ▶ Bridge Toll Only two-axle vehicles are permitted to cross a bridge that leads to Honeymoon Island State Park. The toll for the bridge is 50 cents for motorcycles and $1.00 for cars and trucks. On Saturday, the toll booth attendant collected a total of $150, and the vehicle counter recorded 170 vehicles crossing the bridge. How many motorcycles and how many cars and trucks crossed the bridge that day?

Solution Understand and Translate   We are provided sufficient information in the example to obtain two equations for our system of equations.

$$\text{Let } x = \text{number of motorcycles}$$
$$y = \text{number of cars and trucks.}$$

Since a total of 170 vehicles crossed the bridge, one equation is $x + y = 170$. The second equation comes from the tolls collected.

tolls from motorcycles	+	tolls from cars and trucks	= 150
0.50x	+	1.00y	= 150

System of equations
$$\begin{cases} x + y = 170 \\ 0.50x + 1.00y = 150 \end{cases}$$

INSTRUCTOR EXAMPLE 3
Raffle tickets cost $1.00 for children and $1.50 for adults. If 110 tickets were sold for a total of $140, how many adult tickets and how many children tickets were sold?
Ans.: children: 50, adult: 60

Carry Out   Since the first equation can be easily solved for y, we will solve this system by substitution. Solving for y in $x + y = 170$ gives $y = 170 - x$. Substitute $170 - x$ for y in the second equation and solve for x.

$$0.50x + 1.00y = 150$$
$$0.50x + 1.00(170 - x) = 150$$
$$0.50x + 170 - 1.00x = 150$$
$$170 - 0.5x = 150$$
$$-0.5x = -20$$
$$\frac{-0.5x}{-0.5} = \frac{-20}{-0.5}$$
$$x = 40$$

Answer   Forty motorcycles crossed the bridge. The total number of vehicles that crossed the bridge is 170. Therefore, $170 - 40$ or 130 cars and trucks crossed the bridge that Saturday. A check will show that the total collected for these 170 vehicles is $150.

▶ **Now Try Exercise 9**

EXAMPLE 4 ▶ **Swans** Many cities display statues of animals or other items for artistic, charitable, or other reasons. Kim Enterprise is sponsoring the construction of a swan and is considering two artists for the job. One artist, Pam, has indicated the materials needed will cost $2200, and she will charge $80 per hour to paint the swan. The other artist, Mike, indicated the materials will cost $1825, and he will charge $95 per hour to paint the swan.

a) How many hours would the painting need to take for the total cost for both artists to be the same?

b) If both artists estimate the time required for painting the swan to be 20 hours, which artist would be less expensive?

Solution   a) Understand and Translate   We will write equations for the total cost for both Pam and Mike.

Let n = number of hours for painting

c = total cost of swan

Pam	Mike
total cost = materials + labor	total cost = materials + labor
$c = 2200 + 80n$	$c = 1825 + 95n$

Now we have our system of equations.

System of equations
$$\begin{cases} c = 2200 + 80n \\ c = 1825 + 95n \end{cases}$$

Carry Out
$$\text{total cost for Pam} = \text{total cost for Mike}$$
$$2200 + 80n = 1825 + 95n$$
$$375 + 80n = 95n$$
$$375 = 15n$$
$$25 = n$$

Answer   If 25 hours of painting is required, the cost would be equal.

b) If the painting takes 20 hours, Mike would be less expensive, as shown below.

Pam	Mike
$c = 2200 + 80n$	$c = 1825 + 95n$
$c = 2200 + 80(20)$	$c = 1825 + 95(20)$
$c = 3800$	$c = 3725$

▶ **Now Try Exercise 17**

Motion Problems with Two Rates

We introduced the distance formula, distance = rate · time or $d = rt$, in Section 2.6. Now we introduce a method using two variables and a system of equations to solve motion problems that involve two rates. Often when working motion problems with two different rates it is helpful to construct a table to summarize the information given. We will do this in Example 5.

Bob   Restaurant   Jim
Speed: x Speed: y

|← 420 miles →|
|← 4 hours →|← 4 hours →|

FIGURE 5.13

EXAMPLE 5 ▶ **Meeting for Lunch** Bob and Jim are good friends who live 420 miles apart. Sometimes they will meet for lunch at a restaurant somewhere between the towns where they live. On one occasion, they left their houses at the same time. They both arrived at the restaurant 4 hours after they began. Determine Bob's and Jim's speed if Bob drove at an average speed of 5 miles per hour faster than Jim.

Solution **Understand and Translate** We are asked to find Bob's and Jim's speed. We are given sufficient information in the example to obtain two equations for our system of equations.

$$\text{Let } x = \text{Bob's speed.}$$
$$\text{Let } y = \text{Jim's speed.}$$

We will draw a sketch to help understand the problem. See **Figure 5.13**. We will use the formula, distance = rate · time. They both traveled for 4 hours.

Traveler	Rate	Time	Distance
Bob	x	4	$4x$
Jim	y	4	$4y$

Since the total distance covered is 420 miles, our first equation is

$$4x + 4y = 420$$

The second equation comes from the fact that Bob's speed was 5 miles per hour greater than Jim's speed. Therefore, we can add 5 miles per hour to Jim's speed to get Bob's speed.

$$x = y + 5$$

Our system of equations is

$$4x + 4y = 420$$
$$x = y + 5$$

Carry Out The equation $x = y + 5$ is already solved for x. Substituting $y + 5$ for x in the first equation gives

$$4x + 4y = 420$$
$$4(y + 5) + 4y = 420$$
$$4y + 20 + 4y = 420$$
$$8y + 20 = 420$$
$$8y = 400$$
$$y = 50$$

Jim's speed is 50 miles per hour. Bob's speed is

$$x = y + 5$$
$$x = 50 + 5$$
$$x = 55$$

Check and Answer The answer seems reasonable. We can check to see if the equation $4x + 4y = 420$ holds true for $x = 55$ and $y = 50$.

$$4x + 4y = 420$$
$$4(55) + 4(50) \stackrel{?}{=} 420$$
$$220 + 200 \stackrel{?}{=} 420$$
$$420 = 420 \quad \textit{True}$$

Thus Bob's speed is 55 miles per hour and Jim's speed is 50 miles per hour.

▶ **Now Try Exercise 23**

Mixture Problems

Mixture problems were solved with one variable in Section 3.4. Now we will solve mixture problems using two variables and systems of equations. Recall that any problem in which two or more quantities are combined to produce a different quantity, or a single quantity is separated into two or more quantities, may be considered a mixture problem. Again, we will use a table to summarize the information given.

EXAMPLE 6 ▶ Candy Shop A customer comes into a candy shop and explains that he needs a mixture of chocolate-covered cherries and chocolate-covered pecans. The chocolate-covered cherries sell for $7.50 per pound and the chocolate-covered pecans sell for $6.00 per pound.

a) How many pounds of the chocolate-covered pecans must be mixed with 2 pounds of chocolate-covered cherries to obtain a mixture that sells for $6.50 per pound?

b) How many pounds of the mixture will there be?

Solution   **a) Understand and Translate** We are asked to find the number of pounds of chocolate-covered pecans to be mixed with 2 pounds of chocolate-covered cherries. We are given sufficient information in the example to obtain two equations for our system of equations.

Let x = number of pounds of chocolate-covered pecans

y = number of pounds of mixture.

Often it is helpful to make a sketch of the situation. After we draw a sketch, we will construct a table. In our sketch we will use bins to mix the candy (**Fig. 5.14**).

FIGURE 5.14

	CHOCOLATE COVERED PECANS		CHOCOLATE COVERED CHERRIES		MIXTURE
Price per pound	$6.00 lb		$7.50 lb		$6.50 lb
Number of pounds	x	+	2	=	y

The value of the candy is found by multiplying the number of pounds by the price per pound.

Candy	Price	Number of Pounds	Value of Candy
Pecans	6	x	$6x$
Cherries	7.50	2	7.50(2)
Mixture	6.50	y	6.50y

Our two equations come from the following information:

$$\left(\begin{array}{c}\text{number of pounds}\\\text{of pecans}\end{array}\right) + \left(\begin{array}{c}\text{number of pounds}\\\text{of cherries}\end{array}\right) = \left(\begin{array}{c}\text{number of pounds}\\\text{of mixture}\end{array}\right)$$

$$x \qquad + \qquad 2 \qquad = \qquad y$$

value of pecans $+$ value of cherries $=$ value of mixture

$$6x \qquad + \qquad 7.50(2) \qquad = \qquad 6.50y$$

System of equations $\begin{cases} x + 2 = y \\ 6x + 7.50(2) = 6.50y \end{cases}$

Carry Out Since $y = x + 2$, we substitute $x + 2$ for y in the second equation and solve for x.

$$6x + 7.50(2) = 6.50y$$
$$6x + 7.50(2) = 6.50(x + 2)$$
$$6x + 15 = 6.50x + 13$$
$$15 = 0.50x + 13$$
$$2 = 0.50x$$
$$4 = x$$

Answer Thus, 4 pounds of the chocolate-covered pecans must be mixed with 2 pounds of the chocolate-covered cherries.

b) The total mixture will weigh $4 + 2$ or 6 pounds.

▸ **Now Try Exercise 33**

Now we will work an example similar to Example 7 in Section 3.4, but this time we will use a system of equations to solve the problem.

EXAMPLE 7 ▸ **Chemistry Lab** Eilish Main is a chemistry professor. She has a number of labs coming up shortly in which her students will need to use a 15% solution of sulfuric acid. Her assistant informs her that they are out of the 15% solution. Eilish checks the supply room and finds they have a large supply of both 5% and 30% sulfuric acid solutions. She decides to use the 5% and 30% solutions to make 60 liters of a 15% solution. How many liters of the 5% solution and the 30% solution should she mix?

Solution **Understand and Translate** Eilish will combine the 5% and 30% solutions to get 60 liters of a 15% solution of sulfuric acid. We need to determine how much of each should be mixed.

$$\text{Let } x = \text{number of liters of 5\% solution}$$
$$y = \text{number of liters of 30\% solution}.$$

The problem is displayed in **Figure 5.15** and the information is summarized in the following table.

FIGURE 5.15

Solution	Number of Liters	Concentration	Acid Content
5% Solution	x	0.05	$0.05x$
30% Solution	y	0.30	$0.30y$
Mixture	60	0.15	$0.15(60)$

Because the total volume of the combination is 60 liters, we have

$$x + y = 60$$

From the table we see that

$$\left(\begin{array}{c}\text{acid content of}\\ \text{5\% solution}\end{array}\right) + \left(\begin{array}{c}\text{acid content of}\\ \text{30\% solution}\end{array}\right) = \left(\begin{array}{c}\text{acid content}\\ \text{of mixture}\end{array}\right)$$

$$0.05x \qquad + \qquad 0.30y \qquad = \qquad 0.15(60)$$

System of equations
$$\begin{cases} x + y = 60 \\ 0.05x + 0.30y = 0.15(60) \end{cases}$$

Carry Out   We will solve this system by substitution. First we solve for y in the first equation.

$$x + y = 60$$
$$y = 60 - x$$

Then we substitute $60 - x$ for y in the second equation.

$$0.05x + 0.30y = 0.15(60)$$
$$0.05x + 0.30(60 - x) = 9$$
$$0.05x + 18 - 0.30x = 9$$
$$-0.25x + 18 = 9$$
$$-0.25x = -9$$
$$x = \frac{-9}{-0.25} = 36$$

Now we solve for y.

$$y = 60 - x$$
$$y = 60 - 36$$
$$y = 24$$

Answer   Thus, 36 liters of the 5% acid solution should be mixed with 24 liters of the 30% acid solution to obtain 60 liters of a 15% acid solution.

▶ **Now Try Exercise 31**

EXERCISE SET 5.4

MathXL®   MyMathLab

Practice the Skills and Problem Solving

In Exercises 1–38, use a system of linear equations to find the solution. Use a calculator where appropriate.

1. **Sum of Integers** The sum of two integers is 43. Find the numbers if one number is 9 greater than the other.   17, 26

2. **Difference of Integers** The difference of two integers is 20. Find the two numbers if the larger is 4 less than three times the smaller.   12, 32

3. **Complementary Angles** Angles A and B are complementary angles. If angle B is 18° greater than angle A, find the measure of each angle. (See Example 1.) $A = 36°$, $B = 54°$

4. **Supplementary Angles** Two angles are **supplementary angles** when the sum of their measures is 180°. If angles A and B are supplementary angles, and angle A is five times as large as angle B, find the measure of each angle. $A = 150°$, $B = 30°$

5. **Supplementary Angles** If angles A and B are supplementary angles (see Exercise 4) and angle A is 44° greater than angle B, find the measure of each angle. $A = 112°$, $B = 68°$

6. **Vegetable Garden** Fred MacDonald bought 60 feet of fence to make a rectangular vegetable garden. What dimensions will the vegetable garden have if the length is 10 feet greater than the width?   *w:* 10 ft, *l:* 20 ft

7. **American Flag** The satellite photo shown is of a floral flag planted by Bodger Seeds, Ltd., that covers 6.65 acres in Lompoc, California. The flag maintains the proper flag dimensions. The perimeter of the flag is 2260 feet. Determine the flag's length and width if the length is 350 feet greater than the width.   *w* = 390 ft, *l* = 740 ft

8. **Letters** Peter Collins, an insurance agent, sent out a total of 150 envelopes by first class mail. Some weighed under 1 ounce and required a 39-cent stamp. The rest weighed 1 ounce or more but less than 2 ounces and required 63-cents postage. If his total postage cost was $70.50 determine how many envelopes were sent at each postage rate.   100 at 39 ¢, 50 at 63 ¢

9. **Population** The population of Birch Mountain is 40,000 and it is growing by 800 per year. The population of Hidden Valley is 67,000 and it is decreasing by 550 per year. How long will it take for both areas to have the same population?   20 yr

10. **Coin Collection** Darren collects coins. His collection has a total of 40 old coins containing only dimes and quarters. If the face value of the coins in his collection is $7.30, how many dimes and how many quarters are in the collection?   18 dimes, 22 quarters

11. **Kayaking** Shane Stagg is kayaking in the St. Lawrence River. He can paddle 4.7 miles per hour with the current and 3.4 miles per hour against the current. Find the speed of the kayak in still water and the current.   kayak, 4.05 mph; current, 0.65 mph

12. **Airline Flights** Two commercial airplanes are flying in the same vicinity but in opposite directions. The American Airlines jet, flying with the wind, is flying at 570 miles per hour. The US Airways jet, flying against the wind, is flying at 500 miles per hour. If it were not for the wind, the two planes would be flying at identical speeds. Find the speed of the planes in still air and the speed of the wind.   planes, 535 mph; wind, 35 mph

13. **Farming** Celeste Nossiter plants corn and wheat on her 100-acre farm near Albuquerque, New Mexico. She estimates that her income after deducting expenses is $500 per acre of corn and $475 per acre of wheat. Find the number of acres of corn and wheat planted if her total income after expenses is $49,000.   60 acres corn, 40 acres wheat

14. **Discount Warehouse** Sol's Club Discount Warehouse has two membership plans. Under plan A the customer pays a $50 annual membership and 85% of the manufacturer's recommended list price. Under plan B the annual membership fee is $100 and the customer pays 80% of the manufacturer's recommended list price. How much merchandise, in dollars, would one have to purchase to pay the same amount under both plans? $1000

15. **Six Flags** The Meyer family had a family reunion in Texas. They all purchased tickets to visit the Six Flags Amusement Park. The adult tickets cost $40 and the children's cost $30. If 27 tickets were purchased, and the total cost for all the adult and all the children's tickets was $930, how many adults' and how many children's tickets were purchased?   12 adults, 15 children

16. **Sales Position** Susan Summerlin, a salesperson, is considering two job offers. At the Medtec Company, Susan's salary would be $300 per week plus a 5% commission of sales. At the Genzone Company, her salary would be $210 per week plus an 8% commission of sales.

   a) What weekly dollar volume of sales would Susan need to make for the total income from both companies to be the same? $3000

   b) If she expects to make sales of $4000, which company would give the greater salary?   Genzone

17. **Copier Contract** Carol Juncker just purchased a high speed copier for her office and wants a service contract on the copier. She is considering two sources for the contract. The Kate Spence Copier Sales and Service Company charges $18 a month plus 2 cents a copy. Office Copier Depot charges $25 a month but only 1.5 cents a copy.

   a) Assuming the prices do not change, how many copies would Carol need to make for the monthly cost of both plans to be the same?   1400 copies

   b) If Carol plans to make 2500 copies a month, which plan would be the least expensive?   Office Copier Depot

18. **Financial Planner** Chris Suit is a financial planner for Walsh and Associates. His salary is a flat 40% commission of sales. As an employee he has no overhead. He is considering starting his own company. Then 100% of sales would be income to him. However, he estimates his monthly overhead for office rent, secretary, utilities, and so on, would be about $1500. How much in sales would Chris's own company need to make in a month for him to make the same income he does as an employee of Walsh and Associates? $2500

19. **Savings Accounts** Mr. and Mrs. Vinny McAdams invest a total of $8000 in two savings accounts. One account yields 5% simple interest and the other 4% simple interest. Find the amount placed in each account if they receive a total of $375 in interest after 1 year. Use interest = principal · rate · time. $2500 at 4%, $5500 at 5%

20. **Investments** Carol Horton invested a total of $10,000. Part of the money was placed in a savings account paying 5.5% simple interest. The rest was placed in a fixed annuity paying 6% simple interest. If the total interest received for the year was $570, how much had been invested in each account? $6000 in savings, $4000 in annuity

21. **Carpeting** The following bar graph shows the cost per square yard of the same carpet at two different carpet stores along with the installation cost (including matting) at each store.

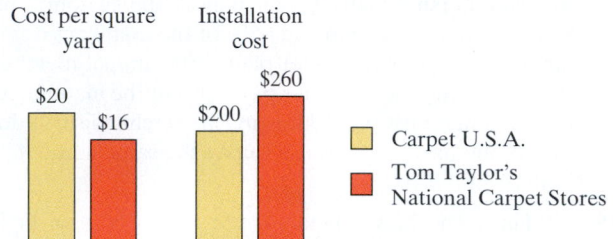

a) Find the number of square yards of carpet that Dorothy Rosene must purchase for the total cost of the carpet plus installation to be the same from both stores.   15 sq yd

b) If she needs to purchase and have installed 25 square yards of carpet, which store will be less expensive?   Tom Taylor's

22. **Self-Publishing** Jorge Perez has written a book that he plans to self-publish. He has consulted two printers to determine the cost of printing his book. Each company has a one-time setup charge and a charge for each book printed. The cost information is shown on the following bar graph.

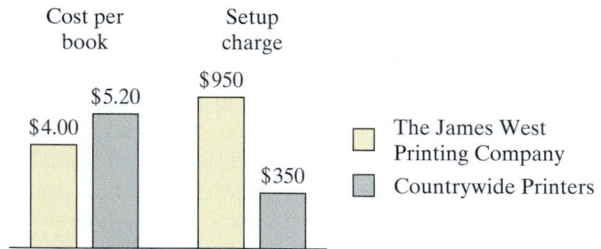

a) How many books would Jorge need to have printed for the total cost of his books to be the same from both printers?   500 copies

b) If he plans to print 1000 books, which printer would be the least expensive?   The James West Company

Review Example 5 before working Exercises 23–30.

23. **Road Trip** Dave Visser started driving from Columbus, Ohio, toward Lincoln, Nebraska—a distance of 903 miles. At the same time Alice Harra started driving to Columbus, Ohio, from Lincoln, Nebraska. If the two meet after 7 hours and Alice's speed averages 15 miles per hour greater than Dave's speed, find the speed of each car.   Dave, 57 mph; Alice, 72 mph

24. **Laying Cable** Two Lucent Technology cable crews are digging a ditch to lay fiber-optic cable. One crew, headed by John Mayleben, and a second crew, headed by Leigh Sumeral, start at opposite ends of a 30-mile stretch of land. John's crew digs at an average speed that is 0.1 miles per hour faster than Leigh's crew. If the two crews meet after 50 hours, find the average speed of each crew.   John's, 0.35 mph; Leigh's, 0.25 mph

25. **Speed Boat** During a race, Elizabeth Kell's speed boat travels 4 miles per hour faster than Melissa Suarez's boat. If Elizabeth's boat finishes the race in 3 hours and Melissa's finishes the race in 3.4 hours, find the speed of each boat.   Melissa, 30 mph; Elizabeth, 34 mph

26. **Trains** Two trains are 560 miles apart on a parallel set of tracks traveling toward each other. One train is traveling 10 miles per hour faster than the other. The trains will pass each other in 4 hours. Find the speed of the trains.   65 and 75 mph

27. **Jogging** Amanda Rodriguez and Delores Melendez go jogging along the River Walk Trail in San Antonio, Texas. They start at the same point, but Amanda starts 1.2 hours before Delores does. If Amanda jogs at a rate of 5 miles per hour and Delores jogs at a rate of 8 miles per hour, how long after Delores starts will Delores catch up to Amanda?   2 hr

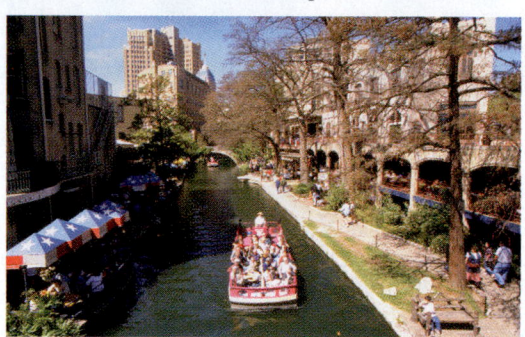

San Antonio, Texas

28. **Horseback Riding** Bill Leonard trots his horse Trixie east at 8 miles per hour. One half-hour later, Mary Mullaley starts at the same point and canters her horse Pegarno west at 12 miles per hour. How long after Mary starts riding will Mary and Bill be separated by 14 miles?   0.5 hr

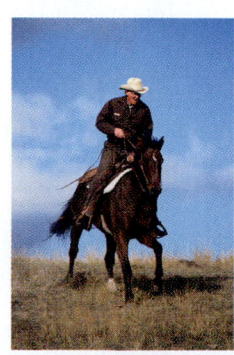

29. **Riding on the Trail** Terri Teegarden has been rollerblading at 5 miles per hour for 0.75 hour along a trail near Pebble Beach, California. She receives a phone call on her cellular phone from her friend Randy Taylor. Randy tells her that he is where she started, at the beginning of the trail. He tells her to keep rollerblading and says that he will ride his bike to catch up with her. Randy plans to ride at 10.5 miles per hour. How long after Randy starts will they meet?   ≈0.68 hr

30. **Dude Ranch** Kate and Ernie Danforth are at a dude ranch. Kate has been horseback riding for 0.5 hours on the trail at 6 miles per hour when Ernie starts riding his horse on the trail. If Ernie rides at 10 miles per hour, how long will it be before he catches up to Kate?   0.75 hr

Review Examples 6 and 7 before working Exercises 31–38.

31. **Chemist** Karl Schmid, a chemist, has a 15% hydrochloric acid solution and a 40% hydrochloric acid solution. How many liters of each should he mix to get 20 liters of a hydrochloric acid solution with a 30% acid concentration?

32. **Pharmacist** Tamuka Williams, a pharmacist, needs 500 milliliters of a 10% phenobarbital solution. She has only 5% and 25% phenobarbital solutions available. How many milliliters of each solution should she mix to obtain the desired solution?

33. **Laying Tile** Julie Hildebrand is selecting tile for her foyer and living room. She wants to make a pattern using two different colors and types of tile. One type costs $3 per tile (per square foot) and the other type costs $5 per tile (per square foot). She needs a total of 380 tiles but does not want to spend more than $1500 on the tile. What is the maximum number of $5 tiles she can purchase?   180 tiles

34. **Melted Ice** A fruit drink is 8% juice by volume. Ice is added to the drink. After the ice melts the juice contents of the 12 ounce mixture is 6%. Find the volume of fruit drink and the volume of ice that was added.   9 oz fruit drink, 3 oz ice

35. **Dairy Farm** Wayne Froelich, a dairy farmer, has milk that is 5% butterfat and skim milk without butterfat. How much 5% milk and how much skim milk should he mix to make 200 gallons of milk that is 3.5% butterfat?   140 gal 5%, 60 gal skim

36. **Soybean Mix** Lynn Hicks wishes to mix soybean meal that is 18% protein and cornmeal that is 6% protein to get a 150-pound mixture that is 10% protein. How much of each should be used?   cornmeal, 100 lb; soybean, 50 lb

37. **Juice** The All Natural Juice Company sells apple juice for 12 cents an ounce and apple drink for 6 cents an ounce. They wish to market and sell for 10 cents an ounce cans of juice drink that are part juice and part drink. How many ounces of each will be used if the juice drink is to be sold in 8-ounce cans?

38. **Quiche** Pierre LaRue's recipe for quiche lorraine calls for 16 ounces (or 2 cups) of light cream, which is 20% buttermilk. It is often difficult to find light cream with 20% butter-

milk at the supermarket. What is commonly found is heavy cream, which is 36% buttermilk, and half-and-half, which is 10.5% buttermilk. How many ounces of the heavy cream and how much of the half-and-half should be mixed to obtain 16 ounces of light cream that is 20% buttermilk?   ≈5.96 oz heavy cream, ≈10.04 oz half-and-half

39. **Chinese Population** The following graph shows that more and more people in China are moving from rural regions to urban cities. We can estimate the percent, p, of the Chinese population living in rural regions by the equation $p = -1.4t + 72$ and the percent of the Chinese population living in urban cities by the equation $p = 1.4t + 28$. In both equations, t represents the years since 1995. That is, $t = 0$ corresponds to 1995, $t = 1$ corresponds to 1996, and so on. Assuming this trend continues, solve the system of equations to estimate the year in which the percent of the Chinese population living in the rural regions would be equal to the percent of the Chinese population living in the urban cities.   2010

Chinese Population

Source: National Bureau of Statistics, *The Wall Street Journal (4/26/05)*

31. 8 L of 15%, 12 L of 40%
32. 375 mL of 5%, 125 mL of 25%
37. $2\frac{2}{3}$ oz drink, $5\frac{1}{3}$ oz juice

40. **Internal Revenue Service** The following graph shows the number of paper Form 1040 tax returns and the number of online Forms 1040–1040A–1040 EZ tax returns filed with the IRS in the years from 2002 to 2005 and projected to 2010. If t represents the number of years since 2002, the number of paper Form 1040 tax returns, in millions, filed with the IRS can be estimated by the function $p(t) = -2.73t + 59.5$ and the number of online Forms 1040–1040A–1040EZ tax returns, in millions, filed with the IRS can be estimated by the function $o(t) = 1.95t + 9.4$. Assuming this trend continues, solve the systems of equations to estimate in which year the number of paper Form 1040 tax returns would equal the number of online Forms 1040–1040A–1040EZ tax returns?   2012

Tax Returns

Source: www.irs.gov/pubs

Challenge Problems

41. Jogging A brother and sister, Sean and Moira O'Donnell, jog to school daily. Sean, who is older, jogs at 9 miles per hour. Moira jogs at 5 miles per hour. When Sean reached the school, Moira is $\frac{1}{2}$ mile away. How far is the school from their house?   1.125 mi

42. Alloys By weight, an alloy of brass is 70% copper and 30% zinc. Another alloy of brass is 40% copper and 60% zinc. How many grams of each of these alloys must be melted and combined to obtain 300 grams of a brass alloy that is 60% copper and 40% zinc?   200 g of first alloy, 100 g of second alloy

43. Pressurized Tanks Two pressurized tanks are connected by a controlled pressure valve, as shown in the figure. Initially, the internal pressure in tank 1 is 200 pounds per square inch, and

the internal pressure in tank 2 is 20 pounds per square inch. The pressure valve is opened slightly to reduce the pressure in tank 1 by 2 pounds per square inch per minute. This increases the pressure in tank 2 by 2 pounds per square inch per minute. At this rate, how long will it take for the pressure to be equal in both tanks?   45 min

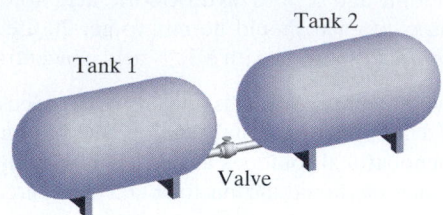

Group Activity

Discuss and work Exercise 44 as a group.

44. Car Purchase Debby Patterson is considering 2 cars for purchase. Car A has a list price of $23,000 and gets an average of 40 miles per gallon. Car B has a list price of $21,500 and gets an average of 20 miles per gallon. Being a conservationist, Debby wishes to purchase car A but is concerned about its

greater initial cost. She plans to keep the car for many years. If she purchases car A, how many miles would she need to drive for the total cost of car A to equal the total cost of car B? Assume gasoline costs $3.00 per gallon.   20,000 mi

Cumulative Review Exercises

[1.10] **45.** Name the properties illustrated.

    a) $x + 4 = 4 + x$ commutative property of addition

    b) $(3x)y = 3(xy)$ associative property of multiplication

    c) $4(x + 2) = 4x + 8$ distributive property

[2.5] **46.** Solve the equation $5x + 4 = -(x - 7)$. $\frac{1}{2}$

[3.3] **47. Perimeter** The perimeter of a rectangle is 22 feet. Find the length and width of the rectangle if the length is two more than twice the width. $w = 3$ ft, $l = 8$ ft

[5.1] **48.** Solve the system of equations.

$$3x + y = -6$$
$$2x = 1 + y$$ $(-1, -3)$

5.5 Solving Systems of Linear Inequalities

1 Solve systems of linear inequalities graphically.

1 Solve Systems of Linear Inequalities Graphically

In Section 4.5, we learned how to graph linear inequalities in two variables. In Section 5.1, we learned how to solve systems of equations graphically. In this section, we discuss how to solve systems of linear inequalities graphically. The **solution to a system of linear inequalities** is the set of points that satisfies all inequalities in the system. Although a system of linear inequalities may contain more than two inequalities, in this book, except in the Group Activity exercises, we will consider systems with only two inequalities.

> **To Solve a System of Linear Inequalities Graphically**
>
> Graph each inequality on the same axes. The solution is the set of points that satisfies all the inequalities in the system.

EXAMPLE 1 ▶ Determine the solution to the following system of inequalities.

$$x + 2y \le 6$$
$$y > 2x - 4$$

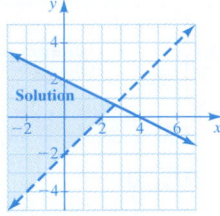
Solution   First graph the inequality $x + 2y \le 6$ (**Fig. 5.16**) as explained in Section 4.5. Now, on the same axes, graph the inequality $y > 2x - 4$ (**Fig. 5.17**). Note that the line is dashed. Why?

FIGURE 5.16

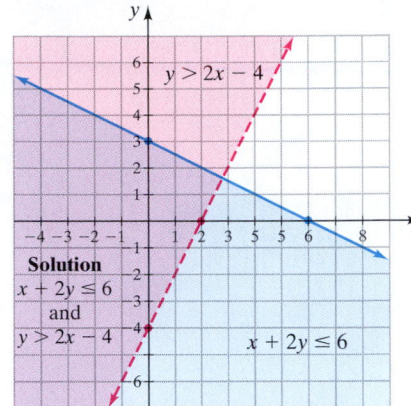

FIGURE 5.17

The solution is the set of points common to both inequalities—the part of the graph that contains both shadings (the purple color). The dashed line is not part of the solution. However, the part of the solid line that satisfies both inequalities is part of the solution.

▶ **Now Try Exercise 7**

In Example 1, the ordered pairs of each of the points in the solution (the purple colored area) satisfies both inequalities in the system. We should be able to choose any point in the shaded region, substitute its x and y values into *both* inequalities and obtain true statements. Let us choose the origin, which is in the shaded area. Let (x, y) be $(0, 0)$.

$$x + 2y \le 6 \qquad\qquad\qquad y > 2x - 4$$
$$0 + 2(0) \overset{?}{\le} 6 \qquad\qquad\qquad 0 \overset{?}{>} 2(0) - 4$$
$$0 \le 6 \quad \textit{True} \qquad\qquad\qquad 0 > -4 \quad \textit{True}$$

As we expected, the ordered pair $(0, 0)$ checks in both inequalities.

EXAMPLE 2 ▶ Determine the solution to the following system of inequalities.

$$2x + 3y > 4$$
$$2x - y \ge -6$$

Solution   Graph $2x + 3y > 4$ (**Fig. 5.18**). Graph $2x - y \ge -6$ on the same axes (**Fig. 5.19**). The solution is the part of the graph with both shadings and the part of the solid line that satisfies both inequalities.

FIGURE 5.18

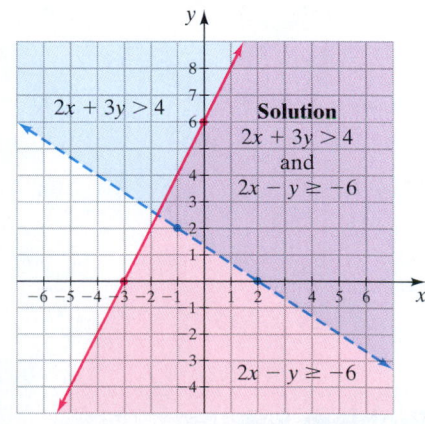

FIGURE 5.19

▶ **Now Try Exercise 11**

EXAMPLE 3 ▶ Determine the solution to the following system of inequalities.

$$y < 2$$

$$x > -3$$

Solution   Graph both inequalities on the same axes (**Fig. 5.20**). The solution is the part of the graph that contains both shadings.

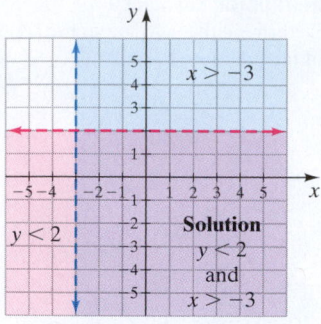

FIGURE 5.20

▶ **Now Try Exercise 15**

It is possible for a system of linear inequalities to have no solution. This can occur if the graphs of the inequalities are lines that have the same slope and are parallel to each other. For example, the system of inequalities $x + y \leq 2$ and $x + y \geq 4$ has no solution.

EXERCISE SET 5.5

Concept/Writing Exercises

3. yes, when the lines are parallel: $x + y > 2, x + y < 1$

1. If an ordered pair satisfies both inequalities in a system of linear inequalities, must that ordered pair be in the solution to the system? Explain.   yes

2. If an ordered pair satisfies only one inequality in a system of linear inequalities, is it possible for that ordered pair to be in the solution to the system? Explain.   no

3. Can a system of linear inequalities have no solution? Explain your answer with the use of your own example.

4. Is it possible to construct a system of two nonparallel linear inequalities that has no solution? Explain.   no

Practice the Skills

Determine the solution to each system of inequalities.   **5.–24.** See graphing answer section.

5. $x + y > 2$
   $x - y < 2$

6. $y \leq 3x - 2$
   $y > -4x$

7. $y \leq x$
   $y < -2x + 2$

8. $2x + 3y < 6$
   $4x - 2y \geq 8$

9. $y < -2x - 3$
   $y \geq 3x + 2$

10. $x + 3y \geq 6$
   $2x - y > 4$

11. $x - 2y < 6$
   $y \leq -x + 4$

12. $3x - 4y \leq 12$
   $y > -x + 4$

13. $4x + 5y < 20$
   $x \geq -3$

14. $y \leq 3x + 4$
   $y < 2$

15. $x \leq 4$
   $y \geq -2$

16. $x \leq 0$
   $y \leq 0$

17. $x > -3$
   $y > 1$

18. $4x + 2y > 8$
   $y \leq 2$

19. $2x - y \leq 3$
   $4x + 2y > 8$

20. $-2x + 3y \geq 6$
   $x + 4y \geq 4$

21. $2x - y < 4$
   $4x - 2y \geq -10$

22. $x - 3y > 3$
   $2x - 6y < 6$

23. $2x + 4y > 6$
   $4x + 8y < 4$

24. $x - 3y \leq 6$
   $x + 3y \leq 6$

Problem Solving

25. Is it possible for a system of two linear inequalities to have only one solution? Explain.   no

26. Construct a system of two linear inequalities that has no solution. Explain how you determined your answer.
   Answers will vary.

Group Activity

In more advanced mathematics courses and when working in many industries, you may need to graph more than two linear inequalities. When a system has more than two inequalities, the solution is the point or points that satisfy all inequalities in the system. As a group, determine the solutions to the systems of inequalities in Exercises 27 and 28.

27. $x + 2y \leq 6$
   $2x - y < 2$
   $y > 2$ See graphing answer section.

28. $x \geq 0$
   $y \geq 0$
   $y \leq 2x + 4$
   $y \leq -x + 6$ See graphing answer section.

Cumulative Review Exercises

29. all real numbers, <img axis>   **31.** See graphing answer section.   **32.** $-\dfrac{8}{7}$

[2.8]   **29.** Solve the inequality and graph the solution on a number line: $6(x - 2) < 4x - 3 + 2x$.

[2.6]   **30.** Solve the equation $3x - 5y = 6$ for y. $y = \dfrac{3}{5}x - \dfrac{6}{5}$

[4.2]   **31.** Graph $2x + y = 4$ by plotting points.

[4.3]   **32.** A line passes through the points $(-4, 6)$ and $(3, -2)$. Find the slope of the line.

Chapter 5 Summary

IMPORTANT FACTS AND CONCEPTS	EXAMPLES
Section 5.1	

A **system of linear equations** is a system having two or more linear equations.	$y = 2x - 5$ $y = -4x + 7$
The **solution to a system of equations** is the ordered pair or pairs that satisfy all the equations in the system.	The solution to the above system is $(2, -1)$.

A linear system of equations may have exactly one solution (intersecting lines) no solution (parallel lines) or an infinite number of solutions (same line).

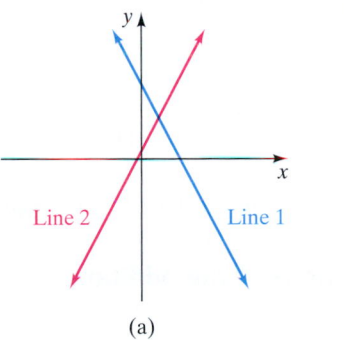

Consistent, exactly 1 solution

(a)

Inconsistent, no solution

(b)

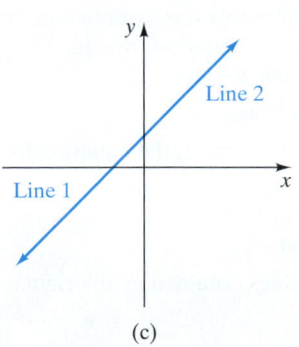

Dependent, infinite number of solutions

(c)

IMPORTANT FACTS AND CONCEPTS	EXAMPLES

Section 5.1 (continued)

To **solve a system of equations graphically**, graph each equation and determine the point or points of intersection.

Solve the system of equations graphically.

$$y = -x + 5$$
$$y = x + 3$$

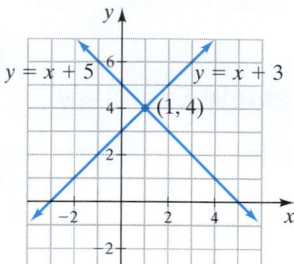

The solution is $(1, 4)$.

Section 5.2

To Solve a System of Equations by Substitution

1. Solve for a variable in either equation.
2. Substitute the expression found for the variable in step 1 into the other equation.
3. Solve the equation determined in step 2 to find the value of one variable.
4. Substitute the value found in step 3 into the equation obtained in step 1 to find the value of the other variable.
5. Check by substituting both values in both original equations.

Solve the system of equations by substitution.

$$y = -x + 5$$
$$y = x + 3$$

Substitute $x + 3$ for y in the first equation.

$$x + 3 = -x + 5$$
$$2x + 3 = 5$$
$$2x = 2$$
$$x = 1$$

Now, solve for y.

$$y = -x + 5$$
$$y = -1 + 5$$
$$= 4$$

The solution is $(1, 4)$.

Section 5.3

To Solve a System of Equations by the Addition (or Elimination) Method

1. If necessary, rewrite each equation so that the terms containing variables appear on the left side of the equal sign and any constants appear on the right side of the equal sign.
2. If necessary, multiply one or both equations by a constant(s) so that when the equations are added the resulting sum will contain only one variable.
3. Add the equations.
4. Solve for the variable in the equation from step 3.
5. Substitute the value found in step 4 into either of the original equations. Solve that equation to find the value of the remaining variable.
6. Check the values obtained in all original equations.

Solve the system of equations by the addition method.
$$2x + 3y = -4 \qquad (eq.\,1)$$
$$3x - y = -17. \qquad (eq.\,2)$$
Multiply $(eq.\,2)$ by 3, then add:
$$
\begin{array}{l}
2x + 3y = -\,4 \\
\underline{9x - 3y = -51} \quad (eq.\,2) \;\text{Multiplied by 3} \\
11x \qquad\;\; = -55 \\
\qquad x = -\,5
\end{array}
$$
Substitute -5 for x into $(eq.\,2)$.

$$3x - y = -17$$
$$3(-5) - y = -17$$
$$-15 - y = -17$$
$$-y = -2$$
$$y = 2$$

The solution is $(-5, 2)$.

IMPORTANT FACTS AND CONCEPTS	EXAMPLES

Section 5.4

Complementary Angles
Two angles are complementary angles if the sum of their measures is 90°.

If angle A is 64° and angle B is 26°, then angles A and B are complementary angles.

Many real-life applications may be solved using systems of equations.

See Examples 1–7 in Section 5.4.

Section 5.5

A **system of linear inequalities** is a system having two or more linear inequalities. The **solution** to a system of linear inequalities is the set of points that satisfies all inequalities in the system. To solve a system of linear inequalities graphically, graph each inequality on the same axes. The solution is the set of points that satisfies all the inequalities in the system.

Determine the solution to the system of inequalities:
$$x + y < 4$$
$$y \geq 2x - 3$$

Chapter 5 Review Exercises

[5.1] *Determine which, if any, of the ordered pairs satisfy each system of equations.*

1. $y = 4x - 2$
$2x + 3y = 8$

a) $(2, 6)$ **b)** $(4, 0)$ **c)** $(1, 2)$ **c)**

2. $y = -x + 4$
$3x + 5y = 15$

a) $\left(\dfrac{5}{2}, \dfrac{3}{2}\right)$ **b)** $(-1, 5)$ **c)** $\left(\dfrac{1}{2}, \dfrac{3}{5}\right)$ **a)**

Identify each system of linear equations as consistent, inconsistent, or dependent. State whether the system has exactly one solution, no solution, or an infinite number of solutions.

3.

consistent, one solution

4.

inconsistent, no solution

5.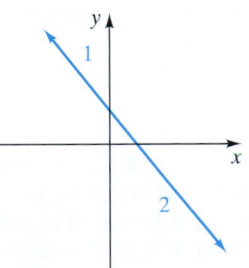

dependent, infinite number of solutions

6.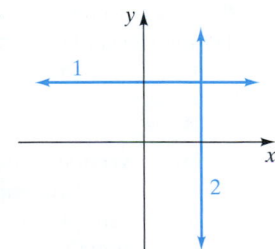

consistent, one solution

Write each equation in slope-intercept form. Without graphing or solving the system of equations, state whether the system of linear equations has exactly one solution, no solution, or an infinite number of solutions.

7. $x + 2y = 10$
$4x = -8y + 16$

no solution

8. $y = -2x + 5$
$2x + 5y = 10$

one solution

9. $y = \dfrac{1}{3}x + \dfrac{2}{3}$
$6y - 2x = 4$

infinite number of solutions

10. $6x = 4y - 20$
$4x = 6y + 20$

one solution

Determine the solution to each system of equations graphically.

11. $y = x - 4$
$y = 2x - 7$ $(3, -1)$

12. $x = -2$
$y = 5$ $(-2, 5)$

13. $x + 2y = 8$
$2x - y = -4$ $(0, 4)$

14. $x + 4y = 8$
$y = 2$ $(0, 2)$

15. $y = 3$
$y = -2x + 5$ $(1, 3)$

16. $y = x - 3$
$3x - 3y = 9$
infinite number of solutions

17. $3x + y = 0$
$3x - 3y = 12$ $(1, -3)$

18. $x + 5y = 10$
$\dfrac{1}{5}x + y = -1$
no solution

[5.2] *Find the solution to each system of equations by substitution.*

19. $y = 4x - 18$
$2x - 5y = 0$ $(5, 2)$

20. $x = 3y - 9$
$x + 2y = 1$ $(-3, 2)$

21. $2x - y = 7$
$x + 2y = 6$ $(4, 1)$

22. $x = -3y$
$x + 4y = 5$ $(-15, 5)$

23. $4x - 2y = 7$
$y = 2x + 3$ no   solution

24. $2x - 4y = 7$
$-4x + 8y = -14$
infinite number of solutions

25. $2x - 3y = 8$
$6x - 5y = 20$ $\left(\dfrac{5}{2}, -1\right)$

26. $3x - y = -5$
$x + 2y = 8$ $\left(-\dfrac{2}{7}, \dfrac{29}{7}\right)$

[5.3] *Find the solution to each system of equations using the addition method.*

27. $x - y = -4$
$-x + 6y = -6$ $(-6, -2)$

28. $x + 2y = -3$
$5x - 2y = 9$ $(1, -2)$

29. $x + y = 12$
$2x + y = 5$ $(-7, 19)$

30. $4x - 3y = 8$
$2x + 5y = 8$ $\left(\dfrac{32}{13}, \dfrac{8}{13}\right)$

31. $-2x + 3y = 15$
$7x + 3y = 6$ $\left(-1, \dfrac{13}{3}\right)$

32. $2x + y = 3$
$-4x - 2y = 5$
no solution

33. $3x = -4y + 15$
$8y = -6x + 30$
infinite number of solutions

34. $2x - 5y = 12$
$3x - 4y = -6$
$\left(-\dfrac{78}{7}, -\dfrac{48}{7}\right)$

[5.4] *Use a system of linear equations to find the solution.*

35. Sum of Integers The sum of two integers is 22. Find the two numbers if the larger is 8 less than twice the smaller.   10, 12

36. Plane Flight A plane flies 580 miles per hour with the wind and 520 miles per hour against the wind. Find the speed of the wind and the speed of the plane in still air.
plane, 550 mph; wind, 30 mph

37. Truck Rental Katz's Truck Rental charges \$35 per day plus 50 cents per mile, while Willie's Truck Rental charges \$40 per day plus 40 cents per mile. How far would you have to travel in one day for the total cost from both rental companies to be the same?   50 mi

38. Savings Account Moura Hakala invested a total of \$16,000. Part of the money was placed in a savings account paying 4% simple interest. The rest was placed in a savings account paying 6% simple interest. If the total interest received for the year was \$760, how much had she invested in each account?   \$10,000 at 4%, \$6000 at 6%

39. Road Trip Liz Wood drives from Charleston, South Carolina, to Louisville, Kentucky—a distance of 600 miles. At the same time, Mary Mayer starts driving from Louisville to Charleston along the same route. If the two meet after driving 5 hours and Mary's average speed was 6 miles per hour greater than Liz's, find the average speed of each car.   Liz, 57 mph; Mary, 63 mph

40. Grass Seed Green Turf's grass seed costs 60 cents a pound and Agway's grass seed costs 45 cents a pound. How many pounds of each were used to make a 50-pound mixture that cost \$25.50?   20 lb of Green Turf's, 30 lb of Agway's

41. Chemist A chemist has a 25% acid solution and a 55% acid solution. How much of each must be mixed to get 10 liters of a 40% acid solution?   5 liters of each

[5.5] *Determine the solution to each system of inequalities.*   42.–45. See graphing answer section.

42. $2x - 6y > 6$
$x > -2$

43. $x < 2$
$y \geq -3$

44. $2x + y > 2$
$2x - y \leq 4$

45. $2x - 3y \leq 6$
$2x + 8y > 8$

Chapter 5 Practice Test

*To find out how well you understand the chapter material, take this practice test. The answers, and the section where the material was initially discussed, are given in the back of the book. Each problem is also fully worked out on the **Chapter Test Prep Video CD**. Review any questions that you answered incorrectly.*

1. Determine which, if any, of the ordered pairs satisfy the system of equations.

$$x + 2y = -6$$
$$3x + 2y = -12$$

a) $(-6, 0)$ **b)** $\left(-3, -\dfrac{3}{2}\right)$ **c)** $(2, -4)$ **b)**

Identify each system as consistent, inconsistent, or dependent. State whether the system has exactly one solution, no solution, or an infinite number of solutions.

2.

consistent—one solution

3.

inconsistent—no solution

4.

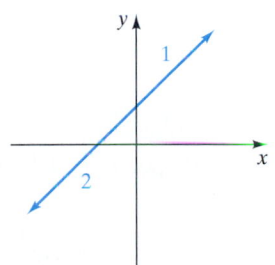

dependent—infinite number of solutions

Write each equation in slope-intercept form. Then determine, without graphing or solving the system, whether the system of equations has exactly one solution, no solution, or an infinite number of solutions.

5. $-3y = 6x - 10$
$2x + y = 5$ no solution

6. $5x + 2y = 12$
$5x - 2y = 16$
one solution

7. $4x = 6y - 12$
$2x - 3y = -6$ infinite number of solutions

8. When solving a system of linear equations by the substitution or the addition methods, how will you know if the system is

a) inconsistent,   You will obtain a false statement, such as $6 = 0$.

b) dependent?   You will obtain a true statement, such as $0 = 0$.

Solve each system of equations graphically.

9. $y = 2x - 4$
$y = -2x + 8$ $(3, 2)$

10. $3x - 2y = -3$
$3x + y = 6$ $(1, 3)$

11. $y = 2x + 4$
$4x - 2y = 6$ no solution

Solve each system of equations by substitution.

12. $y = 5x - 9$
$y = 3x + 3$ $(6, 21)$

13. $3x + y = 8$
$x - y = 6$ $\left(\dfrac{7}{2}, -\dfrac{5}{2}\right)$

14. $3x - 2y = 2$
$-5x + 4y = 0$ $(4, 5)$

Solve each system of equations using the addition method.

15. $4x + y = -6$
$x + 3y = 4$ $(-2, 2)$

16. $4x - y = 8$
$10x + 3y = -13$ $\left(\dfrac{1}{2}, -6\right)$

17. $5x - 10y = 20$
$2x = 4y + 8$ infinite number of solutions

Solve each system of equations using the method of your choice.

18. $y = 5x - 13$
$y = -2x + 8$ $(3, 2)$

19. $3x - 4y = 1$
$-2x + 5y = -10$ $(-5, -4)$

20. $3x + 5y = 20$
$6x + 3y = -12$ $\left(-\dfrac{40}{7}, \dfrac{52}{7}\right)$

Use a system of linear equations to find the solution.

21. **Truck Rental** Charley's Rent a Truck Agency charges $47 per day plus 8 cents per mile to rent a certain truck. Hugh's Rent a truck charges $40 per day plus 15 cents per mile to rent the same truck. How many miles will have to be driven in one day for the cost of Charley's truck to equal the cost of Hugh's truck?   100 mi

22. **Candies** Albert's Grocery sells individually wrapped lemon candies for $6.00 a pound and individually wrapped butterscotch candies for $4.50 a pound. How much of each must Albert mix to get 20 pounds of a mixture that he can sell for $5.00 per pound? $13\dfrac{1}{3}$ lb butterscotch, $6\dfrac{2}{3}$ lb lemon

23. **Boat Race** During a race, Dante Hull's speed boat travels 4 miles per hour faster than Deja Rocket's speed boat. If Dante's boat finishes the race in 2.5 hours and Deja's finishes the race in 3 hours, find the speed of each boat.
Deja's boat, 20 mph; Dante's boat, 24 mph

Determine the solution to each system of inequalities.

24. $x + 3y \geq 6$
$y < 3$ See graphing answer section.

25. $2x + 4y < 8$
$x - 3y \geq 6$ See graphing answer section.

Cumulative Review Test

Take the following test and check your answers with those given in the back of the book. Review any questions that you answered incorrectly. The section where the material was covered is indicated after the answer.

1. **Women in the Military** Women are playing an increasingly important role in the U.S. military. Women have been serving in the U.S. armed forces since 1901 when the Army Nurse Corps was established. The number of women serving in the military has grown dramatically since 1967 when the military abolished the 2% cap on women serving in the armed forces. The following graphs provide information about women and the military.

Percent of Military Branches That Are Women

Percent of Military Positions Open to Women

Source: Defense Department; Women's Research and Education Institute

a) Which branches of the military are composed of at least 15% women? Air Force, Army

b) Which branches of the military are composed of at least 10% women *and* have at least 70% of the military positions open to women? Air Force, Army, Navy

2. Mallory Volcy's first five exam scores were 87, 92, 78, 80, and 89. Find her median test score. 87

3. Find the mean of the five test scores in Exercise 2. 85.2

4. Perform the indicated operation $\dfrac{3}{8} \div \dfrac{9}{10}$. $\dfrac{5}{12}$

5. Consider the set of numbers
$$\left\{ -5, -0.6, \frac{3}{5}, \sqrt{10}, -\sqrt{2}, 7, 0, -\frac{5}{9}, 1.34 \right\}$$

List the elements that are

a) natural numbers. 7

b) rational numbers. $-5, -0.6, \dfrac{3}{5}, 7, 0, -\dfrac{5}{9}, 1.34$

c) irrational numbers. $\sqrt{10}, -\sqrt{2}$

d) real numbers. $-5, -0.6, \dfrac{3}{5}, \sqrt{10}, -\sqrt{2}, 7, 0, -\dfrac{5}{9}, 1.34$

6. Insert either $>$, $<$, or $=$ in the shaded area to make a true statement.
$$3 \quad \boxed{} \quad |-3| \quad =$$

7. Simplify $-115 + 63 + (-192)$. -244

8. Simplify $10 - (3a - 2) + 4(a + 3)$. $a + 24$

9. Solve the equation $2(x - 4) + 2 = 3x - 4$. -2

10. Solve the formula $P = 2l + 2w$ for w. $w = \dfrac{P - 2l}{2}$

11. Solve the inequality $3x - 2 \le x + 8$. Graph the solution on a number line. $x \le 5$;

12. **Cutting a Board** A 39-foot length of board is cut into two pieces. If one of the pieces has length y, what is the length of the other piece? $39 - y$

13. **Select a Salary Plan** Maria Gentile recently graduated from college and has accepted a position selling software. She is given a choice of two salary plans. Plan A is a straight 12% commission on sales. Plan B is $348 per week plus 6% commission on sales. How much must Maria sell in a week for both plans to have the same weekly salary? $5800

14. **Angles of a Triangle** One angle of a triangle measures 30° greater than the smallest angle. The third angle measures 8 times the smallest angle. Find the measure of all three angles. 15°, 45°, 120°

15. Graph $2x - 4y = 8$. See graphing answer section.

16. Graph $\dfrac{1}{3}x + \dfrac{1}{2}y = 12$. See graphing answer section.

17. Find the slope of the line through the points $(-4, 7)$ and $(5, -3)$.

18. Determine if the system of equations
$$3x - y = 6$$
$$\frac{3}{2}x - 3 = \frac{1}{2}y$$
has one solution, no solution, or an infinite number of solutions. Explain how you determined your answer.

19. Solve the following system of equations graphically.
$$2x + y = 5$$
$$x - 2y = 0 \qquad (2, 1)$$

20. Solve the following system of equations using the addition method.
$$3x + 5y = 6$$
$$-6x + 7y = -29 \qquad \left(\frac{11}{3}, -1 \right)$$

17. $-\dfrac{10}{9}$ 18. infinite number of solutions

6 Exponents and Polynomials

MOST AREAS OF science and technology deal with very small and very large numbers. Computers, for example, perform calculations in microseconds and their hard drives hold gigabytes of data. Scientific notation is a convenient way to work with small and large quantities. In Exercise 84 on page 370 we use scientific notation to determine how long it takes light from the sun to reach the earth.

6.1 Exponents

1 Review exponents.

2 Learn the rules of exponents.

3 Simplify an expression before using the expanded power rule.

1 Review Exponents

To be able to work the examples and exercises in this chapter, we need to expand our knowledge of exponents. Exponents were introduced in Section 1.9. Let's review the fundamental concepts. In the expression x^n, x is referred to as the **base** and n is called the **exponent**. x^n is read "x to the nth power."

$$x^2 = \underbrace{x \cdot x}_{2 \text{ factors of } x}$$

$$x^4 = \underbrace{x \cdot x \cdot x \cdot x}_{4 \text{ factors of } x}$$

$$x^m = \underbrace{x \cdot x \cdot x \cdot \,\cdots\, \cdot x}_{m \text{ factors of } x}$$

EXAMPLE 1 ▶ Write *xxxxyyy* using exponents.

Solution

$$\underbrace{xxxx}_{\substack{4 \text{ factors} \\ \text{of } x}} \quad \underbrace{yyy}_{\substack{3 \text{ factors} \\ \text{of } y}} = x^4 y^3$$

▶ **Now Try Exercise 7**

Remember, when a term containing a variable is given without a numerical coefficient, the numerical coefficient of the term is assumed to be 1. For example, $x = 1x$ and $x^2 y = 1x^2 y$.

Also recall that when a variable or numerical value is given without an exponent, the exponent of that variable or numerical value is assumed to be 1. For example, $x = x^1$, $xy = x^1 y^1$, $x^2 y = x^2 y^1$, and $2xy^2 = 2^1 x^1 y^2$.

2 Learn the Rules of Exponents

Now we will learn the rules of exponents.

EXAMPLE 2 ▶ Multiply $x^4 \cdot x^3$.

Solution

$$\underbrace{x^4}_{x \cdot x \cdot x \cdot x} \cdot \underbrace{x^3}_{x \cdot x \cdot x} = x^7$$

▶ **Now Try Exercise 11**

Example 2 illustrates that when multiplying expressions with the same base we keep the base and *add* the exponents. This is the **product rule for exponents**.

Product Rule for Exponents
$x^m \cdot x^n = x^{m+n}$

In Example 2, we showed that $x^4 \cdot x^3 = x^7$. This problem could also be done using the product rule: $x^4 \cdot x^3 = x^{4+3} = x^7$.

EXAMPLE 3 ▶ Multiply each expression using the product rule.

a) $3^2 \cdot 3$ **b)** $2^4 \cdot 2^2$ **c)** $x \cdot x^4$ **d)** $x^3 \cdot x^6$ **e)** $y^4 \cdot y^7$

Solution

a) $3^2 \cdot 3 = 3^2 \cdot 3^1 = 3^{2+1} = 3^3$ or 27   **b)** $2^4 \cdot 2^2 = 2^{4+2} = 2^6$ or 64

c) $x \cdot x^4 = x^1 \cdot x^4 = x^{1+4} = x^5$ **d)** $x^3 \cdot x^6 = x^{3+6} = x^9$

e) $y^4 \cdot y^7 = y^{4+7} = y^{11}$

▶ **Now Try Exercise 19**

Avoiding Common Errors

Note in Example 3**a)** that $3^2 \cdot 3^1$ is 3^3 and not 9^3. When multiplying powers of the same base, *do not multiply the bases.*

<table>
<tr><td>CORRECT</td><td>INCORRECT</td></tr>
<tr><td>$3^2 \cdot 3^1 = 3^3$</td><td>$3^2 \cdot 3^1 = 9^3$</td></tr>
</table>

Example 4 will help you understand the **quotient rule for exponents**.

INSTRUCTOR EXAMPLE
Divide $y^8 \div y^2$.
Ans.: y^6

EXAMPLE 4 ▸ Divide $x^5 \div x^3$.

Solution

$$\frac{x^5}{x^3} = \frac{\overset{1}{\cancel{x}} \cdot \overset{1}{\cancel{x}} \cdot \overset{1}{\cancel{x}} \cdot x \cdot x}{\underset{1}{\cancel{x}} \cdot \underset{1}{\cancel{x}} \cdot \underset{1}{\cancel{x}}} = \frac{1x^2}{1} = x^2$$

▸ **Now Try Exercise 23**

TEACHING TIP
When discussing Example 4, point out that if all factors are divided out of the denominator (or numerator), the denominator (or numerator) equals 1.

When dividing expressions with the same base, keep the base and *subtract* the exponent in the denominator from the exponent in the numerator.

Quotient Rule for Exponents

$$\frac{x^m}{x^n} = x^{m-n}, \qquad x \neq 0$$

In Example 4, we showed that $\frac{x^5}{x^3} = x^2$. This problem could also be done using the quotient rule: $\frac{x^5}{x^3} = x^{5-3} = x^2$.

INSTRUCTOR EXAMPLE
Divide each expression using the quotient rule.

a) $\frac{2^6}{2^4}$ **b)** $\frac{z^7}{z^3}$

Ans.:

a) 2^2 or 4   **b)** z^4

EXAMPLE 5 ▸ Divide each expression using the quotient rule.

a) $\dfrac{3^5}{3^2}$ **b)** $\dfrac{6^4}{6}$ **c)** $\dfrac{x^{12}}{x^5}$ **d)** $\dfrac{y^{10}}{y^8}$ **e)** $\dfrac{z^8}{z}$

Solution

a) $\dfrac{3^5}{3^2} = 3^{5-2} = 3^3$ or 27   **b)** $\dfrac{6^4}{6} = \dfrac{6^4}{6^1} = 6^{4-1} = 6^3$ or 216

c) $\dfrac{x^{12}}{x^5} = x^{12-5} = x^7$ **d)** $\dfrac{y^{10}}{y^8} = y^{10-8} = y^2$

e) $\dfrac{z^8}{z} = \dfrac{z^8}{z^1} = z^{8-1} = z^7$

▸ **Now Try Exercise 25**

Avoiding Common Errors

Note in Example 5**a)** that $\dfrac{3^5}{3^2}$ is 3^3 and not 1^3. When dividing powers of the same base, *do not divide out the bases.*

<table>
<tr><td>CORRECT</td><td>INCORRECT</td></tr>
<tr><td>$\dfrac{3^3}{3^1} = 3^2$ or 9</td><td>$\dfrac{3^3}{3^1} = 1^2$</td></tr>
</table>

The answer to Example 5**c)**, $\dfrac{x^{12}}{x^5}$, is x^7. We obtained this answer using the quotient rule. This answer could also be obtained by dividing out the common factors in both the numerator and denominator as follows.

$$\frac{x^{12}}{x^5} = \frac{(\cancel{x} \cdot \cancel{x} \cdot \cancel{x} \cdot \cancel{x} \cdot \cancel{x}) \cdot x \cdot x \cdot x \cdot x \cdot x \cdot x \cdot x}{(\cancel{x} \cdot \cancel{x} \cdot \cancel{x} \cdot \cancel{x} \cdot \cancel{x})} = x^7$$

We divided out the product of five x's, which is x^5. We can indicate this process in shortened form as follows.

$$\frac{x^{12}}{x^5} = \frac{\overset{1}{\cancel{x^5}} \cdot x^7}{\underset{1}{\cancel{x^5}}} = x^7$$

In this section, to simplify an expression when the numerator and denominator have the same base and the exponent in the denominator is greater than the exponent in the numerator, we divide out common factors. For example, $\dfrac{x^5}{x^{12}}$ can be simplified by dividing out the common factor, x^5, as follows.

$$\frac{x^5}{x^{12}} = \frac{\overset{1}{\cancel{x^5}}}{\underset{1}{\cancel{x^5}} \cdot x^7} = \frac{1}{x^7}$$

We will now simplify some expressions by dividing out common factors.

EXAMPLE 6 ▶ Simplify each expression by dividing out a common factor in both the numerator and denominator.

    a) $\dfrac{x^9}{x^{12}}$ **b)** $\dfrac{y^4}{y^9}$

Solution

a) Since the numerator is x^9, we write the denominator with a factor of x^9. Since $x^9 \cdot x^3 = x^{12}$, we rewrite x^{12} as $x^9 \cdot x^3$.

$$\frac{x^9}{x^{12}} = \frac{\overset{1}{\cancel{x^9}}}{\underset{1}{\cancel{x^9}} \cdot x^3} = \frac{1}{x^3}$$

b) $\dfrac{y^4}{y^9} = \dfrac{\overset{1}{\cancel{y^4}}}{\underset{1}{\cancel{y^4}} \cdot y^5} = \dfrac{1}{y^5}$

▶ **Now Try Exercise 27**

In the next section, we will show another way to simplify expressions like $\dfrac{x^9}{x^{12}}$ by using the negative exponent rule.

Example 7 leads us to our next rule, the **zero exponent rule**.

EXAMPLE 7 ▶ Divide $\dfrac{x^3}{x^3}$.

Solution By the quotient rule,

$$\frac{x^3}{x^3} = x^{3-3} = x^0$$

However,

$$\frac{x^3}{x^3} = \frac{1x^3}{1x^3} = \frac{1 \cdot \cancel{x} \cdot \cancel{x} \cdot \cancel{x}}{1 \cdot \cancel{x} \cdot \cancel{x} \cdot \cancel{x}} = \frac{1}{1} = 1$$

Since $\dfrac{x^3}{x^3} = x^0$ and $\dfrac{x^3}{x^3} = 1$, then x^0 must equal 1.

▶ **Now Try Exercise 29**

Zero Exponent Rule

$$x^0 = 1, \qquad x \neq 0$$

By the zero exponent rule, any real number, except 0, raised to the zero power equals 1. Note that 0^0 is undefined.

EXAMPLE 8 ▸ Simplify each expression. Assume $x \neq 0$.

a) 3^0 **b)** x^0 **c)** $3x^0$ **d)** $(3x)^0$ **e)** $4x^2y^3z^0$

Solution

a) $3^0 = 1$

b) $x^0 = 1$

c) $3x^0 = 3(x^0)$ *Remember, the exponent refers only to the immediately preceding symbol*
  $ = 3 \cdot 1 = 3$ *unless parentheses are used.*

d) $(3x)^0 = 1$

e) $4x^2y^3z^0 = 4x^2y^3 \cdot 1 = 4x^2y^3$

▸ **Now Try Exercise 37**

Avoiding Common Errors

An expression raised to the zero power is not equal to 0; it is equal to 1.

CORRECT	INCORRECT
$x^0 = 1$	$x^0 = 0$
$5^0 = 1$	$5^0 = 0$

The **power rule** will be explained with the aid of Example 9.

EXAMPLE 9 ▸ Simplify $(x^3)^2$.

Solution

$$(x^3)^2 = \underbrace{x^3 \cdot x^3}_{2 \text{ factors of } x^3} = x^{3+3} = x^6$$

▸ **Now Try Exercise 45**

Power Rule for Exponents

$$(x^m)^n = x^{m \cdot n}$$

The power rule indicates that when we raise an exponential expression to a power, we keep the base and *multiply* the exponents. Example 9 could also be simplified using the power rule: $(x^3)^2 = x^{3 \cdot 2} = x^6$.

EXAMPLE 10 ▸ Simplify each expression.

a) $(x^3)^5$ **b)** $(3^4)^2$ **c)** $(y^5)^7$

Solution

a) $(x^3)^5 = x^{3 \cdot 5} = x^{15}$ **b)** $(3^4)^2 = 3^{4 \cdot 2} = 3^8$ **c)** $(y^5)^7 = y^{5 \cdot 7} = y^{35}$

▸ **Now Try Exercise 51**

Helpful Hint

Students often confuse the product and power rules. Note the difference carefully.

Product Rule	Power Rule
$x^m \cdot x^n = x^{m+n}$	$(x^m)^n = x^{m \cdot n}$
$2^3 \cdot 2^5 = 2^{3+5} = 2^8$	$(2^3)^5 = 2^{3 \cdot 5} = 2^{15}$

Example 11 will help us in explaining the **expanded power rule**. As the name suggests, this rule is an expansion of the power rule.

INSTRUCTOR EXAMPLE

Simplify $\left(\dfrac{4a}{y}\right)^3$.

Ans.: $\dfrac{64a^3}{y^3}$

EXAMPLE 11 ▶ Simplify $\left(\dfrac{ax}{by}\right)^4$.

Solution
$$\left(\frac{ax}{by}\right)^4 = \frac{ax}{by} \cdot \frac{ax}{by} \cdot \frac{ax}{by} \cdot \frac{ax}{by}$$

$$= \frac{a \cdot a \cdot a \cdot a \cdot x \cdot x \cdot x \cdot x}{b \cdot b \cdot b \cdot b \cdot y \cdot y \cdot y \cdot y} = \frac{a^4 \cdot x^4}{b^4 \cdot y^4} = \frac{a^4 x^4}{b^4 y^4}$$

▶ **Now Try Exercise 67**

Expanded Power Rule for Exponents

$$\left(\frac{ax}{by}\right)^m = \frac{a^m x^m}{b^m y^m}, \qquad b \neq 0, \, y \neq 0$$

The expanded power rule illustrates that every factor within parentheses is raised to the power outside the parentheses when the expression is simplified.

INSTRUCTOR EXAMPLE

Simplify each expression.

a) $(2xy)^5$ **b)** $\left(\dfrac{3y}{4z}\right)^3$

Ans.:

a) $32x^5 y^5$ **b)** $\dfrac{27y^3}{64z^3}$

EXAMPLE 12 ▶ Simplify each expression.

a) $(5x)^2$ **b)** $(-y)^3$ **c)** $(4xy)^4$ **d)** $\left(\dfrac{-2y}{3z}\right)^2$

Solution

a) $(5x)^2 = 5^2 x^2 = 25x^2$ **b)** $(-y)^3 = (-1y)^3 = (-1)^3 y^3 = -1y^3 = -y^3$

c) $(4xy)^4 = 4^4 x^4 y^4 = 256 x^4 y^4$ **d)** $\left(\dfrac{-2y}{3z}\right)^2 = \dfrac{(-2)^2 y^2}{3^2 z^2} = \dfrac{4y^2}{9z^2}$

▶ **Now Try Exercise 69**

3 Simplify an Expression Before Using the Expanded Power Rule

Whenever we have an expression raised to a power, it helps to simplify the expression in parentheses before using the expanded power rule. This procedure is illustrated in Examples 13 and 14.

INSTRUCTOR EXAMPLE

Simplify $\left(\dfrac{8x^3 y^5}{4x^3 y^2}\right)^2$.

Ans.: $4y^6$

EXAMPLE 13 ▶ Simplify $\left(\dfrac{9x^3 y^2}{3xy^2}\right)^3$.

Solution We first simplify the expression within parentheses by dividing out common factors.

$$\left(\frac{9x^3 y^2}{3xy^2}\right)^3 = \left(\frac{9}{3} \cdot \frac{x^3}{x} \cdot \frac{y^2}{y^2}\right)^3 = (3x^2)^3$$

TEACHING TIP
After discussing Example 13, have students verify that the result is the same when the expression within the parentheses is not simplified first. Then ask, "Which method do you prefer?"

Now we use the expanded power rule to simplify further.

$$(3x^2)^3 = 3^3(x^2)^3 = 27x^6$$

Thus, $\left(\dfrac{9x^3y^2}{3xy^2}\right)^3 = 27x^6$.

▸ **Now Try Exercise 93**

Helpful Hint *Study Tip*

Be very careful when writing exponents. Since exponents are generally smaller than regular text, take your time and write them clearly, and position them properly. If exponents are not written clearly it is very easy to confuse exponents such as 2 and 3, or 1 and 4, or 0 and 6. If you write down or carry an exponent from step to step incorrectly, you will obtain an incorrect answer.

INSTRUCTOR EXAMPLE

Simplify $\left(\dfrac{18x^2y^8}{9x^5y^4}\right)^3$.

Ans.: $\dfrac{8y^{12}}{x^9}$

EXAMPLE 14 ▸ Simplify $\left(\dfrac{25x^4y^3}{5x^2y^7}\right)^4$.

Solution Begin by simplifying the expression within parentheses.

$$\left(\frac{25x^4y^3}{5x^2y^7}\right)^4 = \left(\frac{25}{5}\cdot\frac{x^4}{x^2}\cdot\frac{y^3}{y^7}\right)^4 = \left(\frac{5x^2}{y^4}\right)^4$$

Now use the expanded power rule to simplify further.

$$\left(\frac{5x^2}{y^4}\right)^4 = \frac{5^4(x^2)^4}{(y^4)^4} = \frac{625x^8}{y^{16}}$$

Thus, $\left(\dfrac{25x^4y^3}{5x^2y^7}\right)^4 = \dfrac{625x^8}{y^{16}}$.

▸ **Now Try Exercise 95**

Avoiding Common Errors

Students sometimes make errors in simplifying expressions containing exponents. One of the most common errors follows. Study this error carefully to make sure you do not make the same mistake.

CORRECT

$$\frac{4}{2x} = \frac{\overset{2}{\cancel{4}}}{\underset{1}{\cancel{2}}x} = \frac{2}{x}$$

$$\frac{x}{xy} = \frac{\cancel{x}}{\underset{1}{\cancel{x}}y} = \frac{1}{y}$$

$$\frac{5x^3y^2}{y^2} = \frac{5x^3\overset{1}{\cancel{y^2}}}{\underset{1}{\cancel{y^2}}} = 5x^3$$

INCORRECT

$$\frac{4}{x+2} = \frac{\overset{2}{\cancel{4}}}{x+\underset{1}{\cancel{2}}} = \frac{2}{x+1}$$

$$\frac{x}{x+y} = \frac{\cancel{x}}{\underset{1}{\cancel{x}}+y} = \frac{1}{1+y}$$

$$\frac{5x^3+y^2}{y^2} = \frac{5x^3+\overset{1}{\cancel{y^2}}}{\underset{1}{\cancel{y^2}}} = 5x^3 + 1$$

The simplifications on the right side are not correct because only common *factors* can be divided out (remember, factors are multiplied together). In the first denominator on the right, $x + 2$, the x and 2 are terms, not factors, since they are being added. Similarly, in the second denominator, $x + y$, the x and the y are terms, not factors, since they are being added. Also, in the numerator $5x^3 + y^2$, the $5x^3$ and y^2 are terms, not factors. No common factors can be divided out in the fractions on the right.

INSTRUCTOR EXAMPLE
Simplify $(3x^3y^2)^3(x^2y)$.
Ans.: $27x^{11}y^7$

EXAMPLE 15 ▶ Simplify $(2a^5b^3)^5(3a^2b)$.

Solution   First simplify $(2a^5b^3)^5$ by using the expanded power rule.

$$(2a^5b^3)^5 = 2^5a^{5\cdot5}b^{3\cdot5} = 32a^{25}b^{15}$$

Now use the product rule to simplify further.

$$
\begin{aligned}
(2a^5b^3)^5(3a^2b) &= (32a^{25}b^{15})(3a^2b^1) \\
&= 32 \cdot 3 \cdot a^{25} \cdot a^2 \cdot b^{15} \cdot b^1 \\
&= 96a^{25+2}b^{15+1} \\
&= 96a^{27}b^{16}
\end{aligned}
$$

Thus, $(2a^5b^3)^5(3a^2b) = 96a^{27}b^{16}$.

▶ **Now Try Exercise 125**

Summary of the Rules of Exponents Presented in This Section

1. $x^m \cdot x^n = x^{m+n}$		**product rule**
2. $\dfrac{x^m}{x^n} = x^{m-n}$, $\quad x \neq 0$		**quotient rule**
3. $x^0 = 1$, $\quad x \neq 0$		**zero exponent rule**
4. $(x^m)^n = x^{m\cdot n}$		**power rule**
5. $\left(\dfrac{ax}{by}\right)^m = \dfrac{a^m x^m}{b^m y^m}$, $\quad b \neq 0, \quad y \neq 0$		**expanded power rule**

EXERCISE SET 6.1

Math XL MathXL®   *MyMathLab* MyMathLab   **6. a)** $\left(\dfrac{ax}{by}\right)^m = \dfrac{a^m x^m}{b^m y^m}, b \neq 0, y \neq 0$

Concept/Writing Exercises

1. In the exponential expression t^p, what is the t called? What is the p called?   *t: base, p: exponent*

2. a) Write the product rule for exponents. $x^m \cdot x^n = x^{m+n}$

   b) Explain the product rule.   *Answers will vary.*

3. a) Write the quotient rule for exponents. $\dfrac{x^m}{x^n} = x^{m-n}, x \neq 0$

   b) Explain the quotient rule.   *Answers will vary.*

4. a) Write the zero exponent rule. $x^0 = 1, x \neq 0$

   b) Explain the zero exponent rule.   *Answers will vary.*

5. a) Write the power rule for exponents. $(x^m)^n = x^{m\cdot n}$

   b) Explain the power rule.   *Answers will vary.*

6. a) Write the expanded power rule for exponents.

   b) Explain the expanded power rule.   *Answers will vary.*

7. Write *aabbbbb* using exponents. a^2b^5

8. Write *pppqqqqrrrrrr* using exponents. $p^3q^4r^6$

9. Explain the difference between the product rule and the power rule. Give an example of each.   *Answers will vary.*

10. For what value of x is $x^0 \neq 1$?   0

Practice the Skills

Multiply.

11. $x^5 \cdot x^4$ x^9

 15. $y^3 \cdot y^2$ y^5

19. $z^3 \cdot z^5$ z^8

12. $x^6 \cdot x$ x^7

16. $4^2 \cdot 4^3$ 1024

20. $2^4 \cdot 2^2$ 64

13. $-z^4 \cdot z$ $-z^5$

17. $3^2 \cdot 3^3$ 243

14. $x^7 \cdot x^2$ x^9

18. $-x^3 \cdot x^4$ $-x^7$

Divide.

21. $\dfrac{6^2}{6}$ 6

25. $\dfrac{3^6}{3^2}$ 81

29. $\dfrac{c^4}{c^4}$ 1

22. $\dfrac{x^4}{x^3}$ x

26. $\dfrac{4^5}{4^3}$ 16

30. $\dfrac{5^4}{5^4}$ 1

 23. $\dfrac{x^{10}}{x^3}$ x^7

27. $\dfrac{y^4}{y^6}$ $\dfrac{1}{y^2}$

31. $\dfrac{a^3}{a^9}$ $\dfrac{1}{a^6}$

24. $\dfrac{y^9}{y}$ y^8

28. $\dfrac{a^7}{a^9}$ $\dfrac{1}{a^2}$

32. $\dfrac{x^9}{x^{13}}$ $\dfrac{1}{x^4}$

Simplify.

33. x^0 1

34. 5^0 1

35. $3x^0$ 3

36. $-7x^0$ -7

37. $4(5d)^0$ 4

38. $-2(8x)^0$ -2

39. $-9(-4y)^0$ -9

40. $-(-x)^0$ -1

41. $6x^3y^2z^0$ $6x^3y^2$

42. $-5xy^2z^0$ $-5xy^2$

43. $-8r(st)^0$ $-8r$

44. $-3(a^2b^5c^3)^0$ -3

Simplify.

45. $(x^4)^2$ x^8

46. $(a^5)^3$ a^{15}

47. $(x^5)^5$ x^{25}

48. $(y^5)^2$ y^{10}

49. $(x^3)^1$ x^3

50. $(x^6)^2$ x^{12}

51. $(x^4)^3$ x^{12}

52. $(x^5)^4$ x^{20}

53. $(n^6)^3$ n^{18}

54. $(1.3x)^2$ $1.69x^2$

55. $(-2w^2)^3$ $-8w^6$

56. $(-3x)^2$ $9x^2$

57. $(-3x^3)^3$ $-27x^9$

58. $(-xy)^4$ x^4y^4

59. $(4x^3y^2)^3$ $64x^9y^6$

60. $(3a^2b^4)^3$ $27a^6b^{12}$

Simplify.

61. $\left(\dfrac{x}{3}\right)^2$ $\dfrac{x^2}{9}$

62. $\left(\dfrac{-2}{x}\right)^3$ $-\dfrac{8}{x^3}$

63. $\left(\dfrac{y}{x}\right)^4$ $\dfrac{y^4}{x^4}$

64. $\left(\dfrac{2}{y}\right)^4$ $\dfrac{16}{y^4}$

65. $\left(\dfrac{-6}{x}\right)^3$ $-\dfrac{216}{x^3}$

66. $\left(\dfrac{4m}{n}\right)^3$ $\dfrac{64m^3}{n^3}$

67. $\left(\dfrac{2x}{y}\right)^3$ $\dfrac{8x^3}{y^3}$

68. $\left(\dfrac{3s}{t^2}\right)^2$ $\dfrac{9s^2}{t^4}$

69. $\left(\dfrac{4p}{5}\right)^2$ $\dfrac{16p^2}{25}$

70. $\left(\dfrac{2y^3}{x}\right)^4$ $\dfrac{16y^{12}}{x^4}$

71. $\left(\dfrac{3x^4}{y}\right)^3$ $\dfrac{27x^{12}}{y^3}$

72. $\left(\dfrac{-4x^2}{5}\right)^2$ $\dfrac{16x^4}{25}$

Simplify.

73. $\dfrac{a^8b}{ab^4}$ $\dfrac{a^7}{b^3}$

74. $\dfrac{x^3y^5}{x^7y}$ $\dfrac{y^4}{x^4}$

75. $\dfrac{5x^{12}y^2}{10xy^9}$ $\dfrac{x^{11}}{2y^7}$

76. $\dfrac{10x^3y^8}{2xy^{10}}$ $\dfrac{5x^2}{y^2}$

77. $\dfrac{30y^5z^3}{5yz^6}$ $\dfrac{6y^4}{z^3}$

78. $\dfrac{3ab}{27a^3b^4}$ $\dfrac{1}{9a^2b^3}$

79. $\dfrac{35x^4y^9}{15x^9y^{12}}$ $\dfrac{7}{3x^5y^3}$

80. $\dfrac{6m^3n^9}{9m^7n^{12}}$ $\dfrac{2}{3m^4n^3}$

81. $-\dfrac{36xy^7z}{12x^4y^5z}$ $-\dfrac{3y^2}{x^3}$

82. $\dfrac{4x^4y^7z^3}{32x^5y^4z^9}$ $\dfrac{y^3}{8xz^6}$

83. $-\dfrac{6x^2y^7z}{3x^5y^9z^6}$ $-\dfrac{2}{x^3y^2z^5}$

84. $-\dfrac{25x^4y^{10}}{30x^3y^7z}$ $-\dfrac{5xy^3}{6z}$

Simplify.

85. $\left(\dfrac{10x^4}{5x^6}\right)^3$ $\dfrac{8}{x^6}$

86. $\left(\dfrac{4x^4}{8x^8}\right)^3$ $\dfrac{1}{8x^{12}}$

87. $\left(\dfrac{6y^6}{2y^3}\right)^3$ $27y^9$

88. $\left(\dfrac{4xy^5}{y}\right)^3$ $64x^3y^{12}$

89. $\left(\dfrac{6a^2b^4}{3a^7b^9}\right)^0$ 1

90. $\left(\dfrac{16y^6}{24y^{10}}\right)^3$ $\dfrac{8}{27y^{12}}$

91. $\left(\dfrac{x^4y^3}{x^2y^5}\right)^2$ $\dfrac{x^4}{y^4}$

92. $\left(\dfrac{2x^7y^2}{4xy}\right)^3$ $\dfrac{x^{18}y^3}{8}$

93. $\left(\dfrac{9y^2z^7}{18y^9z}\right)^4$ $\dfrac{z^{24}}{16y^{28}}$

94. $\left(\dfrac{y^7z^5}{y^8z^4}\right)^{10}$ $\dfrac{z^{10}}{y^{10}}$

95. $\left(\dfrac{25s^4t}{5s^6t^4}\right)^3$ $\dfrac{125}{s^6t^9}$

96. $\left(\dfrac{-64xy^6}{32xy^9}\right)^4$ $\dfrac{16}{y^{12}}$

Simplify.

97. $(3xy^4)^2$ $9x^2y^8$

98. $(4ab^3)^3$ $64a^3b^9$

99. $(5ab^3)(b)$ $5ab^4$

100. $(6xy^5)(3x^2y^4)$ $18x^3y^9$

101. $(-2xy)(3xy)$ $-6x^2y^2$

102. $(-3x^4y^2)(5x^2y)$ $-15x^6y^3$

103. $(5x^2y)(3xy^5)$ $15x^3y^6$

104. $(-5xy)(-2xy^6)$ $10x^2y^7$

105. $(-3p^2q)^2(-p^2q)$ $-9p^6q^3$

106. $(2c^3d^2)^2(3cd)^0$ $4c^6d^4$

107. $(7r^3s^2)^2(9r^3s^4)^0$ $49r^6s^4$

108. $(3x^2)^4(2xy^5)$ $162x^9y^5$

Simplify.

109. $(-x)^2$ x^2

110. $(2xy^4)^3$ $8x^3y^{12}$

111. $\left(\dfrac{x^5y^5}{xy^5}\right)^3$ x^{12}

112. $(2x^2y^5)(3x^5y^4)^3$ $54x^{17}y^{17}$

113. $(2.5x^3)^2$ $6.25x^6$

114. $(-3a^2b^3c^4)^3$ $-27a^6b^9c^{12}$

115. $\dfrac{x^9y^3}{x^2y^7}$ $\dfrac{x^7}{y^4}$

116. $(xy^4)(xy^4)^3$ x^4y^{16}

117. $\left(-\dfrac{m^4}{n^3}\right)^3$ $-\dfrac{m^{12}}{n^9}$

118. $\left(-\dfrac{12x}{16x^7y^2}\right)^2$ $\dfrac{9}{16x^{12}y^4}$

119. $(-6x^3y^2)^3$ $-216x^9y^6$

120. $(3x^6y)^2(4xy^8)$ $36x^{13}y^{10}$

121. $(-2x^4y^2z)^3$ $-8x^{12}y^6z^3$

122. $\left(\dfrac{z}{4}\right)^3$ $\dfrac{z^3}{64}$

123. $(9r^4s^5)^3$ $729r^{12}s^{15}$

124. $(5x^4z^{10})^2(2x^2z^8)$ $50x^{10}z^{28}$

125. $(4x^2y)(3xy^2)^3$ $108x^5y^7$

126. $\dfrac{x^2y^6}{x^4y}$ $\dfrac{y^5}{x^2}$

127. $(7.3x^2y^4)^2$ $53.29x^4y^8$

128. $\left(\dfrac{-3x^3}{4}\right)^3$ $-\dfrac{27x^9}{64}$

129. $(x^7y^5)(xy^2)^4$ $x^{11}y^{13}$

130. $(4c^3d^2)(2c^5d^3)^2$ $16c^{13}d^8$

131. $\left(\dfrac{-x^4z^7}{x^2z^5}\right)^4$ x^8z^8

132. $(x^4y^6)^3(3x^2y^5)$ $3x^{14}y^{23}$

Study the Avoiding Common Errors box on page 349. Simplify the following expressions by dividing out common factors. If the expression cannot be simplified by dividing out common factors, so state.

133. $\dfrac{a + b}{b}$ **134.** $\dfrac{xy}{x}$ y **135.** $\dfrac{y^2 + 3}{y}$ **136.** $\dfrac{a + 9}{3}$

137. $\dfrac{6yz^4}{yz^2}$ $6z^2$ **138.** $\dfrac{x}{x + 1}$ **139.** $\dfrac{a^2 + b^2}{a^2}$ **140.** $\dfrac{x^4}{x^2y}$ $\dfrac{x^2}{y}$

Problem Solving

133., 135., 136., 138., 139. cannot be simplified

141. What is the value of a^3b if $a = 2$ and $b = 5$? 40

142. What is the value of xy^2 if $x = -3$ and $y = -4$? -48

143. What is the value of $(xy)^0$ if $x = -5$ and $y = 3$? 1

144. What is the value of $(xy)^0$ if $x = 2$ and $y = 4$? 1

145. Consider the expression $(-9x^4y^6)^8$. When the expanded power rule is used to simplify the expression, will the *sign* of the simplified expression be positive or negative? Explain how you determined your answer. positive, even exponent

146. Consider the expression $(-x^5y^7)^9$. When the expanded power rule is used to simplify the expression, will the *sign* of the simplified expression be positive or negative? Explain how you determined your answer. negative, odd exponent

Write an expression for the total area of the figure or figures shown.

147. $8x^2$

148. $x^2 + y^2$

149. 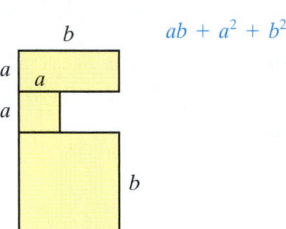 $ab + a^2 + b^2$

150. $3x^2 + 4xy$

Challenge Problems

Simplify.

151. $(3yz^2)^2\left(\dfrac{2y^3z^5}{10y^6z^4}\right)^0(4y^2z^3)^3$ $576y^8z^{13}$

152. $\left(\dfrac{3x^4y^5}{6x^6y^8}\right)^3\left(\dfrac{9x^7y^8}{3x^3y^5}\right)^2$ $\dfrac{9x^2}{8y^3}$

Group Activity

Discuss and answer Exercise 153 as a group, according to the instructions.

153. a) $\dfrac{1}{3}$ d) $\dfrac{1}{2}, 2^{-1}, \dfrac{1}{2} = 2^{-1}$

153. In the next section we will be working with negative exponents. To prepare for that work, use the expression $\dfrac{3^2}{3^3}$ to work parts **a)** through **c)**. Work parts **a)** through **d)** individually, then part **e)** as a group.

  a) Divide out common factors in the numerator and denominator and determine the value of the expression.

  b) Use the quotient rule on the given expression and write down your results. 3^{-1}

  c) Write a statement of equality using the results of part **a)** and **b)** above. $\dfrac{1}{3} = 3^{-1}$

  d) Repeat parts **a)** through **c)** for the expression $\dfrac{2^3}{2^4}$.

  e) As a group, compare your answers to parts **a)** through **d)**, then write an exponential expression for $\dfrac{1}{x^m}$. x^{-m}

Cumulative Review Exercises

157. b) $w = \dfrac{P - 2l}{2}$

[1.9] **154.** Evaluate $3^4 \div 3^3 - (5 - 8) + 7$. 13

[2.1] **155.** Simplify $-4(x - 3) + 5x - 2$. $x + 10$

[2.5] **156.** Solve the equation
$$2(x + 4) - 3 = 5x + 4 - 3x + 1.$$ all real numbers

[2.6] **157.** a) Use the formula $P = 2l + 2w$ to find the length of the sides of the rectangle shown if the perimeter of the rectangle is 26 inches. 4 in., 4 in., 9 in., 9 in.

  b) Solve the formula $P = 2l + 2w$ for w.

6.2 Negative Exponents

1 Understand the negative exponent rule.

2 Simplify expressions containing negative exponents.

INSTRUCTOR EXAMPLE

Repeat parts **a)** and **b)** of Example 1 to simplify $\dfrac{y^4}{y^7}$.

Ans.:

a) y^{-3} **b)** $\dfrac{1}{y^3}$

1 Understand the Negative Exponent Rule

One additional rule that involves exponents is the negative exponent rule. You will need to understand negative exponents to be successful with scientific notation in the next section.

The negative exponent rule will be developed using the quotient rule illustrated in Example 1.

EXAMPLE 1 ▶ Simplify $\dfrac{x^3}{x^5}$ by **a)** using the quotient rule and **b)** dividing out common factors.

Solution

a) By the quotient rule,

$$\frac{x^3}{x^5} = x^{3-5} = x^{-2}$$

b) By dividing out common factors,

$$\frac{x^3}{x^5} = \frac{\cancel{x} \cdot \cancel{x} \cdot \cancel{x}}{\cancel{x} \cdot \cancel{x} \cdot \cancel{x} \cdot x \cdot x} = \frac{1}{x^2}$$

▶ **Now Try Exercise 35**

In Example 1, we see that $\dfrac{x^3}{x^5}$ is equal to both x^{-2} and $\dfrac{1}{x^2}$. Therefore, x^{-2} must equal $\dfrac{1}{x^2}$. That is, $x^{-2} = \dfrac{1}{x^2}$. This is an example of the **negative exponent rule**.

Negative Exponent Rule

$$x^{-m} = \frac{1}{x^m}, \qquad x \neq 0$$

When a variable or number is raised to a negative exponent, the expression may be rewritten as 1 divided by the variable or number raised to that positive exponent.

Examples

$$x^{-6} = \frac{1}{x^6} \qquad 4^{-2} = \frac{1}{4^2} = \frac{1}{16}$$

$$y^{-7} = \frac{1}{y^7} \qquad 5^{-3} = \frac{1}{5^3} = \frac{1}{125}$$

Avoiding Common Errors

Students sometimes believe that a negative exponent automatically makes the value of the expression negative. This is not true.

EXPRESSION	CORRECT	INCORRECT	ALSO INCORRECT
3^{-2}	$\dfrac{1}{3^2} = \dfrac{1}{9}$	-3^2	$-\dfrac{1}{3^2}$ 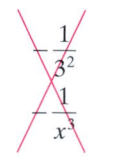
x^{-3}	$\dfrac{1}{x^3}$	$-x^3$	$-\dfrac{1}{x^3}$

To help you see that the negative exponent rule makes sense, consider the following sequence of exponential expressions and their corresponding values.

$$2^3 = 8, \quad 2^2 = 4, \quad 2^1 = 2, \quad 2^0 = 1, \quad 2^{-1} = \frac{1}{2^1} \text{ or } \frac{1}{2}, \quad 2^{-2} = \frac{1}{2^2} \text{ or } \frac{1}{4}, \quad 2^{-3} = \frac{1}{2^3} \text{ or } \frac{1}{8}$$

Note that each time the exponent decreases by 1, the value of the expression is halved. For example, when we go from 2^3 to 2^2, the value of the expression goes from 8 to 4. If we continue decreasing the exponents beyond $2^0 = 1$, the next exponent in the pattern is -1. If we take half of 1 we get $\dfrac{1}{2}$. This pattern illustrates that $x^{-m} = \dfrac{1}{x^m}$.

2 Simplify Expressions Containing Negative Exponents

TEACHING TIP
Ask: "Will a positive base raised to a power ever result in a negative number?"

Generally, when you are asked to simplify an exponential expression **your final answer should contain no negative exponents**. You may simplify exponential expressions using the negative exponent rule and the rules of exponents presented in the previous section. The following examples indicate how exponential expressions containing negative exponents may be simplified.

INSTRUCTOR EXAMPLE
Simplify.

a) y^{-8} b) -4^{-3}

ANS.:

a) $\dfrac{1}{y^8}$ b) $-\dfrac{1}{64}$

EXAMPLE 2 ▶ Use the negative exponent rule to write each expression with a positive exponent. Simplify the expressions further when possible.

a) y^{-5} b) x^{-4} c) 2^{-3} d) 6^{-1} e) -5^{-3} f) $(-5)^{-3}$

Solution

a) $y^{-5} = \dfrac{1}{y^5}$ b) $x^{-4} = \dfrac{1}{x^4}$

c) $2^{-3} = \dfrac{1}{2^3} = \dfrac{1}{8}$ d) $6^{-1} = \dfrac{1}{6}$

e) $-5^{-3} = -\dfrac{1}{5^3} = -\dfrac{1}{125}$ f) $(-5)^{-3} = \dfrac{1}{(-5)^3} = \dfrac{1}{-125} = -\dfrac{1}{125}$

▶ **Now Try Exercise 11**

INSTRUCTOR EXAMPLE
Write each expression with a positive exponent.

a) $\dfrac{1}{x^{-4}}$ b) $\dfrac{1}{3^{-1}}$

Ans.:

a) x^4 b) 3

EXAMPLE 3 ▶ Use the negative exponent rule to write each expression with a positive exponent.

a) $\dfrac{1}{x^{-2}}$ b) $\dfrac{1}{4^{-1}}$

Solution   First use the negative exponent rule on the denominator. Then simplify further.

a) $\dfrac{1}{x^{-2}} = \dfrac{1}{\dfrac{1}{x^2}} = 1 \div \dfrac{1}{x^2} = \dfrac{1}{1} \cdot \dfrac{x^2}{1} = x^2$ b) $\dfrac{1}{4^{-1}} = \dfrac{1}{\dfrac{1}{4}} = 1 \div \dfrac{1}{4} = \dfrac{1}{1} \cdot \dfrac{4}{1} = 4$

▶ **Now Try Exercise 15**

Helpful Hint

From Examples 2 and 3, we can see that when a factor is moved from the denominator to the numerator or from the numerator to the denominator, the sign of the *exponent* changes.

$$x^{-4} = \dfrac{1}{x^4} \qquad\qquad \dfrac{1}{x^{-4}} = x^4$$

$$3^{-5} = \dfrac{1}{3^5} \qquad\qquad \dfrac{1}{3^{-5}} = 3^5$$

Now let's look at additional examples that combine two or more of the rules presented so far.

INSTRUCTOR EXAMPLE
Simplify.
  a) $(a^{-3})^6$ **b)** $(2^3)^{-2}$

Ans.:

  a) $\dfrac{1}{a^{18}}$ **b)** $\dfrac{1}{64}$

EXAMPLE 4 ▶ Simplify.   **a)** $(z^{-5})^4$ **b)** $(4^2)^{-3}$

Solution

  a) $(z^{-5})^4 = z^{(-5)(4)}$ *By the power rule*

  $= z^{-20}$

  $= \dfrac{1}{z^{20}}$ *By the negative exponent rule*

  b) $(4^2)^{-3} = 4^{(2)(-3)}$ *By the power rule*

  $= 4^{-6}$

  $= \dfrac{1}{4^6}$ *By the negative exponent rule*

  ▶ **Now Try Exercise 25**

INSTRUCTOR EXAMPLE
Simplify.
  a) $y^4 \cdot y^{-9}$ **b)** $2^{-2} \cdot 2^{-3}$

Ans.:

  a) $\dfrac{1}{y^5}$ **b)** $\dfrac{1}{32}$

EXAMPLE 5 ▶ Simplify.   **a)** $x^3 \cdot x^{-5}$ **b)** $3^{-4} \cdot 3^{-7}$

Solution

  a) $x^3 \cdot x^{-5} = x^{3+(-5)}$ *By the product rule*

  $= x^{-2}$

  $= \dfrac{1}{x^2}$ *By the negative exponent rule*

  b) $3^{-4} \cdot 3^{-7} = 3^{-4+(-7)}$ *By the product rule*

  $= 3^{-11}$

  $= \dfrac{1}{3^{11}}$ *By the negative exponent rule*

  ▶ **Now Try Exercise 51**

Avoiding Common Errors

What is the sum of $3^2 + 3^{-2}$? Look carefully at the correct solution.

CORRECT	INCORRECT
$3^2 + 3^{-2} = 9 + \dfrac{1}{9}$	$3^2 + 3^{-2} = 0$
$= 9\dfrac{1}{9}$	

Note that $3^2 \cdot 3^{-2} = 3^{2+(-2)} = 3^0 = 1$.

INSTRUCTOR EXAMPLE
Simplify.
  a) $\dfrac{z^{-6}}{z^{11}}$ **b)** $\dfrac{5^{-7}}{5^{-5}}$

Ans.:

  a) $\dfrac{1}{z^{17}}$ **b)** $\dfrac{1}{25}$

EXAMPLE 6 ▶ Simplify.   **a)** $\dfrac{b^{-5}}{b^{13}}$ **b)** $\dfrac{6^{-8}}{6^{-5}}$

Solution

  a) $\dfrac{b^{-5}}{b^{13}} = b^{-5-13}$ *By the quotient rule*

  $= b^{-18}$

  $= \dfrac{1}{b^{18}}$ *By the negative exponent rule*

b) $\dfrac{6^{-8}}{6^{-5}} = 6^{-8-(-5)}$ *By the quotient rule*

$\qquad\quad = 6^{-8+5}$

$\qquad\quad = 6^{-3}$

$\qquad\quad = \dfrac{1}{6^3}$ or $\dfrac{1}{216}$ *By the negative exponent rule*

▸ **Now Try Exercise 81**

The following Helpful Hint should be read carefully.

Helpful Hint

Consider a division problem where a variable has a negative exponent in either its numerator or its denominator, such as in Example **6a)**. Another way to simplify such an expression is to move the variable with the negative exponent from the numerator to the denominator, or from the denominator to the numerator, and change the sign of the exponent. For example,

$$\frac{x^{-4}}{x^5} = \frac{1}{x^5 \cdot x^4} = \frac{1}{x^{5+4}} = \frac{1}{x^9}$$

$$\frac{y^3}{y^{-7}} = y^3 \cdot y^7 = y^{3+7} = y^{10}$$

Now consider a division problem where a number or variable has a negative exponent in both its numerator and its denominator, such as in Example **6b)**. Another way to simplify such an expression is to move the variable with the more negative exponent from the numerator to the denominator, or from the denominator to the numerator, and change the sign of the exponent from negative to positive. For example,

$$\frac{x^{-8}}{x^{-3}} = \frac{1}{x^8 \cdot x^{-3}} = \frac{1}{x^{8-3}} = \frac{1}{x^5} \qquad \text{\textit{Note that} } -8 < -3.$$

$$\frac{y^{-4}}{y^{-7}} = y^7 \cdot y^{-4} = y^{7-4} = y^3 \qquad \text{\textit{Note that} } -7 < -4.$$

EXAMPLE 7 ▸ Simplify.

a) $7x^4(6x^{-9})$ **b)** $\dfrac{16r^3s^{-3}}{8rs^2}$ **c)** $\dfrac{2x^2y^5}{8x^7y^{-3}}$

Solution

a) $7x^4(6x^{-9}) = 7 \cdot 6 \cdot x^4 \cdot x^{-9} = 42x^{-5} = \dfrac{42}{x^5}$

b) $\dfrac{16r^3s^{-3}}{8rs^2} = \dfrac{16}{8} \cdot \dfrac{r^3}{r} \cdot \dfrac{s^{-3}}{s^2}$

$\qquad\qquad = 2 \cdot r^2 \cdot \dfrac{1}{s^5} = \dfrac{2r^2}{s^5}$

c) $\dfrac{2x^2y^5}{8x^7y^{-3}} = \dfrac{2}{8} \cdot \dfrac{x^2}{x^7} \cdot \dfrac{y^5}{y^{-3}}$

$\qquad\qquad = \dfrac{1}{4} \cdot \dfrac{1}{x^5} \cdot y^8 = \dfrac{y^8}{4x^5}$

▸ **Now Try Exercise 121**

In Example **7b)**, the variable with the negative exponent, s^{-3}, was moved from the numerator to the denominator. In Example **7c)**, the variable with the negative exponent, y^{-3}, was moved from the denominator to the numerator. In each case, the sign of the exponent was changed from negative to positive when the variable factor was moved.

EXAMPLE 8 ▶ Simplify.

a) $(5x^{-3})^{-2}$ **b)** $(-5x^{-3})^{-2}$ **c)** $(-5x^{-3})^{-3}$

Solution Begin by using the expanded power rule.

a)
$$(5x^{-3})^{-2} = 5^{-2}x^{(-3)(-2)}$$
$$= 5^{-2}x^6$$
$$= \frac{1}{5^2}x^6$$
$$= \frac{x^6}{25}$$

b)
$$(-5x^{-3})^{-2} = (-5)^{-2}x^{(-3)(-2)}$$
$$= \frac{1}{(-5)^2}x^6$$
$$= \frac{x^6}{25}$$

c)
$$(-5x^{-3})^{-3} = (-5)^{-3}x^{(-3)(-3)}$$
$$= \frac{1}{(-5)^3}x^9$$
$$= \frac{1}{-125}x^9$$
$$= -\frac{x^9}{125}$$

▶ **Now Try Exercise 105**

Avoiding Common Errors

Can you explain why the simplification on the right is incorrect?

CORRECT	INCORRECT
$\dfrac{x^3y^{-2}}{w} = \dfrac{x^3}{wy^2}$	$\dfrac{x^3 + y^{-2}}{w} = \dfrac{x^3}{w + y^2}$

The simplification on the right is incorrect because in the numerator $x^3 + y^{-2}$, the y^{-2} *is not a factor*; it is a term. We will learn how to simplify expressions like this when we study complex fractions in Section 8.5.

EXAMPLE 9 ▶ Simplify $\left(\dfrac{2}{3}\right)^{-2}$.

Solution By the expanded power rule, we may write

$$\left(\frac{2}{3}\right)^{-2} = \frac{2^{-2}}{3^{-2}} = \frac{\dfrac{1}{2^2}}{\dfrac{1}{3^2}} = \frac{1}{2^2} \cdot \frac{3^2}{1} = \frac{3^2}{2^2} = \frac{9}{4}$$

▶ **Now Try Exercise 95**

If we examine the results of Example 9, we see that

$$\left(\frac{2}{3}\right)^{-2} = \frac{3^2}{2^2} = \left(\frac{3}{2}\right)^2.$$

This example illustrates that $\left(\dfrac{a}{b}\right)^{-m} = \left(\dfrac{b}{a}\right)^{m}$ when $a \neq 0$ and $b \neq 0$. Thus, for example, $\left(\dfrac{3}{4}\right)^{-5} = \left(\dfrac{4}{3}\right)^{5}$ and $\left(\dfrac{5}{9}\right)^{-3} = \left(\dfrac{9}{5}\right)^{3}$. We can summarize this information as follows.

A Fraction Raised to a Negative Exponent Rule

For a fraction of the form $\dfrac{a}{b}$, $a \neq 0$ and $b \neq 0$, $\left(\dfrac{a}{b}\right)^{-m} = \left(\dfrac{b}{a}\right)^{m}$.

INSTRUCTOR EXAMPLE
Simplify.

a) $\left(\dfrac{5}{6}\right)^{-2}$ b) $\left(\dfrac{a^3}{b^6}\right)^{-4}$

Ans.:

a) $\dfrac{36}{25}$ b) $\dfrac{b^{24}}{a^{12}}$

EXAMPLE 10 ▶ Simplify.   a) $\left(\dfrac{4}{5}\right)^{-3}$ b) $\left(\dfrac{x^5}{y^7}\right)^{-4}$

Solution   We use the above rule to simplify.

a) $\left(\dfrac{4}{5}\right)^{-3} = \left(\dfrac{5}{4}\right)^{3} = \dfrac{5^3}{4^3} = \dfrac{125}{64}$ b) $\left(\dfrac{x^5}{y^7}\right)^{-4} = \left(\dfrac{y^7}{x^5}\right)^{4} = \dfrac{y^{7 \cdot 4}}{x^{5 \cdot 4}} = \dfrac{y^{28}}{x^{20}}$

▶ **Now Try Exercise 97**

INSTRUCTOR EXAMPLE
Simplify.

a) $\left(\dfrac{x^3 y^{-2}}{z^3}\right)^{-6}$ b) $\left(\dfrac{2x^{-2} y^3 z^2}{x^5}\right)^{3}$

Ans.:

a) $\dfrac{y^{12} z^{18}}{x^{18}}$ b) $\dfrac{8 y^9 z^6}{x^{21}}$

EXAMPLE 11 ▶ Simplify.   a) $\left(\dfrac{x^2 y^{-3}}{z^4}\right)^{-5}$ b) $\left(\dfrac{2x^{-3} y^2 z}{x^2}\right)^{2}$

Solution

a) We will work part **a)** using two different methods. In method 1, we begin by using the expanded power rule. In method 2, we use a fraction raised to a negative exponent rule before we use the expanded power rule. You may use either method.

Method 1 $\left(\dfrac{x^2 y^{-3}}{z^4}\right)^{-5} = \dfrac{x^{2(-5)} y^{(-3)(-5)}}{z^{4(-5)}}$ *Expanded power rule*

$= \dfrac{x^{-10} y^{15}}{z^{-20}}$ *Multiply exponents*

$= \dfrac{y^{15} z^{20}}{x^{10}}$ *Negative exponent rule*

Method 2 $\left(\dfrac{x^2 y^{-3}}{z^4}\right)^{-5} = \left(\dfrac{z^4}{x^2 y^{-3}}\right)^{5}$ $\left(\dfrac{a}{b}\right)^{-m} = \left(\dfrac{b}{a}\right)^{m}$

$= \left(\dfrac{y^3 z^4}{x^2}\right)^{5}$ *Simplify expression within parentheses*

$= \dfrac{y^{3 \cdot 5} z^{4 \cdot 5}}{x^{2 \cdot 5}}$ *Expanded power rule*

$= \dfrac{y^{15} z^{20}}{x^{10}}$ *Multiply exponents*

b) First simplify the expression within parentheses, then square the results. To simplify, we note that $\dfrac{x^{-3}}{x^2}$ becomes $\dfrac{1}{x^5}$.

$$\left(\dfrac{2x^{-3} y^2 z}{x^2}\right)^{2} = \left(\dfrac{2 y^2 z}{x^5}\right)^{2} = \dfrac{2^2 y^{2 \cdot 2} z^{1 \cdot 2}}{x^{5 \cdot 2}} = \dfrac{4 y^4 z^2}{x^{10}}$$

▶ **Now Try Exercise 125**

Summary of Rules of Exponents

1. $x^m \cdot x^n = x^{m+n}$ — product rule

2. $\dfrac{x^m}{x^n} = x^{m-n}$, $\quad x \neq 0$ — quotient rule

3. $x^0 = 1$, $\quad x \neq 0$ — zero exponent rule

4. $(x^m)^n = x^{m \cdot n}$ — power rule

5. $\left(\dfrac{ax}{by}\right)^m = \dfrac{a^m x^m}{b^m y^m}$, $\quad b \neq 0, y \neq 0$ — expanded power rule

6. $x^{-m} = \dfrac{1}{x^m}$, $\quad x \neq 0$ — negative exponent rule

7. $\left(\dfrac{a}{b}\right)^{-m} = \left(\dfrac{b}{a}\right)^m$, $\quad a \neq 0, b \neq 0$ — a fraction raised to a negative exponent rule

EXERCISE SET 6.2

2. no, $\dfrac{1}{x^2}$ 3. no, $\dfrac{x^5}{y^3}$ 4. no, $\dfrac{a^6}{b^2}$ 5. no, $\dfrac{1}{25}$ 7. b) x^5, y^2 8. b) x^{-4}, y^3

Concept/Writing Exercises

1. Describe the negative exponent rule.   Answers will vary.

2. Is the expression x^{-2} simplified? Explain. If not simplified, then simplify.

3. Is the expression $x^5 y^{-3}$ simplified? Explain. If not simplified, then simplify.

4. Can the expression $a^6 b^{-2}$ be simplified to $\dfrac{1}{a^6 b^{-2}}$? If not, what is the correct simplification? Explain.

5. Can the expression 5^{-2} be simplified to -25? If not, what is the correct simplification? Explain.

6. Are the following expressions simplified? If an expression is not simplified, explain why and then simplify.

   a) $\dfrac{5}{x^3}$ yes

   b) n^{-5} no, $\dfrac{1}{n^5}$

   c) $\dfrac{a^{-4}}{2}$ no, $\dfrac{1}{2a^4}$

   d) $\dfrac{x^{-4}}{x^4}$ no, $\dfrac{1}{x^8}$

7. a) Identify the term or terms in the numerator of the expression $\dfrac{x^5 y^2}{z^3}$.   only one term, $x^5 y^2$

   b) Identify the factors in the numerator of the expression.

8. a) Identify the term or terms in the numerator of the expression $\dfrac{x^{-4} y^3}{z^5}$.   only one term, $x^{-4} y^3$

   b) Identify the factors in the numerator of the expression.

9. Describe what happens to the exponent of a factor when the factor is moved from the numerator to the denominator of a fraction.   the sign changes

10. Describe what happens to the exponent of a factor when the factor is moved from the denominator to the numerator of a fraction.   the sign changes

Practice the Skills

Simplify.

11. x^{-6} $\dfrac{1}{x^6}$

12. y^{-5} $\dfrac{1}{y^5}$

13. 5^{-1} $\dfrac{1}{5}$

14. 7^{-2} $\dfrac{1}{49}$

15. $\dfrac{1}{x^{-3}}$ x^3

16. $\dfrac{1}{b^{-4}}$ b^4

17. $\dfrac{1}{a^{-1}}$ a

18. $\dfrac{1}{y^{-4}}$ y^4

19. $\dfrac{1}{6^{-2}}$ 36

20. $\dfrac{1}{4^{-3}}$ 64

21. $(x^{-2})^3$ $\dfrac{1}{x^6}$

22. $(m^{-5})^{-2}$ m^{10}

23. $(y^{-5})^4$ $\dfrac{1}{y^{20}}$

24. $(a^5)^{-4}$ $\dfrac{1}{a^{20}}$

25. $(x^4)^{-2}$ $\dfrac{1}{x^8}$

26. $(x^{-9})^{-2}$ x^{18}

27. $(3^{-2})^{-1}$ 9

28. $(2^{-3})^2$ $\dfrac{1}{64}$

29. $y^4 \cdot y^{-2}$ y^2

30. $x^{-3} \cdot x^1$ $\dfrac{1}{x^2}$

31. $x^7 \cdot x^{-5}$ x^2

32. $d^{-3} \cdot d^{-4}$ $\dfrac{1}{d^7}$

33. $3^{-2} \cdot 3^4$ 9

34. $6^{-3} \cdot 6^6$ 216

35. $\dfrac{r^5}{r^6}$ $\dfrac{1}{r}$

36. $\dfrac{x^2}{x^{-1}}$ x^3

37. $\dfrac{p^0}{p^{-3}}$ p^3

38. $\dfrac{x^{-2}}{x^5}$ $\dfrac{1}{x^7}$

39. $\dfrac{x^{-7}}{x^{-3}}$ $\dfrac{1}{x^4}$

40. $\dfrac{z^{-11}}{z^{-12}}$ z

41. $\dfrac{3^2}{3^{-1}}$ 27

42. $\dfrac{4^2}{4^{-1}}$ 64

43. 5^{-3} $\dfrac{1}{125}$

44. x^{-7} $\dfrac{1}{x^7}$

45. $\dfrac{1}{z^{-9}}$ z^9

46. $\dfrac{1}{3^{-3}}$ 27

47. $\left(p^{-4}\right)^{-6}$ p^{24}

48. $\left(x^{-3}\right)^{-4}$ x^{12}

49. $\left(y^{-2}\right)^{-3}$ y^6

50. $z^9 \cdot z^{-12}$ $\dfrac{1}{z^3}$

51. $x^3 \cdot x^{-7}$ $\dfrac{1}{x^4}$

52. $x^{-3} \cdot x^{-5}$ $\dfrac{1}{x^8}$

53. $x^{-8} \cdot x^{-7}$ $\dfrac{1}{x^{15}}$

54. $8^{-3} \cdot 8^3$ 1

55. -4^{-2} $-\dfrac{1}{16}$

56. $(-4)^{-2}$ $\dfrac{1}{16}$

57. $-(-4)^{-2}$ $-\dfrac{1}{16}$

58. -2^{-3} $-\dfrac{1}{8}$

59. $(-2)^{-3}$ $-\dfrac{1}{8}$

60. $-(-2)^{-3}$ $\dfrac{1}{8}$

61. $(-6)^{-2}$ $\dfrac{1}{36}$

62. -6^{-2} $-\dfrac{1}{36}$

63. $\dfrac{x^{-5}}{x^5}$ $\dfrac{1}{x^{10}}$

64. $\dfrac{y^6}{y^{-8}}$ y^{14}

65. $\dfrac{n^{-5}}{n^{-7}}$ n^2

66. $\dfrac{3^{-4}}{3}$ $\dfrac{1}{243}$

67. $\dfrac{9^{-3}}{9^{-3}}$ 1

68. $\left(7q^5r^2\right)^0$ 1

69. $\left(2^{-1} + 3^{-1}\right)^0$ 1

70. $\left(3^{-1} + 4^2\right)^0$ 1

71. $\dfrac{2}{2^{-5}}$ 64

72. $\left(z^{-5}\right)^{-9}$ z^{45}

73. $\left(x^{-4}\right)^{-2}$ x^8

74. $\left(x^{-7}\right)^0$ 1

75. $\left(x^0\right)^{-2}$ 1

76. $\left(3^{-2}\right)^{-1}$ 9

77. $2^{-3} \cdot 2$ $\dfrac{1}{4}$

78. $7^5 \cdot 7^{-3}$ 49

79. $7^{-5} \cdot 7^3$ $\dfrac{1}{49}$

80. $\dfrac{z^{-3}}{z^{-7}}$ z^4

81. $\dfrac{x^{-1}}{x^{-4}}$ x^3

82. $\dfrac{r^6}{r}$ r^5

83. $\left(4^2\right)^{-1}$ $\dfrac{1}{16}$

84. $\left(2^{-2}\right)^{-2}$ 16

85. $\dfrac{5}{5^{-2}}$ 125

86. $\dfrac{x^6}{x^7}$ $\dfrac{1}{x}$

87. $\dfrac{3^{-4}}{3^{-2}}$ $\dfrac{1}{9}$

88. $x^{-10} \cdot x^8$ $\dfrac{1}{x^2}$

89. $\dfrac{8^{-1}}{8^{-1}}$ 1

90. $2x^{-1}y$ $\dfrac{2y}{x}$

91. $\left(-6x^2\right)^{-2}$ $\dfrac{1}{36x^4}$

92. $\left(-3z^3\right)^{-2}$ $\dfrac{1}{9z^6}$

93. $3x^{-2}y^2$ $\dfrac{3y^2}{x^2}$

94. $-5x^4y^{-1}$ $-\dfrac{5x^4}{y}$

95. $\left(\dfrac{1}{2}\right)^{-2}$ 4

96. $\left(\dfrac{3}{5}\right)^{-2}$ $\dfrac{25}{9}$

97. $\left(\dfrac{5}{4}\right)^{-3}$ $\dfrac{64}{125}$

98. $\left(\dfrac{3}{5}\right)^{-3}$ $\dfrac{125}{27}$

99. $\left(\dfrac{c^4}{d^2}\right)^{-2}$ $\dfrac{d^4}{c^8}$

100. $\left(\dfrac{x^2}{y}\right)^{-2}$ $\dfrac{y^2}{x^4}$

101. $-\left(\dfrac{r^4}{s}\right)^{-4}$ $-\dfrac{s^4}{r^{16}}$

102. $-\left(\dfrac{m^3}{n^4}\right)^{-5}$ $-\dfrac{n^{20}}{m^{15}}$

103. $-7a^{-3}b^{-4}$ $-\dfrac{7}{a^3b^4}$

104. $\left(3x^2y^3\right)^{-2}$ $\dfrac{1}{9x^4y^6}$

105. $\left(4x^5y^{-3}\right)^{-3}$ $\dfrac{y^9}{64x^{15}}$

106. $2w\left(3w^{-5}\right)$ $\dfrac{6}{w^4}$

107. $\left(3z^{-4}\right)\left(6z^{-5}\right)$ $\dfrac{18}{z^9}$

108. $2x^5\left(3x^{-6}\right)$ $\dfrac{6}{x}$

109. $4x^4\left(-2x^{-4}\right)$ -8

110. $\left(9x^5\right)\left(-3x^{-7}\right)$ $-\dfrac{27}{x^2}$

111. $\left(4x^2y\right)\left(3x^3y^{-1}\right)$ $12x^5$

112. $\left(7a^{-6}b^{-1}\right)\left(a^9b^0\right)$ $\dfrac{7a^3}{b}$

113. $\left(-5y^2\right)\left(4y^{-3}z^5\right)$ $-\dfrac{20z^5}{y}$

114. $\left(-3y^{-2}\right)\left(5x^{-1}y^3\right)$ $-\dfrac{15y}{x}$

115. $\dfrac{24d^{12}}{3d^8}$ $8d^4$

116. $\dfrac{8z^{-4}}{32z^{-2}}$ $\dfrac{1}{4z^2}$

117. $\dfrac{36x^{-4}}{9x^{-2}}$ $\dfrac{4}{x^2}$

118. $\dfrac{18m^{-3}n^0}{6m^5n^9}$ $\dfrac{3}{m^8n^9}$

119. $\dfrac{3x^4y^{-2}}{6y^3}$ $\dfrac{x^4}{2y^5}$

120. $\dfrac{16x^{-7}y^{-2}}{4x^5y^2}$ $\dfrac{4}{x^{12}y^4}$

121. $\dfrac{32x^4y^{-2}}{4x^{-2}y^0}$ $\dfrac{8x^6}{y^2}$

122. $\dfrac{21x^{-3}z^2}{7xz^{-3}}$ $\dfrac{3z^5}{x^4}$

123. $\left(\dfrac{5x^4y^{-7}}{z^3}\right)^{-2}$ $\dfrac{y^{14}z^6}{25x^8}$

124. $\left(\dfrac{b^4c^{-2}}{2d^{-3}}\right)^{-1}$ $\dfrac{2c^2}{b^4d^3}$

125. $\left(\dfrac{2r^{-5}s^9}{t^{12}}\right)^{-4}$ $\dfrac{r^{20}t^{48}}{16s^{36}}$

126. $\left(\dfrac{5m^{-1}n^{-3}}{p^2}\right)^{-3}$ $\dfrac{m^3n^9p^6}{125}$

127. $\left(\dfrac{x^3y^{-4}z}{y^{-2}}\right)^{-6}$ $\dfrac{y^{12}}{x^{18}z^6}$

128. $\left(\dfrac{3p^{-1}q^{-2}r^3}{p^2}\right)^3$ $\dfrac{27r^9}{p^9q^6}$

129. $\left(\dfrac{p^6q^{-3}}{4p^8}\right)^2$ $\dfrac{1}{16p^4q^6}$

130. $\left(\dfrac{x^{12}y^5}{y^{-3}z}\right)^{-4}$ $\dfrac{z^4}{x^{48}y^{32}}$

Problem Solving

131. a) Does $p^{-1}q^{-1} = \dfrac{1}{pq}$? Explain your answer.   yes

b) Does $p^{-1} + q^{-1} = \dfrac{1}{p+q}$? Explain your answer.   no

132. a) Does $\dfrac{x^{-1}y^2}{z} = \dfrac{y^2}{xz}$? Explain your answer.   yes

b) Does $\dfrac{x^{-1} + y^2}{z} = \dfrac{y^2}{x+z}$? Explain your answer.   no

Evaluate.

133. $4^2 + 4^{-2}$ $16\frac{1}{16}$

134. $3^2 + 3^{-2}$ $9\frac{1}{9}$

135. $5^3 + 5^{-3}$ $125\frac{1}{125}$

136. $6^{-3} + 6^3$ $216\frac{1}{216}$

Evaluate.

137. $5^0 - 3^{-1}$ $\frac{2}{3}$

138. $4^{-1} - 3^{-1}$ $-\frac{1}{12}$

139. $2^{-3} - 2^3 \cdot 2^{-3}$ $-\frac{7}{8}$

140. $2 \cdot 4^{-1} + 4 \cdot 3^{-1}$ $\frac{11}{6}$

141. $2 \cdot 4^{-1} - 4 \cdot 3^{-1}$ $-\frac{5}{6}$

142. $2 \cdot 4^{-1} - 3^{-1}$ $\frac{1}{6}$

143. $3 \cdot 5^0 - 5 \cdot 3^{-2}$ $\frac{22}{9}$

144. $7 \cdot 2^{-3} - 2 \cdot 4^{-1}$ $\frac{3}{8}$

Determine the number that when placed in the shaded area makes the statement true.

145. $3^{\blacksquare} = \frac{1}{9}$ -2

146. $\frac{1}{2^{\blacksquare}} = 64$ -6

147. $\frac{1}{6^{\blacksquare}} = 216$ -3

148. $4^{\blacksquare} = \frac{1}{256}$ -4

Challenge Problems

In Exercises 149–151, determine the number (or numbers) that when placed in the shaded area (or areas) make the statement true.

149. $(x^{\blacksquare} y^3)^{-2} = \frac{x^4}{y^6}$ -2

150. $(x^4 y^{-3})^{\blacksquare} = \frac{y^9}{x^{12}}$ -3

151. $(\blacksquare x^{\blacksquare} y^{-2})^3 = \frac{8}{x^9 y^6}$ $2, -3$

152. For any nonzero real number a, if $a^{-1} = x$, describe the following in terms of x.

a) $-a^{-1}$ $-x$

b) $\frac{1}{a^{-1}}$ $\frac{1}{x}$

153. Consider $(3^{-1} + 2^{-1})^0$. We know this is equal to 1 by the zero exponent rule. Determine the error in the following calculation. Explain your answer.

$$(3^{-1} + 2^{-1})^0 = (3^{-1})^0 + (2^{-1})^0$$
$$= 3^{-1(0)} + 2^{-1(0)}$$
$$= 3^0 + 2^0$$
$$= 1 + 1 = 2$$

Product rule is $(xy)^m = x^m y^m$ not $(x + y)^m$.

Group Activity

Discuss and answer Exercise 154 as a group.

154. Often problems involving exponents can be done in more than one way. Consider

$$\left(\frac{3x^2 y^3}{x}\right)^{-2}$$

a) Group member 1: Simplify this expression by first simplifying the expression within parentheses.

154. a)–c) $\dfrac{1}{9x^2 y^6}$

b) Group member 2: Simplify this expression by first using the expanded power rule.

c) Group member 3: Simplify this expression by first using the negative exponent rule.

d) Compare your answers. If you did not all get the same answers, determine why.

e) As a group, decide which method—**a)**, **b)**, or **c)**—was the easiest way to simplify this expression.

Cumulative Review Exercises

[2.7] **155.** **Racing** If a race car travels 104 miles in 52 minutes, how far will it travel in 93 minutes (assuming all conditions stay the same)?   186 miles

[3.2] **156.** **Even Integers** The sum of two consecutive even integers is 190. Find the numbers.   94, 96

[3.3] **157.** **Shed** Michael Beattie is building a rectangular shed. The perimeter of the shed is to be 56 feet. Determine the dimensions of the shed if the length is to be 8 feet less than twice the width.   12 ft by 16 ft

[3.4] **158.** **Simple Interest** Mia Kattee invested $9000, part at 3% and part at 4% simple interest for a period of one year. How much was invested in each account if the interest earned in the 3% account was $32 greater than the interest earned in the 4% account?
$3400 at 4%, $5600 at 3%

[6.1] **159.** Simplify $(6xy^5)(3x^2 y^4)$. $18x^3 y^9$

6.3 Scientific Notation

1 Convert numbers to and from scientific notation.

2 Recognize numbers in scientific notation with a coefficient of 1.

3 Do calculations using scientific notation.

1 Convert Numbers to and from Scientific Notation

We often see, and sometimes use, very large or very small numbers. For example, in September 2006, the world population was about 6,539,000,000 people. You may have read that an influenza virus is about 0.0000001 meters in diameter. Because it is difficult to work with many zeros, we can express such numbers using exponents. For example, the number 6,539,000,000 could be written 6.539×10^9 and the number 0.0000001 could be written 1.0×10^{-7}.

Numbers such as 6.539×10^9 and 1.0×10^{-7} are in a form called **scientific notation**. Each number written in scientific notation is written as a number greater than or equal to 1 and less than 10 ($1 \le a < 10$) multiplied by some power of 10. The exponent on the 10 must be an integer.

Examples of Numbers in Scientific Notation

$$1.2 \times 10^6$$
$$3.762 \times 10^3$$
$$8.07 \times 10^{-2}$$
$$1.0 \times 10^{-5}$$

Below we change the number 68,400 to scientific notation.

$$68,400 = 6.84 \times 10,000$$
$$= 6.84 \times 10^4 \qquad \text{Note that } 10,000 = 10 \cdot 10 \cdot 10 \cdot 10 = 10^4.$$

Therefore, $68,400 = 6.84 \times 10^4$. To go from 68,400 to 6.84 the decimal point was moved four places to the left. Note that the exponent on the 10, the 4, is the same as the number of places the decimal point was moved to the left.

Following is a simplified procedure for writing a number in scientific notation.

> ### To Write a Number in Scientific Notation
>
> 1. Move the decimal point in the original number to the right of the first nonzero digit. This will give a number greater than or equal to 1 and less than 10.
>
> 2. Count the number of places you moved the decimal point to obtain the number in step 1. If the original number was 10 or greater, the count is considered positive. If the original number was less than 1, the count is considered negative.
>
> 3. Multiply the number obtained in step 1 by 10 raised to the count (power) found in step 2.

EXAMPLE 1 ▶ Write the following numbers in scientific notation.

a) 18,500   **b)** 0.0000416   **c)** 3,721,000   **d)** 0.0093

Solution

a) The original number is greater than 10; therefore, the exponent is positive. The decimal point in 18,500 belongs after the last zero.

$$18,500. = 1.85 \times 10^4$$
4 places

b) The original number is less than 1; therefore, the exponent is negative.

$$0.0000416 = 4.16 \times 10^{-5}$$
5 places

c) $3,721,000 = 3.721 \times 10^6$

6 places

d) $0.0093 = 9.3 \times 10^{-3}$

3 places

▶ **Now Try Exercise 13**

When we write a number in scientific notation, we are allowed to leave our answer with a negative exponent, as in Example 1**b)** and 1**d)**.

Now we explain how to write a number in scientific notation as a number without exponents, or in decimal form.

To Convert a Number from Scientific Notation to Decimal Form

1. Observe the exponent of the power of 10.

2. **a)** If the exponent is positive, move the decimal point in the number (greater than or equal to 1 and less than 10) to the right the same number of places as the exponent. It may be necessary to add zeros to the number. This will result in a number greater than or equal to 10.

   b) If the exponent is 0, do not move the decimal point. Drop the factor 10^0 since it equals 1. This will result in a number greater than or equal to 1 but less than 10.

   c) If the exponent is negative, move the decimal point in the number to the left the same number of places as the exponent (dropping the negative sign). It may be necessary to add zeros to the number. This will result in a number less than 1.

EXAMPLE 2 ▶ Write each number without exponents.

a) 2.9×10^4 **b)** 6.28×10^{-3} **c)** 7.95×10^8

Solution

a) Move the decimal point four places to the right.

$$2.9 \times 10^4 = 2.9 \times 10,000 = 29,000$$

b) Move the decimal point three places to the left.

$$6.28 \times 10^{-3} = 0.00628$$

c) Move the decimal point eight places to the right.

$$7.95 \times 10^8 = 795,000,000$$

▶ **Now Try Exercise 29**

---

2 Recognize Numbers in Scientific Notation with a Coefficient of 1

We often hear terms like kilograms, milligrams, and gigabytes. For example, an aspirin tablet bottle may indicate that each aspirin contains 325 milligrams of aspirin. Your hard drive on your computer may hold 40 gigabytes of memory. The prefixes kilo, milli, and giga are some of the prefixes used in the *metric system*. The metric system is used in every westernized nation except the United States as the main system of measurement. The prefixes are always used with some type of base unit. The base unit may be measures like meter, m (a unit of length); gram, g (a unit of mass); liter, ℓ (a unit of volume); bits, b (a unit of computer memory); or hertz, Hz (a measure of frequency).

For example, a *milli*meter is $\dfrac{1}{1000}$ meter. A *mega*gram is 1,000,000 grams, and so on. The following table illustrates the meaning of some prefixes.*

Prefix	Meaning	Symbol	Meaning as a Decimal Number
nano	10^{-9}	n	$\dfrac{1}{1,000,000,000}$ or 0.000000001
micro	10^{-6}	μ	$\dfrac{1}{1,000,000}$ or 0.000001
milli	10^{-3}	m	$\dfrac{1}{1000}$ or 0.001
base unit**	10^{0}		1
kilo	10^{3}	k	1000
mega	10^{6}	M	1,000,000
giga	10^{9}	G	1,000,000,000

**The base unit is not a prefix. We included this row to include 10^0 in the chart.

You will sometimes see numbers written as powers of 10, but without a numerical coefficient, as in the table above. If no numerical coefficient is indicated, the numerical coefficient is always assumed to be 1. Thus, for example, $10^{-3} = 1.0 \times 10^{-3}$ and $10^9 = 1.0 \times 10^9$. A computer hard drive that contains 40 gigabytes (40 Gb) contains about $40(1.0 \times 10^9) = 40 \times 10^9 = 40{,}000{,}000{,}000$ bytes. Fifty micrometers (50 μm) is $50(1.0 \times 10^{-6}) = 50 \times 10^{-6} = 0.00005$ meter. Three hundred twenty-five milligrams (325 mg) is $325(1.0 \times 10^{-3}) = 325 \times 10^{-3} = 0.325$ gram. Notice that in the table, each prefix represents a value that is 10^3 or 1000 times greater than the prefix above it. For example, a micrometer is 10^3 or 1000 times greater than a nanometer. A gigameter is 1000 times larger than a megameter, and so on.

In **Figure 6.1**, we see that the frequency of FM radio and VHF TV is about 10^8 hertz (or cycles per second). Thus, the frequency of FM radio is $10^8 = 1.0 \times 10^8 = 100{,}000{,}000$ hertz. This number, one hundred million hertz, can also be expressed as 100×10^6 or 100 megahertz, 100 MHz.

TEACHING TIP
Point out that the FM radio dial spans 88–108 with the units MHz and the AM radio dial spans 530–1700 with the units kHz. After pointing out that MHz = 10^6 Hz and kHz = 10^3 Hz, have students write 88 MHz, 108 MHz, 530 kHz, and 1700 kHz in hertz using scientific notation.

FIGURE 6.1

Now that we know how to interpret powers of 10 that are given without numerical coefficients, we will work some problems using scientific notation.

*There are other prefixes not listed. For example, centi is 10^{-2} or 0.01 times the base unit.

INSTRUCTOR EXAMPLE
Write 76 millimeters without the
metric prefix.
Ans.: 0.076 meter

EXAMPLE 3 ▶ Write each quantity without the metric prefix.

a) 52 kilograms   **b)** 183 nanoseconds

Solution

a) 52 kilograms (52 kg) $= 52 \times 10^3$ grams $= 52{,}000$ grams

b) 183 nanoseconds (183 ns) $= 183 \times 10^{-9}$ seconds $= 0.000000183$ second

▶ **Now Try Exercise 45**

Helpful Hint *Study Tip*

Think about how often in your daily life you come across large and small quantities that may be expressed using scientific notation. This may give you more of an appreciation for scientific notation.

---

3 Do Calculations Using Scientific Notation

We can use the rules of exponents presented in Sections 6.1 and 6.2 when working with numbers written in scientific notation.

INSTRUCTOR EXAMPLE
Multiply $(2.8 \times 10^7)(3.0 \times 10^{-3})$.
Write the answer in decimal form.
Ans.: 84,000

EXAMPLE 4 ▶ Multiply $(4.2 \times 10^6)(2.0 \times 10^{-4})$. Write the answer in decimal form.

Solution   By the commutative and associative properties of multiplication we can rearrange the expression as follows.

$$(4.2 \times 10^6)(2.0 \times 10^{-4}) = (4.2 \times 2.0)(10^6 \times 10^{-4})$$

$$= 8.4 \times 10^{6+(-4)} \qquad \textit{By the product rule}$$

$$= 8.4 \times 10^2 \qquad \textit{Scientific notation}$$

$$= 840 \qquad \textit{Decimal form}$$

▶ **Now Try Exercise 55**

INSTRUCTOR EXAMPLE
Divide $\dfrac{5.6 \times 10^{-3}}{2.8 \times 10^{-7}}$. Write the answer
in scientific notation.

Ans.: 2.0×10^4

EXAMPLE 5 ▶ Divide $\dfrac{3.2 \times 10^{-6}}{5.0 \times 10^{-3}}$. Write the answer in scientific notation.

Solution

$$\frac{3.2 \times 10^{-6}}{5.0 \times 10^{-3}} = \left(\frac{3.2}{5.0}\right)\left(\frac{10^{-6}}{10^{-3}}\right)$$

$$= 0.64 \times 10^{-6-(-3)} \qquad \textit{By the quotient rule}$$

$$= 0.64 \times 10^{-6+3}$$

$$= 0.64 \times 10^{-3}$$

$$= 6.4 \times 10^{-4} \qquad \textit{Scientific notation}$$

The answer to Example 5 in decimal form would be 0.00064.

▶ **Now Try Exercise 59**

USING YOUR CALCULATOR

What will your calculator show when you multiply very large or very small numbers? The answer depends on whether your calculator has the ability to display an answer in scientific notation. On calculators without the ability to express numbers in scientific notation, you will probably get an error message because the answer will be too large or too small for the display. For example, on a calculator without scientific notation:

$$\boxed{8000000} \; \boxed{\times} \; \boxed{600000} \; \boxed{=} \; \boxed{\text{Error}}$$

On scientific calculators and graphing calculators, the answer to this example might be displayed in the following ways.

Possible displays

$$\boxed{8000000} \; \boxed{\times} \; \boxed{600000} \; \boxed{=} \; \boxed{4.8 \qquad 12}$$

$$\boxed{8000000} \; \boxed{\times} \; \boxed{600000} \; \boxed{=} \; \boxed{4.8 \quad ^{12}}$$

$$\boxed{8000000} \; \boxed{\times} \; \boxed{600000} \; \boxed{=} \; \boxed{4.8E12}$$

Each answer means 4.8×10^{12}. Let's look at one more example.

Possible displays

$$\boxed{0.0000003} \; \boxed{\times} \; \boxed{0.004} \; \boxed{=} \; \boxed{1.2 \qquad -9}$$

$$\boxed{0.0000003} \; \boxed{\times} \; \boxed{0.004} \; \boxed{=} \; \boxed{1.2 \quad ^{-9}}$$

$$\boxed{0.0000003} \; \boxed{\times} \; \boxed{0.004} \; \boxed{=} \; \boxed{1.2E-9}$$

Each display means 1.2×10^{-9}. On some calculators you will press the $\boxed{\text{ENTER}}$ key instead of the $\boxed{=}$ key. The TI-84 Plus graphing calculator displays answers using E, such as 4.8E12.

INSTRUCTOR EXAMPLE
The weight of the Earth is
5.972×10^{24} kg. The weight of the
Earth's Moon is 7.35×10^{22} kg.

a) How much greater is the weight
of the Earth than the weight of
its Moon?

b) How many times greater is the
weight of the Earth than the
weight of its Moon?

Ans.:

a) 5.8985×10^{24} kg

b) ≈ 81 times greater

EXAMPLE 6 ▶ **Comparing Big Ships** The *Disney Magic* cruise ship gross tonnage is about 8.3×10^4 tons. The Carnival line's *Destiny* cruise ship gross tonnage is about 1.02×10^5 tons.

a) How much greater is the gross tonnage of the *Destiny* than the *Disney Magic*?

b) How many times greater is the gross tonnage of the *Destiny* than the *Disney Magic*?

Solution

a) Understand   We need to subtract 8.3×10^4 from 1.02×10^5. To add or subtract numbers in scientific notation, we generally make the exponents on the 10's the same. This will allow us to add or subtract the numerical values preceding the base while maintaining the common base and exponent on the base.

Translate   We can write 1.02×10^5 as 10.2×10^4. Now subtract as follows.

Carry Out
$$\begin{array}{r} 10.2 \times 10^4 \\ -8.3 \times 10^4 \\ \hline 1.9 \times 10^4 \end{array}$$

Notice that in subtraction, we did not subtract the 10^4's. This subtraction could also be done as $(10.2 \times 10^4) - (8.3 \times 10^4) = (10.2 - 8.3) \times 10^4 = 1.9 \times 10^4$.

Check   We can check by writing the numbers out in decimal form.

$$\begin{array}{r} 102{,}000 \\ -83{,}000 \\ \hline 19{,}000 \text{ or } 1.9 \times 10^4 \end{array}$$

Answer   Since we obtain the same results, the difference is 1.9×10^4 (or 19,000) tons.

b) Understand   Part **b)** may seem similar to part **a)**, but it is a different question because we are asked to find the *number of times* greater rather than *how much greater*. To find the number of times greater, we perform division.

Translate   Divide the gross tonnage of the *Destiny* by the gross tonnage of the *Disney Magic*.

Carry Out
$$\frac{1.02 \times 10^5}{8.3 \times 10^4} = \frac{1.02}{8.3} \times \frac{10^5}{10^4}$$

$$\approx 0.12 \times 10^{5-4} \qquad \textit{Quotient rule of exponents}$$

$$\approx 0.12 \times 10^1$$

$$\approx 1.2$$

Check   We can check by writing the numbers out in decimal form.

$$\frac{102{,}000}{83{,}000} \approx 1.2$$

INSTRUCTOR EXAMPLE 7
How long would it take the Blue Gene/L System to do 8 trillion calculations?
Ans.: 0.0584 second

Answer   Since we obtain the same result, the tonnage of the *Destiny* is about 1.2 times that of the *Disney Magic*.

▸ **Now Try Exercise 75**

EXAMPLE 7 ▸ **Fastest Computer**   As of June 2005, the fastest computer in the world, called the Blue Gene/L System, located at the Lawrence Livermore National Laboratory in California, could perform a single calculation in about 0.0000000000000073 second. How long would it take this computer to perform 7 billion (7,000,000,000) calculations? *Source:* www.top500.org/news/articles/article_68.php

Solution **Understand**   The computer could perform 1 calculation in 1(0.0000000000000073) second, 2 calculations in 2(0.0000000000000073) second, 3 calculations in 3(0.0000000000000073) second, and 7 billion operations in 7,000,000,000(0.0000000000000073) second.

The Blue Gene/L System

Translate   We will multiply by converting each number to scientific notation.

$$7{,}000{,}000{,}000(0.0000000000000073) = (7.0 \times 10^9)(7.3 \times 10^{-15})$$

Carry Out
$$= (7.0 \times 7.3)(10^9 \times 10^{-15})$$
$$= 51.1 \times 10^{-6}$$
$$= 5.11 \times 10^{-5}$$
$$= 0.0000511$$

Answer   The Blue Gene/L System would take about 0.0000511 of a second to perform 7 billion calculations.

▶ **Now Try Exercise 79**

EXERCISE SET 6.3

MathXL®   MyMathLab

Concept/Writing Exercises

1. a number greater than or equal to 1 and less than 10 multiplied by some power of 10
6. when the number is less than 1   7. when the number is 10 or greater

1. Describe the form of a number given in scientific notation.

2. a) Describe how to write a number 10 or greater in scientific notation.   Answers will vary.

   b) Using the procedure described in part a), write 315,200 in scientific notation. 3.152×10^5

3. a) Describe how to write a number less than 1 in scientific notation.   Answers will vary.

   b) Using the procedure described in part a), write 0.0000723 in scientific notation. 7.23×10^{-5}

4. How many places, and in what direction, will you move the decimal point when you convert a number from scientific notation to decimal form when the exponent on the base 10 is −9?   nine places to the left

5. How many places, and in what direction, will you move the decimal point when you convert a number from scientific notation to decimal form when the exponent on the base 10 is 6?   six places to the right

6. When changing a number to scientific notation, under what conditions will the exponent on the base 10 be negative?

7. When changing a number to scientific notation, under what conditions will the exponent on the base 10 be positive?

8. In writing the number 112,546 in scientific notation, will the exponent on the base 10 be positive or negative? Explain.   positive

9. In writing the number 0.000937 in scientific notation, will the exponent on the base 10 be positive or negative? Explain.   negative

10. Write the number 1,000,000 in scientific notation. 1.0×10^6

11. Write the number 0.000001 in scientific notation. 1.0×10^{-6}

12. a) Is 82.39×10^4 written in scientific notation? If not, how should it be written?   no, 8.239×10^5

    b) Is 0.083×10^{-5} written in scientific notation? If not, how should it be written?   no, 8.3×10^{-7}

Practice the Skills

Express each number in scientific notation.

13. 350,000 3.5×10^5

14. 3,610,000 3.61×10^6

15. 7950 7.950×10^3

16. 0.000089 8.9×10^{-5}

17. 0.053 5.3×10^{-2}

18. 19,000 1.9×10^4

19. 0.000726 7.26×10^{-4}

20. 0.00000186 1.86×10^{-6}

21. 5,260,000,000 5.26×10^9

22. 0.0075 7.5×10^{-3}

23. 0.00000914 9.14×10^{-6}

24. 74,100 7.41×10^4

25. 220,300 2.203×10^5

26. 0.08 8.0×10^{-2}

27. 0.005104 5.104×10^{-3}

28. 416,000 4.16×10^5

Express each number in decimal form (without exponents).

29. 4.3×10^4 43,000

30. 1.63×10^{-4} 0.000163

31. 9.32×10^{-6} 0.00000932

32. 6.15×10^5 615,000

33. 2.13×10^{-5} 0.0000213

34. 7.26×10^{-6} 0.00000726

35. 6.25×10^5 625,000

36. 4.6×10^1 46

37. 9.0×10^6 9,000,000

38. 6.475×10^1 64.75

39. 5.35×10^2 535

40. 3.14×10^{-2} 0.0314

41. 7.73×10^{-7} 0.000000773

42. 6.201×10^{-4} 0.0006201

43. 1.0×10^4 10,000

44. 7.13×10^{-4} 0.000713

In Exercises 45–52, write the quantity without metric prefixes. See Example 3.

45. 8 micrometers   0.000008 meter

46. 29 micrograms   0.000029 gram

47. 125 gigawatts   125,000,000,000 watts

48. 8.7 nanoseconds   0.0000000087 second

49. 15.3 kilometers   15,300 meters

50. 80.2 megahertz   80,200,000 hertz

51. 48.2 millimeters   0.0482 meter

52. 3.12 milligrams   0.00312 gram

Perform each indicated operation and express each number in decimal form (without exponents).

53. $(2.0 \times 10^2)(3.0 \times 10^5)$ 60,000,000
54. $(2.0 \times 10^{-3})(3.0 \times 10^2)$ 0.6
55. $(2.7 \times 10^{-6})(9.0 \times 10^4)$ 0.243

56. $(1.3 \times 10^{-8})(1.74 \times 10^6)$ 0.02262
57. $(1.6 \times 10^{-2})(4.0 \times 10^{-3})$ 0.000064
58. $(4.0 \times 10^5)(1.2 \times 10^{-4})$ 48

59. $\dfrac{3.9 \times 10^{-5}}{3.0 \times 10^{-2}}$ 0.0013
60. $\dfrac{6.0 \times 10^{-3}}{3.0 \times 10^1}$ 0.0002
61. $\dfrac{7.5 \times 10^6}{3.0 \times 10^3}$ 2500

62. $\dfrac{1.4 \times 10^7}{4.0 \times 10^8}$ 0.035
63. $\dfrac{2.0 \times 10^4}{8.0 \times 10^{-2}}$ 250,000
64. $\dfrac{1.6 \times 10^4}{8.0 \times 10^{-3}}$ 2,000,000

Perform each indicated operation by first converting each number to scientific notation. Write the answer in scientific notation.

65. $(700,000)(6,000,000)$ 4.2×10^{12}
66. $(0.003)(0.00015)$ 4.5×10^{-7}
67. $(0.0004)(320)$ 1.28×10^{-1}

68. $(67,000)(200,000)$ 1.34×10^{10}
69. $\dfrac{5,600,000}{8000}$ 7.0×10^2
70. $\dfrac{0.00004}{200}$ 2.0×10^{-7}

71. $\dfrac{0.00035}{0.000002}$ 1.75×10^2
72. $\dfrac{150,000}{0.0005}$ 3.0×10^8

73. List the following numbers from smallest to largest: $7.3 \times 10^2, 3.3 \times 10^{-4}, 1.75 \times 10^6, 5.3$.
$3.3 \times 10^{-4}, 5.3, 7.3 \times 10^2, 1.75 \times 10^6$

74. List the following numbers from smallest to largest: $4.8 \times 10^5, 3.2 \times 10^{-1}, 4.6, 8.3 \times 10^{-4}$.
$8.3 \times 10^{-4}, 3.2 \times 10^{-1}, 4.6, 4.8 \times 10^5$

Problem Solving

80. a) $\approx 918,000,000$ **b)** $\approx 2,515,068$

In Exercises 75–92, write the answer in decimal form (without exponents) unless asked to do otherwise.

75. Population In 2006, the U.S. population was about 2.99×10^8 people and the world population was about 6.55×10^9 people.

  a) How many people lived outside the United States in 2006? $\approx 6,251,000,000$

  b) How many times greater is the world population than the U.S. population? ≈ 21.9

76. Diapers Laid end to end the 18 billion disposable diapers thrown away in the United States each year would reach the moon and back seven times (seven round trips).

  a) Write 18 billion in scientific notation. 1.8×10^{10}

  b) If the distance from earth to the moon is 2.38×10^5 miles, what is the length of all these diapers placed end to end? Write your answer in scientific notation and as a number without exponents. 3.332×10^6 or 3,332,000 mi

77. Niagara Falls A treaty between the United States and Canada requires that during the tourist season a minimum of 100,000 cubic feet of water per second flows over Niagara Falls (another 130,000 to 160,000 cubic feet/sec is diverted for power generation). Find the minimum volume of water that will flow over the falls in a 24-hour period during the tourist season.   8,640,000,000 ft³

78. PGA Tour The top five money leaders from the 2004 PGA Tour are listed below.

Golfer	Approximate Money
1. Vijay Singh	$10,910,000
2. Ernie Els	$5,790,000
3. Phil Michelson	$5,780,000
4. Tiger Woods	$5,370,000
5. Stewart Cink	$4,450,000

Source: USA Today

  a) Write, in scientific notation, Tiger Woods's approximate money total. 5.37×10^6

  b) Determine, in scientific notation, the average daily amount that Tiger Woods earned in 2004. Recall that 2004 was a leap year. $\approx \$1.4672 \times 10^4$

79. Computer Speed If a computer can do a calculation in 0.000002 second, how long, in seconds, would it take the computer to do 8 trillion (8,000,000,000,000) calculations? Write your answer in scientific notation. 1.6×10^7 sec

80. Fortune Cookies Who writes the fortunes in those fortune cookies? Fortune cookies are an American invention. Steven Yang, who runs M & Y Trading Company, a San Francisco Company, prints about 90% of all the 1.02×10^9 fortunes in fortune cookies in America in any given year.

  a) How many fortunes does Yang print in a year?

  b) How many fortunes does Yang print in a day?

81. Movies The gross ticket sales of the top five movies in the United States as of June 29, 2005, are listed below.

Movie	Year Released	Approximate U.S. Gross Ticket Sales
1. *Titanic*	1997	$601,000,000
2. *Star Wars*	1977	$461,000,000
3. *Shrek 2*	2004	$437,000,000
4. *E.T.*	1982	$433,000,000
5. *Star Wars—The Phantom Menace*	1999	$431,000,000

a) How much greater was the gross ticket sales of *Titanic* than *E.T.*? Write your answer in scientific notation. 1.68×10^8

b) How many times greater was the gross ticket sales of *Titanic* than *E.T.*? ≈ 1.39

82. Melanoma The number of new cases of melanoma has increased from 4.03×10^4 in 1997 to about 5.5×10^4 in 2003.

a) How much greater was the number of cases of melanoma in 2003 than in 1997?   14,700

b) How many times greater was the number of cases of melanoma in 2003 than in 1997? ≈ 1.36

Source: Rochester Democrat & Chronicle

83. World's Richest The worth of Bill Gates (the world's richest person in 2005) was 4.65×10^{10}. The worth of Pierre Omidyar (the world's thirty-fifth richest person in 2005) was 9.9×10^9. *Source:* www.forbes.com

a) How much greater was the worth of Bill Gates than the worth of Pierre Omidyar in 2005? $36,600,000,000

b) How many times greater was the worth of Bill Gates than the worth of Pierre Omidyar in 2005? ≈ 4.70

84. Light from the Sun The sun is 9.3×10^7 miles from Earth. Light travels at a speed of 1.86×10^5 miles per second. How long, in both seconds and in minutes, does it take light from the Sun to reach Earth?   500 sec or ≈ 8.33 min

85. Astronomy The mass of Earth, Earth's Moon, and the planet Jupiter are listed below.

Earth: 5,794,000,000,000,000,000,000 metric tons

Moon: 73,400,000,000,000,000,000 metric tons

Jupiter: 1,899,000,000,000,000,000,000,000 metric tons

a) Write the mass of Earth, the Moon, and Jupiter in scientific notation.   Earth, 5.794×10^{24} metric tons; Moon, 7.34×10^{19} metric tons; Jupiter, 1.899×10^{27} metric tons

b) How many times greater is the mass of Earth than the mass of the Moon? $\approx 7.89 \times 10^4$

c) How many times greater is the mass of Jupiter than the mass of Earth? $\approx 3.28 \times 10^2$

86. Missing Persons Of the nearly 47,600 active adult missing-person FBI cases as of May 1, 2005, about 53% were men. Determine, in scientific notation, the approximate number of active adult missing-person FBI cases that were men. *Source: Rochester Democrat & Chronicle* $\approx 2.52 \times 10^4$

87. Camera Products and Services The circle graph below shows the percentage of revenue from digital products and services and from traditional products and services during the first quarter of 2005 for Kodak. The company's total revenue for the first quarter of 2005 was $2,800,000,000. How much revenue was from digital products and services? Write your answer in scientific notation. 1.316×10^9

Kodak First Quarter 2005 Revenue

Source: Rochester Democrat & Chronicle

88. Chesapeake Bay Oysters The following bar graph shows the approximate number of bushels of oysters harvested in the Chesapeake Bay.

Chesapeake Oyster Harvests Declining

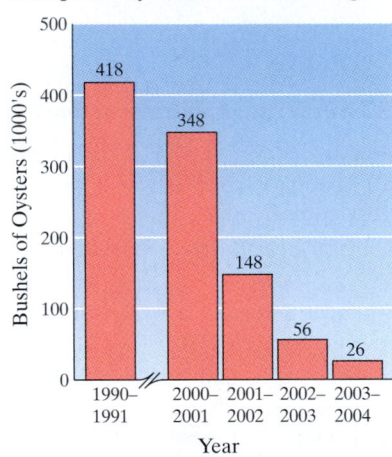

Source: USA Today

a) Give, in scientific notation, the approximate number of bushels of oysters harvested in 1990–1991. 4.18×10^5

b) Give, in scientific notation, the approximate number of bushels of oysters harvested in 2003–2004. 2.6×10^4

c) Determine, in scientific notation, the approximate difference between the number of bushels harvested in 2003–2004 and 1990–1991. 3.92×10^5

89. Federal Government Employees The following bar graph shows the number of federal government employees, by age.

Federal Government Employees by Age (2004)

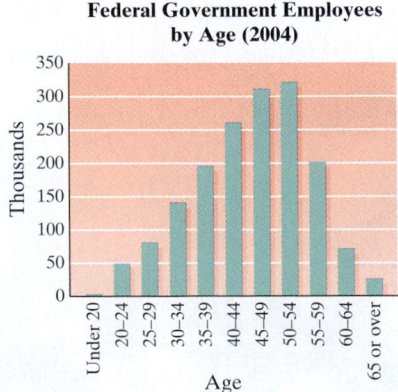

Source: Office of Personnel Management

a) Write, in scientific notation, the approximate number of federal government employees in 2004 who were age 55–59 and the approximate number of federal government employees in 2004 who were age 20–24.

b) Determine, in scientific notation, the approximate total number of federal government employees in 2004 who were age 55–59 or age 20–24. 2.48×10^5

c) Determine, in scientific notation, the approximate difference between the number of federal government employees in 2004 who were age 55–59 and age 20–24. 1.52×10^5

90. The Spice Girls The Spice Girls hold the Guinness World Record as having the highest ever annual earnings by a girl band. The four group members had a total income of $49,000,000 in 1998. If each member of the band received an

89. a) 55–59: 2.0×10^5; 20–24: 5.0×10^4

equal amount, determine, in scientific notation, the amount earned by each group member in 1998. $\$1.225 \times 10^7$

91. Structure of Matter An article in *Scientific American* states that physicists have created a *standard model* that describes the structure of matter down to 10^{-18} meters. If this number is written without exponents, how many zeroes would there be to the right of the decimal point?   17

92. A Large Number Avogadro's number, named after the nineteenth century Italian chemist Amedeo Avogadro, is roughly 6.02×10^{23}. It represents the number of atoms in 12 grams of pure carbon.

a) If this number were written out in decimal form, how many digits would it contain?   24

b) What is the number of atoms in 1 gram of pure carbon? Write your answer in scientific notation. $\approx 5.017 \times 10^{22}$

Challenge Problems

93. The Movie Contact In the movie *Contact*, Jodie Foster plays an astronomer who makes the statement "There are 400 billion stars out there just in our universe alone. If only one out of a million of those had planets, and if just one out of a million of those had life, and if just one out of a million of those had intelligent life, there would be literally millions of civilizations out there." Do you believe this statement is correct? Explain your answer.   Answers will vary.

94. How many times smaller is 1 nanosecond than one millisecond?   1,000,000

95. How many times, either greater or smaller, is 10^{-12} meters than 10^{-18} meters?   1,000,000 times greater

96. Light Year Light travels at a speed of 1.86×10^5 miles per second. A *light year* is the distance light travels in one year. Determine the number of miles in a light year. $\approx 5.87 \times 10^{12}$ mi

Group Activity

Discuss and answer Exercise 97 as a group.

97. A Million versus a Billion Do you have any idea of the difference in size between a million (1,000,000), a billion (1,000,000,000), and a trillion (1,000,000,000,000)?

a) Write a million, a billion, and a trillion in scientific notation. $1.0 \times 10^6, 1.0 \times 10^9, 1.0 \times 10^{12}$

b) Group member 1: Determine how long it would take to spend a million dollars if you spent $1000 a day.
1000 days or about 2.74 years

97. c) 1,000,000 days or about 2740 years   **d)** 1,000,000,000 days or about 2,740,000 years

c) Group member 2: Repeat part **b)** for a billion dollars.

d) Group member 3: Repeat part **b)** for a trillion dollars.

e) As a group, determine how many times greater a billion dollars is than a million dollars.   1000

Cumulative Review Exercises

[1.9] **98.** Evaluate $4x^2 + 3x + \dfrac{x}{2}$ when $x = 0$.   0

[2.3] **99. a)** If $-x = -\dfrac{3}{2}$, what is the value of x? $\dfrac{3}{2}$

   b) If $5x = 0$, what is the value of x?   0

[2.5] **100.** Solve the equation $2x - 3(x - 2) = x + 2$.   2

[6.1] **101.** Simplify $\left(\dfrac{-2x^5y^7}{8x^8y^3}\right)^3$. $-\dfrac{y^{12}}{64x^9}$

Mid-Chapter Test: 6.1–6.3

To find out how well you understand the chapter material to this point, take this brief test. The answers, and the section where the material was initially discussed, are given in the back of the book. Review any questions that you answered incorrectly.

Simplify.

1. $y^{11} \cdot y^2$ y^{13}

2. $\dfrac{x^{13}}{x^{10}}$ x^3

3. $(-3x^5y^7)(-2xy^6)$ $6x^6y^{13}$

4. $\dfrac{6a^{12}b^8}{9a^7b^2}$ $\dfrac{2a^5b^6}{3}$

5. $(-4x^2y^4)^3$ $-64x^6y^{12}$

6. $\left(\dfrac{-5s^4t^6}{10s^6t^3}\right)^2$ $\dfrac{t^6}{4s^4}$

7. $(7x^9y^5)(-3xy^4)^2$ $63x^{11}y^{13}$

8. $\dfrac{p^{-3}}{p^5}$ $\dfrac{1}{p^8}$

9. $x^{-4} \cdot x^{-6}$ $\dfrac{1}{x^{10}}$

10. $(3^{-1} + 5^2)^0$ 1

11. $\left(\dfrac{3}{7}\right)^{-2}$ $\dfrac{49}{9}$

12. $(8x^{-2}y^5)(4x^3y^{-6})$ $\dfrac{32x}{y}$

13. $\dfrac{6m^{-4}n^{-7}}{2m^0n^{-1}}$ $\dfrac{3}{m^4n^6}$

14. $\left(\dfrac{2x^{-3}y^{-4}}{x^3yz^{-2}}\right)^{-2}$ $\dfrac{x^{12}y^{10}}{4z^4}$

15. **a)** Describe how to write a number 10 or greater in scientific notation.   Answers will vary.

   b) Describe how to write a number less than 1 in scientific notation.   Answers will vary.

16. Express 6,540,000,000 in scientific notation. 6.54×10^9

17. Express 3.27×10^{-5} in decimal form (without exponents).   0.0000327

18. Write 18.9 kilometers without metric prefixes.   18,900 meters

19. Multiply $(3.4 \times 10^{-6})(7.0 \times 10^3)$ and express the answer in decimal form (without exponents).   0.0238

20. Divide $\dfrac{0.00006}{200}$ by first converting to scientific notation. Write the answer in scientific notation. 3.0×10^{-7}

6.4 Addition and Subtraction of Polynomials

1. Identify polynomials.
2. Add polynomials.
3. Subtract polynomials.
4. Subtract polynomials in columns.

1 Identify Polynomials

A **polynomial in x** is an expression containing the sum of a finite number of terms of the form ax^n, for any real number a and any *whole number n*.

Examples of Polynomials	Not Polynomials	
$8x$	$4x^{1/2}$	*(Fractional exponent)*
$\dfrac{1}{3}x - 4$	$3x^2 + 4x^{-1} + 5$	*(Negative exponent)*
$x^2 - 2x + 1$	$4 + \dfrac{1}{x}$	$\left(\dfrac{1}{x} = x^{-1}, \text{negative exponent}\right)$

A polynomial is written in **descending order** (or **descending powers**) **of the variable** when the exponents on the variable decrease from left to right.

Example of Polynomial in Descending Order
$$2x^4 + 4x^2 - 6x + 3$$

Note in the example that the constant term 3 is last because it can be written as $3x^0$. Remember that $x^0 = 1$.

A polynomial can be in more than one variable. For example, $3xy + 2$ is a polynomial in two variables, x and y.

A polynomial with one term is called a **monomial**. A **binomial** is a two-termed polynomial. A **trinomial** is a three-termed polynomial. Polynomials containing more

TEACHING TIP
Tell students to give their answers in descending order unless otherwise instructed. Point out that this will make it easier to compare answers.

than three terms are not given special names. The prefix "poly" means "many." The chart that follows summarizes this information.

TEACHING TIP
You may want to use the definition of polynomial to show that a nonzero constant such as 5 is a polynomial.

Type of Polynomial	Number of Terms	Examples
Monomial	One	$8,\ 4x,\ -6x^2$
Binomial	Two	$x + 5,\ x^2 - 6,\ 4y^2 - 5y$
Trinomial	Three	$x^2 - 2x + 3,\ 3z^2 - 6z + 7$

The **degree of a term** of a polynomial in one variable is the exponent on the variable in that term.

Term	Degree of Term	
$4x^2$	Second	
$2y^5$	Fifth	
$-5x$	First	*($-5x$ can be written $-5x^1$.)*
3	Zero	*(3 can be written $3x^0$.)*

For a polynomial in two or more variables, the degree of a term is the sum of the exponents on the variables. For example, the degree of the term $4x^2y^3$ is 5 because $2 + 3 = 5$. The degree of the term $5a^4bc^3$ is 8 because $4 + 1 + 3 = 8$.

The **degree of a polynomial** is the same as that of its highest-degree term.

TEACHING TIP
Point out that polynomials are expressions not equations.

Polynomial	Degree of Polynomial	
$8x^3 + 2x^2 - 3x + 4$	Third	*($8x^3$ is highest-degree term.)*
$x^2 - 4$	Second	*(x^2 is highest-degree term.)*
$6x - 5$	First	*($6x$ or $6x^1$ is highest-degree term.)*
4	Zero	*(4 or $4x^0$ is highest-degree term.)*
$x^2y^4 + 2x + 3$	Sixth	*(x^2y^4 is highest-degree term.)*

2 Add Polynomials

In Section 2.1, we stated that like terms are terms having the same variables and the same exponents. That is, like terms may differ only in their numerical coefficients.

Examples of Like Terms

$$3,\ -5$$
$$2x,\ x$$
$$-2x^2,\ 4x^2$$
$$3y^2,\ 5y^2$$
$$3xy^2,\ 5xy^2$$

To Add Polynomials

To add polynomials, combine the like terms of the polynomials.

INSTRUCTOR EXAMPLE
Add
$(7a^2 + a - 6) + (10a^2 - 3a + 9)$.
Ans.: $17a^2 - 2a + 3$

EXAMPLE 1 ▶ Add $(4x^2 + 6x + 3) + (2x^2 + 5x - 1)$.

Solution   Remember that $(4x^2 + 6x + 3) = 1(4x^2 + 6x + 3)$ and $(2x^2 + 5x - 1) = 1(2x^2 + 5x - 1)$. We can use the distributive property to remove the parentheses, as shown below.

$$(4x^2 + 6x + 3) + (2x^2 + 5x - 1)$$
$$= 1(4x^2 + 6x + 3) + 1(2x^2 + 5x - 1)$$
$$= 4x^2 + 6x + 3 + 2x^2 + 5x - 1 \qquad \text{\textit{Use the distributive property.}}$$
$$= \underline{4x^2 + 2x^2} + \underline{6x + 5x} + \underline{3 - 1} \qquad \text{\textit{Rearrange terms.}}$$
$$= 6x^2 + 11x + 2 \qquad \text{\textit{Combine like terms.}}$$

▶ **Now Try Exercise 67**

In the following examples, we will not show the multiplication by 1 as was shown in Example 1.

EXAMPLE 2 ▶ Add $(5a^2 + 3a + b) + (a^2 - 7a + 3)$.

Solution
$$(5a^2 + 3a + b) + (a^2 - 7a + 3)$$
$$= 5a^2 + 3a + b + a^2 - 7a + 3 \qquad \text{Remove parentheses.}$$
$$= \underline{5a^2 + a^2} + \underline{3a - 7a} + b + 3 \qquad \text{Rearrange terms.}$$
$$= \quad 6a^2 \quad - \quad 4a \quad + b + 3 \qquad \text{Combine like terms.}$$

▶ **Now Try Exercise 75**

EXAMPLE 3 ▶ Add $(3x^2y - 4xy + y) + (x^2y + 2xy + 3y)$.

Solution
$$(3x^2y - 4xy + y) + (x^2y + 2xy + 3y)$$
$$= 3x^2y - 4xy + y + x^2y + 2xy + 3y \qquad \text{Remove parentheses.}$$
$$= \underline{3x^2y + x^2y} \quad \underline{- 4xy + 2xy} \quad \underline{+ y + 3y} \qquad \text{Rearrange terms.}$$
$$= \quad 4x^2y \quad - \quad 2xy \quad + \quad 4y \qquad \text{Combine like terms.}$$

▶ **Now Try Exercise 77**

Usually, when we add polynomials, we will do so as in Examples 1 through 3. That is, we will list the polynomials horizontally. However, in Section 6.6, when we divide polynomials, there will be steps where we add polynomials in columns.

To Add Polynomials in Columns

1. Arrange polynomials in descending order, one under the other with like terms in the same columns.
2. Add the terms in each column.

EXAMPLE 4 ▶ Add $5x^2 - 9x - 3$ and $-3x^2 - 4x + 6$ using columns.

Solution
$$\begin{array}{r} 5x^2 - 9x - 3 \\ -3x^2 - 4x + 6 \\ \hline 2x^2 - 13x + 3 \end{array}$$

▶ **Now Try Exercise 83**

EXAMPLE 5 ▶ Add $5w^3 + 2w - 4$ and $2w^2 - 6w - 3$ using columns.

Solution Since the polynomial $5w^3 + 2w - 4$ does not have a w^2 term, we will add the term $0w^2$ to the polynomial. This procedure sometimes helps in aligning like terms.

$$\begin{array}{r} 5w^3 + 0w^2 + 2w - 4 \\ 2w^2 - 6w - 3 \\ \hline 5w^3 + 2w^2 - 4w - 7 \end{array}$$

▶ **Now Try Exercise 85**

3 Subtract Polynomials

Now let's subtract polynomials.

To Subtract Polynomials

1. Use the distributive property to remove parentheses. (This will have the effect of changing the sign of *every* term within the parentheses of the polynomial being subtracted.)
2. Combine like terms.

EXAMPLE 6 ▶ Subtract $(3x^2 - 2x + 5) - (x^2 - 3x + 4)$.

Solution $(3x^2 - 2x + 5)$ means $1(3x^2 - 2x + 5)$ and $(x^2 - 3x + 4)$ means $1(x^2 - 3x + 4)$. We use this information in the solution, as shown below.

$$(3x^2 - 2x + 5) - (x^2 - 3x + 4) = 1(3x^2 - 2x + 5) - 1(x^2 - 3x + 4)$$
$$= 3x^2 - 2x + 5 - x^2 + 3x - 4 \qquad \textcolor{red}{\textit{Remove parentheses.}}$$
$$= \underline{3x^2 - x^2} \; \underline{- 2x + 3x} \; \underline{+ 5 - 4} \qquad \textcolor{red}{\textit{Rearrange terms.}}$$
$$= \quad 2x^2 \quad + \quad x \quad + \quad 1 \qquad \textcolor{red}{\textit{Combine like terms.}}$$

▶ **Now Try Exercise 97**

Remember from Section 2.1 that when a negative sign precedes the parentheses, the sign of every term within the parentheses is changed when the parentheses are removed. This was shown in Example 6. In Example 7, we will not show the multiplication by -1, as was done in Example 6.

EXAMPLE 7 ▶ Subtract $(-3x^2 - 5x + 3)$ from $(x^3 + 2x + 6)$.

Solution
$$(x^3 + 2x + 6) - (-3x^2 - 5x + 3)$$
$$= x^3 + 2x + 6 + 3x^2 + 5x - 3 \qquad \textcolor{red}{\textit{Remove parentheses.}}$$
$$= x^3 + 3x^2 \; \underline{+ 2x + 5x} \; \underline{+ 6 - 3} \qquad \textcolor{red}{\textit{Rearrange terms.}}$$
$$= x^3 + 3x^2 + \quad 7x \quad + \quad 3 \qquad \textcolor{red}{\textit{Combine like terms.}}$$

▶ **Now Try Exercise 107**

Avoiding Common Errors

One of the most common mistakes occurs when subtracting polynomials. When subtracting one polynomial from another, **the sign of each term in the polynomial being subtracted must be changed, not just the sign of the first term.**

CORRECT	INCORRECT
$6x^2 - 4x + 3 - (2x^2 - 3x + 4)$	$6x^2 - 4x + 3 - (2x^2 - 3x + 4)$
$= 6x^2 - 4x + 3 \; \boxed{-} \; 2x^2 \; \boxed{+} \; 3x \; \boxed{-} \; 4$	$= 6x^2 - 4x + 3 - 2x^2 - 3x + 4$
$= 4x^2 - x - 1$	$= 4x^2 - 7x + 7$

$$\textcolor{red}{\textit{Do not make this mistake!}}$$

4 Subtract Polynomials in Columns

Polynomials can be subtracted as well as added using columns.

To Subtract Polynomials in Columns

1. Write *the polynomial being subtracted* below the polynomial from which it is being subtracted. List like terms in the same column.

2. *Change the sign of each term* in the polynomial being subtracted. (This step can be done mentally, if you like.)

3. Add the terms in each column.

EXAMPLE 8 ▶ Subtract $(2x^2 - 4x + 6)$ from $(4x^2 + 5x + 8)$ using columns.

Solution   Align like terms in columns (step 1).

$$\begin{array}{r} 4x^2 + 5x + 8 \\ -(2x^2 - 4x + 6) \\ \hline \end{array} \qquad \textcolor{red}{\textit{Align like terms.}}$$

Change *all* signs in the second row (step 2); then add (step 3).

$$4x^2 + 5x + 8$$
$$\underline{-2x^2 + 4x - 6} \quad \textit{Change all signs.}$$
$$2x^2 + 9x + 2 \quad \textit{Add.}$$

▸ **Now Try Exercise 113**

EXAMPLE 9 ▸ Subtract $(2x^2 - 6)$ from $(-3x^3 + 4x - 3)$ using columns.

Solution   To help align like terms, write each expression in descending order. If any power of x is missing, write that term with a numerical coefficient of 0.

$$-3x^3 + 4x - 3 = -3x^3 + 0x^2 + 4x - 3$$
$$2x^2 - 6 = 2x^2 + 0x - 6$$

Align like terms.

$$-3x^3 + 0x^2 + 4x - 3$$
$$\underline{-(2x^2 + 0x - 6)}$$

Change all signs in the second row; then add the terms in each column.

$$-3x^3 + 0x^2 + 4x - 3$$
$$\underline{- 2x^2 - 0x + 6}$$
$$-3x^3 - 2x^2 + 4x + 3$$

▸ **Now Try Exercise 115**

NOTE: Many of you will find that you can change the signs mentally and can therefore align and change the signs in one step.

---

1. an expression containing the sum of a finite number of terms of the form ax^n, for any real number a and any whole number n

2. no, contains a fractional exponent   **3.** no, contains a negative exponent   **4.** no, $\dfrac{2}{x} = 2x^{-1}$, negative exponent   **5. a)** a one-termed polynomial

b) a two-termed polynomial   **c)** a three-termed polynomial   **6. a)** The exponent on the variable is the degree of the term.   **b)** same as the degree of the highest-degree term in the polynomial   **10.** should be $3x + 2 - 4x + 6$ **11.** Write with exponents on the variable decreasing from left to right.

12. because the exponent on the variable is 0   **14. a)** Answers will vary.   **b)** $4x^3 + 0x^2 + 5x - 7$ **15.** Use the distributive property to remove parentheses and then combine like terms.   **16. a)** Answers will vary.

EXERCISE SET 6.4

MathXL®   MyMathLab

Concept/Writing Exercises

1. What is a polynomial?

2. Is $6m^3 - 5m^{1/2}$ a polynomial? Explain.

3. Is $4x^{-3} + 9$ a polynomial? Explain.

4. Is $5x + \dfrac{2}{x}$ a polynomial? Explain.

5. a) What is a monomial? Make up three examples.

b) What is a binomial? Make up three examples.

c) What is a trinomial? Make up three examples.

6. a) Explain how to find the degree of a term in one variable.

b) Explain how to find the degree of a polynomial in one variable.

7. Make up your own sixth-degree polynomial with four terms. Explain why it is a sixth-degree polynomial with four terms.   Answers will vary.

8. Explain how to find the degree of a term in a polynomial in more than one variable.   Add the exponents on the variables.

9. Which of the following are fourth-degree terms? Explain your answer.

a) $3xy^2$ **b)** $6r^2s^2$ **c)** $-2mn^3$ **b) and c)**

10. Explain why $(3x + 2) - (4x - 6) \neq 3x + 2 - 4x - 6$.

11. Explain how to write a polynomial in one variable in descending order of the variable.

12. Why is the constant term always written last when writing a polynomial in descending order?

13. Explain how to add polynomials.   Combine like terms.

14. a) Describe how to add polynomials in columns.

b) How will you rewrite $4x^3 + 5x - 7$ in order to add it to $3x^3 + x^2 - 4x + 8$ using columns? Explain.

15. Explain how to subtract polynomials.

16. a) Describe how to subtract polynomials in columns.

b) How will you rewrite $(3x^2 - 4x + 5) - (x^2 + 7x - 4)$ in order to subtract? $3x^2 - 4x + 5 - x^2 - 7x + 4$

Practice the Skills

Indicate the degree of each term.

17. x^5 fifth   **18.** z^{11} eleventh   **19.** $-3b^8$ eighth   **20.** $5a^4$ fourth   **21.** x^2y third

22. a^4b^3 seventh   **23.** $3r^2s^8$ tenth   **24.** $6m^5n^8$ thirteenth   **25.** $-8x^3y^5z$ ninth   **26.** $-12p^4q^7r$ twelfth

Indicate which expressions are polynomials. If the polynomial has a specific name—monomial, binomial, or trinomial—give that name.

27. $2x^2 - 6x + 7$ trinomial   **28.** $x^2 + 3$ binomial   **29.** -6 monomial

30. $4x^{-2}$ not a polynomial   **31.** $9a^4 - 5$ binomial   **32.** $7x + 8$ binomial

33. $8x^9$ monomial   **34.** $3x^{1/2} + 2x$ not a polynomial   **35.** $a^{-1} + 4$ not a polynomial

36. $x^3 - 8x^2 + 8$ trinomial   **37.** $6n^3 - 5n^2 + 4n - 3$ polynomial   **38.** $10x^2$ monomial

39. $4 - 2b^2 - 5b$ trinomial   **40.** $5p^{-3}$ not a polynomial   **41.** $\dfrac{2}{3}x^2 - \dfrac{1}{x}$ not a polynomial

42. $0.6r^4 - \dfrac{1}{2}r^3 - 0.4r^2 - \dfrac{1}{3}$ polynomial

Express each polynomial in descending order. If the polynomial is already in descending order, so state. Give the degree of each polynomial.   **43., 46., 49., 50., 51., 52.,** already in descending order.   **53.** $4x^3 - 3x^2 + x - 4$, third

43. 8 0 degree   **44.** $4 + 5x$ $5x + 4$, first   **45.** $-4 + x^2 - 2x$ $x^2 - 2x - 4$, second

46. $6x - 5$ first   **47.** $x + 3x^2 - 8$ $3x^2 + x - 8$, second   **48.** $4 - 3p^3$ $-3p^3 + 4$, third

49. $-a - 3$ first   **50.** $2x^2 + 5x - 8$ second   **51.** $6w^2 - 5w + 9$ second

52. 15 0 degree   **53.** $-4 + x - 3x^2 + 4x^3$ **54.** $1 - x^3 + 3x$ $-x^3 + 3x + 1$, third

55. $5x + 3x^2 - 6 - 2x^4$ $-2x^4 + 3x^2 + 5x - 6$, fourth   **56.** $-3r - 5r^2 + 2r^4 - 6$ $2r^4 - 5r^2 - 3r - 6$, fourth

Add.

57. $(9x - 2) + (x - 7)$ $10x - 9$ **58.** $(5x - 6) + (2x - 3)$ $7x - 9$

59. $(-3x + 8) + (2x + 3)$ $-x + 11$ **60.** $(-7x - 9) + (-2x + 9)$ $-9x$

61. $(t + 7) + (-3t - 8)$ $-2t - 1$ **62.** $(4x - 3) + (3x - 3)$ $7x - 6$

63. $(x^2 + 2.6x - 3) + (4x + 3.8)$ $x^2 + 6.6x + 0.8$ **64.** $(-4p^2 - 3p - 2) + (-p^2 - 4)$ $-5p^2 - 3p - 6$

65. $(4m - 3) + (5m^2 - 4m + 7)$ $5m^2 + 4$ **66.** $(-x^2 - 2x - 4) + (4x^2 + 3)$ $3x^2 - 2x - 1$

67. $(2x^2 - 3x + 5) + (-x^2 + 6x - 8)$ $x^2 + 3x - 3$ **68.** $(x^2 - 6x + 7) + (-x^2 + 3x + 5)$ $-3x + 12$

69. $(-x^2 - 4x + 8) + \left(5x - 2x^2 + \dfrac{1}{2}\right)$ $-3x^2 + x + \dfrac{17}{2}$ **70.** $(8x^2 + 3x - 5) + \left(x^2 + \dfrac{1}{2}x + 2\right)$ $9x^2 + \dfrac{7}{2}x - 3$

71. $(5.2n^2 - 6n + 1.7) + (3n^2 + 1.2n - 2.3)$ $8.2n^2 - 4.8n - 0.6$ **72.** $(8x^2 + 4) + (-2.6x^2 - 5x - 2.3)$ $5.4x^2 - 5x + 1.7$

73. $(-7x^3 - 3x^2 + 4) + (4x + 5x^3 - 7)$ $-2x^3 - 3x^2 + 4x - 3$ **74.** $(6x^3 - 4x^2 - 7) + (3x^2 + 3x - 3)$ $6x^3 - x^2 + 3x - 10$

75. $(8x^2 + 2x - y) + (3x^2 - 9x + 5)$ $11x^2 - 7x - y + 5$ **76.** $(-7a^2 + 3a - b) + (4a^2 - 2a - 8)$ $-3a^2 + a - b - 8$

77. $(2x^2y + 2x - 3) + (3x^2y - 5x + 5)$ $5x^2y - 3x + 2$ **78.** $(x^2y + x - y) + (2x^2y + 2x - 6y + 3)$ $3x^2y + 3x - 7y + 3$

Add using columns.

79. Add $8x - 7$ and $3x + 4$. $11x - 3$ **80.** Add $-x + 5$ and $-4x - 5$. $-5x$

81. Add $4y^2 - 2y + 4$ and $3y^2 + 1$. $7y^2 - 2y + 5$ **82.** Add $6m^2 - 2m + 1$ and $-10m^2 + 8$. $-4m^2 - 2m + 9$

83. Add $-x^2 - 3x + 3$ and $5x^2 + 5x - 7$. $4x^2 + 2x - 4$ **84.** Add $-2s^2 - s + 5$ and $3s^2 - 6s$. $s^2 - 7s + 5$

85. Add $2x^3 + 3x^2 + 6x - 9$ and $7 - 4x^2$. $2x^3 - x^2 + 6x - 2$ **86.** Add $-3x^3 + 3x + 9$ and $2x^2 - 4$. $-3x^3 + 2x^2 + 3x + 5$

87. Add $4n^3 - 5n^2 + n - 6$ and $-n^3 - 6n^2 - 2n + 8$.   **88.** Add $7x^3 + 5x - 6$ and $3x^3 - 4x^2 - x + 8$.

87. $3n^3 - 11n^2 - n + 2$

88. $10x^3 - 4x^2 + 4x + 2$

Subtract.

89. $(4x - 4) - (2x + 2)$ $2x - 6$ **90.** $(6x - 5) - (2x - 3)$ $4x - 2$

91. $(-2x - 3) - (-5x - 7)$ $3x + 4$ **92.** $(10x - 3) - (-2x + 7)$ $12x - 10$

93. $(-r + 5) - (2r + 5)$ $-3r$ **94.** $(4x + 8) - (3x + 9)$ $x - 1$

95. $(-y^2 + 4y - 5.2) - (5y^2 + 2.1y + 7.5)$ $-6y^2 + 1.9y - 12.7$ **96.** $(9x^2 + 7x - 5) - (3x^2 + 3.5)$ $6x^2 + 7x - 8.5$

97. $(5x^2 - x - 1) - (-3x^2 - 2x - 5)$ $8x^2 + x + 4$ **98.** $(-a^2 + 3a + 12) - (-4a^2 - 3)$ $3a^2 + 3a + 15$

99. $(-4.1n^2 - 3n) - (2.3n^2 - 9n + 7.6)$ $-6.4n^2 + 6n - 7.6$ **100.** $(7x - 0.6) - (-2x^2 + 4x - 8)$ $2x^2 + 3x + 7.4$

103. $2x^3 - \dfrac{23}{5}x^2 + 2x - 2$ 104. $-x^3 - 7x^2 + \dfrac{19}{4}x - 7$ 108. $-4x^2 + 8x + 13$ 109. $-5c^3 - 4c^2 - 7c + 14$

101. $(8x^3 - 2x^2 - 4x + 5) - (5x^2 + 8)$ $8x^3 - 7x^2 - 4x - 3$ 102. $\left(9x^3 - \dfrac{1}{5}\right) - (x^2 + 5x)$ $9x^3 - x^2 - 5x - \dfrac{1}{5}$

103. $(2x^3 - 4x^2 + 5x - 7) - \left(3x + \dfrac{3}{5}x^2 - 5\right)$ 104. $(-3x^2 + 4x - 7) - \left(x^3 + 4x^2 - \dfrac{3}{4}x\right)$

105. Subtract $(7x + 4)$ from $(8x + 2)$. $x - 2$ 106. Subtract $(-4x + 7)$ from $(-3x - 9)$. $x - 16$

107. Subtract $(5x - 6)$ from $(2x^2 - 4x + 8)$. $2x^2 - 9x + 14$ 108. Subtract $(3x^2 - 5x - 3)$ from $(-x^2 + 3x + 10)$.

109. Subtract $(-2c^2 + 7c - 7)$ from $(-5c^3 - 6c^2 + 7)$.   110. Subtract $(4x^3 - 6x^2)$ from $(3x^3 + 5x^2 + 9x - 7)$.

Subtract using columns.   110. $-x^3 + 11x^2 + 9x - 7$ 113. $3a^2 - 16a + 28$ 114. $4x^2 + 12x - 12$ 116. $-3n^3 - 13n + 12$

111. Subtract $(3x - 3)$ from $(6x + 5)$. $3x + 8$ 112. Subtract $(6x + 8)$ from $(2x - 5)$. $-4x - 13$

113. Subtract $(2a^2 + 3a - 9)$ from $(5a^2 - 13a + 19)$.   114. Subtract $(4x^2 - 7x + 3)$ from $(8x^2 + 5x - 9)$.

115. Subtract $(6x^2 - 1)$ from $(7x^2 - 3x - 4)$. $x^2 - 3x - 3$ 116. Subtract $(5n^3 + 7n - 9)$ from $(2n^3 - 6n + 3)$.

117. Subtract $(5x^2 + 4)$ from $(x^2 + 4)$. $-4x^2$ 118. Subtract $(-5m^2 + 6m)$ from $(m - 6)$. $5m^2 - 5m - 6$

119. Subtract $(x^2 + 6x - 7)$ from $(4x^3 - 6x^2 + 7x - 9)$.
     $4x^3 - 7x^2 + x - 2$ 120. Subtract $(2x^3 + 4x^2 - 9x)$ from $(-5x^3 + 4x - 12)$.
     $-7x^3 - 4x^2 + 13x - 12$

Problem Solving

128. sometimes   129. One example is $x^4 - 2x^3 + x$.   130. One example is $x^6 + x^3 + x^2$.

121. Make up your own addition problem where the sum of two binomials is $-5x - 1$.   Answers will vary.

122. Make up your own addition problem where the sum of two trinomials is $3x^3 - 2x - 4$.   Answers will vary.

123. Make up your own subtraction problem where the difference of two trinomials is $7x - 3$.   Answers will vary.

124. Make up your own subtraction problem where the difference of two trinomials is $-x^2 + 4x - 5$.   Answers will vary.

125. When two binomials are added, will the sum always, sometimes, or never be a binomial? Explain your answer and give examples to support your answer.   sometimes

126. When one binomial is subtracted from another, will the difference always, sometimes, or never be a binomial? Explain your answer and give examples to support your answer.   sometimes

127. When two trinomials are added, will the sum always, sometimes, or never be a trinomial? Explain your answer and give examples to support your answer.   sometimes

128. When one trinomial is subtracted from another, will the difference always, sometimes, or never be a trinomial? Explain your answer and give examples to support your answer.

129. Write a fourth-degree trinomial in the variable x that has neither a second-degree term nor a constant term.

130. Write a sixth-degree trinomial in the variable x that has no fifth-, fourth-, first-, or zero-degree terms.

131. Is it possible to have a fourth-degree trinomial in x that has no third-, second-, or zero-degree terms and contains no like terms? Explain.   no

132. Is it possible to have a fifth-degree trinomial in x that has no fourth-, third-, second-, or first-degree terms and contains no like terms? Explain.   no

Write a polynomial that represents the area of each figure shown.

133.   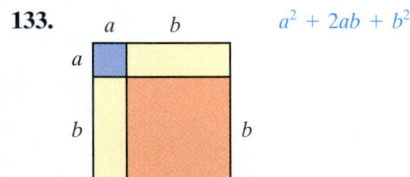 $a^2 + 2ab + b^2$

134. $3x^2 + 3xy$

135. $4x^2 + 3xy$

136.   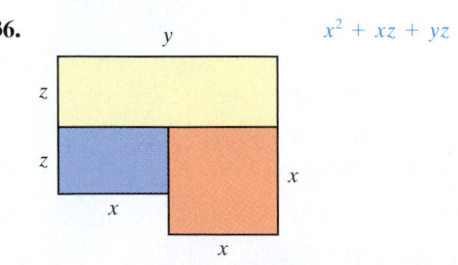 $x^2 + xz + yz$

Challenge Problems

Simplify.   137. $-12x + 18$ 138. $3x^2y - 13xy + 9xy^2 + 3x$

137. $(3x^2 - 6x + 3) - (2x^2 - x - 6) - (x^2 + 7x - 9)$ 138. $3x^2y - 6xy - 2xy + 9xy^2 - 5xy + 3x$

139. $4(x^2 + 2x - 3) - 6(2 - 4x - x^2) - 2x(x + 2)$ $8x^2 + 28x - 24$

Group Activity

Discuss and answer Exercise 140 as a group.

140. Make up a trinomial, a binomial, and a different trinomial such that (first trinomial) + (binomial) − (second trinomial) = 0.
Answers will vary.

Cumulative Review Exercises

142. $n - 5$ **143.** and **144.** See graphing answer section.

[2.7] **141.** Solve $\dfrac{5}{9} = \dfrac{2.5}{x}$ by cross-multiplying.   4.5

[3.1] **142.** Linda Rudolph is n years old now. Write an expression that represents her age 5 years ago.

[4.2] **143.** Graph the equation $3y = 9$.

[4.3] **144.** Graph $y = -2x - 4$.

[6.1] **145.** Simplify $\left(\dfrac{4x^3y^5}{12x^7y^4}\right)^3 \cdot \dfrac{y^3}{27x^{12}}$

[6.3] **146.** Write 3.5×10^{-2} without using exponents.   0.035

6.5 Multiplication of Polynomials

1. Multiply a monomial by a monomial.

2. Multiply a polynomial by a monomial.

3. Multiply binomials using the distributive property.

4. Multiply binomials using the FOIL method.

5. Multiply binomials using formulas for special products.

6. Multiply any two polynomials.

1 Multiply a Monomial by a Monomial

We begin our discussion of multiplication of polynomials by multiplying a monomial by a monomial. To multiply two monomials, multiply their coefficients and use the product rule of exponents to determine the exponents on the variables. Problems of this type were done in Section 6.1.

EXAMPLE 1 ▶ Multiply.

   a) $(7x^3)(6x^5)$ **b)** $(4b^2)(-9b^7)$

Solution

   a) $(7x^3)(6x^5) = 7 \cdot 6 \cdot x^3 \cdot x^5 = 42x^{3+5} = 42x^8$
   b) $(4b^2)(-9b^7) = (4)(-9) \cdot b^2 \cdot b^7 = -36b^{2+7} = -36b^9$
▶ **Now Try Exercise 15**

EXAMPLE 2 ▶ Multiply $(5x^2y)(8x^5y^4)$.

Solution   Remember that when a variable is given without an exponent we assume that the exponent on the variable is 1.

$$(5x^2y)(8x^5y^4) = 40x^{2+5}y^{1+4} = 40x^7y^5$$
▶ **Now Try Exercise 19**

EXAMPLE 3 ▶ Multiply.

   a) $6xy^2z^5(-3x^4y^7z)$ **b)** $(-4x^4z^9)(-3xy^7z^3)$

Solution

   a) $6xy^2z^5(-3x^4y^7z) = -18x^5y^9z^6$
   b) $(-4x^4z^9)(-3xy^7z^3) = 12x^5y^7z^{12}$
▶ **Now Try Exercise 21**

2 Multiply a Polynomial by a Monomial

To multiply a polynomial by a monomial, we use the distributive property presented earlier.

$$a(b + c) = ab + ac$$

The distributive property can be expanded to

$$a(b + c + d + \cdots + n) = ab + ac + ad + \cdots + an$$

EXAMPLE 4 ▶ Multiply $3x(2x^2 + 4)$.

Solution
$$3x(2x^2 + 4) = (3x)(2x^2) + (3x)(4)$$
$$= 6x^3 + 12x$$

▶ **Now Try Exercise 29**

Notice that the use of the distributive property results in monomials being multiplied by monomials. If we study Example 4, we see that the $3x$ and $2x^2$ are both monomials, as are the $3x$ and 4.

EXAMPLE 5 ▶ Multiply $-3n(4n^2 - 2n - 1)$.

Solution $-3n(4n^2 - 2n - 1) = (-3n)(4n^2) + (-3n)(-2n) + (-3n)(-1)$
$$= -12n^3 + 6n^2 + 3n$$

▶ **Now Try Exercise 33**

EXAMPLE 6 ▶ Multiply $5x^2(4x^3 - 2x + 7)$.

Solution $5x^2(4x^3 - 2x + 7) = (5x^2)(4x^3) + (5x^2)(-2x) + (5x^2)(7)$
$$= 20x^5 - 10x^3 + 35x^2$$

▶ **Now Try Exercise 37**

EXAMPLE 7 ▶ Multiply $2x(3x^2y - 6xy + 5)$.

Solution $2x(3x^2y - 6xy + 5) = (2x)(3x^2y) + (2x)(-6xy) + (2x)(5)$
$$= 6x^3y - 12x^2y + 10x$$

▶ **Now Try Exercise 39**

In Example 8, we perform a multiplication where the monomial is placed to the right of the polynomial. Each term of the polynomial is multiplied by the monomial, as illustrated in the example.

EXAMPLE 8 ▶ Multiply $(3x^3 - 2xy + 3)4x$.

Solution $(3x^3 - 2xy + 3)4x = (3x^3)(4x) + (-2xy)(4x) + (3)(4x)$
$$= 12x^4 - 8x^2y + 12x$$

▶ **Now Try Exercise 41**

The problem in Example 8 could be written as $4x(3x^3 - 2xy + 3)$ by the commutative property of multiplication, and then simplified as in Examples 4 through 7.

3 Multiply Binomials Using the Distributive Property

Now we will discuss multiplying a binomial by a binomial. Before we explain how to do this, consider the multiplication problem $43 \cdot 12$.

$$
\begin{array}{rl}
43 & \longleftarrow \textit{Multiplicand} \\
\underline{12} & \longleftarrow \textit{Multiplier} \\
2(4) \longrightarrow \quad 86 & \longleftarrow 2(3) \\
1(4) \longrightarrow \quad \underline{43} & \longleftarrow 1(3) \\
516 & \longleftarrow \textit{Product}
\end{array}
$$

Note how the 2 multiplies both the 3 and the 4, and the 1 also multiplies both the 3 and the 4. That is, every digit in the multiplier multiplies every digit in the multiplicand. We can also illustrate the multiplication process as follows.

$$
\begin{aligned}
(43)(12) &= (40 + 3)(10 + 2) \\
&= (40 + 3)(10) + (40 + 3)(2) \\
&= (40)(10) + (3)(10) + (40)(2) + (3)(2) \\
&= \quad 400 \quad + \quad 30 \quad + \quad 80 \quad + \quad 6 \\
&= 516
\end{aligned}
$$

Whenever any two polynomials are multiplied, the same process must be followed. That is, **every term in one polynomial must multiply every term in the other polynomial**.

Consider multiplying $(a + b)(c + d)$. Treating $(a + b)$ as a single term and using the distributive property, we get

$$(a + b)(c + d) = (a + b)c + (a + b)d$$

Using the distributive property a second time gives

$$= ac + bc + ad + bd$$

Notice how each term of the first polynomial was multiplied by each term of the second polynomial, and all the products were added to obtain the answer.

EXAMPLE 9 ▶ Multiply $(3x + 2)(x - 5)$.

Solution

$$
\begin{aligned}
(3x + 2)(x - 5) &= (3x + 2)x + (3x + 2)(-5) \\
&= 3x(x) + 2(x) + 3x(-5) + 2(-5) \\
&= 3x^2 + 2x - 15x - 10 \\
&= 3x^2 - \quad 13x \quad - 10
\end{aligned}
$$

▶ **Now Try Exercise 43**

Note that after performing the multiplication like terms must be combined.

EXAMPLE 10 ▶ Multiply $(x - 4)(y + 3)$.

Solution

$$
\begin{aligned}
(x - 4)(y + 3) &= (x - 4)y + (x - 4)3 \\
&= xy - 4y + 3x - 12
\end{aligned}
$$

▶ **Now Try Exercise 65**

4 Multiply Binomials Using the FOIL Method

A common method used to multiply two binomials is the **FOIL method**. This procedure also results in each term of one binomial being multiplied by each term in the other binomial. Students often prefer to use this method when multiplying two binomials.

The FOIL method is not actually a different method used to multiply binomials but rather an acronym to help students remember to correctly apply the distributive property. We could have used IFOL or any other arrangement of the four letters. However, FOIL is easier to remember than the other arrangements.

The FOIL Method

Consider $(a + b)(c + d)$.

F   stands for **first**—multiply the first terms of each binomial together:

$$\overset{F}{\overbrace{(a + b)(c}} + d) \qquad \text{product } ac$$

O   stands for **outer**—multiply the two outer terms together:

$$\overset{O}{\overbrace{(a + b)(c + d)}} \qquad \text{product } ad$$

I   stands for **inner**—multiply the two inner terms together:

$$(a + \overset{I}{\overbrace{b)(c}} + d) \qquad \text{product } bc$$

L   stands for **last**—multiply the last terms together:

$$(a + \overset{L}{\overbrace{b)(c + d}}) \qquad \text{product } bd$$

The product of the two binomials is the sum of these four products.

$$(a + b)(c + d) = ac + ad + bc + bd$$

INSTRUCTOR EXAMPLE
Multiply $(3x - 4)(x + 2)$.
Ans.: $3x^2 + 2x - 8$

EXAMPLE 11 ▶ Using the FOIL method, multiply $(2x - 3)(x + 4)$.

Solution

$$(2x - 3)(x + 4)$$

$$\overset{F}{=} (2x)(x) + \overset{O}{(2x)(4)} + \overset{I}{(-3)(x)} + \overset{L}{(-3)(4)}$$
$$= \quad 2x^2 \quad + \quad 8x \quad - \quad 3x \quad - \quad 12$$
$$= 2x^2 + 5x - 12$$

Thus, $(2x - 3)(x + 4) = 2x^2 + 5x - 12$.

▶ **Now Try Exercise 45**

INSTRUCTOR EXAMPLE
Multiply $(8 - 3b)(7 - 5b)$.
Ans.: $15b^2 - 61b + 56$

EXAMPLE 12 ▶ Multiply $(4 - 2x)(6 - 5x)$.

Solution

$$(4 - 2x)(6 - 5x)$$

$$\overset{F}{=} 4(6) + \overset{O}{4(-5x)} + \overset{I}{(-2x)(6)} + \overset{L}{(-2x)(-5x)}$$
$$= \quad 24 \quad - \quad 20x \quad - \quad 12x \quad + \quad 10x^2$$
$$= 10x^2 - 32x + 24$$

Thus, $(4 - 2x)(6 - 5x) = 10x^2 - 32x + 24$.

▶ **Now Try Exercise 63**

EXAMPLE 13 ▶ Multiply $(4p + 5)(4p - 5)$.

Solution

$$
(4p + 5)(4p - 5) = \overset{F}{(4p)(4p)} + \overset{O}{(4p)(-5)} + \overset{I}{(5)(4p)} + \overset{L}{(5)(-5)}
$$

$$
= 16p^2 \quad - \quad 20p \quad + \quad 20p \quad - \quad 25
$$

$$
= 16p^2 - 25
$$

Thus, $(4p + 5)(4p - 5) = 16p^2 - 25$.

▶ **Now Try Exercise 57**

Helpful Hint *Study Tip*

Make sure you have a thorough understanding of multiplication of polynomials. In the next chapter, we will be studying factoring, which is the reverse process of multiplication of polynomials. To understand factoring, you must first understand multiplication of polynomials.

5 Multiply Binomials Using Formulas for Special Products

Example 13 illustrates a special product, the product of the sum and difference of the same two terms.

Product of the Sum and Difference of the Same Two Terms

$$(a + b)(a - b) = a^2 - b^2$$

In this special product, a represents one term and b the other term. Then $(a + b)$ is the sum of the terms and $(a - b)$ is the difference of the terms. This special product is also called the **difference of two squares formula** because the expression on the right side of the equal sign is the difference of two squares. Since multiplication is commutative $(a + b)(a - b) = a^2 - b^2$ can also be written $(a - b)(a + b) = a^2 - b^2$.

EXAMPLE 14 ▶ Use the rule for finding the product of the sum and difference of two quantities to multiply each expression.

a) $(x + 5)(x - 5)$ **b)** $(2x + 4)(2x - 4)$ **c)** $(3x - 2y)(3x + 2y)$

Solution

a) If we let $x = a$ and $5 = b$, then

$$
(a + b)(a - b) = a^2 - b^2
$$

$$
\downarrow \quad \downarrow \quad \downarrow \quad \downarrow \qquad \downarrow \quad \downarrow
$$

$$
(x + 5)(x - 5) = (x)^2 - (5)^2
$$

$$
= x^2 - 25
$$

b)

$$
(a + b)(a - b) = a^2 - b^2
$$

$$
\downarrow \quad \downarrow \quad \downarrow \quad \downarrow \qquad \downarrow \quad \downarrow
$$

$$
(2x + 4)(2x - 4) = (2x)^2 - (4)^2
$$

$$
= 4x^2 - 16
$$

c)

$$
(a - b) \quad (a + b) = a^2 - b^2
$$

$$
\downarrow \quad \downarrow \quad \downarrow \quad \downarrow \qquad \downarrow \quad \downarrow
$$

$$
(3x - 2y)(3x + 2y) = (3x)^2 - (2y)^2
$$

$$
= 9x^2 - 4y^2
$$

▶ **Now Try Exercise 77**

Example 14 could also have been done using the FOIL method.

EXAMPLE 15 ▶ Using the FOIL method, multiply $(x + 3)^2$.

Solution $(x + 3)^2 = (x + 3)(x + 3)$

$$\overset{F\qquad O\qquad I\qquad L}{= x(x) + x(3) + 3(x) + (3)(3)}$$

$$= x^2 + 3x + 3x + 9$$

$$= x^2 + 6x + 9$$

▶ **Now Try Exercise 59**

Example 15 illustrates the **square of a binomial**, another special product.

Square of Binomial Formulas

$$(a + b)^2 = (a + b)(a + b) = a^2 + 2ab + b^2$$
$$(a - b)^2 = (a - b)(a - b) = a^2 - 2ab + b^2$$

To square a binomial, add the square of the first term, twice the product of the terms, and the square of the second term.

EXAMPLE 16 ▶ Use the square of a binomial formula to multiply each expression.

a) $(x + 5)^2$ **b)** $(2x - 4)^2$ **c)** $(3r + 2s)^2$ **d)** $(x - 3)(x - 3)$

Solution

a) If we let $x = a$ and $5 = b$, then

$$(a + b)(a + b) = a^2 + 2\ a\ b + b^2$$
$$\downarrow\ \downarrow\ \downarrow\ \downarrow \qquad \downarrow \qquad \downarrow\ \downarrow \qquad \downarrow$$
$$(x + 5)^2 = (x + 5)(x + 5) = (x)^2 + 2(x)(5) + (5)^2$$
$$= x^2 + 10x + 25$$

b)
$$(a - b)\ (a - b) = a^2 - 2\ a\ b + b^2$$
$$\downarrow\ \downarrow\ \downarrow\ \downarrow \qquad \downarrow \qquad \downarrow\ \downarrow \qquad \downarrow$$
$$(2x - 4)^2 = (2x - 4)(2x - 4) = (2x)^2 - 2(2x)(4) + (4)^2$$
$$= 4x^2 - 16x + 16$$

c)
$$(a + b)\ (a + b) = a^2 + 2\ a\ b + b^2$$
$$\downarrow\ \searrow\ \downarrow\ \searrow \qquad \downarrow \qquad \downarrow\ \downarrow \qquad \downarrow$$
$$(3r + 2s)^2 = (3r + 2s)(3r + 2s) = (3r)^2 + 2(3r)(2s) + (2s)^2$$
$$= 9r^2 + 12rs + 4s^2$$

d)
$$(a - b)(a - b) = a^2 - 2\ a\ b + b^2$$
$$\downarrow\ \downarrow\ \downarrow\ \downarrow \qquad \downarrow \qquad \downarrow\ \downarrow \qquad \downarrow$$
$$(x - 3)(x - 3) = (x - 3)(x - 3) = (x)^2 - 2(x)(3) + (3)^2$$
$$= x^2 - 6x + 9$$

▶ **Now Try Exercise 83**

Example 16 could also have been done using the FOIL method.

TEACHING TIP
Show that $(3 + 5)^2 \neq 3^2 + 5^2$.
Then show that
$(3 + 5)^2 = 3^2 + 2(3)(5) + 5^2$.

Avoiding Common Errors

CORRECT	INCORRECT
$(a + b)^2 = a^2 + 2ab + b^2$	$(a + b)^2 = a^2 + b^2$
$(a - b)^2 = a^2 - 2ab + b^2$	$(a - b)^2 = a^2 - b^2$

Do not forget the middle term when you square a binomial.

$$(x + 2)^2 \neq x^2 + 4$$
$$(x + 2)^2 = (x + 2)(x + 2)$$
$$= x^2 + 4x + 4$$

6 Multiply Any Two Polynomials

When multiplying a binomial by a binomial, we saw that every term in the first binomial was multiplied by every term in the second binomial. When multiplying any two polynomials, each term of one polynomial must be multiplied by each term of the other polynomial. In the multiplication $(3x + 2)(4x^2 - 5x - 3)$, we use the distributive property as follows:

$$(3x + 2)(4x^2 - 5x - 3)$$
$$= 3x(4x^2 - 5x - 3) + 2(4x^2 - 5x - 3)$$
$$= 12x^3 - 15x^2 - 9x + 8x^2 - 10x - 6$$
$$= 12x^3 - 7x^2 - 19x - 6$$

Thus, $(3x + 2)(4x^2 - 5x - 3) = 12x^3 - 7x^2 - 19x - 6$.

Multiplication problems can be performed by using the distributive property, as we just illustrated. However, many students prefer to multiply a polynomial by a polynomial using a vertical procedure. On page 381, we showed that when multiplying the number 43 by the number 12, we multipy each digit in the number 43 by each digit in the number 12. Review that example now. We can follow a similar procedure when multiplying a polynomial by a polynomial, as illustrated in the following examples. We must be careful, however, to align like terms in the same columns when performing the individual multiplications.

INSTRUCTOR EXAMPLE
Multiply $(3y + 7)(4y + 6)$.
Ans.: $12y^2 + 46y + 42$

EXAMPLE 17 ▶ Multiply $(3x + 4)(2x + 5)$.

Solution First write the polynomials one beneath the other.

$$3x + 4$$
$$2x + 5$$

Next, multiply each term in $(3x + 4)$ by 5.

$$3x + 4$$
$$2x + 5$$
$$5(3x + 4) \longrightarrow 15x + 20$$

Next, multiply each term in $(3x + 4)$ by $2x$ and align like terms.

$$3x + 4$$
$$2x + 5$$
$$15x + 20$$
$$2x(3x + 4) \longrightarrow 6x^2 + 8x$$
$$6x^2 + 23x + 20 \quad \text{Add like terms in columns.}$$

▶ **Now Try Exercise 55**

The same answer for Example 17 would be obtained using the FOIL method.

INSTRUCTOR EXAMPLE
Multiply $(3x + 2)(4x^2 + x - 3)$.
Ans.: $12x^3 + 11x^2 - 7x - 6$

EXAMPLE 18 ▸ Multiply $(4y + 3)(2y^2 - 7y - 5)$.

Solution   For convenience, we place the shorter expression on the bottom, as illustrated.

$$
\begin{array}{r}
2y^2 - 7y - 5 \\
4y + 3 \\
\hline
6y^2 - 21y - 15 \\
8y^3 - 28y^2 - 20y \\
\hline
8y^3 - 22y^2 - 41y - 15
\end{array}
$$

Multiply the top polynomial by 3.
Multiply the top polynomial by 4y; align like terms.
Add like terms in columns.

▸ **Now Try Exercise 95**

INSTRUCTOR EXAMPLE
Multiply $(x^2 - 4x + 3)(3x^2 - 4)$.
Ans.: $3x^4 - 12x^3 + 5x^2 + 16x - 12$

EXAMPLE 19 ▸ Multiply $(x^2 - 3x + 2)(2x^2 - 3)$.

Solution

$$
\begin{array}{r}
x^2 - 3x + 2 \\
2x^2 - 3 \\
\hline
-3x^2 + 9x - 6 \\
2x^4 - 6x^3 + 4x^2 \\
\hline
2x^4 - 6x^3 + x^2 + 9x - 6
\end{array}
$$

Multiply the top polynomial by −3.
Multiply the top polynomial by $2x^2$; align like terms.
Add like terms in columns.

▸ **Now Try Exercise 103**

INSTRUCTOR EXAMPLE
Multiply
$(4a^3 + 2a^2 - a + 4)(2a^2 + 2a)$.
Ans.: $8a^5 + 12a^4 + 2a^3 + 6a^2 + 8a$

EXAMPLE 20 ▸ Multiply $(3x^3 - 2x^2 + 4x + 6)(x^2 - 5x)$.

Solution

$$
\begin{array}{r}
3x^3 - 2x^2 + 4x + 6 \\
x^2 - 5x \\
\hline
-15x^4 + 10x^3 - 20x^2 - 30x \\
3x^5 - 2x^4 + 4x^3 + 6x^2 \\
\hline
3x^5 - 17x^4 + 14x^3 - 14x^2 - 30x
\end{array}
$$

Multiply the top polynomial by −5x.
Multiply the top polynomial by x^2; align like terms.
Add like terms in columns.

▸ **Now Try Exercise 105**

---

1. Answers will vary.   **3.** first, outer, inner, last   **6.** because $a^2 - b^2$ is the difference of two squares
7. $(a + b)^2 = a^2 + 2ab + b^2$, $(a - b)^2 = a^2 - 2ab + b^2$ **11., 13.** Answers will vary.

EXERCISE SET 6.5

MathXL®   MyMathLab

Concept/Writing Exercises

✎ **1.** Explain how to multiply a monomial by a monomial.

✎ **2.** What is the name of the property used when multiplying a polynomial by a monomial?   distributive property

✎ **3.** What do the letters in the acronym FOIL represent?

✎ **4.** How does the FOIL method work when multiplying two binomials?   every term multiplies every other term

✎ **5.** When multiplying two binomials, will you get the same answer if you multiply using the order LOIF instead of FOIL? Explain your answer.   yes

✎ **6.** Why is the special product $(a + b)(a - b) = a^2 - b^2$ also called the difference of two squares formula?

7. Write the square of binomial formulas.

✎ **8.** Describe how to square a binomial.   Answers will vary.

✎ **9.** Does $(x - 2)^2 = x^2 - 2^2$? Explain. If not, what is the correct result?   no, $x^2 - 4x + 4$

✎ **10.** Does $(x + 5)^2 = x^2 + 5^2$? Explain. If not, what is the correct result?   no, $x^2 + 10x + 25$

11. Make up a multiplication problem where a monomial in x is multiplied by a binomial in x. Determine the product.

12. Make up a multiplication problem where two binomials in x are multiplied. Determine the product.   Answers will vary.

13. Make up a multiplication problem where a monomial in y is multiplied by a trinomial in y. Determine the product.

14. When multiplying two polynomials, is it necessary for each term in one polynomial to multiply each term in the other polynomial?   yes

Practice the Skills

Multiply.

15. $(3x^4)(-8x^2)$ $-24x^6$

16. $(-7p^5)(-2p^3)$ $14p^8$

17. $5x^3y^5(4x^2y)$ $20x^5y^6$

18. $-5x^2y^4(2x^3y^2)$ $-10x^5y^6$

19. $(4xy^6)(-7x^2y^9)$ $-28x^3y^{15}$

20. $(4a^3b^7)(6a^2b)$ $24a^5b^8$

21. $9xy^6(6x^5y^8)$ $54x^6y^{14}$

22. $(6m^3n^4)(3n^5)$ $18m^3n^9$

23. $(6x^2y)\left(\dfrac{1}{2}x^4\right)$ $3x^6y$

24. $\dfrac{3}{4}x(8x^2y^3)$ $6x^3y^3$

25. $(3.3x^4)(1.8x^4y^3)$ $5.94x^8y^3$

26. $(2.3x^5)(4.1x^2y^4)$ $9.43x^7y^4$

Multiply.

27. $9(x - 5)$ $9x - 45$

28. $4(x + 3)$ $4x + 12$

29. $-3x(2x - 2)$ $-6x^2 + 6x$

30. $-4p(-3p + 6)$ $12p^2 - 24p$

31. $-2(8y + 5)$ $-16y - 10$

32. $2x(x^2 + 3x - 1)$ $2x^3 + 6x^2 - 2x$

33. $-2x(x^2 - 2x + 5)$ $-2x^3 + 4x^2 - 10x$

34. $-6c(-3c^2 + 5c - 6)$ $18c^3 - 30c^2 + 36c$

35. $5x(-4x^2 + 6x - 4)$ $-20x^3 + 30x^2 - 20x$

36. $(3x^2 + x - 6)x$ $3x^3 + x^2 - 6x$

37. $0.5x^2(x^3 - 6x^2 - 1)$ $0.5x^5 - 3x^4 - 0.5x^2$

38. $2.3b^2(2b^2 - b + 3)$ $4.6b^4 - 2.3b^3 + 6.9b^2$

39. $0.3x(2xy + 5x - 6y)$ $0.6x^2y + 1.5x^2 - 1.8xy$

40. $-\dfrac{1}{2}x^3(2x^2 + 4x - 6y^2)$ $-x^5 - 2x^4 + 3x^3y^2$

41. $(x^2 - 4y^3 - 3)y^4$ $x^2y^4 - 4y^7 - 3y^4$

42. $\dfrac{1}{4}y^4(y^2 - 12y + 4x)$ $\dfrac{1}{4}y^6 - 3y^5 + xy^4$

Multiply.

43. $(5x - 2)(x + 4)$ $5x^2 + 18x - 8$

44. $(2x - 3)(x + 5)$ $2x^2 + 7x - 15$

45. $(2x + 5)(3x - 6)$ $6x^2 + 3x - 30$

46. $(4a - 1)(a + 4)$ $4a^2 + 15a - 4$

47. $(2x - 4)(2x + 4)$ $4x^2 - 16$

48. $(4 + 5w)(3 + w)$ $5w^2 + 19w + 12$

49. $(8 - 5x)(6 + x)$ $-5x^2 - 22x + 48$

50. $(-x + 3)(2x + 5)$ $-2x^2 + x + 15$

51. $(6x - 1)(-2x + 5)$ $-12x^2 + 32x - 5$

52. $(7n - 3)(2n + 1)$ $14n^2 + n - 3$

53. $(x - 2)(4x - 2)$ $4x^2 - 10x + 4$

54. $(2x + 3)(x + 5)$ $2x^2 + 13x + 15$

55. $(3k - 6)(4k - 2)$ $12k^2 - 30k + 12$

56. $(3d - 5)(4d - 1)$ $12d^2 - 23d + 5$

57. $(x - 2)(x + 2)$ $x^2 - 4$

58. $(3x - 8)(2x + 3)$ $6x^2 - 7x - 24$

59. $(2x - 3)(2x - 3)$ $4x^2 - 12x + 9$

60. $(7x + 3)(2x + 4)$ $14x^2 + 34x + 12$

61. $(6z - 4)(7 - z)$ $-6z^2 + 46z - 28$

62. $(6 - 2m)(5m - 3)$ $-10m^2 + 36m - 18$

63. $(9 - 2x)(7 - 4x)$ $8x^2 - 50x + 63$

64. $(2 - 5x)(7 - 2x)$ $10x^2 - 39x + 14$

65. $(x + 7)(y - 3)$ $xy - 3x + 7y - 21$

66. $(z + 2y)(4z - 3)$ $4z^2 - 3z + 8yz - 6y$

67. $(2x - 3y)(3x + 2y)$ $6x^2 - 5xy - 6y^2$

68. $(2x + 3)(2y - 5)$ $4xy - 10x + 6y - 15$

69. $(9x + y)(4 - 3x)$ $-27x^2 - 3xy + 36x + 4y$

70. $(2x - 0.1)(x + 2.4)$ $2x^2 + 4.7x - 0.24$

71. $(x + 0.6)(x + 0.3)$ $x^2 + 0.9x + 0.18$

72. $(3x - 6)\left(x + \dfrac{1}{3}\right)$ $3x^2 - 5x - 2$

73. $(x + 4)\left(x - \dfrac{1}{2}\right)$ $x^2 + \dfrac{7}{2}x - 2$

74. $(2y - 4)\left(\dfrac{1}{2}x - 1\right)$ $xy - 2x - 2y + 4$

Multiply using a special product formula.

75. $(x + 6)(x - 6)$ $x^2 - 36$

76. $(x + 3)^2$ $x^2 + 6x + 9$

77. $(3x - 8)(3x + 8)$ $9x^2 - 64$

78. $(r - 4)(r - 4)$ $r^2 - 8r + 16$

79. $(x + y)^2$ $x^2 + 2xy + y^2$

80. $(2x - 7)(2x + 7)$ $4x^2 - 49$

81. $(x - 0.2)^2$ $x^2 - 0.4x + 0.04$

82. $(a + 3b)(a - 3b)$ $a^2 - 9b^2$

83. $(4x + 5)(4x + 5)$ $16x^2 + 40x + 25$

84. $(5x + 4)(5x - 4)$ $25x^2 - 16$

85. $(0.4x + y)^2$ $0.16x^2 + 0.8xy + y^2$

86. $\left(x - \dfrac{1}{2}y\right)^2$ $x^2 - xy + \dfrac{1}{4}y^2$

87. $(4c - 5d)(4c + 5d)$ $16c^2 - 25d^2$

88. $(4 + 3w)(4 - 3w)$ $16 - 9w^2$

89. $(-2x + 6)(-2x - 6)$ $4x^2 - 36$

90. $(-3m + 2n)(-3m - 2n)$ $9m^2 - 4n^2$

91. $(7s - 3t)^2$ $49s^2 - 42st + 9t^2$

92. $(7a + 2)^2$ $49a^2 + 28a + 4$

Multiply.

93. $(4m + 3)(4m^2 - 5m + 6)$ $16m^3 - 8m^2 + 9m + 18$

94. $(x + 4)(3x^2 + 4x - 1)$ $3x^3 + 16x^2 + 15x - 4$

95. $(3x + 2)(4x^2 - x + 5)$ $12x^3 + 5x^2 + 13x + 10$

96. $(x - 1)(3x^2 + 3x + 2)$ $3x^3 - x - 2$

97. $(-2x^2 - 4x + 1)(7x - 3)$ $-14x^3 - 22x^2 + 19x - 3$

98. $(4x^2 + 9x - 2)(x - 2)$ $4x^3 + x^2 - 20x + 4$

99. $(a + b)(a^2 - ab + b^2)$ $a^3 + b^3$

100. $(a - b)(a^2 + ab + b^2)$ $a^3 - b^3$

101. $(3x^2 - 2x + 4)(2x^2 + 3x + 1)$ $6x^4 + 5x^3 + 5x^2 + 10x + 4$

102. $(x^2 - 2x + 3)(x^2 - 4)$ $x^4 - 2x^3 - x^2 + 8x - 12$

103. $(x^2 - x + 3)(x^2 - 2x)$ $x^4 - 3x^3 + 5x^2 - 6x$

104. $(6x + 4)(2x^2 + 2x - 4)$ $12x^3 + 20x^2 - 16x - 16$

105. $(2x^3 - 6x^2 + x - 3)(x^2 + 4x)$ $2x^5 + 2x^4 - 23x^3 + x^2 - 12x$

106. $(3y^3 + 4y^2 - y + 7)(y^2 - 5y)$
$3y^5 - 11y^4 - 21y^3 + 12y^2 - 35y$

Determine the cube of each expression by writing the expression as the square of an expression multiplied by another expression. For example, $(x + 3y)^3 = (x + 3y)^2(x + 3y)$

107. $(b - 1)^3$ $b^3 - 3b^2 + 3b - 1$

108. $(x + 2)^3$ $x^3 + 6x^2 + 12x + 8$

109. $(3a - 5)^3$ $27a^3 - 135a^2 + 225a - 125$

110. $(2z + 3)^3$ $8z^3 + 36z^2 + 54z + 27$

Problem Solving

111. Will the product of a monomial and a monomial always be a monomial? Explain your answer.   yes

112. Will the product of a monomial and a binomial ever be a trinomial? Explain your answer.   no, will always be a binomial

113. Will the product of two binomials after like terms are combined always be a trinomial? Explain your answer.   no

114. Will the product of any polynomial and a binomial always be a polynomial? Explain.   yes

Consider the multiplications in Exercises 115 and 116. Determine the exponents to be placed in the shaded areas.

115. $3x^2(2x^{\square} - 5x^{\square} + 3x^{\square}) = 6x^8 - 15x^5 + 9x^3$.   6, 3, 1

116. $4x^3(x^{\square} + 2x^{\square} - 5x^{\square}) = 4x^7 + 8x^5 - 20x^4$.   4, 2, 1

117. Suppose that one side of a rectangle is represented as $x + 2$ and a second side is represented as $2x + 1$.

 a) Express the area of the rectangle in terms of x.

 b) Find the area if $x = 4$ feet.   54 ft^2

 c) What value of x, in feet, would result in the rectangle being a square? Explain how you determined your answer.   1 ft   **117. a)** $(x + 2)(2x + 1)$ or $2x^2 + 5x + 2$

118. Consider the figure below.

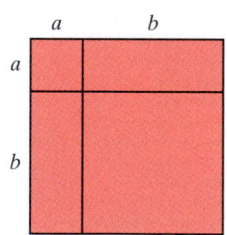

 a) Write an expression for the length of the top. $a + b$

 b) Write an expression for the length of the left side. $a + b$

 c) Is this figure a square? Explain.   yes

 d) Express the area of this square as the square of a binomial. $(a + b)^2$

 e) Determine the area of the square by summing the areas of the four individual pieces. $a^2 + 2ab + b^2$

 f) Using the figure and your answer to part **e)**, complete the following.
$$(a + b)^2 = ?   \quad a^2 + 2ab + b^2$$

119. Suppose that a rectangular solid has length $x + 5$, width $3x + 4$, and height $2x - 2$ (see the figure).

 a) Write a polynomial that represents the area of the base by multiplying the length by the width. $3x^2 + 19x + 20$

 b) The volume of the figure can be found by multiplying the area of the base by the height. Write a polynomial that represents the volume of the figure. $6x^3 + 32x^2 + 2x - 40$

 c) Using the polynomial in part **b)**, find the volume of the figure if x is 4 feet.   864 ft^3

 d) Using the binomials given for the length, width, and height, find the volume if x is 4 feet.   864 ft^3

 e) Are your answers to parts **c)** and **d)** the same? If not, explain why.   yes

Challenge Problems

Multiply.   **120.** $6x^6 - 18x^5 + 3x^4 + 35x^3 - 54x^2 + 38x - 12$

120. $(2x^3 - 6x^2 + 5x - 3)(3x^3 - 6x + 4)$

121. $\left(\dfrac{1}{2}x + \dfrac{2}{3}\right)\left(\dfrac{2}{3}x - \dfrac{2}{5}\right)$ $\dfrac{1}{3}x^2 + \dfrac{11}{45}x - \dfrac{4}{15}$

Group Activity

122. Consider the trinomial $2x^2 + 7x + 3$.

 a) As a group, determine whether there is a maximum number of pairs of binomials whose product is $2x^2 + 7x + 3$. That is, how many different pairs of binomials can go in the shaded areas?
$$2x^2 + 7x + 3 = (\quad\quad)(\quad\quad)   \quad \text{yes, one}$$

 b) Individually, find a pair of binomials whose product is $2x^2 + 7x + 3$. $(x + 3)(2x + 1)$

 c) Compare your answer to part **b)** with the other members of your group. If you did not all arrive at the same answer, explain why.

Cumulative Review Exercises

124. $C = 53°, D = 37°$

[2.5] **123.** Solve the equation $3(x + 7) - 5 = 3x - 17$.

123. no solution

[3.3] **124. Complementary Angles** Angles C and D are complementary angles, and angle D is 16° less than angle C. Find the measures of angle C and angle D.

[6.1] **125.** Simplify $\left(\dfrac{3xy^4}{6y^6}\right)^4 \cdot \dfrac{x^4}{16y^8}$.

[6.1–6.2] **126.** Evaluate the following.

    a) -6^3 −216

    b) 6^{-3} $\dfrac{1}{216}$

[6.4] **127.** Subtract $4x^2 - 4x - 9$ from $-x^2 - 6x + 5$.

$-5x^2 - 2x + 14$

6.6 Division of Polynomials

1 Divide a polynomial by a monomial.

2 Divide a polynomial by a binomial.

3 Check division of polynomial problems.

4 Write polynomials in descending order when dividing.

1 Divide a Polynomial by a Monomial

Now let's see how to divide polynomials. We begin by dividing a polynomial by a monomial.

> **To Divide a Polynomial by a Monomial**
>
> To divide a polynomial by a monomial, divide each term of the polynomial by the monomial.

INSTRUCTOR EXAMPLE
Divide $\dfrac{6x + 20}{2}$.
Ans.: $3x + 10$

EXAMPLE 1 ▶ Divide.

    a) $\dfrac{4x + 20}{4}$ **b)** $\dfrac{9x^2 - 6x}{3x}$

Solution

    a) $\dfrac{4x + 20}{4} = \dfrac{4x}{4} + \dfrac{20}{4} = x + 5$

    b) $\dfrac{9x^2 - 6x}{3x} = \dfrac{9x^2}{3x} - \dfrac{6x}{3x} = 3x - 2$

▶ **Now Try Exercise 17**

> ## Avoiding Common Errors
>
> | CORRECT | INCORRECT |
> |---|---|
> | $\dfrac{x + 2}{2} = \dfrac{x}{2} + \dfrac{2}{2} = \dfrac{x}{2} + 1$ | $\dfrac{x + \overset{1}{\cancel{2}}}{\underset{1}{\cancel{2}}} = \dfrac{x + 1}{1} = x + 1$ |
> | $\dfrac{x + 2}{x} = \dfrac{x}{x} + \dfrac{2}{x} = 1 + \dfrac{2}{x}$ | $\dfrac{\overset{1}{\cancel{x}} + 2}{\underset{1}{\cancel{x}}} = \dfrac{1 + 2}{1} = 3$ |
>
> Can you explain why the procedures on the right are not correct?

INSTRUCTOR EXAMPLE
Divide $\dfrac{6x^5 - 4x^4 + 12x - 5}{2x^2}$.
Ans.: $3x^3 - 2x^2 + \dfrac{6}{x} - \dfrac{5}{2x^2}$

EXAMPLE 2 ▶ Divide $\dfrac{4t^5 - 6t^4 + 8t - 3}{2t^2}$.

Solution

$$\dfrac{4t^5 - 6t^4 + 8t - 3}{2t^2} = \dfrac{4t^5}{2t^2} - \dfrac{6t^4}{2t^2} + \dfrac{8t}{2t^2} - \dfrac{3}{2t^2}$$

$$= 2t^3 - 3t^2 + \dfrac{4}{t} - \dfrac{3}{2t^2}$$

▶ **Now Try Exercise 37**

INSTRUCTOR EXAMPLE

Divide $\dfrac{7x^3 + 9x^2 - 6x + 2}{-3x}$

Ans.: $-\dfrac{7x^2}{3} - 3x + 2 - \dfrac{2}{3x}$

EXAMPLE 3 ▶ Divide $\dfrac{3x^3 - 6x^2 + 4x - 1}{-3x}$.

Solution A negative sign appears in the denominator. Usually, it is easier to divide if the divisor is positive. We can multiply both numerator and denominator by -1 to get a positive denominator.

$$\frac{(-1)(3x^3 - 6x^2 + 4x - 1)}{(-1)(-3x)} = \frac{-3x^3 + 6x^2 - 4x + 1}{3x}$$

$$= \frac{-3x^3}{3x} + \frac{6x^2}{3x} - \frac{4x}{3x} + \frac{1}{3x}$$

$$= -x^2 + 2x - \frac{4}{3} + \frac{1}{3x}$$

▶ **Now Try Exercise 41**

2 Divide a Polynomial by a Binomial

We divide a polynomial by a binomial in much the same way as we perform long division. This procedure will be explained in Example 4.

INSTRUCTOR EXAMPLE

Divide $\dfrac{x^2 - 8x + 15}{x - 5}$.

Ans.: $x - 3$

TEACHING TIP

Before explaining polynomial long division, show an example of arithmetic long division such as 4981 divided by 17.

EXAMPLE 4 ▶ Divide $\dfrac{x^2 + 6x + 8}{x + 2}$.   ⟵ *dividend*
   ⟵ *divisor*

Solution Rewrite the division problem in the following form:

$$x + 2 \overline{) x^2 + 6x + 8}$$

Divide x^2 (the first term in the dividend) by x (the first term in the divisor).

$$\frac{x^2}{x} = x$$

Place the quotient, x, above the like term containing x in the dividend.

$$\begin{array}{r} x \\ x + 2 \overline{) x^2 + 6x + 8} \end{array}$$

Next, multiply the x by $x + 2$ as you would do in long division and place the terms of the product under their like terms.

$$\begin{array}{r} \overset{\textcolor{red}{Times}}{} \quad x \\ x + 2 \overline{) x^2 + 6x + 8} \\ \underset{\textcolor{red}{Equals}}{x^2 + 2x} \quad \leftarrow \textcolor{red}{x(x + 2)} \end{array}$$

Now subtract $x^2 + 2x$ from $x^2 + 6x$. When subtracting, remember to change the sign of the terms being subtracted and then add the like terms.

$$\begin{array}{r} x \\ x + 2 \overline{) x^2 + 6x + 8} \\ \underline{x^2 + 2x } \\ 4x \end{array}$$

Next, bring down the 8, the next term in the dividend.

$$\begin{array}{r} x \\ x + 2 \overline{) x^2 + 6x + 8} \\ \underline{x^2 + 2x } \\ 4x + 8 \end{array}$$

Now divide $4x$, the first term at the bottom, by x, the first term in the divisor.

$$\frac{4x}{x} = +4$$

Write the $+4$ in the quotient above the constant in the dividend.

$$x + 2 \overline{)\begin{array}{l} x + 4 \\ x^2 + 6x + 8 \\ \underline{x^2 + 2x} \\ 4x + 8 \end{array}}$$

Multiply the $x + 2$ by 4 and place the terms of the product under their like terms.

Times

$$x + 2 \overline{)\begin{array}{l} x + 4 \\ x^2 + 6x + 8 \\ \underline{x^2 + 2x} \\ 4x + 8 \\ 4x + 8 \end{array}} \longleftarrow 4(x + 2)$$

Equals

Now subtract.

$$x + 2 \overline{)\begin{array}{l} x + 4 \\ x^2 + 6x + 8 \\ \underline{x^2 + 2x} \\ 4x + 8 \\ \underline{4x + 8} \\ 0 \end{array}} \begin{array}{l} \longleftarrow \text{Quotient} \\ \\ \\ \\ \\ \longleftarrow \text{Remainder} \end{array}$$

Thus,

$$\frac{x^2 + 6x + 8}{x + 2} = x + 4$$

There is no remainder.

▶ **Now Try Exercise 43**

INSTRUCTOR EXAMPLE
Divide $\dfrac{4x^2 + x - 10}{x - 3}$.

Ans.: $4x + 13 + \dfrac{29}{x - 3}$

EXAMPLE 5 ▶ Divide $\dfrac{3x^2 + x - 12}{x + 2}$.

Solution First write the problem in the following form:

$$x + 2 \overline{)3x^2 + x - 12}$$

Since $3x^2$ divided by x is $3x$, place $3x$ above the x-term in the dividend.

$$x + 2 \overline{)\begin{array}{l} 3x \\ 3x^2 + x - 12 \end{array}}$$

Then multiply $3x(x + 2)$ and write the product $3x^2 + 6x$ as shown below. Then subtract to get a difference of $-5x$.

$$x + 2 \overline{)\begin{array}{l} 3x \\ 3x^2 + x - 12 \\ \underline{3x^2 + 6x} \\ -5x \end{array}}$$

TEACHING TIP
Before explaining polynomial long division with a remainder, show an example of arithmetic long division with a remainder such as 5323 divided by 13. Show the final answer as the sum,
$$409 + \frac{6}{13} = 409\frac{6}{13}.$$

Next bring down the -12. Then divide $-5x$ by x, which gives -5. Place -5 over -12 in the dividend, as shown below. Then multiply $-5(x + 2)$. Write the product, $-5x - 10$ below the $-5x - 12$. Then subtract to get a remainder of -2.

$$x + 2 \overline{)\begin{array}{l} 3x - 5 \\ 3x^2 + x - 12 \\ \underline{3x^2 + 6x} \\ -5x - 12 \\ \underline{-5x - 10} \\ -2 \end{array}}$$

When there is a remainder, as in this example, list the quotient plus the remainder above the divisor. Thus,

$$\frac{3x^2 + x - 12}{x + 2} = 3x - 5 - \frac{2}{x + 2}.$$

▶ **Now Try Exercise 45**

INSTRUCTOR EXAMPLE
Divide $\dfrac{4x^2 - 2x + 7}{2x + 5}$.

Ans.: $2x - 6 + \dfrac{37}{2x + 5}$

EXAMPLE 6 ▶ Divide $\dfrac{6x^2 - 5x + 5}{2x + 3}$.

Solution

$$\frac{6x^2}{2x} \qquad \frac{-14x}{2x}$$

$$
\begin{array}{r}
3x - 7 \\
2x + 3\overline{) 6x^2 - 5x + 5} \\
\underline{6x^2 + 9x} \quad \longleftarrow 3x(2x + 3) \\
-14x + 5 \\
\underline{+14x +21} \quad \longleftarrow -7(2x + 3) \\
26 \quad \longleftarrow \text{Remainder}
\end{array}
$$

Thus, $\dfrac{6x^2 - 5x + 5}{2x + 3} = 3x - 7 + \dfrac{26}{2x + 3}.$

▶ **Now Try Exercise 57**

3 Check Division of Polynomial Problems

The answer to a division problem can be checked. Consider the division problem $13 \div 5$.

$$
\begin{array}{r}
2 \\
5\overline{)13} \\
\underline{10} \\
3
\end{array}
$$

Note that the divisor times the quotient, plus the remainder, equals the dividend:

$$(\text{divisor} \times \text{quotient}) + \text{remainder} = \text{dividend}$$
$$(5 \cdot 2) + 3 \overset{?}{=} 13$$
$$10 + 3 \overset{?}{=} 13$$
$$13 = 13 \qquad \textit{True}$$

This same procedure can be used to check all division problems.

> **To Check Division of Polynomials**
>
> $$(\text{divisor} \times \text{quotient}) + \text{remainder} = \text{dividend}$$

Let's check the answer to Example 6. The divisor is $2x + 3$, the quotient is $3x - 7$, the remainder is 26, and the dividend is $6x^2 - 5x + 5$.

Check $(\text{divisor} \times \text{quotient}) + \text{remainder} = \text{dividend}$
$$(2x + 3)(3x - 7) + 26 \overset{?}{=} 6x^2 - 5x + 5$$
$$(6x^2 - 5x - 21) + 26 \overset{?}{=} 6x^2 - 5x + 5$$
$$6x^2 - 5x + 5 = 6x^2 - 5x + 5 \qquad \textit{True}$$

4 Write Polynomials in Descending Order When Dividing

When dividing a polynomial by a binomial, both the polynomial and binomial should be listed in descending order. If a given power term is missing, it is often helpful to include that term with a numerical coefficient of 0 as a place-holder. This will help keep like terms aligned. For example, to divide $(6x^2 + x^3 - 4)/(x - 2)$, we begin by writing $(x^3 + 6x^2 + 0x - 4)/(x - 2)$.

EXAMPLE 7 ▶ Divide $(-x + 9x^3 - 28)$ by $(3x - 4)$.

Solution First we rewrite the dividend in descending order to get $(9x^3 - x - 28) \div (3x - 4)$. Since there is no x^2 term in the dividend, we will add $0x^2$ to help align like terms.

$$\frac{9x^3}{3x} \quad \frac{12x^2}{3x} \quad \frac{15x}{3x}$$
$$\downarrow \qquad \downarrow \qquad \downarrow$$

$$
\begin{array}{r}
3x^2 + 4x + 5 \\
3x - 4 \overline{)9x^3 + 0x^2 - x - 28} \\
\underline{9x^3 - 12x^2} \qquad\qquad \longleftarrow 3x^2(3x-4) \\
12x^2 - x \\
\underline{12x^2 - 16x} \qquad \longleftarrow 4x(3x-4) \\
15x - 28 \\
\underline{15x - 20} \qquad \longleftarrow 5(3x-4) \\
-8 \qquad \longleftarrow \text{Remainder}
\end{array}
$$

Thus, $\dfrac{-x + 9x^3 - 28}{3x - 4} = 3x^2 + 4x + 5 - \dfrac{8}{3x - 4}$. Check this division yourself using the procedure just discussed.

▶ **Now Try Exercise 55**

1. Divide each term in the polynomial by the monomial. **2.** (divisor)(quotient) + remainder = polynomial

EXERCISE SET 6.6

Math XL MathXL® *MyMathLab* MyMathLab

Concept/Writing Exercises

1. Explain how to divide a polynomial by a monomial.

2. Explain how to check a division problem.

3. Explain why $\dfrac{2x + 8}{2} \neq \dfrac{x + 8}{1}$. Then, correctly divide the binomial by the monomial. $x + 4$

4. Explain why $\dfrac{x + 5}{x} \neq \dfrac{1 + 5}{1}$. Then, correctly divide the binomial by the monomial. $1 + \dfrac{5}{y}$

5. How should the terms of a polynomial and binomial be listed when dividing a polynomial by a binomial? in descending order

6. How would you rewrite $\dfrac{x^3 - 14x + 15}{x - 3}$ so that it is easier to complete the division? $\dfrac{x^3 + 0x^2 - 14x + 15}{x - 3}$

7. How would you rewrite $\dfrac{x^2 - 7}{x - 2}$ so that it is easier to complete the division? $\dfrac{x^2 + 0x - 7}{x - 2}$

8. Show that $\dfrac{x^2 - 3x + 7}{x + 2} = x - 5 + \dfrac{17}{x + 2}$ by checking the division. $(x - 5)(x + 2) + 17 = x^2 - 3x + 7$

9. Show that $\dfrac{x^2 + 2x - 17}{x - 3} = x + 5 - \dfrac{2}{x - 3}$ by checking the division. $(x + 5)(x - 3) - 2 = x^2 + 2x - 17$

10. Show that $\dfrac{x^3 + 2x - 3}{x + 1} = x^2 - x + 3 - \dfrac{6}{x + 1}$ by checking the division. $(x^2 - x + 3)(x + 1) - 6 = x^3 + 2x - 3$

Rewrite each multiplication problem as a division problem. There is more than one correct answer.

11. $(x - 7)(x + 6) = x^2 - x - 42$
$\dfrac{x^2 - x - 42}{x - 7} = x + 6$ or $\dfrac{x^2 - x - 42}{x + 6} = x - 7$

12. $(x + 3)(3x - 1) = 3x^2 + 8x - 3$
$\dfrac{3x^2 + 8x - 3}{x + 3} = 3x - 1$ or $\dfrac{3x^2 + 8x - 3}{3x - 1} = x + 3$

13. $(2x + 3)(x + 1) = 2x^2 + 5x + 3$

$\dfrac{2x^2 + 5x + 3}{2x + 3} = x + 1$ or $\dfrac{2x^2 + 5x + 3}{x + 1} = 2x + 3$

14. $(2x - 5)(x + 1) = 2x^2 - 3x - 5$

$\dfrac{2x^2 - 3x - 5}{2x - 5} = x + 1$ or $\dfrac{2x^2 - 3x - 5}{x + 1} = 2x - 5$

15. $(2x + 3)(2x - 3) = 4x^2 - 9$

$\dfrac{4x^2 - 9}{2x + 3} = 2x - 3$ or $\dfrac{4x^2 - 9}{2x - 3} = 2x + 3$

16. $(3n + 4)(n - 5) = 3n^2 - 11n - 20$

$\dfrac{3n^2 - 11n - 20}{3n + 4} = n - 5$ or $\dfrac{3n^2 - 11n - 20}{n - 5} = 3n + 4$

Practice the Skills

37. $3x^2 - 2x + 6 - \dfrac{5}{2x}$ **40.** $4x^3 - 2x + 5 - \dfrac{4}{3x}$ **51.** $x + 5 - \dfrac{3}{2x - 3}$ **60.** $2x^2 - x - 4 + \dfrac{2}{x - 1}$

Divide.

17. $\dfrac{3x + 6}{3}$ $x + 2$

18. $\dfrac{4x - 6}{2}$ $2x - 3$

19. $\dfrac{4n + 10}{2}$ $2n + 5$

20. $(-3x - 8) \div 4$ $-\dfrac{3x}{4} - 2$

21. $\dfrac{7x + 6}{3}$ $\dfrac{7}{3}x + 2$

22. $\dfrac{5x - 10}{5}$ $x - 2$

23. $\dfrac{-6x + 4}{2}$ $-3x + 2$

24. $\dfrac{-5a + 4}{-3}$ $\dfrac{5}{3}a - \dfrac{4}{3}$

25. $\dfrac{-9x - 3}{-3}$ $3x + 1$

26. $\dfrac{8x - 3}{-8}$ $-x + \dfrac{3}{8}$

27. $\dfrac{2x + 16}{4}$ $\dfrac{1}{2}x + 4$

28. $\dfrac{2p - 3}{2p}$ $1 - \dfrac{3}{2p}$

29. $\dfrac{4 - 10w}{-4}$ $-1 + \dfrac{5}{2}w$

30. $\dfrac{6 - 5x}{-3x}$ $-\dfrac{2}{x} + \dfrac{5}{3}$

31. $(4x^2 + 8x - 12) \div 4x^2$ $1 + \dfrac{2}{x} - \dfrac{3}{x^2}$

32. $\dfrac{12x^2 - 6x + 3}{3}$ $4x^2 - 2x + 1$

33. $\dfrac{-4x^5 + 6x + 8}{2x^2}$ $-2x^3 + \dfrac{3}{x} + \dfrac{4}{x^2}$

34. $\dfrac{6t^2 + 3t + 8}{2}$ $3t^2 + \dfrac{3}{2}t + 4$

35. $(x^5 + 3x^4 - 3) \div x^3$ $x^2 + 3x - \dfrac{3}{x^3}$

36. $(6x^2 - 7x + 9) \div 3x$ $2x - \dfrac{7}{3} + \dfrac{3}{x}$

37. $\dfrac{6x^5 - 4x^4 + 12x^3 - 5x^2}{2x^3}$

38. $\dfrac{9x^2 + 18x - 7}{-9}$ $-x^2 - 2x + \dfrac{7}{9}$

39. $\dfrac{8k^3 + 6k^2 - 8}{-4k}$ $-2k^2 - \dfrac{3}{2}k + \dfrac{2}{k}$

40. $\dfrac{-12x^4 + 6x^2 - 15x + 4}{-3x}$

41. $\dfrac{12x^5 + 3x^4 - 10x^2 - 9}{-3x^2}$

42. $\dfrac{-15m^3 - 6m^2 + 15}{-5m^3}$ $3 + \dfrac{6}{5m} - \dfrac{3}{m^3}$

41. $-4x^3 - x^2 + \dfrac{10}{3} + \dfrac{3}{x^2}$

Divide.

63. $w^2 + 3w + 9 + \dfrac{19}{w - 3}$ **69.** $-m^2 - 7m - 5 - \dfrac{8}{m - 1}$ **70.** $-x^2 + 6x - 4 + \dfrac{28}{x + 3}$

43. $\dfrac{x^2 + 4x + 3}{x + 1}$ $x + 3$

44. $(2x^2 + 3x - 35) \div (x + 5)$ $2x - 7$

45. $\dfrac{5y^2 - 34y - 7}{y - 7}$ $5y + 1$

46. $\dfrac{2p^2 - 7p - 15}{p - 5}$ $2p + 3$

47. $\dfrac{6x^2 + 16x + 8}{3x + 2}$ $2x + 4$

48. $\dfrac{3r^2 + 5r - 8}{r - 1}$ $3r + 8$

49. $\dfrac{x^2 - 16}{-4 + x}$ $x + 4$

50. $\dfrac{6t^2 - 7t - 20}{3t + 4}$ $2t - 5$

51. $(2x^2 + 7x - 18) \div (2x - 3)$

52. $(4a^2 - 25) \div (2a - 5)$ $2a + 5$

53. $\dfrac{x^2 - 36}{x - 6}$ $x + 6$

54. $\dfrac{9x^2 - 16}{3x - 4}$ $3x + 4$

55. $\dfrac{-x + 9x^3 - 16}{3x - 4}$ $3x^2 + 4x + 5 + \dfrac{4}{3x - 4}$

56. $\dfrac{10x + 3x^2 + 6}{x + 2}$ $3x + 4 - \dfrac{2}{x + 2}$

57. $\dfrac{6x + 8x^2 - 12}{2x + 3}$ $4x - 3 - \dfrac{3}{2x + 3}$

58. $\dfrac{x^3 + 5x^2 + 2x - 8}{x + 2}$ $x^2 + 3x - 4$

59. $\dfrac{7x^3 + 28x^2 - 5x - 20}{x + 4}$ $7x^2 - 5$

60. $\dfrac{2x^3 - 3x^2 - 3x + 6}{x - 1}$

61. $\dfrac{2x^3 - 4x^2 + 12}{x - 2}$ $2x^2 + \dfrac{12}{x - 2}$

62. $\dfrac{2x^3 + 6x - 4}{x + 4}$ $2x^2 - 8x + 38 - \dfrac{156}{x + 4}$

63. $(w^3 - 8) \div (w - 3)$

64. $\dfrac{x^3 + 8}{x + 2}$ $x^2 - 2x + 4$

65. $\dfrac{x^3 - 27}{x - 3}$ $x^2 + 3x + 9$

66. $\dfrac{x^3 + 64}{x + 4}$ $x^2 - 4x + 16$

67. $\dfrac{4x^3 - 5x}{2x - 1}$ $2x^2 + x - 2 - \dfrac{2}{2x - 1}$

68. $\dfrac{9x^3 - x + 3}{3x - 2}$ $3x^2 + 2x + 1 + \dfrac{5}{3x - 2}$

69. $\dfrac{-m^3 - 6m^2 + 2m - 3}{m - 1}$

70. $\dfrac{-x^3 + 3x^2 + 14x + 16}{x + 3}$

71. $\dfrac{4t^3 - t + 4}{t + 2}$ $4t^2 - 8t + 15 - \dfrac{26}{t + 2}$

72. $\dfrac{9n^3 - 6n + 4}{3n - 3}$ $3n^2 + 3n + 1 + \dfrac{7}{3n - 3}$

Problem Solving

73. When dividing a binomial by a monomial, must the quotient be a binomial? Explain and give an example to support your answer.   no

74. When dividing a trinomial by a monomial, must the quotient be a trinomial? Explain and give an example to support your answer.   no

75. If the divisor is $x + 4$, the quotient is $2x + 3$, and the remainder is 4, find the dividend (or the polynomial being divided). $2x^2 + 11x + 16$

76. If the divisor is $2x - 3$, the quotient is $3x - 1$, and the remainder is -2, find the dividend. $6x^2 - 11x + 1$

77. If a fourth-degree polynomial in x is divided by a first-degree polynomial in x, what will be the degree of the quotient? Explain.   third degree

78. If a second-degree polynomial in x is divided by a first-degree polynomial in x, what will be the degree of the quotient? Explain.   first degree

Determine the expression to be placed in the shaded area to make a true statement. Explain how you determined your answer.

79. $\dfrac{16x^4 + 20x^3 - 4x^2 + 12x}{\boxed{}} = 4x^3 + 5x^2 - x + 3$ $4x$

80. $\dfrac{9x^5 - 6x^4 + 3x^2 + 12}{\boxed{}} = 3x^3 - 2x^2 + 1 + \dfrac{4}{x^2}$ $3x^2$

Determine the exponents to be placed in the shaded areas to make a true statement. Explain how you determined your answer.

81. $\dfrac{8x^{\boxed{}} + 4x^{\boxed{}} - 20x^{\boxed{}} - 5x^{\boxed{}}}{2x^2} = 4x^3 + 2x - 10 - \dfrac{5}{2x}$ $5, 3, 2, 1$

82. $\dfrac{15x^{\boxed{}} + 25x^{\boxed{}} + 5x^{\boxed{}} + 10x^{\boxed{}}}{5x^2} = 3x^5 + 5x^4 + x^2 + 2$ $7, 6, 4, 2$

Challenge Problems

Divide. The quotients in Exercises 83 and 84 will contain fractions.

83. $\dfrac{3x^3 - 5}{3x - 2}$ $x^2 + \dfrac{2}{3}x + \dfrac{4}{9} - \dfrac{37}{9(3x-2)}$

84. $\dfrac{4x^3 - 4x + 6}{2x + 3}$ $2x^2 - 3x + \dfrac{5}{2} - \dfrac{3}{2(2x+3)}$

85. $\dfrac{3x^2 + 6x - 10}{-x - 3}$ $-3x + 3 + \dfrac{1}{x+3}$

Group Activity

Discuss and answer Exercises 86 and 87 as a group. Determine the polynomial that when substituted in the shaded area results in a true statement. Explain how you determined your answer.

86. $\dfrac{\boxed{}}{x + 4} = x + 2 + \dfrac{2}{x + 4}$ $x^2 + 6x + 10$

87. $\dfrac{\boxed{}}{x + 3} = x + 1 - \dfrac{1}{x + 3}$ $x^2 + 4x + 2$

Cumulative Review Exercises

[1.4] **88.** Consider the set of numbers
$$\left\{ 2, -5, 0, \sqrt{7}, \frac{2}{5}, -6.3, \sqrt{3}, -\frac{23}{34} \right\}.$$
List those that are

a) natural numbers; 2

b) whole numbers; $2, 0$

c) rational numbers; $2, -5, 0, \dfrac{2}{5}, -6.3, -\dfrac{23}{34}$

d) irrational numbers; $\sqrt{7}, \sqrt{3}$

e) real numbers. $2, -5, 0, \sqrt{7}, \dfrac{2}{5}, -6.3, \sqrt{3}, -\dfrac{23}{34}$

[1.8] **89.** a) To what is $\dfrac{0}{1}$ equal? 0

b) How do we refer to an expression like $\dfrac{1}{0}$?   undefined

[1.9] **90.** Give the order of operations to be followed when evaluating a mathematical expression.   parentheses, exponents, multiplication or division (left to right), addition or subtraction (left to right)

[2.5] **91.** Solve the equation $2(x + 3) + 2x = x + 4$. $-\dfrac{2}{3}$

[3.2] **92.** **Sale** At a 30% off sale Jennifer Lucking purchased a sweater for $27.65. What is the original price of the sweater? $39.50

[6.2] **93.** Simplify $\dfrac{x^9}{x^{-4}}$. x^{13}

Chapter 6 Summary

IMPORTANT FACTS AND CONCEPTS	EXAMPLES

Section 6.1

In the expression x^n, x is called the **base** and n is called the **exponent**.	base $\rightarrow 3^4 \nwarrow$ exponent

Rules of Exponents

1. $x^m \cdot x^n = x^{m+n}$ product rule

2. $\dfrac{x^m}{x^n} = x^{m-n}$, $x \neq 0$ quotient rule

3. $x^0 = 1$, $x \neq 0$ zero exponent rule

4. $(x^m)^n = x^{m \cdot n}$ power rule

5. $\left(\dfrac{ax}{by}\right)^m = \dfrac{a^m x^m}{b^m y^m}$, $b \neq 0$, $y \neq 0$ expanded power rule

Simplify.

1. $x^5 \cdot x^4 = x^{5+4} = x^9$

2. $\dfrac{x^{12}}{x^7} = x^{12-7} = x^5$

3. $(-3ab^4)^0 = 1$

4. $(x^6)^3 = x^{6 \cdot 3} = x^{18}$

5. $\left(\dfrac{4x}{5y}\right)^2 = \dfrac{4^2 x^2}{5^2 y^2} = \dfrac{16 x^2}{25 y^2}$

Section 6.2

Negative Exponent Rule

$$x^{-m} = \dfrac{1}{x^m}, \qquad x \neq 0$$

$$x^{-2} = \dfrac{1}{x^2}$$

$$\dfrac{1}{y^{-6}} = y^6$$

A Fraction Raised to a Negative Exponent Rule

For a fraction of the form $\dfrac{a}{b}$, $a \neq 0$ and $b \neq 0$, $\left(\dfrac{a}{b}\right)^{-m} = \left(\dfrac{b}{a}\right)^m$

$$\left(\dfrac{7}{8}\right)^{-2} = \left(\dfrac{8}{7}\right)^2 = \dfrac{8^2}{7^2} = \dfrac{64}{49}$$

Section 6.3

Each number written in **scientific notation** is written as a number greater than or equal to 1 and less than 10 multiplied by some power of 10.	1.3×10^7 4.76×10^{-2}

To Write a Number in Scientific Notation

1. Move the decimal point in the original number to the right of the first nonzero digit.

2. Count the number of places you moved the decimal point in step 1. If the original number was 10 or greater, the count is positive. If the original number was less than 1, the count is negative.

3. Multiply the number obtained in step 1 by 10 raised to the count (power) found in step 2.

$25{,}700 = 2.57 \times 10^4$

$0.0000346 = 3.46 \times 10^{-5}$

To Convert a Number from Scientific Notation to Decimal Form

1. Observe the exponent of the power of 10.

2. **a)** If the exponent is positive, move the decimal point in the number to the right the same number of places as the exponent.

    b) If the exponent is 0, do not move the decimal point.

    c) If the exponent is negative, move the decimal point in the number to the left the same number of places as the exponent (dropping the negative sign).

$9.8 \times 10^6 = 9{,}800{,}000$

$5.17 \times 10^{-3} = 0.00517$

IMPORTANT FACTS AND CONCEPTS	EXAMPLES

Section 6.4

A **polynomial in x** is an expression containing the sum of a finite number of terms of the form ax^n, for any real number a and any whole number n.

$\frac{1}{5}x - 2$ and $x^2 - 4x + 7$ are both polynomials in x.

A polynomial is written in **descending order of the variable** when the exponents on the variable decrease from left to right.

$5x^4 - 3x^3 + 7x^2 - 6x + 9$ is written in descending order of the variable.

A **monomial** is a polynomial with one term.

$-7y^2$ is a monomial.

A **binomial** is a two-termed polynomial.

$x^2 - 8$ is a binomial.

A **trinomial** is a three-termed polynomial.

$4z^2 - 9z + 1$ is a trinomial.

The **degree of a term** of a polynomial in **one variable** is the exponent on the variable in that term.

$2y^6$ is a sixth-degree term.

The **degree of a term** of a polynomial in **two or more variables** is the sum of the exponents on those variables.

$3x^2y^5$ is a seventh-degree term

The **degree of a polynomial** is the same as that of its highest-degree term.

$9x^3 + 2x^2 - 5x + 4$ is a third-degree polynomial.

To Add Polynomials

To add polynomials, combine the like terms of the polynomials.

$(3x^2 - 9x + 4) + (2x^2 - 3x - 5) = \underline{3x^2 + 2x^2} \; \underline{- 9x - 3x} \; \underline{+ 4 - 5}$
$$= 5x^2 \quad - 12x \quad - 1$$

To Subtract Polynomials

1. Use the distributive property to remove parentheses.
2. Combine like terms.

$$(9a^2 - 6a + 1) - (a^2 - 5a - 3)$$
$$= 9a^2 - 6a + 1 - a^2 + 5a + 3$$
$$= \underline{9a^2 - a^2} \; \underline{- 6a + 5a} \; \underline{+ 1 + 3}$$
$$= 8a^2 \quad - a \quad + 4$$

Section 6.5

FOIL Method to Multiply Two Binomials (First, Outer, Inner, Last)

$$(a + b)(c + d)$$

$$(3x - 5)(x + 4) = \overset{F}{(3x)(x)} + \overset{O}{(3x)(4)} + \overset{I}{(-5)(x)} + \overset{L}{(-5)(4)}$$
$$= 3x^2 \quad + \quad 12x \quad - \quad 5x \quad - \quad 20$$
$$= 3x^2 \quad + \quad 7x \quad - \quad 20$$

Product of Sum and Difference of the Same Two Terms (also called the difference of two squares):

$$(a + b)(a - b) = a^2 - b^2$$

$$(y + 6)(y - 6) = (y)^2 - (6)^2$$
$$= y^2 - 36$$

Square of a Binomial

$$(a + b)^2 = a^2 + 2ab + b^2$$
$$(a - b)^2 = a^2 - 2ab + b^2$$

1. $(x + 7)^2 = (x)^2 + 2(x)(7) + (7)^2$
$$= x^2 + 14x + 49$$

2. $(z - 3)^2 = (z)^2 - 2(z)(3) + (3)^2$
$$= z^2 - 6z + 9$$

IMPORTANT FACTS AND CONCEPTS	EXAMPLES

Section 6.5 (continued)

To Multiply Any Two Polynomials

To multiply any two polynomials, each term of one polynomial must multiply each term of the second polynomial.

$(x^2 + 3x + 5)(x - 2)$ or

$$
\begin{array}{r}
x^2 + 3x + 5 \\
x - 2 \\
\hline
-2x^2 - 6x - 10 \\
x^3 + 3x^2 + 5x \\
\hline
x^3 + x^2 - x - 10
\end{array}
$$

Section 6.6

To Divide a Polynomial by a Monomial

To divide a polynomial by a monomial, divide each term of the polynomial by the monomial.

$$\frac{6x + 24}{6} = \frac{6x}{6} + \frac{24}{6} = x + 4$$

To Divide a Polynomial by a Binomial

To divide a polynomial by a binomial we perform division in much the same way as we perform long division.

$$\frac{x^2 - 4x + 3}{x + 2}$$

$$
\begin{array}{r}
x - 6 \\
x + 2 \overline{)x^2 - 4x + 3} \\
\underline{x^2 + 2x} \\
-6x + 3 \\
\underline{-6x - 12} \\
15
\end{array}
$$

$$\frac{x^2 - 4x + 3}{x + 2} = x - 6 + \frac{15}{x + 2}$$

Chapter 6 Review Exercises

[6.1] *Simplify.*

1. $x^5 \cdot x^2$ x^7

2. $x^2 \cdot x^4$ x^6

3. $3^2 \cdot 3^3$ 243

4. $2^4 \cdot 2$ 32

5. $\dfrac{x^4}{x}$ x^3

6. $\dfrac{a^5}{a^5}$ 1

7. $\dfrac{5^5}{5^3}$ 25

8. $\dfrac{4^4}{4}$ 64

9. $\dfrac{x^6}{x^8}$ $\dfrac{1}{x^2}$

10. $\dfrac{y^4}{y}$ y^3

11. x^0 1

12. $7y^0$ 7

13. $(-6z)^0$ 1

14. 6^0 1

15. $(5x)^2$ $25x^2$

16. $(3a)^3$ $27a^3$

17. $(-3x)^3$ $-27x^3$

18. $(6s)^3$ $216s^3$

19. $(2x^2)^4$ $16x^8$

20. $(-x^4)^6$ x^{24}

21. $(-p^8)^4$ p^{32}

22. $\left(-\dfrac{2x^3}{y}\right)^2$ $\dfrac{4x^6}{y^2}$

23. $\left(-\dfrac{5y^2}{2b}\right)^2$ $\dfrac{25y^4}{4b^2}$

24. $6x^2 \cdot 4x^3$ $24x^5$

25. $\dfrac{16x^2y}{4xy^2}$ $\dfrac{4x}{y}$

26. $2x(3xy^3)^3$ $54x^4y^9$

27. $\left(\dfrac{9x^2y}{3xy}\right)^2$ $9x^2$

28. $(2x^2y)^3(3xy^4)$ $24x^7y^7$

29. $4x^2y^3(2x^3y^4)^2$ $16x^8y^{11}$

30. $3c^2(2c^4d^3)$ $6c^6d^3$

31. $\left(\dfrac{9a^3b^2}{3ab^7}\right)^3$ $\dfrac{27a^6}{b^{15}}$

32. $\left(\dfrac{21x^4y^3}{7y^2}\right)^3$ $27x^{12}y^3$

[6.2] *Simplify.*

33. b^{-9} $\dfrac{1}{b^9}$

34. 3^{-3} $\dfrac{1}{27}$

35. 5^{-2} $\dfrac{1}{25}$

36. $\dfrac{1}{z^{-2}}$ z^2

37. $\dfrac{1}{x^{-7}}$ x^7

38. $\dfrac{1}{4^{-2}}$ 16

39. $y^5 \cdot y^{-8}$ $\dfrac{1}{y^3}$

40. $x^{-2} \cdot x^{-3}$ $\dfrac{1}{x^5}$

41. $p^{-6} \cdot p^4$ $\dfrac{1}{p^2}$

42. $a^{-2} \cdot a^{-3}$ $\dfrac{1}{a^5}$

43. $\dfrac{m^5}{m^{-5}}$ m^{10}

44. $\dfrac{x^5}{x^{-2}}$ x^7

45. $\dfrac{x^{-3}}{x^3}$ $\dfrac{1}{x^6}$

46. $(3x^4)^{-2}$ $\dfrac{1}{9x^8}$

47. $(4x^{-3}y)^{-3}$ $\dfrac{x^9}{64y^3}$

48. $(-2m^{-3}n)^2$ $\dfrac{4n^2}{m^6}$

49. $6y^{-2} \cdot 2y^4$ $12y^2$

50. $(-5y^{-3}z)^3$ $-\dfrac{125z^3}{y^9}$

51. $(-4x^{-2}y^3)^{-2}$ $\dfrac{x^4}{16y^6}$

52. $2x(3x^{-2})$ $\dfrac{6}{x}$

53. $(5x^{-2}y)(2x^4y)$ $10x^2y^2$

54. $4y^{-2}(3x^2y)$ $\dfrac{12x^2}{y}$

55. $4x^5(6x^{-7}y^2)$ $\dfrac{24y^2}{x^2}$

56. $\dfrac{6xy^4}{2xy^{-1}}$ $3y^5$

57. $\dfrac{12x^{-2}y^3}{3xy^2}$ $\dfrac{4y}{x^3}$

58. $\dfrac{49x^2y^{-3}}{7x^{-3}y}$ $\dfrac{7x^5}{y^4}$

59. $\dfrac{4x^8y^{-2}}{8x^7y^3}$ $\dfrac{x}{2y^5}$

60. $\dfrac{36x^4y^7}{9x^5y^{-3}}$ $\dfrac{4y^{10}}{x}$

[6.3] *Express each number in scientific notation.*

61. 1,720,000 1.72×10^6

62. 0.153 1.53×10^{-1}

63. 0.00763 7.63×10^{-3}

64. 47,000 4.7×10^4

65. 5760 5.76×10^3

66. 0.000314 3.14×10^{-4}

Express each number without exponents.

67. 7.5×10^{-3} 0.0075

68. 6.52×10^{-4} 0.000652

69. 8.9×10^6 8,900,000

70. 5.12×10^4 51,200

71. 3.14×10^{-5} 0.0000314

72. 1.103×10^7 11,030,000

Write each of the following as a base unit without metric prefixes.

73. 92 milliliters   0.092 liter

74. 6 gigameters   6,000,000,000 meters

75. 12.8 micrograms   0.0000128 gram

76. 19.2 kilograms   19,200 grams

Perform each indicated operation and write your answer without exponents.

77. $(2.5 \times 10^2)(3.4 \times 10^{-4})$ 0.085

78. $(4.2 \times 10^{-3})(3.0 \times 10^5)$ 1260

79. $(3.5 \times 10^{-2})(7.0 \times 10^3)$ 245

80. $\dfrac{7.94 \times 10^6}{2.0 \times 10^{-2}}$ 397,000,000

81. $\dfrac{1.5 \times 10^{-2}}{5.0 \times 10^2}$ 0.00003

82. $\dfrac{6.5 \times 10^4}{2.0 \times 10^6}$ 0.0325

Convert each number to scientific notation. Then calculate. Express your answer in scientific notation.

83. $(14,000)(260,000)$ 3.64×10^9

84. $(0.00053)(40,000)$ 2.12×10^1

85. $(12,500)(400,000)$ 5.0×10^9

86. $\dfrac{250}{500,000}$ 5.0×10^{-4}

87. $\dfrac{0.000068}{0.02}$ 3.4×10^{-3}

88. $\dfrac{850,000}{0.025}$ 3.4×10^7

89. Milk Tank A milk tank holds 6.4×10^6 fluid ounces of milk. If one gallon is 1.28×10^2 fluid ounces, determine the number of gallons of milk the tank holds.   50,000 gal

90. Social Security In 2004 there was about $1.5 trillion in the social security trust fund.

   a) Write this amount without scientific notation.

   b) Using scientific notation, determine the annual amount of interest obtained in a year if the interest rate obtained is 7.5% per year. Write the answer in scientific notation.

90. a) 1,500,000,000,000   **b)** 1.125×10^{11}

[6.4] *Indicate whether each expression is a polynomial. If the polynomial is not written in descending order, rewrite it in descending order. If the polynomial has a specific name, give that name. State the degree of each polynomial.*

91. $x^{-4} - 8$ not a polynomial

92. 7   monomial, 0

93. $x^2 - 4 + 3x$ $x^2 + 3x - 4$, trinomial, second

94. $-3 - x + 4x^2$ $4x^2 - x - 3$, trinomial, second

95. $4x^{1/2} - 6$ not a polynomial

96. $13x^3 - 4$ binomial, third

97. $x - 4x^2$ $-4x^2 + x$, binomial, second

98. $y^5 + y^{-3} - 9$ not a polynomial

99. $2x^3 - 7 + 4x^2 - 3x$ $2x^3 + 4x^2 - 3x - 7$, polynomial, third

[6.4–6.6] *Perform each indicated operation.*

100. $(x + 8) + (4x - 11)$ $5x - 3$

101. $(2d - 3) + (5d + 7)$ $7d + 4$

102. $(-x - 10) + (-2x + 5)$ $-3x - 5$

103. $(-3x^2 + 9x + 5) + (-x^2 + 2x - 12)$ $-4x^2 + 11x - 7$

104. $(-m^2 + 5m - 8) + (6m^2 - 5m - 2)$ $5m^2 - 10$

105. $(6.2p - 4.3) + (1.9p + 7.1)$ $8.1p + 2.8$

106. $(-6y - 7) - (-3y + 8)$ $-3y - 15$

107. $(4x^2 - 9x) - (3x + 15)$ $4x^2 - 12x - 15$

108. $(5a^2 - 6a - 9) - (2a^2 - a + 12)$ $3a^2 - 5a - 21$

109. $(x^2 + 7x - 3) - (x^2 + 3x - 5)$ $4x + 2$

110. $(-2x^2 + 8x - 7) - (3x^2 + 12)$ $-5x^2 + 8x - 19$

111. $\frac{1}{7}x(21x + 21)$ $3x^2 + 3x$

112. $-3x(5x + 4)$ $-15x^2 - 12x$

113. $3x(2x^2 - 4x + 7)$ $6x^3 - 12x^2 + 21x$

114. $-c(2c^2 - 3c + 5)$ $-2c^3 + 3c^2 - 5c$

115. $-7b(-4b^2 - 3b - 5)$ $28b^3 + 21b^2 + 35b$

116. $(x + 4)(x + 5)$ $x^2 + 9x + 20$

117. $(3x + 6)(-4x + 1)$ $-12x^2 - 21x + 6$

118. $(-5x + 3)^2$ $25x^2 - 30x + 9$

119. $(6 - 2x)(2 + 3x)$ $-6x^2 + 14x + 12$

120. $(r + 5)(r - 5)$ $r^2 - 25$

121. $(x - 1)(3x^2 + 4x - 6)$ $3x^3 + x^2 - 10x + 6$

122. $(3x + 1)(x^2 + 2x + 4)$ $3x^3 + 7x^2 + 14x + 4$

123. $(-4x + 2)(3x^2 - x + 7)$ $-12x^3 + 10x^2 - 30x + 14$

124. $\dfrac{2x + 4}{2}$ $x + 2$

125. $\dfrac{12y + 18}{3}$ $4y + 6$

126. $\dfrac{8x^2 + 4x}{x}$ $8x + 4$

127. $\dfrac{6x^2 + 9x - 4}{3}$ $2x^2 + 3x - \frac{4}{3}$

128. $\dfrac{6w^2 - 5w + 3}{3w}$ $2w - \frac{5}{3} + \frac{1}{w}$

129. $\dfrac{16x^6 - 8x^5 - 3x^3 + 1}{4x}$

130. $\dfrac{8m - 4}{-2}$ $-4m + 2$

131. $\dfrac{5x^3 + 10x + 2}{2x^2}$ $\frac{5}{2}x + \frac{5}{x} + \frac{1}{x^2}$

132. $\dfrac{5x^2 - 6x + 15}{3x}$ $\frac{5}{3}x - 2 + \frac{5}{x}$

133. $\dfrac{x^2 + x - 12}{x - 3}$ $x + 4$

134. $\dfrac{5x^2 + 28x - 10}{x + 6}$ $5x - 2 + \frac{2}{x + 6}$

135. $\dfrac{6n^2 + 19n + 3}{6n + 1}$ $n + 3$

136. $\dfrac{4x^3 + 12x^2 + x - 12}{2x + 3}$ $2x^2 + 3x - 4$ **137.** $\dfrac{4x^2 - 12x + 9}{2x - 3}$ $2x - 3$

129. $4x^5 - 2x^4 - \frac{3}{4}x^2 + \frac{1}{4x}$

Chapter 6 Practice Test

*To find out how well you understand the chapter material, take this practice test. The answers, and the section where the material was initially discussed, are given in the back of the book. Each problem is also fully worked out on the **Chapter Test Prep Video CD**. Review any questions that you answered incorrectly.*

Simplify each expression.

1. $5x^4 \cdot 3x^2$ $15x^6$

2. $(3xy^2)^3$ $27x^3y^6$

3. $\dfrac{24p^7}{3p^2}$ $8p^5$

4. $\left(\dfrac{3x^2y}{6xy^3}\right)^3$ $\dfrac{x^3}{8y^6}$

5. $(2x^3y^{-2})^{-2}$ $\dfrac{y^4}{4x^6}$

6. $(4x^0)(3x^2)^0$ 4

7. $\dfrac{30x^6y^2}{45x^{-1}y}$ $\dfrac{2x^7y}{3}$

Convert each number to scientific notation and then determine the answer. Express your answer in scientific notation.

8. $(285,000)(50,000)$ 1.425×10^{10}

9. $\dfrac{0.0008}{4000}$ 2.0×10^{-7}

Determine whether each expression is a polynomial. If the polynomial has a specific name, give that name.

10. $4x$ monomial

11. $-8c + 5$ binomial

12. $x^{-2} + 4$ not a polynomial

13. Write the polynomial $-5 + 6x^3 - 2x^2 + 5x$ in descending order, and give its degree. $6x^3 - 2x^2 + 5x - 5$, third degree

In Exercises 14–24, perform each indicated operation.

14. $(6x - 4) + (2x^2 - 5x - 3)$ $2x^2 + x - 7$

15. $(y^2 - 7y + 3) - (4y^2 - 5y - 2)$ $-3y^2 - 2y + 5$

16. $(4x^2 - 5) - (x^2 + x - 8)$ $3x^2 - x + 3$

17. $-5d(-3d + 8)$ $15d^2 - 40d$

18. $(5x + 8)(3x - 4)$ $15x^2 + 4x - 32$

19. $(9 - 4c)(5 + 3c)$ $-12c^2 + 7c + 45$

20. $(3x - 5)(2x^2 + 4x - 5)$ $6x^3 + 2x^2 - 35x + 25$

21. $\dfrac{16x^2 + 8x - 4}{4}$ $4x^2 + 2x - 1$

22. $\dfrac{-12x^2 - 6x + 5}{-3x}$ $4x + 2 - \dfrac{5}{3x}$

23. $\dfrac{8x^2 - 2x - 15}{2x - 3}$ $4x + 5$

24. $\dfrac{12x^2 + 7x - 12}{4x + 5}$ $3x - 2 - \dfrac{2}{4x + 5}$

25. **Half-Life** The half-life of an element is the time it takes one half the amount of a radioactive element to decay. The half-life of carbon 14 (C^{14}) is 5730 years. The half-life of uranium 238 (U^{238}) is 4.46×10^9 years.

   a) Write the half-life of C^{14} in scientific notation. 5.73×10^3

   b) How many times longer is the half-life of U^{238} than C^{14}? $\approx 7.78 \times 10^5$

Cumulative Review Test

Take the following test and check your answers with those given in the back of the book. Review any questions that you answered incorrectly. The section where the material was covered is indicated after the answer.

1. Evaluate $12 + 8 \div 2^2 + 3$. 17

2. Simplify $7 - (2x - 3) + 2x - 8(1 - x)$. $8x + 2$

3. Evaluate $-4x^2 + x - 7$ when $x = -2$. -25

4. Solve the equation $3(x + 2) + 3x - 5 = 4x + 1$. 0

5. Solve the inequality $3x - 11 < 5x - 2$ and graph the solution on a number line.

6. Solve the equation $3x - 2 = y - 7$ for y. $y = 3x + 5$

7. Find the slope of the line through the points $(1, 3)$ and $(5, 1)$.

8. Determine whether the following relation is a function. Give the domain and range of the relation or function. $\{(-4, -5), (1, 5), (2, 7), (5, 13)\}$

9. Find the solution to the following system of equations by substitution. $(4, -1)$

$$3x + 2y = 10$$
$$x - y = 5$$

10. Simplify $\left(\dfrac{5xy^{-3}}{x^{-2}y^5}\right)^2$. $\dfrac{25x^6}{y^{16}}$

11. Write the polynomial $-5x + 2 - 7x^2$ in descending order and give the degree. $-7x^2 - 5x + 2$, second

Perform each indicated operation.

12. $(x^2 + 4x - 3) + (2x^2 + 5x + 1)$ $3x^2 + 9x - 2$

13. $(6a^2 + 3a + 2) - (a^2 - 3a - 3)$ $5a^2 + 6a + 5$

14. $(5t - 3)(2t - 1)$ $10t^2 - 11t + 3$

15. $(2x - 1)(3x^2 - 5x + 2)$ $6x^3 - 13x^2 + 9x - 2$

16. $\dfrac{10d^2 + 12d - 8}{4d}$ $\dfrac{5}{2}d + 3 - \dfrac{2}{d}$

17. $\dfrac{6x^2 + 11x - 10}{3x - 2}$ $2x + 5$

18. **Chicken Soup** At Art's Grocery Store, three cans of chicken soup sell for $1.25. Find the cost of eight cans. $3.33

19. **Average Speed** Bob Dolan drives from Jackson, Mississippi, to Tallulah, Louisiana, a distance of 60 miles. At the same time, Nick Reide starts driving from Tallulah to Jackson along the same route. If Bob and Nick meet after 0.5 hour and Nick's average speed was 7 miles per hour greater than Bob's, find the average speed of each car. Bob, 56.5 mph; Nick, 63.5 mph

20. **Rectangle** The length of a rectangle is 2 less than 3 times the width. Find the dimensions of the rectangle if its perimeter is 28 feet. $l = 10$ ft, $w = 4$ ft

5. $x > -\dfrac{9}{2}$,   ⟵———○———➤   7. $-\dfrac{1}{2}$ 8. Function: Domain, $\{-4, 1, 2, 5\}$, Range, $\{-5, 5, 7, 13\}$

Factoring

7

WE SEE RECTANGLES in our daily lives. Often quadratic equations are used in helping design rectangular structures. For example, in Exercise 21 on page 456, we use quadratic equations to determine the dimensions of a rectangular garden that is to have a specific area.

7.1 Factoring a Monomial from a Polynomial

1   Identify factors.

2   Determine the greatest common factor of two or more numbers.

3   Determine the greatest common factor of two or more terms.

4   Factor a monomial from a polynomial.

TEACHING TIP
This may be a good place to reinforce the difference between a factor and a term.

1   Identify Factors

In Chapter 6, you learned how to multiply polynomials. In this chapter, we focus on factoring, the reverse process of multiplication. In Section 6.5, we showed that $3x(2x^2 + 4) = 6x^3 + 12x$. In this chapter, we start with an expression like $6x^3 + 12x$ and determine that its factors are $3x$ and $2x^2 + 4$, and write $6x^3 + 12x = 3x(2x^2 + 4)$. To **factor an expression** means to write the expression as a product of its factors. Factoring is important because it can be used to solve equations and perform operations on fractions.

If $a \cdot b = c$, then a and b are said to be *factors* of c.

$3 \cdot 5 = 15$; so 3 and 5 are factors of 15.

$x^3 \cdot x^4 = x^7$; so x^3 and x^4 are factors of x^7.

$x(x + 2) = x^2 + 2x$; so x and $x + 2$ are factors of $x^2 + 2x$.

$(x - 1)(x + 3) = x^2 + 2x - 3$; so $x - 1$ and $x + 3$ are factors of $x^2 + 2x - 3$.

A given number or expression may have many factors. Consider the number 30.

$$1 \cdot 30 = 30, \quad 2 \cdot 15 = 30, \quad 3 \cdot 10 = 30, \quad 5 \cdot 6 = 30$$

So, the positive factors of 30 are 1, 2, 3, 5, 6, 10, 15, and 30. Factors can also be negative. Since $(-1)(-30) = 30$, -1 and -30 are also factors of 30. In fact, for each factor a of an expression, $-a$ must also be a factor. Other factors of 30 are therefore $-1, -2, -3, -5, -6, -10, -15$, and -30. When asked to list the factors of an expression that contains a positive numerical coefficient with a variable, we generally list only positive factors.

INSTRUCTOR EXAMPLE
List the factors of $9x^3$.
Ans.:
$1, 3, 9, x, 3x, 9x, x^2, 3x^2, 9x^2, x^3, 3x^3, 9x^3$ and the opposites of these factors.

EXAMPLE 1 ▶ List the factors of $6x^3$.

Solution

$$\overbrace{1}^{factors} \cdot \overbrace{6x^3}{} = 6x^3 \qquad\qquad \overbrace{x}^{factors} \cdot \overbrace{6x^2}{} = 6x^3$$

$$2 \cdot 3x^3 = 6x^3 \qquad\qquad 2x \cdot 3x^2 = 6x^3$$

$$3 \cdot 2x^3 = 6x^3 \qquad\qquad 3x \cdot 2x^2 = 6x^3$$

$$6 \cdot x^3 = 6x^3 \qquad\qquad 6x \cdot x^2 = 6x^3$$

The factors of $6x^3$ are $1, 2, 3, 6, x, 2x, 3x, 6x, x^2, 2x^2, 3x^2, 6x^2, x^3, 2x^3, 3x^3$, and $6x^3$. The opposite (or negative) of each of these factors is also a factor, but these opposites are generally not listed unless specifically asked for.

▶ **Now Try Exercise 7**

Here are examples of multiplying and factoring. Notice again that factoring is the reverse process of multiplying.

TEACHING TIP
Encourage students to multiply factors to check that their product is the original expression. Then have students check if

a) $(x - 5)(x - 4)$ is the factored form of $x^2 - 9x + 20$

b) $7(x + 2)$ is the factored form of $7x + 14$

c) $2(x - 2)(3x + 1)$ is the factored form of $6x^2 - 10x - 4$

Multiplying	Factoring
$3(2x + 5) = 6x + 15$	$6x + 15 = 3(2x + 5)$
$4y(y - 7) = 4y^2 - 28y$	$4y^2 - 28y = 4y(y - 7)$
$(x + 1)(x + 3) = x^2 + 4x + 3$	$x^2 + 4x + 3 = (x + 1)(x + 3)$

2   Determine the Greatest Common Factor of Two or More Numbers

To factor a monomial from a polynomial, we make use of the *greatest common factor (GCF)*. If after studying the following material you wish to see additional material on obtaining the GCF, you may read Appendix B, where one of the topics discussed is finding the GCF.

Recall from Section 1.3 that the **greatest common factor** of two or more numbers is the greatest number that divides into all the numbers. The greatest common factor of the numbers 6 and 8 is 2. Two is the greatest number that divides into both 6 and 8. What is the GCF of 48 and 60? When the GCF of two or more numbers is not easily found, we can find it by writing each number as a product of prime numbers. A **prime number** is an integer greater than 1 that has exactly two factors, itself and one. The first 15 prime numbers are

$$2, 3, 5, 7, 11, 13, 17, 19, 23, 29, 31, 37, 41, 43, 47$$

A positive integer (other than 1) that is not prime is called **composite**. The number 1 is neither prime nor composite, it is called a **unit**. The first 15 composite numbers are

$$4, 6, 8, 9, 10, 12, 14, 15, 16, 18, 20, 21, 22, 24, 25$$

Every even number greater than 2 is a composite number since it has more than two factors, itself, 1, and 2.

To write a number as a product of prime numbers, follow the procedure illustrated in Examples 2 and 3.

EXAMPLE 2 ▶ Write 48 as a product of prime numbers.

Solution   Select any two numbers whose product is 48. Two possibilities are $6 \cdot 8$ and $4 \cdot 12$, but there are other choices. Continue breaking down the factors until all the factors are prime, as illustrated in **Figure 7.1**

Note that no matter how you select your initial factors,

$$48 = 2 \cdot 2 \cdot 2 \cdot 2 \cdot 3 = 2^4 \cdot 3$$

▶ **Now Try Exercise 9**

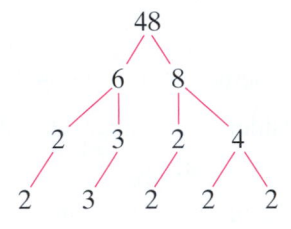

FIGURE 7.1

In Example 2, we found that $48 = 2 \cdot 2 \cdot 2 \cdot 2 \cdot 3 = 2^4 \cdot 3$. The $2 \cdot 2 \cdot 2 \cdot 2 \cdot 3$ or $2^4 \cdot 3$ may also be referred to as **prime factorizations** of 48.

EXAMPLE 3 ▶ Write 60 as a product of its prime factors.

Solution   One way to find the prime factors is shown in **Figure 7.2**. Therefore, $60 = 2 \cdot 2 \cdot 3 \cdot 5 = 2^2 \cdot 3 \cdot 5$.

▶ **Now Try Exercise 11**

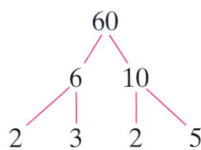

FIGURE 7.2

In the following box, we give the procedure to determine the greatest common factor of two or more numbers.

To Determine the GCF of Two or More Numbers

1. Write each number as a product of prime factors.
2. Determine the prime factors common to all the numbers.
3. Multiply the common factors found in step 2. The product of these factors is the GCF.

EXAMPLE 4 ▶ Determine the greatest common factor of 48 and 60.

Solution   From Examples 2 and 3, we know that

Step 1
$$48 = 2 \cdot 2 \cdot 2 \cdot 2 \cdot 3 = 2^4 \cdot 3$$
$$60 = 2 \cdot 2 \cdot 3 \cdot 5 = 2^2 \cdot 3 \cdot 5$$

Step 2   The common factors are circled. Two factors of 2 and one factor of 3 are common to both numbers. The product of these factors is the GCF of 48 and 60:

Step 3
$$\text{GCF} = 2 \cdot 2 \cdot 3 = 12$$

The GCF of 48 and 60 is 12. Twelve is the greatest number that divides into both 48 and 60.

▶ **Now Try Exercise 15**

EXAMPLE 5 ▶ Determine the GCF of 18 and 24.

Solution

$$18 = 2 \cdot 3 \cdot 3 = 2 \cdot 3^2$$
$$24 = 2 \cdot 2 \cdot 2 \cdot 3 = 2^3 \cdot 3$$

One factor of 2 and one factor of 3 are common to both 18 and 24.

$$GCF = 2 \cdot 3 = 6$$

▶ **Now Try Exercise 19**

3 Determine the Greatest Common Factor of Two or More Terms

The GCF of several terms containing variables is easily found. Consider the terms x^3, x^4, x^5, and x^6. The GCF of these terms is x^3, since x^3 is the largest number of x's common to all four terms. We can illustrate this by writing the terms in factored form, with x^3 as one factor.

$$x^3 = x^3 \cdot 1$$
$$x^4 = x^3 \cdot x$$
$$x^5 = x^3 \cdot x^2$$
$$x^6 = x^3 \cdot x^3$$

GCF of all four terms is x^3.

Notice that x^3 divides all four terms,

$$\frac{x^3}{x^3} = 1, \quad \text{and} \quad \frac{x^4}{x^3} = x, \quad \text{and} \quad \frac{x^5}{x^3} = x^2, \quad \text{and} \quad \frac{x^6}{x^3} = x^3.$$

EXAMPLE 6 ▶ Determine the GCF of the terms m^9, m^5, m^7, and m^3.

Solution The GCF is m^3 because m^3 is the largest number of m's common to all the terms.

▶ **Now Try Exercise 21**

EXAMPLE 7 ▶ Determine the GCF of the terms x^2y^3, x^3y^2 and xy^4.

Solution The largest number of x's common to all three terms is x^1 or x. The largest number of y's common to all three terms is y^2. So the GCF of the three terms is xy^2.

▶ **Now Try Exercise 29**

To Determine the Greatest Common Factor of Two or More Terms

To determine the GCF of two or more terms, take each factor the *largest* number of times that it appears in all of the terms.

EXAMPLE 8 ▶ Determine the GCF of the terms xy, x^2y^2, and x^3.

Solution The GCF is x. The largest power of x that is common to all three terms is x^1, or x. Since the term x^3 does not contain a power of y, the GCF does not contain y.

▶ **Now Try Exercise 25**

EXAMPLE 9 ▶ Determine the GCF of each group of terms.

a) $18y^2, 15y^3, 27y^5$ **b)** $-20x^2, 12x, 40x^3$ **c)** $5s^4, s^7, s^3$

Solution

a) The GCF of 18, 15, and 27 is 3. The GCF of y^2, y^3, and y^5 is y^2. Therefore, the GCF of the three terms is $3y^2$.

b) The GCF of -20, 12, and 40 is 4. The GCF of x^2, x, and x^3 is x. Therefore, the GCF of the three terms is $4x$.

c) The GCF of 5, 1, and 1 is 1. The GCF of s^4, s^7, and s^3 is s^3. Therefore, the GCF of the three terms is $1s^3$, which we write as s^3.

▶ **Now Try Exercise 33**

EXAMPLE 10 ▶ Determine the GCF of each pair of terms.

  a) $a(a - 6)$ and $3(a - 6)$ **b)** $t(t + 4)$ and $t + 4$

  c) $3(p + q)$ and $4p(p + q)$

Solution

  a) The GCF is $(a - 6)$.

  b) $t + 4$ can be written as $1(t + 4)$. Therefore, the GCF of $t(t + 4)$ and $1(t + 4)$ is $t + 4$.

  c) The GCF is $(p + q)$.

▶ **Now Try Exercise 39**

4 Factor a Monomial from a Polynomial

In Section 6.5 we multiplied factors. Factoring is the reverse process of multiplying factors. As mentioned earlier, to *factor an expression* means to write the expression as a product of its factors.

> **To Factor a Monomial from a Polynomial**
>
> 1. Determine the greatest common factor of all terms in the polynomial.
> 2. Write each term as the product of the GCF and its other factor.
> 3. Use the distributive property to factor out the GCF.

In step 3 of the process, we indicate that we use the distributive property. The distributive property is actually used in reverse. For example, if we have $4 \cdot x + 4 \cdot 2$, we use the distributive property in reverse to write $4(x + 2)$.

EXAMPLE 11 ▶ Factor $6x + 18$.

Solution   The GCF is 6.

$$6x + 18 = \boxed{6} \cdot x + \boxed{6} \cdot 3 \qquad \text{\textit{Write each term as a product}}$$
$$\text{\textit{of the GCF and its other factor.}}$$
$$= \boxed{6}(x + 3) \qquad \text{\textit{Distributive property}}$$

▶ **Now Try Exercise 49**

To check the factoring process, multiply the factors using the distributive property. If the factoring is correct, the product will be the polynomial you started with. Following is a check of the factoring in Example 11.

Check $6(x + 3) = 6x + 18$

EXAMPLE 12 ▶ Factor $15x - 20$.

Solution   The GCF is 5.

$$15x - 20 = \boxed{5} \cdot 3x - \boxed{5} \cdot 4$$
$$= \boxed{5}(3x - 4)$$

Check that the factoring is correct by multiplying.

▶ **Now Try Exercise 51**

EXAMPLE 13 ▸ Factor $6y^2 + 9y^5$.

Solution   The GCF is $3y^2$.

$$6y^2 + 9y^5 = \boxed{3y^2} \cdot 2 + \boxed{3y^2} \cdot 3y^3$$
$$= \boxed{3y^2}(2 + 3y^3)$$

Check that the factoring is correct by multiplying.

▸ **Now Try Exercise 59**

EXAMPLE 14 ▸ Factor $8q^3 - 20q^2 - 12q$.

Solution   The GCF is $4q$.

$$8q^3 - 20q^2 - 12q = \boxed{4q} \cdot 2q^2 - \boxed{4q} \cdot 5q - \boxed{4q} \cdot 3$$
$$= \boxed{4q}(2q^2 - 5q - 3)$$

Check $4q(2q^2 - 5q - 3) = 8q^3 - 20q^2 - 12q$

▸ **Now Try Exercise 81**

EXAMPLE 15 ▸ Factor $35x^2 - 25x + 5$.

Solution   The GCF is 5.

$$35x^2 - 25x + 5 = \boxed{5} \cdot 7x^2 - \boxed{5} \cdot 5x + \boxed{5} \cdot 1$$
$$= \boxed{5}(7x^2 - 5x + 1)$$

Check that the factoring is correct by multiplying.

▸ **Now Try Exercise 85**

EXAMPLE 16 ▸ Factor $4x^3 + x^2 + 8x^2y$.

Solution   The GCF is x^2.

$$4x^3 + x^2 + 8x^2y = \boxed{x^2} \cdot 4x + \boxed{x^2} \cdot 1 + \boxed{x^2} \cdot 8y$$
$$= \boxed{x^2}(4x + 1 + 8y)$$

Check that the factoring is correct by multiplying.

▸ **Now Try Exercise 89**

   Notice in Examples 15 and 16 that when one of the terms is itself the GCF, we ex-press it in factored form as the product of the term itself and 1.

EXAMPLE 17 ▸ Factor $x(5x - 2) + 7(5x - 2)$.

Solution   The GCF of $x(5x - 2)$ and $7(5x - 2)$ is $(5x - 2)$. Factoring out the GCF gives

$$x(5x - 2) + 7(5x - 2) = (5x - 2)(x + 7)$$

Check that the factoring is correct by multiplying.

▸ **Now Try Exercise 95**

EXAMPLE 18 ▸ Factor $4x(3x - 5) - 7(3x - 5)$.

Solution   The GCF of $4x(3x - 5)$ and $-7(3x - 5)$ is $(3x - 5)$. Factoring out the GCF gives

$$4x(3x - 5) - 7(3x - 5) = (3x - 5)(4x - 7)$$

Check that the factoring is correct by multiplying.

Recall from Section 1.10 that the commutative property of multiplication states that the order in which any two real numbers are multiplied does not matter. Therefore, $(3x - 5)(4x - 7)$ can also be written $(4x - 7)(3x - 5)$. In the book, we will place the common factor on the left.

▸ **Now Try Exercise 97**

EXAMPLE 19 ▸ Factor $2x(x + 3) - 5(x + 3)$.

Solution   The GCF of $2x(x + 3)$ and $-5(x + 3)$ is $(x + 3)$. Factoring out the GCF gives

$$2x(x + 3) - 5(x + 3) = (x + 3)(2x - 5)$$

Check that the factoring is correct by multiplying.

▸ **Now Try Exercise 93**

Important: Whenever you are factoring a polynomial by any of the methods presented in this chapter, the first step will always be to see if there is a common factor (other than 1) to all the terms in the polynomial. If so, factor the greatest common factor from each term using the distributive property.

Helpful Hint

Checking a Factoring Problem

Every factoring problem may be checked by multiplying the factors. The product of the factors should be identical to the expression that was originally factored. You should check all factoring problems.

1. to write an expression as the product of factors   2. an integer greater than 1 that has exactly two factors, itself and 1
3. a positive integer other than 1 that is not prime   4. no; a unit   6. Answers will vary.
7. $1, 2, 4, x, 2x, 4x, x^2, 2x^2, 4x^2$, and the opposites of these factors   8. by multiplying the factors

EXERCISE SET 7.1   Math XL   MyMathLab
MathXL®   MyMathLab

Concept/Writing Exercises

🖉 **1.** What does it mean to factor an expression?

🖉 **2.** What is a prime number?

🖉 **3.** What is a composite number?

🖉 **4.** Is the number 1 a prime number? If not, what is it called?

🖉 **5.** What is the greatest common factor of two or more numbers?   the greatest number that divides into all the numbers

🖉 **6.** Explain how to factor a monomial from a polynomial.

7. List the factors of $4x^2$.

🖉 **8.** How may any factoring problem be checked?

Practice the Skills

Write each number as a product of prime numbers.

9. 56 $2^3 \cdot 7$ **10.** 120 $2^3 \cdot 3 \cdot 5$ **11.** 90 $2 \cdot 3^2 \cdot 5$ **12.** 540 $2^2 \cdot 3^3 \cdot 5$ **13.** 248 $2^3 \cdot 31$ **14.** 144 $2^4 \cdot 3^2$

Determine the greatest common factor for each pair of numbers.

15. 20, 24   4   **16.** 45, 27   9   **17.** 70, 98   14   **18.** 120, 96   24   **19.** 80, 126   2   **20.** 88, 160   8

Determine the greatest common factor for each group of terms.

21. x^5, x, x^2 x

22. y^3, y^5, y^2 y^2

23. $3x, 6x^2, 9x^3$ $3x$

24. $6p, 4p^2, 8p^3$ $2p$

25. a, ab, ab^2 a

26. x, y, z 1

27. q^3r, q^2r^2, qr^4 qr

28. $4x^2y^2, 3xy^4, 2xy^2$ xy^2

29. $x^3y^7, x^7y^{12}, x^5y^5$ x^3y^5

30. $6x, 12y, 18x^2$ 6

31. $-3, 20x, 30x^2$ 1

32. $24s^5, 6r^3s^3, 15rs^2$ $3s^2$

33. $9x^3y^4, 8x^2y^4, 12x^4y^2$ x^2y^2

34. $16x^9y^{12}, 8x^5y^3, 20x^4y^2$ $4x^4y^2$

35. $40x^3, 27x, 30x^4y^2$ x

36. $6p^4q^3, 9p^2q^5, 9p^4q^2$ $3p^2q^2$

37. $8(x - 4), 7(x - 4)$ $x - 4$

38. $4(x - 5), 3x(x - 5)$ $x - 5$

39. $x^2(2x - 3), 5(2x - 3)$ $2x - 3$

40. $x(9x - 3), 9x - 3$ $9x - 3$

41. $3w + 5, 6(3w + 5)$ $3w + 5$

42. $b(b + 3), b + 3$ $b + 3$

43. $x - 4, y(x - 4)$ $x - 4$

44. $3y(x + 2), 3(x + 2)$ $3(x + 2)$

45. $3(x - 1), 5(x - 1)^2$ $x - 1$

46. $5(n + 2), 7(n + 2)^2$ $n + 2$

47. $(x - 9)(x + 6), (x - 9)(x + 3)$ $x - 9$

48. $(a + 4)(a - 3), 5(a - 3)$ $a - 3$

Factor the GCF from each term in the expression.

49. $4x - 8$ $4(x - 2)$

50. $4x + 2$ $2(2x + 1)$

51. $15x - 5$ $5(3x - 1)$

52. $12x + 15$ $3(4x + 5)$

53. $7q + 28$ $7(q + 4)$

54. $3t^2 - 10t$ $t(3t - 10)$

55. $9x^2 - 12x$ $3x(3x - 4)$

56. $24y - 6y^2$ $6y(4 - y)$

57. $7x^5 - 9x^4$ $x^4(7x - 9)$

58. $9x + 27x^3$ $9x(1 + 3x^2)$

59. $3x^5 - 12x^2$ $3x^2(x^3 - 4)$

60. $26p^2 - 8p$ $2p(13p - 4)$

61. $36x^{12} + 24x^8$ $12x^8(3x^4 + 2)$

62. $45y^{12} + 30y^{10}$ $15y^{10}(3y^2 + 2)$

63. $27y^{15} - 9y^3$ $9y^3(3y^{12} - 1)$

64. $30w^5 + 25w^3$ $5w^3(6w^2 + 5)$

65. $y + 6x^3y$ $y(1 + 6x^3)$

66. $4x^2y - 6x$ $2x(2xy - 3)$

67. $7a^4 + 3a^2$ $a^2(7a^2 + 3)$

68. $3x^2y + 6x^2y^2$ $3x^2y(1 + 2y)$

69. $16xy^2z + 4x^3y$ $4xy(4yz + x^2)$

70. $48m^4n^2 - 16mn^2$ $16mn^2(3m^3 - 1)$

71. $80x^5y^3z^4 - 36x^2yz^3$ $4x^2yz^3(20x^3y^2z - 9)$

72. $56xy^5z^{13} - 24y^4z^2$ $8y^4z^2(7xyz^{11} - 3)$

73. $25x^2yz^3 + 25x^3yz$ $25x^2yz(z^2 + x)$

74. $13y^5z^3 - 11xy^2z^5$ $y^2z^3(13y^3 - 11xz^2)$

75. $19x^4y^{12}z^{13} - 8x^5y^3z^9$ $x^4y^3z^9(19y^9z^4 - 8x)$

76. $16r^4s^5t^3 - 20r^5s^4t$ $4r^4s^4t(4st^2 - 5r)$

77. $8c^2 - 4c - 32$ $4(2c^2 - c - 8)$

78. $x^3 - 4x^2 - 3x$ $x(x^2 - 4x - 3)$

79. $9x^2 + 18x + 3$ $3(3x^2 + 6x + 1)$

80. $4x^2 + 8x + 24$ $4(x^2 + 2x + 6)$

81. $4x^3 - 8x^2 + 12x$ $4x(x^2 - 2x + 3)$

82. $12a^3 - 16a^2 - 4a$ $4a(3a^2 - 4a - 1)$

83. $40b^2 - 48c + 24$ $8(5b^2 - 6c + 3)$

84. $5x^3 - xy^2 + x$ $x(5x^2 - y^2 + 1)$

85. $15p^2 - 6p + 9$ $3(5p^2 - 2p + 3)$

86. $45y^3 - 63y^2 + 27y$ $9y(5y^2 - 7y + 3)$

87. $9a^4 - 6a^3 + 3ab$ $3a(3a^3 - 2a^2 + b)$

88. $45v^4w^2 + 10v^2x - 20vw^5$ $5v(9v^3w^2 + 2vx - 4w^5)$

89. $8x^2y + 12xy^2 + 5xy$ $xy(8x + 12y + 5)$

90. $52x^2y^2 + 16xy^3 + 26z$ $2(26x^2y^2 + 8xy^3 + 13z)$

91. $x(x - 7) + 6(x - 7)$ $(x - 7)(x + 6)$

92. $9x(3x - 4) - 4(3x - 4)$ $(3x - 4)(9x - 4)$

93. $3b(a - 2) - 4(a - 2)$ $(a - 2)(3b - 4)$

94. $3x(7x + 1) - 2(7x + 1)$ $(7x + 1)(3x - 2)$

95. $4x(2x + 1) + 1(2x + 1)$ $(2x + 1)(4x + 1)$

96. $4m(5m - 1) - 3(5m - 1)$ $(5m - 1)(4m - 3)$

97. $5x(2x + 1) + 2x + 1$ $(2x + 1)(5x + 1)$

98. $3x(4x - 5) + 4x - 5$ $(4x - 5)(3x + 1)$

99. $3c(6c + 7) - 2(6c + 7)$ $(6c + 7)(3c - 2)$

100. $5t(t - 2) - 3(t - 2)$ $(t - 2)(5t - 3)$

Problem Solving

Factor each expression, if possible. Treat the unknown symbol as if it were a variable.

101. $12\nabla - 6\nabla^2$ $6\nabla(2 - \nabla)$

102. $3\star + 6$ $3(\star + 2)$

103. $12\square^3 - 4\square^2 + 4\square$ $4\square(3\square^2 - \square + 1)$

104. $\copyright + 11\triangle$ cannot be factored

Challenge Problems

105. Factor $6x^5(2x + 7) + 4x^3(2x + 7) - 2x^2(2x + 7)$.
   $2x^2(2x + 7)(3x^3 + 2x - 1)$

106. Factor $4x^2(x - 3)^3 - 6x(x - 3)^2 + 4(x - 3)$.
   $2(x - 3)[2x^2(x - 3)^2 - 3x(x - 3) + 2]$

107. Factor $x^2 + 2x + 3x + 6$. (*Hint:* Factor the first two terms, then factor the last two terms, then factor the resulting two terms. We will discuss factoring problems of this type in Section 7.2.) $(x + 2)(x + 3)$

Cumulative Review Exercises

[2.1] **108.** Simplify $2x - (x - 5) + 4(3 - x)$. $-3x + 17$

[2.5] **109.** Solve the equation $4 + 3(x - 8) = x - 4(x + 2)$.   2

[2.6] **110.** Solve the equation $4x - 5y = 20$ for y.

111. Find the volume of the cone shown below. ≈ 201.06 in.^{3}

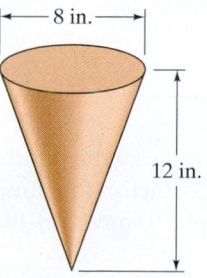

8 in.

12 in.

[3.2] **112.** The sum of two numbers is 41. Find the two numbers if the larger number is one less than twice the smaller number. $14, 27$

[6.1] **113.** Simplify $\left(\dfrac{3x^2y^3}{2x^5y^2}\right)^2$. $\dfrac{9y^2}{4x^6}$

110. $y = \dfrac{4x - 20}{5}$ or $y = \dfrac{4}{5}x - 4$

7.2 Factoring by Grouping

1 Factor a polynomial containing four terms by grouping.

1 Factor a Polynomial Containing Four Terms by Grouping

It may be possible to factor a polynomial containing four or more terms by removing common factors from groups of terms. This process is called **factoring by grouping**. In Sections 7.3 and 7.4, we discuss factoring trinomials. One of the methods we will use in Section 7.4 requires a knowledge of factoring by grouping. Example 1 illustrates the procedure for factoring by grouping.

EXAMPLE 1 ▶ Factor $ax + ay + bx + by$ by grouping.

Solution There is no factor (other than 1) common to all four terms. However, a is common to the first two terms and b is common to the last two terms. Factor a from the first two terms and b from the last two terms.

$$ax + ay + bx + by = a(x + y) + b(x + y)$$

This factoring gives two terms, and $(x + y)$ is common to both terms. Proceed to factor $(x + y)$ from each term, as shown below.

$$a(x + y) + b(x + y) = (x + y)(a + b)$$

Notice that when $(x + y)$ is factored out we are left with $a + b$, which becomes the other factor. Thus, $ax + ay + bx + by = (x + y)(a + b)$.

▶ **Now Try Exercise 7**

To Factor a Four-Term Polynomial Using Grouping

1. Determine whether there are any factors common to all four terms. If so, factor the greatest common factor from each of the four terms.
2. If necessary, arrange the four terms so that the first two terms have a common factor and the last two have a common factor.
3. Use the distributive property to factor each group of two terms.
4. Factor the greatest common factor from the results of step 3.

EXAMPLE 2 ▶ Factor $x^2 + 3x + 4x + 12$ by grouping.

Solution No factor is common to all four terms. However, you can factor x from the first two terms and 4 from the last two terms.

$$x^2 + 3x + 4x + 12 = x(x + 3) + 4(x + 3)$$

Notice that the expression on the right of the equal sign has two *terms* and that the *factor* $(x + 3)$ is common to both terms. Factor out the $(x + 3)$ using the distributive property.

$$x(x + 3) + 4(x + 3) = (x + 3)(x + 4)$$

Thus, $x^2 + 3x + 4x + 12 = (x + 3)(x + 4)$

▶ **Now Try Exercise 11**

In Example 2, the $3x$ and $4x$ are like terms and may be combined. However, if we were to combine them we would not be able to factor the four terms by grouping. Some four-term polynomials, such as in Example 9, have no like terms that can be combined.

EXAMPLE 3 ▶ Factor $15x^2 + 10x + 12x + 8$ by grouping.

Solution

$$15x^2 + 10x + 12x + 8 = 5x(3x + 2) + 4(3x + 2)$$

Factor 5x from the first two terms and 4 from the last two terms.

$$= (3x + 2)(5x + 4)$$

▶ **Now Try Exercise 17**

A factoring by grouping problem can be checked by multiplying the factors using the FOIL method. If you have not made a mistake, your result will be the polynomial you began with. Here is a check of Example 3.

Check   F   O   I   L

$$(3x + 2)(5x + 4) = (3x)(5x) + (3x)(4) + (2)(5x) + (2)(4)$$
$$= 15x^2 + 12x + 10x + 8$$
$$= 15x^2 + 10x + 12x + 8$$

We are able to write $12x + 10x$ as $10x + 12x$ because of the commutative property of addition. Since this is the polynomial we started with, the factoring is correct.

Helpful Hint

In Example 3, when we factored $15x^2 + 10x + 12x + 8$ we obtained

$$5x(3x + 2) + 4(3x + 2)$$

When we factored out the $(3x + 2)$, to be consistent with the way we factored out common factors in Section 7.1, we placed the common factor $(3x + 2)$ on the left. That gave $(3x + 2)(5x + 4)$. We could have just as well placed the common factor on the right to obtain $(5x + 4)(3x + 2)$.

Both answers are correct since $(3x + 2)(5x + 4) = (5x + 4)(3x + 2)$ by the commutative property of multiplication.

EXAMPLE 4 ▶ Factor $15x^2 + 12x + 10x + 8$ by grouping.

Solution $15x^2 + 12x + 10x + 8 = 3x(5x + 4) + 2(5x + 4)$
$$= (5x + 4)(3x + 2)$$

▶ **Now Try Exercise 19**

Notice that Example 4 is the same as Example 3 with the two middle terms interchanged. The answers to Examples 3 and 4 are equivalent since only the order of the factors are changed. When factoring by grouping, if the two middle terms are like terms, the two like terms may be interchanged and the answer will remain the same.

EXAMPLE 5 ▶ Factor $x^2 - 3x + x - 3$ by grouping.

Solution   In the first two terms, x is the common factor. Is there a common factor in the last two terms? Yes; remember that 1 is a factor of every term. Factor 1 from the last two terms.

$$x^2 - 3x + x - 3 = x^2 - 3x + 1 \cdot x - 1 \cdot 3$$
$$= x(x - 3) + 1(x - 3)$$
$$= (x - 3)(x + 1)$$

Note that $x - 3$ was expressed as $1 \cdot x - 1 \cdot 3 = 1(x - 3)$.

▶ **Now Try Exercise 21**

EXAMPLE 6 ▶ Factor $6x^2 - 3x - 2x + 1$ by grouping.

Solution   When $3x$ is factored from the first two terms, we get

$$6x^2 - 3x - 2x + 1 = 3x(2x - 1) - 2x + 1$$

What should we factor from the last two terms? We wish to factor $-2x + 1$ in such a manner that we end up with an expression that is a multiple of $(2x - 1)$.

Whenever we wish to change the sign *of each term of an expression, we can factor out a negative number from each term.* In this case, we factor out -1.

$$-2x + 1 = -1(2x - 1)$$

Now, we rewrite $-2x + 1$ as $-1(2x - 1)$.

$$3x(2x - 1) - 2x + 1 = 3x(2x - 1) - 1(2x - 1)$$

Now we factor out the common factor $(2x - 1)$.

$$3x(2x - 1) - 1(2x - 1) = (2x - 1)(3x - 1)$$

▶ **Now Try Exercise 23**

INSTRUCTOR EXAMPLE
Factor $p^2 + 8p - p - 8$ by grouping.
Ans.: $(p + 8)(p - 1)$

EXAMPLE 7 ▶ Factor $q^2 + 3q - q - 3$ by grouping.

Solution

$$\begin{aligned} q^2 + 3q - q - 3 &= q(q + 3) - q - 3 &&\text{Factor out } q. \\ &= q(q + 3) - 1(q + 3) &&\text{Factor out } -1. \\ &= (q + 3)(q - 1) &&\text{Factor out } (q + 3). \end{aligned}$$

Note that we factored -1 from $-q - 3$ to get $-1(q + 3)$.

▶ **Now Try Exercise 25**

INSTRUCTOR EXAMPLE
Factor $5x^2 - 15x - 2x + 6$ by grouping.
Ans.: $(x - 3)(5x - 2)$

EXAMPLE 8 ▶ Factor $3x^2 - 6x - 4x + 8$ by grouping.

Solution

$$\begin{aligned} 3x^2 - 6x - 4x + 8 &= 3x(x - 2) - 4(x - 2) \\ &= (x - 2)(3x - 4) \end{aligned}$$

Note: $-4x + 8 = -4(x - 2)$.

▶ **Now Try Exercise 27**

Helpful Hint

When factoring four terms by grouping, if the coefficient of the third term is positive, as in Examples 2 through 5, you will generally factor out a positive coefficient from the last two terms. *If the coefficient of the third term is negative*, as in Examples 6 through 8, *you will generally factor out a negative coefficient from the last two terms.* The sign of the coefficient of the third term in the expression *must be included* so that the factoring results in two terms. For example,

$$2x^2 + 8x + 3x + 12 = 2x(x + 4) + 3(x + 4) = (x + 4)(2x + 3)$$
$$3x^2 - 15x - 2x + 10 = 3x(x - 5) - 2(x - 5) = (x - 5)(3x - 2)$$

In the examples illustrated so far, the two middle terms have been like terms. This need not be the case, as illustrated in Example 9.

INSTRUCTOR EXAMPLE
Factor $rt + 3t - 5r - 15$ by grouping.
Ans.: $(r + 3)(t - 5)$

EXAMPLE 9 ▶ Factor $xy + 3x - 2y - 6$ by grouping.

Solution   This problem contains two variables, x and y. The procedure to factor here is basically the same as before. Factor x from the first two terms and -2 from the last two terms.

$$\begin{aligned} xy + 3x - 2y - 6 &= x(y + 3) - 2(y + 3) \\ &= (y + 3)(x - 2) &&\text{Factor out } (y + 3). \end{aligned}$$

▶ **Now Try Exercise 41**

EXAMPLE 10 ▸ Factor $2x^2 + 4xy + 3xy + 6y^2$.

Solution   We will factor out $2x$ from the first two terms and $3y$ from the last two terms.

$$2x^2 + 4xy + 3xy + 6y^2 = 2x(x + 2y) + 3y(x + 2y)$$

Now we factor out the common factor $(x + 2y)$ from each term on the right.

$$2x(x + 2y) + 3y(x + 2y) = (x + 2y)(2x + 3y)$$

Check   F   O   I   L

$$(x + 2y)(2x + 3y) = (x)(2x) + (x)(3y) + (2y)(2x) + (2y)(3y)$$
$$= 2x^2 + 3xy + 4xy + 6y^2$$
$$= 2x^2 + 4xy + 3xy + 6y^2$$

▸ **Now Try Exercise 29**

If Example 10 were given as $2x^2 + 3xy + 4xy + 6y^2$, would the results be the same? Try it and see.

EXAMPLE 11 ▸ Factor $15a^2 - 10ab + 12ab - 8b^2$.

Solution   Factor $5a$ from the first two terms and $4b$ from the last two terms.

$$15a^2 - 10ab + 12ab - 8b^2 = 5a(3a - 2b) + 4b(3a - 2b)$$
$$= (3a - 2b)(5a + 4b)$$

▸ **Now Try Exercise 31**

EXAMPLE 12 ▸ Factor $3x^2 - 15x + 6x - 30$.

Solution   *The first step in any factoring problem is to determine whether all the terms have a common factor. If so, we factor out that common factor.* In this polynomial, 3 is common to every term. Therefore, we begin by factoring out the 3.

$$3x^2 - 15x + 6x - 30 = 3(x^2 - 5x + 2x - 10)$$

Now we factor the expression in parentheses by grouping. We factor out x from the first two terms and 2 from the last two terms.

$$3(x^2 - 5x + 2x - 10) = 3[x(x - 5) + 2(x - 5)]$$
$$= 3[(x - 5)(x + 2)]$$
$$= 3(x - 5)(x + 2)$$

Thus, $3x^2 - 15x + 6x - 30 = 3(x - 5)(x + 2)$.

▸ **Now Try Exercise 49**

1. Factor out the GCF.   2. Multiply the factors to see if the product is the same as the original expression.   3. $x^2 - 3x - 2xy + 6y$
4. $x^2 + 4x - 2x - 8$

EXERCISE SET 7.2   Math XL   MyMathLab
MathXL®   MyMathLab

Concept/Writing Exercises

✎ **1.** What is the first step in any factoring by grouping problem?

✎ **2.** How can you check the answer to a factoring by grouping problem?

✎ **3.** A polynomial of four terms is factored by grouping and the result is $(x - 2y)(x - 3)$. Find a polynomial that was factored, and explain how you determined the answer.

✎ **4.** A polynomial of four terms is factored by grouping and the result is $(x - 2)(x + 4)$. Find a polynomial that was factored, and explain how you determined the answer.

5. What number when factored from each term in an expression changes the sign of each term in the original expression? -1

✎ **6.** Describe the steps you take to factor a polynomial of four terms by grouping.   Answers will vary.

Practice the Skills

Factor by grouping.

7. $x^2 + 3x + 2x + 6$ $(x + 3)(x + 2)$

8. $x^2 + 7x + 3x + 21$ $(x + 7)(x + 3)$

9. $x^2 + 5x + 4x + 20$ $(x + 5)(x + 4)$

10. $x^2 - x + 3x - 3$ $(x - 1)(x + 3)$

11. $x^2 + 2x + 5x + 10$ $(x + 2)(x + 5)$

12. $x^2 - 6x + 5x - 30$ $(x - 6)(x + 5)$

13. $c^2 - 4c + 7c - 28$ $(c - 4)(c + 7)$

14. $r^2 - 4r + 6r - 24$ $(r - 4)(r + 6)$

15. $4x^2 - 6x + 6x - 9$ $(2x - 3)(2x + 3)$

16. $4b^2 - 10b + 10b - 25$ $(2b - 5)(2b + 5)$

17. $3x^2 + 9x + x + 3$ $(x + 3)(3x + 1)$

18. $a^2 + a + 3a + 3$ $(a + 1)(a + 3)$

19. $6x^2 + 3x - 2x - 1$ $(2x + 1)(3x - 1)$

20. $5x^2 + 30x - 3x - 18$ $(x + 6)(5x - 3)$

21. $8x^2 + 32x + x + 4$ $(x + 4)(8x + 1)$

22. $9w^2 - 6w - 6w + 4$ $(3w - 2)(3w - 2) = (3w - 2)^2$

23. $12t^2 - 8t - 3t + 2$ $(3t - 2)(4t - 1)$

24. $12x^2 + 42x - 10x - 35$ $(2x + 7)(6x - 5)$

25. $x^2 + 9x - x - 9$ $(x + 9)(x - 1)$

26. $35x^2 - 40x + 21x - 24$ $(7x - 8)(5x + 3)$

27. $6p^2 + 15p - 4p - 10$ $(2p + 5)(3p - 2)$

28. $10c^2 + 25c - 6c - 15$ $(2c + 5)(5c - 3)$

29. $x^2 + 2xy - 3xy - 6y^2$ $(x + 2y)(x - 3y)$

30. $x^2 - 3xy + 4xy - 12y^2$ $(x - 3y)(x + 4y)$

31. $3x^2 + 2xy - 9xy - 6y^2$ $(3x + 2y)(x - 3y)$

32. $3x^2 - 18xy + 4xy - 24y^2$ $(x - 6y)(3x + 4y)$

33. $10x^2 - 12xy - 25xy + 30y^2$ $(5x - 6y)(2x - 5y)$

34. $6a^2 - 3ab + 4ab - 2b^2$ $(2a - b)(3a + 2b)$

35. $x^2 - bx - ax + ab$ $(x - b)(x - a)$

36. $x^2 + bx + ax + ab$ $(x + b)(x + a)$

37. $xy + 9x - 5y - 45$ $(y + 9)(x - 5)$

38. $x^2 - 2x + ax - 2a$ $(x - 2)(x + a)$

39. $a^2 + 3a + ab + 3b$ $(a + 3)(a + b)$

40. $3x^2 - 15x - 2xy + 10y$ $(x - 5)(3x - 2y)$

41. $xy - x + 5y - 5$ $(y - 1)(x + 5)$

42. $y^2 - yb + ya - ab$ $(y - b)(y + a)$

43. $12 + 8y - 3x - 2xy$ $(3 + 2y)(4 - x)$

44. $7y - 49 - xy + 7x$ $(y - 7)(7 - x)$

45. $z^3 + 5z^2 + z + 5$ $(z + 5)(z^2 + 1)$

46. $x^3 - 3x^2 + 2x - 6$ $(x - 3)(x^2 + 2)$

47. $x^3 - 5x^2 + 8x - 40$ $(x - 5)(x^2 + 8)$

48. $y^3 - 3y + 2y^2 - 6$ $(y^2 - 3)(y + 2)$

49. $2x^2 - 12x + 8x - 48$ $2(x - 6)(x + 4)$

50. $3x^2 - 3x - 3x + 3$ $3(x - 1)(x - 1) = 3(x - 1)^2$

51. $4x^2 + 8x + 8x + 16$ $4(x + 2)(x + 2) = 4(x + 2)^2$

52. $3z^4 - 3z^3 - 7z^3 + 7z^2$ $z^2(z - 1)(3z - 7)$

53. $6x^3 + 9x^2 - 2x^2 - 3x$ $x(2x + 3)(3x - 1)$

54. $9x^3 + 6x^2 - 45x^2 - 30x$ $3x(3x + 2)(x - 5)$

55. $p^3 - 6p^2q + 2p^2q - 12pq^2$ $p(p - 6q)(p + 2q)$

56. $18x^2 + 27xy + 12xy + 18y^2$ $3(2x + 3y)(3x + 2y)$

Rearrange the terms so that the first two terms have a common factor and the last two terms have a common factor (other than 1). Then factor by grouping. There may be more than one way to arrange the factors. However, the answer should be equivalent regardless of the arrangement selected.

57. $5x + 3y + xy + 15$ $(y + 5)(x + 3)$

58. $5m + 2w + mw + 10$ $(m + 2)(w + 5)$

59. $6x + 5y + xy + 30$ $(x + 5)(y + 6)$

60. $ax - 10 - 5x + 2a$ $(a - 5)(x + 2)$

61. $ax + by + ay + bx$ $(a + b)(x + y)$

62. $ax - 21 - 3a + 7x$ $(a + 7)(x - 3)$

63. $rs - 42 + 6s - 7r$ $(r + 6)(s - 7)$

64. $ca - 2b + 2a - cb$ $(c + 2)(a - b)$

65. $dc + 3c - ad - 3a$ $(c - a)(d + 3)$

66. $ac - bd - ad + bc$ $(a + b)(c - d)$

Problem Solving

67. If you know that a polynomial with four terms is factorable by a specific arrangement of the terms, then will *any* arrangement of the terms be factorable by grouping? Explain, and support your answer with an example.
No. $xy + 2x + 5y + 10$ is factorable, $xy + 10 + 2x + 5y$ is not factorable in this arrangement.

Factor each expression, if possible. Treat the unknown symbol as if it were a variable.

68. $\heartsuit^2 + 3\heartsuit + 4\heartsuit + 12$ $(\heartsuit + 3)(\heartsuit + 4)$

69. $\odot^2 + 3\odot - 5\odot - 15$ $(\odot + 3)(\odot - 5)$

70. $\Delta^2 + 2\Delta - \Delta + 6$ cannot be factored

Challenge Problems

In Section 7.4, we will factor trinomials of the form $ax^2 + bx + c$, $a \neq 1$ using grouping. To do this we rewrite the middle term of the trinomial, bx, as a sum or difference of two terms. Then we factor the resulting polynomial of four terms by grouping. For Exercises 71–76,
a) *rewrite the trinomial as a polynomial of four terms by replacing the bx-term with the sum or difference given.* ***b)*** *Factor the polynomial of four terms. Note that the factors obtained are the factors of the trinomial.*

71. $2x^2 - 11x + 15, -11x = -5x - 6x$
  a) $2x^2 - 5x - 6x + 15$ **b)** $(2x - 5)(x - 3)$

72. $3x^2 + 10x + 8, 10x = 4x + 6x$
  a) $3x^2 + 4x + 6x + 8$ **b)** $(3x + 4)(x + 2)$

73. $2x^2 - 11x + 15, -11x = -6x - 5x$
  a) $2x^2 - 6x - 5x + 15$ **b)** $(x - 3)(2x - 5)$

74. $3x^2 + 10x + 8, 10x = 6x + 4x$
  a) $3x^2 + 6x + 4x + 8$ **b)** $(x + 2)(3x + 4)$

75. $4x^2 - 17x - 15, -17x = 3x - 20x$
  a) $4x^2 + 3x - 20x - 15$ **b)** $(4x + 3)(x - 5)$

76. $4x^2 - 17x - 15, -17x = -20x + 3x$
  a) $4x^2 - 20x + 3x - 15$ **b)** $(x - 5)(4x + 3)$

Factor each expression, if possible. Treat the unknown symbols as if they were variables.

77. $\bigstar \odot + 3\bigstar + 2\odot + 6$ $(\odot + 3)(\bigstar + 2)$

78. $2\Delta^2 - 4\Delta\bigstar - 8\Delta\bigstar + 16\bigstar^2$ $2(\Delta - 2\bigstar)(\Delta - 4\bigstar)$

Cumulative Review Exercises

[2.5]   **79.** Solve $5 - 3(2x - 7) = 4(x + 5) - 6$. $\dfrac{6}{5}$

[3.4]   **80.** **Special Mixture** Ed and Beatrice Petrie own a small grocery store near Leesport, Pennsylvania. The store carries a variety of bulk candy. To celebrate the tenth anniversary of the store's opening, the Petries decide to create a special candy mixture containing jelly beans and gumdrops. The jelly beans sell for $6.25 per pound and the gumdrops sell for $2.50 per pound. How many pounds of each type of candy will be needed to make a 50-pound mixture that will sell for $4.75 per pound?   30 lb of jelly beans, 20 lb of gumdrops

See Exercise 80.

[6.6]   **81.** Divide $\dfrac{15x^3 - 6x^2 - 9x + 5}{3x}$. $5x^2 - 2x - 3 + \dfrac{5}{3x}$

82. Divide $\dfrac{a^2 - 16}{a + 4}$. $a - 4$

7.3   Factoring Trinomials of the Form $ax^2 + bx + c, a = 1$

1   Factor trinomials of the form $ax^2 + bx + c$, where $a = 1$.

2   Remove a common factor from a trinomial.

An Important Note Regarding Factoring Trinomials

Factoring trinomials is important in algebra, higher-level mathematics, physics, and other science courses. Because it is important, and also to be successful in Chapter 8, you should study and learn Sections 7.3 and 7.4 well.

    In this section, we learn to factor trinomials of the form $ax^2 + bx + c$, where a, the numerical coefficient of the squared term, is 1. That is, we will be factoring trinomials of the form $x^2 + bx + c$. One example of this type of trinomial is $x^2 + 5x + 6$. Recall that x^2 means $1x^2$.

    In Section 7.4, we will learn to factor trinomials of the form $ax^2 + bx + c$, where $a \neq 1$. One example of this type of trinomial is $2x^2 + 7x + 3$.

1   Factor Trinomials of the Form $ax^2 + bx + c$, where $a = 1$

Now we discuss how to factor trinomials of the form $ax^2 + bx + c$, where a, the numerical coefficient of the squared term, is 1. Examples of such trinomials are

$$x^2 + 7x + 12 \qquad\qquad x^2 - 2x - 24$$
$$a = 1, b = 7, c = 12 \qquad\qquad a = 1, b = -2, c = -24$$

Recall that factoring is the reverse process of multiplication. We can show with the FOIL method of multiplying binomials that

$$(x + 3)(x + 4) = x^2 + 7x + 12 \quad \text{and} \quad (x - 6)(x + 4) = x^2 - 2x - 24$$

Therefore, $x^2 + 7x + 12$ and $x^2 - 2x - 24$ factor as follows:

$$x^2 + 7x + 12 = (x + 3)(x + 4) \quad \text{and} \quad x^2 - 2x - 24 = (x - 6)(x + 4)$$

Notice that each of these trinomials when factored results in the product of two binomials in which the first term of each binomial is x and the second term is a number (including its sign). In general, when we factor a trinomial of the form $x^2 + bx + c$ we will get a pair of binomial factors as follows:

$$x^2 + bx + c = (x + \blacksquare)(x + \blacksquare)$$

Numbers go here.

If, for example, we find that the numbers that go in the shaded areas of the factors are 4 and -6, the factors are written $(x + 4)$ and $(x - 6)$. Notice that instead of listing the second factor as $(x + (-6))$, we list it as $(x - 6)$.

To determine the numbers to place in the shaded areas when factoring a trinomial of the form $x^2 + bx + c$, write down factors of the form $(x + \blacksquare)(x + \blacksquare)$ and then try different sets of factors of the constant, c, in the shaded areas of the parentheses. We multiply each pair of factors using the FOIL method, and continue until we find the pair whose sum of the products of the outer and inner terms is the same as the x-term in the trinomial. For example, to factor the trinomial $x^2 + 7x + 12$ we determine the possible factors of 12. Then we try each pair of factors until we obtain a pair whose product from the FOIL method contains $7x$, the same x-term as in the trinomial. This method for factoring is called **trial and error**. In Example 1, we factor $x^2 + 7x + 12$ by trial and error.

INSTRUCTOR EXAMPLE
Factor $x^2 + 12x + 20$ by trial and error.
Ans.: $(x + 2)(x + 10)$

EXAMPLE 1 ▶ Factor $x^2 + 7x + 12$ by trial and error.

Solution Begin by listing the factors of 12 (see the left-hand column of the chart below. Then list the possible factors of the trinomial, and the products of these factors. Finally, determine which, if any, of these products gives the correct middle term, $7x$.

Factors of 12	Possible Factors of Trinomial	Product of Factors
$(1)(12)$	$(x + 1)(x + 12)$	$x^2 + 13x + 12$
$(2)(6)$	$(x + 2)(x + 6)$	$x^2 + 8x + 12$
$(3)(4)$	$(x + 3)(x + 4)$	$x^2 + 7x + 12$
$(-1)(-12)$	$(x - 1)(x - 12)$	$x^2 - 13x + 12$
$(-2)(-6)$	$(x - 2)(x - 6)$	$x^2 - 8x + 12$
$(-3)(-4)$	$(x - 3)(x - 4)$	$x^2 - 7x + 12$

In the last column, we find the trinomial we are seeking in the third line. Thus,

$$x^2 + 7x + 12 = (x + 3)(x + 4)$$

▶ **Now Try Exercise 17**

Now let's consider how we may more easily determine the correct factors of 12 to place in the shaded areas when factoring the trinomial in Example 1. In Section 6.5, we illustrated how the FOIL method is used to multiply two binomials. Let's multiply $(x + 3)(x + 4)$ using the FOIL method.

$$\begin{array}{l} \quad\quad\quad\quad\quad\quad\quad F \quad\; O \quad\; I \quad\; L \\ (x + 3)(x + 4) = x^2 + 4x + 3x + 12 \\ \quad\quad\quad\quad\quad\quad = x^2 + \quad\; 7x \quad\; + 12 \end{array}$$

We see that $(x + 3)(x + 4) = x^2 + 7x + 12$.

Note that the *sum of the outer and inner terms is 7x and the product of the last terms is 12*. To factor $x^2 + 7x + 12$, we look for two numbers whose product is 12 and whose sum is 7. We list the factors of 12 first and then list the sum of the factors.

Factors of 12	Sum of Factors
$(1)(12) = 12$	$1 + 12 = 13$
$(2)(6) = 12$	$2 + 6 = 8$
$(3)(4) = 12$	$3 + 4 = 7$
$(-1)(-12) = 12$	$-1 + (-12) = -13$
$(-2)(-6) = 12$	$-2 + (-6) = -8$
$(-3)(-4) = 12$	$-3 + (-4) = -7$

The only factors of 12 whose sum is a positive 7 are 3 and 4. The factors of $x^2 + 7x + 12$ will therefore be $(x + 3)$ and $(x + 4)$.

$$x^2 + 7x + 12 = (x + 3)(x + 4)$$

In the previous illustration, all the possible factors of 12 were listed so that you could see them. However, when working a problem, once you find the specific factors you are seeking you need go no further.

TEACHING TIP
Have students create trinomials from the product of 2 factors of the form $(x + c)(x + d)$ for various values of c and d. Have them identify relationships between the signs of c and d, and the coefficients of the simplified trinomial.

To Factor Trinomials of the Form $ax^2 + bx + c$, where $a = 1$

1. Find two numbers whose product equals the constant, c, and whose sum equals the coefficient of the x-term, b.

2. Use the two numbers found in step 1, including their signs, to write the trinomial in factored form. The trinomial in factored form will be

$$(x + \text{one number})(x + \text{second number})$$

How do we find the two numbers mentioned in steps 1 and 2? The sign of the constant, c, is a key in finding the two numbers. *The Helpful Hint that follows is very important and useful. Study it carefully.*

Helpful Hint

When asked to factor a trinomial of the form $x^2 + bx + c$, first observe the sign of the constant.

a) If the constant, c, is positive, both numbers in the factors will have the same sign, either both positive or both negative. Furthermore, that common sign will be the same as the sign of the coefficient of the x-term of the trinomial being factored. That is, if b is positive, both factors will contain positive numbers, and if b is negative, both factors will contain negative numbers.
Example:

$$x^2 + 7x + 12 = (x + 3)(x + 4)$$

The coefficient, b,   The constant, c,   positive   positive
is positive   is positive

Both factors have positive numbers.

(continued on the next page)

Example:

$$x^2 - 5x + 6 = (x - 2)(x - 3)$$

Both factors have negative numbers.

The coefficient, b,   The constant, c,   negative   negative
is negative   is positive

b) If the constant is negative, the two numbers in the factors will have opposite signs. That is, one number will be positive and the other number will be negative.
Example:

$$x^2 + x - 6 = (x + 3)(x - 2)$$

One factor has a positive number and the other factor has a negative number.

The coefficient, b,   The constant, c,   positive   negative
is positive   is negative

Example:

$$x^2 - 3x - 10 = (x + 2)(x - 5)$$

One factor has a positive number and the other factor has a negative number.

The coefficient, b,   The constant, c,   positive   negative
is negative   is negative

We will use this information as a starting point when factoring trinomials.

EXAMPLE 2 ▶ Consider a trinomial of the form $x^2 + bx + c$. Use the signs of b and c given below to determine the signs of the numbers in the factors.

a) b is negative and c is positive   **b)** b is negative and c is negative

c) b is positive and c is negative   **d)** b is positive and c is positive

Solution   In each case we look at the sign of the constant, c, first.

a) Since the constant, c, is positive, both numbers must have the same sign. Since the coefficient of the x-term, b, is negative, both factors will contain negative numbers.

b) Since the constant, c, is negative, one factor will contain a positive number and the other will contain a negative number.

c) Since the constant, c, is negative, one factor will contain a positive number and the other will contain a negative number.

d) Since the constant, c, is positive, both numbers must have the same sign. Since the coefficient of the x-term, b, is positive, both factors will contain positive numbers.

▶ **Now Try Exercise 5**

EXAMPLE 3 ▶ Factor $x^2 + x - 6$.

Solution   We must find two numbers whose product is the constant, -6, and whose sum is the coefficient of the x-term, 1. Remember that x means $1x$. Since the constant is negative, one number must be positive and the other negative. Recall that the product of two numbers with unlike signs is a negative number. We now list the factors of -6 and look for the two factors whose sum is 1.

Factors of -6	Sum of Factors
$1(-6) = -6$	$1 + (-6) = -5$
$2(-3) = -6$	$2 + (-3) = -1$
$3(-2) = -6$	$3 + (-2) = 1$
$6(-1) = -6$	$6 + (-1) = 5$

Note that the factors 1 and -6 in the top row are different from the factors -1 and 6 in the bottom row, and their sums are different.

The numbers 3 and -2 have a product of -6 and a sum of 1. Thus, the factors are $(x + 3)$ and $(x - 2)$.

$$x^2 + x - 6 = (x + 3)(x - 2)$$

The order of the factors is not crucial. Therefore, $x^2 + x - 6 = (x - 2)(x + 3)$ is also an acceptable answer.

▶ **Now Try Exercise 19**

As mentioned earlier, **trinomial factoring problems can be checked by multiplying the factors using the FOIL method.** If the factoring is correct, the product obtained using the FOIL method will be identical to the original trinomial. Let's check the factors obtained in Example 3.

Check $(x + 3)(x - 2) = x^2 - 2x + 3x - 6 = x^2 + x - 6$

Since the product of the factors is identical to the original trinomial, the factoring is correct.

EXAMPLE 4 ▶ Factor $x^2 - x - 6$.

Solution   The factors of -6 are illustrated in Example 3. The factors whose product is -6 and whose sum is -1 are 2 and -3.

Factors of -6	Sum of Factors
$2(-3) = -6$	$2 + (-3) = -1$

Therefore, $x^2 - x - 6 = (x + 2)(x - 3)$

▶ **Now Try Exercise 25**

EXAMPLE 5 ▶ Factor $x^2 - 5x + 6$.

Solution   We must find two numbers whose product is 6 and whose sum is -5. Since the constant, 6, is positive, both numbers must have the same sign. Since the coefficient of the x-term, -5, is negative, both numbers must be negative. Recall that the product of a negative number and a negative number is positive. We now list the negative factors of 6 and look for the pair whose sum is -5.

Factors of 6	Sum of Factors
$(-1)(-6)$	$-1 + (-6) = -7$
$(-2)(-3)$	$-2 + (-3) = -5$

The factors of 6 whose sum is -5 are -2 and -3.
$$x^2 - 5x + 6 = (x - 2)(x - 3)$$

▶ **Now Try Exercise 29**

In Example 5, suppose we were asked to factor $-5x + x^2 + 6$. In order to factor a trinomial, we always write the expression in the form $x^2 + bx + c$ if it is not given in that form. Therefore, the first step in the factoring process would be to rewrite $-5x + x^2 + 6$ as $x^2 - 5x + 6$. Then we would proceed as in Example 5.

EXAMPLE 6 ▶ Factor $r^2 + 2r - 24$.

Solution   In this example, the variable is r, but the factoring procedure is the same. We must find the two factors of -24 whose sum is 2. Since the constant is negative, one factor will be positive and the other factor will be negative.

Factors of -24	Sum of Factors
$(1)(-24)$	$1 + (-24) = -23$
$(2)(-12)$	$2 + (-12) = -10$
$(3)(-8)$	$3 + (-8) = -5$
$(4)(-6)$	$4 + (-6) = -2$
$(6)(-4)$	$6 + (-4) = 2$

Since we have found the two numbers, 6 and -4, whose product is -24 and whose sum is 2, we need go no further.

$$r^2 + 2r - 24 = (r + 6)(r - 4)$$

▸ **Now Try Exercise 33**

INSTRUCTOR EXAMPLE
Factor $x^2 - 14x + 49$.
Ans.: $(x - 7)^2$

EXAMPLE 7 ▸ Factor $x^2 - 8x + 16$.

Solution   We must find the factors of 16 whose sum is -8. Both factors must be negative. (Can you explain why?) The two factors whose product is 16 and whose sum is -8 are -4 and -4.

$$x^2 - 8x + 16 = (x - 4)(x - 4)$$
$$= (x - 4)^2$$

▸ **Now Try Exercise 41**

INSTRUCTOR EXAMPLE
Factor $x^2 - 2x - 63$.
Ans.: $(x - 9)(x + 7)$

EXAMPLE 8 ▸ Factor $x^2 - 11x - 60$.

Solution   We must find two numbers whose product is -60 and whose sum is -11. Since the constant is negative, one number must be positive and the other negative. The desired numbers are -15 and 4 because $(-15)(4) = -60$ and $-15 + 4 = -11$.

$$x^2 - 11x - 60 = (x - 15)(x + 4)$$

▸ **Now Try Exercise 47**

INSTRUCTOR EXAMPLE
Factor $x^2 + 10x + 20$.
Ans.: Prime

EXAMPLE 9 ▸ Factor $x^2 + 5x + 12$.

Solution   Let's first find the two numbers whose product is 12 and whose sum is 5. Since both the constant and the coefficient of the x-term are positive, the two numbers must also be positive.

Factors of 12	Sum of Factors
$(1)(12)$	$1 + 12 = 13$
$(2)(6)$	$2 + 6 = 8$
$(3)(4)$	$3 + 4 = 7$

Note that there are no two integers whose product is 12 and whose sum is 5. When two integers cannot be found to satisfy the given conditions, the trinomial cannot be factored using only integer factors. *A polynomial that cannot be factored using only integer coefficients is called a* **prime polynomial**. If you come across a polynomial that cannot be factored using only integer coefficients, as in Example 9, do not leave the answer blank. Instead, write *prime*. However, before you write the answer *prime*, recheck your work and make sure you have tried every possible combination.

▸ **Now Try Exercise 31**

When factoring a trinomial of the form $x^2 + bx + c$, there is at most one pair of numbers whose product is c and whose sum is b. For example, when factoring

$x^2 - 12x + 32$, the two numbers whose product is 32 and whose sum is -12 are -4 and -8. No other pair of numbers will satisfy these specific conditions. Thus, the only factors of $x^2 - 12x + 32$ are $(x - 4)$ and $(x - 8)$.

In Examples 10 and 11, we will factor trinomials of the form $x^2 + bxy + cy^2$, where b and c are real numbers. An example of a trinomial in this form is $x^2 - 2xy - 15y^2$. When factoring trinomials of this form, the last terms in both factors must contain a y-term in order for the product of the last terms of the factors to give a y^2-term. That is, the factors must be of the form as follows.

$$x^2 + bxy + cy^2 = (x + \blacksquare y)(x + \blacksquare y)$$

Numbers go here.

When finding the factors of $x^2 + bxy + cy^2$, we look for two numbers whose product is c and whose sum is b, just as we did when we factored trinomials of the form $x^2 + bx + c$. When we determine the numbers, we place the numbers in the shaded areas of the factors.

EXAMPLE 10 ▶ Factor $x^2 + 2xy + y^2$.

Solution In this problem, the second term contains two variables, x and y, and the last term is not a constant. The procedure used to factor this trinomial is similar to that outlined previously. You should realize, however, that the product of the first terms of the factors we are looking for must be x^2, and the product of the last terms of the factors must be y^2.

We must find two numbers whose product is 1 (from $1y^2$) and whose sum is 2 (from $2xy$). The two numbers are 1 and 1. Thus

$$x^2 + 2xy + y^2 = (x + 1y)(x + 1y) = (x + y)(x + y) = (x + y)^2$$

▶ **Now Try Exercise 65**

EXAMPLE 11 ▶ Factor $x^2 - 2xy - 15y^2$.

Solution Find two numbers whose product is -15 and whose sum is -2. The numbers are -5 and 3. The last terms must be $-5y$ and $3y$ to obtain $-15y^2$.

$$x^2 - 2xy - 15y^2 = (x - 5y)(x + 3y)$$

▶ **Now Try Exercise 69**

2 Remove a Common Factor from a Trinomial

Sometimes each term of a trinomial has a common factor. When this occurs, factor out the common factor first, as explained in Section 7.1. **The first step in any factoring problem is to factor out any factors common to all the terms in the polynomial. Whenever the numerical coefficient of the highest-degree term is not 1, you should check for a common factor.** After factoring out any common factor, you should factor the remaining trinomial further, if possible.

EXAMPLE 12 ▶ Factor $2x^2 + 2x - 12$.

Solution Since the numerical coefficient of the squared term is not 1, we check for a common factor. Because 2 is common to each term of the polynomial, we factor it out.

$$2x^2 + 2x - 12 = 2(x^2 + x - 6) \qquad \textit{Factor out the common factor.}$$

Now we factor the remaining trinomial $x^2 + x - 6$ into $(x + 3)(x - 2)$. Thus,

$$2x^2 + 2x - 12 = 2(x + 3)(x - 2).$$

Note that the trinomial $2x^2 + 2x - 12$ is now completely factored into *three* factors: two binomial factors, $x + 3$ and $x - 2$, and a monomial factor, 2. After 2 has been factored out, it plays no part in the factoring of the remaining trinomial.

▶ **Now Try Exercise 71**

INSTRUCTOR EXAMPLE
Factor $3m^3 + 9m^2 - 84m$.
Ans.: $3m(m + 7)(m - 4)$

EXAMPLE 13 ▶ Factor $3n^3 + 24n^2 - 60n$.

Solution   We see that $3n$ divides into each term of the polynomial and therefore is a common factor. After factoring out the $3n$, we factor the remaining trinomial.

$$3n^3 + 24n^2 - 60n = 3n(n^2 + 8n - 20) \qquad \textit{Factor out the common factor.}$$
$$= 3n(n + 10)(n - 2) \qquad \textit{Factor the remaining trinomial.}$$

▶ **Now Try Exercise 79**

EXERCISE SET 7.3
MathXL®   MyMathLab

Concept/Writing Exercises

For each trinomial, determine the signs that will appear in the binomial factors. Explain how you determined your answer.

  1. $x^2 + 92x + 960$ both +
  2. $x^2 - 500x + 4000$ both −
  3. $b^2 - 20b - 1500$ one +, one −
  4. $q^2 - 10q - 7200$ one +, one −
  5. $x^2 - 240x + 8000$ both −
  6. $x^2 + 50x + 600$ both +

Write the trinomial whose factors are listed. Explain how you determined your answer.

  7. $(x - 3)(x - 8)$ $x^2 - 11x + 24$
  8. $(x - 2y)(x + 6y)$ $x^2 + 4xy - 12y^2$
  9. $2(x - 5y)(x + y)$ $2x^2 - 8xy - 10y^2$
  10. $5(c + d)(c - d)$ $5c^2 - 5d^2$

  11. On an exam, a student factored $2x^2 - 6x + 4$ as $(2x - 4)(x - 1)$. Even though $(2x - 4)(x - 1)$ does multiply out to $2x^2 - 6x + 4$, why did his or her professor deduct points?   not completely factored

  12. On an exam, a student factored $3x^2 + 3x - 18$ as $(3x - 6)(x + 3)$. Even though $(3x - 6)(x + 3)$ does multiply out to $3x^2 + 3x - 18$, why did his or her professor deduct points?   not completely factored

  13. How can a trinomial factoring problem be checked?   Multiply factors.

  14. Explain how to determine the factors when factoring a trinomial of the form $x^2 + bx + c$.   Find the numbers whose product is c and whose sum is b. The factors are $(x + \text{one number})$ and $(x + \text{second number})$.

Practice the Skills

Factor each polynomial. If the polynomial is prime, so state.

  15. $x^2 - 7x + 10$ $(x - 5)(x - 2)$
  16. $x^2 + 8x + 15$ $(x + 5)(x + 3)$
  17. $x^2 + 6x + 8$ $(x + 2)(x + 4)$
  18. $x^2 - 3x + 2$ $(x - 2)(x - 1)$
  19. $x^2 + 5x - 24$ $(x + 8)(x - 3)$
  20. $x^2 - x - 12$ $(x - 4)(x + 3)$
  21. $x^2 + 4x - 6$ prime
  22. $y^2 - 6y + 8$ $(y - 4)(y - 2)$
  23. $y^2 - 13y + 12$ $(y - 12)(y - 1)$
  24. $x^2 + 3x - 54$ $(x + 9)(x - 6)$
  25. $a^2 - 2a - 8$ $(a - 4)(a + 2)$
  26. $p^2 + 3p - 10$ $(p + 5)(p - 2)$
  27. $r^2 - 2r - 15$ $(r - 5)(r + 3)$
  28. $x^2 - 6x + 8$ $(x - 4)(x - 2)$
  29. $b^2 - 11b + 18$ $(b - 9)(b - 2)$
  30. $x^2 + 11x - 30$ prime
  31. $x^2 - 8x - 15$ prime
  32. $x^2 - 8x + 7$ $(x - 7)(x - 1)$
  33. $q^2 + 4q - 45$ $(q + 9)(q - 5)$
  34. $x^2 + 10x + 25$ $(x + 5)^2$
  35. $x^2 - 7x - 30$ $(x - 10)(x + 3)$
  36. $b^2 - 9b - 36$ $(b - 12)(b + 3)$
  37. $x^2 + 4x + 4$ $(x + 2)^2$
  38. $x^2 - 4x + 4$ $(x - 2)^2$
  39. $s^2 - 8s + 16$ $(s - 4)^2$
  40. $u^2 + 2u + 1$ $(u + 1)^2$
  41. $p^2 - 12p + 36$ $(p - 6)^2$
  42. $x^2 - 10x - 25$ prime
  43. $-18w + w^2 + 45$ $(w - 15)(w - 3)$
  44. $-11x + x^2 + 10$ $(x - 10)(x - 1)$
  45. $10x - 39 + x^2$ $(x + 13)(x - 3)$
  46. $-3x + 8 + x^2$ prime
  47. $x^2 - x - 20$ $(x - 5)(x + 4)$
  48. $t^2 - 28t - 60$ $(t - 30)(t + 2)$
  49. $y^2 + 13y + 40$ $(y + 5)(y + 8)$
  50. $r^2 + 14r + 48$ $(r + 6)(r + 8)$
  51. $x^2 + 12x - 64$ $(x + 16)(x - 4)$
  52. $x^2 - 18x + 80$ $(x - 8)(x - 10)$
  53. $s^2 + 14s - 24$ prime
  54. $x^2 - 13x + 36$ $(x - 4)(x - 9)$
  55. $x^2 - 20x + 64$ $(x - 16)(x - 4)$
  56. $x^2 + 19x + 48$ $(x + 3)(x + 16)$
  57. $a^2 - 20a + 99$ $(a - 9)(a - 11)$
  58. $x^2 + 5x - 24$ $(x - 3)(x + 8)$
  59. $x^2 + 2 + 3x$ $(x + 2)(x + 1)$

60. $m^2 - 11 - 10m$ $(m + 1)(m - 11)$ **61.** $7w - 18 + w^2$ $(w + 9)(w - 2)$ **62.** $30 + y^2 - 13y$ $(y - 10)(y - 3)$

63. $x^2 - 8xy + 15y^2$ $(x - 3y)(x - 5y)$ **64.** $x^2 - 2xy + y^2$ $(x - y)^2$ **65.** $m^2 - 6mn + 9n^2$ $(m - 3n)^2$

66. $b^2 - 2bc - 3c^2$ $(b - 3c)(b + c)$ **67.** $x^2 + 8xy + 12y^2$ $(x + 6y)(x + 2y)$ **68.** $x^2 + 16xy - 17y^2$ $(x + 17y)(x - y)$

69. $m^2 - 5mn - 24n^2$ $(m + 3n)(m - 8n)$ **70.** $c^2 + 2cd - 24d^2$ $(c - 4d)(c + 6d)$

Factor completely.

71. $6x^2 - 30x + 24$ $6(x - 4)(x - 1)$ **72.** $2a^2 - 12a - 32$ $2(a - 8)(a + 2)$

73. $5x^2 + 20x + 15$ $5(x + 3)(x + 1)$ **74.** $4x^2 + 12x - 16$ $4(x + 4)(x - 1)$

75. $2x^2 - 18x + 40$ $2(x - 4)(x - 5)$ **76.** $3y^2 - 33y + 54$ $3(y - 2)(y - 9)$

77. $b^3 - 7b^2 + 10b$ $b(b - 5)(b - 2)$ **78.** $c^3 + 8c^2 - 48c$ $c(c + 12)(c - 4)$

79. $3z^3 - 21z^2 - 54z$ $3z(z - 9)(z + 2)$ **80.** $3x^3 - 36x^2 + 33x$ $3x(x - 11)(x - 1)$

81. $x^3 + 8x^2 + 16x$ $x(x + 4)^2$ **82.** $2x^3y - 12x^2y + 10xy$ $2xy(x - 5)(x - 1)$

83. $7a^2 - 35ab + 42b^2$ $7(a - 2b)(a - 3b)$ **84.** $3x^3 + 3x^2y - 18xy^2$ $3x(x + 3y)(x - 2y)$

85. $3r^3 + 6r^2t - 24rt^2$ $3r(r + 4t)(r - 2t)$ **86.** $r^2s + 7rs^2 + 12s^3$ $s(r + 3s)(r + 4s)$

87. $x^4 - 4x^3 - 21x^2$ $x^2(x - 7)(x + 3)$ **88.** $2z^5 + 14z^4 + 12z^3$ $2z^3(z + 6)(z + 1)$

Problem Solving

89. The first two columns in the following table describe the signs of the coefficient of the x-term and constant term of a trinomial of the form $x^2 + bx + c$. Determine whether the third column should contain "both positive," "both negative," or "one positive and one negative." Explain how you determined your answer.

Sign of Coefficient of x-term	Sign of Constant of Trinomial	Sign of Constant Terms in the Binomial Factors
−	+	both negative
−	−	one positive and one negative
+	−	one positive and one negative
+	+	both positive

90. Assume that a trinomial of the form $x^2 + bx + c$ is factorable. Determine whether the constant terms in the factors are "both positive," "both negative," or "one positive and one negative" for the given signs of b and c. Explain your answer.

a) $b < 0, c > 0$ both negative

b) $b > 0, c > 0$ both positive

c) $b > 0, c < 0$ one positive and one negative

d) $b < 0, c < 0$ one positive and one negative

91. Write a trinomial whose binomial factors contain constant terms that sum to -12 and have a product of 32. Show the factoring of the trinomial. $x^2 - 12x + 32 = (x - 8)(x - 4)$

92. Write a trinomial whose binomial factors contain constant terms that sum to 5 and have a product of 4. Show the factoring of the trinomial. $x^2 + 5x + 4 = (x + 1)(x + 4)$

93. Write a trinomial whose binomial factors contain constant terms that sum to -2 and have a product of -35. Show the factoring of the trinomial. $x^2 - 2x - 35 = (x - 7)(x + 5)$

94. Write a trinomial whose binomial factors contain constant terms that sum to 5 and have a product of -14. Show the factoring of the trinomial. $x^2 + 5x - 14 = (x + 7)(x - 2)$

Challenge Problems

Factor.

95. $x^2 + 0.6x + 0.08$ $(x + 0.4)(x + 0.2)$ **96.** $x^2 - 0.5x - 0.06$ $(x - 0.6)(x + 0.1)$ **97.** $x^2 + \dfrac{2}{5}x + \dfrac{1}{25}$ $\left(x + \dfrac{1}{5}\right)^2$

98. $x^2 - \dfrac{2}{7}x + \dfrac{1}{49}$ $\left(x - \dfrac{1}{7}\right)^2$ **99.** $x^2 - 24x - 256$ $(x + 8)(x - 32)$ **100.** $x^2 + 5x - 300$ $(x + 20)(x - 15)$

Cumulative Review Exercises

104. $2x^3 + x^2 - 16x + 12$ **106.** $(5x + 2)(4x - 3)$

[2.5] **101.** Solve the equation $4(2x - 4) = 5x + 11$.   9

[3.4] **102. Mixing Solutions** Karen Moreau, a chemist, mixes 4 liters of an 18% acid solution with 1 liter of a 26% acid solution. Find the strength of the mixture.   19.6%

[4.2] **103.** Graph $y = 3x - 2$.   See graphing answer section.

[6.5] **104.** Multiply $(2x^2 + 5x - 6)(x - 2)$.

[6.6] **105.** Divide $3x^2 - 10x - 10$ by $x - 4$. $3x + 2 - \dfrac{2}{x - 4}$

[7.2] **106.** Factor $20x^2 + 8x - 15x - 6$ by grouping.   See Exercise 102.

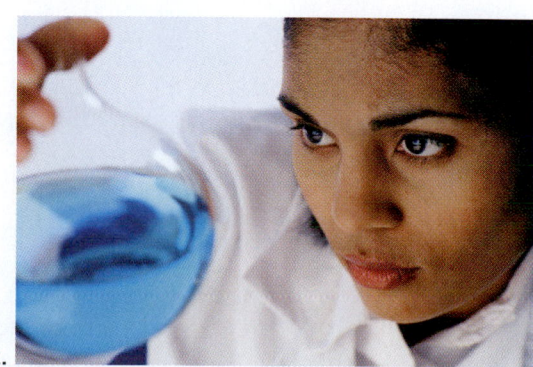

7.4 Factoring Trinomials of the Form $ax^2 + bx + c, a \neq 1$

1 Factor trinomials of the form $ax^2 + bx + c, a \neq 1$, by trial and error.

2 Factor trinomials of the form $ax^2 + bx + c, a \neq 1$, by grouping.

> **An Important Note**
>
> In this section, we discuss two methods of factoring trinomials of the form $ax^2 + bx + c, a \neq 1$. That is, we will be factoring trinomials whose squared term has a numerical coefficient not equal to 1, after removing any common factors. Examples of trinomials with $a \neq 1$ are
>
> $$2x^2 + 11x + 12 \ (a = 2) \qquad 4x^2 - 3x + 1 \ (a = 4)$$
>
> The methods we discuss are (1) **factoring by trial and error** and (2) **factoring by grouping**. We present two different methods for factoring these trinomials because some students, and some instructors, prefer one method, while others prefer the second method. You may use either method unless your instructor asks you to use a specific method. We will use the same examples to illustrate both methods so that you can make a comparison. Each method is treated independently of the other. If your teacher asks you to use a specific method, either factoring by trial and error or factoring by grouping, you need only read the material related to that specific method. Factoring by trial and error was introduced in Section 7.3 and factoring by grouping was introduced in Section 7.2.

1 Factor Trinomials of the Form $ax^2 + bx + c, a \neq 1$, by Trial and Error

Let's now discuss factoring trinomials of the form $ax^2 + bx + c, a \neq 1$, by the trial and error method, introduced in Section 7.3. It may be helpful for you to reread that material before going any further.

Recall that factoring is the reverse of multiplying. Consider the product of the following two binomials:

$$\overset{F \qquad O \qquad I \qquad L}{(2x + 3)(x + 5)} = 2x(x) + (2x)(5) + 3(x) + 3(5)$$
$$= 2x^2 + 10x + 3x + 15$$
$$= 2x^2 + 13x + 15$$

Notice that the product of the first terms of the binomials gives the x-squared term of the trinomial, $2x^2$. Also notice that the product of the last terms of the binomials gives the last term, or constant, of the trinomial, $+15$. Finally, notice that the sum of the products of the outer terms and inner terms of the binomials gives the middle term of the trinomial, $+13x$. When we factor a trinomial using trial and error, we make use of these important facts. Note that $2x^2 + 13x + 15$ in factored form is $(2x + 3)(x + 5)$.

$$2x^2 + 13x + 15 = (2x + 3)(x + 5)$$

When factoring a trinomial of the form $ax^2 + bx + c$ by trial and error, the product of the x-terms in the binomial factors must equal the first term of the trinomial, ax^2. Also, the product of the constants in the binomial factors, including their signs, must equal the constant, c, of the trinomial.

Product of constants in factors must equal c.

$$ax^2 + bx + c = (x\text{-term} + 1\text{st constant})(x\text{-term} + 2\text{nd constant})$$

Product of x-terms in factors must equal ax^2.

For example, when factoring the trinomial $2x^2 + 7x + 6$, each of the following pairs of factors has a product of the first terms equal to $2x^2$ and a product of the last terms equal to 6.

Trinomial	Possible Factors	Product of First Terms	Product of Last Terms
$2x^2 + 7x + 6$	$(2x + 1)(x + 6)$	$2x(x) = 2x^2$	$1(6) = 6$
	$(2x + 2)(x + 3)$	$2x(x) = 2x^2$	$2(3) = 6$
	$(2x + 3)(x + 2)$	$2x(x) = 2x^2$	$3(2) = 6$
	$(2x + 6)(x + 1)$	$2x(x) = 2x^2$	$6(1) = 6$

Each of these pairs of factors is a possible answer, but only one has the correct factors. How do we determine which is the correct factoring of the trinomial $2x^2 + 7x + 6$? The key lies in the x-term. We know that when we multiply two binomials using the FOIL method the sum of the products of the outer and inner terms gives us the x-term of the trinomial. We use this concept in reverse to determine the correct pair of factors. We need to find the pair of factors whose sum of the products of the outer and inner terms is equal to the x-term of the trinomial.

$$ax^2 + bx + c = (\,x\text{-term} + 1\text{st constant}\,)(\,x\text{-term} + 2\text{nd constant}\,)$$

Product of inner terms

Product of outer terms

Sum of products of outer and inner terms must equal bx.

Now look at the possible pairs of factors we obtained for $2x^2 + 7x + 6$ to see if any yield the correct x-term, $7x$.

Trinomial	Possible Factors	Product of the First Terms	Product of the Last Terms	Sum of the Products of Outer and Inner Terms
$2x^2 + 7x + 6$	$(2x + 1)(x + 6)$	$2x^2$	6	$2x(6) + 1(x) = 13x$
	$(2x + 2)(x + 3)$	$2x^2$	6	$2x(3) + 2(x) = 8x$
	$(2x + 3)(x + 2)$	$2x^2$	6	$2x(2) + 3(x) = 7x$
	$(2x + 6)(x + 1)$	$2x^2$	6	$2x(1) + 6(x) = 8x$

Since $(2x + 3)(x + 2)$ yields the correct x-term, $7x$, the factors of the trinomial $2x^2 + 7x + 6$ are $(2x + 3)$ and $(x + 2)$.

$$2x^2 + 7x + 6 = (2x + 3)(x + 2)$$

We can check this factoring using the FOIL method.

Check
$$
\begin{aligned}
(2x + 3)(x + 2) &= \overset{F}{2x(x)} + \overset{O}{2x(2)} + \overset{I}{3(x)} + \overset{L}{3(2)} \\
&= 2x^2 + 4x + 3x + 6 \\
&= 2x^2 + 7x + 6
\end{aligned}
$$

Since we obtained the original trinomial, our factoring is correct.

Note in the preceding illustration that $(2x + 1)(x + 6)$ are different factors than $(2x + 6)(x + 1)$, because in one case 1 is paired with $2x$ and in the second case 1 is paired with x. The factors $(2x + 1)(x + 6)$ and $(x + 6)(2x + 1)$ are, however, the same set of factors with their order reversed.

Helpful Hint

When factoring a trinomial of the form $ax^2 + bx + c$, remember that the sign of the constant, c, and the sign of the x-term, bx, offer valuable information. When factoring a trinomial by trial and error, first check the sign of the constant. If it is positive, the signs in both factors will be the same as the sign of the x-term. If the constant is negative, one factor will contain a plus sign and the other a negative sign.

Now we outline the procedure to factor trinomials of the form $ax^2 + bx + c, a \neq 1$, by trial and error. Keep in mind that the more you practice, the better you will become at factoring.

> **To Factor Trinomials of the Form $ax^2 + bx + c, a \neq 1$, by Trial and Error**
>
> 1. Determine whether there is a factor common to all three terms. If so, factor it out.
> 2. Write all pairs of factors of the coefficient of the squared term, a.
> 3. Write all pairs of factors of the constant term, c.
> 4. Try various combinations of these factors until the correct middle term, bx, is found.

When factoring using this procedure, if there is more than one pair of numbers whose product is a, we generally begin with the middle-size pair. We will illustrate the procedure in Examples 1 through 8.

EXAMPLE 1 ▶ Factor $3x^2 + 20x + 12$.

Solution   We first determine that all three terms have no common factors other than 1. Since the first term is $3x^2$, one factor must contain a $3x$ and the other an x. Therefore, the factors will be of the form $(3x + \blacksquare)(x + \blacksquare)$. Now we must find the numbers to place in the shaded areas. The product of the last terms in the factors must be 12. Since the constant and the coefficient of the x-term are both positive, only the positive factors of 12 need be considered. We will list the positive factors of 12, the possible factors of the trinomial, and the sum of the products of the outer and inner terms. Once we find the factors of 12 that yield the proper sum of the products of the outer and inner terms, $20x$, we can write the answer.

Factors of 12	Possible Factors of Trinomial	Sum of the Products of the Outer and Inner Terms
1(12)	$(3x + 1)(x + 12)$	$37x$
2(6)	$(3x + 2)(x + 6)$	$20x$
3(4)	$(3x + 3)(x + 4)$	$15x$
4(3)	$(3x + 4)(x + 3)$	$13x$
6(2)	$(3x + 6)(x + 2)$	$12x$
12(1)	$(3x + 12)(x + 1)$	$15x$

Since the product of $(3x + 2)$ and $(x + 6)$ yields the correct x-term, $20x$, they are the correct factors.

$$3x^2 + 20x + 12 = (3x + 2)(x + 6)$$

▶ **Now Try Exercise 5**

In Example 1, our first factor could have been written with an x and the second with a $3x$. Had we done this, we still would have obtained the correct answer: $(x + 6)(3x + 2)$. We also could have stopped once we found the pair of factors that yielded the $20x$. Instead, we listed all the factors so that you could study them.

EXAMPLE 2 ▶ Factor $5x^2 - 7x - 6$.

Solution There are no factors common to all three terms. Since the first term is $5x^2$, one factor must contain a $5x$ and the other an x. We now list the factors of -6 and look for the pair of factors that yields $-7x$.

Factors of −6	Possible Factors	Sum of the Products of the Outer and Inner Terms
$-1(6)$	$(5x - 1)(x + 6)$	$29x$
$-2(3)$	$(5x - 2)(x + 3)$	$13x$
$-3(2)$	$(5x - 3)(x + 2)$	$7x$
$-6(1)$	$(5x - 6)(x + 1)$	$-x$

Since we did not obtain the desired quantity, $-7x$, by writing the negative factor with the $5x$, we will now try listing the negative factor with the x.

Factors of −6	Possible Factors	Sum of the Products of the Outer and Inner Terms
$1(-6)$	$(5x + 1)(x - 6)$	$-29x$
$2(-3)$	$(5x + 2)(x - 3)$	$-13x$
$3(-2)$	$(5x + 3)(x - 2)$	$-7x$
$6(-1)$	$(5x + 6)(x - 1)$	x

We see that $(5x + 3)(x - 2)$ gives the $-7x$ we are looking for. Thus,

$$5x^2 - 7x - 6 = (5x + 3)(x - 2)$$

Again we listed all the possible combinations for you to study.

▶ **Now Try Exercise 9**

Helpful Hint

In Example 2, we were asked to factor $5x^2 - 7x - 6$. When we considered the product of $-3(2)$ in the first set of possible factors, we obtained

Factors of −6	Possible Factors	Sum of the Products of the Outer and Inner Terms
$-3(2)$	$(5x - 3)(x + 2)$	$7x$

Later in the solution we tried the factors $3(-2)$ and obtained the correct answer.

$3(-2)$	$(5x + 3)(x - 2)$	$-7x$

When factoring a trinomial with a *negative constant*, if you obtain the x-term whose sign is the opposite of the one you are seeking, *reverse the signs on the constants* in the factors. This should give you the set of factors you are seeking.

EXAMPLE 3 ▶ Factor $8x^2 + 33x + 4$.

Solution There are no factors common to all three terms. Since the first term is $8x^2$, there are a number of possible combinations for the first terms in the factors. Since $8 = 8 \cdot 1$ and $8 = 4 \cdot 2$, the possible factors may be of the form $(8x \quad)(x \quad)$ or $(4x \quad)(2x \quad)$. When this situation occurs, we will generally start with the middle-size pair of factors. Thus, we begin with $(4x \quad)(2x \quad)$. If this pair does not lead to the solution, we will then try $(8x\quad)(x\quad)$. We now list the factors of the constant, 4. Since all signs are positive, we list only the positive factors of 4.

Factors of 4	Possible Factors	Sum of the Products of the Outer and Inner Terms
1(4)	$(4x + 1)(2x + 4)$	$18x$
2(2)	$(4x + 2)(2x + 2)$	$12x$
4(1)	$(4x + 4)(2x + 1)$	$12x$

Since we did not obtain the correct factors with $(4x\quad)(2x\quad)$, we now try $(8x\quad)(x\quad)$.

Factors of 4	Possible Factors	Sum of the Products of the Outer and Inner Terms
1(4)	$(8x + 1)(x + 4)$	$33x$
2(2)	$(8x + 2)(x + 2)$	$18x$
4(1)	$(8x + 4)(x + 1)$	$12x$

Since the product of $(8x + 1)$ and $(x + 4)$ yields the correct x-term, $33x$, they are the correct factors.

$$8x^2 + 33x + 4 = (8x + 1)(x + 4)$$

▶ **Now Try Exercise 19**

INSTRUCTOR EXAMPLE
Factor $16x^2 - 8x + 1$.
Ans.: $(4x - 1)^2$

EXAMPLE 4 ▶ Factor $25t^2 - 10t + 1$.

Solution   The factors must be of the form $(25t\quad)(t\quad)$ or $(5t\quad)(5t\quad)$. We will start with the middle-size factors $(5t\quad)(5t\quad)$. Since the constant is positive and the coefficient of the x-term is negative, both factors must be negative.

Factors of 1	Possible Factors	Sum of the Products of the Outer and Inner Terms
$(-1)(-1)$	$(5t - 1)(5t - 1)$	$-10t$

Since we found the correct factors, we can stop.

$$25t^2 - 10t + 1 = (5t - 1)(5t - 1) = (5t - 1)^2$$

▶ **Now Try Exercise 13**

INSTRUCTOR EXAMPLE
Factor $2x^2 + 11x + 7$.
Ans.: Prime

EXAMPLE 5 ▶ Factor $2x^2 + 3x + 7$.

Solution   The factors will be of the form $(2x\quad)(x\quad)$. We need only consider the positive factors of 7. Can you explain why?

Factors of 7	Possible Factors	Sum of the Products of the Outer and Inner Terms
1(7)	$(2x + 1)(x + 7)$	$15x$
7(1)	$(2x + 7)(x + 1)$	$9x$

Since we have tried all possible combinations and we have not obtained the x-term, $3x$, this trinomial *cannot be factored using only integer factors*. As explained in Section 7.3, the trinomial $2x^2 + 3x + 7$ is a *prime polynomial*.

▶ **Now Try Exercise 17**

EXAMPLE 6 ▶ Factor $6a^2 + 19ab + 3b^2$.

Solution   This trinomial is different from the other trinomials in that the last term is not a constant but contains b^2. Don't let this scare you. The factoring process is the same, except that the second term of both factors will contain b. We begin by considering factors of the form $(3a\quad)(2a\quad)$. If we cannot find the factors, then we try factors of the form $(6a\quad)(a\quad)$.

Factors of 3	Possible Factors	Sum of the Products of the Outer and Inner Terms
1(3)	$(3a + b)(2a + 3b)$	$11ab$
3(1)	$(3a + 3b)(2a + b)$	$9ab$
1(3)	$(6a + b)(a + 3b)$	$19ab$
3(1)	$(6a + 3b)(a + b)$	$9ab$

$$6a^2 + 19ab + 3b^2 = (6a + b)(a + 3b)$$

Check $(6a + b)(a + 3b) = 6a^2 + 18ab + ab + 3b^2 = 6a^2 + 19ab + 3b^2$

▶ **Now Try Exercise 55**

EXAMPLE 7 ▶ Factor $6x^2 - 13xy - 8y^2$.

Solution   We begin with factors of the form $(3x\quad)(2x\quad)$. If we cannot find the solution from these, we will try $(6x\quad)(x\quad)$. Since the last term, $-8y^2$, is negative, one factor will contain a plus sign and the other will contain a minus sign.

Factors of −8	Possible Factors	Sum of the Products of the Outer and Inner Terms
1(−8)	$(3x + y)(2x - 8y)$	$-22xy$
2(−4)	$(3x + 2y)(2x - 4y)$	$-8xy$
4(−2)	$(3x + 4y)(2x - 2y)$	$2xy$
8(−1)	$(3x + 8y)(2x - y)$	$13xy$

We are looking for $-13xy$. When we considered 8(−1), we obtained $13xy$. As explained in the Helpful Hint on page 427, if we reverse the signs of the numbers in the factors, we will obtain the factors we are seeking.

$$(3x + 8y)(2x - y) \quad \text{Gives } 13xy$$
$$(3x - 8y)(2x + y) \quad \text{Gives } -13xy$$

Therefore, $6x^2 - 13xy - 8y^2 = (3x - 8y)(2x + y)$.

▶ **Now Try Exercise 57**

Now we will look at an example in which all the terms of the trinomial have a common factor.

EXAMPLE 8 ▶ Factor $6x^3 + 15x^2 - 36x$.

Solution   *The first step in any factoring problem is to determine whether all the terms contain a common factor. If so, factor out that common factor first.* In this example, $3x$ is common to all three terms. We begin by factoring out the $3x$. Then we continue factoring by trial and error.

$$6x^3 + 15x^2 - 36x = 3x(2x^2 + 5x - 12)$$
$$= 3x(2x - 3)(x + 4)$$

▶ **Now Try Exercise 47**

2 Factor Trinomials of the Form $ax^2 + bx + c, a \neq 1$, by Grouping

We will now discuss the use of grouping. The steps in the box that follow give the procedure for factoring trinomials by grouping.

> ### To Factor Trinomials of the Form $ax^2 + bx + c, a \neq 1$, by Grouping
>
> 1. Determine whether there is a factor common to all three terms. If so, factor it out.
> 2. Find two numbers whose product is equal to the product of a times c, and whose sum is equal to b.
> 3. Rewrite the middle term, bx, as the sum or difference of two terms using the numbers found in step 2.
> 4. Factor by grouping as explained in Section 7.2.

This process will be made clear in Example 9. We will rework Examples 1 through 8 here using factoring by grouping. Example 9, which follows, is the same trinomial given in Example 1. After you study this method and try some exercises, you will gain a feel for which method you prefer using.

EXAMPLE 9 ▶ Factor $3x^2 + 20x + 12$.

Solution First determine whether there is a factor common to all the terms of the polynomial. There are no common factors (other than 1) to the three terms.

$$a = 3 \quad b = 20 \quad c = 12$$

1. We must find two numbers whose product is $a \cdot c$ and whose sum is b. We must therefore find two numbers whose product equals $3 \cdot 12 = 36$ and whose sum equals 20. Only the positive factors of 36 need be considered since all signs of the trinomial are positive.

Factors of 36	Sum of Factors
(1)(36)	$1 + 36 = 37$
(2)(18)	$2 + 18 = 20$
(3)(12)	$3 + 12 = 15$
(4)(9)	$4 + 9 = 13$
(6)(6)	$6 + 6 = 12$

The desired factors are 2 and 18.

2. Rewrite $20x$ as the sum or difference of two terms using the values found in step 1. Therefore, we rewrite $20x$ as $2x + 18x$.

$$3x^2 + 20x + 12$$
$$= 3x^2 \; \overbrace{+ 2x + 18x} \; + 12$$

3. Now factor by grouping. Start by factoring out a common factor from the first two terms and a common factor from the last two terms. This procedure was discussed in Section 7.2.

x is common factor   *6 is common factor*

$$= 3x^2 + 2x + 18x + 12$$
$$= x(3x + 2) + 6(3x + 2)$$
$$= (3x + 2)(x + 6)$$

▶ **Now Try Exercise 7**

Note that in step 2 of Example 9 we rewrote $20x$ as $2x + 18x$. Would it have made a difference if we had written $20x$ as $18x + 2x$? Let's work it out and see.

$$3x^2 + 20x + 12$$
$$= 3x^2 \boxed{+18x + 2x} + 12$$

3x is common factor   2 is common factor

$$= 3x^2 + 18x + 2x + 12$$
$$= 3x(x + 6) + 2(x + 6)$$
$$= (x + 6)(3x + 2)$$

Since $(x + 6)(3x + 2) = (3x + 2)(x + 6)$, the factors are the same. We obtained the same answer by writing the $20x$ as either $2x + 18x$ or $18x + 2x$. *In general, when rewriting the middle term of the trinomial using the specific factors found, the terms may be listed in either order.* You should, however, check after you list the two terms to make sure that the sum of the terms you listed equals the middle term.

INSTRUCTOR EXAMPLE
Factor $3x^2 - 7x - 6$.
Ans.: $(3x + 2)(x - 3)$

EXAMPLE 10 ▶ Factor $5x^2 - 7x - 6$.

Solution   There are no common factors other than 1.

$$a = 5, \quad b = -7, \quad c = -6$$

The product of a times c is $5(-6) = -30$. We must find two numbers whose product is -30 and whose sum is -7.

Factors of -30	Sum of Factors
$(-1)(30)$	$-1 + 30 = 29$
$(-2)(15)$	$-2 + 15 = 13$
$(-3)(10)$	$-3 + 10 = 7$
$(-5)(6)$	$-5 + 6 = 1$
$(-6)(5)$	$-6 + 5 = -1$
$(-10)(3)$	$-10 + 3 = -7$
$(-15)(2)$	$-15 + 2 = -13$
$(-30)(1)$	$-30 + 1 = -29$

Rewrite the middle term of the trinomial, $-7x$, as $-10x + 3x$.

$$5x^2 - 7x - 6$$
$$= 5x^2 \boxed{-10x + 3x} - 6 \qquad \textit{Now factor by grouping.}$$
$$= 5x(x - 2) + 3(x - 2)$$
$$= (x - 2)(5x + 3)$$

▶ **Now Try Exercise 31**

In Example 10, we could have expressed the $-7x$ as $3x - 10x$ and obtained the same answer. Try working Example 10 by rewriting $-7x$ as $3x - 10x$.

Helpful Hint

Notice in Example 10 that we were looking for two factors of -30 whose sum was -7. When we considered the factors -3 and 10, we obtained a sum of 7, which is the opposite of -7. The factors we eventually obtained that gave a sum of -7 were 3 and -10. Note that when the *constant of the trinomial is negative*, if we switch the signs of the constants in the factors, the sign of the sum of the factors changes. Thus, when trying pairs of factors to obtain the middle term, if you obtain the opposite of the coefficient you are seeking, reverse the signs in the factors. This should give you the coefficient you are seeking.

In Example 10, we began factoring $5x^2 - 7x - 6$ by finding two numbers whose product equals -30 and whose sum equals -7. The graphing calculator can be used to help find those numbers.

We can represent two numbers whose product is -30 by x and $-\dfrac{30}{x}$. Notice $x\left(-\dfrac{30}{x}\right) = -30$. Let $Y_1 = -\dfrac{30}{x}$, the second factor in $x\left(-\dfrac{30}{x}\right)$. Let $Y_2 = -\dfrac{30}{x} + x$, the sum of the factors. Use the TABLE feature to create pairs of numbers whose product is -30 (the product of columns X and Y_1 is -30) and whose sum is in column Y_2 (see **Figure 7.3**). Look down the Y_2 column until you find the sum you are looking for, -7.

Use the value for X, 3, and the value for Y_1, -10, to rewrite the middle term of the trinomial, $-7x$, as $3x - 10x$. Continue factoring by grouping.

EXERCISES

Use your graphing calculator as an aid in factoring each trinomial.

1. $6x^2 - 13x - 28$ $(3x + 4)(2x - 7)$
2. $10x^2 - x - 24$ $(5x - 8)(2x + 3)$
3. $12x^2 + 16x - 35$ $(6x - 7)(2x + 5)$
4. $27x^2 + 57x + 20$ $(9x + 4)(3x + 5)$

X	Y1	Y2
1	-30	-29
2	-15	-13
3	-10	-7
4	-7.5	-3.5
5	-6	-1
6	-5	1
7	-4.286	2.7143

X=3

FIGURE 7.3

EXAMPLE 11 ▶ Factor $8x^2 + 33x + 4$.

Solution   There are no common factors other than 1. We must find two numbers whose product is $8 \cdot 4$ or 32 and whose sum is 33. The numbers are 1 and 32.

Factors of 32	Sum of Factors
(1)(32)	$1 + 32 = 33$

Rewrite $33x$ as $32x + x$. Then factor by grouping.

$$8x^2 + 33x + 4$$
$$= 8x^2 + 32x + x + 4$$
$$= 8x(x + 4) + 1(x + 4)$$
$$= (x + 4)(8x + 1)$$

▶ **Now Try Exercise 25**

Notice in Example 11 that we rewrote $33x$ as $32x + x$ rather than $x + 32x$. We did this to reinforce factoring out 1 from the last two terms of an expression. You should obtain the same answer if you rewrite $33x$ as $x + 32x$. Try this now.

EXAMPLE 12 ▶ Factor $25t^2 - 10t + 1$.

Solution   There are no common factors other than 1. We must find two numbers whose product is $25 \cdot 1$ or 25 and whose sum is -10. Since the product of a times c is positive and the coefficient of the t-term is negative, both numerical factors must be negative.

Factors of 25	Sum of Factors
$(-1)(-25)$	$-1 + (-25) = -26$
$(-5)(-5)$	$-5 + (-5) = -10$

The desired factors are -5 and -5.

$$25t^2 - 10t + 1$$
$$= 25t^2 \boxed{-5t - 5t} + 1 \qquad \textcolor{red}{\textit{Rewrite } -10t \textit{ as } -5t - 5t.}$$
$$= 5t(5t - 1) - 5t + 1$$
$$= 5t(5t - 1) - 1(5t - 1) \qquad \textcolor{red}{\textit{Rewrite } -5t + 1 \textit{ as } -1(5t - 1).}$$
$$= (5t - 1)(5t - 1) \text{ or } (5t - 1)^2$$

▸ **Now Try Exercise 29**

Helpful Hint

When attempting to factor a trinomial, if there are no two integers whose product equals $a \cdot c$ and whose sum equals b, the trinomial cannot be factored.

INSTRUCTOR EXAMPLE
Factor $3x^2 + 20x + 5$.
Ans.: Prime

EXAMPLE 13 ▸ Factor $2x^2 + 3x + 7$.

Solution   There are no common factors other than 1. We must find two numbers whose product is 14 and whose sum is 3. We need consider only positive factors of 14. Why?

Factors of 14	Sum of Factors
(1)(14)	$1 + 14 = 15$
(2)(7)	$2 + 7 = 9$

Since there are no factors of 14 whose sum is 3, we conclude that this trinomial cannot be factored. This is an example of a *prime polynomial*.

▸ **Now Try Exercise 21**

INSTRUCTOR EXAMPLE
Factor $5a^2 + 9ab + 4b^2$.
Ans.: $(5a + 4b)(a + b)$

EXAMPLE 14 ▸ Factor $6a^2 + 19ab + 3b^2$.

Solution   There are no common factors other than 1. This trinomial contains two variables. It is factored in basically the same manner as the previous examples. Find two numbers whose product is $6 \cdot 3$ or 18 and whose sum is 19. The two numbers are 18 and 1.

$$6a^2 + 19ab + 3b^2$$
$$= 6a^2 \boxed{+18ab + ab} + 3b^2$$
$$= 6a(a + 3b) + b(a + 3b)$$
$$= (a + 3b)(6a + b)$$

▸ **Now Try Exercise 61**

INSTRUCTOR EXAMPLE
Factor $6x^2 - 25xy - 9y^2$.
Ans.: $(3x + y)(2x - 9y)$

EXAMPLE 15 ▸ Factor $6x^2 - 13xy - 8y^2$.

Solution   There are no common factors other than 1. Find two numbers whose product is $6(-8)$ or -48 and whose sum is -13. Since the product is negative, one factor must be positive and the other negative. Some factors are given below.

Product of Factors	Sum of Factors
(1)(−48)	$1 + (-48) = -47$
(2)(−24)	$2 + (-24) = -22$
(3)(−16)	$3 + (-16) = -13$

There are many other factors, but we have found the pair we were looking for. The two numbers whose product is -48 and whose sum is -13 are 3 and -16.

$$6x^2 - 13xy - 8y^2$$
$$= 6x^2 \boxed{+3xy - 16xy} - 8y^2$$
$$= 3x(2x + y) - 8y(2x + y)$$
$$= (2x + y)(3x - 8y)$$

Check $(2x + y)(3x - 8y)$

$$\begin{array}{cccc} F & O & I & L \end{array}$$

$$= (2x)(3x) + (2x)(-8y) + (y)(3x) + (y)(-8y)$$

$$= \quad 6x^2 \quad - \quad 16xy \quad + \quad 3xy \quad - \quad 8y^2$$

$$= 6x^2 - 13xy - 8y^2$$

▶ **Now Try Exercise 63**

If you rework Example 15 by writing $-13xy$ as $-16xy + 3xy$, what answer would you obtain? Try it now and see.

Remember that in any factoring problem our first step is to determine whether all terms in the polynomial have a common factor other than 1. If so, we use the distributive property to factor the GCF from each term. We then continue to factor the trinomial, if possible.

EXAMPLE 16 ▶ Factor $6x^3 + 15x^2 - 36x$.

Solution   The factor $3x$ is common to all three terms. Factor the $3x$ from each term of the polynomial.

$$6x^3 + 15x^2 - 36x = 3x(2x^2 + 5x - 12)$$

Now continue by factoring $2x^2 + 5x - 12$. The two numbers whose product is $2(-12)$ or -24 and whose sum is 5 are 8 and -3.

$$2x(2x^2 + 5x - 12)$$
$$= 2x(2x^2 + 8x - 3x - 12)$$
$$= 2x[2x(x + 4) - 3(x + 4)]$$
$$= 2x(x + 4)(2x - 3)$$

▶ **Now Try Exercise 49**

Helpful Hint

Which Method Should You Use to Factor a Trinomial?

If your instructor asks you to use a specific method, you should use that method. If your instructor does not require a specific method, you should use the method you feel most comfortable with. You may wish to start with the trial-and-error method if there are only a few possible factors to try. If you cannot find the factors by trial and error or if there are many possible factors to consider, you may wish to use the grouping procedure. With time and practice you will learn which method you feel most comfortable with and which method gives you greater success.

EXERCISE SET 7.4

Concept/Writing Exercises

1. Factoring trinomials is the reverse process of multiplying binomials.

1. What is the relationship between factoring trinomials and multiplying binomials?

2. When factoring a trinomial of the form $ax^2 + bx + c$, what must be the product of the constants in the binomial factors equal?   the constant of the trinomial, c

3. When factoring a trinomial of the form $ax^2 + bx + c$, what must the product of the first terms of the binomial factors equal?   the first term of the trinomial, ax^2

4. Explain the procedure used to factor a trinomial of the form $ax^2 + bx + c, a \neq 1$.   Answers will vary.

Practice the Skills

Factor completely. If the polynomial is prime, so state.

5. $2x^2 + 11x + 5$ $(2x + 1)(x + 5)$

6. $2x^2 + 9x + 4$ $(2x + 1)(x + 4)$

7. $3x^2 + 14x + 8$ $(3x + 2)(x + 4)$

8. $7x^2 + 37x + 10$ $(7x + 2)(x + 5)$

9. $5x^2 - 9x - 2$ $(5x + 1)(x - 2)$

10. $3y^2 + 17y + 10$ $(3y + 2)(y + 5)$

11. $3r^2 + 13r - 10$ $(3r - 2)(r + 5)$

12. $3x^2 - 2x - 8$ $(3x + 4)(x - 2)$

13. $4z^2 - 12z + 9$ $(2z - 3)^2$

14. $4n^2 - 9n + 5$ $(4n - 5)(n - 1)$

15. $6z^2 + z - 12$ $(2z + 3)(3z - 4)$

16. $5m^2 - 17m + 6$ $(5m - 2)(m - 3)$

17. $5a^2 - 12a + 6$ prime

18. $2x^2 - x - 6$ $(2x + 3)(x - 2)$

19. $8x^2 + 19x + 6$ $(8x + 3)(x + 2)$

20. $6y^2 - 11y + 4$ $(3y - 4)(2y - 1)$

21. $3x^2 + 11x + 4$ prime

22. $3a^2 + 7a - 20$ $(3a - 5)(a + 4)$

23. $5y^2 - 16y + 3$ $(5y - 1)(y - 3)$

24. $5x^2 + 2x + 9$ prime

25. $7x^2 + 43x + 6$ $(7x + 1)(x + 6)$

26. $7x^2 - 8x + 1$ $(7x - 1)(x - 1)$

27. $4x^2 + 4x - 15$ $(2x + 5)(2x - 3)$

28. $15x^2 - 19x + 6$ $(5x - 3)(3x - 2)$

29. $49t^2 - 14t + 1$ $(7t - 1)^2$

30. $16z^2 - 8z + 1$ $(4z - 1)^2$

31. $5z^2 - 6z - 8$ $(5z + 4)(z - 2)$

32. $3z^2 - 11z - 6$ prime

33. $4y^2 + 5y - 6$ $(4y - 3)(y + 2)$

34. $5y^2 - 3y - 1$ prime

35. $10x^2 - 27x + 5$ $(5x - 1)(2x - 5)$

36. $6a^2 + 7a - 10$ $(6a - 5)(a + 2)$

37. $10d^2 - 7d - 12$ $(5d + 4)(2d - 3)$

38. $6x^2 + 13x + 3$ prime

39. $8x^2 - 46x - 12$ $2(4x + 1)(x - 6)$

40. $12x^2 - 13x - 35$ $(3x - 7)(4x + 5)$

41. $10t + 3 + 7t^2$ $(7t + 3)(t + 1)$

42. $n - 30 + n^2$ $(n + 6)(n - 5)$

43. $6x^2 + 16x + 10$ $2(3x + 5)(x + 1)$

44. $12z^2 + 32z + 20$ $4(3z + 5)(z + 1)$

45. $6x^3 - 5x^2 - 4x$ $x(2x + 1)(3x - 4)$

46. $8x^3 + 8x^2 - 6x$ $2x(2x - 1)(2x + 3)$

47. $12x^3 + 28x^2 + 8x$ $4x(3x + 1)(x + 2)$

48. $18x^3 - 21x^2 - 9x$ $3x(2x - 3)(3x + 1)$

49. $4x^3 - 2x^2 - 12x$ $2x(2x + 3)(x - 2)$

50. $300x^2 - 400x - 400$ $100(3x + 2)(x - 2)$

51. $48c^2 + 8c - 16$ $8(2c - 1)(3c + 2)$

52. $28x^2 - 28x + 7$ $7(2x - 1)^2$

53. $4p - 12 + 8p^2$ $4(2p + 3)(p - 1)$

54. $72 + 3r^2 - 30r$ $3(r - 4)(r - 6)$

55. $8c^2 + 41cd + 5d^2$ $(8c + d)(c + 5d)$

56. $8x^2 - 8xy - 6y^2$ $2(2x + y)(2x - 3y)$

57. $15x^2 - xy - 6y^2$ $(5x + 3y)(3x - 2y)$

58. $2x^2 - 7xy + 3y^2$ $(2x - y)(x - 3y)$

59. $12x^2 + 10xy - 8y^2$ $2(2x - y)(3x + 4y)$

60. $12a^2 - 34ab + 24b^2$ $2(3a - 4b)(2a - 3b)$

61. $7p^2 + 13pq + 6q^2$ $(7p + 6q)(p + q)$

62. $24x^2 - 92x + 80$ $4(3x - 4)(2x - 5)$

63. $6m^2 - mn - 2n^2$ $(3m - 2n)(2m + n)$

64. $8m^2 + 4mn - 4n^2$ $4(2m - n)(m + n)$

65. $8x^3 + 10x^2y + 3xy^2$ $x(4x + 3y)(2x + y)$

66. $8a^2b + 10ab^2 + 3b^3$ $b(4a + 3b)(2a + b)$

67. $4x^4 + 8x^3y + 3x^2y^2$ $x^2(2x + y)(2x + 3y)$

68. $26u^2v + 6uv^2 + 24u^3$ $2u(3u + v)(4u + 3v)$

Problem Solving

For Exercises 69–74, write the polynomial whose factors are listed. Explain how you determined your answer.

69. $3x + 1, x - 7$ $3x^2 - 20x - 7$

70. $6y - 5, 4y - 3$ $24y^2 - 38y + 15$

71. $5, x + 3, 2x + 1$ $10x^2 + 35x + 15$

72. $3, 2x + 3, x - 4$ $6x^2 - 15x - 36$

73. $t^2, t + 4, 3t - 1$ $3t^4 + 11t^3 - 4t^2$

74. $5x^2, 3x - 7, 2x + 3$ $30x^4 - 25x^3 - 105x^2$

75. a) Trinomial divided by binomial is second factor.

75. a) If you know one binomial factor of a trinomial, explain how you can use division to find the second binomial factor of the trinomial (see Section 6.6).

b) One factor of $18x^2 + 93x + 110$ is $3x + 10$. Use division to find the second factor. $6x + 11$

76. One factor of $30x^2 - 17x - 247$ is $6x - 19$. Find the other factor. $5x + 13$

Challenge Problems

Factor each trinomial.

77. $18x^2 + 9x - 20$ $(6x - 5)(3x + 4)$

78. $9p^2 - 104p + 55$ $(9p - 5)(p - 11)$

79. $15x^2 - 124x + 160$ $(5x - 8)(3x - 20)$

80. $16x^2 - 62x - 45$ $(8x + 5)(2x - 9)$

81. $105a^2 - 220a - 160$ $5(3a - 8)(7a + 4)$

82. $72x^2 + 417x - 420$ $3(8x - 7)(3x + 20)$

83. Two factors of $6x^3 + 235x^2 + 2250x$ are x and $3x + 50$, determine the other factor. Explain how you determined your answer. $2x + 45$

84. Two factors of the polynomial $2x^3 + 11x^2 + 3x - 36$ are $x + 3$ and $2x - 3$. Determine the third factor. Explain how you determined your answer. $x + 4$

Cumulative Review Exercises

[1.9] **85.** Evaluate $-x^2 - 4(y + 3) + 2y^2$ when $x = -3$ and $y = -5$.   49

[2.6] **86.** **Daytona 500** Jimmie Johnson won the 2006 Daytona 500 in a time of about 3.56 hours. If the race covered 507.5 miles, find the average speed of Johnson's car. ≈ 142.56 mph

[7.1] **87.** Factor $36x^4y^3 - 12xy^2 + 24x^5y^6$. $12xy^2(3x^3y - 1 + 2x^4y^4)$

[7.3] **88.** Factor $b^2 + 4b - 96$. $(b + 12)(b - 8)$

See Exercise 86.

Mid-Chapter Test: 7.1–7.4

1. by multiplying the factors

To find out how well you understand the chapter material to this point, take this brief test. The answers, and the section where the material was initially discussed, are given in the back of the book. Review any questions that you answered incorrectly.

1. How may any factoring problem be checked?

2. Determine the greatest common factor of $18xy^2$, $27x^3y^4$, and $12x^2y^3$. $3xy^2$

In Exercises 3–5, factor the GCF from each term in the expression.

3. $4a^2b^3 - 24a^3b$ $4a^2b(b^2 - 6a)$

4. $5c(d - 6) - 3(d - 6)$ $(d - 6)(5c - 3)$

5. $7x(2x + 9) + 2x + 9$ $(2x + 9)(7x + 1)$

In Exercises 6–10, factor by grouping.

6. $x^2 + 4x + 7x + 28$ $(x + 4)(x + 7)$

7. $x^2 + 5x - 3x - 15$ $(x + 5)(x - 3)$

8. $6a^2 + 15ab - 2ab - 5b^2$ $(2a + 5b)(3a - b)$

9. $5x^2 - 2xy - 45x + 18y$ $(5x - 2y)(x - 9)$

10. $8x^3 + 4x^2 - 48x^2 - 24x$ $4x(2x + 1)(x - 6)$

In Exercises 11–20, factor each polynomial completely. If the polynomial is prime, so state.

11. $x^2 - 10x + 21$ $(x - 3)(x - 7)$

12. $t^2 + 9t + 20$ $(t + 4)(t + 5)$

13. $p^2 - 3p - 8$ prime

14. $x^2 + 16x + 64$ $(x + 8)^2$

15. $m^2 - 4mn - 45n^2$ $(m + 5n)(m - 9n)$

16. $3x^2 + 17x + 10$ $(3x + 2)(x + 5)$

17. $4z^2 - 11z + 6$ $(4z - 3)(z - 2)$

18. $3y^2 + 13y + 6$ prime

19. $9x^2 - 6x + 1$ $(3x - 1)^2$

20. $6a^2 + 3ab - 3b^2$ $3(2a - b)(a + b)$

7.5 Special Factoring Formulas and a General Review of Factoring

1 Factor the difference of two squares.

2 Factor the sum and difference of two cubes.

3 Learn the general procedure for factoring a polynomial.

TEACHING TIP
Before beginning this section, have students describe each of the following expressions in words.
a) $r^2 - s^2$ **b)** $a^3 + b^3$ **c)** $x^3 - y^3$

There are special formulas for certain types of factoring problems that are often used. The special formulas we focus on in this section are the *difference of two squares, the sum of two cubes, and the difference of two cubes.* There is no special formula for the sum of two squares; this is because the sum of two squares cannot be factored using the set of real numbers. *You will need to memorize the three highlighted formulas in this section* so that you can use them whenever you need them.

1 Factor the Difference of Two Squares

Let's begin with the difference of two squares. Consider the binomial $x^2 - 9$. Note that each term of the binomial can be expressed as the square of some expression.

$$x^2 - 9 = x^2 - 3^2$$

This is an example of a **difference of two squares**. To factor the difference of two squares, it is convenient to use the difference of two squares formula (which was introduced in Section 6.5).

Difference of Two Squares

$$a^2 - b^2 = (a + b)(a - b)$$

EXAMPLE 1 ▶ Factor $x^2 - 9$.

Solution   If we write $x^2 - 9$ as a difference of two squares, we have $(x)^2 - (3)^2$. Using the difference of two squares formula, where a is replaced by x and b is replaced by 3, we obtain the following:

$$a^2 - b^2 = (a + b)(a - b)$$
$$x^2 - 9 = (x)^2 - (3)^2 = (x + 3)(x - 3)$$

Thus, $x^2 - 9 = (x + 3)(x - 3)$.

▶ **Now Try Exercise 13**

EXAMPLE 2 ▶ Factor using the difference of two squares formula.

a) $x^2 - 16$ **b)** $25x^2 - 4$ **c)** $36x^2 - 49y^2$

Solution

a) $x^2 - 16 = (x)^2 - (4)^2$
$$= (x + 4)(x - 4)$$
b) $25x^2 - 4 = (5x)^2 - (2)^2$
$$= (5x + 2)(5x - 2)$$
c) $36x^2 - 49y^2 = (6x)^2 - (7y)^2$
$$= (6x + 7y)(6x - 7y)$$

▶ **Now Try Exercise 21**

EXAMPLE 3 ▶ Factor each difference of two squares.

a) $16x^4 - 9y^4$ **b)** $x^6 - y^4$

Solution

a) Rewrite $16x^4$ as $(4x^2)^2$ and $9y^4$ as $(3y^2)^2$, then use the difference of two squares formula.

$$16x^4 - 9y^4 = (4x^2)^2 - (3y^2)^2$$
$$= (4x^2 + 3y^2)(4x^2 - 3y^2)$$

b) Rewrite x^6 as $(x^3)^2$ and y^4 as $(y^2)^2$, then use the difference of two squares formula.

$$x^6 - y^4 = (x^3)^2 - (y^2)^2$$
$$= (x^3 + y^2)(x^3 - y^2)$$

▶ **Now Try Exercise 29**

EXAMPLE 4 ▶ Factor $9x^2 - 36y^2$ using the difference of two squares formula.

Solution   First factor out the common factor, 9.

$$9x^2 - 36y^2 = 9(x^2 - 4y^2)$$

Now use the formula for the difference of two squares.

$$9(x^2 - 4y^2) = 9[(x)^2 - (2y)^2]$$
$$= 9(x + 2y)(x - 2y)$$

▶ **Now Try Exercise 23**

Notice in Example 4 that $9x^2 - 36y^2$ is the difference of two squares, $(3x)^2 - (6y)^2$. If you factor this difference of squares without first factoring out the common factor 9, the factoring may be more difficult. After you factor this difference of squares you will need to factor out the common factor 3 from each binomial factor, as illustrated below.

$$9x^2 - 36y^2 = (3x)^2 - (6y)^2$$
$$= (3x + 6y)(3x - 6y)$$
$$= 3(x + 2y)3(x - 2y)$$
$$= 9(x + 2y)(x - 2y)$$

We obtain the same answer as we did in Example 4. However, since we did not factor out the common factor 9 first, we had to work a little harder to obtain the answer.

INSTRUCTOR EXAMPLE
Factor $p^4 - 1$ using the difference of two squares formula.
Ans.: $(p^2 + 1)(p + 1)(p - 1)$

EXAMPLE 5 ▶ Factor $z^4 - 16$ using the difference of two squares formula.

Solution We rewrite z^4 as $(z^2)^2$ and 16 as $(4)^2$, then use the difference of two squares formula.

$$z^4 - 16 = (z^2)^2 - (4)^2$$
$$= (z^2 + 4)(z^2 - 4)$$

Notice that the second factor, $z^2 - 4$, is also the difference of two squares. To complete the factoring, we use the difference of two squares formula again to factor $z^2 - 4$.

$$= (z^2 + 4)(z^2 - 4)$$
$$= (z^2 + 4)(z + 2)(z - 2)$$

▶ **Now Try Exercise 35**

Avoiding Common Errors

The difference of two squares can be factored. However, a sum of two squares, where there is no common factor to the two terms, cannot be factored using real numbers.

CORRECT	INCORRECT
$a^2 - b^2 = (a + b)(a - b)$	~~$a^2 + b^2 = (a + b)(a + b)$~~

---

2 Factor the Sum and Difference of Two Cubes

We begin our discussion of the sum and difference of two cubes with a multiplication of polynomials problem. Consider the product of $(a + b)(a^2 - ab + b^2)$.

$$
\begin{array}{r}
a^2 \quad - ab \ + b^2 \\
a \ + b \\
\hline
a^2b - ab^2 + b^3 \qquad \leftarrow b(a^2 - ab + b^2) \\
a^3 - a^2b + ab^2 \qquad\qquad \leftarrow a(a^2 - ab + b^2) \\
\hline
a^3 \qquad\qquad\qquad + b^3 \qquad \leftarrow \textit{Sum of terms}
\end{array}
$$

Thus, $(a + b)(a^2 - ab + b^2) = a^3 + b^3$. Since factoring is the opposite of multiplying, we may factor $a^3 + b^3$ as follows:

$$a^3 + b^3 = (a + b)(a^2 - ab + b^2)$$

We see, using the same procedure, that $a^3 - b^3 = (a - b)(a^2 + ab + b^2)$. The expression $a^3 + b^3$ is a sum of two cubes and the expression $a^3 - b^3$ is a difference of two cubes. The formulas for factoring **the sum and the difference of two cubes** follow.

Sum of Two Cubes

$$a^3 + b^3 = (a + b)(a^2 - ab + b^2)$$

Difference of Two Cubes

$$a^3 - b^3 = (a - b)(a^2 + ab + b^2)$$

Note that the trinomials $a^2 - ab + b^2$ and $a^2 + ab + b^2$ cannot be factored further. Now let's solve some factoring problems using the sum and the difference of two cubes.

INSTRUCTOR EXAMPLE
Factor $x^3 + 125$.
Ans.: $(x + 5)(x^2 - 5x + 25)$

EXAMPLE 6 ▶ Factor $x^3 + 8$.

Solution   We rewrite $x^3 + 8$ as a sum of two cubes: $x^3 + 8 = (x)^3 + (2)^3$. Using the sum of two cubes formula, if we let a correspond to x and b correspond to 2, we get

$$a^3 + b^3 = (a + b)(a^2 - a \cdot b + b^2)$$
$$x^3 + 8 = (x)^3 + (2)^3 = (x + 2)[x^2 - x \cdot 2 + 2^2]$$
$$= (x + 2)(x^2 - 2x + 4)$$

You can check the factoring by multiplying $(x + 2)(x^2 - 2x + 4)$. If factored correctly, the product of the factors will equal the original expression, $x^3 + 8$. Try it and see.

▶ **Now Try Exercise 41**

Helpful Hint

When factoring the sum or difference of two cubes remember that the sign between the terms in the *binomial factor* will be the same as the sign between the terms of the expression you are factoring. Furthermore, the sign of the ab term will be the opposite of the sign between the terms of the binomial factor. The last term in the trinomial factor will always be positive. Consider

$$a^3 + b^3 = (a + b)(a^2 - ab + b^2)$$

same sign · opposite sign · always positive

$$a^3 - b^3 = (a - b)(a^2 + ab + b^2)$$

same sign · opposite sign · always positive

INSTRUCTOR EXAMPLE
Factor $z^3 - 216$.
Ans.: $(z - 6)(z^2 + 6z + 36)$

EXAMPLE 7 ▶ Factor $y^3 - 125$.

Solution   We rewrite $y^3 - 125$ as a difference of two cubes: $(y)^3 - (5)^3$. Using the difference of two cubes formula, if we let a correspond to y and b correspond to 5, we get

$$a^3 - b^3 = (a - b)(a^2 + a \cdot b + b^2)$$
$$y^3 - 125 = (y)^3 - (5)^3 = (y - 5)[y^2 + y \cdot 5 + 5^2]$$
$$= (y - 5)(y^2 + 5y + 25)$$

▶ **Now Try Exercise 43**

TEACHING TIP
Have students work by themselves or in pairs to verify the formula for the difference of two cubes.

EXAMPLE 8 ▶ Factor $64a^3 - b^3$.

Solution   We rewrite $64a^3 - b^3$ as a difference of two cubes. Since $(4a)^3 = 64a^3$, we write

$$64a^3 - b^3 = (4a)^3 - (b)^3$$

$$= (4a - b)[(4a)^2 + (4a)(b) + b^2]$$

$$= (4a - b)(16a^2 + 4ab + b^2)$$

▶ **Now Try Exercise 49**

EXAMPLE 9 ▶ Factor $8r^3 + 27s^3$.

Solution   We rewrite $8r^3 + 27s^3$ as a sum of two cubes. Since $8r^3 = (2r)^3$ and $27s^3 = (3s)^3$, we write

$$8r^3 + 27s^3 = (2r)^3 + (3s)^3$$

$$= (2r + 3s)[(2r)^2 - (2r)(3s) + (3s)^2]$$

$$= (2r + 3s)(4r^2 - 6rs + 9s^2)$$

▶ **Now Try Exercise 53**

Avoiding Common Errors

Recall that $a^2 + b^2 \neq (a + b)^2$ and $a^2 - b^2 \neq (a - b)^2$. The same principle applies to the sum and difference of two cubes.

CORRECT	INCORRECT
$a^3 + b^3 = (a + b)(a^2 - ab + b^2)$	$a^3 + b^3 = (a + b)^3$
$a^3 - b^3 = (a - b)(a^2 + ab + b^2)$	$a^3 - b^3 = (a - b)^3$

Since $(a + b)^3 = (a + b)(a + b)(a + b)$, it cannot possibly equal $a^3 + b^3$. Also, since $(a - b)^3 = (a - b)(a - b)(a - b)$, it cannot possibly equal $a^3 - b^3$. At this point, we suggest you determine the products of $(a + b)(a + b)(a + b)$ and $(a - b)(a - b)(a - b)$.

It may be easier to see that, for example, $a^3 + b^3 = (a + b)(a^2 - ab + b^2)$ and not $(a + b)^3$ by substituting numbers for a and b. Suppose $a = 3$ and $b = 4$, then

$$3^3 + 4^3 = (3 + 4)[3^2 - 3(4) + 4^2]$$

$$27 + 64 = 7(13)$$

$$91 = 91$$

$$\text{but}\quad 3^3 + 4^3 \neq (3 + 4)^3$$

$$91 \neq 343$$

---

3 Learn the General Procedure for Factoring a Polynomial

In this chapter, we have presented several methods of factoring. We now combine techniques from this and previous sections to give you an overview of a general factoring procedure.

Here is a general procedure for factoring any polynomial:

> ### General Procedure for Factoring a Polynomial
>
> 1. If all the terms of the polynomial have a greatest common factor other than 1, factor it out.
>
> 2. If the polynomial has two terms (or is a binomial), determine whether it is a difference of two squares or a sum or a difference of two cubes. If so, factor using the appropriate formula.
>
> 3. If the polynomial has three terms, factor the trinomial using the methods discussed in Sections 7.3 and 7.4.
>
> 4. If the polynomial has more than three terms, try factoring by grouping.
>
> 5. As a final step, examine your factored polynomial to determine whether the terms in any factors have a common factor. If you find a common factor, factor it out at this point.

INSTRUCTOR EXAMPLE
Factor $5x^4 - 405x^2$.
Ans.: $5x^2(x + 9)(x - 9)$

EXAMPLE 10 ▶ Factor $3x^4 - 27x^2$.

Solution First determine whether the terms have a greatest common factor other than 1. Since $3x^2$ is common to both terms, factor it out.

$$3x^4 - 27x^2 = 3x^2(x^2 - 9)$$
$$= 3x^2(x + 3)(x - 3)$$

Note that $x^2 - 9$ is a difference of two squares.

▶ **Now Try Exercise 69**

INSTRUCTOR EXAMPLE
Factor $3p^2q^2 + 12p^2q - 36p^2$.
Ans.: $3p^2(q + 6)(q - 2)$

EXAMPLE 11 ▶ Factor $2m^2n^2 + 6m^2n - 36m^2$.

Solution Begin by factoring the GCF, $2m^2$, from each term. Then factor the remaining trinomial.

$$2m^2n^2 + 6m^2n - 36m^2 = 2m^2(n^2 + 3n - 18)$$
$$= 2m^2(n + 6)(n - 3)$$

▶ **Now Try Exercise 81**

INSTRUCTOR EXAMPLE
Factor $3t^3r^2 - 12tr^2 + 15r^2$.
Ans.: $3r^2(t^3 - 4t + 5)$

EXAMPLE 12 ▶ Factor $15c^2d - 10cd + 20d$.

Solution

$$15c^2d - 10cd + 20d = 5d(3c^2 - 2c + 4)$$

Since $3c^2 - 2c + 4$ cannot be factored, we stop here.

▶ **Now Try Exercise 77**

INSTRUCTOR EXAMPLE
Factor $5rt + 5r - 15t - 15$.
Ans.: $5(t + 1)(r - 3)$

EXAMPLE 13 ▶ Factor $3xy + 6x + 3y + 6$.

Solution Always begin by determining whether all the terms in the polynomial have a common factor. In this example, 3 is the GCF. Factor 3 from each term.

$$3xy + 6x + 3y + 6 = 3(xy + 2x + y + 2)$$

Now factor by grouping.

$$= 3[x(y + 2) + 1(y + 2)]$$
$$= 3(y + 2)(x + 1)$$

▶ **Now Try Exercise 79**

In Example 13, what would happen if we forgot to factor out the common factor 3? Let's rework the problem without first factoring out the 3, and see what happens. Factor $3x$ from the first two terms, and 3 from the last two terms.

$$3xy + 6x + 3y + 6 = 3x(y + 2) + 3(y + 2)$$
$$= (y + 2)(3x + 3)$$

In step 5 of the general factoring procedure on page 441, we are reminded to examine the factored polynomial to see whether the terms in any factor have a common factor. If we study the factors, we see that the factor $3x + 3$ has a common factor of 3. If we factor out the 3 from $3x + 3$ we will obtain the same answer obtained in Example 13.

$$(y + 2)(3x + 3) = 3(y + 2)(x + 1)$$

INSTRUCTOR EXAMPLE
Factor $45x^2 - 45x - 50$.
Ans.: $5(3x + 2)(3x - 5)$

EXAMPLE 14 ▶ Factor $12x^2 + 12x - 9$.

Solution   First factor out the common factor, 3. Then factor the remaining trinomial by one of the methods discussed in Section 5.4 (either by grouping or trial and error).

$$12x^2 + 12x - 9 = 3(4x^2 + 4x - 3)$$
$$= 3(2x + 3)(2x - 1)$$

▶ **Now Try Exercise 59**

INSTRUCTOR EXAMPLE
Factor $3m^4n + 192mn$.
Ans.: $3mn(m + 4)(m^2 - 4m + 16)$

EXAMPLE 15 ▶ Factor $2x^4y + 54xy$.

Solution   First factor out the common factor, $2xy$.

$$2x^4y + 54xy = 2xy(x^3 + 27)$$
$$= 2xy(x + 3)(x^2 - 3x + 9)$$

Note that $x^3 + 27$ is a sum of two cubes.

▶ **Now Try Exercise 95**

EXERCISE SET 7.5   MathXL®   MyMathLab

Concept/Writing Exercises   1. b), 2. b), 3. b) Answers will vary.

1. **a)** Write the formula for factoring the difference of two squares. $a^2 - b^2 = (a + b)(a - b)$
   b) Explain how to factor the difference of two squares.

2. **a)** Write the formula for factoring the difference of two cubes. $a^3 - b^3 = (a - b)(a^2 + ab + b^2)$
   b) Explain how to factor the difference of two cubes.

3. **a)** Write the formula for factoring the sum of two cubes. $a^3 + b^3 = (a + b)(a^2 - ab + b^2)$

4. Why is it important to memorize the special factoring formulas?   to be able to use them whenever needed

5. Is there a special formula for factoring the sum of two squares?   no

6. Describe the general procedure for factoring a polynomial.   Answers will vary.

In Exercises 7–12, the binomial is a sum of squares. There is no formula for factoring the sum of squares. However, sometimes a common factor can be factored out from a sum of squares. Factor those polynomials that are factorable. If the polynomial is not factorable, write the word prime.

7. $x^2 + 9$ prime

8. $4y^2 + 1$ prime

9. $3b^2 + 48$ $3(b^2 + 16)$

10. $16s^2 + 64t^2$ $16(s^2 + 4t^2)$

11. $16m^2 + 36n^2$ $4(4m^2 + 9n^2)$

12. $9y^2 + 16z^2$ prime

Practice the Skills

Factor each difference of two squares.

13. $y^2 - 25$ $(y + 5)(y - 5)$

14. $x^2 - 4$ $(x + 2)(x - 2)$

15. $81 - z^2$ $(9 + z)(9 - z)$

16. $64 - z^2$ $(8 + z)(8 - z)$

17. $x^2 - 49$ $(x + 7)(x - 7)$

18. $c^2 - d^2$ $(c + d)(c - d)$

19. $x^2 - y^2$ $(x + y)(x - y)$

20. $16x^2 - 9$ $(4x + 3)(4x - 3)$

21. $9y^2 - 25z^2$ $(3y + 5z)(3y - 5z)$

22. $64z^2 - 9$ $(8z + 3)(8z - 3)$ **23.** $64a^2 - 36b^2$ $4(4a + 3b)(4a - 3b)$ **24.** $100x^2 - 81y^2$ $(10x + 9y)(10x - 9y)$

25. $36 - 49x^2$ $(6 + 7x)(6 - 7x)$ **26.** $100 - y^4$ $(10 + y^2)(10 - y^2)$ **27.** $z^4 - 81x^2$ $(z^2 + 9x)(z^2 - 9x)$

28. $9x^4 - 81y^2$ $9(x^2 + 3y)(x^2 - 3y)$ **29.** $25x^4 - 49y^4$ $(5x^2 + 7y^2)(5x^2 - 7y^2)$ **30.** $4x^4 - 25y^4$ $(2x^2 + 5y^2)(2x^2 - 5y^2)$

31. $36m^4 - 49n^2$ $(6m^2 + 7n)(6m^2 - 7n)$ **32.** $10x^2 - 160$ $10(x + 4)(x - 4)$ **33.** $2x^4 - 50y^2$ $2(x^2 + 5y)(x^2 - 5y)$

34. $4x^3 - xy^2$ $x(2x + y)(2x - y)$ **35.** $x^4 - 81$ $(x^2 + 9)(x + 3)(x - 3)$ **36.** $36x^4 - 4y^2$ $4(3x^2 + y)(3x^2 - y)$

Factor each sum or difference of two cubes.

37. $x^3 + y^3$ $(x + y)(x^2 - xy + y^2)$ **38.** $a^3 - b^3$ $(a - b)(a^2 + ab + b^2)$ **39.** $x^3 - y^3$ $(x - y)(x^2 + xy + y^2)$

40. $a^3 + b^3$ $(a + b)(a^2 - ab + b^2)$ **41.** $x^3 + 64$ $(x + 4)(x^2 - 4x + 16)$ **42.** $x^3 - 8$ $(x - 2)(x^2 + 2x + 4)$

43. $x^3 - 27$ $(x - 3)(x^2 + 3x + 9)$ **44.** $a^3 + 27$ $(a + 3)(a^2 - 3a + 9)$ **45.** $a^3 + 1$ $(a + 1)(a^2 - a + 1)$

46. $t^3 - 1$ $(t - 1)(t^2 + t + 1)$ **47.** $27x^3 - 1$ $(3x - 1)(9x^2 + 3x + 1)$ **48.** $64y^3 + 125$ $(4y + 5)(16y^2 - 20y + 25)$

49. $27a^3 - 125$ $(3a - 5)(9a^2 + 15a + 25)$ **50.** $125 + x^3$ $(5 + x)(25 - 5x + x^2)$ **51.** $27 - 8y^3$ $(3 - 2y)(9 + 6y + 4y^2)$

52. $8 + 27y^3$ $(2 + 3y)(4 - 6y + 9y^2)$ **53.** $64m^3 + 27n^3$ **54.** $64x^3 - 125y^3$

55. $8a^3 - 27b^3$ $(2a - 3b)(4a^2 + 6ab + 9b^2)$ **56.** $27c^3 + 125d^3$ $(3c + 5d)(9c^2 - 15cd + 25d^2)$

Factor completely.

57. $4x^2 - 24x + 36$ $4(x - 3)^2$ **58.** $3x^2 - 9x - 12$ $3(x + 1)(x - 4)$ **59.** $50x^2 - 10x - 12$ $2(5x + 2)(5x - 3)$

60. $3x^2 - 48$ $3(x + 4)(x - 4)$ **61.** $2d^2 + 16d + 32$ $2(d + 4)^2$ **62.** $3x^2 + 9x + 12x + 36$ $3(x + 4)(x + 3)$

63. $5x^2 - 10x - 15$ $5(x - 3)(x + 1)$ **64.** $3xy - 6x + 9y - 18$ $3(x + 3)(y - 2)$ **65.** $5x^2 - 20$ $5(x + 2)(x - 2)$

66. $x^2y + 2xy - 6xy - 12y$ **67.** $2x^2 - 50$ $2(x + 5)(x - 5)$ **68.** $4a^2y - 64y^3$ $4y(a + 4y)(a - 4y)$

69. $2x^2y - 18y$ $2y(x + 3)(x - 3)$ **70.** $3x^3 - 147x$ $3x(x + 7)(x - 7)$ **71.** $3x^3y^2 + 3y^2$ $3y^2(x + 1)(x^2 - x + 1)$

72. $x^4 - 125x$ $x(x - 5)(x^2 + 5x + 25)$ **73.** $2x^3 - 16$ $2(x - 2)(x^2 + 2x + 4)$ **74.** $x^3 - 27y^3$ $(x - 3y)(x^2 + 3xy + 9y^2)$

75. $18x^2 - 50$ $2(3x + 5)(3x - 5)$ **76.** $54a^3 - 16$ $2(3a - 2)(9a^2 + 6a + 4)$ **77.** $6t^2r - 15tr + 21r$ $3r(2t^2 - 5t + 7)$

78. $12n^2 + 4n - 16$ $4(3n + 4)(n - 1)$ **79.** $6x^2 - 4x + 24x - 16$ $2(3x - 2)(x + 4)$ **80.** $4ab^2 + 4ab - 24a$ $4a(b + 3)(b - 2)$

81. $2rs^2 - 10rs - 48r$ $2r(s + 3)(s - 8)$ **82.** $4x^4 - 26x^3 + 30x^2$ **83.** $4x^2 + 5x - 6$ $(x + 2)(4x - 3)$

84. $12a^2 + 36a + 27$ $3(2a + 3)^2$ **85.** $25b^2 - 100$ $25(b + 2)(b - 2)$ **86.** $3b^2 - 75c^2$ $3(b + 5c)(b - 5c)$

87. $a^5b^2 - 4a^3b^4$ $a^3b^2(a + 2b)(a - 2b)$ **88.** $12x^2 + 36x - 3x - 9$ $3(x + 3)(4x - 1)$ **89.** $5x^4 + 10x^3 + 5x^2$ $5x^2(x + 1)^2$

90. $3c^6 + 12c^4d^2$ $3c^4(c^2 + 4d^2)$ **91.** $x^3 + 25x$ $x(x^2 + 25)$ **92.** $8y^2 - 23y - 3$ $(8y + 1)(y - 3)$

93. $y^4 - 16$ $(y^2 + 4)(y + 2)(y - 2)$ **94.** $36a^2 - 15ab - 6b^2$ **95.** $16m^3 + 250$

96. $2ab - 3b + 4a - 6$ $(2a - 3)(b + 2)$ **97.** $ac + 2a + bc + 2b$ $(a + b)(c + 2)$ **98.** $x^3 - 100x$ $x(x + 10)(x - 10)$

99. $9 - 9y^4$ $9(1 + y^2)(1 + y)(1 - y)$ **53.** $(4m + 3n)(16m^2 - 12mn + 9n^2)$ **54.** $(4x - 5y)(16x^2 + 20xy + 25y^2)$ **66.** $y(x + 2)(x - 6)$

82. $2x^2(2x - 3)(x - 5)$ **94.** $3(3a - 2b)(4a + b)$ **95.** $2(2m + 5)(4m^2 - 10m + 25)$

Problem Solving

100. Explain why the sum of two squares, $a^2 + b^2$, cannot be factored using real numbers.   Answers will vary.

101. Have you ever seen the proof that 1 is equal to 2? Here it is.

Let $a = b$, then square both sides of the equation:

$$a^2 = b^2$$
$$a^2 = b \cdot b$$
$$a^2 = ab \qquad \text{Substitute } a = b.$$
$$a^2 - b^2 = ab - b^2 \qquad \text{Subtract } b^2 \text{ from both sides of the equation.}$$
$$(a + b)(a - b) = b(a - b) \qquad \text{Factor both sides of the equation.}$$
$$\frac{(a + b)\cancel{(a - b)}}{\cancel{(a - b)}} = \frac{b\cancel{(a - b)}}{\cancel{(a - b)}} \qquad \text{Divide both sides of the equation by } (a - b) \text{ and divide out common factors.}$$
$$a + b = b$$
$$b + b = b \qquad \text{Substitute } a = b.$$
$$2b = b$$
$$\frac{2\overset{1}{\cancel{b}}}{\underset{1}{\cancel{b}}} = \frac{\overset{1}{\cancel{b}}}{\underset{1}{\cancel{b}}} \qquad \text{Divide both sides of the equation by } b.$$
$$2 = 1$$

Obviously, $2 \neq 1$. Therefore, we must have made an error somewhere. Can you find it?
cannot divide both sides of the equation by $a - b$, because it equals 0

Factor each expression. Treat the unknown symbols as if they were variables.

102. $\blacklozenge \maltese + 2\blacklozenge + \odot \maltese + 2\odot$ $(\maltese + 2)(\blacklozenge + \odot)$

103. $2\blacklozenge^6 + 4\blacklozenge^4 \maltese^2$ $2\blacklozenge^4(\blacklozenge^2 + 2\maltese^2)$

104. $4\blacklozenge^2 \maltese - 6\blacklozenge \maltese - 20\maltese \blacklozenge + 30\maltese$ $2\maltese(2\blacklozenge - 3)(\blacklozenge - 5)$

Challenge Problems

105. Factor $x^6 - 27y^9$. $(x^2 - 3y^3)(x^4 + 3x^2y^3 + 9y^6)$

106. Factor $x^6 + 1$. $(x^2 + 1)(x^4 - x^2 + 1)$

107. Factor $x^2 - 6x + 9 - 4y^2$. (*Hint:* Write the first three terms as the square of a binomial.) $(x - 3 + 2y)(x - 3 - 2y)$

108. Factor $x^6 - y^6$. (*Hint:* Factor initially as the difference of two squares.) $(x - y)(x + y)(x^2 + xy + y^2)(x^2 - xy + y^2)$

109. Factor $x^2 + 10x + 25 - y^2 + 4y - 4$. (*Hint:* Group the first three terms and the last three terms.) $(x + y + 3)(x - y + 7)$

Cumulative Review Exercises

[2.8] **110.** Solve the inequality $3x - 2(x + 4) \geq 2x - 9$ and graph the solution on a number line.

[2.6] **111.** Use the formula $A = \dfrac{1}{2}h(b + d)$ to find h in the following trapezoid if the area of the trapezoid is 36 square inches. 4 in.

6 in.

h

12 in.

[6.1] **112.** Simplify $-9\,(a^3\,b^2\,c^6)^0$. -9

[6.1] **113.** Simplify $\left(\dfrac{4x^4 y}{6xy^5}\right)^3$. $\dfrac{8x^9}{27y^{12}}$

[6.2] **114.** Simplify $a^{-4}a^{-7}$. $\dfrac{1}{a^{11}}$

110. $x \leq 1$; ⟵━━━●━⟶
                       1

7.6 Solving Quadratic Equations Using Factoring

1 Recognize quadratic equations.

2 Solve quadratic equations using factoring.

1 Recognize Quadratic Equations

In this section, we introduce **quadratic equations**, which are equations that contain a second-degree term and no term of a higher degree.

Quadratic Equation

Quadratic equations have the form

$$ax^2 + bx + c = 0$$

where a, b, and c are real numbers, $a \neq 0$.

Examples of Quadratic Equations

$$x^2 + 4x - 12 = 0$$
$$2x^2 - 5x = 0$$
$$3x^2 - 2 = 0$$

Quadratic equations like these, in which one side of the equation is written in descending order of the variable and the other side of the equation is 0, are said to be in **standard form**.

Some quadratic equations can be solved by factoring. Two methods for solving quadratic equations that cannot be solved by factoring are given in Chapter 10. To solve a quadratic equation by factoring, we use the **zero-factor property**.

You know that if you multiply by 0, the product is 0. That is, if $a = 0$ or $b = 0$, then $ab = 0$. The reverse is also true. If a product equals 0, at least one of its factors must be 0.

TEACHING TIP
Before discussing the zero-factor property, have students investigate $ab = c$ for $c = 6$ and for $c = 0$ by asking, "What do you know about a and/or b if their product is ... 6? 0?"

Zero-Factor Property

If $ab = 0$, then $a = 0$ or $b = 0$.

We now illustrate how the zero-factor property is used in solving equations.

EXAMPLE 1 ▸ Solve the equation $(x + 3)(x + 4) = 0$.

Solution   Since the product of the factors equals 0, according to the zero-factor property, one or both factors must equal 0. Set each factor equal to 0, and solve each resulting equation.

$$
\begin{array}{ccc}
x + 3 = 0 & \text{or} & x + 4 = 0 \\
x + 3 - 3 = 0 - 3 & & x + 4 - 4 = 0 - 4 \\
x = -3 & & x = -4
\end{array}
$$

Thus, if x is either -3 or -4, the product of the factors is 0. The solutions to the equation are -3 and -4.

Check

$$
\begin{array}{cc}
x = -3 & x = -4 \\
(x + 3)(x + 4) = 0 & (x + 3)(x + 4) = 0 \\
(-3 + 3)(-3 + 4) \stackrel{?}{=} 0 & (-4 + 3)(-4 + 4) \stackrel{?}{=} 0 \\
0(1) \stackrel{?}{=} 0 & -1(0) \stackrel{?}{=} 0 \\
0 = 0 \quad \textit{True} & 0 = 0 \quad \textit{True}
\end{array}
$$

▸ **Now Try Exercise 7**

EXAMPLE 2 ▸ Solve the equation $(3x - 2)(4x + 1) = 0$.

Solution   Set each factor equal to 0 and solve for x.

$$
\begin{array}{ccc}
3x - 2 = 0 & \text{or} & 4x + 1 = 0 \\
3x = 2 & & 4x = -1 \\
x = \dfrac{2}{3} & & x = -\dfrac{1}{4}
\end{array}
$$

The solutions to the equation are $\dfrac{2}{3}$ and $-\dfrac{1}{4}$.

▸ **Now Try Exercise 11**

2 Solve Quadratic Equations Using Factoring

Now we give a general procedure for solving quadratic equations using factoring.

> **To Solve a Quadratic Equation Using Factoring**
>
> 1. Write the equation in standard form with the squared term having a positive coefficient. This will result in one side of the equation being 0.
> 2. Factor the side of the equation that is not 0.
> 3. Set each factor *containing a variable* equal to 0 and solve each equation.
> 4. Check each solution found in step 3 in the *original* equation.

EXAMPLE 3 ▸ Solve the equation $3x^2 = 12x$.

Solution   To make the right side of the equation equal to 0, we subtract $12x$ from both sides of the equation. Then we factor out $3x$ from both terms. Why did we make the right side of the equation equal to 0 instead of the left side?

$$
\begin{aligned}
3x^2 &= 12x \\
3x^2 - 12x &= 12x - 12x \\
3x^2 - 12x &= 0 \\
3x(x - 4) &= 0
\end{aligned}
$$

Now set each factor equal to 0.

$$3x = 0 \quad \text{or} \quad x - 4 = 0$$

$$x = \frac{0}{3} \qquad\qquad x = 4$$

$$x = 0$$

The solutions to the quadratic equation are 0 and 4. Check by substituting $x = 0$, then $x = 4$ in $3x^2 = 12x$.

▶ **Now Try Exercise 47**

EXAMPLE 4 ▶ Solve the equation $x^2 + 10x + 28 = 4$.

Solution   To make the right side of the equation equal to 0, we subtract 4 from both sides of the equation. Then we factor and solve.

$$x^2 + 10x + 24 = 0$$

$$(x + 4)(x + 6) = 0$$

$$x + 4 = 0 \quad \text{or} \quad x + 6 = 0$$

$$x = -4 \qquad\qquad x = -6$$

The solutions are -4 and -6. We will check these values in the original equation.

Check

$x = -4$	$x = -6$
$x^2 + 10x + 28 = 4$	$x^2 + 10x + 28 = 4$
$(-4)^2 + 10(-4) + 28 \overset{?}{=} 4$	$(-6)^2 + 10(-6) + 28 \overset{?}{=} 4$
$16 - 40 + 28 \overset{?}{=} 4$	$36 - 60 + 28 \overset{?}{=} 4$
$-24 + 28 \overset{?}{=} 4$	$-24 + 28 \overset{?}{=} 4$
$4 = 4$ *True*	$4 = 4$ *True*

▶ **Now Try Exercise 23**

EXAMPLE 5 ▶ Solve the equation $4y^2 + 5y - 20 = -11y$.

Solution   Since all terms are not on the same side of the equation, add $11y$ to both sides of the equation.

$$4y^2 + 16y - 20 = 0$$

Factor out the common factor.

$$4(y^2 + 4y - 5) = 0$$

Factor the remaining trinomial.

$$4(y + 5)(y - 1) = 0$$

Now solve for y.

$$y + 5 = 0 \quad \text{or} \quad y - 1 = 0$$

$$y = -5 \qquad\qquad y = 1$$

Since 4 is a factor that does not contain a variable, we do not set it equal to 0. The solutions to the quadratic equation are -5 and 1.

▶ **Now Try Exercise 25**

EXAMPLE 6 ▸ Solve the equation $-x^2 + 5x + 6 = 0$.

Solution   When the squared term is negative, we generally make it positive by multiplying both sides of the equation by -1.

$$-1(-x^2 + 5x + 6) = -1 \cdot 0$$
$$x^2 - 5x - 6 = 0$$

Note that the sign of each term on the left side of the equation changed and that the right side of the equation remained 0. Why? Now proceed as before.

$$x^2 - 5x - 6 = 0$$
$$(x - 6)(x + 1) = 0$$
$$x - 6 = 0 \quad \text{or} \quad x + 1 = 0$$
$$x = 6 \qquad\qquad x = -1$$

A check using the original equation will show that the solutions are 6 and -1.

▸ **Now Try Exercise 33**

Avoiding Common Errors

Be careful not to confuse factoring a polynomial with using factoring as a method to solve an equation.

	CORRECT		INCORRECT
Factor:	$x^2 + 3x + 2$	Factor:	$x^2 + 3x + 2$
	$(x + 2)(x + 1)$		$(x + 2)(x + 1)$

$$\cancel{x + 2 = 0 \quad \text{or} \quad x + 1 = 0}$$
$$\cancel{x = -2 \qquad\qquad x = -1}$$

Do you know what is wrong with the example on the right? It goes too far. The expression $x^2 + 3x + 2$ is a polynomial (a trinomial), not an equation. Since it is not an equation, it cannot be solved. When you are given a polynomial, you cannot just include "$= 0$" to change it to an equation.

CORRECT

Solve: $x^2 + 3x + 2 = 0$
$$(x + 2)(x + 1) = 0$$
$$x + 2 = 0 \quad \text{or} \quad x + 1 = 0$$
$$x = -2 \qquad\qquad x = -1$$

EXAMPLE 7 ▸ Solve the equation $x^2 = 49$.

Solution   Subtract 49 from both sides of the equation; then factor using the difference of two squares formula.

$$x^2 - 49 = 0$$
$$(x + 7)(x - 7) = 0$$
$$x + 7 = 0 \quad \text{or} \quad x - 7 = 0$$
$$x = -7 \qquad\qquad x = 7$$

The solutions are -7 and 7.

▸ **Now Try Exercise 45**

EXAMPLE 8 ▶ Solve the equation $(x - 3)(x + 1) = 5$.

Solution   Begin by multiplying the factors, then write the quadratic equation in standard form.

$$(x - 3)(x + 1) = 5$$
$$x^2 - 2x - 3 = 5 \qquad \text{\textit{Multiply the factors.}}$$
$$x^2 - 2x - 8 = 0 \qquad \text{\textit{Write the equation in standard form.}}$$
$$(x - 4)(x + 2) = 0 \qquad \text{\textit{Factor.}}$$
$$x - 4 = 0 \quad \text{or} \quad x + 2 = 0 \qquad \text{\textit{Zero-factor property}}$$
$$x = 4 \qquad\qquad x = -2$$

The solutions are 4 and -2. We will check these values in the original equation.

Check
$$\begin{array}{cc}
x = 4 & x = -2 \\
(x - 3)(x + 1) = 5 & (x - 3)(x + 1) = 5 \\
(4 - 3)(4 + 1) \overset{?}{=} 5 & (-2 - 3)(-2 + 1) \overset{?}{=} 5 \\
1(5) \overset{?}{=} 5 & (-5)(-1) \overset{?}{=} 5 \\
5 = 5 \quad \textit{True} & 5 = 5 \quad \textit{True}
\end{array}$$

▶ **Now Try Exercise 51**

Helpful Hint

In Example 8, you might have been tempted to start the problem by writing

$$x - 3 = 5 \quad \text{or} \quad x + 1 = 5.$$

This would lead to an incorrect solution. Remember, the zero-factor property only holds when one side of the equation is equal to 0. In Example 8, once we obtained $(x - 4)(x + 2) = 0$, we were able to use the zero-factor property.

USING YOUR GRAPHING CALCULATOR

If you solve the equation $x^2 - x - 6 = 0$ by factoring, you should obtain the solutions -2 and 3. Solve the equation now. The solutions to this equation can be found on a graphing calculator in a number of ways. If we replace the 0 with y we obtain $y = x^2 - x - 6$. **Figure 7.4** shows the graph of $Y_1 = x^2 - x - 6$ using the standard window settings.

Some graphing calculators have a TABLE feature which shows a table of values. On the TI-84 Plus press $\boxed{2^{\text{nd}}}$ $\boxed{\text{GRAPH}}$ to use the TABLE feature. In the Using Your Graphing Calculator Box on page 248, we explained how to use the TABLE feature. Please re-read that material now and notice how to change the table settings. From the graph, observe that both x-intercepts occur to the right of $x = -3$. We will therefore set TblStart $= -3$. We will let ΔTbl $= 1$. After you get the table, you can scroll up and down the table using the up and down arrows. **Figure 7.5** shows a table of values for $Y_1 = x^2 - x - 6$. Note that $Y_1 = 0$ when $X = -2$ and $X = 3$. These values are the solution to the equation $x^2 - x - 6 = 0$. The values -2 and 3 are also called **zeros**, for when they are substituted for x in $y = x^2 - x - 6$, y has a value of zero. One drawback to using the TABLE feature to find the zeros is that if you do not use the appropriate table settings, you may not find the zeroes. Observe the TABLE when we use ΔTbl $= 2$, (see **Figure 7.6**.) Note that the value of Y_1 is zero only when $X = 3$. The other zero is not displayed because only odd values of x are shown in the table. If an x-intercept is not at an integer value, then it will not show up in a table in ΔTbl $= 1$. Can you explain why? If this happens you can change your table setting, or use the CALC menu, as explained on the next page.

FIGURE 7.4

FIGURE 7.5

FIGURE 7.6

(continued on the next page)

Another method that can be used to find the solution to $x^2 - x - 6 = 0$ is to graph $y = x^2 - x - 6$ and use the CALC (which stands for calculate) menu to find the x-intercepts. On the TI-84 Plus you press $\boxed{2^{nd}}$ $\boxed{\text{TRACE}}$ to get to the CALC menu. The CALC menu is shown in **Figure 7.7**.

Scroll down to option 2: zero and press $\boxed{\text{ENTER}}$ which then gives the screen in **Figure 7.8**. Under the words *Left Bound?* you see $x = 0$. Use the arrow key to move the cursor to the right until it is just to the left of the positive x-intercept (this puts the cursor slightly below the x-axis). Note that the value of Y is negative. Press $\boxed{\text{ENTER}}$. The screen now shows *Right Bound?* Move the cursor so it is slightly to the right of the x-intercept (this puts the cursor slightly above the x-axis), then press $\boxed{\text{ENTER}}$.

Note that the sign of the value of Y has changed, and is positive. The screen now shows *Guess?* Press $\boxed{\text{ENTER}}$ again and the screen shows that the zero is 3 (see **Figure 7.9**.) That is, when $x = 3$, $y = 0$. If you make a mistake, clear your calculator, re-enter $Y_1 = x^2 - x - 6$, and start the procedure again.

FIGURE 7.7

FIGURE 7.8

FIGURE 7.9

You can also use this procedure to determine the other zero, or the other solution to $x^2 - x - 6 = 0$. To obtain the other zero, press $\boxed{2^{nd}}$ $\boxed{\text{TRACE}}$ to get to the CALC menu again. Then using the left arrow, move the cursor from its current position to just left of the other x-intercept. In this case, it will be slightly *above* the x-axis, and the value of Y will be *positive*. Press $\boxed{\text{ENTER}}$ to get *Left Bound?* Finish the procedure by moving the cursor right until it is slightly *below* the x-axis. Press $\boxed{\text{ENTER}}$ to get the *Right Bound?* and once more to get *Guess?* The screen shows that the zero is -2.

EXERCISES

Use your graphing calculator to determine the solutions to each of the following quadratic equations. You may have to adjust the window settings to see the entire graph.

1. $x^2 - 2x - 8 = 0$ $4, -2$

2. $x^2 - 7x + 10 = 0$ $2, 5$

3. $2x^2 - 6x + 4 = 0$ $2, 1$

4. $2x^2 - 8x - 10 = 0$ $-1, 5$

---

2. an equation that contains a second-degree term and no term of a higher degree   **3.** $ax^2 + bx + c = 0, a \neq 0$ **4.** Answers will vary.
5. a) The zero-factor property may only be used when one side of the equation is 0.

EXERCISE SET 7.6   Math XL   MyMathLab

MathXL®   MyMathLab

Concept/Writing Exercises

1. Explain the zero-factor property.   Answers will vary.

2. What is a quadratic equation?

3. What is the standard form of a quadratic equation?

4. Explain the procedure to use to solve a quadratic equation.

5. a) When solving the equation $(x + 1)(x - 2) = 4$, explain why we **cannot** solve the equation by first writing

$x + 1 = 4$ or $x - 2 = 4$ and then solving each equation for x.

b) Solve the equation $(x + 1)(x - 2) = 4$. $-2, 3$

6. When solving an equation such as $3(x - 4)(x + 5) = 0$, we set the factors $x - 4$ and $x + 5$ equal to 0, but we do not set the 3 equal to 0. Can you explain why?   3 cannot equal 0

Practice the Skills

Solve.

7. $(x + 6)(x - 7) = 0$ $-6, 7$

8. $-2x(x + 9) = 0$ $0, -9$

9. $7x(x - 8) = 0$ $0, 8$

10. $(x + 3)(x + 5) = 0$ $-3, -5$

11. $(3x + 7)(2x - 11) = 0$ $-\dfrac{7}{3}, \dfrac{11}{2}$

12. $(3x - 2)(x - 5) = 0$ $\dfrac{2}{3}, 5$

13. $x^2 - 16 = 0$ $4, -4$

14. $x^2 - 9 = 0$ $3, -3$

15. $x^2 - 12x = 0$ $0, 12$

16. $9x^2 + 27x = 0$ $0, -3$

17. $x^2 + 7x = 0$ $0, -7$

18. $a^2 - 4a - 12 = 0$ $-2, 6$

19. $x^2 - 8x + 16 = 0$ 4

20. $x^2 + 12x + 36 = 0$ -6

21. $x^2 + 12x = -20$ $-2, -10$

22. $3y^2 - 4 = -4y$ $\dfrac{2}{3}, -2$

23. $x^2 + 12x + 22 = 2$ $-2, -10$

24. $3x^2 = -21x - 18$ $-1, -6$

25. $2x^2 - 5x - 24 = -3x$ $-3, 4$

26. $x^2 = 4x + 21$ $-3, 7$

27. $23p - 24 = -p^2$ $1, -24$

28. $3x^2 - 9x - 30 = 0$ $5, -2$

29. $33w + 90 = -3w^2$ $-5, -6$

30. $t^2 + 44 + 15t = 0$ $-11, -4$

31. $-2x - 15 = -x^2$ $5, -3$

32. $-9x + 20 = -x^2$ $4, 5$

33. $-x^2 + 29x + 30 = 0$ $30, -1$

34. $12y - 11 = y^2$ $1, 11$

35. $-15 = 4m^2 + 17m$ $-3, -\dfrac{5}{4}$

36. $z^2 + 8z = -16$ -4

37. $9p^2 = -21p - 6$ $-\dfrac{1}{3}, -2$

38. $2x^2 - 5 = 3x$ $-1, \dfrac{5}{2}$

39. $3r^2 + 13r = 10$ $\dfrac{2}{3}, -5$

40. $3x^2 = 7x + 20$ $-\dfrac{5}{3}, 4$

41. $4x^2 + 4x - 48 = 0$ $-4, 3$

42. $6x^2 - 7x - 5 = 0$ $-\dfrac{1}{2}, \dfrac{5}{3}$

43. $8x^2 + 2x = 3$ $-\dfrac{3}{4}, \dfrac{1}{2}$

44. $2x^2 + 4x - 6 = 0$ $-3, 1$

45. $c^2 = 64$ $8, -8$

46. $2n^2 + 36 = -18n$ $-3, -6$

47. $2x^2 = 50x$ $0, 25$

48. $4x^2 - 25 = 0$ $\dfrac{5}{2}, -\dfrac{5}{2}$

49. $x^2 = 100$ $10, -10$

50. $3x^2 - 48 = 0$ $4, -4$

51. $(x - 2)(x - 1) = 12$ $-2, 5$

52. $(x + 2)(x + 5) = -2$ $-4, -3$

53. $(3x + 2)(x + 1) = 4$ $-2, \dfrac{1}{3}$

54. $(x - 1)(2x - 5) = 9$ $-\dfrac{1}{2}, 4$

55. $2(a^2 + 9) = 15a$ $\dfrac{3}{2}, 6$

56. $x(x + 5) = 6$ $-6, 1$

Problem Solving

In Exercises 57–60, create a quadratic equation with the given solutions. Explain how you determined your answers.

57. $6, -4$ $x^2 - 2x - 24 = 0$

58. $-3, -5$ $x^2 + 8x + 15 = 0$

59. $6, 0$ $x^2 - 6x = 0$

60. $0, -9$ $x^2 + 9x = 0$

61. The solutions to a quadratic equation are $\dfrac{1}{2}$ and $-\dfrac{1}{3}$.

    a) What factors with integer coefficients were set equal to 0 to obtain these solutions? $(2x - 1)$ and $(3x + 1)$

    b) Write a quadratic equation whose solutions are $\dfrac{1}{2}$ and $-\dfrac{1}{3}$. $6x^2 - x - 1 = 0$

62. The solutions to a quadratic equation are $\dfrac{2}{3}$ and $-\dfrac{3}{4}$.

    a) What factors with integer coefficients were set equal to 0 to obtain these solutions? $(3x - 2)$ and $(4x + 3)$

    b) Write a quadratic equation whose solutions are $\dfrac{2}{3}$ and $-\dfrac{3}{4}$. $12x^2 + x - 6 = 0$

Challenge Problems

63. Solve the equation
$(2x - 3)(x - 4) = (x - 5)(x + 3) + 7$. $4, 5$

64. Solve the equation
$(x - 3)(x - 2) = (x + 5)(2x - 3) + 21$. $0, -12$

65. Solve the equation $x(x - 3)(x + 2) = 0$. $0, 3, -2$

66. Solve the equation $x^3 - 10x^2 + 24x = 0$. $0, 4, 6$

Cumulative Review Exercises

[1.7] **67.** Subtract $\dfrac{3}{5} - \dfrac{2}{9}$. $\dfrac{17}{45}$

[2.5] **68.** **a)** What is the name given to an equation that has an infinite number of solutions?   identity

    b) What is the name given to an equation that has no solution?   contradiction

[2.7] **69.** **Cyprus Gardens** At Cyprus Gardens, there is a long line of people waiting to go through the entrance. If 160 people are admitted in 13 minutes, how many people will be admitted in 60 minutes? Assume the rate stays the same. ≈ 738 people

[6.1] **70.** Simplify $\left(\dfrac{3p^5q^7}{p^9q^8}\right)^2$. $\dfrac{9}{p^8q^2}$

Cyprus Gardens; see Exercise 69

[6.4] *Identify the following as a monomial, binomial, trinomial or not a polynomial. If an expression is not a polynomial, explain why.*

71. $2x$ monomial

72. $x - 3$ binomial

73. $\dfrac{1}{x}$ not a polynomial

74. $x^2 - 6x + 9$ trinomial

7.7 Applications of Quadratic Equations

1 Solve applications by factoring quadratic equations.

2 Learn the Pythagorean Theorem.

1 Solve Applications by Factoring Quadratic Equations

In Section 7.6, we learned how to solve quadratic equations by factoring. In this section, we will discuss and solve application problems that require solving quadratic equations to obtain the answer. In Example 1, we will solve a problem involving a relationship between two numbers.

EXAMPLE 1 ▶ **Number Problem** The product of two numbers is 78. Find the two numbers if one number is 7 more than the other.

Solution   Understand and Translate   Our goal is to find the two numbers.

$$\text{Let } x = \text{smaller number.}$$

$$x + 7 = \text{larger number.}$$

$$x(x + 7) = 78$$

Carry Out

$$x^2 + 7x = 78$$

$$x^2 + 7x - 78 = 0$$

$$(x - 6)(x + 13) = 0$$

$$x - 6 = 0 \quad \text{or} \quad x + 13 = 0$$

$$x = 6 \qquad\qquad x = -13$$

Remember that x represents the smaller of the two numbers. This problem has two possible solutions.

	Solution 1	Solution 2
Smaller number	6	−13
Larger number	$x + 7 = 6 + 7 = 13$	$x + 7 = -13 + 7 = -6$

Thus, the two possible solutions are 6 and 13, and -13 and -6.

Check	6 and 13	−13 and −6
Product of the two numbers is 78.	$6 \cdot 13 = 78$	$(-13)(-6) = 78$
One number is 7 more than the other number.	13 is 7 more than 6.	-6 is 7 more than -13.

Answer   One solution is: smaller number 6, larger number 13. A second solution is: smaller number -13, larger number -6. You must give both solutions. If the question had stated "the product of two *positive* numbers is 78," the only solution would be 6 and 13.

▶ **Now Try Exercise 13**

Now let us work an application problem involving geometry.

EXAMPLE 2 ▶ **Advertising** The marketing department of a large publishing company is planning to make a large rectangular sign to advertise a new book at a convention. They want the length of the sign to be 3 feet longer than the width (**Fig. 7.10** on page 452). Signs at the convention may have a maximum area of 54 square feet. Find the length and width of the sign if the area is to be 54 square feet.

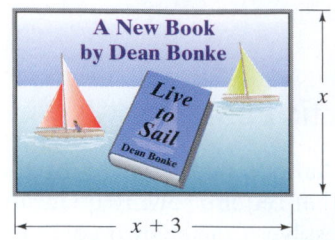

A New Book
by Dean Bonke

Live
to
Sail
Dean Bonke

x

$x + 3$

FIGURE 7.10

TEACHING TIP
Before discussing the solution to
Example 3, have students guess how
long it takes for the eyeglasses to
reach the ground.

Solution   Understand and Translate   We need to find the length and width of the sign. We will use the formula for the area of a rectangle.

$$\text{Let } x = \text{width.}$$
$$x + 3 = \text{length.}$$
$$\text{area} = \text{length} \cdot \text{width}$$

Carry Out

$$54 = (x + 3)x$$
$$54 = x^2 + 3x$$
$$0 = x^2 + 3x - 54$$
$$\text{or} \quad x^2 + 3x - 54 = 0$$
$$(x - 6)(x + 9) = 0$$
$$x - 6 = 0 \quad \text{or} \quad x + 9 = 0$$
$$x = 6 \qquad\qquad x = -9$$

Check and Answer   Since the width of the sign cannot be a negative number, the only solution is

$$\text{width} = x = 6 \text{ feet,} \quad \text{length} = x + 3 = 6 + 3 = 9 \text{ feet}$$

The area, length · width, is 54 square feet, and the length is 3 feet more than the width, so the answer checks.

▸ **Now Try Exercise 21**

EXAMPLE 3 ▸ **Earth's Gravitational Field**   In earth's gravitational field, the distance, d, in feet, that an object falls t seconds after it has been released is given by the formula $d = 16t^2$. While at the top of a roller coaster, a rider's eyeglasses slide off his head and fall out of the cart. How long does it take the eyeglasses to reach the ground 64 feet below?

Solution   Understand and Translate   Substitute 64 for d in the formula and then solve for t.

$$d = 16t^2$$
$$64 = 16t^2$$

Carry Out

$$\frac{64}{16} = t^2$$
$$4 = t^2$$

INSTRUCTOR EXAMPLE 3
In Example 3, how long would it take
the eyeglasses to reach the ground
144 feet below?
Ans.: 3 seconds

Now subtract 4 from both sides of the equation and write the equation with 0 on the right side to put the quadratic equation in standard form.

$$4 - 4 = t^2 - 4$$
$$0 = t^2 - 4$$
$$\text{or} \quad t^2 - 4 = 0$$
$$(t + 2)(t - 2) = 0$$
$$t + 2 = 0 \quad \text{or} \quad t - 2 = 0$$
$$t = -2 \qquad\qquad t = 2$$

Check and Answer   Since t represents the number of seconds, it must be a positive number. Thus, the only possible answer is 2 seconds. It takes 2 seconds for the eyeglasses (or any other object falling under the influence of gravity) to fall 64 feet.

▸ **Now Try Exercise 25**

2   Learn The Pythagorean Theorem

Now we will introduce the Pythagorean Theorem, which describes an important relationship between the length of the sides of a right triangle. The Pythagorean Theorem is named after Pythagoras of Samos ($\approx$569 B.C.–475 B.C.) who was born in Samos, Ionia. Pythagoras is often described as the first pure mathematician. Unlike many later

Pythagoras of Samos

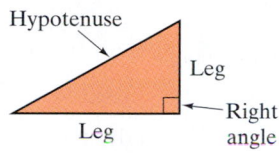

Hypotenuse

Leg

Leg

Right angle

FIGURE 7.11

Greek mathematicians, relatively little is known about his life. The society he led, the Pythagorians, was half religious and half scientific. They followed a code of secrecy and did not publish any of their writings. There is fairly good agreement on the main events of Pythagoras's life, but many of the dates are disputed by scholars. Now let's discuss the Pythagorean Theorem.

A **right triangle** is a triangle that contains a right, or 90°, angle (**Fig. 7.11**). The two shorter sides of a right triangle are called the **legs** and the largest side, which is always opposite the right angle is called the **hypotenuse**. The **Pythagorean Theorem** expresses the relationship between the lengths of the legs of a right triangle and its hypotenuse.

Pythagorean Theorem

The square of the hypotenuse of a right triangle is equal to the sum of the squares of the two legs.

$$(\text{leg})^2 + (\text{leg})^2 = (\text{hypotenuse})^2$$

If a and b represent the legs, and c represents the hypotenuse, then

$$a^2 + b^2 = c^2$$

c

b

a

When you use the Pythagorean Theorem, it makes no difference which leg you designate as a and which leg you designate as b, but the hypotenuse is always designated as c.

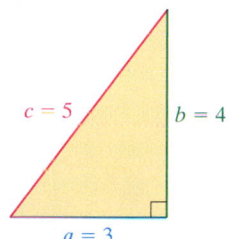

$c = 5$ $b = 4$

$a = 3$

FIGURE 7.12

EXAMPLE 4 ▶ Verifying Right Triangles Determine if a right triangle can have the following sides.

a) 3 inches, 4 inches, 5 inches   **b)** 2 inches, 5 inches, 7 inches

Solution

a) Understand   To determine if a right triangle can have the sides given, we will use the Pythagorean Theorem. If the results show the Pythagorean Theorem holds true, the triangle can have the given sides. If the results are false, then the sides given cannot be those of a right triangle.

Translate   We must always select the largest size to represent the hypotenuse, c. We will designate the length of leg a to be 3 inches and the length of leg b to be 4 inches. The length of the hypotenuse, c, will be 5 inches. See **Figure 7.12**.

$$a^2 + b^2 = c^2$$
$$3^2 + 4^2 \stackrel{?}{=} 5^2$$

Carry Out
$$9 + 16 \stackrel{?}{=} 25$$
$$25 = 25 \quad \textit{True}$$

Check and Answer   Since using the Pythagorean Theorem results in a true statement, a right triangle can have the given sides.

b) We will work this part using the Pythagorean Theorem, as we did in part **a)**. We will let leg a have a length of 2 inches, leg b have a length of 5 inches, and the hypotenuse, c, have a length of 7 inches.

$$a^2 + b^2 = c^2$$
$$2^2 + 5^2 \stackrel{?}{=} 7^2$$
$$4 + 25 \stackrel{?}{=} 49$$
$$29 = 49 \quad \textit{False}$$

Since 29 is not equal to 49, the Pythagorean Theorem does not hold for these lengths. Therefore, no right triangle can have sides with lengths of 2 inches, 5 inches and 7 inches.

▸ **Now Try Exercise 27**

Helpful Hint

When drawing a right triangle, the hypotenuse, c, is always the side opposite the right angle. See Figures **7.13 (a)–(d)**.

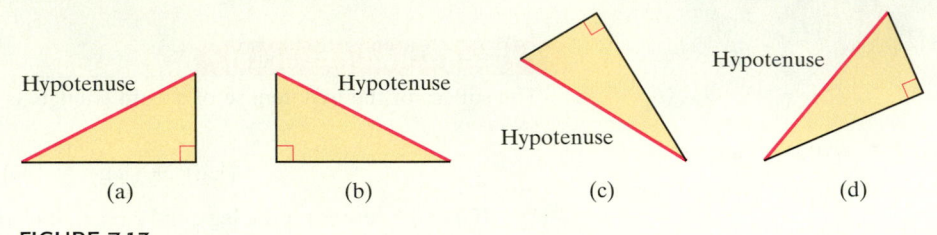

FIGURE 7.13

Notice that the hypotenuse is always the longest side of a right triangle.

EXAMPLE 5 ▸ **Using the Pythagorean Theorem** One leg of a right triangle is 7 feet longer than the other leg. The hypotenuse is 13 feet. Find the dimensions of the right triangle.

Solution **Understand and Translate**   We will first draw a diagram of the situation. See **Figure 7.14**.

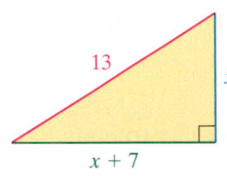

FIGURE 7.14

Now we will use the Pythagorean Theorem to determine the dimensions of the right triangle.

$$a^2 + b^2 = c^2$$
$$x^2 + (x + 7)^2 = 13^2$$

Carry Out
$$x^2 + (x^2 + 14x + 49) = 169$$
$$2x^2 + 14x - 120 = 0$$
$$2(x^2 + 7x - 60) = 0$$
$$2(x + 12)(x - 5) = 0$$
$$x + 12 = 0 \quad \text{or} \quad x - 5 = 0$$
$$x = -12 \qquad\qquad x = 5$$

Check and Answer   Since a length cannot be a negative number, the only answer is 5. The dimensions of the right triangle are 5 feet, $x + 7$ or 12 feet, and 13 feet. One leg is 5 feet, the other leg is 12 feet, and the hypotenuse is 13 feet.

▸ **Now Try Exercise 35**

INSTRUCTOR EXAMPLE
One leg of a right triangle is 14 feet longer than the other leg. The hypotenuse is 26 feet. Find the length of the legs of the right triangle.
Ans.: 10 ft, 24 ft

INSTRUCTOR EXAMPLE
The diagonal of a picture frame is 13 inches. If the length of the frame is 7 inches greater than its width, find the dimensions of the frame.
Ans.: $w = 5$ in., $l = 12$ in.

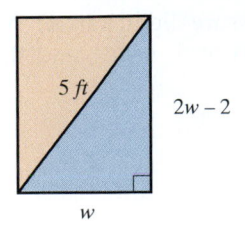

FIGURE 7.15

EXAMPLE 6 ▸ **Sand and Water Table** Clayton Jackson is building a rectangular table for his son to hold sand in one area and water in a different area (**Fig. 7.15**). The length of the table will be 2 feet less than twice the width. He is placing a divider that is 5 feet in length along the diagonal of the table to separate the sand from the water. Find the dimensions of the table.

Solution **Understand and Translate**   Our goal is to find the dimensions of the table. After looking at **Figure 7.15**, you should realize that we are working with a right triangle. Therefore, we will use the Pythagorean Theorem to answer the question. To do so, we must express the dimensions of the table in mathematical terms.

$$\text{Let } w = \text{width of the table.}$$
$$\text{Then } 2w - 2 = \text{length of the table.}$$

Figure 7.15 illustrates the relationship. Now we use the Pythagorean Theorem. We will let w represent leg a, $2w - 2$ represent leg b, and 5 represent the hypotenuse, c.

Carry Out

$$a^2 + b^2 = c^2$$
$$w^2 + (2w - 2)^2 = 5^2$$
$$w^2 + 4w^2 - 8w + 4 = 25$$
$$5w^2 - 8w + 4 = 25$$
$$5w^2 - 8w - 21 = 0$$
$$(5w + 7)(w - 3) = 0$$
$$5w + 7 = 0 \quad \text{or} \quad w - 3 = 0$$
$$5w = -7 \qquad\qquad w = 3$$
$$w = -\frac{7}{5}$$

Check and Answer Since the width of the table cannot be a negative number, the only solution is 3. Therefore, the width of the sand and water table is 3 feet. The length of the sand and water table is $2w - 2 = 2(3) - 2 = 6 - 2 = 4$ feet.

▶ **Now Try Exercise 37**

In the Exercise Set, we use the terms consecutive integers, consecutive even integers, and consecutive odd integers. Recall from Section 3.1 that **consecutive integers** may be represented as x and $x + 1$. **Consecutive even** or **consecutive odd integers** may be represented as x and $x + 2$.

EXERCISE SET 7.7

Concept/Writing Exercises

1. What is a right triangle? a triangle with a 90° angle

2. a) What are the smaller sides of a right triangle called? legs

    b) What is the longest side of a right triangle called? hypotenuse

3. State the Pythagorean Theorem formula. $a^2 + b^2 = c^2$

4. When designating the legs of a right triangle as a and b, does it make any difference which leg you call a and which leg you call b? Explain your answer. no

Practice the Skills

In Exercises 5–8, determine the value of the question mark.

5.

6.

7.

8.

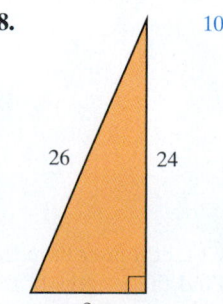

In Exercises 9–12, a and b represent two legs of a right triangle and c represents the hypotenuse. Determine the value of the question mark (?).

9. $a = 24, c = 30, b = ?$ 18

10. $a = 12, b = 16, c = ?$ 20

11. $a = 15, b = 36, c = ?$ 39

12. $b = 20, c = 25, a = ?$ 15

Problem Solving

Express each problem as an equation, then solve.

13. Product of Numbers The product of two positive numbers is 117. Determine the two numbers if one is 4 more than the other.   9, 13

14. Positive Numbers The product of two positive numbers is 245. Determine the two numbers if one number is 5 times the other.   7, 35

15. Positive Numbers The product of two positive numbers is 84. Find the two numbers if one number is 2 more than twice the other.   6, 14

16. Consecutive Integers The product of two consecutive positive integers is 56. Find the two integers.   7, 8

17. Consecutive Even Integers The product of two consecutive positive even integers is 288. Find the two integers.   16, 18

18. Consecutive Odd Integers The product of two consecutive positive odd integers is 143. Determine the two integers.   11, 13

19. Area of Rectangle The area of a rectangle is 36 square feet. Determine the length and width if the length is 4 times the width. $w = 3$ ft, $l = 12$ ft

20. Rectangular Scrapbook A scrapbook page has an area of 180 square inches. Find the length and width if the width is 3 inches less than the length. $l = 15$ in., $w = 12$ in.

21. $w = 10$ ft, $l = 15$ ft

21. Rectangular Garden Maureen Woolhouse has a rectangular garden whose width is 2/3 its length. If its area is 150 square feet, determine the length and width of the garden.

22. Buying Wallpaper Alejandro Ibanez wishes to buy a wallpaper border to go along the top of one wall in his living room. The length of the wall is 7 feet greater than its height.

 a) Find the length and height of the wall if the area of the wall is 120 square feet. $h = 8$ ft, $l = 15$ ft

 b) What is the length of the border he will need?   15 ft

 c) If the border costs $4 per linear foot, how much will the border cost? $60

23. Square If each side of a square is increased by 5 meters, the area becomes 81 square meters. Determine the length of a side of the original square.   4 m

24. Sign If the length of the sign in Example 2 is to be 2 feet longer than the width and the area is to be 35 square feet, determine the dimensions of the sign. $w = 5$ ft, $l = 7$ ft

25. Dropped Egg How long would it take for an egg dropped from a helicopter to fall 256 feet to the ground? See Example 3.   4 sec

26. Falling Rock How long would it take a rock that falls from a cliff 400 feet above the sea to hit the sea?   5 sec

In Exercises 27–30, determine if a right triangle can have the following sides where a and b represent the legs and c represents the hypotenuse. Explain your answer.

27. $a = 7, b = 24, c = 25$ yes

28. $a = 16, c = 20, b = 22$ no

29. $a = 9, b = 40, c = 41$ yes

30. $a = 13, b = 18, c = 28$ no

In Exercises 31–34, find the value of the question mark.

31.

16 ft

32.

18 in.

33.

41 ft

34.

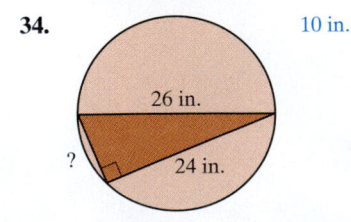

10 in.

35. Triangle One leg of a right triangle is 2 feet longer than the other leg. The hypotenuse is 10 feet. Find the lengths of the three sides of the triangle.   6 ft, 8 ft, 10 ft

36. Triangle One leg of a right triangle is two inches more than twice the other leg. The hypotenuse is 13 inches. Find the lengths of the three sides of the triangle.   5 in., 12 in., 13 in.

37. Artwork Rachel bought a framed piece of artwork as a souvenir from her trip to Disney World. The diagonal of the frame is 15 inches. If the length of the frame is 3 inches greater than its width, find the dimensions of the frame.

$w = 9$ in., $l = 12$ in.

38. Laptop The top of a new experimental rectangular laptop computer has a diagonal of 17 inches. If the length of the computer is 1 inch less than twice its width, find the dimensions of the computer. $w = 8$ in., $l = 15$ in.

39. Rectangular Garden Mary Ann Tuerk has constructed a rectangular garden. The length of the garden is 3 feet more than three times its width. The diagonal of the garden is 4 feet more than three times the width. Find the length and width of the garden. $w = 7$ ft, $l = 24$ ft

40. Height of Tree A tree is supported by ropes. One rope goes from the top of the tree to a point on the ground. The height

of the tree is 4 feet more than twice the distance between the base of the tree and the rope anchored in the ground. The length of the rope is 6 feet more than twice the distance between the base of the tree and the rope anchored in the ground. Find the height of the tree.   24 ft

41. Book Store A book store owner finds that her daily profit, P, is approximated by the formula $P = x^2 - 15x - 50$, where x is the number of books she sells. How many books must she sell in a day for her profit to be $400?   30 books

42. Water Sprinklers The cost, C, for manufacturing x water sprinklers is given by the formula $C = x^2 - 27x - 20$. Determine the number of water sprinklers manufactured at a cost of $70.   30 sprinklers

43. Sum of Numbers The sum, s, of the first n even numbers is given by the formula $s = n^2 + n$. Determine n for the given sums:

a) $s = 20$ 4   **b)** $s = 90$ 9

44. Telephone Lines For a switchboard that handles n telephone lines, the maximum number of telephone connections, C, that it can make simultaneously is given by the formula

$$C = \frac{n(n-1)}{2}.$$

a) How many telephone connections can a switchboard make simultaneously if it handles 15 lines?   105

b) How many lines does a switchboard have if it can make 55 telephone connections simultaneously?   11

Challenge Problems

45. Area Determine the area of the rectangle.   432 sq ft

46. Area Determine the area of the circle.   ≈227 sq ft

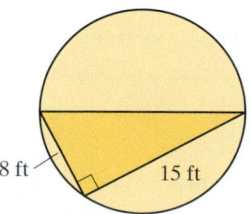

47. Solve the equation $x^3 - 4x^2 - 32x = 0$. $0, 8, -4$

48. Solve the equation $x^3 + 2x^2 - 15x = 0$. $0, -5, 3$

49. Create an equation whose solutions are -2, 0, and 3. Explain how you determined your answer. $x^3 - x^2 - 6x = 0$

50. Numbers The product of two numbers is -63. Determine the numbers if their sum is -2. -9 and 7

51. Numbers The sum of two numbers is 9. The sum of the squares of the two numbers is 45. Determine the two numbers.   3 and 6

52. Wizard of Oz Near the end of the movie *The Wizard of Oz*, when the scarecrow receives his brain, he starts talking rapidly and seems to impress us with his new found intelligence. One of the things that the scarecrow *attempts* to say is the Pythagorean Theorem. The only problem is that he says it incorrectly! Rent or borrow a videotape or DVD of the movie and write down exactly what the scarecrow says about the Pythagorean Theorem. Then see if you can rewrite the script to make it mathematically correct.

Group Activity

Discuss and solve Exercises 53 and 54 in groups.

53. Cost and Revenue The break-even point for a manufacturer occurs when its cost of production, C, is equal to its revenue, R. The cost equation for a company is $C = 2x^2 - 20x + 600$ and its revenue equation is $R = x^2 + 50x - 400$, where x is the number of units produced and sold. How many units must be produced and sold for the manufacturer to break even? There are two values.   20 and 50 units

54. Cannonball When a certain cannon is fired, the height, in feet, of the cannonball at time t can be found by using the formula $h = -16t^2 + 128t$.

a) Determine the height of the cannonball 3 seconds after being fired.   240 ft

b) Determine the time it takes for the cannonball to hit the ground. (*Hint:* What is the value of h at impact?)   8 sec

Cumulative Review Exercises

[3.1] **55.** Express the statement "seven less than three times a number" as a mathematical expression. $3x - 7$

[6.4] **56.** Subtract $x^2 - 4x + 6$ from $3x + 2$. $-x^2 + 7x - 4$

[6.5] **57.** Multiply $(3x^2 + 2x - 4)(2x - 1)$.
       $6x^3 + x^2 - 10x + 4$

[6.6] **58.** Divide $\dfrac{6x^2 - 19x + 15}{3x - 5}$ by dividing the numerator by the denominator. $2x - 3$

[7.4] **59.** Divide $\dfrac{6x^2 - 19x + 15}{3x - 5}$ by factoring the numerator and dividing out common factors. $2x - 3$

Chapter 7 Summary

IMPORTANT FACTS AND CONCEPTS	EXAMPLES
Section 7.1	
To **factor an expression** means to write the expression as a product of its factors.	$x^2 + 2x - 35 = (x + 7)(x - 5)$
If $a \cdot b = c$, then a and b are **factors** of c.	6 and 4 are factors of 24.
The **greatest common factor (GCF)** of two or more numbers is the greatest number that divides into all the numbers.	The GCF of 36 and 48 is 12.
A **prime number** is an integer greater than 1 that has exactly two factors, itself and 1. A positive integer (other than 1) that is not prime is called **composite**. The number 1 is neither prime nor composite; it is called a **unit**.	23 is a prime number. 72 is a composite number.
To Determine the GCF of Two or More Numbers 1. Write each number as a product of prime factors. 2. Determine the prime factors common to all the numbers. 3. Multiply the common factors found in step 2. The product is the GCF.	$40 = 2^3 \cdot 5$ $140 = 2^2 \cdot 5 \cdot 7$ The GCF of 40 and 140 is $2^2 \cdot 5 = 4 \cdot 5 = 20$.
To Determine the Greatest Common Factor of Two or More Terms To determine the GCF of two or more terms, take each factor the *largest* number of times that it appears in all of the terms.	The GCF of xy^2, x^3y^4, and x^2y^3 is xy^2.
To Factor a Monomial from a Polynomial 1. Determine the greatest common factor of all terms in the polynomial. 2. Write each term as the product of the GCF and its other factor. 3. Use the distributive property to factor out the GCF.	$6a^4 + 27a^3 - 18a^2 = 3a^2(2a^2 + 9a - 6)$

IMPORTANT FACTS AND CONCEPTS	EXAMPLES

Section 7.2

To Factor a Four-Term Polynomial Using Grouping

1. Determine whether there are any factors common to all four terms. If so, factor the GCF from each of the four terms.

2. If necessary, arrange the four terms so that the first two terms have a common factor and the last two have a common factor.

3. Use the distributive property to factor each group of two terms.

4. Factor the GCF from the results of step 3.

$$xy + 5x - 3y - 15 = x(y + 5) - 3(y + 5)$$
$$= (y + 5)(x - 3)$$

Section 7.3

To Factor Trinomials of the Form $ax^2 + bx + c$, where $a = 1$

1. Find two numbers whose product equals the constant, c, and whose sum equals the coefficient of the x-term, b.

2. Use the two numbers found in step 1, including their signs, to write the trinomial in factored form. The trinomial in factored form will be

$$(x + \text{one number})(x + \text{second number}).$$

Factor $x^2 + 5x - 36$.

The two numbers whose product is -36 and whose sum is 5 are 9 and -4.

Therefore,

$$x^2 + 5x - 36 = (x + 9)(x - 4).$$

A **prime polynomial** is a polynomial that cannot be factored using only integer coefficients

$x^2 - 7x + 11$ is a prime polynomial.

Section 7.4

To Factor Trinomials of the Form $ax^2 + bx + c, a \neq 1$, by Trial and Error

1. Factor out any factor common to all three terms.

2. Write all pairs of factors of the coefficient of the squared term, a.

3. Write all pairs of factors of the constant term, c.

4. Try various combinations of these factors until the correct middle term, bx, is found.

Factor $3x^2 - 2x - 8$.

Factors of -8	Possible Factors	Sum of the Products of the Outer and Inner Terms
$-1(8)$	$(3x - 1)(x + 8)$	$23x$
$-2(4)$	$(3x - 2)(x + 4)$	$10x$
$-4(2)$	$(3x - 4)(x + 2)$	$2x$
$-8(1)$	$(3x - 8)(x + 1)$	$-5x$
$4(-2)$	$(3x + 4)(x - 2)$	$-2x$

Therefore, $3x^2 - 2x - 8 = (3x + 4)(x - 2)$.

To Factor Trinomials of the Form $ax^2 + bx + c, a \neq 1$, by Grouping

1. Factor out any factor common to all three terms.

2. Find two numbers whose product is equal to the product of a times c, and whose sum is equal to b.

3. Rewrite the middle term, bx, as the sum or difference of two terms using the numbers found in step 2.

4. Factor by grouping as explained in Section 7.2.

Factor $4x^2 + 19x - 30$.
$$ac = 4(-30) = -120$$

Two numbers whose product is -120 and whose sum is 19 are 24 and -5.

$$\overset{\overbrace{\hspace{3em}}^{19x}}{4x^2 + 19x - 30 = 4x^2 + 24x - 5x - 30}$$
$$= 4x(x + 6) - 5(x + 6)$$
$$= (x + 6)(4x - 5)$$

IMPORTANT FACTS AND CONCEPTS	EXAMPLES

Section 7.5

Difference of Two Squares

$$a^2 - b^2 = (a + b)(a - b)$$

$$y^2 - 49 = (y + 7)(y - 7)$$

Sum of Two Cubes

$$a^3 + b^3 = (a + b)(a^2 - ab + b^2)$$

$$
\begin{aligned}
8p^3 + q^3 &= (2p)^3 + (q)^3 \\
&= (2p + q)[(2p)^2 - (2p)(q) + (q)^2] \\
&= (2p + q)(4p^2 - 2pq + q^2)
\end{aligned}
$$

Difference of Two Cubes

$$a^3 - b^3 = (a - b)(a^2 + ab + b^2)$$

$$
\begin{aligned}
8p^3 - q^3 &= (2p)^3 - (q)^3 \\
&= (2p - q)[(2p)^2 + (2p)(q) + (q)^2] \\
&= (2p - q)(4p^2 + 2pq + q^2)
\end{aligned}
$$

General Procedure for Factoring a Polynomial

1. If all the terms of the polynomial have a GCF other than 1, factor it out.

2. If the polynomial has two terms, determine whether it is a difference of two squares or a sum or a difference of two cubes. If so, factor using the appropriate formula.

3. If the polynomial has three terms, factor the trinomial using the methods discussed in Sections 7.3 and 7.4.

4. If the polynomial has more than three terms, try factoring by grouping.

5. Examine your factored polynomial to determine whether the terms in any factors have a common factor. If you find a common factor, factor it out.

Factor $3x^2 - 48$.

$$
\begin{aligned}
3x^2 - 48 &= 3(x^2 - 16) \\
&= 3(x + 4)(x - 4)
\end{aligned}
$$

Section 7.6

Quadratic Equation

Quadratic equations have the form

$$ax^2 + bx + c = 0$$

where a, b, and c are real numbers, $a \neq 0$.

$6x^2 - 7x + 3 = 0$ is a quadratic equation in **standard form**.

Zero-Factor Property

If $ab = 0$, then $a = 0$ or $b = 0$.

If $(x + 3)(x - 1) = 0$, then $x + 3 = 0$ or $x - 1 = 0$.

To Solve a Quadratic Equation Using Factoring

1. Write the equation in standard form with the squared term having a positive coefficient.

2. Factor the side of the equation that is not 0.

3. Set each factor *containing a variable* equal to 0 and solve each equation.

4. Check each solution found in step 3 in the *original* equation.

Solve the equation $x^2 - 3x - 52 = -12$.

$$
\begin{aligned}
x^2 - 3x - 40 &= 0 \\
(x - 8)(x + 5) &= 0 \\
x - 8 = 0 \quad &\text{or} \quad x + 5 = 0 \\
x = 8 \qquad &\qquad x = -5
\end{aligned}
$$

IMPORTANT FACTS AND CONCEPTS	EXAMPLES

Section 7.7

A **right triangle** is a triangle that contains a right, or 90°, angle.

Right angle

Pythagorean Theorem
If a and b represent the legs of a right triangle, and c represents the hypotenuse, then

$$a^2 + b^2 = c^2$$

Hypotenuse
Leg
Leg
Right angle
c b
a

Determine the value of x.

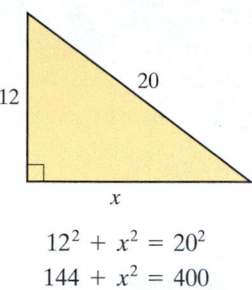

12   20
x

$$12^2 + x^2 = 20^2$$
$$144 + x^2 = 400$$
$$x^2 = 256$$
$$x = 16$$

---

15. $4x^3y^2(5 + 2x^6y - 4x^2)$ **18.** $(5x + 3)(x - 2)$ **28.** $(5x - y)(x + 4y)$ **29.** $(x + 3y)(4x - 5y)$ **30.** $(3a - 5b)(2a - b)$ **32.** $(x - 3y)(3x + 2y)$
33. $(a + 2b)(7a - b)$ **46.** $4x(x + 5y)(x + 3y)$

Chapter 7 Review Exercises

[7.1] *Find the greatest common factor for each set of terms.*

1. $3y^5, y^4, y^3$ y^3
2. $3p, 6p^2, 9p^3$ $3p$
3. $18c^4, 12c^2, 30c^5$ $6c^2$
4. $20x^2y^3, 25x^3y^4, 10x^5y^2z$ $5x^2y^2$
5. $9xyz, 12xz, 36, x^2y$ 1
6. $9st, 16s^2t, 24s, s^3t^3$ s
7. $8(x - 3), x - 3$ $x - 3$
8. $x(x + 5), x + 5$ $x + 5$

Factor each expression. If an expression is prime, so state.

9. $7x - 35$ $7(x - 5)$
10. $35x - 5$ $5(7x - 1)$
11. $24y^2 - 4y$ $4y(6y - 1)$
12. $55p^3 - 20p^2$ $5p^2(11p - 4)$
13. $60a^2b - 36ab^2$ $12ab(5a - 3b)$
14. $9xy - 36x^3y^2$ $9xy(1 - 4x^2y)$
15. $20x^3y^2 + 8x^9y^3 - 16x^5y^2$
16. $24x^2 - 13y^2 + 6xy$ prime
17. $14a^2b - 7b - a^3$ prime
18. $x(5x + 3) - 2(5x + 3)$
19. $3x(x - 1) + 4(x - 1)$ $(x - 1)(3x + 4)$
20. $2x(4x - 3) + 4x - 3$ $(4x - 3)(2x + 1)$

[7.2] *Factor by grouping.*

21. $x^2 + 6x + 2x + 12$ $(x + 6)(x + 2)$
22. $x^2 - 5x + 4x - 20$ $(x - 5)(x + 4)$
23. $y^2 - 6y - 6y + 36$ $(y - 6)^2$
24. $3xy + 3x + 2y + 2$ $(y + 1)(3x + 2)$
25. $4a^2 - 4ab - a + b$ $(a - b)(4a - 1)$
26. $2x^2 + 12x - x - 6$ $(x + 6)(2x - 1)$
27. $x^2 + 3x - 2xy - 6y$ $(x + 3)(x - 2y)$
28. $5x^2 - xy + 20xy - 4y^2$
29. $4x^2 + 12xy - 5xy - 15y^2$
30. $6a^2 - 10ab - 3ab + 5b^2$
31. $pq - 3q + 4p - 12$ $(p - 3)(q + 4)$
32. $3x^2 - 9xy + 2xy - 6y^2$
33. $7a^2 + 14ab - ab - 2b^2$
34. $8x^2 - 4x + 6x - 3$ $(2x - 1)(4x + 3)$

[7.3] *Factor completely. If an expression is prime, so state.*

35. $x^2 - x - 6$ $(x - 3)(x + 2)$
36. $x^2 + 4x - 15$ prime
37. $x^2 + 11x + 18$ $(x + 2)(x + 9)$
38. $n^2 + 3n - 40$ $(n + 8)(n - 5)$
39. $b^2 + b - 20$ $(b + 5)(b - 4)$
40. $x^2 - 15x + 56$ $(x - 8)(x - 7)$
41. $c^2 - 10c - 20$ prime
42. $y^2 - 10y - 22$ prime
43. $x^3 - 17x^2 + 72x$ $x(x - 9)(x - 8)$
44. $t^3 - 5t^2 - 36t$ $t(t - 9)(t + 4)$
45. $x^2 - 2xy - 15y^2$ $(x + 3y)(x - 5y)$
46. $4x^3 + 32x^2y + 60xy^2$

[7.4] *Factor completely. If an expression is prime, so state.*

47. $2x^2 - x - 15$ $(2x + 5)(x - 3)$
48. $6x^2 - 29x - 5$ $(6x + 1)(x - 5)$
49. $4x^2 - 9x + 5$ $(4x - 5)(x - 1)$
50. $5m^2 - 14m + 8$ $(5m - 4)(m - 2)$
51. $16y^2 + 8y - 3$ $(4y + 3)(4y - 1)$
52. $5x^2 - 32x + 12$ $(5x - 2)(x - 6)$

53. $2t^2 + 14t + 9$ prime

54. $5x^2 + 37x - 24$ $(5x - 3)(x + 8)$

55. $6s^2 + 13s + 5$ $(2s + 1)(3s + 5)$

56. $6x^2 + 11x - 10$ $(3x - 2)(2x + 5)$

57. $12x^2 + 2x - 4$ $2(3x + 2)(2x - 1)$

58. $25x^2 - 30x + 9$ $(5x - 3)^2$

59. $9x^3 - 12x^2 + 4x$ $x(3x - 2)^2$

60. $18x^3 + 12x^2 - 16x$ $2x(3x + 4)(3x - 2)$ **61.** $4a^2 - 16ab + 15b^2$ $(2a - 3b)(2a - 5b)$

62. $16a^2 - 22ab - 3b^2$ $(8a + b)(2a - 3b)$

[7.5] *Factor completely.*

63. $x^2 - 100$ $(x + 10)(x - 10)$

64. $x^2 - 36$ $(x + 6)(x - 6)$

65. $3x^2 - 48$ $3(x + 4)(x - 4)$

66. $81x^2 - 9y^2$ $9(3x + y)(3x - y)$

67. $81 - a^2$ $(9 + a)(9 - a)$

68. $64 - x^2$ $(8 + x)(8 - x)$

69. $16x^4 - 49y^2$ $(4x^2 + 7y)(4x^2 - 7y)$

70. $64x^6 - 49y^6$ $(8x^3 + 7y^3)(8x^3 - 7y^3)$

71. $a^3 + b^3$ $(a + b)(a^2 - ab + b^2)$

72. $x^3 - y^3$ $(x - y)(x^2 + xy + y^2)$

73. $x^3 - 1$ $(x - 1)(x^2 + x + 1)$

74. $x^3 + 8$ $(x + 2)(x^2 - 2x + 4)$

75. $a^3 + 27$ $(a + 3)(a^2 - 3a + 9)$

76. $b^3 - 64$ $(b - 4)(b^2 + 4b + 16)$

77. $125a^3 + b^3$ $(5a + b)(25a^2 - 5ab + b^2)$

78. $27 - 8y^3$ $(3 - 2y)(9 + 6y + 4y^2)$

79. $3x^3 - 192y^3$ $3(x - 4y)(x^2 + 4xy + 16y^2)$ **80.** $27x^4 - 75y^2$ $3(3x^2 + 5y)(3x^2 - 5y)$

[7.1–7.5] *Factor completely.*   **92.** $3x(2x + 3)(x + 5)$ **100.** $2x(2x + 5y)(x + 2y)$

81. $x^2 - 14x + 48$ $(x - 6)(x - 8)$

82. $3x^2 - 18x + 27$ $3(x - 3)^2$

83. $5q^2 - 5$ $5(q + 1)(q - 1)$

84. $8x^2 + 16x - 24$ $8(x + 3)(x - 1)$

85. $4y^2 - 36$ $4(y + 3)(y - 3)$

86. $x^2 - 6x - 27$ $(x - 9)(x + 3)$

87. $9x^2 - 6x + 1$ $(3x - 1)^2$

88. $7x^2 + 25x - 12$ $(7x - 3)(x + 4)$

89. $6b^3 - 6$ $6(b - 1)(b^2 + b + 1)$

90. $x^3y - 27y$ $y(x - 3)(x^2 + 3x + 9)$

91. $a^2b - 2ab - 15b$ $b(a + 3)(a - 5)$

92. $6x^3 + 30x^2 + 9x^2 + 45x$

93. $x^2 - 4xy + 3y^2$ $(x - 3y)(x - y)$

94. $3m^2 + 2mn - 8n^2$ $(3m - 4n)(m + 2n)$ **95.** $4x^2 + 12xy + 9y^2$ $(2x + 3y)^2$

96. $25a^2 - 49b^2$ $(5a + 7b)(5a - 7b)$

97. $xy - 7x + 2y - 14$ $(x + 2)(y - 7)$

98. $16y^5 - 25y^7$ $y^5(4 + 5y)(4 - 5y)$

99. $6x^2 + 5xy - 21y^2$ $(2x - 3y)(3x + 7y)$ **100.** $4x^3 + 18x^2y + 20xy^2$

101. $16x^4 - 8x^3 - 3x^2$ $x^2(4x + 1)(4x - 3)$

102. $d^4 - 16$ $(d^2 + 4)(d + 2)(d - 2)$

[7.6] *Solve.*

103. $x(x + 9) = 0$ $0, -9$

104. $(a - 2)(a + 6) = 0$ $2, -6$

105. $(x + 5)(4x - 3) = 0$ $-5, \dfrac{3}{4}$

106. $x^2 + 7x = 0$ $0, -7$

107. $6x^2 + 30x = 0$ $0, -5$

108. $6x^2 + 18x = 0$ $0, -3$

109. $r^2 + 9r + 18 = 0$ $-3, -6$

110. $x^2 - 3x = -2$ $1, 2$

111. $x^2 - 12 = -x$ $-4, 3$

112. $15x + 12 = -3x^2$ $-1, -4$

113. $x^2 - 6x + 8 = 0$ $2, 4$

114. $3p^2 + 6p = 45$ $3, -5$

115. $8x^2 - 3 = -10x$ $\dfrac{1}{4}, -\dfrac{3}{2}$

116. $3p^2 - 11p = 4$ $-\dfrac{1}{3}, 4$

117. $4x^2 - 16 = 0$ $2, -2$

118. $49x^2 - 100 = 0$ $\dfrac{10}{7}, -\dfrac{10}{7}$

119. $8x^2 - 14x + 3 = 0$ $\dfrac{3}{2}, \dfrac{1}{4}$

120. $-48x = -12x^2 - 45$ $\dfrac{3}{2}, \dfrac{5}{2}$

[7.7]

121. State the Pythagorean Theorem. $a^2 + b^2 = c^2$

122. What is the longest side of a right triangle called?   hypotenuse

In Exercises 123 and 124, determine the value of the question mark (?).

123.   6 ft   10 ft
              8 ft

              ?

124.

Express each problem as an equation, then solve.

125. Product of Integers The product of two consecutive positive odd integers is 99. Determine the two integers. 9, 11

126. Product of Integers The product of two positive integers is 56. Determine the integers if the larger is 6 more than twice the smaller. 4, 14

127. Area of Rectangle The area of a rectangle is 180 square feet. Determine the length and width of the rectangle if the length is 3 feet greater than the width. $w = 12$ ft, $l = 15$ ft

128. Right Triangle One leg of a right triangle is 7 feet longer than the other leg. The hypotenuse is 9 feet longer than the shortest leg. Find the lengths of the three sides of the triangle. 8 ft, 15 ft, 17 ft

129. Square The length of each side of a square is made smaller by 4 inches. If the area of the resulting square is 25 square inches, determine the length of a side of the original square. 9 in.

130. Table Brian has a rectangular table. The length of the table is 2 feet greater than the width of the table. A diagonal across the table is 4 feet greater than the width of the table. Find the length of the diagonal across the table. 10 ft

131. Falling Pear How long would it take a pear that falls off a 16-foot tree to hit the ground? 1 sec

132. Baking Brownies The Pine Hills Neighborhood Association has determined that the cost, C, to make x dozen brownies can be estimated by the formula $C = x^2 - 79x + 20$. If they have $100 to be used to make the brownies, how many dozen brownies can the association make to sell at a fund-raiser? 80 dozen

Chapter 7 Practice Test

*To find how well you understand the chapter material, take this practice test. The answers, and the section where the material was initially discussed, are given in the back of the book. Each problem is also fully worked out on the **Chapter Test Prep Video CD**. Review any questions that you answered incorrectly..*

1. Determine the greatest common factor of $9y^5, 15y^3$, and $27y^4$. $3y^3$

2. Determine the greatest common factor of $8p^3q^2, 32p^2q^5$, and $24p^4q^3$. $8p^2q^2$

Factor completely.

3. $5x^2y^3 - 15x^5y^2$ $5x^2y^2(y - 3x^3)$

4. $8a^3b - 12a^2b^2 + 28a^2b$ $4a^2b(2a - 3b + 7)$

5. $4x^2 - 20x + x - 5$ $(x - 5)(4x + 1)$

6. $a^2 - 4ab - 5ab + 20b^2$ $(a - 4b)(a - 5b)$

7. $r^2 + 5r - 24$ $(r + 8)(r - 3)$

8. $25a^2 - 5ab - 6b^2$ $(5a - 3b)(5a + 2b)$

9. $4x^2 - 16x - 48$ $4(x + 2)(x - 6)$

10. $2y^3 - y^2 - 3y$ $y(2y - 3)(y + 1)$

11. $12x^2 - xy - 6y^2$ $(3x + 2y)(4x - 3y)$

12. $x^2 - 9y^2$ $(x + 3y)(x - 3y)$

13. $x^3 - 64$ $(x - 4)(x^2 + 4x + 16)$

Solve.

14. $(6x - 5)(x + 3) = 0$ $\frac{5}{6}, -3$

15. $x^2 - 6x = 0$ $0, 6$

16. $x^2 = 64$ $-8, 8$

17. $x^2 + 18x + 81 = 0$ -9

18. $x^2 - 7x + 12 = 0$ $3, 4$

19. $x^2 + 6 = -5x$ $-2, -3$

20. Right Triangle Find the length of the side indicated with a question mark. 24 in.

21. Right Triangle In a right triangle, one leg is 2 feet less than twice the length of the smaller leg. The hypotenuse is 2 feet more than twice the length of the smaller leg. Determine the hypotenuse of the triangle. 34 ft

22. Product of Integers The product of two positive integers is 36. Determine the two integers if the larger is 1 more than twice the smaller. 4, 9

23. Consecutive Even Integers The product of two positive consecutive even integers is 168. Determine the integers. 12, 14

24. Rectangle The area of a rectangle is 24 square meters. Determine the length and width of the rectangle if its length is 2 meters greater than its width. $l = 6$ m, $w = 4$ m

25. Fallen Object How long would it take for an object dropped from a hot air balloon to fall 1600 feet to the ground? 10 sec

Cumulative Review Test

Take the following test and check your answers with those given in the back of the book. Review any questions that you answered incorrectly. The section where the material was covered is indicated after the answer.

1. Evaluate $4 - 5(2x + 4x^2 - 21)$ when $x = -4$. -171

2. Evaluate $5x^2 - 3y + 7(2 + y^2 - 4x)$ when $x = 3$ and $y = -2$.   9

3. **Motel Room** The cost of a motel room including a 12% state tax and 3% county tax is $103.50. Determine the cost of the room before tax. $90

4. Consider the set of numbers

$$\left\{-6, -0.2, \frac{3}{5}, \sqrt{7}, -\sqrt{2}, 7, 0, -\frac{5}{9}, 1.34\right\}$$

List the elements that are

a) natural numbers.   7

b) rational numbers. $-6, -0.2, \frac{3}{5}, 7, 0, -\frac{5}{9}, 1.34$

c) irrational numbers. $\sqrt{7}, -\sqrt{2}$

d) real numbers. $-6, -0.2, \frac{3}{5}, \sqrt{7}, -\sqrt{2}, 7, 0, -\frac{5}{9}, 1.34$

5. Which is greater, $|-8|$ or $-|8|$? Explain your answer. $|-8|$

6. Solve the equation $4x - 2 = 4(x - 7) + 2x$ for x.   13

7. Solve the proportion $\dfrac{5}{12} = \dfrac{8}{x}$ for x by cross-multiplying.   19.2

8. Solve the inequality $3x - 5 \geq 10(6 - x)$, and graph the solution on a number line. $x \geq 5$

9. Solve the equation $4x + 3y = 7$ for y. Write your answer in $y = mx + b$ form.

10. **Acid Solution** How many liters of a 10% acid solution must be mixed with three liters of a 4% acid solution to get an 8% acid solution?   6 L

11. **Cross-Country Skiing** Two cross-country skiers follow the same trail in a local park. Brooke Stoner skis at a rate of 8 kilometers per hour and Bob Thoresen skis at a rate of

4 kilometers per hour. How long will it take Brooke to catch Bob if she leaves 15 minutes after he does? $\frac{1}{4}$ hr

12. Find an equation of a line through the points $(3, 7)$ and $(-2, 4)$. Write the equation in slope-intercept form.

13. Solve the following system of equations.

$$5x - 2y = -7$$
$$5 = y - 3x \quad (-3, -4)$$

14. Simplify $(2x^{-3})^{-2}(4x^{-3}y^2)^3$. $\dfrac{16y^6}{x^3}$

15. Subtract $(4x^3 - 3x^2 + 7)$ from $(x^3 - x^2 + 6x - 5)$.

Perform the operations indicated.

16. $(3x - 2)(x^2 + 5x - 6)$ $3x^3 + 13x^2 - 28x + 12$

17. $\dfrac{x^2 - 2x + 6}{x + 3}$ $x - 5 + \dfrac{21}{x + 3}$

18. Factor $qr + 2q - 8r - 16$ by grouping. $(r + 2)(q - 8)$

19. Factor $5x^2 - 7x - 6$. $(5x + 3)(x - 2)$

20. Factor $7y^3 - 63y$. $7y(y + 3)(y - 3)$

9. $y = -\dfrac{4}{3}x + \dfrac{7}{3}$ 12. $y = \dfrac{3}{5}x + \dfrac{26}{5}$ 15. $-3x^3 + 2x^2 + 6x - 12$

8 Rational Expressions and Equations

WHEN TWO PEOPLE perform a task, it takes less time than for each person to do the task separately. In Exercise 29 on page 520, we will determine how long it takes two people working together to load baskets of peaches onto a truck when we know how long it takes for each person to do the task separately.

8.1 Simplifying Rational Expressions

1. Determine the values for which a rational expression is defined.

2. Understand the three signs of a fraction.

3. Simplify rational expressions.

4. Factor a negative 1 from a polynomial.

1 Determine the Values for Which a Rational Expression Is Defined

We begin this chapter by defining a *rational expression*.

Rational Expression

A **rational expression** is an expression of the form p/q, where p and q are polynomials and $q \neq 0$.

Examples of Rational Expressions

$$\frac{4}{5}, \quad \frac{x-6}{x}, \quad \frac{x^2+8x}{x-3}, \quad \frac{a}{a^2-4}$$

TEACHING TIP
You may want to use arithmetic fractions to introduce the various operations with rational expressions.

The denominator of a rational expression cannot equal 0 since division by 0 is not defined. In the expression $\dfrac{x+3}{x}$, the value of x cannot be 0 because the denominator would then equal 0. We say that the expression $\dfrac{x+3}{x}$ is *defined* for all real numbers except 0. It is *undefined* when x is 0. In $\dfrac{x^2+8x}{x-3}$, the value of x cannot be 3 because the denominator would then be 0. What values of x cannot be used in the expression $\dfrac{x}{x^2-4}$? If you answered 2 and -2, you answered correctly. **Whenever we have a rational expression containing a variable in the denominator, we always assume that the value or values of the variable that make the denominator 0 are excluded.**

One method that can be used to determine the value or values of the variable that are excluded is to set the denominator equal to 0 and then solve the resulting equation for the variable.

INSTRUCTOR EXAMPLE
Determine the values for which each rational expression is defined.

a) $\dfrac{x-1}{3x-8}$ b) $\dfrac{x+5}{x^2-4x-12}$

Ans.:

a) $x \neq \dfrac{8}{3}$ b) $x \neq -2, x \neq 6$

EXAMPLE 1 ▶ Determine the value or values of the variable for which the rational expression is defined.

a) $\dfrac{7}{x-4}$ b) $\dfrac{3x+4}{2x-7}$ c) $\dfrac{x+5}{x^2+6x-7}$

Solution

a) We need to determine the value or values of x that make $x-4$ equal to 0 and exclude these values. By looking at the denominator we can see that when $x=4$, the denominator is $4-4$ or 0. Thus, we do not consider $x=4$ when we consider the rational expression $\dfrac{7}{x-4}$. This expression is defined for all real numbers except 4. We will sometimes shorten our answer and write $x \neq 4$.

b) We need to determine the value or values of x that make $2x-7$ equal to 0 and exclude these. We can do this by setting $2x-7$ equal to 0 and solving the equation for x.

$$2x - 7 = 0$$
$$2x = 7$$
$$x = \frac{7}{2}$$

TEACHING TIP
After discussing Example 1, show students how to create a rational expression that is not defined for a certain value. Have students write a rational expression that is defined for all real numbers except

a) 5   b) -3 c) -3 and 5

Thus, we do not consider $x = \dfrac{7}{2}$ when we consider the rational expression $\dfrac{3x+4}{2x-7}$. This expression is defined for all real numbers except $x = \dfrac{7}{2}$.

We will sometimes shorten our answer and write $x \neq \dfrac{7}{2}$.

c) To determine the value or values that are excluded, we set the denominator equal to zero and solve the equation for the variable.

$$x^2 + 6x - 7 = 0$$
$$(x + 7)(x - 1) = 0$$
$$x + 7 = 0 \quad \text{or} \quad x - 1 = 0$$
$$x = -7 \qquad\qquad x = 1$$

Therefore, we do not consider the values $x = -7$ or $x = 1$ when we consider the rational expression $\dfrac{x + 5}{x^2 + 6x + 7}$. Both $x = -7$ and $x = 1$ make the denominator zero. This expression is defined for all real numbers except $x = -7$ and $x = 1$. Thus, $x \neq -7$ and $x \neq 1$.

▶ **Now Try Exercise 15**

2   Understand the Three Signs of a Fraction

Three **signs** are associated with any fraction: the sign of the numerator, the sign of the denominator, and the sign of the fraction.

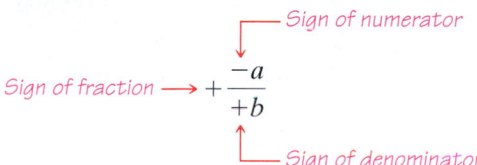

Whenever any of the three signs is omitted, we assume it to be positive. For example,

$$\frac{a}{b} \quad \text{means} \quad +\frac{+a}{+b}$$

$$\frac{-a}{b} \quad \text{means} \quad +\frac{-a}{+b}$$

$$-\frac{a}{b} \quad \text{means} \quad -\frac{+a}{+b}$$

TEACHING TIP
Point out that the value of the fraction is either positive or negative, or zero. For class consistency, suggest that students give their positive answers without any signs and their negative answer with only 1 negative sign in front of the fraction.

> ### Negative Fractions
>
> Changing any two of the three signs of a fraction does not change the value of a fraction. Thus,
>
> $$\frac{-a}{b} = -\frac{a}{b} = \frac{a}{-b}$$

Generally, we do not write a fraction with a negative denominator. For example, the expression $\dfrac{2}{-5}$ would be written as either $\dfrac{-2}{5}$ or $-\dfrac{2}{5}$. The expression $\dfrac{x}{-(4 - x)}$ can be written $\dfrac{x}{x - 4}$ since $-(4 - x) = -4 + x$ or $x - 4$.

3   Simplify Rational Expressions

A rational expression is **simplified** or **reduced to its lowest terms** when the numerator and denominator have no common factors other than 1. The fraction $\dfrac{9}{12}$ is not simplified because 9 and 12 both contain the common factor 3. When the 3 is factored out, the simplified fraction is $\dfrac{3}{4}$.

$$\frac{9}{12} = \frac{\overset{1}{\cancel{3}} \cdot 3}{\underset{1}{\cancel{3}} \cdot 4} = \frac{3}{4}$$

The rational expression $\dfrac{ab - b^2}{2b}$ is not simplified because both the numerator and denominator have a common factor, b. To simplify this expression, factor b from each term in the numerator, then divide it out.

$$\frac{ab - b^2}{2b} = \frac{\overset{1}{\cancel{b}}(a - b)}{2\underset{1}{\cancel{b}}} = \frac{a - b}{2}$$

Thus, $\dfrac{ab - b^2}{2b}$ becomes $\dfrac{a - b}{2}$ when simplified.

TEACHING TIP
Before discussing Examples 2–5, ask, "Is the numerator in factored form? Is the denominator in factored form?" Suggest that students ask themselves these questions whenever simplifying rational expressions.

INSTRUCTOR EXAMPLE
Simplify $\dfrac{6x^4 + 12x^3 - 24x^2}{18x^3}$.

Ans.: $\dfrac{x^2 + 2x - 4}{3x}$

> **To Simplify Rational Expressions**
>
> 1. Factor both the numerator and denominator as completely as possible.
> 2. Divide out any factors common to both the numerator and denominator.

EXAMPLE 2 ▶ Simplify $\dfrac{5x^3 + 10x^2 - 35x}{10x^2}$.

Solution Factor the greatest common factor, $5x$, from each term in the numerator. Since $5x$ is a factor common to both the numerator and denominator, divide it out.

$$\frac{5x^3 + 10x^2 - 35x}{10x^2} = \frac{\overset{1}{\cancel{5x}}(x^2 + 2x - 7)}{\underset{1}{\cancel{5x}} \cdot 2x} = \frac{x^2 + 2x - 7}{2x}$$

▶ **Now Try Exercise 33**

Helpful Hint

Study the expression on the left. The explanation on the right indicates whether a common factor may be divided out of both the numerator and denominator. If an expression can be simplified, the simplified expression is shown on the right.

Expression	Simplified Expression
$\dfrac{x}{x + 3}$	This expression cannot be simplified further because the x in the denominator is not a factor of the denominator.
$\dfrac{x}{3x}$	Since the x is a factor of both the numerator and the denominator, we can factor out an x and we can simplify as follows: $$\frac{\overset{1}{\cancel{x}}}{3\underset{1}{\cancel{x}}} = \frac{1}{3}$$
$\dfrac{(x + 3)(x - 4)}{x + 3}$	Since $x + 3$ can be written as $1(x + 3)$, the $x + 3$ can be considered a factor of the denominator. Since $(x + 3)$ is also a factor of the numerator, the $x + 3$ can be factored out of both the numerator and denominator, as shown below. $$\frac{\overset{1}{\cancel{(x + 3)}}(x - 4)}{1\underset{1}{\cancel{(x + 3)}}} = \frac{x - 4}{1} = x - 4$$

Helpful Hint

In Example 2 we *simplified* a polynomial divided by a monomial using factoring. In Section 6.6 we *divided* polynomials by monomials by writing each term in the numerator over the expression in the denominator. For example,

$$\frac{5x^3 + 10x^2 - 35x}{10x^2} = \frac{5x^3}{10x^2} + \frac{10x^2}{10x^2} - \frac{35x}{10x^2}$$

$$= \frac{x}{2} + 1 - \frac{7}{2x}$$

The answer above, $\frac{x}{2} + 1 - \frac{7}{2x}$, is equivalent to the answer $\frac{x^2 + 2x - 7}{2x}$, which was obtained by factoring in Example 2. We show this below.

$$\frac{x}{2} + 1 - \frac{7}{2x}$$

$$= \frac{x}{x} \cdot \frac{x}{2} + \frac{2x}{2x} \cdot 1 - \frac{7}{2x} \qquad \textit{\textcolor{red}{Write each term with LCD 2x.}}$$

$$= \frac{x^2}{2x} + \frac{2x}{2x} - \frac{7}{2x}$$

$$= \frac{x^2 + 2x - 7}{2x}$$

When asked to *simplify* an expression we will factor numerators and denominators, when possible, then divide out common factors. This process was illustrated in Example 2 and will be further illustrated in Examples 3 through 5.

INSTRUCTOR EXAMPLE

Simplify $\dfrac{x^2 + 3x - 10}{x - 2}$.

Ans.: $x + 5$

EXAMPLE 3 ▶ Simplify $\dfrac{x^2 - x - 12}{x + 3}$.

Solution Factor the numerator; then divide out the common factor.

$$\frac{x^2 - x - 12}{x + 3} = \frac{\overset{1}{\cancel{(x + 3)}}(x - 4)}{\underset{1}{\cancel{x + 3}}} = x - 4$$

▶ **Now Try Exercise 35**

INSTRUCTOR EXAMPLE

Simplify $\dfrac{m^2 - 49}{m - 7}$.

Ans.: $m + 7$

EXAMPLE 4 ▶ Simplify $\dfrac{r^2 - 25}{r - 5}$.

Solution Factor the numerator; then divide out common factors.

$$\frac{r^2 - 25}{r - 5} = \frac{(r + 5)\overset{1}{\cancel{(r - 5)}}}{\underset{1}{\cancel{r - 5}}} = r + 5$$

▶ **Now Try Exercise 61**

INSTRUCTOR EXAMPLE

Simplify $\dfrac{2x^2 + 3x - 5}{x^2 + 2x - 3}$.

Ans.: $\dfrac{2x + 5}{x + 3}$

EXAMPLE 5 ▶ Simplify $\dfrac{3x^2 - 10x - 8}{x^2 + 3x - 28}$.

Solution Factor both the numerator and denominator, then divide out common factors.

$$\frac{3x^2 - 10x - 8}{x^2 + 3x - 28} = \frac{(3x + 2)\overset{1}{\cancel{(x - 4)}}}{(x + 7)\underset{1}{\cancel{(x - 4)}}} = \frac{3x + 2}{x + 7}.$$

Note that $\dfrac{3x + 2}{x + 7}$ cannot be simplified any further.

▶ **Now Try Exercise 41**

Avoiding Common Errors

Remember: Only common *factors* can be divided out from expressions.

<table>
<tr><td align="center">CORRECT</td><td align="center">INCORRECT</td></tr>
</table>

$$\frac{\overset{5}{\cancel{20}}\,\overset{x}{\cancel{x^2}}}{\underset{1}{\cancel{4}}\,\underset{1}{\cancel{x}}} = 5x \qquad\qquad \frac{\overset{x}{\cancel{x^2}} - \overset{5}{\cancel{20}}}{\underset{1}{\cancel{x}} - \underset{4}{\cancel{4}}}$$

In the denominator of the example on the left, $4x$, the 4 and x are factors since they are *multiplied* together. The 4 and the x are also both factors of the numerator $20x^2$, since $20x^2$ can be written $4 \cdot x \cdot 5x$.

Some students incorrectly divide out *terms*. In the expression $\dfrac{x^2 - 20}{x - 4}$, the x and -4 are *terms* of the denominator, not factors, and therefore cannot be divided out.

USING YOUR GRAPHING CALCULATOR

The graphing calculator can be used to determine whether a rational expression has been simplified correctly. To check the simplification below,

$$\frac{3x + 6}{6x^2 - 24} = \frac{1}{2(x - 2)}$$

we let $Y_1 = \dfrac{3x + 6}{6x^2 - 24}$ and $Y_2 = \dfrac{1}{2(x - 2)}$. Then we use the TABLE feature to compare results, as shown in **Figure 8.1**.

FIGURE 8.1

Since Y_1 and Y_2 have the same values for each value of x, we have not made a mistake. This procedure can only tell you if a mistake has been made. It cannot tell you if the fraction has been simplified completely. For example, $\dfrac{3x + 6}{6x^2 - 24}$ and $\dfrac{3}{6x - 12}$ will give you the same set of values, but $\dfrac{3}{6x - 12}$ is not simplified completely. Try this example again, using TblMin $= -3$. What do you notice about the values for Y_1 and Y_2? Do you know why the table is slightly different?

EXERCISES

Use the TABLE feature of your graphing calculator to determine whether the following rational expressions are equal for all values of x where the expression on the left is defined.

1. $\dfrac{x^2 - 4x + 4}{x^2 - 2x}$; $\dfrac{x - 2}{x}$ yes   **2.** $\dfrac{x + 8}{x^2 - 64}$; $\dfrac{1}{x - 8}$ yes   **3.** $\dfrac{x^2 - 4x + 4}{x^2 - 3x - 10}$; $\dfrac{x - 2}{x - 5}$ no   **4.** $\dfrac{5x^2 + 30x}{x + 6}$; $5x$ yes

---

4 Factor a Negative 1 from a Polynomial

Recall from Section 7.2 that when -1 is factored from a polynomial, the sign of each term in the polynomial changes.

Examples

$$-3x + 10 = -1(3x - 10) = -(3x - 10)$$

$$5 - 2x = -1(-5 + 2x) = -(2x - 5)$$

$$-2x^2 + 3x - 4 = -1(2x^2 - 3x + 4) = -(2x^2 - 3x + 4)$$

Whenever the terms in a numerator and denominator differ only in their signs (one is the opposite or additive inverse of the other), we can factor out -1 from either the numerator or denominator and then divide out the common factor. This procedure is illustrated in Example 6.

Simplify $\dfrac{2x - 1}{1 - 2x}$.

Ans.: -1

TEACHING TIP
After discussing Example 6, have students work in pairs to create rational expressions that simplify to -1 having the following criteria:

a) Numerator is a monomial.

b) Denominator is a binomial.

c) Numerator is a trinomial.

d) Denominator is the difference of 2 variables.

Then ask, "How could we change each expression so that it simplifies to -2?"

EXAMPLE 6 ▶ Simplify $\dfrac{3x - 8}{8 - 3x}$.

Solution Since each term in the numerator differs only in sign from its like term in the denominator, we will factor -1 from each term in the denominator.

$$\frac{3x - 8}{8 - 3x} = \frac{3x - 8}{-1(-8 + 3x)}$$

$$= \frac{\overset{1}{\cancel{3x - 8}}}{-\underset{1}{\cancel{(3x - 8)}}}$$

$$= -1$$

▶ **Now Try Exercise 43**

Helpful Hint

In Example 6 we found that $\dfrac{3x - 8}{8 - 3x} = -1$. Note that the numerator, $3x - 8$, and the denominator, $8 - 3x$, are opposites since they differ only in sign. That is,

$$\frac{3x - 8}{8 - 3x} = \frac{3x - 8}{-(3x - 8)} = -1$$

Whenever we have the quotient of two expressions that are opposites, such as $\dfrac{a - b}{b - a}$, $a \ne b$, the quotient can be replaced by -1.

We will use this Helpful Hint in Example 7.

Simplify $\dfrac{3z^2 - 8z + 4}{2 - z}$.

Ans.: $-(3z - 2)$ or $-3z + 2$

EXAMPLE 7 ▶ Simplify $\dfrac{4n^2 - 23n - 6}{6 - n}$.

Solution $\dfrac{4n^2 - 23n - 6}{6 - n} = \dfrac{(4n + 1)\boxed{(n - 6)}}{\boxed{6 - n}}$ *The terms in $n - 6$ differ only in sign from the terms in $6 - n$.*

$$= (4n + 1)(-1)$$ *Replace $\dfrac{n - 6}{6 - n}$ with -1.*

$$= -(4n + 1)$$

Note that $-4n - 1$ is also an acceptable answer.

▶ **Now Try Exercise 49**

EXERCISE SET 8.1
MathXL®   MyMathLab

Concept/Writing Exercises
1. a) and **b)** Answers will vary. **3.** The value of the variable does not make the denominator equal to 0.

✎ **1. a)** Define a rational expression.

   b) Give three examples of rational expressions.

✎ **2.** Explain how to determine the value or values of the variable that makes a rational expression undefined.

✎ **3.** In any rational expression with a variable in the denominator, what do we always assume about the variable?

✎ **4.** Explain how to simplify a rational expression. Answers will vary.

2. Set the denominator equal to zero and then solve the resulting equation.

Explain why the following expressions cannot be simplified.

✎ **5.** $\dfrac{4 + 3x}{9}$ **5.** and **6.** There is no factor common in both the numerator and the denominator.

✎ **6.** $\dfrac{5x + 7y}{12xy}$

Explain why x can represent any real number in the following expressions.

✎ **7.** $\dfrac{x - 3}{x^2 + 2}$ **7.** and **8.** The denominator cannot be 0.

✎ **8.** $\dfrac{x + 6}{x^2 + 4}$

In Exercises 9 and 10, determine what values, if any, x cannot represent. Explain.

9. $\dfrac{x+5}{x-2}$ $x \ne 2$

10. $\dfrac{x}{(x+4)^2}$ $x \ne -4$

11. Is $-\dfrac{x+8}{8-x}$ equal to -1? Explain.   no

12. Is $-\dfrac{3x+2}{-3x-2}$ equal to 1? Explain.   yes

Practice the Skills

13. all real numbers except $x = 0$ **14.** all real numbers except $r = -3$ **15.** all real numbers except $n = 4$

Determine the value or values of the variable where each expression is defined.

13. $\dfrac{x-2}{x}$

14. $\dfrac{8}{r+3}$

15. $\dfrac{7}{4n-16}$

16. $\dfrac{7}{2x-3}$

17. $\dfrac{x+4}{x^2-4}$

18. $\dfrac{9}{x^2+4x-5}$

19. $\dfrac{2x-3}{2x^2-9x+9}$

20. $\dfrac{x^2+2}{2x^2-13x+15}$

21. $\dfrac{x}{x^2+36}$ all real numbers

22. $\dfrac{4}{9+x^2}$ all real numbers

23. $\dfrac{p+8}{4p^2-25}$

24. $\dfrac{10}{9r^2-16}$

16. all real numbers except $x = \dfrac{3}{2}$ **17.** all real numbers except $x = 2, x = -2$ **18.** all real numbers except $x = -5, x = 1$

Simplify the following rational expressions which contain a monomial divided by a monomial. This material was covered in Sections 6.1 and 6.2, and it will help prepare you for the next section.

25. $\dfrac{8x^3y}{24x^2y^5}$ $\dfrac{x}{3y^4}$

26. $\dfrac{18x^3y^2}{30x^4y^5}$ $\dfrac{3}{5xy^3}$

27. $\dfrac{(2a^4b^5)^3}{2a^{12}b^{20}}$ $\dfrac{4}{b^5}$

28. $\dfrac{(5r^2s^3)^2}{(3r^4s)^3}$ $\dfrac{25s^3}{27r^8}$

19. all real numbers except $x = \dfrac{3}{2}, x = 3$ **20.** all real numbers except $x = 5, x = \dfrac{3}{2}$ **23.** all real numbers except $p = \dfrac{5}{2}, p = -\dfrac{5}{2}$

24. all real numbers except $r = \dfrac{4}{3}, r = -\dfrac{4}{3}$

Simplify.

29. $\dfrac{2x}{x+xy}$ $\dfrac{2}{1+y}$

30. $\dfrac{12x}{3x+9}$ $\dfrac{4x}{x+3}$

31. $\dfrac{5x+15}{x+3}$ 5

32. $\dfrac{3x^2+6x}{3x^2+9x}$ $\dfrac{x+2}{x+3}$

33. $\dfrac{x^3+6x^2+7x}{2x}$ $\dfrac{x^2+6x+7}{2}$

34. $\dfrac{x^2y^2-2xy+5y}{y}$ $x^2y-2x+5$

35. $\dfrac{r^2-r-2}{r-2}$ $r+1$

36. $\dfrac{b-6}{b^2-8b+12}$ $\dfrac{1}{b-2}$

37. $\dfrac{x^2+2x}{x^2+4x+4}$ $\dfrac{x}{x+2}$

38. $\dfrac{x^2+3x-18}{4x-12}$ $\dfrac{x+6}{4}$

39. $\dfrac{z^2-10z+25}{z^2-25}$ $\dfrac{z-5}{z+5}$

40. $\dfrac{k^2-6k+9}{k^2-9}$ $\dfrac{k-3}{k+3}$

41. $\dfrac{x^2-2x-3}{x^2-x-6}$ $\dfrac{x+1}{x+2}$

42. $\dfrac{4x^2-12x-40}{2x^2-16x+30}$ $\dfrac{2x+4}{x-3}$

43. $\dfrac{4x-3}{3-4x}$ -1

44. $\dfrac{10a-6}{3-5a}$ -2

45. $\dfrac{x^2-2x-8}{4-x}$ $-(x+2)$

46. $\dfrac{7-s}{s^2-12s+35}$ $-\dfrac{1}{s-5}$

47. $\dfrac{x^2+3x-18}{-2x^2+6x}$ $-\dfrac{x+6}{2x}$

48. $\dfrac{3p^2-13p-10}{3p+2}$ $p-5$

49. $\dfrac{2x^2+5x-3}{1-2x}$ $-(x+3)$

50. $\dfrac{x^2-25}{x^2-2x-15}$ $\dfrac{x+5}{x+3}$

51. $\dfrac{m-2}{4m^2-13m+10}$ $\dfrac{1}{4m-5}$

52. $\dfrac{2x^2-13x+21}{(x-3)^2}$ $\dfrac{2x-7}{x-3}$

53. $\dfrac{x^2-25}{(x+5)^2}$ $\dfrac{x-5}{x+5}$

54. $\dfrac{16x^2+24x+9}{4x+3}$ $4x+3$

55. $\dfrac{6x^2-13x+6}{3x-2}$ $2x-3$

56. $\dfrac{6t^2-7t-5}{3t-5}$ $2t+1$

57. $\dfrac{x^2-3x+4x-12}{x+4}$ $x-3$

58. $\dfrac{x^2-2x+4x-8}{2x^2+3x+8x+12}$ $\dfrac{x-2}{2x+3}$

59. $\dfrac{2x^2-8x+3x-12}{2x^2+8x+3x+12}$ $\dfrac{x-4}{x+4}$

60. $\dfrac{x^3-125}{x^2-25}$ $\dfrac{x^2+5x+25}{x+5}$

61. $\dfrac{a^3-8}{a-2}$ a^2+2a+4

62. $\dfrac{x^3+1}{x+1}$ x^2-x+1

63. $\dfrac{9s^2-16t^2}{3s-4t}$ $3s+4t$

64. $\dfrac{a+6b}{a^2-36b^2}$ $\dfrac{1}{a-6b}$

65. $\dfrac{6x+9y}{2x^2+xy-3y^2}$ $\dfrac{3}{x-y}$

66. $\dfrac{3k^2+6kr-9r^2}{k^2+5kr+6r^2}$ $\dfrac{3(k-r)}{k+2r}$

Problem Solving

Simplify the following expressions, if possible. Treat the unknown symbol as if it were a variable.

67. $\dfrac{3\text{☺}}{15}$ $\dfrac{\text{☺}}{5}$

68. $\dfrac{\text{☺}}{\text{☺} + 8\text{☺}^2}$ $\dfrac{1}{1 + 8\text{☺}}$

69. $\dfrac{7\Delta}{14\Delta + 63}$ $\dfrac{\Delta}{2\Delta + 9}$

70. $\dfrac{\Delta^2 + 2\Delta}{\Delta^2 + 4\Delta + 4}$ $\dfrac{\Delta}{\Delta + 2}$

71. $\dfrac{3\Delta - 4}{4 - 3\Delta}$ -1

72. $\dfrac{(\Delta - 3)^2}{\Delta^2 - 6\Delta + 9}$ 1

Determine the denominator that will make each statement true. Explain how you obtained your answer.

73. $\dfrac{x^2 - x - 6}{\boxed{}} = x - 3$ $x + 2$

74. $\dfrac{2x^2 + 11x + 12}{\boxed{}} = 2x + 3$ $x + 4$

Determine the numerator that will make each statement true. Explain how you obtained your answer.

75. $\dfrac{\boxed{}}{x + 4} = x + 5$ $x^2 + 9x + 20$

76. $\dfrac{\boxed{}}{x - 5} = 2x - 1$ $2x^2 - 11x + 5$

Challenge Problems

In Exercises 77–79, **a)** determine the value or values that x cannot represent. **b)** Simplify the expression.

77. $\dfrac{x - 2}{x^2 - 2x + 3x - 6}$ **a)** $x \neq -3, x \neq 2$ **b)** $\dfrac{1}{x + 3}$

78. $\dfrac{x - 4}{2x^2 - 5x - 8x + 20}$ **a)** $x \neq 4, x \neq \dfrac{5}{2}$ **b)** $\dfrac{1}{2x - 5}$

79. $\dfrac{x + 5}{2x^3 + 7x^2 - 15x}$ **a)** $x \neq 0, x \neq -5, x \neq \dfrac{3}{2}$ **b)** $\dfrac{1}{x(2x - 3)}$

Simplify. Explain how you determined your answer.

80. $\dfrac{\dfrac{1}{6}x^5 - \dfrac{2}{3}x^4}{x^4}$ $\dfrac{1}{6}x - \dfrac{2}{3}$

81. $\dfrac{\dfrac{1}{5}x^5 - \dfrac{2}{3}x^4}{\dfrac{1}{5}x^5 - \dfrac{2}{3}x^4}$ 1

82. $\dfrac{\dfrac{1}{5}x^5 - \dfrac{2}{3}x^4}{\dfrac{2}{3}x^4 - \dfrac{1}{5}x^5}$ -1

Group Activity

Discuss and answer Exercise 83 as a group.

83. a) As a group, determine the values of the variable where the expression $\dfrac{x^2 - 25}{x^3 + 2x^2 - 15x}$ is undefined.

b) As a group, simplify the rational expression. $\dfrac{x - 5}{x(x - 3)}$

c) Group member 1: Substitute 6 in the *original expression* and evaluate.

d) Group member 2: Substitute 6 in the *simplified expression* from part **b)** and compare your result to that of Group member 1.

e) Group member 3: Substitute -2 in the original expression and in the simplified expression in part **b)**. Compare your answers.

f) As a group, discuss the results of your work in parts **c)**–**e)**.

g) Now, as a group, substitute -5 in the original expression and in the simplified expression. Discuss your results.

h) Is $\dfrac{x^2 - 25}{x^3 + 2x^2 - 15x}$ always equal to its simplified form for *any* value of x? Explain your answer.
no, only for those values for which the expression is defined

83. a) Undefined at $x = 0$, $x = 3$, and $x = -5$ **c)** $\dfrac{11}{198} = \dfrac{1}{18}$ **d)** $\dfrac{1}{18}$

e) $-\dfrac{21}{30} = -\dfrac{7}{10}$ **g)** undefined in the original; $-\dfrac{1}{4}$ in the simplified form

Cumulative Review Exercises

[2.6] **84.** Solve the formula $z = \dfrac{x - y}{4}$ for y. $y = x - 4z$

[3.3] **85. Triangle** Find the measures of the three angles of a triangle if one angle is 30° greater than the smallest angle, and the third angle is 10° greater than 3 times the smallest angle.   28°, 58°, 94°

[6.1] **86.** Simplify $\left(\dfrac{5x^2y^2}{9x^4y^3}\right)^2 \cdot \dfrac{25}{81x^4y^2}$

[6.4] **87.** Subtract $3x^2 - 4x - 8 - (-5x^2 + 6x + 11)$.
$8x^2 - 10x - 19$

[7.3] **88.** Factor $3a^2 - 6a - 72$ completely. $3(a + 4)(a - 6)$

[7.7] **89.** Find the length of the hypotenuse of the right triangle.   13 in.

12 in.

5 in.

8.2 Multiplication and Division of Rational Expressions

1 Multiply rational expressions.

2 Divide rational expressions.

1 Multiply Rational Expressions

In Section 1.3 we reviewed multiplication of numerical fractions. Recall that to multiply two fractions we multiply their numerators together and multiply their denominators together.

> **To Multiply Two Fractions**
>
> $$\frac{a}{b} \cdot \frac{c}{d} = \frac{a \cdot c}{b \cdot d}, \quad b \neq 0 \quad \text{and} \quad d \neq 0$$

EXAMPLE 1 ▶ Multiply $\left(\dfrac{3}{5}\right)\left(\dfrac{-2}{9}\right)$.

Solution   First divide out common factors; then multiply.

$$\frac{\overset{1}{\cancel{3}}}{5} \cdot \frac{-2}{\underset{3}{\cancel{9}}} = \frac{1 \cdot (-2)}{5 \cdot 3} = -\frac{2}{15}$$

▶ **Now Try Exercise 7**

The same principles apply when multiplying rational expressions containing variables. Before multiplying, you should first divide out any factors common to both a numerator and a denominator.

> **To Multiply Rational Expressions**
>
> 1. Factor all numerators and denominators completely.
> 2. Divide out common factors.
> 3. Multiply numerators together and multiply denominators together.

EXAMPLE 2 ▶ Multiply $\dfrac{3x^2}{2y} \cdot \dfrac{4y^3}{3x}$.

Solution   This problem can be represented as

$$\frac{3x^2}{2y} \cdot \frac{4y^3}{3x} = \frac{3xx}{2y} \cdot \frac{4yyy}{3x}$$

$$= \frac{\overset{1\;1}{\cancel{3}\cancel{x}x}}{2y} \cdot \frac{4yyy}{\underset{1\;1}{\cancel{3}\cancel{x}}} \qquad \textit{Divide out the 3's and x's.}$$

$$= \frac{\overset{1\;1}{\cancel{3}\cancel{x}x}}{\underset{1\;1}{\cancel{2}\cancel{y}}} \cdot \frac{\overset{2\;1}{\cancel{4}\cancel{y}yy}}{\underset{1\;1}{\cancel{3}\cancel{x}}} \qquad \textit{Divide both the 4 and the 2 by 2, and divide out the y's.}$$

Now we multiply the remaining numerators together and the remaining denominators together.

$$= \frac{2xy^2}{1} \quad \text{or} \quad 2xy^2$$

▶ **Now Try Exercise 19**

Rather than illustrating this entire process when multiplying rational expressions, we will often proceed as follows:

$$\frac{3x^2}{2y} \cdot \frac{4y^3}{3x}$$

$$= \frac{\overset{1}{\cancel{3}}\overset{x}{\cancel{x^2}}}{\underset{1}{\cancel{2}}\underset{1}{\cancel{y}}} \cdot \frac{\overset{2}{\cancel{4}}\overset{y^2}{\cancel{y^3}}}{\underset{1}{\cancel{3}}\underset{1}{\cancel{x}}} = 2xy^2$$

INSTRUCTOR EXAMPLE

Multiply $-\dfrac{2m^2}{7n^4} \cdot \dfrac{8n}{3m^2}$.

Ans.: $-\dfrac{16}{21n^3}$

EXAMPLE 3 ▶ Multiply $-\dfrac{5y^2}{2x^3} \cdot \dfrac{3x^2}{7y^2}$.

Solution
$$-\frac{5\overset{1}{\cancel{y^2}}}{2\underset{x}{\cancel{x^3}}} \cdot \frac{3\overset{1}{\cancel{x^2}}}{7\underset{1}{\cancel{y^2}}} = -\frac{15}{14x}$$

▶ **Now Try Exercise 53**

From this point on when a common factor is factored out from a numerator and a denominator, we will generally not show the 1s above the expression factored out in the numerator and below the expression factored out in the denominator. After the common factor is factored out, if the remaining expression is any number or expression other than 1, we will indicate that by using small numbers above the numerator or below the denominator.

INSTRUCTOR EXAMPLE

Multiply $(x + 4) \cdot \dfrac{3}{x^3 + 4x^2}$.

Ans.: $\dfrac{3}{x^2}$

EXAMPLE 4 ▶ Multiply $(x - 6) \cdot \dfrac{4}{x^3 - 6x^2}$.

Solution
$$(x - 6) \cdot \frac{4}{x^3 - 6x^2} = \frac{\cancel{x - 6}}{1} \cdot \frac{4}{x^2\cancel{(x - 6)}} = \frac{4}{x^2}$$

▶ **Now Try Exercise 27**

INSTRUCTOR EXAMPLE

Multiply $\dfrac{(x + 3)^2}{8x^2} \cdot \dfrac{2x}{x^2 - 9}$.

Ans.: $\dfrac{x + 3}{4x(x - 3)}$

EXAMPLE 5 ▶ Multiply $\dfrac{(x + 2)^2}{6x^2} \cdot \dfrac{3x}{x^2 - 4}$.

Solution
$$\frac{(x + 2)^2}{6x^2} \cdot \frac{3x}{x^2 - 4} = \frac{(x + 2)(x + 2)}{6x^2} \cdot \frac{3x}{(x + 2)(x - 2)}$$

$$= \frac{\cancel{(x + 2)}(x + 2)}{\underset{2}{6}\underset{x}{\cancel{x^2}}} \cdot \frac{\overset{1}{\cancel{3}}\overset{1}{\cancel{x}}}{\cancel{(x + 2)}(x - 2)} = \frac{x + 2}{2x(x - 2)}$$

▶ **Now Try Exercise 61**

In Example 5 we could have multiplied the factors in the denominator to get $\dfrac{x + 2}{2x^2 - 4x}$. This is also a correct answer. In this section we will leave rational answers with the numerator as a polynomial (in unfactored form) and the denominators in factored form, as was given in Example 5. This is consistent with how we will leave rational answers when we add and subtract rational expressions in later sections.

INSTRUCTOR EXAMPLE

Multiply $\dfrac{m-6}{5m} \cdot \dfrac{20m}{6-m}$.

Ans.: -4

EXAMPLE 6 ▶ Multiply $\dfrac{b-4}{5b} \cdot \dfrac{10b}{4-b}$.

Solution
$$\frac{b-4}{\overset{}{\underset{1}{5b}}} \cdot \frac{\overset{2}{10b}}{4-b} = \frac{2(b-4)}{4-b}.$$

This solution is still not complete. In Section 8.1 we showed that $4-b$ is $-1(-4+b)$ or $-1(b-4)$. Thus,

$$\frac{2(b-4)}{4-b} = \frac{2(b-4)}{-1(b-4)} = -2$$

▶ **Now Try Exercise 23**

Helpful Hint

When only the signs differ in a numerator and denominator in a multiplication problem, factor out -1 *from either the numerator or denominator;* then divide out the common factor.

$$\frac{a-b}{x} \cdot \frac{y}{b-a} = \frac{a-b}{x} \cdot \frac{y}{-1(a-b)} = -\frac{y}{x}$$

INSTRUCTOR EXAMPLE

Multiply $\dfrac{2x+5}{3x-1} \cdot \dfrac{2-6x}{2x+5}$.

Ans.: -2

EXAMPLE 7 ▶ Multiply $\dfrac{3x+2}{2x-1} \cdot \dfrac{4-8x}{3x+2}$.

Solution
$$\frac{3x+2}{2x-1} \cdot \frac{4-8x}{3x+2} = \frac{3x+2}{2x-1} \cdot \frac{4(1-2x)}{3x+2} \qquad \textit{Factor.}$$

$$= \frac{3x+2}{2x-1} \cdot \frac{4(1-2x)}{3x+2}. \qquad \textit{Divide out common factors.}$$

Note that the factor $(1-2x)$ in the numerator of the second fraction differs only in sign from $2x-1$, the denominator of the first fraction. We will therefore factor -1 from each term of the $(1-2x)$ in the numerator of the second fraction.

$$= \frac{3x+2}{2x-1} \cdot \frac{4(-1)(2x-1)}{3x+2} \qquad \textit{Factor -1 from the second numerator.}$$

$$= \frac{3x+2}{2x-1} \cdot \frac{-4(2x-1)}{3x+2} \qquad \textit{Divide out common factors.}$$

$$= \frac{-4}{1} = -4$$

▶ **Now Try Exercise 25**

INSTRUCTOR EXAMPLE

Multiply
$\dfrac{3x^2+13x-10}{3x^2+x-2} \cdot \dfrac{2x^2+x-1}{2x^2+9x-5}$.

Ans.: 1

EXAMPLE 8 ▶ Multiply $\dfrac{2x^2+5x-12}{6x^2-11x+3} \cdot \dfrac{3x^2+2x-1}{x^2+5x+4}$.

Solution   Factor all numerators and denominators, and then divide out common factors.

$$\frac{2x^2+5x-12}{6x^2-11x+3} \cdot \frac{3x^2+2x-1}{x^2+5x+4} = \frac{(2x-3)(x+4)}{(2x-3)(3x-1)} \cdot \frac{(3x-1)(x+1)}{(x+1)(x+4)}$$

$$= \frac{(2x-3)(x+4)}{(2x-3)(3x-1)} \cdot \frac{(3x-1)(x+1)}{(x+1)(x+4)} = 1$$

▶ **Now Try Exercise 67**

EXAMPLE 9 ▶ Multiply $\dfrac{2x^3 - 18x^2 + 16x}{6y^2} \cdot \dfrac{-2y}{3x^2 - 3x}$.

Solution

$$\frac{2x^3 - 18x^2 + 16x}{6y^2} \cdot \frac{-2y}{3x^2 - 3x} = \frac{2x(x^2 - 9x + 8)}{6y^2} \cdot \frac{-2y}{3x(x - 1)}$$

$$= \frac{2x(x - 8)(x - 1)}{6y^2} \cdot \frac{-2y}{3x(x - 1)}$$

$$= \frac{\overset{}{2x}(x - 8)\cancel{(x - 1)}}{\underset{3}{\cancel{6}}\underset{y}{y^2}} \cdot \frac{-2\cancel{y}}{\cancel{3x}\cancel{(x - 1)}}$$

$$= \frac{-2(x - 8)}{9y} = \frac{-2x + 16}{9y}$$

▶ **Now Try Exercise 29**

EXAMPLE 10 ▶ Multiply $\dfrac{x^2 - y^2}{x + y} \cdot \dfrac{x + 2y}{2x^2 - 3xy + y^2}$.

Solution

$$\frac{x^2 - y^2}{x + y} \cdot \frac{x + 2y}{2x^2 - 3xy + y^2} = \frac{(x + y)(x - y)}{x + y} \cdot \frac{x + 2y}{(2x - y)(x - y)}$$

$$= \frac{\cancel{(x + y)}\cancel{(x - y)}}{\cancel{x + y}} \cdot \frac{x + 2y}{(2x - y)\cancel{(x - y)}}$$

$$= \frac{x + 2y}{2x - y}$$

▶ **Now Try Exercise 33**

2 Divide Rational Expressions

In Chapter 1 we learned that to divide one fraction by a second fraction, we multiply the first fraction by the reciprocal of the second fraction (or by the reciprocal of the divisor).

To Divide Two Fractions
$\dfrac{a}{b} \div \dfrac{c}{d} = \dfrac{a}{b} \cdot \dfrac{d}{c} = \dfrac{ad}{bc}, \quad b \neq 0, \quad d \neq 0, \quad \text{and} \quad c \neq 0$

EXAMPLE 11 ▶ Divide.

a) $\dfrac{2}{7} \div \dfrac{9}{7}$ **b)** $\dfrac{3}{4} \div \dfrac{10}{6}$

Solution

a) $\dfrac{2}{7} \div \dfrac{9}{7} = \dfrac{2}{\underset{1}{\cancel{7}}} \cdot \dfrac{\overset{1}{\cancel{7}}}{9} = \dfrac{2 \cdot 1}{1 \cdot 9} = \dfrac{2}{9}$

b) $\dfrac{3}{4} \div \dfrac{10}{6} = \dfrac{3}{\underset{2}{\cancel{4}}} \cdot \dfrac{\overset{3}{\cancel{6}}}{10} = \dfrac{3 \cdot 3}{2 \cdot 10} = \dfrac{9}{20}$

▶ **Now Try Exercise 13**

TEACHING TIP
After discussing division in terms of multiplication, have students rewrite Examples 1, 9, and 10 as division problems that give the same answers as the original problems.

The same principles are used to **divide rational expressions**.

> **To Divide Rational Expressions**
>
> Multiply the first fraction by the reciprocal of the second fraction.

INSTRUCTOR EXAMPLE

Divide $\dfrac{2a^3}{b^2} \div \dfrac{3b^2}{7}$.

Ans.: $\dfrac{14a^3}{3b^4}$

EXAMPLE 12 ▶ Divide $\dfrac{8x^3}{z} \div \dfrac{5z^3}{3}$.

Solution   Multiply the first fraction by the reciprocal of the second fraction.

$$\frac{8x^3}{z} \div \frac{5z^3}{3} = \frac{8x^3}{z} \cdot \frac{3}{5z^3} = \frac{24x^3}{5z^4}$$

▶ **Now Try Exercise 35**

INSTRUCTOR EXAMPLE

Divide $\dfrac{x^2 - 16}{x + 2} \div \dfrac{x + 4}{x + 2}$.

Ans.: $x - 4$

EXAMPLE 13 ▶ Divide $\dfrac{x^2 - 9}{x + 4} \div \dfrac{x - 3}{x + 4}$.

Solution

$$\frac{x^2 - 9}{x + 4} \div \frac{x - 3}{x + 4} = \frac{x^2 - 9}{x + 4} \cdot \frac{x + 4}{x - 3}$$

Multiply the first fraction by the reciprocal of the second fraction.

$$= \frac{(x + 3)\cancel{(x - 3)}}{\cancel{x + 4}} \cdot \frac{\cancel{x + 4}}{\cancel{x - 3}} = x + 3$$

Factor, and divide out common factors.

▶ **Now Try Exercise 49**

INSTRUCTOR EXAMPLE

Divide $\dfrac{-1}{5x - 2} \div \dfrac{4}{2 - 5x}$.

Ans.: $\dfrac{1}{4}$

EXAMPLE 14 ▶ Divide $\dfrac{-1}{2x - 3} \div \dfrac{8}{3 - 2x}$.

Solution

$$\frac{-1}{2x - 3} \div \frac{8}{3 - 2x} = \frac{-1}{2x - 3} \cdot \frac{3 - 2x}{8}$$

Multiply the first fraction by the reciprocal of the second fraction.

$$= \frac{-1}{\cancel{2x - 3}} \cdot \frac{-1\cancel{(2x - 3)}}{8}$$

Factor out −1, then divide out common factors.

$$= \frac{(-1)(-1)}{(1)(8)} = \frac{1}{8}$$

▶ **Now Try Exercise 41**

INSTRUCTOR EXAMPLE

Divide $\dfrac{x^2 + 3x - 18}{x^3} \div (x + 6)^2$.

Ans.: $\dfrac{x - 3}{x^3(x + 6)}$

EXAMPLE 15 ▶ Divide $\dfrac{w^2 - 11w + 30}{w^2} \div (w - 5)^2$.

Solution $(w - 5)^2$ means $\dfrac{(w - 5)^2}{1}$. Factor the numerator of the first fraction and multiply by the reciprocal of the second fraction.

$$\frac{w^2 - 11w + 30}{w^2} \div (w - 5)^2 = \frac{w^2 - 11w + 30}{w^2} \cdot \frac{1}{(w - 5)^2}$$

$$= \frac{(w - 6)\cancel{(w - 5)}}{w^2} \cdot \frac{1}{\cancel{(w - 5)}(w - 5)}$$

$$= \frac{w - 6}{w^2(w - 5)}$$

▶ **Now Try Exercise 43**

INSTRUCTOR EXAMPLE

Divide

$$\frac{6x^2 + 15x - 36}{10x} \div \frac{2x^2 - x - 3}{4x^2 + 4x}.$$

Ans.: $\dfrac{6x + 24}{5}$

EXAMPLE 16 ▶ Divide $\dfrac{12x^2 - 22x + 8}{7x} \div \dfrac{3x^2 + 2x - 8}{2x^2 + 4x}$.

Solution

$$\frac{12x^2 - 22x + 8}{7x} \div \frac{3x^2 + 2x - 8}{2x^2 + 4x} = \frac{12x^2 - 22x + 8}{7x} \cdot \frac{2x^2 + 4x}{3x^2 + 2x - 8}$$

$$= \frac{2(6x^2 - 11x + 4)}{7x} \cdot \frac{2x(x + 2)}{(3x - 4)(x + 2)}$$

$$= \frac{2\cancel{(3x - 4)}(2x - 1)}{7\cancel{x}} \cdot \frac{2\cancel{x}\cancel{(x + 2)}}{\cancel{(3x - 4)}\cancel{(x + 2)}}$$

$$= \frac{4(2x - 1)}{7} = \frac{8x - 4}{7}$$

▶ **Now Try Exercise 45**

EXERCISE SET 8.2

MathXL MathXL®   *MyMathLab* MyMathLab

Concept/Writing Exercises   **1.** and **2.** Answers will vary.

✎ **1.** Explain how to multiply rational expressions.   ✎ **2.** Explain how to divide rational expressions.

What polynomial should be in the shaded area of the second fraction to make each statement true? Explain how you determined your answer.   **3.** $x^2 + x - 20$; numerator must be $(x - 4)(x + 5)$ **4.** $2x^2 + x - 6$; numerator must be $(x + 2)(2x - 3)$

✎ **3.** $\dfrac{x + 3}{x - 4} \cdot \dfrac{}{x + 3} = x + 5$ ✎ **4.** $\dfrac{x - 5}{x + 2} \cdot \dfrac{}{x - 5} = 2x - 3$ ✎ **5.** $\dfrac{x - 5}{x + 5} \cdot \dfrac{x + 5}{} = \dfrac{1}{x + 7}$ ✎ **6.** $\dfrac{2x - 1}{x - 3} \cdot \dfrac{x - 3}{} = \dfrac{1}{x - 6}$

5. $x^2 + 2x - 35$; denominator must be $(x + 7)(x - 5)$ **6.** $2x^2 - 13x + 6$; denominator must be $(2x - 1)(x - 6)$

Practice the Skills

Multiply or divide as indicated.

7. $\left(\dfrac{2}{5}\right)\left(\dfrac{15}{19}\right)$ $\dfrac{6}{19}$ **8.** $\left(\dfrac{3}{8}\right)\left(-\dfrac{9}{33}\right)$ $-\dfrac{9}{88}$ **9.** $\left(\dfrac{6}{8}\right)\left(-\dfrac{10}{14}\right)$ $-\dfrac{15}{28}$ **10.** $\left(\dfrac{7}{9}\right)\left(\dfrac{81}{98}\right)$ $\dfrac{9}{14}$ **11.** $\left(-\dfrac{4}{11}\right)\left(-\dfrac{55}{64}\right)$ $\dfrac{5}{16}$

12. $\left(-\dfrac{12}{13}\right)\left(-\dfrac{65}{42}\right)$ $\dfrac{10}{7}$ **13.** $\dfrac{3}{7} \div \dfrac{5}{7}$ $\dfrac{3}{5}$ **14.** $\dfrac{3}{8} \div \dfrac{15}{44}$ $\dfrac{11}{10}$ **15.** $-\dfrac{2}{9} \div \dfrac{32}{39}$ $-\dfrac{13}{48}$ **16.** $\left(-\dfrac{3}{4}\right) \div \left(-\dfrac{15}{16}\right)$ $\dfrac{4}{5}$

Multiply.

17. $\dfrac{6x}{4y} \cdot \dfrac{y^2}{12}$ $\dfrac{xy}{8}$ **18.** $\dfrac{15x^3y^2}{2z} \cdot \dfrac{z}{5xy^3}$ $\dfrac{3x^2}{2y}$ **19.** $\dfrac{14x^2}{y^4} \cdot \dfrac{5x^2}{y^2}$ $\dfrac{70x^4}{y^6}$

20. $\dfrac{7n^3}{16m} \cdot \dfrac{-4}{21m^2n^3}$ $-\dfrac{1}{12m^3}$ 💿 **21.** $\dfrac{6x^5y^3}{5z^3} \cdot \dfrac{6x^4}{5yz^4}$ $\dfrac{36x^9y^2}{25z^7}$ **22.** $\dfrac{x^2 - 4}{x^2 - 16} \cdot \dfrac{x - 4}{x - 2}$ $\dfrac{x + 2}{x + 4}$

23. $\dfrac{3x - 2}{3x + 2} \cdot \dfrac{x - 1}{1 - x}$ $\dfrac{-3x + 2}{3x + 2}$ **24.** $\dfrac{m - 5}{2m + 5} \cdot \dfrac{8m}{-m + 5}$ $-\dfrac{8m}{2m + 5}$ **25.** $\dfrac{x^2 + 7x + 6}{x + 6} \cdot \dfrac{1}{x + 1}$ 1

26. $\dfrac{b^2 + 7b + 12}{6b} \cdot \dfrac{b^2 - 4b}{b^2 - b - 12}$ $\dfrac{b + 4}{6}$ 💿 **27.** $\dfrac{a}{a^2 - b^2} \cdot \dfrac{a + b}{a^2 + ab}$ $\dfrac{1}{a^2 - b^2}$ **28.** $\dfrac{t^2 - 36}{t^2 + t - 30} \cdot \dfrac{t - 5}{4t}$ $\dfrac{t - 6}{4t}$

29. $\dfrac{6x^2 - 14x - 12}{6x + 4} \cdot \dfrac{2x + 4}{2x^2 - 2x - 12}$ 1 **30.** $\dfrac{2x^2 - 9x + 9}{8x - 12} \cdot \dfrac{4x}{x^2 - 3x}$ 1 **31.** $\dfrac{3x^2 - 13x - 10}{x^2 - 2x - 15} \cdot \dfrac{x^2 + x - 2}{3x^2 - x - 2}$ $\dfrac{x + 2}{x + 3}$

32. $\dfrac{2t^2 - t - 6}{2t^2 - 3t - 2} \cdot \dfrac{2t^2 - 5t - 3}{2t^2 + 11t + 12}$ $\dfrac{t - 3}{t + 4}$ **33.** $\dfrac{x + 9}{x - 3} \cdot \dfrac{x^3 - 27}{x^2 + 3x + 9}$ $x + 9$ **34.** $\dfrac{x^3 + 8}{x^2 - x - 6} \cdot \dfrac{x + 5}{x^2 - 2x + 4}$ $\dfrac{x + 5}{x - 3}$

Divide.

35. $\dfrac{12x^3}{y^2} \div \dfrac{3x}{y^3}$ $4x^2y$

36. $\dfrac{9x^3}{5} \div \dfrac{1}{20y^2}$ $36x^3y^2$

37. $\dfrac{15xy^2}{4z} \div \dfrac{5x^2y^2}{12z^2}$ $\dfrac{9z}{x}$

38. $\dfrac{36y}{5z^2} \div \dfrac{3xy}{2z}$ $\dfrac{24}{5xz}$

39. $\dfrac{11xy}{7ab^2} \div \dfrac{6xy}{7}$ $\dfrac{11}{6ab^2}$

40. $3xz \div \dfrac{6xy}{z}$ $\dfrac{z^2}{2y}$

41. $\dfrac{12r + 6}{r} \div \dfrac{2r + 1}{r^3}$ $6r^2$

42. $\dfrac{x - 3}{10y^2} \div \dfrac{x^2 - 9}{5xy}$ $\dfrac{x}{2y(x + 3)}$

43. $\dfrac{x^2 + 11x + 18}{x} \div \dfrac{x + 2}{x}$ $x + 9$

44. $\dfrac{1}{x^2 + 7x - 18} \div \dfrac{1}{x^2 - 17x + 30}$

45. $\dfrac{x^2 - 12x + 32}{x^2 - 6x - 16} \div \dfrac{x^2 - x - 12}{x^2 - 5x - 24}$ $\dfrac{x - 8}{x + 2}$

46. $\dfrac{a - b}{9a + 9b} \div \dfrac{a^2 - b^2}{a^2 + 2a + 7}$ $\dfrac{a^2 + 2a + 7}{9(a + b)^2}$

47. $\dfrac{2x^2 + 9x + 4}{x^2 + 7x + 12} \div \dfrac{2x^2 - x - 1}{(x + 3)^2}$ $\dfrac{x + 3}{x - 1}$

48. $\dfrac{a^2 - b^2}{9} \div \dfrac{3a - 3b}{27x^2}$ $ax^2 + bx^2$

49. $\dfrac{x^2 - y^2}{x^2 - 2xy + y^2} \div \dfrac{x + y}{y - x}$ -1

50. $\dfrac{9x^2 - 9y^2}{18x^2y^2} \div \dfrac{3x + 3y}{12x^2y^5}$ $2xy^3 - 2y^4$

51. $\dfrac{5x^2 - 4x - 1}{5x^2 + 6x + 1} \div \dfrac{x^2 - 5x + 4}{x^2 + 2x + 1}$ $\dfrac{x + 1}{x - 4}$

52. $\dfrac{7n^2 - 15n + 2}{n^2 + n - 6} \div \dfrac{n^2 - 3n - 10}{n^2 - 2n - 15}$ $\dfrac{7n - 1}{n + 2}$

Perform each indicated operation.

44. $\dfrac{x - 15}{x + 9}$ **71.** $\dfrac{2w - 7}{w + 1}$ **72.** $\dfrac{3z + 2}{z - 2}$ **73.** $\dfrac{q - 5}{2q + 3}$

53. $\dfrac{11z}{6y^2} \cdot \dfrac{24x^2y^4}{11z}$ $4x^2y^2$

54. $\dfrac{5z^3}{7} \cdot \dfrac{9x^2}{15z}$ $\dfrac{3x^2z^2}{7}$

55. $\dfrac{63a^2b^3}{20c^3} \cdot \dfrac{4c^4}{9a^3b^5}$ $\dfrac{7c}{5ab^2}$

56. $\dfrac{-2xw}{y^5} \div \dfrac{8x^2}{y^6}$ $-\dfrac{wy}{4x}$

57. $\dfrac{-xy}{a} \div \dfrac{-2ax}{6y}$ $\dfrac{3y^2}{a^2}$

58. $\dfrac{27x}{8y^2} \div 3x^2y^2$ $\dfrac{9}{8xy^4}$

59. $\dfrac{64m^6}{21x^5y^7} \cdot \dfrac{14x^{12}y^5}{16m^5}$ $\dfrac{8mx^7}{3y^2}$

60. $\dfrac{-18x^2y}{11z^2} \cdot \dfrac{22z^3}{x^2y^5}$ $-\dfrac{36z}{y^4}$

61. $\dfrac{(x + 3)^2}{5x^2} \cdot \dfrac{10x}{x^2 - 9}$ $\dfrac{2(x + 3)}{x(x - 3)}$

62. $\dfrac{1}{4x - 3} \cdot (24x - 18)$ 6

63. $\dfrac{1}{5x^2y^2} \div \dfrac{1}{35x^3y}$ $\dfrac{7x}{y}$

64. $\dfrac{x^2y^5}{3z} \div \dfrac{7z}{2x}$ $\dfrac{2x^3y^5}{21z^2}$

65. $\dfrac{(4m)^2}{8n^3} \div \dfrac{m^6n^8}{2}$ $\dfrac{4}{m^4n^{11}}$

66. $\dfrac{11r^5s^2}{(r^2s^3)^3} \cdot \dfrac{6r^4}{4s}$ $\dfrac{33r^3}{2s^8}$

67. $\dfrac{r^2 + 5r + 6}{r^2 + 9r + 18} \cdot \dfrac{r^2 + 4r - 12}{r^2 - 5r + 6}$ $\dfrac{r + 2}{r - 3}$

68. $\dfrac{z^2 - z - 20}{z^2 - 3z - 10} \cdot \dfrac{(z + 2)^2}{(z + 4)^2}$ $\dfrac{z + 2}{z + 4}$

69. $\dfrac{x^2 - 12x + 36}{x^2 - 8x + 12} \div \dfrac{x^2 - 7x + 12}{x^2 - 6x + 8}$ $\dfrac{x - 6}{x - 3}$

70. $\dfrac{p^2 - 5p + 6}{p^2 - 10p + 16} \div \dfrac{p^2 + 2p}{p^2 - 6p - 16}$ $\dfrac{p - 3}{p}$

71. $\dfrac{2w^2 + 3w - 35}{w^2 - 7w - 8} \cdot \dfrac{w^2 - 5w - 24}{w^2 + 8w + 15}$

72. $\dfrac{3z^2 - 4z - 4}{z^2 - 4} \cdot \dfrac{2z^2 + 5z + 2}{2z^2 - 3z - 2}$

73. $\dfrac{q^2 - 11q + 30}{2q^2 - 7q - 15} \div \dfrac{q^2 - 2q - 24}{q^2 - q - 20}$

74. $\dfrac{2x^2 - 19x + 24}{x^2 - 12x + 32} \div \dfrac{2x^2 + x - 6}{x^2 + 7x + 10}$ $\dfrac{x + 5}{x - 4}$

75. $\dfrac{4n^2 - 9}{9n^2 - 1} \cdot \dfrac{3n^2 - 2n - 1}{2n^2 - 5n + 3}$ $\dfrac{2n + 3}{3n - 1}$

76. $\dfrac{2z^2 + 9z + 9}{4z^2 - 9} \div \dfrac{(z + 3)^2}{(2z - 3)^2}$ $\dfrac{2z - 3}{z + 3}$

Problem Solving

Perform each indicated operation. Treat Δ and ☺ as if they were variables.

77. $\dfrac{6\Delta^2}{13} \cdot \dfrac{13}{36\Delta^5}$ $\dfrac{1}{6\Delta^3}$

78. $\dfrac{\Delta - 7}{2\Delta + 5} \cdot \dfrac{3\Delta}{-\Delta + 7}$ $-\dfrac{3\Delta}{2\Delta + 5}$

79. $\dfrac{\Delta - ☺}{9\Delta - 9☺} \div \dfrac{\Delta^2 - ☺^2}{\Delta^2 + 2\Delta☺ + ☺^2}$ $\dfrac{\Delta + ☺}{9(\Delta - ☺)}$

80. $\dfrac{\Delta^2 - ☺^2}{\Delta^2 - 2\Delta☺ + ☺^2} \div \dfrac{\Delta + ☺}{☺ - \Delta}$ -1

For each equation, fill in the shaded area with a binomial or trinomial to make the statement true. Explain how you determined your answer.

81. $\dfrac{\boxed{}}{x + 2} = x + 3$ $x^2 + 5x + 6$

82. $\dfrac{x + 5}{\boxed{}} = \dfrac{1}{x - 5}$ $x^2 - 25$

83. $\dfrac{\boxed{}}{x - 6} = x + 2$ $x^2 - 4x - 12$

84. $\dfrac{\boxed{}}{x^2 - 7x + 10} = \dfrac{1}{x - 2}$ $x - 5$

85. $\dfrac{\boxed{}}{x^2 - 4} \cdot \dfrac{x + 2}{x - 1} = 1$ $x^2 - 3x + 2$

86. $\dfrac{x + 4}{x^2 + 9x + 20} \cdot \dfrac{\boxed{}}{x - 2} = 1$ $x^2 + 3x - 10$

Challenge Problems

Simplify.

87. $\left(\dfrac{x + 2}{x^2 - 4x - 12} \cdot \dfrac{x^2 - 9x + 18}{x - 2} \right) \div \dfrac{x^2 + 5x + 6}{x^2 - 4}$ $\dfrac{x - 3}{x + 3}$

88. $\left(\dfrac{x^2 + 4x + 3}{x^2 - 6x - 16} \right) \div \left(\dfrac{x^2 + 5x + 6}{x^2 - 9x + 8} \cdot \dfrac{x^2 - 1}{x^2 + 4x + 4} \right)$ 1

89. $\left(\dfrac{x^2 - x - 6}{2x^2 - 9x + 9} \div \dfrac{x^2 + x - 12}{x^2 + 3x - 4} \right) \cdot \dfrac{2x^2 - 5x + 3}{x^2 + x - 2}$ $\dfrac{x - 1}{x - 3}$

90. $\dfrac{(x + 1)^2(x - 1)^2}{(x + 2)^4}$

90. $\left(\dfrac{x^2 + 4x + 3}{x^2 - 6x - 16} \div \dfrac{x^2 + 5x + 6}{x^2 - 9x + 8} \right) \cdot \left(\dfrac{x^2 - 1}{x^2 + 4x + 4} \right)$

For Exercises 91 and 92, determine the polynomials that when placed in the shaded areas make the statement true. Explain how you determined your answer.

91. $\dfrac{\boxed{}}{\boxed{}} \cdot \dfrac{x^2 + 3x - 4}{x^2 - 4x + 3} = \dfrac{x - 2}{x - 5}$ $x^2 - 5x + 6, x^2 - x - 20$

92. $\dfrac{\boxed{}}{x^2 + x - 2} \cdot \dfrac{x^2 + 6x + 8}{\boxed{}} = \dfrac{x + 3}{x + 5}$ $x^2 + 2x - 3, x^2 + 9x + 20$

Group Activity

93. Consider the three problems that follow:

1. $\left(\dfrac{x + 2}{x - 3} \right) \div \left(\dfrac{x^2 - 5x + 6}{x - 2} \cdot \dfrac{x + 2}{x - 3} \right)$ $\dfrac{1}{x - 3}$

2. $\left(\dfrac{x + 2}{x - 3} \div \dfrac{x^2 - 5x + 6}{x - 2} \right) \cdot \left(\dfrac{x + 2}{x - 3} \right)$ $\dfrac{(x + 2)^2}{(x - 3)^3}$

3. $\left(\dfrac{x + 2}{x - 3} \right) \div \left(\dfrac{x^2 - 5x + 6}{x - 2} \right) \cdot \left(\dfrac{x + 2}{x - 3} \right)$ $\dfrac{(x + 2)^2}{(x - 3)^3}$

a) Without working the problem, decide as a group which of the problems will have the same answer. Explain.   (2) and (3)

b) Individually, simplify each of the three problems.

c) Compare your answers to part **b)** with the other members of your group. If you did not get the same answers, determine why.

Cumulative Review Exercises

[3.4] **94. Tug Boat** A tug boat leaves its dock traveling at an average of 15 miles per hour towards a barge it is to pull back to the dock. On the return trip, pulling the barge, the tug averages 5 miles per hour. If the trip back to the dock took 2 hours longer than the trip out, find the time it took the tug boat to reach the barge.   1 hr

[6.5] **95.** Multiply $(4x^3y^2z^4)(3xy^3z^7)$. $12x^4y^5z^{11}$

[6.6] **96.** Divide $\dfrac{4x^3 - 5x}{2x - 1}$. $2x^2 + x - 2 - \dfrac{2}{2x - 1}$

[7.4] **97.** Factor $6x^2 - 18x - 60$. $6(x - 5)(x + 2)$

[7.6] **98.** Solve $3x^2 - 9x - 30 = 0$. $5, -2$

8.3 Addition and Subtraction of Rational Expressions with a Common Denominator and Finding the Least Common Denominator

1 Add and subtract rational expressions with a common denominator.

2 Find the least common denominator.

1 Add and Subtract Rational Expressions with a Common Denominator

Recall that when adding (or subtracting) two arithmetic fractions with a common denominator we add (or subtract) the numerators while keeping the common denominator.

> **To Add or Subtract Two Fractions**
>
> $$\frac{a}{c} + \frac{b}{c} = \frac{a+b}{c}, c \neq 0 \qquad \frac{a}{c} - \frac{b}{c} = \frac{a-b}{c}, c \neq 0$$

EXAMPLE 1 ▶ **a)** Add $\frac{7}{16} + \frac{8}{16}$.   **b)** Subtract $\frac{4}{9} - \frac{1}{9}$.

Solution

a) $\frac{7}{16} + \frac{8}{16} = \frac{7+8}{16} = \frac{15}{16}$ **b)** $\frac{4}{9} - \frac{1}{9} = \frac{4-1}{9} = \frac{3}{9} = \frac{1}{3}$

▶ **Now Try Exercise 13**

Note in Example **1a)** that we did not simplify $\frac{8}{16}$ to $\frac{1}{2}$. The fractions are given with a common denominator, 16. If $\frac{8}{16}$ was simplified to $\frac{1}{2}$, you would lose the common denominator that is needed to add or subtract fractions.

The same principles apply when **adding or subtracting rational expressions** containing variables.

> **To Add or Subtract Rational Expressions with a Common Denominator**
>
> 1. Add or subtract the numerators.
> 2. Place the sum or difference of the numerators found in step 1 over the common denominator.
> 3. Simplify the fraction if possible.

EXAMPLE 2 ▶ Add $\frac{3}{x-4} + \frac{x+8}{x-4}$.

Solution

$$\frac{3}{x-4} + \frac{x+8}{x-4} = \frac{3+(x+8)}{x-4} = \frac{x+11}{x-4}$$

▶ **Now Try Exercise 19**

EXAMPLE 3 ▶ Add $\frac{2x^2+7}{x+3} + \frac{6x-7}{x+3}$.

Solution

$$\frac{2x^2+7}{x+3} + \frac{6x-7}{x+3} = \frac{(2x^2+7)+(6x-7)}{x+3}$$

$$= \frac{2x^2+7+6x-7}{x+3}$$

$$= \frac{2x^2+6x}{x+3}$$

Now factor $2x$ from each term in the numerator and simplify.

$$= \frac{2x\cancel{(x+3)}}{\cancel{x+3}} = 2x$$

▶ **Now Try Exercise 21**

EXAMPLE 4 ▶ Add $\dfrac{x^2 + 2x - 2}{(x + 5)(x - 2)} + \dfrac{5x + 12}{(x + 5)(x - 2)}.$

Solution

$$\frac{x^2 + 2x - 2}{(x + 5)(x - 2)} + \frac{5x + 12}{(x + 5)(x - 2)} = \frac{(x^2 + 2x - 2) + (5x + 12)}{(x + 5)(x - 2)}$$ *Write as a single fraction.*

$$= \frac{x^2 + 2x - 2 + 5x + 12}{(x + 5)(x - 2)}$$ *Remove parentheses in the numerator.*

$$= \frac{x^2 + 7x + 10}{(x + 5)(x - 2)}$$ *Combine like terms.*

$$= \frac{\cancel{(x + 5)}(x + 2)}{\cancel{(x + 5)}(x - 2)}$$ *Factor, divide out common factor.*

$$= \frac{x + 2}{x - 2}$$

▶ **Now Try Exercise 27**

When subtracting rational expressions, be sure to subtract the entire numerator of the fraction being subtracted. Study the following Avoiding Common Errors box very carefully.

Avoiding Common Errors

Consider the subtraction

$$\frac{4x}{x - 2} - \frac{2x + 1}{x - 2}$$

Many people begin problems of this type incorrectly. Here are the correct and incorrect ways of working this problem.

CORRECT	INCORRECT
$\dfrac{4x}{x - 2} - \dfrac{2x + 1}{x - 2} = \dfrac{4x - (2x + 1)}{x - 2}$	$\dfrac{\cancel{4x}}{\cancel{x - 2}} - \dfrac{\cancel{2x + 1}}{\cancel{x - 2}} \dfrac{\cancel{4x - 2x + 1}}{\cancel{x - 2}}$
$= \dfrac{4x - 2x - 1}{x - 2}$	
$= \dfrac{2x - 1}{x - 2}$	

Note that the entire numerator of the second fraction (not just the first term) **must be subtracted**. Also note that the sign of *each* term of the numerator being subtracted will change when the parentheses are removed.

INSTRUCTOR EXAMPLE
Subtract
$\dfrac{x^2 + 7x - 13}{x^2 + 8x + 12} - \dfrac{x^2 + 8x - 7}{x^2 + 8x + 12}$.
Ans.: $-\dfrac{1}{x + 2}$

EXAMPLE 5 ▶ Subtract $\dfrac{x^2 - 6x + 3}{x^2 + 7x + 12} - \dfrac{x^2 - 8x - 5}{x^2 + 7x + 12}$.

Solution

$$\dfrac{x^2 - 6x + 3}{x^2 + 7x + 12} - \dfrac{x^2 - 8x - 5}{x^2 + 7x + 12} = \dfrac{(x^2 - 6x + 3) - (x^2 - 8x - 5)}{x^2 + 7x + 12}$$ *Write as a single fraction.*

$$= \dfrac{x^2 - 6x + 3 - x^2 + 8x + 5}{x^2 + 7x + 12}$$ *Remove parentheses.*

$$= \dfrac{2x + 8}{x^2 + 7x + 12}$$ *Combine like terms.*

$$= \dfrac{2\cancel{(x + 4)}}{(x + 3)\cancel{(x + 4)}}$$ *Factor, divide out common factor.*

$$= \dfrac{2}{x + 3}$$

▶ **Now Try Exercise 43**

The variable used when working with rational expressions is irrelevant. In Example 6 we work with rational expressions in variable *r*.

INSTRUCTOR EXAMPLE
Subtract $\dfrac{3m}{m + 4} - \dfrac{4m^2 + 20m + 4}{m + 4}$.
Ans.: $-(4m + 1)$ or $-4m - 1$

EXAMPLE 6 ▶ Subtract $\dfrac{6r}{r - 5} - \dfrac{4r^2 - 17r + 15}{r - 5}$

Solution

$$\dfrac{6r}{r - 5} - \dfrac{4r^2 - 17r + 15}{r - 5} = \dfrac{6r - (4r^2 - 17r + 15)}{r - 5}$$ *Write as a single fraction.*

$$= \dfrac{6r - 4r^2 + 17r - 15}{r - 5}$$ *Remove parentheses.*

$$= \dfrac{-4r^2 + 23r - 15}{r - 5}$$ *Combine like terms.*

$$= \dfrac{-(4r^2 - 23r + 15)}{r - 5}$$ *Factor out −1.*

$$= \dfrac{-(4r - 3)\cancel{(r - 5)}}{\cancel{r - 5}}$$ *Factor, divide out common factor.*

$$= -(4r - 3) \quad \text{or} \quad -4r + 3$$

▶ **Now Try Exercise 31**

2 Find the Least Common Denominator

To add two fractions with unlike denominators, we must first obtain a common denominator. Now we explain how to find the **least common denominator** for rational expressions. We will use this information in Section 8.4 when we add and subtract rational expressions.

INSTRUCTOR EXAMPLE
Add $\dfrac{1}{2} + \dfrac{3}{5}$.
Ans.: $\dfrac{11}{10}$ or $1\dfrac{1}{10}$

EXAMPLE 7 ▶ Add $\dfrac{4}{7} + \dfrac{2}{3}$.

Solution   The least common denominator (LCD) of the fractions $\dfrac{4}{7}$ and $\dfrac{2}{3}$ is 21.

Twenty-one is the smallest number that is divisible by both denominators, 7 and 3. Rewrite each fraction so that its denominator is 21.

$$\dfrac{4}{7} + \dfrac{2}{3} = \dfrac{3}{3} \cdot \dfrac{4}{7} + \dfrac{2}{3} \cdot \dfrac{7}{7}$$

$$= \dfrac{12}{21} + \dfrac{14}{21} = \dfrac{26}{21} \quad \text{or} \quad 1\dfrac{5}{21}$$

▶ **Now Try Exercise 95**

To add or subtract rational expressions, we must write each expression with a common denominator.

> ### To Find the Least Common Denominator of Rational Expressions
>
> 1. Factor each denominator completely. Any factors that occur more than once should be expressed as powers. For example, $(x - 3)(x - 3)$ should be expressed as $(x - 3)^2$.
>
> 2. List all different factors (other than 1) that appear in any of the denominators. When the same factor appears in more than one denominator, write that factor with the highest power that appears.
>
> 3. The least common denominator is the product of all the factors listed in step 2.

TEACHING TIP
Emphasize that the LCD is the product of the highest power of each factor found in any of the denominators.

INSTRUCTOR EXAMPLE
Find the LCD.
$$\frac{1}{5} + \frac{1}{x}$$
Ans.: $5x$

EXAMPLE 8 ▶ Find the least common denominator.
$$\frac{1}{7} + \frac{1}{y}$$

Solution   The only factor (other than 1) of the first denominator is 7. The only factor (other than 1) of the second denominator is y. The LCD is therefore $7 \cdot y = 7y$.

▶ **Now Try Exercise 53**

INSTRUCTOR EXAMPLE
Find the LCD.
$$\frac{2}{x^3} + \frac{4}{9x}$$
Ans.: $9x^3$

EXAMPLE 9 ▶ Find the LCD.
$$\frac{8}{x^2} - \frac{3}{5x}$$

Solution   The factors that appear in the denominators are 5 and x. List each factor with its highest power. The LCD is the product of these factors.

$$\overset{\text{Highest power of } x}{\text{LCD} = 5 \cdot x^2 = 5x^2}$$

▶ **Now Try Exercise 59**

INSTRUCTOR EXAMPLE
Find the LCD.
$$\frac{7}{12xy^4} - \frac{11}{18x^2y^2}$$
Ans.: $36x^2y^4$

EXAMPLE 10 ▶ Find the LCD.
$$\frac{11}{18x^3y} + \frac{5}{27x^2y^3}$$

Solution   Write both 18 and 27 as products of prime factors: $18 = 2 \cdot 3^2$ and $27 = 3^3$. *If you have forgotten how to write a number as a product of prime factors, read Section 7.1 or Appendix B now.*

$$\frac{11}{18x^3y} + \frac{5}{27x^2y^3} = \frac{11}{2 \cdot 3^2 x^3 y} + \frac{5}{3^3 x^2 y^3}$$

The factors that appear are 2, 3, x, and y. List the highest powers of each of these factors.

$$\text{LCD} = 2 \cdot 3^3 \cdot x^3 \cdot y^3 = 54x^3y^3$$

▶ **Now Try Exercise 61**

INSTRUCTOR EXAMPLE
Find the LCD.
$$\frac{4}{x} - \frac{2y}{x + 5}$$
Ans.: $x(x + 5)$

EXAMPLE 11 ▶ Find the LCD.
$$\frac{9}{x} - \frac{2z}{x + 3}$$

Solution   The factors in the denominators are x and $x + 3$. *Note that the x in the second denominator, $x + 3$, is a term, not a factor.*
$$\text{LCD} = x(x + 3)$$

▶ **Now Try Exercise 65**

INSTRUCTOR EXAMPLE
Find the LCD.

$$\frac{3}{4x^2 - 12x} + \frac{2x^2}{x^2 - 6x + 9}$$

Ans.: $4x(x - 3)^2$

EXAMPLE 12 ▸ Find the LCD.

$$\frac{7}{3x^2 - 6x} + \frac{8x^2}{x^2 - 4x + 4}$$

Solution   Factor both denominators.

$$\frac{7}{3x^2 - 6x} + \frac{8x^2}{x^2 - 4x + 4} = \frac{7}{3x(x - 2)} + \frac{8x^2}{(x - 2)(x - 2)}$$

$$= \frac{7}{3x(x - 2)} + \frac{8x^2}{(x - 2)^2}$$

The factors in the denominators are $3, x$, and $x - 2$. List the highest power of each of these factors.

$$LCD = 3 \cdot x \cdot (x - 2)^2 = 3x(x - 2)^2.$$

▸ **Now Try Exercise 85**

INSTRUCTOR EXAMPLE
Find the LCD.

$$\frac{3x}{x^2 + 2x - 15} + \frac{9x^2}{x^2 + 4x - 5}$$

Ans.: $(x - 3)(x + 5)(x - 1)$

EXAMPLE 13 ▸ Find the LCD.

$$\frac{11x}{x^2 - x - 12} - \frac{6x^2}{x^2 - 7x + 12}$$

Solution   Factor both denominators.

$$\frac{11x}{x^2 - x - 12} - \frac{6x^2}{x^2 - 7x + 12} = \frac{11x}{(x + 3)(x - 4)} - \frac{6x^2}{(x - 3)(x - 4)}$$

The factors in the denominators are $x + 3$, $x - 4$, and $x - 3$.

$$LCD = (x + 3)(x - 4)(x - 3)$$

Although $x - 4$ is a common factor of each denominator, the highest power of that factor that appears in each denominator is 1.

▸ **Now Try Exercise 81**

INSTRUCTOR EXAMPLE
Find the LCD.

$$\frac{12n}{n^2 + 4n - 32} + 2n + 9$$

Ans.: $(n + 8)(n - 4)$

EXAMPLE 14 ▸ Find the LCD.

$$\frac{6w}{w^2 - 14w + 45} + w + 8$$

Solution   Factor the denominator of the first term.

$$\frac{6w}{w^2 - 14w + 45} + w + 8 = \frac{6w^2}{(w - 5)(w - 9)} + w + 8$$

Since the denominator of $w + 8$ is 1, the expression can be rewritten as

$$\frac{6w}{(w - 5)(w - 9)} + \frac{w + 8}{1}$$

The LCD is therefore $1(w - 5)(w - 9)$ or simply $(w - 5)(w - 9)$.

▸ **Now Try Exercise 89**

EXERCISE SET 8.3

<small>MathXL®</small>   <small>MyMathLab</small>

Concept/Writing Exercises

  1. Explain how to add or subtract rational expressions with a common denominator. *Answers will vary.*

  2. When subtracting rational expressions, what must happen to the sign of each term of the numerator being subtracted? *signs change*

  3. Explain how to find the least common denominator of two rational expressions. *Answers will vary.*

  4. In the addition $\dfrac{1}{x} + \dfrac{1}{x + 1}$, is the least common denominator x, $x + 1$, or $x(x + 1)$? Explain. *$x(x + 1)$*

Determine the LCD to be used to perform each indicated operation. Explain how you determined the LCD. Do not perform the operations.

5. $\dfrac{9}{x+6} - \dfrac{2}{x}$ $x(x+6)$

6. $\dfrac{10}{x-2} + \dfrac{3}{7}$ $7(x-2)$

7. $\dfrac{2}{x+3} + \dfrac{1}{x} + \dfrac{1}{4}$ $4x(x+3)$

8. $\dfrac{6}{x-3} + \dfrac{1}{x} - \dfrac{1}{8}$ $8x(x-3)$

In Exercises 9–12, **a)** *Explain why the expression on the left side of the equal sign is not equal to the expression on the right side of the equal sign.* **b)** *Show what the expression on the right side should be for it to be equal to the one on the left.*

9. $\dfrac{4x-3}{5x+4} - \dfrac{2x-9}{5x+4} \neq \dfrac{4x-3-2x-9}{5x+4}$ **b)** $\dfrac{4x-3-2x+9}{5x+4}$

10. $\dfrac{5x}{2x-3} - \dfrac{-3x-7}{2x-3} \neq \dfrac{5x+3x-7}{2x-3}$ **b)** $\dfrac{5x+3x+7}{2x-3}$

11. $\dfrac{8x-2}{x^2-4x+3} - \dfrac{3x^2-4x+5}{x^2-4x+3} \neq \dfrac{8x-2-3x^2-4x+5}{x^2-4x+3}$ **b)** $\dfrac{8x-2-3x^2+4x-5}{x^2-4x+3}$

12. $\dfrac{2x+5}{x^2-6x} - \dfrac{-x^2+3x+6}{x^2-6x} \neq \dfrac{2x+5+x^2+3x+6}{x^2-6x}$ **b)** $\dfrac{2x+5+x^2-3x-6}{x^2-6x}$

Practice the Skills

27. $\dfrac{1}{m-3}$ **28.** $\dfrac{x+5}{x+6}$

Add or subtract.

13. $\dfrac{4}{7} + \dfrac{2}{7}$ $\dfrac{6}{7}$

14. $\dfrac{8}{5} - \dfrac{6}{5}$ $\dfrac{2}{5}$

15. $\dfrac{5r+2}{4} - \dfrac{3}{4}$ $\dfrac{5r-1}{4}$

16. $\dfrac{3x+6}{2} - \dfrac{x}{2}$ $x+3$

17. $\dfrac{2}{x} + \dfrac{x+4}{x}$ $\dfrac{x+6}{x}$

18. $\dfrac{3x+1}{x+1} + \dfrac{6x+8}{x+1}$ 9

19. $\dfrac{6}{n+1} + \dfrac{n+2}{n+1}$ $\dfrac{n+8}{n+1}$

20. $\dfrac{7}{x-2} - \dfrac{x+4}{x-2}$ $\dfrac{-x+3}{x-2}$

21. $\dfrac{x}{x-3} + \dfrac{4x+9}{x-3}$ $\dfrac{5x+9}{x-3}$

22. $\dfrac{4x-3}{x-7} - \dfrac{2x+8}{x-7}$ $\dfrac{2x-11}{x-7}$

23. $\dfrac{4t+7}{5t^2} - \dfrac{3t+4}{5t^2}$ $\dfrac{t+3}{5t^2}$

24. $\dfrac{3w+6}{w^2+2w+1} + \dfrac{-2w-5}{w^2+2w+1}$ $\dfrac{1}{w+1}$

25. $\dfrac{5x+4}{x^2-x-12} + \dfrac{-4x-1}{x^2-x-12}$ $\dfrac{1}{x-4}$

26. $\dfrac{-x-6}{x^2-16} + \dfrac{2(x+5)}{x^2-16}$ $\dfrac{1}{x-4}$

27. $\dfrac{2m+5}{(m+4)(m-3)} - \dfrac{m+1}{(m+4)(m-3)}$

28. $\dfrac{x^2+3x}{(x+6)(x-3)} - \dfrac{x+15}{(x+6)(x-3)}$

29. $\dfrac{2p-6}{p-5} - \dfrac{p+6}{p-5}$ $\dfrac{p-12}{p-5}$

30. $\dfrac{x^2-6}{3x} - \dfrac{x^2+4x-11}{3x}$ $\dfrac{-4x+5}{3x}$

31. $\dfrac{x^2+4x+1}{x+2} - \dfrac{5x+7}{x+2}$ $x-3$

32. $\dfrac{-4x+2}{3x+6} + \dfrac{4(x-1)}{3x+6}$ $\dfrac{-2}{3x+6}$

33. $\dfrac{3x+13}{2x+10} - \dfrac{2(x+4)}{2x+10}$ $\dfrac{1}{2}$

34. $\dfrac{x^2}{x+4} - \dfrac{16}{x+4}$ $x-4$

35. $\dfrac{b^2-2b-2}{b^2-b-6} + \dfrac{b-4}{b^2-b-6}$ 1

36. $\dfrac{4x+17}{3-x} - \dfrac{3x+20}{3-x}$ -1

37. $\dfrac{t-3}{t+3} - \dfrac{-3t-15}{t+3}$ 4

38. $\dfrac{x+8}{3x+2} - \dfrac{x+8}{3x+2}$ 0

39. $\dfrac{3x^2+15x}{x^3+2x^2-8x} + \dfrac{2x^2+5x}{x^3+2x^2-8x}$ $\dfrac{5}{x-2}$

40. $\dfrac{x^2-12}{x+5} - \dfrac{13}{x+5}$ $x-5$

41. $\dfrac{3x^2-9x}{4x^2-8x} + \dfrac{3x}{4x^2-8x}$ $\dfrac{3}{4}$

42. $\dfrac{x^3-10x^2+35x}{x(x-6)} - \dfrac{x^2+5x}{x(x-6)}$ $x-5$

43. $\dfrac{3x^2-4x+6}{3x^2+7x+2} - \dfrac{10x+11}{3x^2+7x+2}$ $\dfrac{x-5}{x+2}$

44. $\dfrac{x^2-2}{x^2+6x-7} - \dfrac{-4x+19}{x^2+6x-7}$ $\dfrac{x-3}{x-1}$

45. $\dfrac{x^2+3x-6}{x^2-5x+4} - \dfrac{-2x^2+4x-4}{x^2-5x+4}$ $\dfrac{3x+2}{x-4}$

46. $\dfrac{4x^2+15}{9x^2-64} - \dfrac{x^2-x+39}{9x^2-64}$ $\dfrac{x+3}{3x+8}$

47. $\dfrac{5x^2+30x+8}{x^2-64} + \dfrac{x^2+19x}{x^2-64}$ $\dfrac{6x+1}{x-8}$

48. $\dfrac{20x^2+8x+1}{6x^2+x-2} - \dfrac{8x^2-9x-5}{6x^2+x-2}$ $\dfrac{4x+3}{2x-1}$

56. $(x+3)(x-9)$ **69.** $4n-1$ or $1-4n$ **70.** $2a-3b$ or $-2a+3b$ **71.** $4k-5r$ or $-4k+5r$ **72.** $2p(2p+1)$

Find the least common denominator for each expression.

49. $\dfrac{x}{5} + \dfrac{x+4}{5}$ 5

50. $\dfrac{2+r}{7} - \dfrac{12}{7}$ 7

51. $\dfrac{3}{n} + \dfrac{1}{9n}$ $9n$

52. $\dfrac{6}{x+1} - \dfrac{4}{7}$ $7(x+1)$

53. $\dfrac{3}{5x} + \dfrac{7}{3}$ $15x$

54. $\dfrac{1}{8} + \dfrac{1}{z}$ $8z$

55. $\dfrac{6}{p} + \dfrac{9}{p^3}$ p^3

56. $\dfrac{2x}{x+3} + \dfrac{6}{x-9}$

57. $\dfrac{m+3}{3m-4} + m$ $3m-4$

58. $\dfrac{x+4}{2x} + \dfrac{8}{7x}$ $14x$

59. $\dfrac{x}{6x} + \dfrac{4}{x^2}$ $6x^2$

60. $\dfrac{x}{5x^2} + \dfrac{9}{7x^3}$ $35x^3$

61. $\dfrac{x+1}{12x^2y} - \dfrac{7}{9x^3}$ $36x^3y$

62. $\dfrac{-3}{8x^2y^2} + \dfrac{5}{12x^4y^5}$ $24x^4y^5$

63. $\dfrac{4}{2r^4s^5} - \dfrac{5}{9r^3s^7}$ $18r^4s^7$

64. $\dfrac{5}{4w^5z^4} + \dfrac{4}{9wz^2}$ $36w^5z^4$

65. $\dfrac{3}{m} - \dfrac{17m}{m+2}$ $m(m+2)$

66. $\dfrac{x-3}{17} - \dfrac{6}{x-5}$ $17(x-5)$

67. $\dfrac{5x-2}{x^2+x} - \dfrac{13}{x}$ $x(x+1)$

68. $\dfrac{3t}{t-5} + \dfrac{2}{5-t}$ $t-5$ or $5-t$

69. $\dfrac{n}{4n-1} + \dfrac{n-8}{1-4n}$

70. $\dfrac{3}{-2a+3b} - \dfrac{10}{2a-3b}$

71. $\dfrac{3}{4k-5r} - \dfrac{10}{-4k+5r}$

72. $\dfrac{p}{4p^2+2p} - \dfrac{7}{2p+1}$

73. $\dfrac{4}{2q^2 + 2q} - \dfrac{5}{9q}$ $18q(q + 1)$

74. $\dfrac{10}{(x + 4)(x + 2)} - \dfrac{6 + x}{x + 2}$ $(x + 4)(x + 2)$

75. $\dfrac{21}{24x^2y} + \dfrac{x + 4}{15xy^3}$ $120x^2y^3$

76. $\dfrac{p^2 + 4}{p^2 - 25} + \dfrac{9}{p - 5}$ $(p + 5)(p - 5)$

77. $\dfrac{11}{3x + 12} + \dfrac{3x + 1}{2x + 4}$ $6(x + 4)(x + 2)$

78. $6x^2 + \dfrac{8x}{x - 7}$ $x - 7$

79. $\dfrac{9x + 4}{x + 1} - \dfrac{2x - 6}{x + 8}$ $(x + 1)(x + 8)$

80. $\dfrac{x + 3}{x^2 + 11x + 18} - \dfrac{x^2 - 11}{x^2 - 3x - 10}$

81. $\dfrac{x - 2}{x^2 - 5x - 24} + \dfrac{3}{x^2 + 11x + 24}$

82. $\dfrac{6n}{n^2 - 4} - \dfrac{n - 3}{n^2 - 5n - 14}$

83. $\dfrac{5}{(a - 4)^2} - \dfrac{a + 2}{a^2 - 7a + 12}$ $(a - 4)^2(a - 3)$

84. $\dfrac{3x + 5}{x^2 - 1} + \dfrac{x^2 - 18}{(x + 1)^2}$ $(x + 1)^2(x - 1)$

85. $\dfrac{9x}{x^2 + 6x + 5} - \dfrac{5x^2}{x^2 + 4x + 3}$

86. $\dfrac{6x + 5}{x + 2} + \dfrac{3x}{(x + 2)^2}$ $(x + 2)^2$

87. $\dfrac{3x - 5}{x^2 - 6x + 9} + \dfrac{3}{x - 3}$ $(x - 3)^2$

88. $\dfrac{2n + 11}{(n + 5)(n + 2)} - \dfrac{3n - 5}{(n - 3)(n + 5)}$

89. $\dfrac{8x^2}{x^2 - 7x + 6} + x - 9$ $(x - 6)(x - 1)$

90. $\dfrac{2x - 1}{x^2 - 25} + x - 10$ $(x + 5)(x - 5)$

91. $\dfrac{t - 1}{3t^2 + 10t - 8} - \dfrac{11}{3t^2 + 11t - 4}$

92. $\dfrac{-4x + 9}{2x^2 + 5x + 2} + \dfrac{x^2}{3x^2 + 4x - 4}$

93. $\dfrac{3x - 1}{4x^2 + 4x + 1} + \dfrac{x^2 + x - 9}{8x^2 + 10x + 3}$

94. $\dfrac{3x + 7}{6x^2 + 11x - 10} + \dfrac{x^2 - 8}{9x^2 - 12x + 4}$ $(3x - 2)^2(2x + 5)$

80. $(x + 9)(x + 2)(x - 5)$ **81.** $(x - 8)(x + 3)(x + 8)$

82. $(n + 2)(n - 2)(n - 7)$ **85.** $(x + 5)(x + 1)(x + 3)$

88. $(n + 5)(n + 2)(n - 3)$ **91.** $(3t - 2)(t + 4)(3t - 1)$

92. $(2x + 1)(x + 2)(3x - 2)$ **93.** $(2x + 1)^2(4x + 3)$

Add or subtract using the technique from Example 7.

95. $\dfrac{1}{7} + \dfrac{2}{5}$ $\dfrac{19}{35}$

96. $\dfrac{3}{8} + \dfrac{1}{4}$ $\dfrac{5}{8}$

97. $\dfrac{2}{9} + \dfrac{3}{4}$ $\dfrac{35}{36}$

98. $\dfrac{5}{6} - \dfrac{1}{3}$ $\dfrac{1}{2}$

99. $\dfrac{5}{9} - \dfrac{1}{2}$ $\dfrac{1}{18}$

100. $\dfrac{6}{5} - \dfrac{3}{10}$ $\dfrac{9}{10}$

Problem Solving

List the polynomial to be placed in each shaded area to make a true statement. Explain how you determined your answer.

101. $\dfrac{x^2 - 6x + 3}{x + 3} + \dfrac{\boxed{}}{x + 3} = \dfrac{2x^2 - 5x - 6}{x + 3}$

$x^2 + x - 9$, sum of numerators must be $2x^2 - 5x - 6$

102. $\dfrac{4x^2 - 6x - 7}{x^2 - 4} - \dfrac{\boxed{}}{x^2 - 4} = \dfrac{2x^2 + x - 3}{x^2 - 4}$

$2x^2 - 7x - 4$, difference of numerators must be $2x^2 + x - 3$

103. $\dfrac{-x^2 - 4x + 3}{2x + 5} + \dfrac{\boxed{}}{2x + 5} = \dfrac{5x - 7}{2x + 5}$

$x^2 + 9x - 10$, sum of numerators must be $5x - 7$

104. $\dfrac{-3x^2 - 9}{(x + 4)(x - 2)} - \dfrac{\boxed{}}{(x + 4)(x - 2)} = \dfrac{x^2 + 3x}{(x + 4)(x - 2)}$

$-4x^2 - 3x - 9$, difference of numerators must be $x^2 + 3x$

Find the least common denominator of each expression.

105. $\dfrac{3}{☺} + \dfrac{4}{5☺}$ $5☺$

106. $\dfrac{5}{8\Delta^2☺^2} + \dfrac{6}{5\Delta^4☺^5}$ $40\Delta^4☺^5$

107. $\dfrac{8}{\Delta^2 - 9} - \dfrac{2}{\Delta + 3}$ $(\Delta + 3)(\Delta - 3)$

108. $\dfrac{6}{\Delta + 3} - \dfrac{\Delta + 5}{\Delta^2 - 4\Delta + 3}$ $(\Delta + 3)(\Delta - 3)(\Delta - 1)$

Challenge Problems

Perform each indicated operation.

109. $\dfrac{4x - 1}{x^2 - 25} - \dfrac{3x^2 - 8}{x^2 - 25} + \dfrac{8x - 7}{x^2 - 25}$ $\dfrac{-3x^2 + 12x}{x^2 - 25}$

110. $\dfrac{x^2 - 8x + 2}{x + 7} + \dfrac{2x^2 - 5x}{x + 7} - \dfrac{3x^2 + 7x + 10}{x + 7}$ $\dfrac{-20x - 8}{x + 7}$

Find the least common denominator for each expression.

111. $\dfrac{17}{6x^5y^9} - \dfrac{9}{2x^3y} + \dfrac{6}{5x^{12}y^2}$ $30x^{12}y^9$

112. $\dfrac{2x}{x - 3} - \dfrac{3}{x^2 - 9} + \dfrac{5}{x + 3}$ $(x - 3)(x + 3)$

113. $\dfrac{3x}{x^2 - x - 12} + \dfrac{2}{x^2 - 6x + 8} + \dfrac{3}{x^2 + x - 6}$

$(x - 4)(x + 3)(x - 2)$

114. $\dfrac{9}{x^2 - 4} - \dfrac{8}{3x^2 + 5x - 2} + \dfrac{7}{3x^2 - 7x + 2}$

$(x - 2)(x + 2)(3x - 1)$

Cumulative Review Exercises

[1.3] 115. Subtract $4\dfrac{3}{5} - 2\dfrac{5}{9}$. $\dfrac{92}{45}$ or $2\dfrac{2}{45}$

[2.5] 116. Solve $6x + 4 = -(x + 2) - 3x + 4$. $-\dfrac{1}{5}$

[2.7] **117. Hummingbird Food** The instructions on a bottle of concentrated hummingbird food indicate that 6 ounces of the concentrate should be mixed with 1 gallon (128 ounces) of water. If you wish to mix the concentrate with only 48 ounces of water, how much concentrate should you use?   2.25 oz

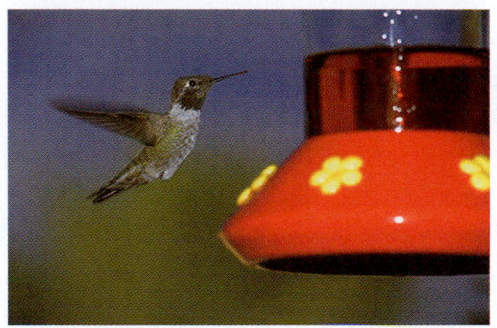

[3.2] **118. Tennis Club** A Tennis Club has two payment plans. Plan 1 is a yearly membership fee of $250 plus $5.00

per hour for use of the tennis court. Plan 2 is an annual membership fee of $600 with no charge for court time. How many hours would Malcolm Wu have to play in a year to make the cost of Plan 1 equal to the cost of Plan 2?   70 hr

[4.3] **119.** What is the slope of the line in the graph below?

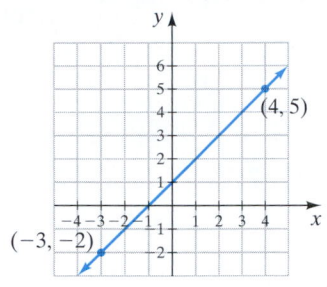

[6.3] **120.** Use scientific notation to evaluate $\dfrac{840{,}000{,}000}{0.0021}$. Leave your answer in scientific notation. 4.0×10^{11}

[7.6] **121.** Solve $2x^2 - 3 = x$. $\dfrac{3}{2}, -1$

8.4 Addition and Subtraction of Rational Expressions

1 Add and subtract rational expressions.

In Section 8.3 we discussed how to add and subtract rational expressions with a common denominator. Now we discuss adding and subtracting rational expressions that are not given with a common denominator.

1 Add and Subtract Rational Expressions

The method used to add and subtract rational expressions with unlike denominators is outlined in Example 1.

EXAMPLE 1 ▶ Add $\dfrac{7}{x} + \dfrac{6}{y}$.

Solution First we determine the LCD as outlined in Section 8.3.

$$LCD = xy$$

We write each fraction with the LCD. We do this by multiplying **both** the numerator and denominator of each fraction by any factors needed to obtain the LCD.

In this problem, the fraction on the left must be multiplied by y/y and the fraction on the right must be multiplied by x/x.

$$\frac{7}{x} + \frac{6}{y} = \frac{y}{y} \cdot \frac{7}{x} + \frac{6}{y} \cdot \frac{x}{x} = \frac{7y}{xy} + \frac{6x}{xy}$$

By multiplying both the numerator and denominator by the same factor, we are in effect multiplying by 1, which does not change the value of the fraction, only its appearance. Thus, the new fraction is equivalent to the original fraction.

Now we add the numerators, while leaving the LCD alone.

$$\frac{7y}{xy} + \frac{6x}{xy} = \frac{7y + 6x}{xy} \quad \text{or} \quad \frac{6x + 7y}{xy}$$

▶ **Now Try Exercise 7**

To Add or Subtract Two Rational Expressions with Unlike Denominators

1. Determine the LCD.
2. Rewrite each fraction as an equivalent fraction with the LCD. This is done by multiplying both the numerator and denominator of each fraction by any factors needed to obtain the LCD.
3. Add or subtract the numerators while maintaining the LCD.
4. When possible, factor the remaining numerator and simplify the fraction.

EXAMPLE 2 ▶ Add $\dfrac{1}{4x^2y} + \dfrac{3}{14xy^3}$.

Solution   The LCD is $28x^2y^3$. We must write each fraction with the denominator $28x^2y^3$. To do this, we multiply the fraction on the left by $\dfrac{7y^2}{7y^2}$ and the fraction on the right by $\dfrac{2x}{2x}$.

$$\dfrac{1}{4x^2y} + \dfrac{3}{14xy^3} = \dfrac{7y^2}{7y^2} \cdot \dfrac{1}{4x^2y} + \dfrac{3}{14xy^3} \cdot \dfrac{2x}{2x}$$

$$= \dfrac{7y^2}{28x^2y^3} + \dfrac{6x}{28x^2y^3}$$

$$= \dfrac{7y^2 + 6x}{28x^2y^3} \quad \text{or} \quad \dfrac{6x + 7y^2}{28x^2y^3}$$

▶ **Now Try Exercise 15**

Helpful Hint

In Example 2 we multiplied the first fraction by $\dfrac{7y^2}{7y^2}$ and the second fraction by $\dfrac{2x}{2x}$ to get two fractions with a common denominator. How did we know what to multiply each fraction by? Many of you can determine this by observing the LCD and then determining what each denominator needs to be multiplied by to get the LCD. If this is not obvious, you can divide the LCD by the given denominator to determine what the numerator and denominator of each fraction should be multiplied by. In Example 2, the LCD is $28x^2y^3$. If we divide $28x^2y^3$ by each given denominator, $4x^2y$ and $14xy^3$, we can determine what the numerator and denominator of each respective fraction should be multiplied by

$$\dfrac{28x^2y^3}{4x^2y} = 7y^2 \qquad \dfrac{28x^2y^3}{14xy^3} = 2x$$

Thus, $\dfrac{1}{4x^2y}$ should be multiplied by $\dfrac{7y^2}{7y^2}$ and $\dfrac{3}{14xy^3}$ should be multiplied by $\dfrac{2x}{2x}$ to obtain the LCD $28x^2y^3$.

EXAMPLE 3 ▶ Add $\dfrac{3}{x + 2} + \dfrac{5}{x}$.

Solution   We must write each fraction with the LCD, which is $x(x + 2)$. To do this, we multiply the fraction on the left by x/x and the fraction on the right by $(x + 2)/(x + 2)$.

$$\dfrac{3}{x + 2} + \dfrac{5}{x} = \dfrac{x}{x} \cdot \dfrac{3}{x + 2} + \dfrac{5}{x} \cdot \dfrac{x + 2}{x + 2}$$

$$= \dfrac{3x}{x(x + 2)} + \dfrac{5(x + 2)}{x(x + 2)} \qquad \textit{Rewrite each fraction as an equivalent fraction with the LCD.}$$

$$= \dfrac{3x}{x(x + 2)} + \dfrac{5x + 10}{x(x + 2)} \qquad \textit{Distributive property.}$$

$$= \dfrac{3x + (5x + 10)}{x(x + 2)} \qquad \textit{Write as a single fraction.}$$

$$= \dfrac{3x + 5x + 10}{x(x + 2)} \qquad \textit{Remove parentheses in the numerator.}$$

$$= \dfrac{8x + 10}{x(x + 2)} \qquad \textit{Combine like terms in the numerator.}$$

▶ **Now Try Exercise 25**

Helpful Hint

Look at the answer to Example 3, $\dfrac{8x + 10}{x(x + 2)}$. Notice that the numerator could have been factored to obtain $\dfrac{2(4x + 5)}{x(x + 2)}$. Also notice that the denominator could have been multiplied to get $\dfrac{8x + 10}{x^2 + 2x}$. All three of these answers are equivalent and each is correct. In this section, when writing answers, unless there is a common factor in the numerator and denominator we will leave the numerator in unfactored form and the denominator in factored form. If both the numerator and denominator have a common factor, we will factor the numerator and simplify the fraction.

INSTRUCTOR EXAMPLE

Subtract $\dfrac{m}{m + 8} - \dfrac{2}{m - 1}$.

Ans.: $\dfrac{m^2 - 3m - 16}{(m + 8)(m - 1)}$

EXAMPLE 4 ▶ Subtract $\dfrac{w}{w - 7} - \dfrac{6}{w - 4}$.

Solution The LCD is $(w - 7)(w - 4)$. The fraction on the left must be multiplied by $(w - 4)/(w - 4)$ to obtain the LCD. The fraction on the right must be multiplied by $(w - 7)/(w - 7)$ to obtain the LCD.

$$\frac{w}{w - 7} - \frac{6}{w - 4} = \frac{w - 4}{w - 4} \cdot \frac{w}{w - 7} - \frac{6}{w - 4} \cdot \frac{w - 7}{w - 7}$$

$$= \frac{w(w - 4)}{(w - 4)(w - 7)} - \frac{6(w - 7)}{(w - 4)(w - 7)} \qquad \text{\textit{Rewrite each fraction as an equivalent fraction with the LCD.}}$$

$$= \frac{w^2 - 4w}{(w - 4)(w - 7)} - \frac{6w - 42}{(w - 4)(w - 7)} \qquad \text{\textit{Distributive property.}}$$

$$= \frac{(w^2 - 4w) - (6w - 42)}{(w - 4)(w - 7)} \qquad \text{\textit{Write as a single fraction.}}$$

$$= \frac{w^2 - 4w - 6w + 42}{(w - 4)(w - 7)} \qquad \text{\textit{Remove parentheses in the numerator.}}$$

$$= \frac{w^2 - 10w + 42}{(w - 4)(w - 7)} \qquad \text{\textit{Combine like terms in the numerator.}}$$

▶ **Now Try Exercise 29**

INSTRUCTOR EXAMPLE

Subtract $\dfrac{x + 1}{x - 2} - \dfrac{x + 4}{x + 2}$.

Ans.: $\dfrac{x + 10}{(x + 2)(x - 2)}$

EXAMPLE 5 ▶ Subtract $\dfrac{x + 2}{x - 4} - \dfrac{x + 3}{x + 4}$.

Solution The LCD is $(x - 4)(x + 4)$.

$$\frac{x + 2}{x - 4} - \frac{x + 3}{x + 4} = \frac{x + 4}{x + 4} \cdot \frac{x + 2}{x - 4} - \frac{x + 3}{x + 4} \cdot \frac{x - 4}{x - 4}$$

$$= \frac{(x + 4)(x + 2)}{(x + 4)(x - 4)} - \frac{(x + 3)(x - 4)}{(x + 4)(x - 4)} \qquad \text{\textit{Rewrite each fraction as an equivalent fraction with the LCD.}}$$

Use the FOIL method to multiply each numerator.

$$= \frac{x^2 + 6x + 8}{(x + 4)(x - 4)} - \frac{x^2 - x - 12}{(x + 4)(x - 4)}$$

$$= \frac{(x^2 + 6x + 8) - (x^2 - x - 12)}{(x + 4)(x - 4)} \qquad \text{\textit{Write as a single fraction.}}$$

$$= \frac{x^2 + 6x + 8 - x^2 + x + 12}{(x + 4)(x - 4)} \qquad \text{\textit{Remove parentheses in the numerator.}}$$

$$= \frac{7x + 20}{(x + 4)(x - 4)} \qquad \text{\textit{Combine like terms in the numerator.}}$$

▶ **Now Try Exercise 37**

Consider the problem

$$\frac{13}{x-2} + \frac{x+8}{2-x}$$

How do we add these rational expressions? We could write each fraction with the denominator $(x-2)(2-x)$. However, there is an easier way. Study the following Helpful Hint.

Helpful Hint

When adding or subtracting fractions whose denominators are opposites (and therefore differ only in signs), multiply both the numerator *and* the denominator of *either* fraction by -1. Then both fractions will have the same denominator.

$$\frac{x}{a-b} + \frac{y}{b-a} = \frac{x}{a-b} + \frac{y}{b-a} \cdot \frac{-1}{-1}$$

$$= \frac{x}{a-b} + \frac{-y}{a-b}$$

$$= \frac{x-y}{a-b}$$

INSTRUCTOR EXAMPLE
Add $\dfrac{3}{x-5} + \dfrac{x+2}{5-x}$.
Ans.: $\dfrac{-x+1}{x-5}$

EXAMPLE 6 ▶ Add $\dfrac{4}{x-2} + \dfrac{x+3}{2-x}$.

Solution Since the denominators differ only in sign, we may multiply both the numerator and the denominator of either fraction by -1. Here we will multiply the numerator and denominator of the second fraction by -1 to obtain the common denominator $x-2$.

$$\frac{4}{x-2} + \frac{x+3}{2-x} = \frac{4}{x-2} + \frac{x+3}{2-x} \cdot \frac{-1}{-1} \qquad \text{\textit{Multiply numerator and denominator by} } -1.$$

$$= \frac{4}{x-2} + \frac{(-x-3)}{x-2}$$

$$= \frac{4 + (-x-3)}{x-2} \qquad \text{\textit{Write as a single fraction.}}$$

$$= \frac{4-x-3}{x-2} \qquad \text{\textit{Remove parentheses in the numerator.}}$$

$$= \frac{-x+1}{x-2} \qquad \text{\textit{Combine like terms in the numerator.}}$$

▶ **Now Try Exercise 31**

Let's work another example where the denominators differ only in sign.

INSTRUCTOR EXAMPLE
Subtract $\dfrac{a+3}{2a-7} - \dfrac{2a+5}{7-2a}$.
Ans.: $\dfrac{3a+8}{2a-7}$

EXAMPLE 7 ▶ Subtract $\dfrac{a-9}{3a-4} - \dfrac{2a-5}{4-3a}$.

Solution The denominators of the two fractions differ only in sign. We will work this problem in a similar manner to how we worked Example 6. We will multiply both the numerator and denominator of the second fraction by -1 to obtain the common denominator $3a-4$.

$$\frac{a-9}{3a-4} - \frac{2a-5}{4-3a} = \frac{a-9}{3a-4} - \frac{2a-5}{4-3a} \cdot \frac{-1}{-1} \qquad \text{\textit{Multiply numerator and denominator by} } -1.$$

$$= \frac{a-9}{3a-4} - \frac{(-2a+5)}{3a-4}$$

$$= \frac{(a-9)-(-2a+5)}{3a-4} \qquad \textit{Write as a single fraction.}$$

$$= \frac{a-9+2a-5}{3a-4} \qquad \textit{Remove parentheses in the numerator.}$$

$$= \frac{3a-14}{3a-4} \qquad \textit{Combine like terms in the numerator.}$$

▸ **Now Try Exercise 33**

EXAMPLE 8 ▸ Add $\dfrac{3}{x^2+5x+6} + \dfrac{1}{3x^2+8x-3}$.

Solution

$$\frac{3}{x^2+5x+6} + \frac{1}{3x^2+8x-3} = \frac{3}{(x+2)(x+3)} + \frac{1}{(3x-1)(x+3)}$$

The LCD is $(x+2)(x+3)(3x-1)$.

$$= \frac{3x-1}{3x-1} \cdot \frac{3}{(x+2)(x+3)} + \frac{1}{(3x-1)(x+3)} \cdot \frac{x+2}{x+2}$$

$$= \frac{9x-3}{(3x-1)(x+2)(x+3)} + \frac{x+2}{(3x-1)(x+2)(x+3)}$$

$$= \frac{(9x-3)+(x+2)}{(3x-1)(x+2)(x+3)}$$

$$= \frac{9x-3+x+2}{(3x-1)(x+2)(x+3)}$$

$$= \frac{10x-1}{(3x-1)(x+2)(x+3)}$$

▸ **Now Try Exercise 55**

EXAMPLE 9 ▸ Subtract $\dfrac{5}{x^2-5x} - \dfrac{x}{5x-25}$.

Solution

$$\frac{5}{x^2-5x} - \frac{x}{5x-25} = \frac{5}{x(x-5)} - \frac{x}{5(x-5)}$$

The LCD is $5x(x-5)$.

$$= \frac{5}{5} \cdot \frac{5}{x(x-5)} - \frac{x}{5(x-5)} \cdot \frac{x}{x}$$

$$= \frac{25}{5x(x-5)} - \frac{x^2}{5x(x-5)}$$

$$= \frac{25-x^2}{5x(x-5)}$$

$$= \frac{(5-x)(5+x)}{5x(x-5)} \qquad \textit{Factor the numerator.}$$

$$= \frac{-1(x-5)(x+5)}{5x(x-5)} \qquad 5-x=-1(x-5)$$

$$= \frac{-1(x-5)(x+5)}{5x(x-5)} \qquad \textit{Simplify.}$$

$$= \frac{-1(x+5)}{5x} \quad \text{or} \quad -\frac{x+5}{5x}$$

▸ **Now Try Exercise 65**

Avoiding Common Errors

A common error in an addition or subtraction problem is to add or subtract the numerators and the denominators. Here is one such example.

CORRECT

$$\frac{1}{x} + \frac{x}{1} = \frac{1}{x} + \frac{x}{1} \cdot \boxed{\frac{x}{x}}$$

$$= \frac{1}{x} + \frac{x^2}{x}$$

$$= \frac{1 + x^2}{x} \text{ or } \frac{x^2 + 1}{x}$$

INCORRECT

$$\cancel{\frac{1}{x} + \frac{x}{1} = \frac{1 + x}{x + 1}}$$

$$\cancel{\frac{1}{x} - \frac{x}{1} = \frac{1 - x}{x - 1}}$$

Remember that to add or subtract fractions you must first have a common denominator. Then you add or subtract the numerators while maintaining the common denominator.

Another common mistake is to treat an addition or subtraction problem as a multiplication problem. You can divide out common factors only when *multiplying* expressions, not when adding or subtracting them.

CORRECT

$$\frac{1}{x} \cdot \frac{x}{1} = \frac{1}{\cancel{x}} \cdot \frac{\cancel{x}^1}{1}$$

$$= 1 \cdot 1 = 1$$

INCORRECT

$$\cancel{\frac{1}{x} + \frac{x}{1} = \frac{1}{\cancel{x}} + \frac{\cancel{x}^1}{1}}$$

$$= 1 + 1 = 2$$

---

1. For each fraction, divide the LCD by the denominator.   **2.** in effect, multiplying by 1   **3. a)** Answers will vary.   **5. b)** $\dfrac{3yz + 10}{12z^2}$

EXERCISE SET 8.4

MathXL®   MyMathLab

Concept/Writing Exercises

1. When adding or subtracting fractions with unlike denominators, how can you determine what each denominator should be multiplied by to get the LCD?

2. When you multiply both the numerator and denominator of a fraction by the factors needed to obtain the LCD, why are you not changing the value of the fraction?

3. a) Give a step-by-step procedure to add or subtract two rational expressions that have unlike denominators.

   b) Using the procedure outlined in part **a)**, add

$$\frac{x}{x^2 - x - 6} + \frac{3}{x^2 - 4}. \quad \frac{x^2 + x - 9}{(x + 2)(x - 3)(x - 2)}$$

4. Explain how to add or subtract fractions whose denominators are opposites. Give an example.   Multiply both the numerator and the denominator of either fraction by -1.

5. Consider $\dfrac{y}{4z} + \dfrac{5}{6z^2}$

   a) What is the LCD? $12z^2$

   b) Perform the indicated operation.

   c) If you mistakenly used $24z^2$ for the LCD when adding, would you eventually obtain the correct answer? Explain.   yes

6. Would you use the LCD to perform the following indicated operations? Explain.

   a) $\dfrac{3}{x + 3} - \dfrac{4}{x} + \dfrac{5}{3}$ yes   **b)** $\dfrac{1}{x + 2} \cdot \dfrac{5}{x}$ no

   c) $x + \dfrac{2}{9}$ yes   **d)** $\dfrac{5}{x^2 - 9} \div \dfrac{2}{x - 3}$ no

Practice the Skills

Add or subtract.

7. $\dfrac{2}{x} + \dfrac{3}{y}$ $\dfrac{3x + 2y}{xy}$

8. $\dfrac{5}{x} - \dfrac{1}{y}$ $\dfrac{5y - x}{xy}$

9. $\dfrac{5}{x^2} + \dfrac{1}{2x}$ $\dfrac{x + 10}{2x^2}$

10. $7 - \dfrac{1}{x^2}$ $\dfrac{7x^2 - 1}{x^2}$

11. $3 + \dfrac{8}{x}$ $\dfrac{3x + 8}{x}$

12. $\dfrac{5}{6y} + \dfrac{3}{5y^2}$ $\dfrac{25y + 18}{30y^2}$

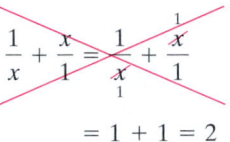 **13.** $\dfrac{2}{x^2} + \dfrac{3}{5x}$ $\dfrac{3x + 10}{5x^2}$

14. $\dfrac{6}{x} - \dfrac{5}{x^2}$ $\dfrac{6x - 5}{x^2}$

15. $\dfrac{9}{4x^2y} + \dfrac{3}{5xy^2}$ $\dfrac{45y + 12x}{20x^2y^2}$

16. $\dfrac{7}{12x^4y} - \dfrac{1}{5x^2y^3}$ $\dfrac{35y^2 - 12x^2}{60x^4y^3}$

17. $4y + \dfrac{x}{y}$ $\dfrac{4y^2 + x}{y}$

18. $x + \dfrac{2x}{y}$ $\dfrac{xy + 2x}{y}$

19. $\dfrac{3a - 1}{2a} + \dfrac{2}{3a}$ $\dfrac{9a + 1}{6a}$

20. $\dfrac{11}{n} + 5$ $\dfrac{5n + 11}{n}$

21. $\dfrac{6x}{y} + \dfrac{2y}{xy}$ $\dfrac{6x^2 + 2y}{xy}$

22. $\dfrac{4}{5p} - \dfrac{5}{2p^2}$ $\dfrac{8p - 25}{10p^2}$

23. $\dfrac{9}{b} - \dfrac{4}{5a^2}$ $\dfrac{45a^2 - 4b}{5a^2b}$

24. $\dfrac{x-3}{x} - \dfrac{1}{6x}$ $\dfrac{6x - 19}{6x}$

25. $\dfrac{4}{x} + \dfrac{9}{x-3}$ $\dfrac{13x - 12}{x(x-3)}$

26. $10 - \dfrac{3}{x-3}$ $\dfrac{10x - 33}{x-3}$

27. $\dfrac{9}{p+3} + \dfrac{2}{p}$ $\dfrac{11p + 6}{p(p+3)}$

28. $\dfrac{2a}{a+b} + \dfrac{a-b}{a}$ $\dfrac{3a^2 - b^2}{a(a+b)}$

29. $\dfrac{5}{d+1} - \dfrac{d}{3d+5}$ $\dfrac{-d^2 + 14d + 25}{(d+1)(3d+5)}$

30. $\dfrac{2}{x-3} - \dfrac{5}{x-1}$ $\dfrac{-3x + 13}{(x-3)(x-1)}$

31. $\dfrac{8}{p-3} + \dfrac{2}{3-p}$ $\dfrac{6}{p-3}$

32. $\dfrac{3}{n-5} - \dfrac{7}{5-n}$ $\dfrac{10}{n-5}$

33. $\dfrac{9}{x+7} - \dfrac{5}{-x-7}$ $\dfrac{14}{x+7}$

34. $\dfrac{6}{7x-1} - \dfrac{3}{1-7x}$ $\dfrac{9}{7x-1}$

35. $\dfrac{8}{a-2} + \dfrac{a}{2a-4}$ $\dfrac{a+16}{2(a-2)}$

36. $\dfrac{4}{y-1} + \dfrac{3}{y+1}$ $\dfrac{7y+1}{(y+1)(y-1)}$

37. $\dfrac{x+5}{x-5} - \dfrac{x-5}{x+5}$ $\dfrac{20x}{(x-5)(x+5)}$

38. $\dfrac{x+7}{x+3} - \dfrac{x+3}{x+7}$ $\dfrac{8x+40}{(x+3)(x+7)}$

39. $\dfrac{5}{6n+3} - \dfrac{2}{n}$ $\dfrac{-7n-6}{3n(2n+1)}$

40. $\dfrac{x}{4x-4} - \dfrac{1}{3x}$ $\dfrac{3x^2 - 4x + 4}{12x(x-1)}$

41. $\dfrac{3}{2w+10} + \dfrac{6}{w+2}$ $\dfrac{15w + 66}{2(w+5)(w+2)}$

42. $\dfrac{5k}{4k-8} - \dfrac{k}{k+2}$ $\dfrac{k^2 + 18k}{4(k-2)(k+2)}$

43. $\dfrac{z}{z^2 - 16} + \dfrac{4}{z+4}$ $\dfrac{5z - 16}{(z+4)(z-4)}$

44. $\dfrac{5}{(x+4)^2} + \dfrac{3}{x+4}$ $\dfrac{3x + 17}{(x+4)^2}$

45. $\dfrac{x+2}{x^2 - 4} - \dfrac{2}{x+2}$ $\dfrac{-x+6}{(x+2)(x-2)}$

46. $\dfrac{3}{(x-2)(x+3)} + \dfrac{5}{(x+2)(x+3)}$

47. $\dfrac{3r+4}{r^2 - 10r + 24} - \dfrac{2}{r-6}$ $\dfrac{r+12}{(r-4)(r-6)}$

48. $\dfrac{x+9}{x^2 - 3x - 10} - \dfrac{2}{x-5}$ $\dfrac{-x+5}{(x-5)(x+2)}$

49. $\dfrac{x^2 - 3}{x^2 + 2x - 8} - \dfrac{x-4}{x+4}$ $\dfrac{6x - 11}{(x+4)(x-2)}$

50. $\dfrac{x+8}{x^2 - 4x + 4} - \dfrac{x+1}{x-2}$ $\dfrac{-x^2 + 2x + 10}{(x-2)^2}$

51. $\dfrac{x-6}{x^2 + 10x + 25} + \dfrac{x-3}{x+5}$ $\dfrac{x^2 + 3x - 21}{(x+5)^2}$

52. $\dfrac{x}{x^2 - xy} - \dfrac{y}{xy - x^2}$ $\dfrac{x+y}{x(x-y)}$

53. $\dfrac{5}{a^2 - 9a + 8} - \dfrac{6}{a^2 - 6a - 16}$

54. $\dfrac{4}{a^2 + 2a - 15} - \dfrac{1}{a^2 - 9}$

55. $\dfrac{2}{x^2 + 6x + 9} + \dfrac{7}{x^2 + x - 6}$

56. $\dfrac{x}{2x^2 + 7x - 4} + \dfrac{4}{x^2 - x - 20}$

57. $\dfrac{x}{2x^2 + 7x + 3} - \dfrac{5}{3x^2 + 7x - 6}$

58. $\dfrac{x}{6x^2 + 7x + 2} + \dfrac{5}{2x^2 - 3x - 2}$

59. $\dfrac{x}{4x^2 + 11x + 6} - \dfrac{2}{8x^2 + 2x - 3}$

60. $\dfrac{x}{5x^2 - 9x - 2} - \dfrac{1}{3x^2 - 7x + 2}$

61. $\dfrac{3w + 12}{w^2 + w - 12} - \dfrac{2}{w-3}$ $\dfrac{1}{w-3}$

62. $\dfrac{5x + 10}{x^2 - 5x - 14} - \dfrac{4}{x-7}$ $\dfrac{1}{x-7}$

63. $\dfrac{4r}{2r^2 - 10r + 12} + \dfrac{4}{r-2}$ $\dfrac{6}{r-3}$

64. $\dfrac{6m}{3m^2 - 24m + 48} - \dfrac{2}{m-4}$ $\dfrac{8}{(m-4)^2}$

65. $\dfrac{4}{x^2 - 4x} - \dfrac{x}{4x - 16}$ $\dfrac{-x+4}{4x}$

66. $\dfrac{6}{x^2 - 6x} - \dfrac{x}{6x - 36}$ $\dfrac{x+6}{6x}$

46. $\dfrac{8x - 4}{(x+2)(x-2)(x+3)}$ **53.** $\dfrac{-a+16}{(a-8)(a-1)(a+2)}$ **54.** $\dfrac{3a+7}{(a+5)(a-3)(a+3)}$

Problem Solving

55. $\dfrac{9x + 17}{(x+3)^2(x-2)}$ **56.** $\dfrac{x^2 + 3x - 4}{(2x-1)(x+4)(x-5)}$ **57.** $\dfrac{3x^2 - 12x - 5}{(2x+1)(3x-2)(x+3)}$ **58.** $\dfrac{x^2 + 13x + 10}{(3x+2)(2x+1)(x-2)}$

For what value(s) of x is each expression defined?

67. $\dfrac{8}{x} + 6$

68. $\dfrac{6}{x-1} - \dfrac{5}{x}$

69. $\dfrac{3}{x-4} + \dfrac{7}{x+6}$

70. $\dfrac{4}{x^2 - 9} - \dfrac{9}{x+3}$

67. all real numbers except $x = 0$ **68.** all real numbers except $x = 1, x = 0$ **69.** all real numbers except $x = 4, x = -6$

Add or subtract. Treat the unknown symbols as if they were variables.   **70.** all real numbers except $x = 3, x = -3$

71. $\dfrac{3}{\Delta - 2} - \dfrac{4}{2 - \Delta}$ $\dfrac{7}{\Delta - 2}$

72. $\dfrac{\Delta}{2\Delta^2 + 7\Delta - 4} + \dfrac{2}{\Delta^2 - \Delta - 20}$ $\dfrac{\Delta^2 - \Delta - 2}{(2\Delta - 1)(\Delta + 4)(\Delta - 5)}$

Challenge Problems

59. $\dfrac{2x^2 - 3x - 4}{(4x+3)(x+2)(2x-1)}$ **60.** $\dfrac{3x^2 - 6x - 1}{(5x+1)(x-2)(3x-1)}$

Under what conditions is each expression defined? Explain your answers.

73. $\dfrac{5}{a+b} + \dfrac{4}{a}$ all real numbers except $a = 0, a = -b$

74. $\dfrac{x+2}{x+5y} - \dfrac{y-2}{3x}$ all real numbers except $x = 0, x = -5y$

79. $\dfrac{6x + 5}{(x+2)(x-3)(x+1)}$

Perform each indicated operation.

75. $\dfrac{x}{x^2 - 9} + \dfrac{2x}{x+3} + \dfrac{2x^2 - 5x}{9 - x^2}$ 0

76. $\dfrac{8x + 9}{x^2 + x - 6} + \dfrac{x}{x+3} - \dfrac{5}{x-2}$ 1

77. $\dfrac{x+6}{4 - x^2} - \dfrac{x+3}{x+2} + \dfrac{x-3}{2-x}$ $\dfrac{2x-3}{2-x}$

78. $\dfrac{3x-1}{x+2} + \dfrac{x}{x-3} - \dfrac{4}{2x+3}$ $\dfrac{8x^3 - 8x^2 - 14x + 33}{(x+2)(x-3)(2x+3)}$

79. $\dfrac{2}{x^2 - x - 6} + \dfrac{3}{x^2 - 2x - 3} + \dfrac{1}{x^2 + 3x + 2}$

80. $\dfrac{3x}{x^2 - 4} + \dfrac{4}{x^3 + 8}$ $\dfrac{3x^3 - 6x^2 + 16x - 8}{(x+2)(x-2)(x^2 - 2x + 4)}$

Group Activity

Discuss and answer Exercise 81 as a group.

81. a) As a group, find the LCD of

$$\frac{x + 3y}{x^2 + 3xy + 2y^2} + \frac{y - x}{2x^2 + 3xy + y^2}$$

b) As a group, perform the indicated operation, but do not simplify your answer.

c) As a group, simplify your answer.

d) Group member 1: Substitute 2 for x and 1 for y in the fraction on the left in part **a)** and evaluate.

e) Group member 2: Substitute 2 for x and 1 for y in the fraction on the right in part **a)** and evaluate.

f) Group member 3: Add the numerical fractions found in parts **d)** and **e)**.

g) Individually, substitute 2 for x and 1 for y in the expression obtained in part **b)** and evaluate.

h) Individually, substitute 2 for x and 1 for y in the expression obtained in part **c)**, evaluate, and compare your answers.

i) As a group, discuss what you discovered from this activity.

j) Do you think your results would have been similar for any numbers substituted for x and y (for which the denominator is not 0)? Why? yes

81. a) $(x + y)(x + 2y)(2x + y)$ **b)** $\dfrac{x^2 + 6xy + 5y^2}{(x + y)(x + 2y)(2x + y)}$ **c)** $\dfrac{x + 5y}{(x + 2y)(2x + y)}$ **d)** $\dfrac{5}{12}$ **e)** $-\dfrac{1}{15}$ **f)** $\dfrac{7}{20}$ **g)** $\dfrac{21}{60} = \dfrac{7}{20}$ **h)** $\dfrac{7}{20}$

Cumulative Review Exercises

[2.7] 82. White Pass Railroad The White Pass Railroad is a narrow gauge railroad that travels slowly through the mountains of Alaska. If the train travels 22 miles in 0.8 hours, how long will it take to travel 42 miles? Assume the train travels at the same rate throughout the trip. ≈ 1.53 hr

[2.8] 83. Solve the inequality $3(x - 2) + 2 < 4(x + 1)$ and graph the solution on a number line.

[6.6] 84. Divide $(8x^2 + 6x - 15) \div (2x + 3)$.

[8.2] 85. Multiply $\dfrac{x^2 + xy - 6y^2}{x^2 - xy - 2y^2} \cdot \dfrac{y^2 - x^2}{x^2 + 2xy - 3y^2}$. -1

83. $x > -8$; **84.** $4x - 3 - \dfrac{6}{2x + 3}$

Mid-Chapter Test: 8.1–8.4

To find out how well you understand the chapter material to this point, take this brief test. The answers, and the section where the material was initially discussed, are given in the back of the book. Review any questions that you answered incorrectly.

Determine the value or values of the variable where each expression is defined.

1. $\dfrac{9}{3x - 2}$ all real numbers except $x = \dfrac{2}{3}$

2. $\dfrac{2x + 1}{x^2 - 5x - 14}$ all real numbers except $x = -2, x = 7$

Simplify each rational expression.

3. $\dfrac{9x + 18}{x + 2}$ 9

4. $\dfrac{2x^2 + 13x + 15}{3x^2 + 14x - 5}$ $\dfrac{2x + 3}{3x - 1}$

5. $\dfrac{25r^2 - 36t^2}{5r - 6t}$ $5r + 6t$

Multiply or divide as indicated.

6. $\dfrac{15x^2}{2y} \cdot \dfrac{4y^4}{5x^5} \cdot \dfrac{6y^3}{x^3}$

7. $\dfrac{m - 3}{m + 4} \cdot \dfrac{m^2 + 8m + 16}{3 - m}$ $-(m + 4)$ or $-m - 4$

8. $\dfrac{x^3 + 27}{x^2 - 2x - 15} \cdot \dfrac{x^2 - 7x + 10}{x^2 - 3x + 9}$ $x - 2$

9. $\dfrac{5x - 1}{x^2 + 11x + 10} \div \dfrac{10x - 2}{x^2 + 17x + 70}$ $\dfrac{x + 7}{2(x + 1)}$

10. $\dfrac{5x^2 + 7x + 2}{x^2 + 6x + 5} \div \dfrac{7x^2 - 39x - 18}{x^2 - x - 30}$ $\dfrac{5x + 2}{7x + 3}$

Add or subtract as indicated.

11. $\dfrac{x^2}{x+6} - \dfrac{36}{x+6}$ $x-6$

12. $\dfrac{2x^2-2x}{2x+5} + \dfrac{x-15}{2x+5}$ $x-3$

13. $\dfrac{3x^2-x}{4x^2-9x+2} - \dfrac{3x+4}{4x^2-9x+2}$ $\dfrac{3x+2}{4x-1}$

Find the least common denominator.

14. $\dfrac{2m}{6m^2+3m} + \dfrac{m+7}{2m+1}$ $3m(2m+1)$

15. $\dfrac{9x+8}{2x^2-5x-12} + \dfrac{2x+3}{x^2-9x+20}$ $(2x+3)(x-4)(x-5)$

For Exercises 16–19, add or subtract as indicated.

16. $\dfrac{x+1}{2x} + \dfrac{4x-3}{5x}$ $\dfrac{13x-1}{10x}$

17. $\dfrac{2a+5}{a+3} - \dfrac{3a+1}{a-4}$ $-\dfrac{a^2+13a+23}{a^2-a-12}$

18. $\dfrac{x^2+5}{2x^2+13x+6} + \dfrac{3x-1}{2x+1}$ $\dfrac{4x^2+17x-1}{2x^2+13x+6}$

19. $\dfrac{x}{x^2+3x+2} - \dfrac{4}{x^2-x-6}$ $\dfrac{x^2-7x-4}{(x+1)(x+2)(x-3)}$

20. To add the rational expressions $\dfrac{7}{x+1} + \dfrac{8}{x}$, Samuel Ditsi decided to add both numerators and then add both denominators to get $\dfrac{7+8}{(x+1)+x}$, which simplified to $\dfrac{15}{2x+1}$. This procedure is wrong. Why is it wrong? Explain your answer. Then add the rational expressions $\dfrac{7}{x+1} + \dfrac{8}{x}$ correctly.

need common denominator of $x(x+1)$, $\dfrac{15x+8}{x(x+1)}$

8.5 Complex Fractions

1 Simplify complex fractions by combining terms.

2 Simplify complex fractions using multiplication first to clear fractions.

1 Simplify Complex Fractions by Combining Terms

A **complex fraction** is one that has a fraction in its numerator or its denominator or in both its numerator and denominator.

Examples of Complex Fractions

$$\dfrac{\frac{3}{5}}{7} \qquad \dfrac{\frac{x+9}{x}}{4x} \qquad \dfrac{\frac{x}{y}}{x+1} \qquad \dfrac{\frac{a+b}{a}}{\frac{a-b}{b}}$$

The expression above the main fraction line is the numerator of the complex fraction, and the expression below the main fraction line is the denominator of the complex fraction.

Numerator of complex fraction $\Big\{$ $\dfrac{a+b}{a}$

$\longleftarrow$ Main fraction line

Denominator of complex fraction $\Big\{$ $\dfrac{a+b}{a}$

There are two methods to simplify complex fractions. The first reinforces many of the concepts used in this chapter because we may need to add, subtract, multiply, and divide simpler fractions as we simplify the complex fraction. Many students prefer to use the second method because the answer may be obtained more quickly. We will give two examples using the first method and then work three examples using the second method.

Method 1—To Simplify a Complex Fraction by Combining Terms

1. Add or subtract the fractions in both the numerator and denominator of the complex fraction to obtain single fractions in both the numerator and the denominator.

2. Multiply the fraction in the numerator by the reciprocal of the divisor (that is, by the reciprocal of the fraction in the denominator).

3. Simplify further if possible.

EXAMPLE 1 ▶ Simplify $\dfrac{\frac{ab^2}{c^3}}{\frac{a}{bc^2}}$.

Solution   Since both numerator and denominator are already single fractions, we omit step 1 and begin with step 2. When we multiply the fraction in the numerator by the reciprocal of the fraction in the denominator we obtain the following.

$$\frac{\frac{ab^2}{c^3}}{\frac{a}{bc^2}} = \frac{ab^2}{c^3} \cdot \frac{bc^2}{a} = \frac{b^3}{c}$$

Thus the expression simplifies to $\dfrac{b^3}{c}$.

▶ **Now Try Exercise 11**

EXAMPLE 2 ▶ Simplify $\dfrac{a + \frac{1}{x}}{x + \frac{1}{a}}$.

Solution   Express both the numerator and denominator of the complex fraction as single fractions. The LCD of the numerator is x and the LCD of the denominator is a.

$$\frac{a + \frac{1}{x}}{x + \frac{1}{a}} = \frac{\frac{x}{x} \cdot a + \frac{1}{x}}{\frac{a}{a} \cdot x + \frac{1}{a}} = \frac{\frac{ax}{x} + \frac{1}{x}}{\frac{ax}{a} + \frac{1}{a}} = \frac{\frac{ax+1}{x}}{\frac{ax+1}{a}}$$

Now multiply the numerator by the reciprocal of the denominator.

$$= \frac{ax+1}{x} \cdot \frac{a}{ax+1} = \frac{a}{x}$$

▶ **Now Try Exercise 25**

In Example 4 on page 499 we will rework Example 2. However, at that time we will work the example using method 2. Most students will agree that method 2 is simpler to use for problems of this type, where the numerator or denominator consists of a sum or difference of terms. We illustrated Example 2 here to show you that method 1 works for problems of this type, and to give you more practice with method 1.

2 Simplify Complex Fractions Using Multiplication First to Clear Fractions

Here is the second method for simplifying complex fractions.

> **Method 2—To Simplify a Complex Fraction Using Multiplication First**
>
> 1. Find the least common denominator of *all* the denominators appearing in the complex fraction.
> 2. Multiply both the numerator and denominator of the complex fraction by the LCD found in step 1.
> 3. Simplify when possible.

EXAMPLE 3 ▶ Simplify $\dfrac{\dfrac{2}{3} + \dfrac{1}{5}}{\dfrac{4}{5} - \dfrac{1}{3}}$.

Solution   The denominators in the complex fraction are 3 and 5. The LCD of 3 and 5 is 15. Thus 15 is the LCD of the complex fraction. Multiply both the numerator and denominator of the complex fraction by 15.

$$\dfrac{\dfrac{2}{3} + \dfrac{1}{5}}{\dfrac{4}{5} - \dfrac{1}{3}} = \dfrac{15}{15} \cdot \dfrac{\left(\dfrac{2}{3} + \dfrac{1}{5}\right)}{\left(\dfrac{4}{5} - \dfrac{1}{3}\right)} = \dfrac{15\left(\dfrac{2}{3}\right) + 15\left(\dfrac{1}{5}\right)}{15\left(\dfrac{4}{5}\right) - 15\left(\dfrac{1}{3}\right)}$$

Now simplify.

$$= \dfrac{10 + 3}{12 - 5} = \dfrac{13}{7} \text{ or } 1\dfrac{6}{7}$$

▶ **Now Try Exercise 9**

Now we will rework Example 2 using method 2.

EXAMPLE 4 ▶ Simplify $\dfrac{a + \dfrac{1}{x}}{x + \dfrac{1}{a}}$.

Solution   The denominators in the complex fraction are x and a. Therefore, the LCD of the complex fraction is ax. Multiply both the numerator and denominator of the complex fraction by ax.

$$\dfrac{a + \dfrac{1}{x}}{x + \dfrac{1}{a}} = \dfrac{ax}{ax} \cdot \dfrac{\left(a + \dfrac{1}{x}\right)}{\left(x + \dfrac{1}{a}\right)} = \dfrac{a^2x + a}{ax^2 + x}$$

$$= \dfrac{a\,\cancel{(ax + 1)}}{x\,\cancel{(ax + 1)}} = \dfrac{a}{x}$$

▶ **Now Try Exercise 25**

Note that the answers to Examples 2 and 4 are the same.

EXAMPLE 5 ▶ Simplify $\dfrac{y^2}{\dfrac{1}{x} + \dfrac{1}{y}}$.

Solution   The denominators in the complex fraction are x and y. Therefore, the LCD of the complex fraction is xy. Multiply both the numerator and denominator of the complex fraction by xy.

$$\dfrac{y^2}{\dfrac{1}{x} + \dfrac{1}{y}} = \dfrac{xy}{xy} \cdot \dfrac{y^2}{\left(\dfrac{1}{x} + \dfrac{1}{y}\right)}$$

$$= \dfrac{xy^3}{xy\left(\dfrac{1}{x}\right) + xy\left(\dfrac{1}{y}\right)}$$

$$= \dfrac{xy^3}{y + x}$$

▶ **Now Try Exercise 33**

When asked to simplify a complex fraction, you may use either method unless you are told by your instructor to use a specific method. Read the Helpful Hint that follows.

Helpful Hint

We have presented two methods for simplifying complex fractions. Which method should you use? Although either method can be used to simplify complex fractions, most students prefer to use method 1 when both the numerator and denominator consist of a single term, as in Example 1. When the complex fraction has a sum or difference of expressions in either the numerator or denominator, as in Examples 2, 3, 4, or 5, most students prefer to use method 2.

EXERCISE SET 8.5

MathXL®   MyMathLab

Concept/Writing Exercises

1. What is a complex fraction?

2. What is the numerator and denominator of each complex fraction?

a) $\dfrac{\dfrac{5}{3}}{x^2 + 5x + 6}$ **b)** $\dfrac{\dfrac{5}{3}}{x^2 + 5x + 6}$

3. What is the numerator and denominator of each complex fraction?

a) $\dfrac{\dfrac{x+9}{4}}{\dfrac{7}{x^2 + 5x + 6}}$ **b)** $\dfrac{\dfrac{1}{2y} + x}{\dfrac{3}{y} + x^2}$

4. a) Select the method you prefer to use to simplify complex fractions. Then write a step-by-step procedure for simplifying complex fractions using that method.   Answers will vary.

b) Using the procedure you wrote in part **a)**, simplify the following complex fraction.

$$\dfrac{\dfrac{4}{x} - \dfrac{3}{y}}{x + \dfrac{1}{y}} \qquad \dfrac{4y - 3x}{x^2 y + x}$$

1. A fraction that contains a fraction in its numerator or its denominator or in both.

2. a) numerator, 5; denominator, $\dfrac{3}{x^2 + 5x + 6}$ **b)** numerator, $\dfrac{5}{3}$; denominator, $x^2 + 5x + 6$

3. a) numerator, $\dfrac{x+9}{4}$; denominator, $\dfrac{7}{x^2 + 5x + 6}$ **b)** numerator, $\dfrac{1}{2y} + x$; denominator, $\dfrac{3}{y} + x^2$

Practice the Skills

Simplify.

5. $\dfrac{4 + \dfrac{2}{3}}{5 + \dfrac{1}{3}}$ $\dfrac{7}{8}$

6. $\dfrac{2 + \dfrac{4}{5}}{1 - \dfrac{9}{16}}$ $\dfrac{224}{35}$

7. $\dfrac{2 + \dfrac{3}{8}}{1 + \dfrac{1}{3}}$ $\dfrac{57}{32}$

8. $\dfrac{\dfrac{1}{4} + \dfrac{5}{6}}{\dfrac{2}{3} + \dfrac{3}{5}}$ $\dfrac{65}{76}$

9. $\dfrac{\dfrac{2}{3} + \dfrac{1}{4}}{\dfrac{5}{6} - \dfrac{1}{3}}$ $\dfrac{11}{6}$

10. $\dfrac{\dfrac{5}{8} + \dfrac{1}{3}}{\dfrac{11}{12} - \dfrac{1}{6}}$ $\dfrac{23}{18}$

11. $\dfrac{\dfrac{xy^2}{7}}{\dfrac{3}{x^2}}$ $\dfrac{x^3 y^2}{21}$

12. $\dfrac{\dfrac{11a}{b^3}}{\dfrac{b^2}{4}}$ $\dfrac{44a}{b^5}$

13. $\dfrac{\dfrac{6a^2 b}{7}}{\dfrac{9ac^2}{b^2}}$ $\dfrac{2ab^3}{21c^2}$

14. $\dfrac{\dfrac{18x^4}{5y^4 z^5}}{\dfrac{9xy^2}{15z^5}}$ $\dfrac{6x^3}{y^6}$

15. $\dfrac{a - \dfrac{a}{b}}{\dfrac{3 + a}{b}}$ $\dfrac{ab - a}{3 + a}$

16. $\dfrac{a + \dfrac{2}{b}}{\dfrac{a}{b}}$ $\dfrac{ab + 2}{a}$

17. $\dfrac{\dfrac{9}{x} + \dfrac{3}{x^2}}{3 + \dfrac{1}{x}}$ $\dfrac{3}{x}$

18. $\dfrac{\dfrac{4}{a} + \dfrac{1}{2a}}{a + \dfrac{a}{2}}$ $\dfrac{3}{a^2}$

19. $\dfrac{5 - \dfrac{1}{x}}{4 - \dfrac{1}{x}}$ $\dfrac{5x - 1}{4x - 1}$

20. $\dfrac{\dfrac{2x}{x - y}}{\dfrac{x^2}{y}}$ $\dfrac{2y}{x(x - y)}$

21. $\dfrac{\dfrac{m}{n} - \dfrac{n}{m}}{\dfrac{m + n}{n}}$ $\dfrac{m - n}{m}$

22. $\dfrac{\dfrac{5}{\frac{1}{x} + y}}{}$ $\dfrac{5x}{1 + xy}$

23. $\dfrac{\dfrac{a^2}{b} - b}{\dfrac{b^2}{a} - a}$ $-\dfrac{a}{b}$

24. $\dfrac{\dfrac{1}{x^2} - \dfrac{8}{x}}{3 + \dfrac{1}{x^2}}$ $\dfrac{1 - 8x}{3x^2 + 1}$

25. $\dfrac{2 - \dfrac{a}{b}}{\dfrac{a}{b} - 2}$ -1

26. $\dfrac{\dfrac{x}{y} - 9}{\dfrac{-x}{y} + 9}$ -1

27. $\dfrac{\dfrac{4}{x^2} + \dfrac{4}{x}}{\dfrac{4}{x} + \dfrac{4}{x^2}}$ 1

28. $\dfrac{\dfrac{a^2 - b^2}{a}}{\dfrac{a + b}{a^4}}$ $a^3(a - b)$

29. $\dfrac{\dfrac{1}{a} - \dfrac{1}{b}}{\dfrac{1}{ab}}$ $b - a$

30. $\dfrac{\dfrac{1}{a} - \dfrac{1}{b}}{\dfrac{1}{a} + \dfrac{1}{b}}$ $\dfrac{b - a}{a + b}$

31. $\dfrac{\dfrac{a}{b} + \dfrac{1}{a}}{\dfrac{b}{a} + \dfrac{1}{a}}$ $\dfrac{a^2 + b}{b(b + 1)}$

32. $\dfrac{\dfrac{2}{a} + \dfrac{3}{b}}{\dfrac{1}{a}}$ $\dfrac{2b + 3a}{b}$

33. $\dfrac{x}{\dfrac{1}{x} - \dfrac{1}{y}}$ $\dfrac{x^2 y}{y - x}$

34. $\dfrac{\dfrac{1}{a} + \dfrac{1}{b}}{ab}$ $\dfrac{b + a}{a^2 b^2}$

35. $\dfrac{\dfrac{5}{a} + \dfrac{5}{a^2}}{\dfrac{5}{b} + \dfrac{5}{b^2}}$ $\dfrac{ab^2 + b^2}{a^2(b + 1)}$

36. $\dfrac{\dfrac{x}{y} - \dfrac{2}{x}}{\dfrac{y}{x} + \dfrac{1}{y}}$ $\dfrac{x^2 - 2y}{x + y^2}$

40. $\dfrac{27x + 23y}{2x + 8y}$ **41. a)** $\dfrac{\dfrac{5}{12x}}{\dfrac{8}{x^2} - \dfrac{4}{3x}}$ **b)** $\dfrac{5x}{96 - 16x}$ **42. a)** $\dfrac{\dfrac{6}{x} - \dfrac{3}{2x}}{x + \dfrac{1}{x}}$; **b)** $\dfrac{9}{2x^2 + 2}$

Problem Solving

For the complex fractions in Exercises 37–40,

a) *Determine which of the two methods discussed in this section you would use to simplify the fraction. Explain why.*

b) *Simplify by the method you selected in part* **a)**.

c) *Simplify by the method you did not select in part* **a)**. *If your answers to parts* **b)** *and* **c)** *are not the same, explain why.*

37. $\dfrac{5 + \dfrac{3}{5}}{\dfrac{1}{8} - 4}$ $-\dfrac{224}{155}$

38. $\dfrac{\dfrac{x + y}{x^3} - \dfrac{1}{x}}{\dfrac{x - y}{x^5} + 5}$ $\dfrac{x^3 + x^2 y - x^4}{x - y + 5x^5}$

39. $\dfrac{\dfrac{x - y}{x + y} + \dfrac{6}{x + y}}{2 - \dfrac{7}{x + y}}$ $\dfrac{x - y + 6}{2x + 2y - 7}$

40. $\dfrac{\dfrac{25}{x - y} + \dfrac{2}{x + y}}{\dfrac{5}{x - y} - \dfrac{3}{x + y}}$

In Exercises 41 and 42, **a)** *write the complex fraction, and* **b)** *simplify the complex fraction.*

41. The numerator of the complex fraction consists of one term: 5 is divided by $12x$. The denominator of the complex fraction consists of two terms: 4 divided by $3x$ is subtracted from 8 divided by x^2.

42. The numerator of the complex fraction consists of two terms: 3 divided by $2x$ is subtracted from 6 divided by x. The denominator of the complex fraction consists of two terms: the sum of x and the quantity 1 divided by x.

Challenge Problems

Simplify. (Hint: Refer to Section 6.2, which discusses negative exponents.)

43. $\dfrac{x^{-1} + y^{-1}}{3}$ $\dfrac{y + x}{3xy}$

44. $\dfrac{x^{-1} + y^{-1}}{y^{-1}}$ $\dfrac{y + x}{x}$

45. $\dfrac{x^{-1} + y^{-1}}{x^{-1} y^{-1}}$ $x + y$

46. $\dfrac{x^{-2} - y^{-2}}{y^{-1} - x^{-1}}$ $-\dfrac{x + y}{xy}$

47. Jack The efficiency of a jack, E, is expressed by the formula

$$E = \dfrac{\dfrac{1}{2}h}{h + \dfrac{1}{2}},$$ where h is determined by the pitch of the

jack's thread. Determine the efficiency of a jack if h is

a) $\dfrac{2}{3}$ $\dfrac{2}{7}$ **b)** $\dfrac{4}{5}$ $\dfrac{4}{13}$

Pitch

Simplify.

48. $\dfrac{\dfrac{x}{y} + \dfrac{y}{x} + \dfrac{2}{x}}{\dfrac{x}{y} + y}$ $\dfrac{x^2 + y^2 + 2y}{x^2 + xy^2}$

49. $\dfrac{\dfrac{a}{b} + b - \dfrac{1}{a}}{\dfrac{a}{b^2} - \dfrac{b}{a} + \dfrac{3}{a^2}}$ $\dfrac{a^3 b + a^2 b^3 - ab^2}{a^3 - ab^3 + 3b^2}$

50. $\dfrac{x}{4 + \dfrac{x}{1 + x}}$ $\dfrac{x^2 + x}{5x + 4}$

Cumulative Review Exercises

[2.5] **51.** Solve the equation

$2x - 8(5 - x) = 9x - 3(x + 2)$. $\dfrac{17}{2}$

[6.4] **52.** What is a polynomial? An expression containing a finite number of terms of the form ax^n where a is a real number and n is a whole number.

[7.3] **53.** Factor $x^2 - 13x + 40$. $(x - 5)(x - 8)$

[8.4] **54.** Subtract $\dfrac{x}{3x^2 + 17x - 6} - \dfrac{2}{x^2 + 3x - 18}$.

$\dfrac{x^2 - 9x + 2}{(3x - 1)(x + 6)(x - 3)}$

8.6 Solving Rational Equations

1. Solve rational equations with integer denominators.

2. Solve rational equations where a variable appears in a denominator.

1 Solve Rational Equations with Integer Denominators

In Sections 8.1 through 8.5, we focused on how to add, subtract, multiply, and divide rational expressions. Now we are ready to solve rational equations. A **rational equation** is one that contains one or more rational (or fractional) expressions. A rational equation may be one that contains rational coefficients, such as $\dfrac{1}{2}x + \dfrac{3}{5}x = 8$ or $\dfrac{x}{2} + \dfrac{3x}{5} = 8$, or one that contains rational terms, with a variable in a denominator, such as $\dfrac{4}{x - 2} = 5$. We solved linear equations with rational coefficients in Sections 6.4 and 6.5.

The emphasis of this section will be on solving rational equations where a variable appears in a denominator. The following procedure that we will use to solve rational equations in this section is very similar to the procedure we used in Chapter 2.

To Solve Rational Equations

1. Determine the least common denominator (LCD) of all fractions in the equation.

2. Multiply **both** sides of the equation by the LCD. **This will result in every term in the equation being multiplied by the LCD**.

3. Remove any parentheses and combine like terms on each side of the equation.

4. Solve the equation using the properties discussed in earlier chapters.

5. Check your solution in the *original* equation.

TEACHING TIP
Point out that the strategy we will use to solve rational equations is to change the rational equation into the kind of equation we can solve.

The purpose of multiplying both sides of the equation by the LCD (step 2) is to eliminate all fractions from the equation. After both sides of the equation are multiplied by the LCD, the resulting equation should contain no fractions. We will omit some of the checks to save space.

Before we solve rational equations where a variable appears in a denominator, let's review how to solve equations with rational coefficients. Examples 1 and 2 illustrate the procedure to follow.

INSTRUCTOR EXAMPLE

Solve $\dfrac{x}{2} - \dfrac{x}{3} = 1$.

Ans.: 6

EXAMPLE 1 ▶ Solve $\dfrac{t}{4} - \dfrac{t}{5} = 1$ for t.

Solution   The LCD of 4 and 5 is 20. Multiply both sides of the equation by 20.

$$\frac{t}{4} - \frac{t}{5} = 1$$

$$20\left(\frac{t}{4} - \frac{t}{5}\right) = 20 \cdot 1 \qquad \textit{Multiply both sides by the LCD, 20.}$$

$$20\left(\frac{t}{4}\right) - 20\left(\frac{t}{5}\right) = 20 \qquad \textit{Distributive property}$$

$$5t - 4t = 20$$

$$t = 20$$

Check $\dfrac{t}{4} - \dfrac{t}{5} = 1$

$\dfrac{20}{4} - \dfrac{20}{5} \overset{?}{=} 1$

$5 - 4 \overset{?}{=} 1$

$1 = 1$ *True*

The solution is 20.

▶ **Now Try Exercise 13**

EXAMPLE 2 ▶ Solve $\dfrac{x-5}{30} = \dfrac{4}{5} - \dfrac{x-1}{10}$.

Solution   The least common denominator is 30. Multiply both sides of the equation by 30.

$$\dfrac{x-5}{30} = \dfrac{4}{5} - \dfrac{x-1}{10}$$

$$\boxed{30}\left(\dfrac{x-5}{30}\right) = \boxed{30}\left(\dfrac{4}{5} - \dfrac{x-1}{10}\right) \qquad \textit{Multiply both sides by the LCD, 30.}$$

$$x - 5 = \boxed{30}\left(\dfrac{4}{5}\right) - \boxed{30}\left(\dfrac{x-1}{10}\right) \qquad \textit{Distributive property}$$

$$x - 5 = 24 - 3(x - 1)$$

$$x - 5 = 24 - 3x + 3 \qquad \textit{Distributive property}$$

$$x - 5 = -3x + 27 \qquad \textit{Combine like terms.}$$

$$4x - 5 = 27 \qquad \textit{3x was added to both sides.}$$

$$4x = 32 \qquad \textit{5 was added to both sides.}$$

$$x = 8 \qquad \textit{Both sides were divided by 4.}$$

A check will show that the answer is 8. We suggest you check this answer now to get practice at checking answers.

▶ **Now Try Exercise 27**

In Example 2, the equation could also have been written as

$$\dfrac{1}{30}(x - 5) = \dfrac{4}{5} - \dfrac{1}{10}(x - 1).$$

For additional examples of solving rational equations with integers in the denominators, review Sections 2.4 and 2.5.

2 Solve Rational Equations Where a Variable Appears in a Denominator

Now we are ready to solve rational equations where a variable appears in a denominator. When solving a rational equation where a variable appears in any denominator, you *must* check your answer. See the following warning!

Warning   **Whenever a variable appears in any denominator of a rational equation, it is necessary to check your answer in the original equation. If the answer obtained makes any denominator equal to zero, that value is not a solution to the equation. Such values are called extraneous roots or extraneous solutions.**

EXAMPLE 3 ▶ Solve $4 - \dfrac{5}{x} = \dfrac{3}{2}$.

Solution Multiply both sides of the equation by the LCD, $2x$.

$$2x\left(4 - \frac{5}{x}\right) = \left(\frac{3}{2}\right) \cdot 2x \qquad \textit{Multiply both sides by the LCD, 2x.}$$

$$2x(4) - 2x\left(\frac{5}{x}\right) = \left(\frac{3}{2}\right) \cdot 2x \qquad \textit{Distributive property}$$

$$8x - 10 = 3x$$

$$5x - 10 = 0 \qquad \textit{3x was subtracted from both sides.}$$

$$5x = 10 \qquad \textit{10 was added to both sides.}$$

$$x = 2$$

Check $\qquad 4 - \dfrac{5}{x} = \dfrac{3}{2}$

$$4 - \frac{5}{2} \overset{?}{=} \frac{3}{2}$$

$$\frac{8}{2} - \frac{5}{2} \overset{?}{=} \frac{3}{2}$$

$$\frac{3}{2} = \frac{3}{2} \qquad \textit{True}$$

Since 2 does check, it is the solution to the equation.

▶ **Now Try Exercise 17**

EXAMPLE 4 ▶ Solve $\dfrac{p - 5}{p + 3} = \dfrac{1}{5}$.

Solution The LCD is $5(p + 3)$. Multiply both sides of the equation by the LCD.

$$5(p + 3) \cdot \frac{(p - 5)}{p + 3} = \frac{1}{5} \cdot 5(p + 3)$$

$$5(p - 5) = 1(p + 3)$$

$$5p - 25 = p + 3$$

$$4p - 25 = 3$$

$$4p = 28$$

$$p = 7$$

A check will show that 7 is the solution.

▶ **Now Try Exercise 43**

In Section 2.7 we illustrated that proportions of the form

$$\frac{a}{b} = \frac{c}{d}$$

can be cross-multiplied to obtain $a \cdot d = b \cdot c$. Example 4 is a proportion and can also be solved by cross-multiplying, as done in Example 5.

EXAMPLE 5 ▶ Use cross-multiplication to solve $\dfrac{9}{x + 1} = \dfrac{5}{x - 3}$.

Solution

$$\frac{9}{x + 1} = \frac{5}{x - 3}$$

$$9(x - 3) = 5(x + 1) \qquad \textit{Cross-multiply.}$$

$$9x - 27 = 5x + 5 \qquad \textit{Distributive property}$$

$$4x - 27 = 5$$

$$4x = 32$$

$$x = 8$$

A check will show that 8 is the solution to the equation.

▶ **Now Try Exercise 41**

Now let's examine some examples that involve quadratic equations. Recall from Section 7.6 that quadratic equations have the form $ax^2 + bx + c = 0$, where $a \neq 0$.

EXAMPLE 6 ▶ Solve $x + \dfrac{12}{x} = -7$.

Solution

$$x + \frac{12}{x} = -7$$

$$x \cdot \left(x + \frac{12}{x} \right) = -7 \cdot x \qquad \textit{Multiply both sides by x.}$$

$$x(x) + x\left(\frac{12}{x}\right) = -7x \qquad \textit{Distributive property}$$

$$x^2 + 12 = -7x$$

$$x^2 + 7x + 12 = 0 \qquad \textit{7x was added to both sides.}$$

$$(x + 3)(x + 4) = 0 \qquad \textit{Factor.}$$

$$x + 3 = 0 \quad \text{or} \quad x + 4 = 0 \qquad \textit{Zero-factor property}$$

$$x = -3 \qquad\qquad x = -4$$

Check

$$x = -3 \qquad\qquad\qquad x = -4$$

$$x + \frac{12}{x} = -7 \qquad\qquad\qquad x + \frac{12}{x} = -7$$

$$-3 + \frac{12}{-3} \overset{?}{=} -7 \qquad\qquad -4 + \frac{12}{-4} \overset{?}{=} -7$$

$$-3 + (-4) \overset{?}{=} -7 \qquad\qquad -4 + (-3) \overset{?}{=} -7$$

$$-7 = -7 \quad \textit{True} \qquad\qquad -7 = -7 \quad \textit{True}$$

The solutions are -3 and -4.

▶ **Now Try Exercise 57**

EXAMPLE 7 ▶ Solve $\dfrac{x^2 - 2x}{x - 6} = \dfrac{24}{x - 6}$.

Solution   If we try to solve this equation using cross-multiplication we will get a cubic equation. We will solve this equation by multiplying both sides of the equation by the LCD, $x - 6$.

$$\frac{x^2 - 2x}{x - 6} = \frac{24}{x - 6}$$

$$\cancel{x - 6} \cdot \frac{x^2 - 2x}{\cancel{x - 6}} = \frac{24}{\cancel{x - 6}} \cdot \cancel{x - 6} \qquad \textit{Multiply both sides by the LCD, } x - 6.$$

$$x^2 - 2x = 24$$

$$x^2 - 2x - 24 = 0 \qquad \textit{24 was subctracted from both sides.}$$

$$(x + 4)(x - 6) = 0 \qquad \textit{Factor}$$

$$x + 4 = 0 \quad \text{or} \quad x - 6 = 0 \qquad \textit{Zero-factor property}$$

$$x = -4 \qquad\qquad x = 6$$

Check $x = -4$ $x = 6$

$$\frac{x^2 - 2x}{x - 6} = \frac{24}{x - 6} \qquad\qquad \frac{x^2 - 2x}{x - 6} = \frac{24}{x - 6}$$

$$\frac{(-4)^2 - 2(-4)}{-4 - 6} \overset{?}{=} \frac{24}{-4 - 6} \qquad\qquad \frac{6^2 - 2(6)}{6 - 6} \overset{?}{=} \frac{24}{6 - 6}$$

$$\frac{16 + 8}{-10} \overset{?}{=} \frac{24}{-10} \qquad\qquad\qquad\qquad \frac{24}{0} = \frac{24}{0}$$

$$\frac{24}{-10} = \frac{24}{-10} \quad \textit{True} \qquad\qquad \uparrow \quad \uparrow$$

Since the denominator is 0, and we cannot divide by 0, 6 is not a solution.

Since $\dfrac{24}{0}$ is not a real number, 6 is an extraneous solution. Thus, this equation has only one solution, -4.

▶ **Now Try Exercise 47**

Helpful Hint

Remember, when solving a rational equation in which a variable appears in a denominator, you must check *all* your answers to make sure that none is an extraneous root. Extraneous roots can usually be spotted quickly. If any of your answers make any denominator 0, that answer is an extraneous root and not a true solution.

Generally speaking, if none of your answers makes any denominator 0, and you have not made a mistake when solving the equation, the answers you obtained when solving the equation will be solutions to the equation.

EXAMPLE 8 ▶ Solve $\dfrac{5w}{w^2 - 4} + \dfrac{1}{w - 2} = \dfrac{4}{w + 2}$.

Solution   First factor $w^2 - 4$.

$$\frac{5w}{(w + 2)(w - 2)} + \frac{1}{w - 2} = \frac{4}{w + 2}$$

Multiply both sides of the equation by the LCD, $(w + 2)(w - 2)$.

$$(w + 2)(w - 2)\left[\frac{5w}{(w + 2)(w - 2)} + \frac{1}{w - 2}\right] = \frac{4}{w + 2} \cdot (w + 2)(w - 2)$$

$$(w + 2)(w - 2) \cdot \frac{5w}{(w + 2)(w - 2)} + (w + 2)(w - 2) \cdot \frac{1}{w - 2} = \frac{4}{w + 2} \cdot (w + 2)(w - 2)$$

$$(w + 2)(w - 2) \cdot \frac{5w}{(w + 2)(w - 2)} + (w + 2)(w - 2) \cdot \frac{1}{w - 2} = \frac{4}{w + 2} \cdot (w + 2)(w - 2)$$

$$5w + (w + 2) = 4(w - 2)$$

$$6w + 2 = 4w - 8$$

$$2w + 2 = -8$$

$$2w = -10$$

$$w = -5$$

A check will show that -5 is the solution to the equation.

▶ **Now Try Exercise 65**

Helpful Hint

Some students confuse adding and subtracting rational expressions with solving rational equations. When adding or subtracting rational expressions, we must rewrite each expression with a common denominator. When solving a rational equation, we multiply both sides of the equation by the LCD to eliminate fractions from the equation. Consider the following two problems. Note that the one on the right is an equation because it contains an equal sign. We will work both problems. The LCD for both problems is $x(x + 4)$.

Adding Rational Expressions	Solving Rational Equations
$\dfrac{x + 2}{x + 4} + \dfrac{3}{x}$	$\dfrac{x + 2}{x + 4} = \dfrac{3}{x}$

We rewrite each fraction with the LCD, $x(x + 4)$.

$$= \frac{x}{x} \cdot \frac{x + 2}{x + 4} + \frac{3}{x} \cdot \frac{x + 4}{x + 4}$$

$$= \frac{x(x + 2)}{x(x + 4)} + \frac{3(x + 4)}{x(x + 4)}$$

$$= \frac{x^2 + 2x}{x(x + 4)} + \frac{3x + 12}{x(x + 4)}$$

$$= \frac{x^2 + 2x + 3x + 12}{x(x + 4)}$$

$$= \frac{x^2 + 5x + 12}{x(x + 4)}$$

We eliminate fractions by multiplying both sides of the equation by the LCD, $x(x + 4)$.

$$(x)(x + 4)\left(\frac{x + 2}{x + 4}\right) = \frac{3}{x}(x)(x + 4)$$

$$x(x + 2) = 3(x + 4)$$

$$x^2 + 2x = 3x + 12$$

$$x^2 - x - 12 = 0$$

$$(x - 4)(x + 3) = 0$$

$$x - 4 = 0 \quad \text{or} \quad x + 3 = 0$$

$$x = 4 \qquad\qquad x = -3$$

The numbers 4 and -3 on the right will both check and are thus solutions to the equation.

Note that when adding and subtracting rational expressions we usually end up with an algebraic expression. When solving rational equations, the solution will be a numerical value or values. The equation on the right could also be solved using cross-multiplication.

EXERCISE SET 8.6

MathXL®   MyMathLab

Concept/Writing Exercises

1. a) Explain the steps to use to solve rational equations.

b) Using the procedure you wrote in part **a)**, solve the equation $\dfrac{1}{x-1} - \dfrac{1}{x+1} = \dfrac{3x}{x^2-1}$. $\dfrac{2}{3}$

2. a) Without solving the equations, determine whether the answer to the two equations that follow will be the same or different. Explain your answer.

$$\dfrac{3}{x-2} + \dfrac{2}{x+2} = \dfrac{4x}{x^2-4}, \quad \dfrac{4x}{x^2-4} - \dfrac{2}{x+2} = \dfrac{3}{x-2}$$

b) Determine the answer to both questions.   no solution

3. Consider the following problems.

Simplify: Solve:

$$\dfrac{x}{3} - \dfrac{x}{4} + \dfrac{1}{x-1} \qquad \dfrac{x}{3} - \dfrac{x}{4} = \dfrac{1}{x-1}$$

a) Explain the difference between the two types of problems.   Left: expression, Right: equation

b) Explain how you would work each problem to obtain the correct answer.

c) Find the correct answer to each problem.

4. Consider the following problems.

Simplify: Solve:

$$\dfrac{x}{2} - \dfrac{x}{3} + \dfrac{5}{2x+7} \qquad \dfrac{x}{2} - \dfrac{x}{3} = \dfrac{5}{2x+7}$$

a) Explain the difference between the two types of problems.   Left: expression, Right: equation

b) Explain how you would work each problem to obtain the correct answer.

c) Find the correct answer to each problem.

5. Under what conditions must you check rational equations for extraneous solutions?

6. Which of the following numbers, 3, 1, or, 0 cannot be a solution to the equation $3 - \dfrac{1}{x} = 4$? Explain.   0

7. Which of the following numbers, 0, 3, or 2 cannot be a solution to the equation $\dfrac{3}{x-2} + 5x = 6$? Explain.   2

8. Which of the following numbers, 0, −5 or 2 cannot be a solution to the equation $4x - \dfrac{2}{x+5} = 3$? Explain.   −5

1. a) Answers will vary.   **2. a)** will be the same   **3. b)** **Left:** Write fractions with LCD $12(x-1)$, combine numerators. **Right:** Multiply both sides by LCD, $12(x-1)$, then solve.   **3. c)** **Left:** $\dfrac{x^2 - x + 12}{12(x-1)}$; **Right:** $4, -3$

In Exercises 9–12, indicate whether it is necessary to check the solution obtained to see if it is extraneous. Explain your answer.

9. $\dfrac{4}{7} + \dfrac{x-2}{6} = 5$ no   **10.** $\dfrac{5}{x-2} + \dfrac{1}{x} = 6$ yes   **11.** $\dfrac{2}{x+4} + 1 = 6$ yes   **12.** $\dfrac{z}{3} + \dfrac{7}{z} = 8$ yes

4. b) Left: Write fractions with LCD $6(2x+7)$, combine numerators. **Right:** Multiply both sides by LCD $6(2x+7)$, then solve.

c) Left: $\dfrac{2x^2 + 7x + 30}{6(2x+7)}$, **Right:** $\dfrac{5}{2}, -6$ **5.** when there is a variable in the denominator

Practice the Skills

Solve each equation and check your solution. See Examples 1 and 2.

13. $\dfrac{x}{3} - \dfrac{x}{4} = 1$ 12   **14.** $\dfrac{t}{5} - \dfrac{t}{6} = 2$ 60   **15.** $\dfrac{r}{6} = \dfrac{r}{4} + \dfrac{1}{3}$ −4   **16.** $\dfrac{n}{5} = \dfrac{n}{6} + \dfrac{2}{3}$ 20

17. $\dfrac{z}{2} + 6 = \dfrac{z}{5}$ −20   **18.** $\dfrac{3w}{5} - 6 = w$ −15   **19.** $\dfrac{z}{6} + \dfrac{2}{3} = \dfrac{z}{5} - \dfrac{1}{3}$ 30   **20.** $\dfrac{m-2}{6} = \dfrac{2}{3} + \dfrac{m}{12}$ 12

21. $d + 7 = \dfrac{3}{2}d + 5$ 4   **22.** $\dfrac{q}{5} + \dfrac{q}{2} = \dfrac{21}{10}$ 3   **23.** $3k + \dfrac{1}{6} = 4k - 4$ $\dfrac{25}{6}$ **24.** $\dfrac{p}{4} + \dfrac{1}{4} = \dfrac{p}{3} - \dfrac{1}{2}$ 9

25. $\dfrac{n+6}{3} = \dfrac{5(n-8)}{10}$ 36   **26.** $\dfrac{3(x-6)}{5} = \dfrac{4(x+2)}{8}$ 46   **27.** $\dfrac{x-5}{15} = \dfrac{3}{5} - \dfrac{x-4}{10}$ 8   **28.** $\dfrac{z+4}{6} = \dfrac{3}{2} - \dfrac{2z+2}{12}$ 2

29. $\dfrac{-p+1}{4} + \dfrac{13}{20} = \dfrac{p}{5} - \dfrac{p-1}{2}$ −8   **30.** $\dfrac{1}{10} - \dfrac{n+1}{6} = \dfrac{1}{5} - \dfrac{n+10}{15}$ 4

31. $\dfrac{d-3}{4} + \dfrac{1}{15} = \dfrac{2d+1}{3} - \dfrac{34}{15}$ 3   **32.** $\dfrac{t+4}{5} = \dfrac{5}{8} + \dfrac{t+7}{40}$ 0

Solve each equation and check your solution. See Examples 3–8.

33. $2 + \dfrac{3}{x} = \dfrac{11}{4}$ 4   **34.** $3 - \dfrac{1}{x} = \dfrac{14}{5}$ 5   **35.** $7 - \dfrac{5}{x} = \dfrac{9}{2}$ 2   **36.** $4 + \dfrac{3}{z} = \dfrac{9}{2}$ 6

37. $\dfrac{4}{n} - \dfrac{3}{2n} = \dfrac{1}{2}$ 5   **38.** $\dfrac{5}{3x} + \dfrac{2}{x} = 1$ $\dfrac{11}{3}$ **39.** $\dfrac{x-1}{x-5} = \dfrac{4}{x-5}$ no solution   **40.** $\dfrac{2x+3}{x+2} = \dfrac{3}{2}$ 0

41. $\dfrac{5}{a+3} = \dfrac{4}{a+1}$ 7

42. $\dfrac{5}{x+2} = \dfrac{1}{x-4}$ $\dfrac{11}{2}$

43. $\dfrac{y+3}{y-3} = \dfrac{6}{4}$ 15

44. $\dfrac{x}{x+6} = \dfrac{2}{5}$ 4

45. $\dfrac{2x-3}{x-4} = \dfrac{5}{x-4}$ no solution

46. $\dfrac{3}{x} + 9 = \dfrac{3}{x}$ no solution

47. $\dfrac{x^2}{x-3} = \dfrac{9}{x-3}$ -3

48. $\dfrac{x^2}{x+5} = \dfrac{25}{x+5}$ 5

49. $\dfrac{n-3}{n+2} = \dfrac{n+4}{n+10}$ 38

50. $\dfrac{x+5}{x+1} = \dfrac{x-6}{x-3}$ $\dfrac{9}{7}$

51. $\dfrac{1}{r} = \dfrac{3r}{8r+3}$ $-\dfrac{1}{3}, 3$

52. $\dfrac{1}{r} = \dfrac{2r}{r+15}$ $-\dfrac{5}{2}, 3$

53. $\dfrac{k}{k+2} = \dfrac{3}{k-2}$ $6, -1$

54. $\dfrac{3a-2}{2a+2} = \dfrac{3}{a-1}$ $-\dfrac{1}{3}, 4$

55. $\dfrac{4}{r} + r = \dfrac{20}{r}$ $4, -4$

56. $a + \dfrac{5}{a} = \dfrac{14}{a}$ $3, -3$

57. $x + \dfrac{20}{x} = -9$ $-4, -5$

58. $x - \dfrac{32}{x} = 4$ $8, -4$

59. $\dfrac{3y-2}{y+1} = 4 - \dfrac{y+2}{y-1}$ 4

60. $\dfrac{2b}{b+1} = 2 - \dfrac{5}{2b}$ -5

61. $\dfrac{1}{x+3} + \dfrac{1}{x-3} = \dfrac{-5}{x^2-9}$ $-\dfrac{5}{2}$

62. $\dfrac{t+2}{t-5} - \dfrac{3}{4} = \dfrac{6}{t-5}$ 1

63. $\dfrac{x}{x-3} + \dfrac{3}{2} = \dfrac{3}{x-3}$ no solution

64. $\dfrac{y}{2y+2} + \dfrac{2y-16}{4y+4} = \dfrac{y-3}{y+1}$

65. $\dfrac{3}{x-5} - \dfrac{4}{x+5} = \dfrac{11}{x^2-25}$ 24

66. $\dfrac{2n^2-15}{n^2+n-6} = \dfrac{n+1}{n+3} + \dfrac{n-3}{n-2}$ 4

67. $\dfrac{3x}{x^2-9} + \dfrac{1}{x-3} = \dfrac{3}{x+3}$ -12

68. $\dfrac{3}{x+3} + \dfrac{5}{x+4} = \dfrac{12x+7}{x^2+7x+12}$ 5

69. $\dfrac{1}{y-1} + \dfrac{1}{2} = \dfrac{2}{y^2-1}$ -3

70. $\dfrac{2y}{y+2} = \dfrac{y}{y+3} - \dfrac{3}{y^2+5y+6}$ -1

71. $\dfrac{3t}{6t+6} + \dfrac{t}{2t+2} = \dfrac{2t-3}{t+1}$ 3

72. $\dfrac{2}{x-2} - \dfrac{1}{x+1} = \dfrac{2}{x^2-x-2}$ -2

Problem Solving   **64.** no solution   **76.** x can be any real number.   **77.** x can be any real number.   **78.** x can be any real number except 0.

In Exercises 73–78, determine the solution by observation. Explain how you determined your answer.

73. $\dfrac{3}{x-2} = \dfrac{x-2}{x-2}$ 5

74. $\dfrac{1}{2} + \dfrac{x}{2} = \dfrac{5}{2}$ 4

75. $\dfrac{x}{x-6} + \dfrac{x}{x-6} = 0$ 0

76. $\dfrac{x}{4} + \dfrac{3x}{4} = x$

77. $\dfrac{x-2}{3} + \dfrac{x-2}{3} = \dfrac{2x-4}{3}$

78. $\dfrac{3}{x} - \dfrac{1}{x} = \dfrac{2}{x}$

79. Optics A formula frequently used in optics is

$$\dfrac{1}{p} + \dfrac{1}{q} = \dfrac{1}{f}$$

where p represents the distance of the object from a mirror (or lens), q represents the distance of the image from the mirror (or lens), and f represents the focal length of the mirror (or lens). If a mirror has a focal length of 10 centimeters, how far from the mirror will the image appear when the object is 30 centimeters from the mirror?   15 cm

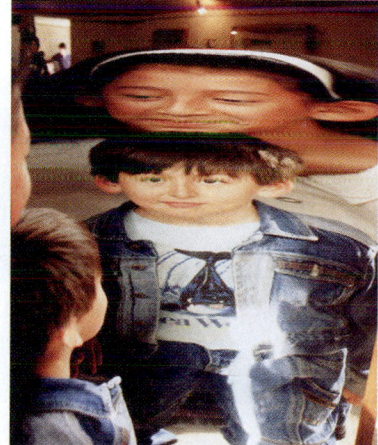

80. a) You would obtain a cubic equation.   **83.** No; it is impossible for both sides of the equation to be equal.

Challenge Problems

80. a) Explain why the equation $\dfrac{x^2}{x-3} = \dfrac{9}{x-3}$ cannot be solved by cross-multiplying using the material presented in the book.

   b) Solve the equation given in part a). -3

81. Solve the equation $\dfrac{x-4}{x^2-2x} = \dfrac{-4}{x^2-4}$ -4

82. Electrical Resistance In electronics the total resistance R_T, of resistors wired in a parallel circuit is determined by the formula

$$\dfrac{1}{R_T} = \dfrac{1}{R_1} + \dfrac{1}{R_2} + \dfrac{1}{R_3} + \cdots + \dfrac{1}{R_n}$$

where $R_1, R_2, R_3, \ldots, R_n$ are the resistances of the individual resistors (measured in ohms) in the circuit.

   a) Find the total resistance if two resistors, one of 200 ohms and the other of 300 ohms, are wired in a parallel circuit.   120 ohms

   b) If three identical resistors are to be wired in parallel, what should be the resistance of each resistor if the total resistance of the circuit is to be 300 ohms?   900 ohms

83. Can an equation of the form $\dfrac{a}{x} + 1 = \dfrac{a}{x}$ have a real number solution for any real number a? Explain your answer.

Group Activity

Discuss and answer Exercise 84 as a group.

84. **a)** cross-multiply or use the LCD **c)** $\dfrac{5}{x+3} = \dfrac{4}{x}$ **f)** $\dfrac{x}{1} + \dfrac{3}{1} = \dfrac{x}{2}$

84. **a)** As a group, discuss two different methods you can use to solve the equation $\dfrac{x+3}{5} = \dfrac{x}{4}$.

  b) Group member 1: Solve the equation by obtaining a common denominator.
  Group member 2: Solve the equation by cross-multiplying.
  Group member 3: Check the results of group member 1 and group member 2.   12

  c) Individually, create another equation by taking the reciprocal of each term in the equation in part **a)**. Compare your results. Do you think that the reciprocal of the answer you found in part **b)** will be the solution to this equation? Explain.

  d) Individually, solve the equation you found in part **c)** and check your answer. Compare your work with the other group members. Was the conclusion you came to in part **c)** correct? Explain.   12

  e) As a group, solve the equation $\dfrac{1}{x} + \dfrac{1}{3} = \dfrac{2}{x}$. Check your result.   3

  f) As a group, create another equation by taking the reciprocal of each term of the equation in part **e)**. Do you think that the reciprocal of the answer you found in part **e)** will be the solution to this equation? Explain.

  g) Individually, solve the equation you found in part **f)** and check your answer. Compare your work with the other group members. Did your group make the correct conclusion in part **f)**? Explain.   −6

  h) As a group, discuss the relationship between the solution to the equation $\dfrac{7}{x-9} = \dfrac{3}{x}$ and the solution to the equation $\dfrac{x-9}{7} = \dfrac{x}{3}$. Explain your answer.

  h) The solution will be the same.

Cumulative Review Exercises

[3.2] **85. Internet Plans** An Internet service offers two plans for its customers. One plan includes 5 hours of use and costs $7.95 per month. Each additional minute after the 5 hours costs $0.15. The second plan costs $19.95 per month and provides unlimited Internet access. How many hours would Jake LaRue have to use the Internet monthly to make the second plan the less expensive?   more than $6\frac{1}{3}$ hours

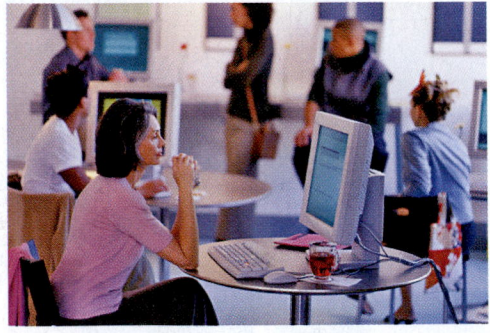

86. Filling a Jacuzzi How long will it take to fill a 600-gallon Jacuzzi if water is flowing into the Jacuzzi at a rate of 4 gallons a minute?   150 min

[3.3] **87. Supplementary Angles** Two angles are supplementary angles if the sum of their measures is 180°. Find the two supplementary angles if the smaller angle is 30° less than half the larger angle.   40°, 140°

[6.6] **88.** Multiply $(3.4 \times 10^{-5})(2 \times 10^{13})$. 6.8×10^8

[7.6] **89.** Explain the difference between a linear equation and a quadratic equation, and give an example of each.
  linear equation: $ax + b = c, a \neq 0$;
  quadratic equation: $ax^2 + bx + c = 0, a \neq 0$

8.7 Rational Equations: Applications and Problem Solving

1 Set up and solve applications containing rational expressions.

2 Set up and solve motion problems.

3 Set up and solve work problems.

1 Set Up and Solve Applications Containing Rational Expressions

Many applications of algebra involve rational equations. After we represent the application as an equation, we solve the rational equation as we did in Section 8.6.

The first type of application we will consider is a *geometry problem*.

EXAMPLE 1 ▶ A New Rug Mary and Larry Armstrong are interested in purchasing a carpet whose area is 60 square feet. Determine the length and width if the width is 5 feet less than $\dfrac{3}{5}$ of the length, see **Figure 8.2**.

FIGURE 8.2

INSTRUCTOR EXAMPLE
The area of a rectangle is 160 square meters. Determine the length and width if the width is 6 meters less than the length.
Ans.: *l*: 16 m, *w*: 10 m

Solution

Understand and Translate   Let x = length.

Then $\frac{3}{5}x - 5$ = width.

$$\text{area} = \text{length} \cdot \text{width}$$

$$60 = x\left(\frac{3}{5}x - 5\right)$$

Carry Out

$$60 = \frac{3}{5}x^2 - 5x$$

$$5\,(60) = 5\left(\frac{3}{5}x^2 - 5x\right) \quad \text{Multiply both sides by 5.}$$

$$300 = 3x^2 - 25x \quad \text{Distributive property}$$

$$0 = 3x^2 - 25x - 300 \quad \text{Subtract 300 from both sides.}$$

$$\text{or} \quad 3x^2 - 25x - 300 = 0$$

$$(3x + 20)(x - 15) = 0 \quad \text{Factor.}$$

$$3x + 20 = 0 \quad \text{or} \quad x - 15 = 0 \quad \text{Zero-factor property}$$

$$3x = -20 \qquad\qquad x = 15$$

$$x = -\frac{20}{3}$$

Check and Answer   Since the length of a rectangle cannot be negative, we can eliminate $-\frac{20}{3}$ as an answer to our problem.

$$\text{length} = x = 15 \text{ feet}$$

$$\text{width} = \frac{3}{5}(15) - 5 = 4 \text{ feet}$$

Check

$$a = lw$$

$$60 \stackrel{?}{=} 15(4)$$

$$60 = 60 \qquad \textit{True}$$

Therefore, the length is 15 feet and the width is 4 feet.

▶ **Now Try Exercise 5**

Now we will work with a problem that expresses the relationship between two numbers. Problems like this are sometimes referred to as *number problems*.

INSTRUCTOR EXAMPLE
One number is 5 times another. The difference of their reciprocals is $\frac{2}{5}$. Determine the numbers.
Ans.: 2 and 10

EXAMPLE 2 ▶ **Reciprocals** One number is 4 times another number. The sum of their reciprocals is $\frac{5}{2}$. Determine the numbers.

Solution   **Understand and Translate**

Let x = first number.

Then $4x$ = second number.

The reciprocal of the first number is $\frac{1}{x}$ and the reciprocal of the second number is $\frac{1}{4x}$.

The sum of their reciprocals is $\frac{5}{2}$, thus:

$$\frac{1}{x} + \frac{1}{4x} = \frac{5}{2}$$

Carry Out

$$4x\left(\frac{1}{x} + \frac{1}{4x}\right) = 4x\left(\frac{5}{2}\right) \quad \textcolor{red}{\textit{Multiply both sides by the LCD, 4x.}}$$

$$4x\left(\frac{1}{x}\right) + 4x\left(\frac{1}{4x}\right) = 10x \quad \textcolor{red}{\textit{Distributive property}}$$

$$4 + 1 = 10x$$

$$5 = 10x$$

$$\frac{5}{10} = x$$

$$\frac{1}{2} = x$$

Check   The first number is $\frac{1}{2}$. The second number is therefore $4x = 4\left(\frac{1}{2}\right) = 2$.
Let's now check if the sum of the reciprocals is $\frac{5}{2}$. The reciprocal of $\frac{1}{2}$ is 2. The reciprocal of 2 is $\frac{1}{2}$. The sum of the reciprocals is

$$2 + \frac{1}{2} = \frac{4}{2} + \frac{1}{2} = \frac{5}{2}$$

Answer   Since the sum of the reciprocals is $\frac{5}{2}$, the two numbers are 2 and $\frac{1}{2}$.

▶ **Now Try Exercise 11**

---

2 Set Up and Solve Motion Problems

In Chapter 3 we discussed *motion problems*. Recall that

$$\text{distance} = \text{rate} \cdot \text{time}$$

If we solve this equation for time, we obtain

$$\text{time} = \frac{\text{distance}}{\text{rate}} \quad \text{or} \quad t = \frac{d}{r}$$

INSTRUCTOR EXAMPLE 3
The current in the river is 3 mph. If it takes the same amount of time to travel 14 miles downstream as 2 miles upstream, find the speed of the boat in still water.
Ans.: 4 mph

This equation is useful in solving motion problems when the total time of travel for two objects or the time of travel between two points is known.

EXAMPLE 3 ▶ **Canoeing** Cindy Kilborn went canoeing in the Colorado River. The current in the river was 2 miles per hour. If it took Cindy the same amount of time to travel 10 miles downstream as 2 miles upstream, determine the speed at which Cindy's canoe would travel in still water.

Solution   Understand and Translate

Let r = the canoe's speed in still water.

Then $r + 2$ = the canoe's speed traveling downstream (with current)

and $r - 2$ = the canoe's speed traveling upstream (against current.)

Direction	Distance	Rate	Time
Downstream	10	$r + 2$	$\dfrac{10}{r + 2}$
Upstream	2	$r - 2$	$\dfrac{2}{r - 2}$

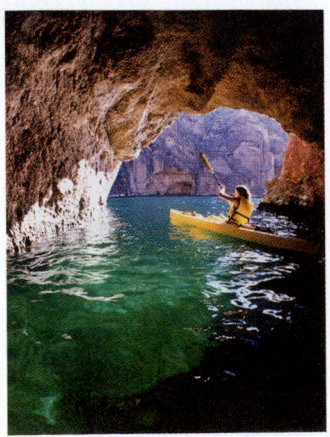

Since the time it takes to travel 10 miles downstream is the same as the time to travel 2 miles upstream, we set the times equal to each other and then solve the resulting equation.

$$\text{time downstream} = \text{time upstream}$$

$$\frac{10}{r + 2} = \frac{2}{r - 2}$$

Carry Out

$$10(r - 2) = 2(r + 2) \qquad \textit{Cross-multiply.}$$

$$10r - 20 = 2r + 4$$

$$8r = 24$$

$$r = 3$$

Check and Answer   Since this rational equation contains a variable in a denominator, the solution must be checked. A check will show that 3 satisfies the equation. Thus, the canoe would travel at 3 miles per hour in still water.

▶ **Now Try Exercise 15**

EXAMPLE 4 ▶ **Scenic Route** Mazie Akana drives along Route 72 along the shore-line in Oahu, Hawaii. Because of the beautiful scenery she drives an average of 20 miles per hour. Then she drives inland and averages 65 miles per hour. If the total distance she drove was 100 miles and the total time she drove was 3.5 hours, how long did she drive at each speed?

Solution   Understand and Translate

Let d = distance traveled at 20 miles per hour.

Then $100 - d$ = distance traveled at 65 miles per hour.

Direction	Distance	Rate	Time
Shoreline	d	20	$\dfrac{d}{20}$
Inland	$100 - d$	65	$\dfrac{100 - d}{65}$

Since the total time spent driving is 3.5 hours, we write

$$\text{time along shoreline} + \text{time inland} = 3.5 \text{ hours}$$

$$\frac{d}{20} + \frac{100 - d}{65} = 3.5$$

Carry Out

$$260\left(\frac{d}{20} + \frac{100 - d}{65}\right) = (260)(3.5) \qquad \textit{Multiply both sides by the LCD, 260.}$$

$$\overset{13}{\cancel{260}}\left(\frac{d}{\cancel{20}}\right) + \overset{4}{\cancel{260}}\left(\frac{100 - d}{\cancel{65}}\right) = 910 \qquad \textit{Distributive property}$$

$$13d + 4(100 - d) = 910$$

$$13d + 400 - 4d = 910$$

$$9d + 400 = 910$$

$$9d = 510$$

$$d = \frac{510}{9}$$

$$d \approx 57$$

Answer   The answer to the problem is not 57. Remember that the question asked us to *find the time spent* traveling at each speed. The variable d does not represent time but represents the distance traveled at 20 miles per hour. To find the time traveled and to answer the question asked, we need to evaluate $\dfrac{d}{20}$ and $\dfrac{100 - d}{65}$ for $d = 57$.

Time at 20 mph

$$\frac{d}{20} = \frac{57}{20} \approx 2.9$$

Time at 65 mph

$$\frac{100 - d}{65} = \frac{100 - 57}{65} = \frac{43}{65} \approx 0.6$$

Thus, Mazie drove about 2.9 hours along the shoreline and about 0.6 hours inland. The total time was $2.9 + 0.6$ or 3.5 hours.

▶ **Now Try Exercise 17**

EXAMPLE 5 ▶ **Distance of a Marathon**   At a fund-raising marathon participants can either bike, walk, or run. Kim Clark, who rode a bike, completed the entire distance of the marathon with an average speed of 16 kilometers per hour (kph). Steve Schwartz, who jogged, completed the entire distance with an average speed of 5 kph. If Kim completed the race in 2.75 hours less time than Steve did, determine the distance the marathon covered.

Solution   **Understand and Translate**   Let d = the distance from the start to the finish of the marathon. Then we can construct the following table. To determine the time, we divide the distance by the rate.

Person	Distance	Rate	Time
Kim	d	16	$\dfrac{d}{16}$
Steve	d	5	$\dfrac{d}{5}$

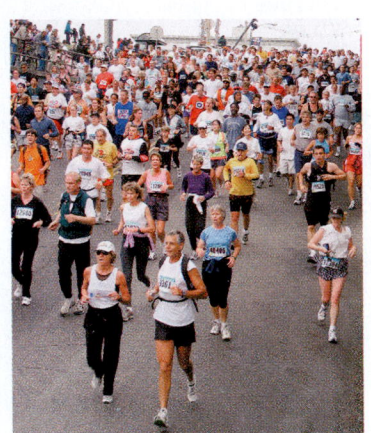

We are given that Kim completed the marathon in 2.75 hours less time than Steve did. Therefore, to make Kim's and Steve's times equal, we need to subtract 2.75 hours from Steve's time (or add 2.75 hours to Kim's time; see the paragraph following this example). We will subtract 2.75 hours from Steve's time and use the following equation to solve the problem.

$$\text{Time for Kim} = \text{Time for Steve} - 2.75 \text{ hours}$$

$$\frac{d}{16} = \frac{d}{5} - 2.75$$

Carry Out

$$80\left(\frac{d}{16}\right) = 80\left(\frac{d}{5} - 2.75\right)$$ *Multiply both sides by the LCD, 80.*

$$5d = 80\left(\frac{d}{5}\right) - 80(2.75)$$ *Distributive property*

$$5d = 16d - 220$$
$$-11d = -220$$
$$d = 20$$

Check and Answer   The distance from the starting point to the ending point of the marathon appears to be 20 kilometers. To check this answer we will determine the times it took Kim and Steve to complete the marathon and see if the difference between the times is 2.75 hours. To determine the times, divide the distance, 20 kilometers, by the rate.

$$\text{Kim's time} = \frac{20}{16} = 1.25 \text{ hours}$$

$$\text{Steve's time} = \frac{20}{5} = 4 \text{ hours}$$

Since $4 - 1.25 = 2.75$ hours, the answer checks. Therefore the distance the marathon covers is 20 kilometers.

▶ **Now Try Exercise 25**

In Example 5 we subtracted 2.75 hours from Steve's time to obtain an equation. We could have added 2.75 hours to Kim's time to obtain an equivalent equation. Rework Example 5 now by adding 2.75 hours to Kim's time.

3 Set Up and Solve Work Problems

Problems in which two or more machines or people work together to complete a specific task are sometimes referred to as *work problems*. Work problems often involve equations containing fractions. Generally, work problems are based on the fact that the fractional part of the work done by person 1 (or machine 1) plus the fractional part of the work done by person 2 (or machine 2) is equal to the total amount of work done by both people (or both machines). *We represent the total amount of work done by the number 1, which represents one whole job completed.*

$$\begin{pmatrix} \text{part of task done} \\ \text{by first person} \\ \text{or machine} \end{pmatrix} + \begin{pmatrix} \text{part of task done} \\ \text{by second person} \\ \text{or machine} \end{pmatrix} = \begin{pmatrix} 1 \\ \text{(one whole task} \\ \text{completed)} \end{pmatrix}$$

To determine the part of the task completed by each person or machine, we use the formula

$$\textbf{part of task completed} = \textbf{rate} \cdot \textbf{time}$$

This formula is very similar to the formula

$$\text{amount} = \text{rate} \cdot \text{time}$$

that was discussed in Section 3.4. To determine the part of the task completed, we need to determine the rate. Suppose that Paul can do a particular task in 6 hours. Then he would complete 1/6 of the task per hour. Thus, his rate is 1/6 of the task per hour. If Audrey can do a particular task in 5 minutes, her rate is 1/5 of the task per minute. In general, if a person or machine can complete a task in t units of time, the rate is $1/t$.

EXAMPLE 6 ▶ **Plowing a Field** Bob Smith can plow a field by himself in 20 hours. His wife, Mary, by herself can plow the same field in 30 hours. How long will it take them to plow the field if they work together?

Solution   Understand and Translate   Let t = the time, in hours, for Mr. and Mrs. Smith working together, to plow the field. We will construct a table to help us in finding the part of the task completed by Mr. Smith and Mrs. Smith in t hours.

Landscaper	Rate of Work (part of the task completed per hour)	Time Worked	Part of Task
Mr. Smith	$\dfrac{1}{20}$	t	$\dfrac{t}{20}$
Mrs. Smith	$\dfrac{1}{30}$	t	$\dfrac{t}{30}$

$$\begin{pmatrix} \text{part of the field plowed} \\ \text{by Mr. Smith in } t \text{ hours} \end{pmatrix} + \begin{pmatrix} \text{part of the field plowed} \\ \text{by Mrs. Smith in } t \text{ hours} \end{pmatrix} = 1 (\text{entire field plowed})$$

$$\dfrac{t}{20} \qquad\qquad + \qquad\qquad \dfrac{t}{30} \qquad\qquad = \qquad\qquad 1$$

Carry Out   Now multiply both sides of the equation by the LCD, 60.

$$60\left(\frac{t}{20} + \frac{t}{30}\right) = 60 \cdot 1$$

$$\overset{3}{\cancel{60}}\left(\frac{t}{\cancel{20}}\right) + \overset{2}{\cancel{60}}\left(\frac{t}{\cancel{30}}\right) = 60 \qquad \textit{Distributive property}$$

$$3t + 2t = 60$$

$$5t = 60$$

$$t = 12$$

Answer   Thus, Mr. and Mrs. Smith working together can plow the field in 12 hours. We leave the check for you.

▸ **Now Try Exercise 27**

Helpful Hint

In Example 6, Mr. Smith could plow the field by himself in 20 hours, and Mrs. Smith could plow the field by herself in 30 hours. We determined that together they could plow the field in 12 hours. Does this answer make sense? Since you would expect the time to plow the field together to be less than the time either of them could plow it alone, the answer makes sense. When solving a work problem, always examine your answer to see if it makes sense. If not, rework the problem and find your error.

EXAMPLE 7 ▸ **Storing Wine**   At a winery in Napa Valley, California, one pipe can fill a tank with wine in 3 hours and another pipe can empty the tank in 5 hours. If the valves to both pipes are open, how long will it take to fill the empty tank?

Solution   **Understand and Translate**   Let t = amount of time to fill the tank with both valves open.

Pipe	Rate of Work	Time	Part of Task
Pipe filling tank	$\dfrac{1}{3}$	t	$\dfrac{t}{3}$
Pipe emptying tank	$\dfrac{1}{5}$	t	$\dfrac{t}{5}$

As one pipe is filling, the other is emptying the tank. Thus, the pipes are working against each other. Therefore, instead of adding the parts of the task, as was done in Example 6 where the people worked together, we will subtract the parts of the task.

$$\left(\begin{array}{c}\text{part of tank}\\\text{filled in } t \text{ hours}\end{array}\right) - \left(\begin{array}{c}\text{part of tank}\\\text{emptied in } t \text{ hours}\end{array}\right) = 1(\text{total tank filled})$$

$$\frac{t}{3} - \frac{t}{5} = 1$$

Carry Out

$$15\left(\frac{t}{3} - \frac{t}{5}\right) = 15 \cdot 1 \qquad \textit{Multiply both sides by the LCD, 15.}$$

$$\overset{5}{\cancel{15}}\left(\frac{t}{\cancel{3}}\right) - \overset{3}{\cancel{15}}\left(\frac{t}{\cancel{5}}\right) = 15 \qquad \textit{Distributive property}$$

$$5t - 3t = 15$$

$$2t = 15$$

$$t = 7\frac{1}{2}$$

Check and Answer   The tank will be filled in $7\frac{1}{2}$ hours. This answer is reasonable because we expect it to take longer than 3 hours when the tank is being drained at the same time.

▶ **Now Try Exercise 35**

EXAMPLE 8 ▶ **Cleaning Service** Linda and John Franco own a house cleaning service. When Linda cleans Damon's house by herself, it takes 7 hours. When Linda and John work together, they can clean the house in 4 hours. How long will it take John to clean the house by himself?

Solution   Let t = time for John to clean the house by himself. Then John's rate is $\frac{1}{t}$. Let's make a table to help analyze the problem. Since Linda can clean the house by herself in 7 hours, her rate is $\frac{1}{7}$ of the job per hour. In the table, we use the fact that together they can clean the house in 4 hours.

Worker	Rate of Work	Time	Part of Task
Linda	$\frac{1}{7}$	4	$\frac{4}{7}$
John	$\frac{1}{t}$	4	$\frac{4}{t}$

$$\left(\begin{array}{c}\text{part of house}\\\text{cleaned by Linda}\end{array}\right) + \left(\begin{array}{c}\text{part of house}\\\text{cleaned by John}\end{array}\right) = 1$$

$$\frac{4}{7} \qquad + \qquad \frac{4}{t} \qquad = 1$$

Carry Out
$$7t\left(\frac{4}{7} + \frac{4}{t}\right) = 7t \cdot 1 \qquad \textit{Multiply both sides by the LCD, 7t.}$$

$$7t\left(\frac{4}{7}\right) + 7t\left(\frac{4}{t}\right) = 7t \qquad \textit{Distributive property}$$

$$4t + 28 = 7t$$

$$28 = 3t$$

$$\frac{28}{3} = t$$

$$9\frac{1}{3} = t$$

Check and Answer   Thus, it takes John, $9\frac{1}{3}$ hours, or 9 hours 20 minutes, to clean the house by himself. This answer is reasonable because we expect it to take longer for John to clean the house by himself than it would for Linda and John working together.

▶ **Now Try Exercise 39**

EXAMPLE 9 ▶ Thank-You Notes Peter and Kaitlyn Kewin are handwriting thank-you notes to guests who attended their 20th wedding anniversary party. Kaitlyn by herself could write all the notes in 6 hours and Peter could write all the notes by himself in 10 hours. After Kaitlyn has been writing thank-you notes for 4 hours by herself, she must leave town on business. Peter then continues the task of writing the thank-you notes. How long will it take Peter to finish writing the remaining notes?

Solution   **Understand and Translate**   Let t = time it will take Peter to finish writing the notes.

Person	Rate of Work	Time	Part of Task
Kaitlyn	$\dfrac{1}{6}$	4	$\dfrac{4}{6} = \dfrac{2}{3}$
Peter	$\dfrac{1}{10}$	t	$\dfrac{t}{10}$

$$\left(\begin{array}{c}\text{part of notes written}\\ \text{by Kaitlyn}\end{array}\right) + \left(\begin{array}{c}\text{part of notes written}\\ \text{by Peter}\end{array}\right) = 1$$

$$\frac{2}{3} \quad + \quad \frac{t}{10} \quad = 1$$

Carry Out

$$30\left(\frac{2}{3} + \frac{t}{10}\right) = 30 \cdot 1 \qquad \textcolor{magenta}{\textit{Multiply both sides by the LCD, 30.}}$$

$$\overset{10}{\cancel{30}}\left(\frac{2}{\underset{1}{\cancel{3}}}\right) + \overset{3}{\cancel{30}}\left(\frac{t}{\underset{1}{\cancel{10}}}\right) = 30 \qquad \textcolor{magenta}{\textit{Distributive property}}$$

$$20 + 3t = 30$$

$$3t = 10$$

$$t = \frac{10}{3} \quad \text{or} \quad 3\frac{1}{3}$$

Answer   Thus, it will take Peter $3\dfrac{1}{3}$ hours to complete the cards.

▶ **Now Try Exercise 37**

EXERCISE SET 8.7

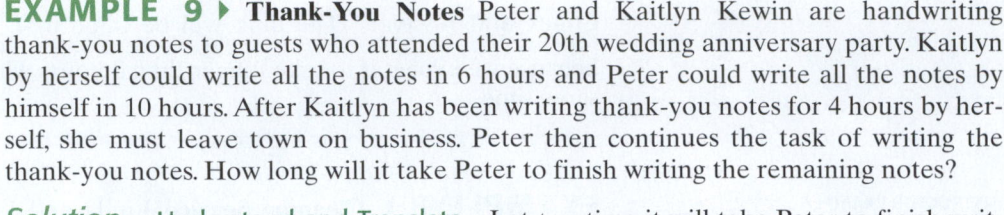

Concept/Writing Exercises

1. Geometric formulas, which were discussed in Section 2.6, are often rational equations. Give three formulas that are rational equations.

2. Suppose that car 1 and car 2 are traveling to the same location 60 miles away and that car 1 travels 10 miles per hour faster than car 2.

   a) Let r represent the speed of car 2. Write an expression, using time $= \dfrac{\text{distance}}{\text{rate}}$, for the time it takes car 1 to reach its destination. $t = \dfrac{60}{r + 10}$

   b) Now let r represent the speed of car 1. Write an expression, using time $= \dfrac{\text{distance}}{\text{rate}}$, for the time it takes car 2 to reach its destination. $t = \dfrac{60}{r - 10}$.

3. In an equation for a work problem, one side of the equation is set equal to 1. What does the 1 represent in the problem?   1 complete task

4. Suppose Tracy Augustine can complete a particular task in 3 hours, while the same task can be completed by John Bailey in 7 hours. How would you represent the part of the task completed by Tracy in 1 hour? By John in 1 hour?
   Tracy, $\dfrac{1}{3}$; John, $\dfrac{1}{7}$

1. Some examples are: $A = \dfrac{1}{2}bh$, $A = \dfrac{1}{2}h(b_1 + b_2)$, $V = \dfrac{1}{3}\pi r^2 h$, $V = \dfrac{4}{3}\pi r^3$

Practice the Skills/Problem Solving

In Exercises 5–36, solve the problem and answer the questions.

Geometry Problems; see Example 1. **7.** base = 12 cm, height = 7 cm

5. Packaging Computers The Phillips Paper Company makes rectangular pieces of cardboard for packing computers. The sheets of cardboard are to have an area of 99 square inches, and the length of a sheet is to be 5 inches more than $\frac{2}{3}$ its width. Determine the length and width of the cardboard to be manufactured. *l* = 11 in., *w* = 9 in.

6. Carry-on Luggage On most airlines carry-on luggage can have a maximum width of 10 inches with a maximum volume of 3840 cubic inches, see the figure. If the height of the luggage is $\frac{2}{3}$ the length, determine the dimensions of the largest piece of carry-on luggage. Use $V = lwh$.
w = 10 in., *l* = 24 in., *h* = 16 in.

7. Triangles of Dough Pillsbury Crescent Rolls are packaged in tubes that contain perforated triangles of dough. The base of the triangular piece of dough is about 5 centimeters more than its height. Determine the base and height of a piece of dough if the area is about 42 square centimeters.

8. Yield Sign Yield right of way signs used in the United States are triangles. The area of the sign is about 558 square inches. The height of the sign is about 5 inches less than its base. Determine the length of the base of a yield right of way sign. 36 in.

9. Triangular Garden A triangular area is 20 square feet. Find the base of the triangular area if the height is 1 foot more than $\frac{1}{2}$ the base. base: 8 ft

10. Billboard A billboard sign is in the shape of a trapezoid. The area of the sign is 10 square feet. If the height of the sign is $\frac{1}{5}$ the length of the sum of the 2 bases, determine the height of the sign. 2 ft

Number Problems; see Example 2.

11. Difference of Numbers One number is 9 times larger than another. The difference of their reciprocals is 1. Determine the two numbers. $\frac{8}{9}$, 8

12. Sum of Numbers One number is 3 times larger than another. The sum of their reciprocals is $\frac{4}{3}$. Determine the two numbers. 1, 3

13. Increased Numerator The numerator of the fraction $\frac{3}{4}$ is increased by an amount so that the value of the resulting fraction is $\frac{5}{2}$. Determine the amount by which the numerator was increased. 7

14. Decreased Denominator The denominator of the fraction $\frac{8}{21}$ is decreased by an amount so that the value of the resulting fraction is $\frac{1}{2}$. Determine the amount by which the denominator was decreased. 5

Motion Problems; see Examples 3–5.

15. Paddleboat Ride In the Mississippi River near New Orleans, the Creole Queen paddleboat travels 6 miles upstream (against the current) in the same amount of time it travels 12 miles downstream (with the current). If the current of the river is 3 miles per hour, determine the speed of the Creole Queen in still water. 9 mph

16. Kayak Ride Kathy Boothby-Sestak can paddle her kayak 6 miles per hour in still water. It takes her as long to paddle 5 miles upstream as 10 miles downstream in the Wabash River near Lafayette, Indiana. Determine the river's current. 2 mph

17. Trolley Ride A trolley travels in one direction at an average of 12 miles per hour, then turns around and travels on the same track in the opposite direction at 12 miles per hour. If the total time traveling on the trolley is $2\frac{1}{2}$ hours, how far did the trolley travel in one direction? 15 mi

18. Motorcycle Trip Brandy Dawson and Jason Dodge start a motorcycle trip at the same point a little north of Fort Worth, Texas. Both are traveling to San Antonio, Texas, a distance of about 400 kilometers. Brandy rides 30 kilometers per hour faster than Jason does. When Brandy reaches her destination, Jason has only traveled to Austin, Texas, a distance of about 250 kilometers. Determine the approximate speed of each motorcycle. 50 km/hr, 80 km/hr

19. Jet Flight Elenore Morales traveled 1600 miles by commercial jet from Kansas City, Missouri, to Spokane, Washington. She then traveled an additional 500 miles on a private propeller plane from Spokane to Billings, Montana. If the speed of the jet was 4 times the speed of the propeller plane and the total time in the air was 6 hours, determine the speed of each plane. 150 mph, 600 mph

20. Exercise Regimen As part of his exercise regimen, Chris Barker walks a distance of 2 miles on an indoor track and then jogs at twice his walking speed for another 2 miles. If the total time spent on the track was one hour, determine the speeds at which he walks and jogs. walks at 3 mph, jogs at 6 mph

21. No Wake Zone Alisha is traveling by motorboat from her dock to Paradise Island. While she is in a no wake zone, her average speed is 4 miles per hour. Once she leaves the no wake zone, her average speed is 28 miles per hour. If the total distance traveled from her dock to the island is 36.6 miles and the total time of the trip is 1.7 hours, determine the distance from her dock to the end of the no wake zone and the distance from the end of the no wake zone to Paradise Island. No wake zone: ≈1.83 mi; zone to Island: ≈34.77 mi

22. Jogging and Walking Kristen Taylor jogs a certain distance and then walks a certain distance. When she jogs she averages 5 miles per hour and when she walks she averages 3 miles per hour. If she walks and jogs a total of 5 miles in a total of 1.4 hours, how far does she jog and how far does she walk? jogs 2 mi, walks 3 mi

23. Headwind and Tailwind A Boeing 747 flew from San Francisco to Honolulu, a distance of 2900 miles. Flying with the wind, it averaged 600 miles per hour. When the wind changed from a tailwind to a headwind, the plane's speed dropped to 550 miles per hour. If the total time of the trip was 5 hours, determine the length of time it flew at each speed. 3 hr at 600 mph, 2 hr at 550 mph

24. Thalys Train The Thalys train in Europe has been known to travel an average 240 kilometers per hour (kph). Prior to using the Thalys (bullet) trains in Europe, trains traveled an average speed of 120 kph. If a Thalys train traveling from Brussels to Amsterdam can complete its trip in 0.88 hour less

27. $3\frac{3}{7}$ hr

Work Problems; see Examples 6–9.

27. Wallpaper Reynaldo and Felicia Fernandez decide to wallpaper their family room. Felicia, who has wallpapering experience, can wallpaper the room in 6 hours. Reynaldo can wallpaper the same room in 8 hours. How long will it take them to wallpaper the family room if they work together?

28. Conveyor Belt At a salt mine, one conveyor belt requires 20 minutes to fill a large truck with ore. A second conveyor belt requires 30 minutes to fill the same truck with ore. How long would it take if both conveyor belts were working together to fill the truck with ore? 12 min

29. Picking Peaches In a peach orchard in Williamson, New York, Gary Rominger can load his truck with peaches in 6 hours. His friend, Alex Taurke, takes twice as long to load Gary's truck with peaches. How long will it take them working together to load the truck with peaches? 4 hr

time than an older train, determine the distance from Brussels to Amsterdam. 211.2 km

25. Water Skiers At a water show a boat pulls a water skier at a speed of 30 feet per second. When it reaches the end of the lake, more skiers are added to be pulled by the boat, so the boat's speed drops to 25 feet per second. If the boat traveled the same distance with additional skiers as it did with the single skier, and the trip back with the additional skiers took 8 seconds longer than the trip with the single skier, how far, in feet, in one direction, had the boat traveled? 1200 ft

26. Cross-Country Skiing Alana Bradley and her father Tim begin skiing the same cross-country ski trail in Elmwood Park in Sioux Falls, South Dakota, at the same time. If Alana, who averages 9 miles per hour, finishes the trail 0.25 hours sooner than her father, who averages 6 miles per hour, determine the length of the trail. 4.5 m

30. Watering Plants In a small nursery, Becky Hailey can water all the plants in 30 minutes. Her co-worker, Karen Grizzaffi, can water all the plants in 20 minutes. How long will it take them working together to water the plants? 12 min

31. Painting a Room Eric Kweeder can paint a room in 60 minutes. His brother, Jessup, can paint the same room in 40 minutes. How long will it take them working together to paint the room?   24 min

32. Laying a Floor Robert Struckland can lay a new hardwood floor in 6.5 hours. His neighbor, Andrea Vorwark, can lay the same floor in 7 hours. How long will it take them working together to lay the hardwood floor?   ≈3.37 hr

33. Hot Tub Pam and Loren Fornieri know that their hot tub can be filled in 40 minutes and drained completely in 60 minutes. If the water is turned on and the drain is left open, how long would it take the tub to fill completely?   120 min or 2 hr

37. $8\frac{3}{4}$ days

34. Filling a Tank During a rainstorm, the rain is flowing into a large holding tank. At the rate the rain is falling, the empty tank would fill in 8 hours. At the bottom of the tank is a spigot to dispense water. Typically, it takes about 12 hours with the spigot wide open to empty the water in a full tank. If the tank is empty and the spigot has been accidentally left open, and the rain falls at the constant rate, how long would it take for the tank to fill completely?   24 hr

35. Payroll Checks At the Community Savings Bank, it takes a computer 40 minutes to process and print payroll checks. When a second computer is used and the two computers work together, the checks can be processed and printed in 24 minutes. How long would it take the second computer by itself to process and print the payroll checks?   60 min or 1 hr

36. Flowing Water When the water is turned on and passes through a one-half inch diameter hose, a small above-ground pool can be filled in 6 hours. When the water is turned on at two spigots and passes through both the one-half inch diameter hose and a three-quarter inch diameter hose, the pool can be filled in 2 hours. How long would it take to fill the pool using only the three-quarter inch diameter hose?   3 hr

37. Digging a Trench A construction company with two backhoes has contracted to dig a long trench for drainage pipes. The larger backhoe can dig the entire trench by itself in 12 days. The smaller backhoe can dig the entire trench by itself in 15 days. The large backhoe begins working on the trench by itself, but after 5 days it is transferred to a different job and the smaller backhoe begins working on the trench. How long will it take for the smaller backhoe to complete the job?

38. Delivery of Food Ian and Nicole Murphy deliver food to various restaurants. If Ian drove the entire trip, the trip would take about 10 hours. If Nicole drove the entire trip, the trip would take about 8 hours. After Nicole had been driving for 4 hours, Ian takes over the driving. About how much longer will Ian drive before they reach their final destination?   5 hr

39. Snowstorm Following a severe snowstorm, Ken and Bettina Reeves must clear their driveway and sidewalk. Ken can clear the snow by himself in 4 hours, and Bettina can clear the snow by herself in 6 hours. After Bettina has been working for 3 hours, Ken is able to join her. How much longer will it take them working together to remove the rest of the snow?

$\frac{6}{5}$ hr or 1 hr, 12 min

40. a) $\frac{3}{4}$ hr, **b)** $281\frac{1}{4}$ hr

40. Farm Cooperative A large farming cooperative near Hutchinson, Kansas, owns three hay balers. The oldest baler can pick up and bale an acre of hay in 3 hours and each of the two new balers can work an acre in 2 hours.
  a) How long would it take the three balers working together to pick up and bale 1 acre?
  b) How long would it take for the three balers working together to pick up and bale the farm's 375 acres of hay?

41. Skimming Oil A boat designed to skim oil off the surface of the water has two skimmers. One skimmer can fill the boat's holding tank in 60 hours while the second skimmer can fill the boat's holding tank in 50 hours. There is also a valve in the holding tank that is used to transfer the oil to a larger vessel. If no new oil is coming into the holding tank, a full holding tank of skimmed oil can be transferred to a larger tank in 30 hours. If both skimmers begin skimming and the valve on the holding tank is opened, how long will it take for the empty holding tank on the boat to fill?   300 hr

42. Flower Garden Bob can plant a flower garden by himself in 8 hours. Mary can plant the same garden by herself in 10 hours, and Gloria can plant the same garden by herself in 12 hours. How long would it take them working together to plant the garden?   ≈3.24 hr

Challenge Problems

43. Reciprocal of a Number If 2 times a number is added to 3 times the reciprocal of the number, the answer is 7. Determine the number(s). $3 \text{ or } \frac{1}{2}$

44. Determine a Number The reciprocal of the difference of a certain number and 5 is twice the reciprocal of the difference of twice the number and 10. Determine the number(s).

45. Picking Blueberries Ed and Samantha Weisman, whose parents own a fruit farm, must each pick the same number of pints of blueberries each day during the season. Ed picks an

average of 8 pints per hour, while Samantha picks an average of 4 pints per hour. If Ed and Samantha begin picking blueberries at the same time, and Samantha finishes 1 hour after Ed, how many pints of blueberries must each pick?   8 pints

46. Sorting Mail A mail processing machine can sort a large bin of mail in 1 hour. A newer model can sort the same quantity of mail in 30 minutes. If they operate together, how long will it take them to sort the bin of mail?   20 min

44. all real numbers except 5

Cumulative Review Exercises

[2.1] **47.** Simplify $\frac{1}{2}(x + 3) - (2x + 5)$. $-\frac{3}{2}x - \frac{7}{2}$

[4.2] **48.** Graph $x = -2$.   See graphing answer section.

[8.2] **49.** Divide $\dfrac{x^2 - 14x + 48}{x^2 - 5x - 24} \div \dfrac{2x^2 - 13x + 6}{2x^2 + 5x - 3}$.   1

[8.4] **50.** Subtract $\dfrac{x}{6x^2 - x - 15} - \dfrac{5}{9x^2 - 12x - 5}$.

$$\frac{3x^2 - 9x - 15}{(2x + 3)(3x - 5)(3x + 1)}$$

8.8 Variation

1 Set up and solve direct variation problems.

2 Set up and solve inverse variation problems.

Many scientific formulas are expressed as variations. Many of our daily activities also involve variation. A **variation** is an equation that relates one variable to one or more other variables using the operations of multiplication or division (or both operations). In this book we will discuss two types of variation: **direct variation** and **inverse variation.** We will first discuss direct variation.

1 Set Up and Solve Direct Variation Problems

In direct variation, the two variables both increase together or both decrease together; that is, as one variable increases, so does the other, and as one variable decreases, so does the other.

Suppose water is coming out of a garden hose for a specific amount of time and going into a bucket. The greater the flow rate of water coming out of the hose, the greater the volume of water in the bucket, and the smaller the flow rate of water coming out of the hose, the smaller the volume of water in the bucket. This is an example of direct variation. The volume of water in the bucket varies directly as the flow rate from the hose.

Consider a car traveling at 60 miles per hour. The car travels 60 miles in 1 hour, 120 miles in 2 hours, 180 miles in 3 hours. Notice that as the time increases the distance traveled increases. This is also an example of direct variation. Notice that for a constant speed, as the time increases, so does the distance traveled, and as the time decreases, so does the distance traveled.

The formula used to calculate distance is

$$\text{distance} = \text{rate} \cdot \text{time}$$

Since the rate is constant, 60 miles per hour, the formula can be written

$$d = 60t$$

We say that the distance, d, *varies directly* as the time, t, or that the distance is *directly proportional* to the time t. In the equation, the 60 is a constant referred to as a **constant of proportionality.** Now we will define direct variation.

TEACHING TIP
You may wish to mention, that, if the direct variation is linear, k represents the slope of a line. You may want to come back to direct variation briefly when slope is covered.

Direct Variation

If a variable y varies directly as a variable x, then

$$y = kx$$

where k is the *constant of proportionality* (or the variation constant).

When we are told that one quantity varies directly as another, we generally start with an equation in the form $y = kx$; however letters other than x and y may be used for the variables.

INSTRUCTOR EXAMPLE
When a bowl of water is heated in a microwave oven, the temperature of the water, w, increases directly with the time, t.

a) Write the variation as an equation.

b) If $k = 2.2$, find the increase in the temperature of the water 5 seconds later.

Ans.:

a) $w = kt$ b) $11°$

EXAMPLE 1 ▶ **Heating Up a Jacuzzi** When the heater is turned on to warm the water in a jacuzzi, the temperature of the water, w, increases directly with the time, t, the heater is on.

a) Write the variation as an equation.

b) If the constant of proportionality, k, is 0.8, find the increase in temperature of the water after 40 minutes.

Solution

a) We are told that the water temperature varies directly with the time. Thus we set up the direct proportion, as follows.

$$w = kt$$

b) To find the increase in water temperature we will substitute 0.8 for k, and 40 for t.

$$w = kt$$
$$w = 0.8(40) = 32$$

Thus, after 40 minutes the water temperature has increased by 32°.

▶ **Now Try Exercise 35**

In many variation problems you will first have to solve for the constant of proportionality before you can solve for the variable you are asked to find. To determine the constant of proportionality, substitute the values given for the variables, and solve for k. We illustrate this procedure in Example 2.

INSTRUCTOR EXAMPLE
x varies directly as y. If $x = 100$ when $y = 20$, find x when $y = 60$.
Ans.: 300

EXAMPLE 2 ▶ **Direct Variation Problem** s varies directly as the square of m. If $s = 125$ when $m = 5$, find s when $m = 12$.

Solution   a) **Understand and Translate** We begin by setting up the equation. Notice that we are told that s varies directly as the square of m. The square of m is written m^2. Therefore, the equation is $s = km^2$. Since we are not given the constant of proportionality, we find it by substituting the values we are given for the variables.

$$s = km^2$$
$$125 = k(5^2) \qquad \textit{Substitute values.}$$
$$125 = k(25)$$
$$125 = 25k$$
$$5 = k$$

Now that we have determined k, we can answer the question by substituting 5 for k, and 12 for m.

Carry Out
$$s = km^2$$
$$s = 5(12)^2$$
$$s = 5(144)$$
$$s = 720$$

Answer   Thus, when $m = 12$, $s = 720$.

▶ **Now Try Exercise 27**

EXAMPLE 3 ▸ **Drug Dosage** The amount of the drug, d, given to a person is directly proportional to the person's weight, w. If an adult who weighs 75 kilograms is given 300 milligrams (mg) of allopurinol, determine how many milligrams of allopurinol are given to an adult who weighs 96 kg.

Solution **Understand and Translate** We are told that the amount of the drug is directly proportional to the person's weight. Thus we set up the equation

$$d = kw$$

Now we determine k by substituting the values given for d and w.

Carry Out

$$d = kw$$
$$300 = k(75)$$
$$\frac{300}{75} = k$$
$$4 = k$$

Now we proceed to find the number of milligrams of the drug to be given by substituting 4 for k and 96 for w.

$$d = kw$$
$$d = 4(96) = 384$$

Check and Answer Since we expect the amount of the drug to be greater than 300 milligrams, our answer is reasonable. A 96 kg adult should be given 384 milligrams of the drug.

▸ **Now Try Exercise 39**

Example 3 could also be solved using a proportion.

2 Set Up and Solve Inverse Variation Problems

Now we will discuss inverse variation. When two quantities vary inversely, it means that as one quantity increases, the other quantity decreases, and vice versa.

Suppose you are making a casserole in the oven. Generally speaking, the higher the temperature of the oven, the shorter the period of time needed for the casserole to cook. That is, as the temperature increases, the time decreases, and vice versa. Thus, the time and temperature are inversely proportional to one another, or vary inversely with one another.

To explain inverse variation, we again use the distance formula,

$$\text{distance} = \text{rate} \cdot \text{time}$$

If we solve the formula for time, we get time $= \dfrac{\text{distance}}{\text{rate}}$. Assume the distance is fixed at 100 miles; then

$$\text{time} = \frac{100}{\text{rate}}$$

At a rate of 100 miles per hour it would take 1 hour to cover the 100 mile distance. At 50 miles per hour it would take 2 hours to cover the distance. At 25 mph it would take 4 hours. Note that as the rate (or speed) decreases, the time increases, and vice versa. The preceding equation can be written

$$t = \frac{100}{r}$$

This is an example of an inverse variation in which the time and rate are inversely proportional and the constant of proportionality is 100. We define inverse variation and then work two examples.

Inverse Variation

If a variable y varies inversely as a variable x, then

$$y = \frac{k}{x} \text{ (or } xy = k\text{)}$$

where k is the constant of proportionality.

EXAMPLE 4 ▶ **Chartering a Sailboat** A group of friends is going to charter a sailboat for a pleasure trip. The cost per person for chartering the boat, c, is inversely proportional to the number of people chartering the boat, n. If 8 friends decide to charter the boat, the cost per person is $60. Determine the cost per person if 15 friends decide to charter the boat.

Solution

Understand and Translate   We are told this is an inverse variation. Therefore, we will set up an equation to represent the inverse proportion.

$$c = \frac{k}{n}$$

Since we are not given the constant of proportionality, we determine k by substituting the values given for c and n.

$$60 = \frac{k}{8}$$
$$480 = k$$

Now we can determine the answer to the question by using $k = 480$ and $n = 15$.

Carry Out
$$c = \frac{k}{n}$$
$$c = \frac{480}{15}$$
$$c = 32$$

Check and Answer   The cost to each person would be $32 if 15 friends decided to charter the sailboat.

▶ **Now Try Exercise 41**

EXAMPLE 5 ▶ **Speaker Loudness** The loudness, l, of a stereo speaker, measured in decibels (dB), varies inversely as the square of the distance, d, of the listener from the speaker. Assuming that for a particular speaker the loudness is 20 dB when the listener is 6 feet from the speaker.

a) Determine an equation that expresses the relationship between the loudness and the distance.

b) Using the equation obtained in part **a)**, determine the loudness when a person is 3 feet from the speaker.

Solution   This problem is broken down into two parts. The first part asks us to find a general formula, while the second part asks us to use the formula.

a) Understand and Translate   We are told that the loudness varies inversely as the *square* of the distance. Thus we write the following equation and solve for *k*.

Carry Out

$$l = \frac{k}{d^2}$$

$$20 = \frac{k}{6^2}$$

$$20 = \frac{k}{36}$$

$$720 = k$$

Check and Answer   The constant of proportionality, *k*, is 720. Since for this speaker *k* = 720, the equation we are seeking is

$$l = \frac{720}{d^2}$$

b) Understand and Translate   In part **a)** we determined the equation used to find the loudness. We substitute 3 for *d* in the formula and solve for *l*.

$$l = \frac{720}{d^2}$$

$$l = \frac{720}{3^2}$$

Carry Out

$$l = \frac{720}{9}$$

$$l = 80$$

Check and Answer   Thus at 3 feet the loudness is 80 decibels. This is reasonable because at a shorter distance (3 feet versus 6 feet) the sound will be louder.

▶ **Now Try Exercise 49**

EXERCISE SET 8.8

MathXL®   MyMathLab

Concept/Writing Exercises

1. What is the value of the constant of proportionality in the direct variation *m* = 30*t*?   30

2. What is the value of the constant of proportionality in the inverse variation $w = \frac{50}{r}$?   50

3. Give the general form of direct variation.   *y* = *kx*

4. Give the general form of inverse variation. $y = \frac{k}{x}$

Practice the Skills

Determine if the following are direct or inverse variations. Explain your answer.

5. The radius of a hose and the amount of water coming out of the hose.   direct

6. The lens opening on a camera and the amount of light reaching the film.   direct

7. The speed of a turtle and the length of time it takes the turtle to cross a road.   inverse

8. The age of a car, up to 8 years old, and the value of a car.   inverse

9. The temperature of water and the time it takes for an ice cube placed in the water to melt.   inverse

10. The number of people in line at the rock concert and the time it takes for all people in line to purchase tickets.   direct

11. The length of a roll of Scotch tape and the number of 2 inch strips that can be obtained from the roll.   *direct*

12. A person's reading speed and the time it takes to read a novel.   *inverse*

13. The cubic-inch displacement, in liters, and the horsepower of the engine.   *direct*

14. The speed of a riding lawn mower and the time it takes to cut the lawn.   *inverse*

In Exercises 15–22, find the quantity indicated.

15. x varies directly as z. Find x when $z = 11$ and $k = 4$.   *44*

16. x varies directly as y. Find x when $y = 9$ and $k = 6$.   *54*

17. x varies inversely as y. Find x when $y = 25$ and $k = 5$. $\frac{1}{5}$

18. R varies inversely as W. Find R when $W = 80$ and $k = 120$.   *1.5*

19. C varies directly as the square of Z. Find C when $Z = 5$ and $k = 3$.   *75*

20. L varies directly as the square of R. Find L when $R = 9$ and $k = 2$.   *162*

21. y varies inversely as the square of x. Find y when $x = 10$ and $k = 250$.   *2.5*

22. y varies inversely as the square of w. Find y when $w = 8$ and $k = 288$.   *4.5*

For Exercises 23–30, find the quantity indicated.

23. x varies directly as y. If $x = 9$ when $y = 18$, find x when $y = 40$.   *20*

24. Z varies directly as W. If $Z = 7$ when $W = 21$, find Z when $W = 51$.   *17*

25. C varies inversely as J. If $C = 7$ when $J = 1$ find C when $J = 2$.   *3.5*

26. H varies inversely as L. If $H = 15$ when $L = 60$, find H when $L = 10$.   *90*

27. y varies directly as the square of R. If $y = 4$ when $R = 4$, find y when $R = 12$.   *36*

28. A varies directly as the square of B. If $A = 245$ when $B = 7$, find A when $B = 9$.   *405*

29. L varies inversely as the square of P. If L is 320 when $P = 20$, find L when $P = 40$.   *80*

30. x varies inversely as the square of P. If $x = 10$ when $P = 6$, find x when $P = 20$.   *0.9*

Problem Solving

31. Assume a varies directly as b. If b is doubled, how will it affect a? Explain.   *doubled*

32. Assume a varies directly as b^2. If b is doubled, how will it affect a? Explain.   *quadrupled*

33. Assume y varies inversely as x. If x is doubled, how will it affect y? Explain.   *halved*

34. Assume y varies inversely as a^2. If a is doubled, how will it affect y? Explain.   *quartered*

In Exercises 35–54, determine the quantity you are asked to find.

35. Distance and Speed The distance, d, a car travels is directly proportional to the speed, s, the car is traveling. Determine the distance traveled if the constant of proportionality, k, is 2 and the speed is 55 miles per hour.   *110 mi*

36. Swimming Pool The time, t, it takes to fill an inground pool is directly proportional to the amount of water coming out of the hose, w. Determine the time it takes a hose to fill the pool if the constant of proportionality is 0.3 and the amount of water coming out of the hose is 200 gallons per hour.   *60 hr*

37. Reaching a Destination The time it takes to reach a certain destination, t, is inversely proportional to the speed a car is traveling, s. Determine the time it takes to reach the destination if the constant of proportionality is 150 and the speed, s, is 50 miles per hour.   *3 hr*

38. Light through Water The percent of light that filters through water, l, is inversely proportional to the depth of the water, d. Determine the percent of light that filters down to a depth of 10 feet if the constant of proportionality is 200.   *20*

39. Kiddie Train The income, I, for a kiddie train at an amusement park is directly proportional to the number of tickets sold, n. If the income, I, is \$33 when 22 tickets are sold, determine the income when 38 tickets are sold.   *\$57*

40. Cutting a Lawn The time it takes Don to cut a lawn, t, is directly proportional to the area of the lawn, A. If it takes Don 0.5 hour to cut an area of 1200 square feet, how long will it take him to cut an area of 1800 square feet?   *0.75 hr*

41. Roofing The time, t, it takes to nail in shingles on a roof is inversely proportional to the number of people nailing in the shingles, n. When three people are nailing in the shingles it takes 7 hours to complete the job. How long will it take to complete the job if five people are nailing in the shingles?   *4.2 hr*

42. Baking a Turkey The time, t, it takes to bake a turkey is inversely proportional to the oven temperature, T. If it takes 3 hours to bake a turkey at 300°F, how long will it take to bake the turkey at 250°F?   *3.6 hr*

43. Basketball Game The receipts, r, at a baseball game are directly proportional to the number of people attending the game, n. If the receipts for a game are \$18,000 when 800 people attend, determine how many people attend if the receipts for a game are \$22,500.   *1000 people*

44. Daily Newspaper The time, t, it takes to print a specific number of copies of a daily newspaper is inversely proportional to the number of presses it has working, n. When 6 presses are working, the newspapers are printed in 8 hours. Determine the number of presses working if the newspapers are printed in 3 hours.   16 presses

45. Pollution The amount of carbon dioxide (CO_2) generated, A, is directly proportional to the amount of energy used, E. The April 3, 2006 issue of *Time* magazine mentioned that Salt Lake City, Utah, has converted 1630 traffic stop lights to energy-efficient signals, which saves 500 tons of CO_2 pollution annually. If another city similar to Salt Lake City were to exchange 2500 traffic stop signals to energy-efficient signals, how much CO_2 pollution would be saved annually?   ≈766.9 tons

46. Cleaning Windows The time, t, it takes to clean all the windows in a large office building is inversely proportional to the number of teams, n, of window workers used. If 6 teams can clean all the windows in 20 days, how many teams are used if the windows are cleaned in 12 days?   10 teams

47. Area of a Circle The area of a circle, A, is directly proportional to the square of the radius of a circle, r. If the area of a circle is about 78.5 square inches when the radius is 5 inches, determine the area when the radius is 12 inches.   ≈452.16 sq in.

48. Falling Object The velocity, v, of a falling object is directly proportional to the square of the time, t, it has been in free fall. An object that has been in free fall for 2 seconds has a velocity of 64 feet per second. Determine the velocity of an object that has been falling for 8 seconds.   1024 ft/sec

49. Electrical Circuit In an electrical circuit the resistance, r, of an appliance is inversely proportional to the square of the current, c. If the resistance is 100 ohms when the current is 0.4 amps, determine the resistance if the current is 0.6 amps.   ≈44.44 ohms

50. Volume of a Cylinder For a cylinder of a specific volume, the height, h, of the cylinder is inversely proportional to the square of the radius of the cylinder, r. When the radius is 6 inches, the height is 10 inches. Determine the height when the radius is 5 inches.   14.4 in.

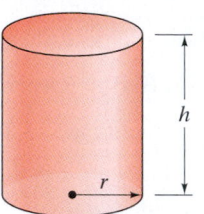

51. Finding Interest The amount of interest earned on an investment, I, varies directly as the interest rate, r. If the interest earned is $40 when the interest rate is 4%, find the amount of interest earned when the interest rate is 5%. $50

52. Brick Wall The time, t, required to build a brick wall varies inversely as the number of people, n, working on the wall. If it takes 9 hours for six bricklayers to build a wall, how long will it take two bricklayers to build a wall?   27 hr

53. Volume of Gas The volume of a gas, V, varies inversely as its pressure, P. If the volume, V, is 800 cubic centimeters when the pressure is 200 millimeters (mm) of mercury, find the volume when the pressure is 25 mm of mercury.   6400 cc

54. Hooke's Law Hooke's law states that the length a spring will stretch, S, varies directly with the force (or weight), F, attached to the spring. If a spring stretches 1.4 inches when 20 pounds is attached, how far will it stretch when 10 pounds is attached?   0.7 in.

Challenge Problems

*In addition to direct variation and inverse variations, there is also joint variation and combined variation. In **joint variation**, one quantity may vary directly (as the product of) two or more quantities. In **combined variation**, one quantity may vary directly with some variables and inversely with other variables. Exercise 55 is a joint variation problem, and Exercise 56 is a combined variation problem. For Exercises 55 and 56,* **a)** *write the variation, and* **b)** *find the quantity indicated.*

55. x varies jointly as y and z. If x is 72 when $y = 18$ and $z = 2$, find x when $y = 36$ and $z = 3$.   **a)** $x = kyz$,   **b)** 216

56. T varies directly as the square of D and inversely as F. If $T = 18$ when $D = 6$ and $F = 4$, find T when $D = 8$ and $F = 8$.   **56. a)** $T = \dfrac{kD^2}{F}$,   **b)** 16

Cumulative Review Exercises

[6.6]   **57.** Divide $\dfrac{8x^2 + 6x - 21}{4x + 9}$ $2x - 3 + \dfrac{6}{4x + 9}$

[7.1]   **58.** Factor $y(z - 2) + 8(z - 2)$ $(z - 2)(y + 8)$

[7.6]   **59.** Solve $3x^2 - 24 = -6x$ $-4, 2$

[8.2]   **60.** Multiply $\dfrac{x + 8}{x - 3} \cdot \dfrac{x^3 - 27}{x^2 + 3x + 9}$ $x + 8$

Chapter 8 Summary

IMPORTANT FACTS AND CONCEPTS	EXAMPLES

Section 8.1

A **rational expression** is an expression of the form p/q, where p and q are polynomials and $q \neq 0$.

$\dfrac{x + 2}{x}$ and $\dfrac{x^2 + x}{x - 1}$ are rational expressions.

Whenever we have a rational expression containing a variable in the denominator, we always assume that the value or values of the variable that make the denominator 0 are excluded.

The rational expression $\dfrac{x - 5}{x - 3}$ is defined for all real numbers except 3.

A rational expression is simplified or reduced to its lowest term when the numerator and denominator have no common factors other than 1.

$\dfrac{1}{8}$ and $\dfrac{x^2 + x + 1}{2x^2 + 3x + 7}$ are expressions reduced to lowest terms.

To Simplify Rational Expressions

1. Factor both the numerator and denominator completely.

2. Divide out common factors.

$\dfrac{12x^2 - 11x - 5}{9x^2 + 6x + 1} = \dfrac{\cancel{(3x + 1)}(4x - 5)}{\cancel{(3x + 1)}(3x + 1)} = \dfrac{4x - 5}{3x + 1}$

Section 8.2

To Multiply Two Fractions

$$\frac{a}{b} \cdot \frac{c}{d} = \frac{a \cdot c}{b \cdot d}, \quad b \neq 0 \quad \text{and} \quad d \neq 0$$

$\dfrac{1}{3} \cdot \dfrac{4}{5} = \dfrac{1 \cdot 4}{3 \cdot 5} = \dfrac{4}{15}$

To Multiply Rational Expressions

1. Factor all numerators and denominators completely.

2. Divide out common factors.

3. Multiply numerators together and multiply denominators together.

$\dfrac{4x^3}{7y^2} \cdot \dfrac{14y^3}{6x} = \dfrac{\overset{2}{\cancel{4}} \overset{x^2}{\cancel{x^3}} \cdot \overset{2}{\cancel{14}} \overset{y}{\cancel{y^3}}}{\cancel{7} \cancel{y^2} \cdot \underset{3}{\cancel{6}} \cancel{x}} = \dfrac{4x^2 y^2}{3}$

To Divide Two Fractions

$$\frac{a}{b} \div \frac{c}{d} = \frac{a}{b} \cdot \frac{d}{c} = \frac{ad}{bc}, \quad b \neq 0, \ d \neq 0, \ \text{and} \ c \neq 0$$

$\dfrac{3}{5} \div \dfrac{6}{7} = \dfrac{3}{5} \cdot \dfrac{7}{\underset{2}{\cancel{6}}}^{1} = \dfrac{7}{10}$

To Divide Rational Expressions

Multiply the first fraction by the reciprocal of the second fraction.

$\dfrac{x + 4}{x + 3} \div \dfrac{3x + 12}{x + 3} = \dfrac{\cancel{x + 4}}{\cancel{x + 3}} \cdot \dfrac{\cancel{x + 3}}{3\cancel{(x + 4)}} = \dfrac{1}{3}$

Section 8.3

To Add or Subtract Two Fractions

$$\frac{a}{c} + \frac{b}{c} = \frac{a + b}{c}, c \neq 0 \qquad \frac{a}{c} - \frac{b}{c} = \frac{a - b}{c}, c \neq 0$$

$\dfrac{3}{11} + \dfrac{4}{11} = \dfrac{7}{11}, \qquad \dfrac{18}{19} - \dfrac{5}{19} = \dfrac{13}{19}$

To Add or Subtract Rational Expressions with a Common Denominator

1. Add or subtract the numerators.

2. Place the sum or difference of the numerators over the common denominator.

3. Simplify the fraction if possible.

$\dfrac{2}{x - 3} + \dfrac{x + 5}{x - 3} = \dfrac{2 + x + 5}{x - 3} = \dfrac{x + 7}{x - 3}$

IMPORTANT FACTS AND CONCEPTS	EXAMPLES

Section 8.3 (continued)

To Find the Least Common Denominator of Rational Expressions

1. Factor each denominator completely.
2. List all different factors of each denominator. When the same factor appears in more than one denominator, write that factor with the highest power that appears.
3. The least common denominator is the product of all the factors listed in step 2.

Find the least common denominator.

$$\frac{1}{9x^3y^4} + \frac{1}{6x^5y^3}$$

$$9x^3y^4 = 3 \cdot 3x^3y^4$$
$$6x^5y^3 = 3 \cdot 2x^5y^3$$

LCD is $2 \cdot 3^2 x^5 y^4 = 18x^5y^4$.

Section 8.4

To Add or Subtract Two Rational Expressions with Unlike Denominators

1. Determine the LCD.
2. Rewrite each fraction as an equivalent fraction with the LCD.
3. Add or subtract the numerators while maintaining the LCD.
4. When possible, factor the remaining numerator and simplify the fraction.

$$\frac{9}{m} + \frac{5}{m-1} = \frac{m-1}{m-1} \cdot \frac{9}{m} + \frac{5}{m-1} \cdot \frac{m}{m}$$

$$= \frac{9(m-1)}{m(m-1)} + \frac{5m}{m(m-1)}$$

$$= \frac{9m - 9 + 5m}{m(m-1)}$$

$$= \frac{14m - 9}{m(m-1)}$$

Section 8.5

A **complex fraction** is one that has a fraction in its numerator or its denominator or in both its numerator and denominator.

$$\frac{\frac{2}{3}}{\frac{4}{7}}, \quad \frac{\frac{1}{x} + \frac{1}{y}}{\frac{1}{a} + \frac{1}{b}}$$

Method 1—To Simplify a Complex Fraction by Combining Terms

1. Add or subtract the fractions in both the numerator and denominator of the complex fraction to obtain single fractions in both.
2. Multiply the fraction in the numerator by the reciprocal of the fraction in the denominator.
3. Simplify further if possible.

$$\frac{1 + \frac{1}{x}}{x} = \frac{\frac{x}{x} + \frac{1}{x}}{x} = \frac{\frac{x+1}{x}}{x}$$

$$= \frac{x+1}{x} \cdot \frac{1}{x} = \frac{x+1}{x^2}$$

Method 2—To Simplify a Complex Fraction Using Multiplication First

1. Find the LCD of *all* the denominators appearing in the complex fraction.
2. Multiply both the numerator and denominator of the complex fraction by the LCD found in step 1.
3. Simplify when possible.

$$\frac{1 + \frac{1}{x}}{x} = \frac{x}{x} \cdot \frac{1 + \frac{1}{x}}{x} = \frac{x(1) + x\left(\frac{1}{x}\right)}{x(x)} = \frac{x+1}{x^2}$$

Note: LCD = x.

Section 8.6

A **rational equation** is an equation that contains one or more rational expressions.

$$\frac{1}{3}x - \frac{1}{7}x = 10, \qquad x + \frac{9}{x} = \frac{1}{3}$$

IMPORTANT FACTS AND CONCEPTS	EXAMPLES

Section 8.6 (continued)

To Solve Rational Equations

1. Determine the LCD of all fractions in the equation.
2. Multiply **both** sides of the equation by the LCD.
3. Remove any parentheses and combine like terms on each side of the equation.
4. Solve the equation using the properties discussed in earlier chapters.
5. Check your solution in the *original* equation.

$$\frac{x}{5} - \frac{x}{8} = 1$$

$$40\left(\frac{x}{5} - \frac{x}{8}\right) = 40(1)$$

$$8x - 5x = 40$$

$$3x = 40$$

$$x = \frac{40}{3}$$

A check shows that $\frac{40}{3}$ is the solution.

Section 8.7

Applications

A **geometric problem** involves geometric figures and formulas.

A rectangle has an area of 70 square meters. Find the dimensions if the width is 3 meters shorter than the length.

The answer is 7 meters by 10 meters.

A **motion problem** involves distance, rate, and time and uses the formula

$$\text{distance} = \text{rate} \cdot \text{time}$$

or

$$\text{time} = \frac{\text{distance}}{\text{rate}}$$

or

$$\text{rate} = \frac{\text{distance}}{\text{time}}$$

A cyclist can travel 20 miles with the wind to his back in the same time he can travel 12 miles going into the wind. If the wind is blowing at 2 miles per hour, find the speed of the cyclist without any wind.

The answer is 8 miles per hour.

A **work problem** involves two or more machines or people working together to complete a specific task.

Tom can paint a room in 6 hours and Bill can paint the same room in 4 hours. How long will it take them working together to paint this room?
The answer is 2.4 hours.

Section 8.8

A **variation** is an equation that relates one variable to one or more other variables using the operations of multiplication or division.

Direct Variation

In direct variation, as one variable increases, so does the other, and as one variable decreases, so does the other.

If a variable y varies directly as a variable x, then

$$y = kx$$

where k is the *constant of proportionality* (or the variation constant).

m varies directly as the square of n. Find m when $n = 5$ and $k = 4$.

$$m = kn^2$$
$$= 4(5)^2$$
$$= 4(25)$$
$$= 100$$

Inverse Variation

In inverse variation, as one variable increases, the other quantity decreases, and vice versa.

If a variable y varies inversely as a variable x, then

$$y = \frac{k}{x} \text{ (or } xy = k)$$

where k is the constant of proportionality.

y varies inversely as the square root of x. Find y when $x = 4$ and $k = 30$.

$$y = \frac{k}{\sqrt{x}}$$
$$= \frac{30}{\sqrt{4}}$$
$$= \frac{30}{2}$$
$$= 15$$

Chapter 8 Review Exercises

2. all real numbers except $x = 3$, $x = 5$ **3.** all real numbers except $x = \frac{1}{5}$, $x = -1$

[8.1] *Determine the values of the variable for which the following expressions are defined.*

1. $\dfrac{5}{2x - 18}$ all real numbers except $x = 9$

2. $\dfrac{2x + 1}{x^2 - 8x + 15}$

3. $\dfrac{7x - 1}{5x^2 + 4x - 1}$

Simplify.

4. $\dfrac{y}{xy - 3y}$ $\dfrac{1}{x - 3}$

5. $\dfrac{x^3 + 5x^2 + 12x}{x}$ $x^2 + 5x + 12$

6. $\dfrac{9x^2 + 3xy}{3x}$ $3x + y$

7. $\dfrac{x^2 + 2x - 8}{x - 2}$ $x + 4$

8. $\dfrac{a^2 - 81}{a - 9}$ $a + 9$

9. $\dfrac{-2x^2 + 7x + 4}{x - 4}$ $-(2x + 1)$

10. $\dfrac{b^2 - 7b + 10}{b^2 - 3b - 10}$ $\dfrac{b - 2}{b + 2}$

11. $\dfrac{4x^2 - 11x - 3}{4x^2 - 7x - 2}$ $\dfrac{x - 3}{x - 2}$

12. $\dfrac{2x^2 - 21x + 40}{4x^2 - 4x - 15}$ $\dfrac{x - 8}{2x + 3}$

[8.2] *Multiply.*

13. $\dfrac{5a^2}{6b} \cdot \dfrac{2}{4a^2b}$ $\dfrac{5}{12b^2}$

14. $\dfrac{30x^2y^3}{3z} \cdot \dfrac{6z^3}{5xy^3}$ $12xz^2$

15. $\dfrac{20a^3b^4}{7c^3} \cdot \dfrac{14c^7}{5a^5b}$ $\dfrac{8b^3c^4}{a^2}$

16. $\dfrac{1}{x - 4} \cdot \dfrac{4 - x}{9}$ $-\dfrac{1}{9}$

17. $\dfrac{-m + 4}{15m} \cdot \dfrac{10m}{m - 4}$ $-\dfrac{2}{3}$

18. $\dfrac{a - 2}{a + 3} \cdot \dfrac{a^2 + 4a + 3}{a^2 - a - 2}$ 1

Divide.

19. $\dfrac{9x^6}{y^2} \div \dfrac{x^4}{4y}$ $\dfrac{36x^2}{y}$

20. $\dfrac{5xy^2}{z} \div \dfrac{x^4y^2}{4z^2}$ $\dfrac{20z}{x^3}$

21. $\dfrac{6a + 6b}{a^2} \div \dfrac{a^2 - b^2}{a^2}$ $\dfrac{6}{a - b}$

22. $\dfrac{1}{a^2 + 8a + 15} \div \dfrac{8}{a + 5}$ $\dfrac{1}{8(a + 3)}$

23. $(t + 8) \div \dfrac{t^2 + 5t - 24}{t - 3}$ 1

24. $\dfrac{x^2 + xy - 2y^2}{2y} \div \dfrac{x + 2y}{12y^2}$ $6y(x - y)$

[8.3] *Add or subtract.*

25. $\dfrac{n}{n + 5} - \dfrac{2}{n + 5}$ $\dfrac{n - 2}{n + 5}$

26. $\dfrac{4x}{x + 7} + \dfrac{28}{x + 7}$ 4

27. $\dfrac{5x - 4}{x + 8} + \dfrac{44}{x + 8}$ 5

28. $\dfrac{7x - 3}{x^2 + 7x - 30} - \dfrac{3x + 9}{x^2 + 7x - 30}$ $\dfrac{4}{x + 10}$

29. $\dfrac{5h^2 + 12h - 1}{h + 5} - \dfrac{h^2 - 5h + 14}{h + 5}$ $4h - 3$

30. $\dfrac{6x^2 - 4x}{2x - 3} - \dfrac{-3x + 12}{2x - 3}$ $3x + 4$

Find the least common denominator for each expression.

31. $\dfrac{a}{8} + \dfrac{5a}{3}$ 24

32. $\dfrac{10}{x + 3} + \dfrac{2x}{x + 3}$ $x + 3$

33. $\dfrac{10}{4xy^3} - \dfrac{11}{10x^2y}$ $20x^2y^3$

34. $\dfrac{6}{x - 3} - \dfrac{2}{x}$ $x(x - 3)$

35. $\dfrac{8}{n + 5} + \dfrac{2n - 3}{n - 4}$ $(n + 5)(n - 4)$

36. $\dfrac{5x - 12}{x^2 + 2x} - \dfrac{4}{x + 2}$ $x(x + 2)$

37. $\dfrac{2r + 1}{r - s} - \dfrac{6}{r^2 - s^2}$ $(r + s)(r - s)$

38. $\dfrac{3x^2}{x - 9} + 10x^3$ $x - 9$

39. $\dfrac{19x - 5}{x^2 + 2x - 35} + \dfrac{-10x + 1}{x^2 + 9x + 14}$
$(x + 7)(x - 5)(x + 2)$

[8.4] *Add or subtract.*

40. $\dfrac{5}{3y^2} + \dfrac{y}{2y}$ $\dfrac{3y^2 + 10}{6y^2}$

41. $\dfrac{3x}{xy} + \dfrac{1}{4x}$ $\dfrac{12x + y}{4xy}$

42. $\dfrac{5x}{3xy} - \dfrac{6}{x^2}$ $\dfrac{5x^2 - 18y}{3x^2y}$

43. $7 - \dfrac{2}{x + 2}$ $\dfrac{7x + 12}{x + 2}$

44. $\dfrac{x - y}{y} - \dfrac{x + y}{x}$ $\dfrac{x^2 - 2xy - y^2}{xy}$

45. $\dfrac{7}{x + 4} + \dfrac{2}{x}$ $\dfrac{9x + 8}{x(x + 4)}$

46. $\dfrac{2}{3x} - \dfrac{3}{3x - 6}$ $\dfrac{-x - 4}{3x(x - 2)}$

47. $\dfrac{1}{(z + 5)} + \dfrac{9}{(z + 5)^2}$ $\dfrac{z + 14}{(z + 5)^2}$

48. $\dfrac{x + 2}{x^2 - x - 6} + \dfrac{x - 3}{x^2 - 8x + 15}$
$\dfrac{2x - 8}{(x - 3)(x - 5)}$

[8.2–8.4] *Perform each indicated operation.*

49. $\dfrac{x + 4}{x + 6} - \dfrac{x - 5}{x + 2}$ $\dfrac{5x + 38}{(x + 6)(x + 2)}$

50. $2 + \dfrac{x}{x - 4}$ $\dfrac{3x - 8}{x - 4}$

51. $\dfrac{a + 2}{b} \div \dfrac{a - 2}{5b^2}$ $\dfrac{5ab + 10b}{a - 2}$

52. $\dfrac{x + 5}{x^2 - 9} + \dfrac{2}{x + 3}$ $\dfrac{3x - 1}{(x + 3)(x - 3)}$

53. $\dfrac{6p + 12q}{p^2 q} \cdot \dfrac{p^4}{p + 2q}$ $\dfrac{6p^2}{q}$

54. $\dfrac{8}{(x + 2)(x - 3)} - \dfrac{6}{(x - 2)(x + 2)}$ $\dfrac{2x + 2}{(x + 2)(x - 3)(x - 2)}$

55. $\dfrac{x + 7}{x^2 + 9x + 14} - \dfrac{x - 10}{x^2 - 49}$ $\dfrac{8x - 29}{(x + 2)(x - 7)(x + 7)}$

56. $\dfrac{x - y}{x + y} \cdot \dfrac{xy + x^2}{x^2 - y^2}$ $\dfrac{x}{x + y}$

57. $\dfrac{3x^2 - 27y^2}{30} \div \dfrac{(x - 3y)^2}{6}$ $\dfrac{3(x + 3y)}{5(x - 3y)}$

58. $\dfrac{a^2 - 11a + 30}{a - 6} \cdot \dfrac{a^2 - 8a + 15}{a^2 - 10a + 25}$ $a - 3$

59. $\dfrac{a}{a^2 - 1} - \dfrac{3}{3a^2 - 2a - 5}$ $\dfrac{3a^2 - 8a + 3}{(a + 1)(a - 1)(3a - 5)}$

60. $\dfrac{2x^2 + 6x - 20}{x^2 - 2x} \div \dfrac{x^2 + 7x + 10}{2x^2 - 8}$ $\dfrac{4x - 8}{x}$

[8.5] *Simplify each complex fraction.*

61. $\dfrac{5 + \dfrac{2}{3}}{\dfrac{3}{4}}$ $\dfrac{68}{9}$

62. $\dfrac{1 + \dfrac{5}{8}}{3 - \dfrac{9}{16}}$ $\dfrac{2}{3}$

63. $\dfrac{\dfrac{12ab}{9c}}{\dfrac{4a}{c^2}}$ $\dfrac{bc}{3}$

64. $\dfrac{\dfrac{18x^4 y^2}{9xy^5}}{\dfrac{4z^2}{}}$ $\dfrac{8x^3 z^2}{y^3}$

65. $\dfrac{a - \dfrac{a}{b}}{\dfrac{1 + a}{b}}$ $\dfrac{ab - a}{a + 1}$

66. $\dfrac{r^2 + \dfrac{7}{s}}{s^2}$ $\dfrac{r^2 s + 7}{s^3}$

67. $\dfrac{\dfrac{3}{x} + \dfrac{2}{x^2}}{5 - \dfrac{1}{x}}$ $\dfrac{3x + 2}{x(5x - 1)}$

68. $\dfrac{\dfrac{x}{x + y}}{\dfrac{x^2}{4x + 4y}}$ $\dfrac{4}{x}$

69. $\dfrac{\dfrac{9}{x}}{\dfrac{9}{x^2}}$ x

70. $\dfrac{\dfrac{1}{a} + 2}{\dfrac{1}{a} + \dfrac{3}{a}}$ $\dfrac{2a + 1}{4}$

71. $\dfrac{\dfrac{1}{x^2} - \dfrac{1}{x}}{\dfrac{1}{x^2} + \dfrac{1}{x}}$ $\dfrac{-x + 1}{x + 1}$

72. $\dfrac{\dfrac{8x}{y} - x}{\dfrac{y}{x} - 1}$ $\dfrac{8x^2 - x^2 y}{y(y - x)}$

[8.6] *Solve.*

73. $\dfrac{5}{9} = \dfrac{10}{x + 3}$ 15

74. $\dfrac{x}{4} = \dfrac{x - 3}{2}$ 6

75. $\dfrac{12}{n} + 2 = \dfrac{n}{4}$ 12

76. $\dfrac{10}{m} + \dfrac{3}{2} = \dfrac{m}{10}$ 20

77. $\dfrac{-4}{d} = \dfrac{3}{2} + \dfrac{4 - d}{d}$ -16

78. $\dfrac{1}{x - 7} + \dfrac{1}{x + 7} = \dfrac{1}{x^2 - 49}$ $\dfrac{1}{2}$

79. $\dfrac{x - 3}{x - 2} + \dfrac{x + 1}{x + 3} = \dfrac{2x^2 + x + 1}{x^2 + x - 6}$ -6

80. $\dfrac{a}{a^2 - 64} + \dfrac{4}{a + 8} = \dfrac{3}{a - 8}$ 28

81. $\dfrac{d}{d - 4} - 4 = \dfrac{4}{d - 4}$ no solution

[8.7] *Solve.*

82. Sandcastles It takes John and Amy Brogan 6 hours to build a sandcastle. It takes Paul and Cindy Carter 4 hours to make the same sandcastle. How long will it take all four people together to build the sandcastle? 2.4 hr

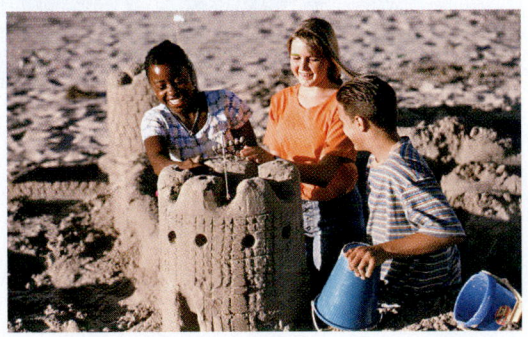

83. Filling a Pool A $\dfrac{3}{4}$-inch-diameter hose can fill a swimming pool in 7 hours. A $\dfrac{5}{16}$-inch-diameter hose can siphon all the water out of a full pool in 12 hours. How long will it take to fill the pool if while one hose is filling the pool the other hose is siphoning water from the pool? $16\dfrac{4}{5}$ hr

84. Sum of Numbers One number is six times as large as another. The sum of their reciprocals is 7. Determine the numbers. 1/6, 1

85. Rollerblading and Motorcycling Robert Johnston can travel 3 miles on his rollerblades in the same time Tran Lee can travel 8 miles on his mountain bike. If Tran's speed on his bike is 3.5 miles per hour faster than that of Robert on his rollerblades, determine Robert's and Tran's speeds. Robert, 2.1 mph; Tran, 5.6 mph

[8.8]

86. Drug Dosage The recommended dosage, d, of the antibiotic drug vancomycin is directly proportional to a person's weight, w. If Carmen Brown, who is 132 pounds is given 182 milligrams, find the recommended dosage for Bill Glenn, who is 198 pounds. 273 mg

87. Runners' Speed The time, t, it takes a runner to cover a specified distance is inversely proportional to the runner's speed. If Nhat Chung runs at an average of 6 miles per hour, he will finish a race in 1.4 hours. How long will it take Leif Lundgren, who runs at 5 miles per hour, to finish the same race? 1.68 hr

Chapter 8 Practice Test

To find out how well you understand the chapter material, take this practice test. The answers, and the section where the material was initially discussed, are given in the back of the book. Each problem is also fully worked out on the **Chapter Test Prep Video CD**. *Review any questions that you answered incorrectly.*

Simplify.

1. $\dfrac{-8+x}{x-8}$ 1

2. $\dfrac{x^3-1}{x^2-1}$ $\dfrac{x^2+x+1}{x+1}$

Perform each indicated operation.

3. $\dfrac{20x^2y^3}{4z^2} \cdot \dfrac{8xz^3}{5xy^4}$ $\dfrac{8x^2z}{y}$

4. $\dfrac{a^2-9a+14}{a-2} \cdot \dfrac{a^2-4a-21}{(a-7)^2}$ $a+3$

5. $\dfrac{x^2-x-6}{x^2-9} \cdot \dfrac{x^2-6x+9}{x^2+4x+4}$ $\dfrac{x^2-6x+9}{(x+3)(x+2)}$

6. $\dfrac{x^2-1}{x+2} \cdot \dfrac{x+2}{1-x^2}$ -1

7. $\dfrac{x^2-4y^2}{5x+20y} \div \dfrac{x+2y}{x+4y}$ $\dfrac{x-2y}{5}$

8. $\dfrac{15}{y^2+2y-15} \div \dfrac{5}{y-3}$ $\dfrac{3}{y+5}$

9. $\dfrac{m^2+3m-18}{m-3} \div \dfrac{m^2-8m+15}{3-m}$ $-\dfrac{m+6}{m-5}$

10. $\dfrac{4x+3}{8y} + \dfrac{2x-5}{8y}$ $\dfrac{3x-1}{4y}$

11. $\dfrac{7x^2-4}{x+3} - \dfrac{6x+9}{x+3}$ $\dfrac{7x^2-6x-13}{x+3}$

12. $\dfrac{2}{xy} - \dfrac{8}{xy^3}$ $\dfrac{2y^2-8}{xy^3}$

13. $3 - \dfrac{5z}{z-5}$ $-\dfrac{2z+15}{z-5}$

14. $\dfrac{x-5}{x^2-16} - \dfrac{x-2}{x^2+2x-8}$ $\dfrac{-1}{(x+4)(x-4)}$

Simplify.

15. $\dfrac{2+\dfrac{1}{2}}{3-\dfrac{1}{5}}$ $\dfrac{25}{28}$

16. $\dfrac{x+\dfrac{x}{y}}{\dfrac{7}{x}}$ $\dfrac{x^2+x^2y}{7y}$

17. $\dfrac{4+\dfrac{3}{x}}{\dfrac{9}{x}-5}$ $\dfrac{4x+3}{9-5x}$

Solve.

18. $2 + \dfrac{8}{x} = 6$ 2

19. $\dfrac{2x}{3} - \dfrac{x}{4} = x+1$ $-\dfrac{12}{7}$

20. $\dfrac{x}{x-8} + \dfrac{6}{x-2} = \dfrac{x^2}{x^2-10x+16}$ 12

Solve.

21. Working Together Mr. Jackson, on his tractor, can clear a 1-acre field in 10 hours. Mr. Hackett, on his tractor, can clear a 1-acre field in 15 hours. If they work together, how long will it take them to clear a 1-acre field?   6 hr

22. Determine a Number The sum of a positive number and its reciprocal is 2. Determine the number.   1

23. Area of Triangle The area of a triangle is 30 square inches. If the height is 2 inches less than 2 times the base, determine the height and base of the triangle.   base, 6 in.; height, 10 in.

24. Exercising LaConya Bertrell exercises for $1\dfrac{1}{2}$ hours each day. During the first part of her routine, she rides a bicycle and averages 10 miles per hour. For the remainder of the time, she rollerblades and averages 4 miles per hour. If the total distance she travels is 12 miles, how far did she travel on the rollerblades?   2 mi

25. Making Music The wavelength of sound waves, w, is inversely proportional to the frequency, f (or pitch). If a frequency of 263 cycles per second (middle C on a piano) produces a wavelength of about 4.3 feet, determine the length of a wavelength of a frequency of 1000 cycles per second. ≈ 1.13 ft

Cumulative Review Test

17. no solution

Take the following test and check your answers with those given in the back of the book. Review any questions that you answered incorrectly. The section where the material was covered is indicated after the answer.

1. Evaluate $3x^2 - 5xy^2 - 7$, when $x = -4$ and $y = -2$.   121

2. Evaluate $[6 - [3(8 \div 4)]^2 + 9 \cdot 4]^2$.   36

3. Solve $5z + 4 = -3(z - 7)$. $\dfrac{17}{8}$

4. The cost of a 2006 Chevrolet Corvette increased by 1.2% over the cost of the 2005 Corvette. Write an expression for the sum of the costs of a 2006 and a 2005 Corvette. $c + (c + 0.012c)$

5. Find the slope of the line through the points $(-7, 8)$ and $(3, 8)$.   0

6. Write the equation $3x - 4y = 12$ in slope-intercept form.

7. Simplify $(6x^2 - 3x - 5) - (-2x^2 - 8x - 19)$.

8. Multiply $(3n^2 - 4n + 3)(2n - 5)$. $6n^3 - 23n^2 + 26n - 15$

9. Divide $\dfrac{4x - 38}{8}$. $\dfrac{1}{2}x - \dfrac{19}{4}$

10. Factor $8a^2 - 8a - 5a + 5$. $(8a - 5)(a - 1)$

11. Factor $13x^2 + 26x - 39$. $13(x + 3)(x - 1)$

12. Solve $2x^2 = 11x - 12$. $4, \dfrac{3}{2}$

13. Multiply $\dfrac{x^2 + x - 12}{x^2 - x - 6} \cdot \dfrac{x^2 - 2x - 8}{2x^2 - 7x - 4}$. $\dfrac{x + 4}{2x + 1}$

14. Subtract $\dfrac{r}{r + 2} - \dfrac{3}{r - 5}$. $\dfrac{r^2 - 8r - 6}{(r + 2)(r - 5)}$

15. Add $\dfrac{4}{x^2 - 3x - 10} + \dfrac{6}{x^2 + 5x + 6}$. $\dfrac{10x - 18}{(x - 5)(x + 2)(x + 3)}$

16. Solve the equation $\dfrac{x}{9} - \dfrac{x}{6} = \dfrac{1}{12}$. $-\dfrac{3}{2}$

17. Solve the equation $\dfrac{7}{x + 3} + \dfrac{5}{x + 2} = \dfrac{5}{x^2 + 5x + 6}$.

18. **Medical Plans** A school district allows its employees to choose from two medical plans. With plan 1, the employee pays 10% of all medical bills (the school district pays the balance). With plan 2, the employee pays the school district a one-time payment of $150, then the employee pays 5% of all medical bills. What total medical bills would result in the employee paying the same amount with the two plans? $3000

19. **Bird Seed** A feed store owner wishes to make his own store-brand mixture of bird seed by mixing sunflower seed that costs $0.50 per pound with a premixed assorted seed that costs $0.20 per pound. How many pounds of each will he have to use to make a 50-pound mixture that will cost $16.00?   20 lb sunflower seed, 30 lb premixed assorted seed mix

20. **Sailing** During the first leg of a race, the sailboat *Thumper* sailed at an average speed of 6.5 miles per hour. During the second leg of the race, the winds increased and *Thumper* sailed at an average speed of 9.5 miles per hour. If the total distance sailed by *Thumper* was 12.75 miles, and the total time spent racing was 1.5 hours, determine the distance traveled by *Thumper* on each leg of the race.   1st leg: 3.25 mi; 2nd leg: 9.5 mi

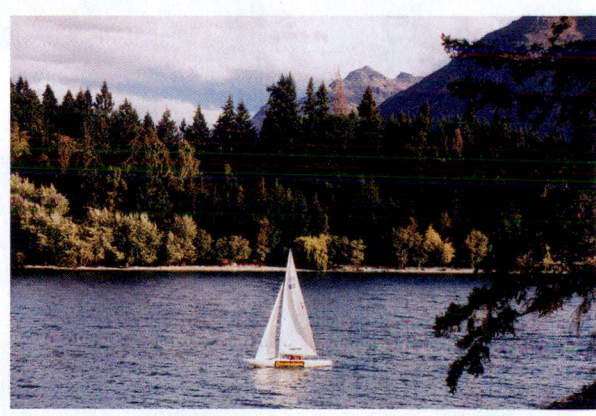

6. $y = \dfrac{3}{4}x - 3$ 7. $8x^2 + 5x + 14$

Roots and Radicals

9

WHEN WE DETERMINE A distance or other items that are measured, the answer obtained is often an irrational number, which involves a radical (for example, a square root), which we often round off to a decimal number. Many scientific and mathematical formulas involve square roots. For example, the formula for finding the period of a pendulum, in Example 6 on page 574, contains a square root.

9.1 Evaluating Square Roots

1 Evaluate square roots of real numbers.

2 Recognize that not all square roots represent real numbers.

3 Determine whether the square root of a real number is rational or irrational.

4 Write square roots as exponential expressions.

1 Evaluate Square Roots of Real Numbers

Earlier we discussed determining the square of a number. Recall that when we square a number we multiply the number by itself. For example,

$$\text{If } a = 5, \text{ then } a^2 = 5 \cdot 5 = 25.$$

$$\text{If } a = -5, \text{ then } a^2 = (-5)(-5) = 25.$$

In this chapter we consider the opposite problem. That is, if we know the square of a number, what is the number? For example,

$$\text{If } a^2 = 25, \text{ then what are the values of } a?$$

To find a in the above statement, we must find the values that when multiplied by themselves result in a product of 25. Since $5 \cdot 5 = 25$ and $(-5)(-5) = 25$, a has two values, -5 and 5.

Finding the **square root** of a given number is the reverse process of squaring a number. When we find the square root of a given number, we are determining what numbers, when multiplied by themselves, result in the given number. Every real number greater than 0 has two square roots, a positive square root and a negative square root. For example, the number 25 has two square roots, -5 and 5. We use the symbol $\sqrt{}$ to indicate the **positive** or **principal square root** of a number. For example,

$$\sqrt{25} = 5 \quad \text{(The principal square root of 25 is 5.)}$$

The symbol $-\sqrt{}$ is used to denote the negative square root of a number. For example,

$$-\sqrt{25} = -5 \quad \text{(The negative square root of 25 is } -5.)$$

The negative square root is the additive inverse or opposite of the principal square root. The following boxed material summarizes this information and provides additional information about square roots.

> **Square Root**
>
> The **positive** or **principal** **square root** of a positive number a is written as $\sqrt{a}$. The negative square root is written as $-\sqrt{a}$.
>
> $$\sqrt{a} = b \quad \text{if} \quad b^2 = a$$
>
> Also, the square root of 0 is 0, written $\sqrt{0} = 0$.

Note that **the principal square root of a positive number, a, is the positive number whose square equals a. Whenever we use the term square root in this book, we mean the positive or principal square root**.

Square roots are one type of radical expression that you will use in both mathematics and science.

$$\sqrt{x} \text{ is read "the square root of } x."$$

The $\sqrt{}$ is called the **radical sign**. The number or expression inside the radical sign is called the **radicand**.

Radical sign

$\sqrt{x}$

Radicand

The entire expression, including the radical sign and radicand, is called the **radical expression**.

Another part of a radical expression is its **index**. The index tells the "root" of the expression. Square roots have an index of 2. The index of a square root is generally not written.

$$\overset{\text{Index}}{\underset{\downarrow}{}}$$

$$\sqrt{x} \quad \text{means} \quad \sqrt[2]{x}$$

Other types of radical expressions have different indices. For example, $\sqrt[3]{x}$, which is read "the cube root of x," has an index of 3. Cube roots are discussed in Section 9.7.

Now let's find some square roots.

Examples

$$\sqrt{25} = 5 \qquad\qquad \text{since } 5^2 = 5 \cdot 5 = 25$$

$$\sqrt{64} = 8 \qquad\qquad \text{since } 8^2 = 8 \cdot 8 = 64$$

$$\sqrt{\frac{1}{4}} = \frac{1}{2} \qquad\qquad \text{since } \left(\frac{1}{2}\right)^2 = \left(\frac{1}{2}\right)\left(\frac{1}{2}\right) = \frac{1}{4}$$

$$\sqrt{\frac{4}{9}} = \frac{2}{3} \qquad\qquad \text{since } \left(\frac{2}{3}\right)^2 = \left(\frac{2}{3}\right)\left(\frac{2}{3}\right) = \frac{4}{9}$$

EXAMPLE 1 ▶ Evaluate. **a)** $\sqrt{81}$ **b)** $\sqrt{121}$ **c)** $\sqrt{\dfrac{9}{100}}$

Solution

a) $\sqrt{81} = 9$ since $9^2 = (9)(9) = 81$

b) $\sqrt{121} = 11$ since $(11)^2 = (11)(11) = 121$

c) $\sqrt{\dfrac{9}{100}} = \dfrac{3}{10}$ since $\left(\dfrac{3}{10}\right)^2 = \left(\dfrac{3}{10}\right)\left(\dfrac{3}{10}\right) = \dfrac{9}{100}$

▶ **Now Try Exercise 23**

EXAMPLE 2 ▶ Evaluate. **a)** $-\sqrt{81}$ **b)** $-\sqrt{100}$

Solution

a) $\sqrt{81} = 9$. Now we take the opposite of both sides to get

$$-\sqrt{81} = -9$$

b) Similarly, $-\sqrt{100} = -10$.

▶ **Now Try Exercise 21**

2   Recognize That Not All Square Roots Represent Real Numbers

You must understand that **square roots of negative numbers are not real numbers**. Consider $\sqrt{-4}$; to what is $\sqrt{-4}$ equal? To evaluate $\sqrt{-4}$, we must find some number whose square equals -4. But we know that the square of any nonzero real number must be a positive number. Therefore, no real number squared equals -4, so $\sqrt{-4}$ has no real value. Numbers like $\sqrt{-4}$, or square roots of any negative numbers, are called **imaginary numbers**. Imaginary numbers are discussed further in Section 10.5.

EXAMPLE 3 ▶ Indicate whether the radical expression is a real or an imaginary number.

a) $-\sqrt{16}$ **b)** $\sqrt{-16}$ **c)** $\sqrt{-43}$ **d)** $-\sqrt{43}$

Solution

a) Real (equal to -4)   **b)** Imaginary   **c)** Imaginary   **d)** Real

▶ **Now Try Exercise 53**

TEACHING TIP
Point out that the words indexes or indices can both be used for the plural of the word index.

INSTRUCTOR EXAMPLE
Evaluate.

a) $\sqrt{49}$ **b)** $\sqrt{\dfrac{36}{121}}$

Ans.:

a) 7   **b)** $\dfrac{6}{11}$

INSTRUCTOR EXAMPLE
Evaluate.

a) $-\sqrt{49}$ **b)** $-\sqrt{64}$
Ans.:

a) -7 **b)** -8

TEACHING TIP
Ask, "How do we know that the square of any nonzero real number must be a positive number?"

INSTRUCTOR EXAMPLE
Indicate whether the radical expression is a real or an imaginary number.

a) $-\sqrt{36}$ **b)** $\sqrt{-36}$
Ans.:

a) Real   **b)** Imaginary

Helpful Hint

The square root of any nonnegative number will be a real number. The square root of any negative number will be an imaginary number.

Examples of *Real* Numbers	Examples of *Imaginary* Numbers
$-\sqrt{9}, \quad -\sqrt{\dfrac{1}{2}}, \quad -\sqrt{6.74}, \quad -\sqrt{16}$	$\sqrt{-9}, \quad \sqrt{-\dfrac{1}{2}}, \quad \sqrt{-6.74}, \quad \sqrt{-16}$
↑ ↑ ↑ ↑	↑ ↑ ↑ ↑
Radicands are positive numbers	Radicands are negative numbers

Suppose we have an expression like $\sqrt{x}$, where x represents some number. For the radical $\sqrt{x}$ to be a real number, and not imaginary, we must assume that x is a nonnegative number.

In this chapter, unless stated otherwise, we will assume that all expressions that are radicands represent nonnegative numbers.

3   Determine Whether the Square Root of a Real Number Is Rational or Irrational

To help in our discussion of rational and irrational numbers, we will define perfect squares. The numbers 1, 4, 9, 16, 25, 36, 49, ... are called **perfect squares** because each number is *the square of a natural number*. When a perfect square is a factor of a radicand, we may refer to it as a **perfect square factor**.

$$1, \quad 2, \quad 3, \quad 4, \quad 5, \quad 6, \quad 7, \quad \ldots \qquad \textit{Natural numbers}$$
$$1^2, \quad 2^2, \quad 3^2, \quad 4^2, \quad 5^2, \quad 6^2, \quad 7^2, \quad \ldots \qquad \textit{The squares of the natural numbers}$$
$$1, \quad 4, \quad 9, \quad 16, \quad 25, \quad 36, \quad 49, \quad \ldots \qquad \textit{Perfect squares}$$

What are the next two perfect squares? Note that the square root of a perfect square is an integer. That is, $\sqrt{1} = 1$, $\sqrt{4} = 2$, $\sqrt{9} = 3$, $\sqrt{16} = 4$, and so on.

Table 9.1 illustrates the first 20 perfect squares. You may wish to refer to this table when simplifying radical expressions.

TEACHING TIP

Have students graph the positive and negative square roots of perfect squares from 1 to 100 on a number line. Then have them estimate the location of $\sqrt{5}$, $-\sqrt{35}$, $\sqrt{50}$, $-\sqrt{72}$, $\sqrt{86}$, and $-\sqrt{95}$.

Table 9.1

Perfect Square	Square Root of Perfect Square		Value	Perfect Square	Square Root of Perfect Square		Value
1	$\sqrt{1}$	=	1	121	$\sqrt{121}$	=	11
4	$\sqrt{4}$	=	2	144	$\sqrt{144}$	=	12
9	$\sqrt{9}$	=	3	169	$\sqrt{169}$	=	13
16	$\sqrt{16}$	=	4	196	$\sqrt{196}$	=	14
25	$\sqrt{25}$	=	5	225	$\sqrt{225}$	=	15
36	$\sqrt{36}$	=	6	256	$\sqrt{256}$	=	16
49	$\sqrt{49}$	=	7	289	$\sqrt{289}$	=	17
64	$\sqrt{64}$	=	8	324	$\sqrt{324}$	=	18
81	$\sqrt{81}$	=	9	361	$\sqrt{361}$	=	19
100	$\sqrt{100}$	=	10	400	$\sqrt{400}$	=	20

A **rational number** is a number that can be written in the form $\frac{a}{b}$, where a and b are integers, and $b \neq 0$. Examples of rational numbers are $\frac{1}{2}, \frac{3}{5}, -\frac{9}{2}, 4$, and 0. All integers are rational numbers since they can be expressed with a denominator of 1. For example, $4 = \frac{4}{1}$ and $0 = \frac{0}{1}$. The square roots of perfect squares are also rational numbers since each is an integer. When a rational number is written as a decimal, it will be either a terminating or repeating decimal.

TEACHING TIP
Have students describe and give an example of
a) terminating decimal
b) repeating decimal
c) nonterminating, nonrepeating decimal

Terminating Decimals	Repeating Decimals
$\frac{1}{2} = 0.5$	$\frac{1}{3} = 0.333\ldots$
$\frac{5}{8} = 0.625$	$\frac{4}{9} = 0.444\ldots$
$\sqrt{4} = 2.0$	$\frac{1}{6} = 0.1666\ldots$

Real numbers that are not rational numbers are called **irrational numbers**. Irrational numbers when written as decimals are nonterminating, nonrepeating decimals. The square root of every positive integer that is not a perfect square is an irrational number. For example, $\sqrt{2}$ and $\sqrt{3}$ are irrational numbers. The 20 square roots listed in **Table 9.1** are rational numbers. All other square roots of integers between 1 and 400 are irrational numbers. For example, since $\sqrt{50}$ is less than $\sqrt{400}$ and is not in **Table 9.1**, it is an irrational number. Furthermore, since $\sqrt{50}$ is between $\sqrt{49}$ and $\sqrt{64}$ in **Table 9.1**, the value of $\sqrt{50}$ is between 7 and 8. If you evaluate $\sqrt{50}$ on a calculator, as explained in the calculator box below, you will find that $\sqrt{50} \approx 7.07$, rounded to the nearest hundredth. Notice that since $\sqrt{50}$ is just slightly larger than $\sqrt{49}$, the value of $\sqrt{50}$ is just slightly larger than 7.

TEACHING TIP
Instruct students to round their answer, rather than truncate, when using the approximately equal sign.

When evaluating radicals, we may use the *is approximately equal to* symbol, $\approx$. For example, we may write $\sqrt{2} \approx 1.414$. This is read "the square root of 2 is approximately equal to 1.414." Recall that $\sqrt{2}$ is not a perfect square, so its square root cannot be evaluated exactly.

USING YOUR CALCULATOR Evaluating Square Roots on a Calculator

The square root key on calculators can be used to find square roots of nonnegative numbers. On some scientific calculators, to find the square root of 4, we press

On the TI-84 Plus graphing calculator, to find the square root of 4, we press

Both calculators display the answer 2. Since 2 is an integer, $\sqrt{4}$ is a rational number.

What would the calculator display if we evaluate $\sqrt{7}$? The display would show 2.6457513. Note that $\sqrt{7}$ is an irrational number, or a nonrepeating, nonterminating decimal. The decimal value of $\sqrt{7}$, or any other irrational number, can never be given exactly. The answers given on a calculator display are only close approximations of their value.

(continued on the next page)

Suppose we tried to evaluate $\sqrt{-4}$ on a calculator. What would the calculator give as an answer? On a scientific calculator, we press

Answer displayed

4 $\boxed{+/-}$ $\boxed{\sqrt{x}}$ Error

On a TI-84 Plus graphing calculator, we press

Answer displayed

$\boxed{2^{nd}}$ $\boxed{x^2}$ $\boxed{(}$ $\boxed{(-)}$ 4 $\boxed{)}$ $\boxed{\text{ENTER}}$ ERR: NONREAL ANS

Both calculators would give an error message, because the square root of -4, or the square root of any other negative number, is not a real number.

EXERCISES

Use your calculator to evaluate each square root.

1. $\sqrt{15}$ 3.872983346
2. $\sqrt{151}$ 12.28820573
3. $\sqrt{-16}$ Error
4. $\sqrt{27}$ 5.196152423

Figure 9.1 shows the relationship between the different types of numbers we discussed. Notice that the rational numbers plus the irrational numbers form the real numbers, and imaginary numbers are not real numbers, and vice versa.

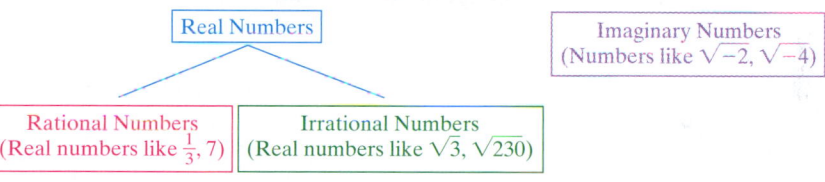

FIGURE 9.1

EXAMPLE 4 ▶ Use your calculator or **Table 9.1**, on page 539, to determine whether the following square roots are rational or irrational numbers.

a) $\sqrt{73}$ b) $\sqrt{196}$ c) $\sqrt{238}$ d) $\sqrt{324}$

Solution

a) Irrational   b) Rational, equal to 14

c) Irrational   d) Rational, equal to 18

▶ **Now Try Exercise 61**

4 Write Square Roots as Exponential Expressions

Radical expressions can be written in exponential form. Since we are discussing square roots, we will show how to write square roots in exponential form. Writing other radicals in exponential form will be discussed in Section 9.7. We introduce this information here because your instructor may wish to use exponential form to help explain certain concepts.

Recall that the index of square roots is 2. For example,

$$\sqrt{x} \quad \text{means} \quad \sqrt[2]{x}$$

We use the index, 2, when writing square roots in exponential form. To change from an expression in square root form to an expression in exponential form, simply write the radicand of the square root to the 1/2 power, as follows:

Writing a Square Root in Exponential Form

For example, $\sqrt{8}$ in exponential form is $8^{1/2}$, and $\sqrt{5ab} = (5ab)^{1/2}$. Other examples are

Square Root Form		Exponential Form
$\sqrt{25}$	$=$	$(25)^{1/2}$
$\sqrt{2x}$	$=$	$(2x)^{1/2}$
$\sqrt{35x^2 y}$	$=$	$(35x^2 y)^{1/2}$

EXAMPLE 5 ▶ Write each radical expression in exponential form.

a) $\sqrt{3}$ **b)** $\sqrt{26x}$

Solution

a) $3^{1/2}$ **b)** $(26x)^{1/2}$

         ▶ Now Try Exercise 69

We can also convert an expression from exponential form to radical form. To do so, we reverse the process. For example, $(8x)^{1/2}$ can be written $\sqrt{8x}$ and $(20x^4)^{1/2}$ can be written $\sqrt{20x^4}$.

The rules of exponents presented in Sections 6.1 and 6.2 apply to rational (or fractional) exponents. For example,

$$(x^2)^{1/2} = x^{2(1/2)} = x^1 = x$$
$$(xy)^{1/2} = x^{1/2} y^{1/2}$$

and $\quad x^{1/2} \cdot x^{3/2} = x^{(1/2)+(3/2)} = x^{4/2} = x^2$

1. positive number whose square equals a **2. a)** the root of the expression   **b)** radicand   **3.** Rational numbers can be written in the form a/b, $b \neq 0$, a and b integers. Irrational numbers are real numbers that are not rational.   **4.** It is nonnegative. The square root of a negative number is not a real number.

EXERCISE SET 9.1

5. b) rational if number appears in Table 9.1

Concept/Writing Exercises

1. What is the principal square root of a positive real number a?

2. a) What does the index indicate in a radical expression?

  b) What is the expression inside the radical sign called?

3. Explain the difference between a rational number and an irrational number.

4. Whenever we see an expression in a square root, what assumption do we make about the expression? Why do we make this assumption?

5. Explain how you would determine whether the square root of a positive integer less than 400 is a rational or irrational number

  a) by using a calculator, and   rational if answer is an integer

  b) without the use of a calculator.

6. Explain why the square root of a negative number is not a real number.   No real number when squared will be a negative number.

7. Is $\sqrt{25} = 5$? Explain.   yes

8. Is $\sqrt{25} = -5$? Explain.   no

9. Is $\sqrt{-25} = -5$? Explain.   no

10. Is $-\sqrt{25} = -5$? Explain.   yes

11. Is $\sqrt{\dfrac{16}{25}}$ a rational number? Explain.   yes

12. Is $\sqrt{\dfrac{13}{15}}$ a rational number? Explain.   no

Practice the Skills

Evaluate each square root.

13. $\sqrt{0}$ 0   **14.** $\sqrt{1}$ 1   **15.** $\sqrt{36}$ 6   **16.** $\sqrt{4}$ 2

17. $-\sqrt{49}$ -7 **18.** $\sqrt{81}$ 9   **19.** $\sqrt{400}$ 20   **20.** $\sqrt{196}$ 14

21. $-\sqrt{16}$ -4 **22.** $-\sqrt{36}$ -6 **23.** $\sqrt{144}$ 12   **24.** $\sqrt{49}$ 7

25. $\sqrt{225}$ 15   **26.** $\sqrt{169}$ 13   **27.** $-\sqrt{1}$ -1 **28.** $-\sqrt{100}$ -10

29. $-\sqrt{144}$ -12 **30.** $-\sqrt{81}$ -9 **31.** $-\sqrt{121}$ -11 **32.** $-\sqrt{196}$ -14

33. $\sqrt{\dfrac{1}{4}}$ $\dfrac{1}{2}$

34. $\sqrt{\dfrac{36}{49}}$ $\dfrac{6}{7}$

35. $\sqrt{\dfrac{25}{4}}$ $\dfrac{5}{2}$

36. $\sqrt{\dfrac{9}{64}}$ $\dfrac{3}{8}$

37. $-\sqrt{\dfrac{25}{36}}$ $-\dfrac{5}{6}$

38. $-\sqrt{\dfrac{49}{144}}$ $-\dfrac{7}{12}$

39. $\sqrt{\dfrac{81}{100}}$ $\dfrac{9}{10}$

40. $\sqrt{\dfrac{121}{225}}$ $\dfrac{11}{15}$

Use your calculator to evaluate each square root. Write your answer to seven decimal places.

41. $\sqrt{12}$ 3.4641016

42. $\sqrt{2}$ 1.4142136

43. $\sqrt{15}$ 3.8729833

44. $\sqrt{30}$ 5.4772256

45. $\sqrt{80}$ 8.9442719

46. $\sqrt{79}$ 8.8881944

47. $\sqrt{324}$ 18

48. $\sqrt{361}$ 19

49. $\sqrt{97}$ 9.8488578

50. $\sqrt{43}$ 6.5574385

51. $\sqrt{30}$ 5.4772256

52. $\sqrt{40}$ 6.3245553

Indicate whether each statement is true or false.

53. $\sqrt{28}$ is a rational number. false

54. $\sqrt{-25}$ is a real number. false

55. $\sqrt{25}$ is a rational number. true

56. $\sqrt{6}$ is an irrational number. true

57. $\sqrt{9}$ is an irrational number. false

58. $\sqrt{\dfrac{1}{4}}$ is a rational number. true

59. $\sqrt{\dfrac{9}{16}}$ is a rational number. true

60. $\sqrt{232}$ is a rational number. false

61. $\sqrt{125}$ is an irrational number. true

62. $\sqrt{29}$ is an irrational number. true

63. $\sqrt{(12)^2}$ is an integer. true

64. $\sqrt{(13)^2}$ is an integer. true

Write in exponential form.

65. $\sqrt{7}$ $7^{1/2}$

66. $\sqrt{23}$ $(23)^{1/2}$

67. $\sqrt{29}$ $(29)^{1/2}$

68. $\sqrt{83}$ $(83)^{1/2}$

69. $\sqrt{8x}$ $(8x)^{1/2}$

70. $\sqrt{5x}$ $(5x)^{1/2}$

71. $\sqrt{12x^2}$ $(12x^2)^{1/2}$

72. $\sqrt{25x^2y}$ $(25x^2y)^{1/2}$

73. $\sqrt{17ab^2}$ $(17ab^2)^{1/2}$

74. $\sqrt{84x^3y}$ $(84x^3y)^{1/2}$

75. $\sqrt{38n^3}$ $(38n^3)^{1/2}$

76. $\sqrt{59x^3y^3}$ $(59x^3y^3)^{1/2}$

77. rational: $9.83, \dfrac{3}{5}, 0.333\ldots, 5, \sqrt{\dfrac{4}{49}}, \dfrac{3}{7}, -\sqrt{9}$; irrational: $\sqrt{\dfrac{5}{16}}$; imaginary: $\sqrt{-4}, -\sqrt{-16}$

Problem Solving

77. Classify each number as rational, irrational, or imaginary.

$$9.83, \sqrt{-4}, \frac{3}{5}, 0.333\ldots, 5, \sqrt{\frac{4}{49}}, \frac{3}{7}, \sqrt{\frac{5}{16}}, -\sqrt{9}, -\sqrt{-16}$$

78. Classify each number as rational, irrational, or imaginary.

$$\sqrt{5}, 8.23, \sqrt{-7}, 10, \frac{1}{3}, 0.33, \sqrt{\frac{25}{64}}, -\sqrt{90}$$

79. Between what two integers is the square root of 47? Do not use your calculator or **Table 9.1**. Explain how you determined your answer. 6 and 7

80. Between what two integers is the square root of 88? Do not use your calculator or **Table 9.1**. Explain how you determined your answer. 9 and 10

81. a) Explain how you can determine without using a calculator whether 4.6 or $\sqrt{20}$ is greater. Square 4.6 and compare to 20.

b) Without using a calculator, determine which is greater. 4.6

82. a) Explain how you can determine without using a calculator whether 7.2 or $\sqrt{58}$ is greater. Square 7.2 and compare to 58.

b) Without using a calculator, determine which is greater. $\sqrt{58}$

83. Arrange the following list from smallest to largest. Do not use a calculator or **Table 9.1**.

$$5, -\sqrt{9}, -\sqrt{7}, 12, 2.5, -\frac{1}{2}, 4.01, \sqrt{16}$$

84. Arrange the following list from smallest to largest. Do not use a calculator or **Table 9.1**.

$$-\frac{1}{3}, -\sqrt{9}, 5, 0, \sqrt{9}, 8, -2, 3.25$$

85. Match each number in the column on the left with the corresponding answer in the column on the right.

$\sqrt{4}$ imaginary number $\sqrt{4} = 2$,

$6^{1/2}$ 2 $6^{1/2} \approx 2.45$,

$-\sqrt{9}$ ≈ 2.45 $-\sqrt{9} = -3$,

$-(25)^{1/2}$ -5 $-(25)^{1/2} = -5$,

$(30)^{1/2}$ -3 $(30)^{1/2} \approx 5.48$,

$(-4)^{1/2}$ ≈ 5.48 $(-4)^{1/2}$, imaginary number

86. Match each number in the column on the left with the corresponding answer in the column on the right.

$-\sqrt{36}$ 10 $-\sqrt{36} = -6$,

$(40)^{1/2}$ -7 $(40)^{1/2} \approx 6.32$

$\sqrt{100}$ imaginary number $\sqrt{100} = 10$,

$(10)^{1/2}$ ≈ 6.32 $(10)^{1/2} \approx 3.16$,

$-(49^{1/2})$ ≈ 3.16 $-(49^{1/2}) = -7$

$(-16)^{1/2}$ -6 $(-16)^{1/2}$, imaginary number

87. Is $\sqrt{0}$

a) a real number? yes

b) a positive number? no

c) a negative number? no

d) a rational number? yes

e) an irrational number? Explain your answer. no

78. rational: $8.23, 10, \dfrac{1}{3}, 0.33, \sqrt{\dfrac{25}{64}}$; irrational: $\sqrt{5}, -\sqrt{90}$; imaginary: $\sqrt{-7}$ **83.** $-\sqrt{9}, -\sqrt{7}, -\dfrac{1}{2}, 2.5, \sqrt{16}, 4.01, 5, 12$ **84.** $-\sqrt{9}, -2, -\dfrac{1}{3}, 0, \sqrt{9}, 3.25, 5, 8$

Challenge Problems

We discuss the following concepts in Sections 9.2 and 9.3.

90. c) $\sqrt{\dfrac{a}{b}}$

88. **a)** Is $\sqrt{4} \cdot \sqrt{9}$ equal to $\sqrt{4 \cdot 9}$?   yes

   b) Is $\sqrt{9} \cdot \sqrt{25}$ equal to $\sqrt{9 \cdot 25}$?   yes

   c) Using these two examples, can you guess what $\sqrt{a} \cdot \sqrt{b}$ is equal to (provided that $a \geq 0, b \geq 0$)? $\sqrt{a \cdot b}$

   d) Create your own problem like those given in parts **a)** and **b)** and see if the answer you gave in part **c)** works with your numbers.   Answers will vary.

89. **a)** Is $\sqrt{3^2}$ equal to 3?   yes

   b) Is $\sqrt{8^2}$ equal to 8?   yes

   c) Using these two examples, can you guess what $\sqrt{a^2}, a \geq 0$, is equal to? a

   d) Create your own problem like those given in parts **a)** and **b)** and see if the answer you gave in part **c)** works with your numbers.   Answers will vary.

90. **a)** Is $\dfrac{\sqrt{16}}{\sqrt{4}}$ equal to $\sqrt{\dfrac{16}{4}}$?   yes

   b) Is $\dfrac{\sqrt{36}}{\sqrt{49}}$ equal to $\sqrt{\dfrac{36}{49}}$?   yes

   c) Using these two examples, can you guess what $\dfrac{\sqrt{a}}{\sqrt{b}}$ is equal to (provided that $a \geq 0, b > 0$)?

   d) Create your own problem like those given in parts **a)** and **b)** and see if the answer you gave in part **c)** works with your numbers.   Answers will vary.

The rules of exponents we discussed in Chapter 6 also apply with rational exponents. Use the rules of exponents to simplify the following expressions. We will discuss problems like this in Section 9.7.

91. $(x^3)^{1/2}$ $x^{3/2}$

92. $(x^6)^{1/2}$ x^3

93. $x^{1/2} \cdot x^{5/2}$ x^3

94. $x^{7/2} \cdot x^{1/2}$ x^4

Cumulative Review Exercises

[3.2] **95. Jumping on a Trampoline** Allison jumped on the trampoline for a minute, and then her mother Elizabeth jumped on the trampoline for a minute. If Allison made twice as many jumps as her mother did, and the total number of jumps was 78, determine the number of jumps Allison made.   52 jumps

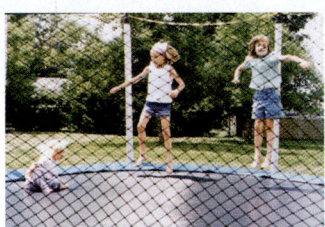

[8.6] *Solve.*

96. $\dfrac{2x}{x^2 - 4} + \dfrac{1}{x - 2} = \dfrac{2}{x + 2}$ -6

97. $\dfrac{4x}{x^2 + 6x + 9} - \dfrac{2x}{x + 3} = \dfrac{x + 1}{x + 3}$ -1

[4.3] **98.** Determine the slope of the line through the points $(-5, 2)$ and $(6, 7)$. $\dfrac{5}{11}$

[4.6] **99.** If $f(x) = x^2 - 4x - 15$, find $f(-3)$.   6

9.2 Simplifying Square Roots

1 Use the product rule to simplify square roots containing constants.

2 Use the product rule to simplify square roots containing variables.

1 Use the Product Rule to Simplify Square Roots Containing Constants

To simplify square roots in this section we will make use of the **product rule for square roots**.

> **Product Rule for Square Roots**
>
> $$\sqrt{a} \cdot \sqrt{b} = \sqrt{a \cdot b}, \quad \text{provided} \quad a \geq 0, b \geq 0 \qquad \text{Rule 1}$$

TEACHING TIP
Before discussing the product rule for square roots, have students describe the rule in words.

The product rule states that the product of two square roots is equal to the square root of the product. The product rule applies only when both a and b are nonnegative, since the square roots of negative numbers are not real numbers.

Examples of the Product Rule

$$\left.\begin{array}{l}\sqrt{1}\cdot\sqrt{60}=\sqrt{1\cdot60}\\ \sqrt{2}\cdot\sqrt{30}=\sqrt{2\cdot30}\\ \sqrt{3}\cdot\sqrt{20}=\sqrt{3\cdot20}\\ \sqrt{4}\cdot\sqrt{15}=\sqrt{4\cdot15}\\ \sqrt{6}\cdot\sqrt{10}=\sqrt{6\cdot10}\end{array}\right\}=\sqrt{60}$$

Note that $\sqrt{60}$ can be factored into any of these forms.

When two square roots are placed next to one another, the square roots are to be multiplied. Thus $\sqrt{a}\sqrt{b}$ means $\sqrt{a}\cdot\sqrt{b}$.

To Simplify the Square Root of a Constant

1. Write the constant as a product of the largest perfect square factor and another factor.

2. Use the product rule to write the expression as a product of square roots, with each square root containing one of the factors.

3. Find the square root of the perfect square factor.

EXAMPLE 1 ▶ Simplify $\sqrt{60}$.

Solution   The only perfect square factor of 60 is 4.

$$\begin{aligned}\sqrt{60}&=\sqrt{4\cdot15}\\ &=\sqrt{4}\cdot\sqrt{15}\\ &=2\sqrt{15}\end{aligned}$$

Since 15 is not a perfect square and has no perfect square factors, this expression cannot be simplified further. The expression $2\sqrt{15}$ is read "two times the square root of fifteen."

▶ **Now Try Exercise 15**

EXAMPLE 2 ▶ Simplify $\sqrt{12}$.

Solution

$$\begin{aligned}\sqrt{12}=\sqrt{4\cdot3}&=\sqrt{4}\cdot\sqrt{3}\\ &=2\sqrt{3}\end{aligned}$$

▶ **Now Try Exercise 13**

EXAMPLE 3 ▶ Simplify $\sqrt{80}$.

Solution

$$\begin{aligned}\sqrt{80}=\sqrt{16\cdot5}&=\sqrt{16}\cdot\sqrt{5}\\ &=4\sqrt{5}\end{aligned}$$

▶ **Now Try Exercise 19**

EXAMPLE 4 ▶ Simplify $\sqrt{245}$.

Solution

$$\begin{aligned}\sqrt{245}=\sqrt{49\cdot5}&=\sqrt{49}\cdot\sqrt{5}\\ &=7\sqrt{5}\end{aligned}$$

▶ **Now Try Exercise 29**

Helpful Hint

When simplifying a square root, it is not uncommon to use a perfect square factor that is not the *largest* perfect square factor of the radicand. Let's consider Example 3 again. Four is also a perfect square factor of 80.

$$\sqrt{80} = \sqrt{4 \cdot 20} = \sqrt{4} \cdot \sqrt{20} = 2\sqrt{20}$$

Since 20 itself contains a perfect square factor of 4, the solution is not complete. Rather than starting the entire solution again, you can continue the simplification process as follows.

$$\sqrt{80} = 2\sqrt{20} = 2\sqrt{4 \cdot 5} = 2\sqrt{4} \cdot \sqrt{5} = 2 \cdot 2 \cdot \sqrt{5} = 4\sqrt{5}$$

Now the result checks with the answer in Example 3.

EXAMPLE 5 ▶ Simplify $\sqrt{135}$.

Solution

$$\sqrt{135} = \sqrt{9 \cdot 15} = \sqrt{9} \cdot \sqrt{15}$$
$$= 3\sqrt{15}$$

Although 15 can be factored into $5 \cdot 3$, neither of these factors is a perfect square. Thus, the answer cannot be simplified any further.

▶ **Now Try Exercise 21**

2 Use the Product Rule to Simplify Square Roots Containing Variables

Now we will simplify square roots that contain variables in the radicand.

In Section 9.1 we noted that certain numbers were **perfect squares**. We will also refer to certain expressions that contain a variable as perfect squares. When a radical contains a variable (or number) raised to an **even exponent**, that variable (or number) and exponent together also form a perfect square. For example, in the expression $\sqrt{x^4}$, the x^4 is a perfect square since the exponent 4, is even. In the expression $\sqrt{x^5}$, the x^5 is not a perfect square since the exponent is odd. However, x^4 is a **perfect square factor** of x^5 because x^4 is a perfect square and x^4 is a factor of x^5. Note that $x^5 = x^4 \cdot x$.

To evaluate square roots when the radicand is a perfect square, we use the following rule.

Square Root of a Perfect Square
$\sqrt{a^{2 \cdot n}} = a^n, \qquad a \geq 0 \qquad$ Rule 2

This rule states that **the square root of a variable raised to an even power equals the variable raised to one-half that power**. To explain this rule, we can write the square root expression $\sqrt{a^{2n}}$ in exponential form, and then simplify as follows.

$$\sqrt{a^{2n}} = (a^{2n})^{1/2} = a^{2n(1/2)} = a^n$$

Examples of rule 2 follow. Remember that we are assuming the variables represent nonnegative real numbers.

Examples

$$\sqrt{x^2} = x$$
$$\sqrt{a^4} = a^2$$
$$\sqrt{y^{20}} = y^{10}$$
$$\sqrt{z^{28}} = z^{14}$$

A special case of rule 2 (when $n = 1$) is

$$\sqrt{a^2} = a, \qquad a \geq 0$$

EXAMPLE 6 ▶ Simplify. **a)** $\sqrt{x^{32}}$ **b)** $\sqrt{x^4 y^8}$ **c)** $\sqrt{a^{10} b^2}$ **d)** $\sqrt{y^{12} z^{16}}$

Solution

a) $\sqrt{x^{32}} = x^{16}$

b) $\sqrt{x^4 y^8} = \sqrt{x^4}\,\sqrt{y^8} = x^2 y^4$

c) $\sqrt{a^{10} b^2} = \sqrt{a^{10}}\,\sqrt{b^2} = a^5 b$

d) $\sqrt{y^{12} z^{16}} = \sqrt{y^{12}}\,\sqrt{z^{16}} = y^6 z^8$

▶ **Now Try Exercise 35**

> **To Simplify the Square Root of a Radicand Containing a Variable Raised to an Odd Power**
>
> 1. Express the variable as the product of two factors, one of which has an exponent of 1 (the other will therefore be a perfect square factor).
> 2. Use the product rule to simplify.

The radicand of your simplified answer should not contain any perfect square factors or any variables with an exponent greater than 1.

Examples 7 and 8 illustrate the above procedure.

EXAMPLE 7 ▶ Simplify. **a)** $\sqrt{x^3}$ **b)** $\sqrt{y^7}$ **c)** $\sqrt{a^{49}}$

Solution

a) $\sqrt{x^3} = \sqrt{x^2 \cdot x} = \sqrt{x^2} \cdot \sqrt{x}$

$\qquad = x \cdot \sqrt{x}$ or $x\sqrt{x}$ *(Remember that x means x^1.)*

b) $\sqrt{y^7} = \sqrt{y^6 \cdot y^1} = \sqrt{y^6} \cdot \sqrt{y}$

$\qquad = y^3 \sqrt{y}$

c) $\sqrt{a^{49}} = \sqrt{a^{48} \cdot a} = \sqrt{a^{48}} \cdot \sqrt{a}$

$\qquad = a^{24}\sqrt{a}$

▶ **Now Try Exercise 33**

More complex radicals can be simplified using the product rule for radicals and the principles discussed in this section.

EXAMPLE 8 ▶ Simplify. **a)** $\sqrt{36 x^3}$ **b)** $\sqrt{50 x^2}$ **c)** $\sqrt{50 x^3}$

Solution Write each expression as the product of square roots, one of which has a radicand that is a perfect square.

a) $\sqrt{36 x^3} = \sqrt{36 x^2} \cdot \sqrt{x} = 6x\sqrt{x}$

b) $\sqrt{50 x^2} = \sqrt{25 x^2} \cdot \sqrt{2} = 5x\sqrt{2}$

c) $\sqrt{50 x^3} = \sqrt{25 x^2} \cdot \sqrt{2x} = 5x\sqrt{2x}$

▶ **Now Try Exercise 41**

EXAMPLE 9 ▶ Simplify. **a)** $\sqrt{72 x^2 y}$ **b)** $\sqrt{45 x^3 y^4}$ **c)** $\sqrt{98 a^9 b^7}$

Solution

a) $\sqrt{72 x^2 y} = \sqrt{36 x^2} \cdot \sqrt{2y}$ *Write $\sqrt{72 x^2 y}$ as a product of a perfect square factor and another factor.*

$\qquad = 6x\sqrt{2y}$ *Simplify the perfect square factor.*

b) $\sqrt{45 x^3 y^4} = \sqrt{9 x^2 y^4} \cdot \sqrt{5x}$ *Write $\sqrt{45 x^3 y^4}$ as a product of a perfect square factor and another factor.*

$\qquad = 3xy^2 \sqrt{5x}$ *Simplify the perfect square factor.*

c) $\sqrt{98 a^9 b^7} = \sqrt{49 a^8 b^6} \cdot \sqrt{2ab}$ *Write $\sqrt{98 a^9 b^7}$ as a product of a perfect square factor and another factor.*

$\qquad = 7 a^4 b^3 \sqrt{2ab}$ *Simplify the perfect square factor.*

▶ **Now Try Exercise 45**

Now let's look at an example where we use the product rule to multiply two radicals before simplifying.

EXAMPLE 10 ▶ Multiply and then simplify.

a) $\sqrt{2} \cdot \sqrt{8}$ **b)** $\sqrt{2x} \cdot \sqrt{8}$ **c)** $\left(\sqrt{5x}\right)^2$

INSTRUCTOR EXAMPLE
Multiply and simplify.
 a) $\sqrt{3x} \cdot \sqrt{12}$ **b)** $\left(\sqrt{7x}\right)^2$
Ans.:
 a) $6\sqrt{x}$ **b)** $7x$

Solution

a) $\sqrt{2} \cdot \sqrt{8} = \sqrt{2 \cdot 8} = \sqrt{16} = 4$

b) $\sqrt{2x} \cdot \sqrt{8} = \sqrt{16x} = \sqrt{16} \cdot \sqrt{x} = 4\sqrt{x}$

c) $\left(\sqrt{5x}\right)^2 = \sqrt{5x} \cdot \sqrt{5x} = \sqrt{25x^2} = 5x$

▶ **Now Try Exercise 55**

EXAMPLE 11 ▶ Multiply and then simplify.

a) $\sqrt{8x^3y}\,\sqrt{4xy^5}$ **b)** $\sqrt{7ab^8}\,\sqrt{6a^5b}$

INSTRUCTOR EXAMPLE
Multiply and simplify
  $\sqrt{10x^2y} \cdot \sqrt{5xy^7}$.
Ans.: $5xy^4\sqrt{2x}$

Solution

a) $\sqrt{8x^3y}\,\sqrt{4xy^5} = \sqrt{32x^4y^6} = \sqrt{16x^4y^6} \cdot \sqrt{2}$
$$= 4x^2y^3\sqrt{2}$$

b) $\sqrt{7ab^8}\,\sqrt{6a^5b} = \sqrt{42a^6b^9} = \sqrt{a^6b^8} \cdot \sqrt{42b}$
$$= a^3b^4\sqrt{42b}$$

In part **b)**, 42 can be factored in many ways. However, none of the factors are perfect squares, so we leave the answer as given.

▶ **Now Try Exercise 63**

---

2. b) $2\sqrt{5}$ **5. a)** Answers will vary.   **b)** $x^6\sqrt{x}$ **6. a), 7. a)** There can be no perfect square factors or any exponents greater than 1 in the radicand.

EXERCISE SET 9.2

MathXL®   MyMathLab

7. a) There can be no perfect square factors or any exponents greater than 1 in the radicand.

Concept/Writing Exercises

1. State the product rule for square roots and explain what it means.   Answers will vary.

2. a) Explain how to simplify a square root containing only a constant.   Answers will vary.

  b) Simplify $\sqrt{20}$ using the procedure you gave in part **a)**.

3. Explain why the product rule cannot be used to simplify the problem $\sqrt{-4} \cdot \sqrt{-9}$.   Radicands cannot be negative.

4. We learned that for $a \geq 0$, $\sqrt{a^{2 \cdot n}} = a^n$. Explain what this means.   Answers will vary.

5. a) Explain how to simplify the square root of a radical containing a variable raised to an odd power.

  b) Simplify $\sqrt{x^{13}}$ using the procedure you gave in part **a)**.

6. a) Explain why $\sqrt{32x^3}$ is not a simplified expression.

  b) Simplify $\sqrt{32x^3}$. $4x\sqrt{2x}$

7. a) Explain why $\sqrt{75x^5}$ is not a simplified expression.

  b) Simplify $\sqrt{75x^5}$. $5x^2\sqrt{3x}$

8. Use the product rule to write $\sqrt{40}$ as four different products of factors. $\sqrt{40} \cdot \sqrt{1}, \sqrt{20} \cdot \sqrt{2}, \sqrt{10} \cdot \sqrt{4}, \sqrt{8} \cdot \sqrt{5}$

Determine whether the square root on the right-hand side of the equal sign is the simplified form of the square root on the left-hand side of the equal sign. If not, simplify it properly.

9. $\sqrt{75} = 5\sqrt{3}$ yes   **10.** $\sqrt{x^5} = x^2\sqrt{x}$ yes   **11.** $\sqrt{32} = 2\sqrt{8}$ no; $4\sqrt{2}$ **12.** $\sqrt{x^9} = x\sqrt{x^7}$ no; $x^4\sqrt{x}$

Practice the Skills

Simplify.

13. $\sqrt{18}$ $3\sqrt{2}$ **14.** $\sqrt{24}$ $2\sqrt{6}$ **15.** $\sqrt{8}$ $2\sqrt{2}$ **16.** $\sqrt{45}$ $3\sqrt{5}$

17. $\sqrt{28}$ $2\sqrt{7}$ **18.** $\sqrt{75}$ $5\sqrt{3}$ **19.** $\sqrt{20}$ $2\sqrt{5}$ **20.** $\sqrt{52}$ $2\sqrt{13}$

21. $\sqrt{160}$ $4\sqrt{10}$ **22.** $\sqrt{44}$ $2\sqrt{11}$ **23.** $\sqrt{80}$ $4\sqrt{5}$ **24.** $\sqrt{98}$ $7\sqrt{2}$

25. $\sqrt{72}$ $6\sqrt{2}$ **26.** $\sqrt{108}$ $6\sqrt{3}$ **27.** $\sqrt{120}$ $2\sqrt{30}$ **28.** $\sqrt{125}$ $5\sqrt{5}$

29. $\sqrt{243}$ $9\sqrt{3}$ **30.** $\sqrt{140}$ $2\sqrt{35}$ **31.** $\sqrt{150}$ $5\sqrt{6}$ **32.** $\sqrt{x^4}$ x^2

33. $\sqrt{x^6}$ x^3 **34.** $\sqrt{y^{15}}$ $y^7\sqrt{y}$ **35.** $\sqrt{x^2y^8}$ xy^4 **36.** $\sqrt{x^2y^6}$ xy^3

37. $\sqrt{a^{12}b^9}$ $a^6b^4\sqrt{b}$ **38.** $\sqrt{x^4y^5z^6}$ $x^2y^2z^3\sqrt{y}$ **39.** $\sqrt{a^2b^4c}$ $ab^2\sqrt{c}$ **40.** $\sqrt{a^3b^9c^{11}}$ $ab^4c^5\sqrt{abc}$

41. $\sqrt{3n^3}$ $n\sqrt{3n}$ **42.** $\sqrt{12x^4y^2}$ $2x^2y\sqrt{3}$ **43.** $\sqrt{108a^3b^2}$ $6ab\sqrt{3a}$ **44.** $\sqrt{150m^4n^3}$ $5m^2n\sqrt{6n}$

45. $\sqrt{300a^5b^{11}}$ $10a^2b^5\sqrt{3ab}$ **46.** $\sqrt{64xyz^7}$ $8z^3\sqrt{xyz}$ **47.** $\sqrt{243x^3y^4}$ $9xy^2\sqrt{3x}$ **48.** $\sqrt{500ab^4c^3}$ $10b^2c\sqrt{5ac}$

49. $\sqrt{108a^2b^9c}$ $6ab^4\sqrt{3bc}$ **50.** $\sqrt{112x^6y^{10}}$ $4x^3y^5\sqrt{7}$ **51.** $\sqrt{180r^3s^{10}t^5}$ $6rs^5t^2\sqrt{5rt}$ **52.** $\sqrt{98x^6y^4z}$ $7x^3y^2\sqrt{2z}$

Simplify.

53. $\sqrt{7}\cdot\sqrt{7}$ 7 **54.** $\sqrt{11}\cdot\sqrt{11}$ 11 **55.** $\sqrt{24}\cdot\sqrt{3}$ $6\sqrt{2}$

56. $\sqrt{60}\cdot\sqrt{5}$ $10\sqrt{3}$ **57.** $\sqrt{48}\cdot\sqrt{15}$ $12\sqrt{5}$ **58.** $\sqrt{35}\cdot\sqrt{5}$ $5\sqrt{7}$

59. $\sqrt{2x}\,\sqrt{7x}$ $x\sqrt{14}$ **60.** $\sqrt{6x^3}\,\sqrt{6x}$ $6x^2$ **61.** $\sqrt{4a^2}\,\sqrt{12ab^2}$ $4ab\sqrt{3a}$

62. $\sqrt{30b^2}\,\sqrt{6b^5}$ $6b^3\sqrt{5b}$ **63.** $\sqrt{3xy^3}\,\sqrt{24x^2y}$ $6xy^2\sqrt{2x}$ **64.** $\sqrt{40xy^4}\,\sqrt{6x^5}$ $4x^3y^2\sqrt{15}$

65. $\sqrt{3r^4s^7}\,\sqrt{21r^6s^5}$ $3r^5s^6\sqrt{7}$ **66.** $\sqrt{20x^3y}\,\sqrt{6x^3y^5}$ $2x^3y^3\sqrt{30}$ **67.** $\sqrt{15xy^6}\,\sqrt{6xyz}$ $3xy^3\sqrt{10yz}$

68. $\sqrt{14xyz^5}\,\sqrt{5xy^2z^6}$ $xyz^5\sqrt{70yz}$ **69.** $\sqrt{6a^2b^4}\,\sqrt{9a^4b^6}$ $3a^3b^5\sqrt{6}$ **70.** $\sqrt{6a^4b^5c^6}\,\sqrt{3a^3bc^6}$ $3a^3b^3c^6\sqrt{2a}$

71. $(\sqrt{2x})^2$ $2x$ **72.** $(\sqrt{5x^2})^2$ $5x^2$ **73.** $(\sqrt{13x^4y^6})^2$ $13x^4y^6$

74. $\sqrt{49x^2y^7}\,\sqrt{2x^4y}$ $7x^3y^4\sqrt{2}$ **75.** $(\sqrt{5a})^2(\sqrt{7a})^2$ $35a^2$ **76.** $(\sqrt{4ab})^2(\sqrt{9ab})^2$ $36a^2b^2$

Problem Solving

81. coefficient, 8; exponent on x, 12; on y, 7   **82.** coefficient, 2; exponent on x, 6; on z, 7

Which coefficients and exponents should be placed in the shaded areas to make a true statement? Explain how you obtained your answer.

77. $\sqrt{25x^{\blacksquare}y^6} = 5x^4y^3$ 8

78. $\sqrt{\blacksquare x^4y^{\blacksquare}} = 6x^2y^4$ coefficient, 36; exponent on y, 8

79. $\sqrt{4x^{\blacksquare}y^{\blacksquare}} = 2x^6y^2\sqrt{y}$ exponent on x, 12; on y, 5

80. $\sqrt{3x^4y^{\blacksquare}}\cdot\sqrt{3x^{\blacksquare}y^5} = 3x^5y^7\sqrt{xy}$ exponent on y, 10; on x, 7

81. $\sqrt{2x^{\blacksquare}y^5}\cdot\sqrt{\blacksquare x^3y^{\blacksquare}} = 4x^7y^6\sqrt{x}$

82. $\sqrt{32x^4z^{\blacksquare}}\cdot\sqrt{\blacksquare x^{\blacksquare}z^{12}} = 8x^5z^9\sqrt{z}$

83. **a)** Showing all steps, simplify $(\sqrt{7x^4})^2$. $7x^4$

b) Showing all steps, simplify $\sqrt{(7x^4)^2}$. $7x^4$

c) Compare your results in part **a)** and part **b)**. Are they the same? yes

84. **a)** Showing all steps, simplify $(\sqrt{23x^3})^2$. $23x^3$

b) Showing all steps, simplify $\sqrt{(23x^3)^2}$. $23x^3$

c) Compare your results in part **a)** and part **b)**. Are they the same? yes

Challenge Problems

89. rational; $\sqrt{6.25} = 2.5$ and 2.5 is a terminating decimal number   **91. a)** 4 ft

Below we show two simplifications involving square roots.

$$\sqrt{x^4} = (x^4)^{1/2} = x^{4(1/2)} = x^2$$

$$\sqrt{x^{2/4}} = (x^{2/4})^{1/2} = x^{(2/4)(1/2)} = x^{1/4}$$

In Section 9.1 we indicated that the square root of an expression may be written as the expression to the $\frac{1}{2}$ power. The rules for exponents that were discussed in Section 6.1 also apply when the exponents are rational numbers. Use the two examples illustrated and the rules for exponents to simplify Exercises 85–88. We will discuss rational exponents further in Section 9.7.

85. $\sqrt{x^{2/6}}$ $x^{1/6}$ **86.** $\sqrt{y^{10/14}}$ $y^{5/14}$ **87.** $\sqrt{4x^{4/5}}$ $2x^{2/5}$ **88.** $\sqrt{25y^{8/3}}$ $5y^{4/3}$

89. Is $\sqrt{6.25}$ a rational or an irrational number? Explain how you determined your answer.

90. **a)** In Section 9.4 we will be multiplying expressions like $(\sqrt{a} + \sqrt{b})(\sqrt{a} - \sqrt{b})$ using the FOIL method. Can you find this product now? $a - b$

b) Multiply $(\sqrt{7} + \sqrt{3})(\sqrt{7} - \sqrt{3})$. 4

91. The area of a square is found by the formula $A = s^2$. We will learn later that we can rewrite this formula as $s = \sqrt{A}$.

a) If the area is 16 square feet, what is the length of a side?

b) If the area is doubled, is the length of a side doubled? Explain. no, increased $\sqrt{2}$ or ≈ 1.414 times

c) To double the length of a side of a square, how much must the area be increased? Explain. 4 times

92. We know that $\sqrt{a}\cdot\sqrt{b} = \sqrt{a\cdot b}$ if $a \geq 0$ and $b \geq 0$. Does $\sqrt{\dfrac{a}{b}} = \dfrac{\sqrt{a}}{\sqrt{b}}$ if $a \geq 0$ and $b > 0$? Try several pairs of values for a and b and see. yes

93. **a)** Will the product of two rational numbers always be a rational number? Explain and give an example to support your answer. yes

b) Will the product of two irrational numbers always be an irrational number? Explain and give an example to support your answer. no; for example, $\sqrt{2}\cdot\sqrt{2} = 2$.

Group Activity

We learned earlier that $\sqrt{\blacksquare} = \blacksquare^{1/2}$. *For example,* $\sqrt{x^6} = (x^6)^{1/2} = x^3$. *We can simplify* $\sqrt{x^{2n}}$ *by writing the expression in exponential form,* $\sqrt{x^{2n}} = (x^{2n})^{1/2} = x^{(2n)(1/2)} = x^n$. *As a group, simplify the following square roots by writing the expression in exponential form. Show all the steps in the simplification process.*

94. $\sqrt{x^{10a}}$ x^{5a}

95. $\sqrt{x^{8b}}$ x^{4b}

96. $\sqrt{x^{4a}y^{12b}}$ $x^{2a}y^{6b}$

97. $\sqrt{x^{10b}y^{6c}}$ $x^{5b}y^{3c}$

Cumulative Review Exercises

[2.6] **98. Area** Find the area of the trapezoid.

Use $A = \dfrac{1}{2}h(b + d)$.   148.5 in.^{2}

15 in.

9 in.

18 in.

99. Volume Find the volume of the cone.

Use $V = \dfrac{1}{3}\pi r^2 h$. ≈ 25.13 ft^3

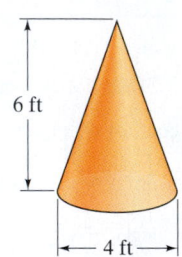

6 ft

4 ft

[8.2] **100.** Divide $\dfrac{3x^2 - 16x - 12}{3x^2 - 10x - 8} \div \dfrac{x^2 - 7x + 6}{3x^2 - 11x - 4}$. $\dfrac{3x + 1}{x - 1}$

[4.4] **101.** Write the equation $5x + 10y = 15$ in slope-intercept form and indicate the slope and the y-intercept.

[4.5] **102.** Graph $6x - 5y \geq 30$.   See graphing answer section.

[5.3] **103.** Solve the system of equations.

$$2x + 3y = -8$$
$$6x - y = 6$$ $\left(\dfrac{1}{2}, -3\right)$

101. $y = -\dfrac{1}{2}x + \dfrac{3}{2}, m = -\dfrac{1}{2}, \left(0, \dfrac{3}{2}\right)$

9.3 Adding, Subtracting, and Multiplying Square Roots

1 Add and subtract square roots.

2 Multiply square roots.

1 Add and Subtract Square Roots

Like square roots are square roots having the same radicands. Like square roots are added in much the same manner that like terms are added, as illustrated below.

Examples of Adding Like Terms

$$2x + 3x = (2 + 3)x = 5x$$
$$4x + x = 4x + 1x = (4 + 1)x = 5x$$

Examples of Adding Like Square Roots

$$2\sqrt{7} + 3\sqrt{7} = (2 + 3)\sqrt{7} = 5\sqrt{7}$$
$$8\sqrt{x} + \sqrt{x} = 8\sqrt{x} + 1\sqrt{x} = (8 + 1)\sqrt{x} = 9\sqrt{x}$$

Note that adding like square roots is an application of the distributive property.

$$2\sqrt{7} + 3\sqrt{7} = (2 + 3)\sqrt{7}$$
$$= 5\sqrt{7}$$

Other Examples of Adding and Subtracting Like Square Roots

$$2\sqrt{5} - 8\sqrt{5} = (2 - 8)\sqrt{5} = -6\sqrt{5}$$
$$\sqrt{x} + \sqrt{x} = 1\sqrt{x} + 1\sqrt{x} = (1 + 1)\sqrt{x} = 2\sqrt{x}$$
$$9\sqrt{2} + 3\sqrt{2} - \sqrt{2} = (9 + 3 - 1)\sqrt{2} = 11\sqrt{2}$$
$$\frac{2\sqrt{3}}{5} + \frac{1\sqrt{3}}{5} = \left(\frac{2}{5} + \frac{1}{5}\right)\sqrt{3} = \frac{3}{5}\sqrt{3} \quad \text{or} \quad \frac{3\sqrt{3}}{5}$$

EXAMPLE 1 ▶ Simplify if possible.

a) $4\sqrt{5} + 3\sqrt{5} - 8$ **b)** $\sqrt{6} - 4\sqrt{6} + 10$

c) $5\sqrt{3} + 4\sqrt{y} - 2\sqrt{3} - 6\sqrt{y}$ **d)** $2\sqrt{3} + 9\sqrt{2}$

Solution

a) $4\sqrt{5} + 3\sqrt{5} - 8 = (4 + 3)\sqrt{5} - 8$ *Only $4\sqrt{5}$ and $3\sqrt{5}$ can be combined.*

$= 7\sqrt{5} - 8$ *Simplify.*

b) $\sqrt{6} - 4\sqrt{6} + 10 = (1 - 4)\sqrt{6} + 10 = -3\sqrt{6} + 10$

c) $5\sqrt{3} + 4\sqrt{y} - 2\sqrt{3} - 6\sqrt{y} = 5\sqrt{3} - 2\sqrt{3} + 4\sqrt{y} - 6\sqrt{y}$ *Place like radicals together.*

$= 3\sqrt{3} - 2\sqrt{y}$ *Simplify.*

d) Cannot be simplified since the radicands are different.

▶ **Now Try Exercise 13**

The answers in Example 1 could be written differently. For example, the answer to part **a)** could be written $-8 + 7\sqrt{5}$ because of the commutative property of addition.

EXAMPLE 2 ▶ Simplify.

a) $3\sqrt{x} - 4\sqrt{x} + 6\sqrt{x}$ **b)** $2\sqrt{a} + a + 9\sqrt{a}$

c) $x + \sqrt{x} + 7\sqrt{x} + 3$ **d)** $x\sqrt{x} + 5\sqrt{x} + x$

e) $\sqrt{xy} + 8\sqrt{xy} - \sqrt{x}$

Solution

a) $3\sqrt{x} - 4\sqrt{x} + 6\sqrt{x} = (3 - 4 + 6)\sqrt{x}$ *All three terms are like radicals.*

$= 5\sqrt{x}$

b) $2\sqrt{a} + a + 9\sqrt{a} = a + 2\sqrt{a} + 9\sqrt{a}$ *Place like radicals together.*

$= a + 11\sqrt{a}$ *Simplify.*

c) $x + \sqrt{x} + 7\sqrt{x} + 3 = x + 1\sqrt{x} + 7\sqrt{x} + 3$ *$\sqrt{x}$ means $1\sqrt{x}$.*

$= x + 8\sqrt{x} + 3$ *Add $1\sqrt{x} + 7\sqrt{x}$ to get $8\sqrt{x}$.*

d) $x\sqrt{x} + 5\sqrt{x} + x = (x + 5)\sqrt{x} + x$ *Only $x\sqrt{x}$ and $5\sqrt{x}$ can be combined.*

e) $\sqrt{xy} + 8\sqrt{xy} - \sqrt{x} = 9\sqrt{xy} - \sqrt{x}$ *Only $\sqrt{xy}$ and $8\sqrt{xy}$ can be combined.*

▶ **Now Try Exercise 19**

Unlike square roots are square roots having different radicands. It is sometimes possible to change unlike square roots into like square roots by simplifying the radicals in an expression. After simplifying, if the terms contain the same radicand they can be combined. Otherwise, they cannot. Examples 3, 4, and 5 illustrate this.

EXAMPLE 3 ▶ Simplify $\sqrt{3} + \sqrt{75}$.

Solution Since 75 has a perfect square factor, 25, we write 75 as a product of the perfect square factor and another factor.

$$\sqrt{3} + \sqrt{75} = \sqrt{3} + \sqrt{25 \cdot 3}$$

$$= \sqrt{3} + \sqrt{25} \cdot \sqrt{3} \qquad \text{\textit{Product rule}}$$

$$= \sqrt{3} + 5\sqrt{3} \qquad \text{\textit{Now the terms are like terms.}}$$

$$= 6\sqrt{3} \qquad \text{\textit{Add like square roots.}}$$

▶ **Now Try Example 25**

INSTRUCTOR EXAMPLE
Simplify $\sqrt{20} - \sqrt{45}$.
Ans.: $-\sqrt{5}$

EXAMPLE 4 ▶ Simplify $\sqrt{63} - \sqrt{28}$.

Solution   Write each radicand as a product of a perfect square factor and another factor.

$$\sqrt{63} - \sqrt{28} = \sqrt{9 \cdot 7} - \sqrt{4 \cdot 7}$$

$$= \sqrt{9} \cdot \sqrt{7} - \sqrt{4} \cdot \sqrt{7} \qquad \textit{Product rule}$$

$$= 3\sqrt{7} - 2\sqrt{7} \qquad \textit{Now the terms are like terms.}$$

$$= \sqrt{7} \qquad \textit{Subtract like square roots.}$$

▶ **Now Try Exercise 27**

EXAMPLE 5 ▶ Simplify.

a) $2\sqrt{8} - \sqrt{32}$ **b)** $3\sqrt{12} + 5\sqrt{27} + 6$ **c)** $\sqrt{120} - \sqrt{125}$

INSTRUCTOR EXAMPLE
Simplify.
 a) $4\sqrt{3} - \sqrt{48}$
 b) $2\sqrt{8} + 5\sqrt{18} + 7$
Ans.:
 a) 0
 b) $19\sqrt{2} + 7$

Solution   In each part we begin by writing each square root as a product of its largest perfect square factor and another factor. Then we simplify the perfect square factor.

a) $2\sqrt{8} - \sqrt{32} = 2\sqrt{4 \cdot 2} - \sqrt{16 \cdot 2}$

$$= 2\sqrt{4}\,\sqrt{2} - \sqrt{16}\,\sqrt{2} \qquad \textit{Product rule}$$

$$= 2 \cdot 2\sqrt{2} - 4\sqrt{2} \qquad \textit{Simplify perfect square factors.}$$

$$= 4\sqrt{2} - 4\sqrt{2} \qquad \textit{Simplify.}$$

$$= 0$$

b) $3\sqrt{12} + 5\sqrt{27} + 6 = 3\sqrt{4 \cdot 3} + 5\sqrt{9 \cdot 3} + 6$

$$= 3\sqrt{4}\,\sqrt{3} + 5\sqrt{9}\,\sqrt{3} + 6 \qquad \textit{Product rule}$$

$$= 3 \cdot 2\sqrt{3} + 5 \cdot 3\sqrt{3} + 6 \qquad \textit{Simplify perfect square factors.}$$

$$= 6\sqrt{3} + 15\sqrt{3} + 6 \qquad \textit{Simplify.}$$

$$= 21\sqrt{3} + 6$$

c) $\sqrt{120} - \sqrt{125} = \sqrt{4 \cdot 30} - \sqrt{25 \cdot 5}$

$$= \sqrt{4}\,\sqrt{30} - \sqrt{25}\,\sqrt{5} \qquad \textit{Product rule}$$

$$= 2\sqrt{30} - 5\sqrt{5} \qquad \textit{Simplify perfect square factors.}$$

Since 30 has no perfect square factors and since the radicands are different, the expression $2\sqrt{30} - 5\sqrt{5}$ cannot be simplified any further.

▶ **Now Try Exercise 33**

Avoiding Common Errors

The product rule presented in Section 9.2 was $\sqrt{a} \cdot \sqrt{b} = \sqrt{a \cdot b}$. The same principle **does not apply to** addition.

INCORRECT

$$\sqrt{a} + \sqrt{b} = \sqrt{a + b}$$

For example, to evaluate $\sqrt{9} + \sqrt{16}$,

<table>
<tr><td style="color:green;">CORRECT</td><td style="color:red;">INCORRECT</td></tr>
<tr><td>

$\sqrt{9} + \sqrt{16} = 3 + 4$

$= 7$

</td><td>

$\sqrt{9} + \sqrt{16} = \sqrt{9 + 16}$

$= \sqrt{25}$

$= 5$

</td></tr>
</table>

2 Multiply Square Roots

Now let's discuss multiplying square roots. We introduced the product rule for radicals earlier. Now we will expand on multiplying radical expressions.

The distributive property can be used to multiply radical expressions. When the distributive property is used, each term within the parentheses is multiplied by the term preceding the parentheses. Some examples follow.

$$\sqrt{6}\left(\sqrt{6}+3\right)=\left(\sqrt{6}\right)\left(\sqrt{6}\right)+\left(\sqrt{6}\right)(3)=6+3\sqrt{6}$$
$$\sqrt{5}\left(\sqrt{x}+y\right)=\left(\sqrt{5}\right)\left(\sqrt{x}\right)+\left(\sqrt{5}\right)(y)=\sqrt{5x}+y\sqrt{5}$$

Now let's work an example.

EXAMPLE 6 ▸ Multiply. **a)** $\sqrt{3}\left(\sqrt{6}-8\right)$ **b)** $\sqrt{2x}\left(\sqrt{x}+\sqrt{2y}\right)$

Solution

a) Use the distributive property. This gives

$$\sqrt{3}\left(\sqrt{6}-8\right)=\left(\sqrt{3}\right)\left(\sqrt{6}\right)-\left(\sqrt{3}\right)(8)$$
$$=\sqrt{18}-8\sqrt{3} \qquad \text{Product rule}$$
$$=\sqrt{9\cdot2}-8\sqrt{3}$$
$$=\sqrt{9}\cdot\sqrt{2}-8\sqrt{3} \qquad \text{Product rule}$$
$$=3\sqrt{2}-8\sqrt{3}$$

b)
$$\sqrt{2x}\left(\sqrt{x}+\sqrt{2y}\right)=\left(\sqrt{2x}\right)\left(\sqrt{x}\right)+\left(\sqrt{2x}\right)\left(\sqrt{2y}\right)$$
$$=\sqrt{2x^2}+\sqrt{4xy} \qquad \text{Product rule}$$
$$=\sqrt{x^2}\cdot\sqrt{2}+\sqrt{4}\cdot\sqrt{xy} \qquad \text{Product rule}$$
$$=x\sqrt{2}+2\sqrt{xy}$$

▸ **Now Try Exercise 41**

INSTRUCTOR EXAMPLE
Multiply.
$$\sqrt{3x}\left(\sqrt{x}+\sqrt{5y}\right)$$
Ans.: $x\sqrt{3}+\sqrt{15xy}$

To multiply two binomials with square root terms, each term in the first binomial must be multiplied by each term in the second binomial. This can be accomplished using the FOIL method.

EXAMPLE 7 ▸ Multiply $\left(3+\sqrt{5}\right)\left(4-2\sqrt{5}\right)$ using the FOIL method.

Solution

INSTRUCTOR EXAMPLE
Multiply.
$$\left(4+\sqrt{2}\right)\left(3-5\sqrt{2}\right)$$
Ans.: $2-17\sqrt{2}$

$$\left(3+\sqrt{5}\right)\left(4-2\sqrt{5}\right)=3(4)+3(-2\sqrt{5})+4\sqrt{5}+\sqrt{5}(-2\sqrt{5})$$
$$=12-6\sqrt{5}+4\sqrt{5}-2\sqrt{25}$$
$$=12-2\sqrt{5}-2(5)$$
$$=12-2\sqrt{5}-10$$
$$=2-2\sqrt{5}$$

▸ **Now Try Exercise 55**

EXAMPLE 8 ▶ Multiply using the FOIL method.

a) $\left(\sqrt{2} - \sqrt{7}\right)\left(\sqrt{2} + \sqrt{7}\right)$

b) $\left(x - \sqrt{y}\right)\left(x + \sqrt{y}\right)$

Solution

a)

$$\left(\sqrt{2} - \sqrt{7}\right)\left(\sqrt{2} + \sqrt{7}\right) = (\sqrt{2})(\sqrt{2}) + (\sqrt{2})(\sqrt{7}) + (-\sqrt{7})(\sqrt{2}) + (-\sqrt{7})(\sqrt{7})$$

$$= \sqrt{4} + \sqrt{14} - \sqrt{14} - \sqrt{49}$$

$$= (\sqrt{4} - \sqrt{49}$$

$$= 2 - 7 = -5$$

b) $(x - \sqrt{y})(x + \sqrt{y}) = (x)(x) + x(\sqrt{y}) + (-\sqrt{y})(x) + (-\sqrt{y})(\sqrt{y})$

$$= x^2 + x\sqrt{y} - x\sqrt{y} - \sqrt{y^2}$$

$$= x^2 - \sqrt{y^2}$$

$$= x^2 - y$$

▶ **Now Try Exercise 73**

Notice that both parts in Example 8 may be considered as the product of the sum and difference of the same two terms. In Section 6.5 we learned that $(a + b)(a - b) = a^2 - b^2$. In part **a)** if we let $a = \sqrt{2}$ and $b = \sqrt{7}$, then

$$a^2 - b^2 = \left(\sqrt{2}\right)^2 - \left(\sqrt{7}\right)^2 = 2 - 7 = -5$$

In part **b)** if we let $a = x$ and $b = \sqrt{y}$, then

$$a^2 - b^2 = (x)^2 - \left(\sqrt{y}\right)^2 = x^2 - y$$

Both answers agree with the answers obtained in Example 8.

---

1. square roots having the same radicand; one example is $\sqrt{3}, 5\sqrt{3}$ **2.** square roots having a different radicand; one example is $\sqrt{2}, \sqrt{5}$.

EXERCISE SET 9.3

Math XL · MathXL®   *MyMathLab* · MyMathLab

Concept/Writing Exercises

1. What are like square roots? Give an example.

2. What are unlike square roots? Give an example.

3. Under what conditions can two square roots be added or subtracted?   Only like square roots can be added or subtracted.

4. Explain how to add like square roots.   Answers will vary.

Practice the Skills

Simplify each expression.

5. $7\sqrt{5} - 4\sqrt{5}$ $3\sqrt{5}$

6. $9\sqrt{3} + \sqrt{3}$ $10\sqrt{3}$

7. $9\sqrt{5} - 11\sqrt{5}$ $-2\sqrt{5}$

8. $3\sqrt{7} - 4\sqrt{7} - \sqrt{7} + 6$ $-2\sqrt{7} + 6$

9. $\sqrt{7} + 4\sqrt{7} - 3\sqrt{7} + 8$ $2\sqrt{7} + 8$

10. $10\sqrt{13} - 6\sqrt{13} + 15\sqrt{13}$ $19\sqrt{13}$

11. $6\sqrt{x} + \sqrt{x}$ $7\sqrt{x}$

12. $14\sqrt{x} - 8\sqrt{x}$ $6\sqrt{x}$

13. $-\sqrt{y} + 3\sqrt{y} - 6\sqrt{y}$ $-4\sqrt{y}$

14. $3\sqrt{y} - 6\sqrt{y} + 12$ $-3\sqrt{y} + 12$

15. $-6\sqrt{t} + 2\sqrt{t} - 11$ $-4\sqrt{t} - 11$

16. $3\sqrt{5} - \sqrt{x} + 4\sqrt{5} + 3\sqrt{x}$

17. $\sqrt{x} + \sqrt{y} + x + 7\sqrt{y}$

18. $9 + 4\sqrt{x} - 6\sqrt{x}$ $9 - 2\sqrt{x}$

19. $11 + 4\sqrt{m} - 6\sqrt{m} + 5m - 2$

20. $2\sqrt{p} - 3p - 5\sqrt{p} + 8\sqrt{p}$

21. $-3\sqrt{7} + \sqrt{7} - 2\sqrt{x} - 7\sqrt{x}$

22. $4\sqrt{5} - 2\sqrt{5} + 3\sqrt{y} - 9\sqrt{y}$

(answers for 16–22) **16.** $7\sqrt{5} + 2\sqrt{x}$ **17.** $\sqrt{x} + 8\sqrt{y} + x$ **19.** $5m - 2\sqrt{m} + 9$ **20.** $-3p + 5\sqrt{p}$ **21.** $-2\sqrt{7} - 9\sqrt{x}$ **22.** $2\sqrt{5} - 6\sqrt{y}$

Simplify each expression.

23. $\sqrt{40} + \sqrt{18}$ $2\sqrt{10} + 3\sqrt{2}$

24. $\sqrt{8} - \sqrt{27}$ $2\sqrt{2} - 3\sqrt{3}$

25. $\sqrt{300} - \sqrt{12}$ $8\sqrt{3}$

26. $\sqrt{125} + \sqrt{20}$ $7\sqrt{5}$

27. $\sqrt{75} + \sqrt{108}$ $11\sqrt{3}$

28. $\sqrt{15} - \sqrt{135}$ $-2\sqrt{15}$

29. $4\sqrt{50} - \sqrt{72} + \sqrt{8}$ $16\sqrt{2}$ **30.** $-4\sqrt{99} + 3\sqrt{44} + 5\sqrt{11}$ $-\sqrt{11}$ **31.** $-3\sqrt{125} + 8\sqrt{75}$ $-15\sqrt{5} + 40\sqrt{3}$

32. $7\sqrt{40} - 2\sqrt{50}$ $14\sqrt{10} - 10\sqrt{2}$ **33.** $2\sqrt{360} + 4\sqrt{160}$ $28\sqrt{10}$ **34.** $6\sqrt{180} - 2\sqrt{108}$ $36\sqrt{5} - 12\sqrt{3}$

35. $7\sqrt{16} - \sqrt{48}$ $28 - 4\sqrt{3}$ **36.** $3\sqrt{250} + 5\sqrt{160}$ $35\sqrt{10}$

Multiply. **39.** $3\sqrt{x} - 3\sqrt{2}$ **43.** $2\sqrt{10} - 3\sqrt{5}$ **47.** $9\sqrt{a} - a\sqrt{2}$ **48.** $5\sqrt{d} + d\sqrt{2}$ **51.** $12x^2 - 9x\sqrt{x}$

37. $\sqrt{3}(2 + \sqrt{3})$ $2\sqrt{3} + 3$ **38.** $\sqrt{2}(7 + \sqrt{2})$ $7\sqrt{2} + 2$ **39.** $3(\sqrt{x} - \sqrt{2})$ **40.** $8(\sqrt{5} - \sqrt{x})$ $8\sqrt{5} - 8\sqrt{x}$

41. $y(\sqrt{y} + y)$ $y\sqrt{y} + y^2$ **42.** $z(z^2 - \sqrt{z})$ $z^3 - z\sqrt{z}$ **43.** $\sqrt{5}(\sqrt{8} - 3)$ **44.** $\sqrt{6}(9 + \sqrt{8})$ $9\sqrt{6} + 4\sqrt{3}$

45. $\sqrt{x}(\sqrt{x} + \sqrt{3})$ $x + \sqrt{3x}$ **46.** $\sqrt{y}(\sqrt{y} - \sqrt{2})$ $y - \sqrt{2y}$ **47.** $\sqrt{a}(9 - \sqrt{2a})$ **48.** $\sqrt{d}(5 + \sqrt{2d})$

49. $x(x + 8\sqrt{y})$ $x^2 + 8x\sqrt{y}$ **50.** $x(10x - 3\sqrt{y})$ $10x^2 - 3x\sqrt{y}$ **51.** $3x(4x - 3\sqrt{x})$ **52.** $6y(y + \sqrt{y})$ $6y^2 + 6y\sqrt{y}$

Multiply.

53. $(6 + \sqrt{3})(1 - \sqrt{2})$ $6 - 6\sqrt{2} + \sqrt{3} - \sqrt{6}$ **54.** $(7 + \sqrt{5})(6 - \sqrt{2})$ $42 - 7\sqrt{2} + 6\sqrt{5} - \sqrt{10}$

55. $(\sqrt{5} - 4)(\sqrt{6} + 3)$ $\sqrt{30} + 3\sqrt{5} - 4\sqrt{6} - 12$ **56.** $(\sqrt{10} + 5)(\sqrt{10} - 2)$ $3\sqrt{10}$

57. $(6 - 2\sqrt{7})(8 - 2\sqrt{7})$ $76 - 28\sqrt{7}$ **58.** $(8 + 3\sqrt{6})(8 + 3\sqrt{6})$ $118 + 48\sqrt{6}$

59. $(4 - \sqrt{x})(4 - \sqrt{x})$ $16 - 8\sqrt{x} + x$ **60.** $(5 - 3\sqrt{y})(2 + \sqrt{y})$ $10 - \sqrt{y} - 3y$

61. $(\sqrt{3z} - 4)(\sqrt{5z} + 1)$ $z\sqrt{15} + \sqrt{3z} - 4\sqrt{5z} - 4$ **62.** $(x - \sqrt{z})(2x - 3\sqrt{z})$ $2x^2 - 5x\sqrt{z} + 3z$

63. $(r + 6\sqrt{s})(2r - 3\sqrt{s})$ $2r^2 + 9r\sqrt{s} - 18s$ **64.** $(\sqrt{5} - 3\sqrt{z})(\sqrt{10} - 5\sqrt{z})$ $5\sqrt{2} - 5\sqrt{5z} - 3\sqrt{10z} + 15z$

65. $(x - \sqrt{2y})(2x - 2\sqrt{2y})$ $2x^2 - 4x\sqrt{2y} + 4y$ **66.** $(n - 6\sqrt{w})(2n + 5\sqrt{w})$ $2n^2 - 7n\sqrt{w} - 30w$

67. $(4p - 2\sqrt{3q})(p + 2\sqrt{3q})$ $4p^2 + 6p\sqrt{3q} - 12q$ **68.** $(8n - \sqrt{7x})(2n - 5\sqrt{7x})$ $16n^2 - 42n\sqrt{7x} + 35x$

Multiply.

69. $(1 + \sqrt{3})(1 - \sqrt{3})$ -2 **70.** $(\sqrt{3} + 7)(\sqrt{3} - 7)$ -46

71. $(5 - \sqrt{2})(5 + \sqrt{2})$ 23 **72.** $(\sqrt{10} - 4)(\sqrt{10} + 4)$ -6

73. $(\sqrt{x} + 2)(\sqrt{x} - 2)$ $x - 4$ **74.** $(\sqrt{a} + 8)(\sqrt{a} - 8)$ $a - 64$

75. $(\sqrt{7} + m)(\sqrt{7} - m)$ $7 - m^2$ **76.** $(\sqrt{5} - y)(\sqrt{5} + y)$ $5 - y^2$

77. $(\sqrt{5x} + \sqrt{y})(\sqrt{5x} - \sqrt{y})$ $5x - y$ **78.** $(\sqrt{x} + \sqrt{y})(\sqrt{x} - \sqrt{y})$ $x - y$

79. $(6\sqrt{x} + 3\sqrt{y})(6\sqrt{x} - 3\sqrt{y})$ $36x - 9y$ **80.** $(4\sqrt{2c} + \sqrt{3d})(4\sqrt{2c} - \sqrt{3d})$ $32c - 3d$

81. a) Is $\sqrt{10}$ twice as large as $\sqrt{5}$? no

    b) What number is twice as large as $\sqrt{5}$? Explain how you determined your answer. $2\sqrt{5}$

82. a) Is $\sqrt{21}$ three times as large as $\sqrt{7}$? no

    b) What number is three times as large as $\sqrt{7}$? Explain how you determined your answer. $3\sqrt{7}$

Problem Solving

83. If $x > -3$, what is $\sqrt{x + 3} \cdot \sqrt{x + 3}$ equal to? $x + 3$

84. If $x > -6$, what is $\sqrt{x + 6} \cdot \sqrt{x + 6}$ equal to? $x + 6$

85. Is the sum or difference of two rational expressions always a rational expression? Explain and give an example. yes

86. Is the sum or difference of two irrational expressions always an irrational expression? Explain and give an example. no; for example, $\sqrt{3} - \sqrt{3} = 0$

Fill in the shaded area to make each statement true. Explain how you determined your answer.

87. $\sqrt{\blacksquare} - \sqrt{63} = 4\sqrt{7}$ 343

88. $\sqrt{180} + \sqrt{\blacksquare} = 9\sqrt{5}$ 45

Find the perimeter and area of the following figures.

89.

perimeter, $4(\sqrt{2} + \sqrt{3})$ units; area, $5 + 2\sqrt{6}$ square units

$\sqrt{2} + \sqrt{3}$

$\sqrt{2} + \sqrt{3}$

90.

perimeter, $4\sqrt{5}$ units; area, 4 square units

$\sqrt{5} - 1$

$\sqrt{5} + 1$

91.

$\sqrt{22}$

$\sqrt{7}$

$\sqrt{15}$

perimeter, $\sqrt{7} + \sqrt{15} + \sqrt{22}$ units; area, $\frac{1}{2}\sqrt{105}$ square units

92.

$\sqrt{2}$

1

1

perimeter, $2 + \sqrt{2}$ units; area, $\frac{1}{2}$ square unit

*In Section 7.6, we solved quadratic equations of the form $ax^2 + bx + c = 0$, by factoring. Not all quadratic equations can be solved by factoring. In Chapter 10, we will be introducing another way to solve quadratic equations, called the **quadratic formula**. The quadratic formula contains the expression $\sqrt{b^2 - 4ac}$. Evaluate this expression for the following quadratic equations. Note, for example, in the quadratic equation $2x^2 - 4x - 5 = 0$ that $a = 2$, $b = -4$, and $c = -5$.*

93. $x^2 + 3x + 2 = 0$ 1

94. $x^2 + 7x + 12 = 0$ 1

95. $x^2 - 14x - 5 = 0$ $\sqrt{216} = 6\sqrt{6}$

96. $x^2 + 4x - 3 = 0$ $\sqrt{28} = 2\sqrt{7}$

97. $-2x^2 + 4x + 7 = 0$ $\sqrt{72} = 6\sqrt{2}$

98. $-3x^2 + 6x + 2 = 0$ $\sqrt{60} = 2\sqrt{15}$

Challenge Problems

In Exercises 99 and 100, fill in the shaded area to make each statement true. Explain how you determined your answer.

99. $-5\sqrt{\blacksquare} + \sqrt{3} + 3\sqrt{27} = -10\sqrt{3}$ 48

100. $20\sqrt{2} - 4\sqrt{\blacksquare} + 5\sqrt{18} = 15\sqrt{2}$ 50

Cumulative Review Exercises

[3.4] **101. Sleigh Ride** Riding a sled down a hill, Jason averages 10 miles per hour. Walking up the same hill to where he started, he averages 2 miles per hour. If it took Jason 0.2 hours longer to come up the hill than to go down the hill, how long was Jason's sled ride?
0.05 hour or 3 min

[7.4] **102.** Factor $3x^2 - 12x - 96$. $3(x + 4)(x - 8)$

[8.1] **103.** Simplify $\dfrac{x^2 - 1}{x^3 - 1} \cdot \dfrac{x + 1}{x^2 + x + 1}$

[8.6] **104.** Solve the equation $x - \dfrac{24}{x} = 2$. $6, -4$

[5.1] **105.** Solve the system of equations graphically.
$$y = 2x - 2$$
$$2x + 3y = 10 \quad (2, 2)$$

9.4 Dividing Square Roots

1 Understand what it means for a square root to be simplified.

2 Use the quotient rule to simplify square roots.

3 Rationalize denominators.

4 Rationalize a denominator that contains a binomial.

1 Understand What It Means for a Square Root to Be Simplified

In this section we will use a new rule, the quotient rule, to simplify square roots containing fractions. Before we do that, let's discuss what it means for a square root to be simplified.

A Square Root Is Simplified When

1. No radicand has a factor that is a perfect square.

2. No radicand contains a fraction.

3. No denominator contains a square root.

All three criteria must be met for an expression to be simplified. Let's look at some radical expressions that *are not simplified*.

Radical	Reason Not Simplified	
$\sqrt{8}$	Contains perfect square factor, 4. $\left(\sqrt{8} = \sqrt{4} \cdot \sqrt{2} = 2\sqrt{2}\right)$	(Criteria 1)
$\sqrt{x^3}$	Contains perfect square factor, x^2. $\left(\sqrt{x^3} = \sqrt{x^2} \cdot \sqrt{x} = x\sqrt{x}\right)$	
$\sqrt{\dfrac{1}{3}}$	Radicand contains a fraction.	(Criteria 2)
$\dfrac{1}{\sqrt{5}}$	Square root in the denominator.	(Criteria 3)

Before we discuss the procedure to divide and simplify square roots containing fractions, we need to understand when common factors can and cannot be divided out.

Common factors in the numerator and denominator of a fraction within a radical sign *can* be divided out. For example, the following are correct.

$$\sqrt{\frac{\overset{2}{\cancel{6}}}{\underset{1}{\cancel{3}}}} = \sqrt{\frac{2}{1}} = \sqrt{2} \quad \text{and} \quad \sqrt{\frac{\overset{x}{\cancel{x^3}}}{\underset{1}{\cancel{x^2}}}} = \sqrt{\frac{x}{1}} = \sqrt{x}$$

However, we cannot divide out common factors directly if one expression containing the common factor is within a radical sign and the other expression is not. See the following common error.

Avoiding Common Errors

An expression under a square root *cannot* be divided by an expression not under a square root.

CORRECT	INCORRECT
$\dfrac{\sqrt{6}}{3}$ cannot be simplified any further.	$\dfrac{\sqrt{\cancel{6}}}{\cancel{3}} = \sqrt{2}$
$\dfrac{\sqrt{x^3}}{x} = \dfrac{\sqrt{x^2}\sqrt{x}}{x} = \dfrac{\cancel{x}\sqrt{x}}{\cancel{x}} = \sqrt{x}$	$\dfrac{\sqrt{\cancel{x^3}}}{\cancel{x}} = \sqrt{x^2} = x$

Each of the following simplifications is correct because the constant or variable divided out are not under square roots.

CORRECT	CORRECT
$\dfrac{\overset{2}{\cancel{6}}\sqrt{2}}{\underset{1}{\cancel{3}}} = 2\sqrt{2}$	$\dfrac{\cancel{x}\sqrt{2}}{\cancel{x}} = \sqrt{2}$
$\dfrac{\overset{1}{\cancel{4}}\sqrt{3}}{\underset{2}{\cancel{8}}} = \dfrac{\sqrt{3}}{2}$	$\dfrac{3\overset{x}{\cancel{x^2}}\sqrt{5}}{\cancel{x}} = 3x\sqrt{5}$

Now we will discuss the quotient rule.

2 Use the Quotient Rule to Simplify Square Roots

The quotient rule for square roots states that the quotient of two square roots is equal to the square root of the quotient.

Quotient Rule for Square Roots

$$\frac{\sqrt{a}}{\sqrt{b}} = \sqrt{\frac{a}{b}}, \quad \text{provided} \quad a \geq 0, b > 0 \qquad \text{Rule 3}$$

Examples 1 through 4 illustrate how the quotient rule is used to simplify square roots.

EXAMPLE 1 ▶ Simplify. **a)** $\sqrt{\dfrac{30}{5}}$ **b)** $\sqrt{\dfrac{64}{4}}$ **c)** $\sqrt{\dfrac{4}{49}}$

Solution When the square root contains a fraction, divide out any factor common to both the numerator and denominator. If the square root still contains a fraction, use the quotient rule to simplify.

a) $\sqrt{\dfrac{30}{5}} = \sqrt{6}$ **b)** $\sqrt{\dfrac{64}{4}} = \sqrt{16} = 4$ **c)** $\sqrt{\dfrac{4}{49}} = \dfrac{\sqrt{4}}{\sqrt{49}} = \dfrac{2}{7}$

▶ **Now Try Exercise 13**

TEACHING TIP
Before discussing the quotient rule for square roots, have students compare $\dfrac{\sqrt{64}}{\sqrt{16}}$ and $\sqrt{\dfrac{64}{16}}$. Then have them work in pairs to investigate the following question "Does $\dfrac{\sqrt{a}}{\sqrt{b}} = \sqrt{\dfrac{a}{b}}$? Explain."

TEACHING TIP
Have students describe the quotient rule for square roots in words.

INSTRUCTOR EXAMPLE
Simplify.

a) $\sqrt{\dfrac{40}{8}}$ **b)** $\sqrt{\dfrac{25}{81}}$

Ans.:

a) $\sqrt{5}$ **b)** $\dfrac{5}{9}$

EXAMPLE 2 ▸ Simplify. **a)** $\sqrt{\dfrac{10x^2}{5}}$ **b)** $\sqrt{\dfrac{80a^2b}{2b}}$ **c)** $\sqrt{\dfrac{3x^2y^4}{48x^4}}$ **d)** $\sqrt{\dfrac{35ab^5c^2}{7a^5bc}}$

Solution First divide out any factors common to both the numerator and denominator; then simplify.

a) $\sqrt{\dfrac{10x^2}{5}} = \sqrt{2x^2}$ *Simplify the radicand.*

$= \sqrt{x^2}\,\sqrt{2}$ *Product rule*

$= x\sqrt{2}$ *Simplify.*

b) $\sqrt{\dfrac{80a^2b}{2b}} = \sqrt{40a^2}$ *Simplify the radical.*

$= \sqrt{4a^2}\,\sqrt{10}$ *Product rule*

$= 2a\sqrt{10}$ *Simplify.*

c) $\sqrt{\dfrac{3x^2y^4}{48x^4}} = \sqrt{\dfrac{y^4}{16x^2}}$ *Simplify the radicand.*

$= \dfrac{\sqrt{y^4}}{\sqrt{16x^2}}$ *Quotient rule*

$= \dfrac{y^2}{4x}$ *Simplify.*

d) $\sqrt{\dfrac{35ab^5c^2}{7a^5bc}} = \sqrt{\dfrac{5b^4c}{a^4}} = \dfrac{\sqrt{5b^4c}}{\sqrt{a^4}} = \dfrac{\sqrt{b^4}\,\sqrt{5c}}{\sqrt{a^4}} = \dfrac{b^2\sqrt{5c}}{a^2}$

▸ **Now Try Exercise 27**

When you are given a fraction containing a radical expression in both the numerator and the denominator, use the quotient rule to simplify, as in Examples 3 and 4.

EXAMPLE 3 ▸ Simplify. **a)** $\dfrac{\sqrt{2}}{\sqrt{8}}$ **b)** $\dfrac{\sqrt{147}}{\sqrt{3}}$

Solution

a) $\dfrac{\sqrt{2}}{\sqrt{8}} = \sqrt{\dfrac{2}{8}}$ *Quotient rule*

$= \sqrt{\dfrac{1}{4}}$ *Simplify the radicand.*

$= \dfrac{\sqrt{1}}{\sqrt{4}}$ *Quotient rule*

$= \dfrac{1}{2}$ *Simplify.*

b) $\dfrac{\sqrt{147}}{\sqrt{3}} = \sqrt{\dfrac{147}{3}} = \sqrt{49} = 7$

▸ **Now Try Exercise 15**

Now we will work another example.

EXAMPLE 4 ▶ Simplify. **a)** $\dfrac{\sqrt{32x^4y^3}}{\sqrt{8xy}}$ **b)** $\dfrac{\sqrt{125x^8y^4}}{\sqrt{5x^5y^8}}$

Solution

a) $\dfrac{\sqrt{32x^4y^3}}{\sqrt{8xy}} = \sqrt{\dfrac{32x^4y^3}{8xy}}$ *Quotient rule*

$= \sqrt{4x^3y^2}$ *Simplify radical.*

$= \sqrt{4x^2y^2}\sqrt{x}$ *Product rule*

$= 2xy\sqrt{x}$ *Simplify.*

b) $\dfrac{\sqrt{125x^8y^4}}{\sqrt{5x^5y^8}} = \sqrt{\dfrac{125x^8y^4}{5x^5y^8}} = \sqrt{\dfrac{25x^3}{y^4}} = \dfrac{\sqrt{25x^3}}{\sqrt{y^4}} = \dfrac{\sqrt{25x^2}\sqrt{x}}{\sqrt{y^4}} = \dfrac{5x\sqrt{x}}{y^2}$

▶ **Now Try Exercise 31**

If you observe all the answers in Examples 1 through 4 you will notice they all meet the three criteria needed for a square root to be simplified.

3 Rationalize Denominators

Suppose we are asked to simplify expressions like $\dfrac{1}{\sqrt{2}}$ or $\sqrt{\dfrac{1}{2}}$. How do we simplify them? To simplify such expressions we use a process called **rationalizing the denominator. To rationalize a denominator means to remove all radicals from the denominator.** We rationalize the denominator because it is easier (without a calculator) to obtain the approximate value of a number like $\dfrac{\sqrt{2}}{2}$ than a number like $\dfrac{1}{\sqrt{2}}$. Also, sometimes we may need to rationalize denominators to add or subtract radical expressions. When the denominator of a fraction contains the square root of a number that is not a perfect square, we generally simplify the expression by **rationalizing the denominator.**

> **Rationalizing a Denominator**
>
> **To rationalize a denominator with a square root,** multiply *both* the numerator and the denominator of the fraction by the square root that appears in the denominator or by the square root of a number that makes the denominator a perfect square.

EXAMPLE 5 ▶ Simplify $\dfrac{1}{\sqrt{5}}$.

Solution Since $\sqrt{5} \cdot \sqrt{5} = \sqrt{25} = 5$, we multiply both the numerator and denominator by $\sqrt{5}$.

$$\dfrac{1}{\sqrt{5}} = \dfrac{1}{\sqrt{5}} \cdot \dfrac{\sqrt{5}}{\sqrt{5}} = \dfrac{\sqrt{5}}{\sqrt{25}} = \dfrac{\sqrt{5}}{5}$$

The answer $\dfrac{\sqrt{5}}{5}$ is simplified because it satisfies the three requirements stated earlier.

▶ **Now Try Exercise 39**

In Example 5, multiplying both the numerator and denominator by $\sqrt{5}$ is equivalent to multiplying the fraction by 1, which does not change its value.

INSTRUCTOR EXAMPLE

Simplify.

a) $\sqrt{\dfrac{3}{7}}$ b) $\sqrt{\dfrac{x^2}{32}}$

Ans.:

a) $\dfrac{\sqrt{21}}{7}$ b) $\dfrac{x\sqrt{2}}{8}$

EXAMPLE 6 ▶ Simplify. **a)** $\sqrt{\dfrac{2}{3}}$ **b)** $\sqrt{\dfrac{z^2}{18}}$

Solution

a) $\sqrt{\dfrac{2}{3}} = \dfrac{\sqrt{2}}{\sqrt{3}}$ *Quotient rule*

$\phantom{\sqrt{\dfrac{2}{3}}} = \dfrac{\sqrt{2}}{\sqrt{3}} \cdot \dfrac{\sqrt{3}}{\sqrt{3}}$ *Multiply numerator and denominator by $\sqrt{3}$.*

$\phantom{\sqrt{\dfrac{2}{3}}} = \dfrac{\sqrt{6}}{\sqrt{9}}$ *Product rule*

$\phantom{\sqrt{\dfrac{2}{3}}} = \dfrac{\sqrt{6}}{3}$ *Simplify.*

b) $\sqrt{\dfrac{z^2}{18}} = \dfrac{\sqrt{z^2}}{\sqrt{18}} = \dfrac{z}{\sqrt{9}\,\sqrt{2}} = \dfrac{z}{3\sqrt{2}}$

Now rationalize the denominator.

$$\dfrac{z}{3\sqrt{2}} \cdot \dfrac{\sqrt{2}}{\sqrt{2}} = \dfrac{z\sqrt{2}}{3\sqrt{4}} = \dfrac{z\sqrt{2}}{3 \cdot 2} = \dfrac{z\sqrt{2}}{6}$$

Part **b)** can also be rationalized as follows:

$$\sqrt{\dfrac{z^2}{18}} = \dfrac{\sqrt{z^2}}{\sqrt{18}} = \dfrac{z}{\sqrt{18}} \cdot \dfrac{\sqrt{2}}{\sqrt{2}} = \dfrac{z\sqrt{2}}{\sqrt{36}} = \dfrac{z\sqrt{2}}{6}$$

Note that $\dfrac{z}{\sqrt{18}} \cdot \dfrac{\sqrt{18}}{\sqrt{18}}$ will also give us the same result when simplified.

▶ **Now Try Exercise 63**

Now we will discuss rationalizing a denominator where the denominator is a binomial that contains one or more radical expressions.

4 Rationalize a Denominator That Contains a Binomial

When the denominator of a rational expression is a binomial with a square root term, we again **rationalize the denominator**. We do this by multiplying both the numerator and the denominator of the fraction by the conjugate of the denominator. The **conjugate of a binomial** is a binomial having the same two terms with the sign of the second term changed.

Binomial	Its Conjugate
$8 + \sqrt{2}$	$8 - \sqrt{2}$
$\sqrt{3} - 4$	$\sqrt{3} + 4$
$9\sqrt{3} - \sqrt{5}$	$9\sqrt{3} + \sqrt{5}$
$-x + \sqrt{3}$	$-x - \sqrt{3}$

When a binomial is multiplied by its conjugate using the FOIL method, the sum of the outer and inner terms will be zero.

Now let's try some examples where we rationalize the denominator when the denominator is a binomial with one or more radical terms.

EXAMPLE 7 ▶ Simplify $\dfrac{8}{2 + \sqrt{3}}$.

Solution To rationalize the denominator, multiply both the numerator and the denominator of the fraction by $2 - \sqrt{3}$, which is the conjugate of $2 + \sqrt{3}$.

$$\frac{8}{2 + \sqrt{3}} \cdot \frac{2 - \sqrt{3}}{2 - \sqrt{3}} = \frac{8(2 - \sqrt{3})}{(2 + \sqrt{3})(2 - \sqrt{3})} \qquad \text{Multiply numerator and denominator by } 2 - \sqrt{3}.$$

$$= \frac{8(2 - \sqrt{3})}{4 - 3} \qquad \text{Multiply factors in denominator, as discussed in Section 9.3.}$$

$$= \frac{8(2 - \sqrt{3})}{1} \qquad \text{Simplify.}$$

$$= 8(2 - \sqrt{3}) = 16 - 8\sqrt{3}$$

Note that $-8\sqrt{3} + 16$ is also an acceptable answer.

▶ **Now Try Exercise 83**

EXAMPLE 8 ▶ Simplify $\dfrac{9}{\sqrt{2} - \sqrt{5}}$.

Solution Multiply both the numerator and the denominator of the fraction by $\sqrt{2} + \sqrt{5}$, the conjugate of $\sqrt{2} - \sqrt{5}$.

$$\frac{9}{\sqrt{2} - \sqrt{5}} \cdot \frac{\sqrt{2} + \sqrt{5}}{\sqrt{2} + \sqrt{5}} = \frac{9(\sqrt{2} + \sqrt{5})}{(\sqrt{2} - \sqrt{5})(\sqrt{2} + \sqrt{5})} \qquad \text{Multiply numerator and denominator by } \sqrt{2} + \sqrt{5}.$$

$$= \frac{9(\sqrt{2} + \sqrt{5})}{2 - 5} \qquad \text{Multiply factors in denominator.}$$

$$= \frac{9(\sqrt{2} + \sqrt{5})}{-3} \qquad \text{Simplify.}$$

$$= \frac{-\overset{3}{9}(\sqrt{2} + \sqrt{5})}{\cancel{3}}$$

$$= -3(\sqrt{2} + \sqrt{5}) = -3\sqrt{2} - 3\sqrt{5}$$

▶ **Now Try Exercise 87**

EXAMPLE 9 ▶ Simplify $\dfrac{\sqrt{3}}{2 - \sqrt{6}}$.

Solution Multiply both the numerator and the denominator of the fraction by $2 + \sqrt{6}$, the conjugate of $2 - \sqrt{6}$.

$$\frac{\sqrt{3}}{2 - \sqrt{6}} \cdot \frac{2 + \sqrt{6}}{2 + \sqrt{6}} = \frac{\sqrt{3}(2 + \sqrt{6})}{4 - 6}$$

$$= \frac{2\sqrt{3} + \sqrt{3}\,\sqrt{6}}{-2} \qquad \text{Distributive property}$$

$$= \frac{2\sqrt{3} + \sqrt{18}}{-2} \qquad \text{Product rule}$$

$$= \frac{2\sqrt{3} + \sqrt{9}\,\sqrt{2}}{-2} \qquad \text{Product rule}$$

$$= \frac{2\sqrt{3} + 3\sqrt{2}}{-2} \qquad \text{Simplify.}$$

$$= \frac{-2\sqrt{3} - 3\sqrt{2}}{2} \qquad \text{Multiply numerator and denominator by } -1.$$

▶ **Now Try Exercise 85**

Simplify $\dfrac{a}{\sqrt{a}-b}$.

Ans.: $\dfrac{a\sqrt{a}+ab}{a-b^2}$

EXAMPLE 10 ▶ Simplify $\dfrac{x}{x-\sqrt{y}}$.

Solution Multiply both the numerator and the denominator of the fraction by $x+\sqrt{y}$, the conjugate of the denominator.

$$\frac{x}{x-\sqrt{y}}\cdot\frac{x+\sqrt{y}}{x+\sqrt{y}}=\frac{x\left(x+\sqrt{y}\right)}{x^2-y}=\frac{x^2+x\sqrt{y}}{x^2-y}$$

Remember, you cannot divide out the x^2 terms because they are not factors.

▶ **Now Try Exercise 93**

---

7. no perfect square factors in any radicand, no radicand contains a fraction, no square roots in any denominator   **9. a)** $\sqrt{27}$ has a perfect square factor, 9   **b)** radicand contains a fraction   **c)** square root in the denominator

---

EXERCISE SET 9.4   MathXL   MyMathLab

Concept/Writing Exercises

In Exercises 1–6, indicate if a common factor can be divided out from both the numerator and denominator of the fraction. If a common factor can be divided out, do so and show the simplified answer. See the Avoiding Common Errors box on page 557.

1. $\dfrac{\sqrt{7}}{7}$ cannot be simplified

2. $\dfrac{4\sqrt{5}}{2}$ yes, $2\sqrt{5}$

3. $\dfrac{x^2\sqrt{3}}{x}$ yes, $x\sqrt{3}$

4. $\dfrac{\sqrt{6}}{2}$ cannot be simplified

5. $\dfrac{\sqrt{x}}{x}$ cannot be simplified

6. $\dfrac{\sqrt{15}}{5}$ cannot be simplified

7. What are the three requirements for a square root to be considered simplified?

8. State the quotient rule for square roots and explain what it means.   Answers will vary.

9. Explain why each expression is not simplified.

   a) $\sqrt{27}$ **b)** $\sqrt{\dfrac{1}{3}}$ **c)** $\dfrac{8}{\sqrt{5}}$

10. What does it mean to rationalize a denominator?   remove all radicals from the denominator

Practice the Skills

Simplify each expression.

11. $\sqrt{\dfrac{27}{3}}$ 3

12. $\sqrt{\dfrac{24}{6}}$ 2

13. $\sqrt{\dfrac{63}{7}}$ 3

14. $\sqrt{\dfrac{20}{5}}$ 2

15. $\dfrac{\sqrt{18}}{\sqrt{2}}$ 3

16. $\dfrac{\sqrt{28}}{\sqrt{7}}$ 2

17. $\dfrac{\sqrt{3}}{\sqrt{12}}$ $\dfrac{1}{2}$

18. $\dfrac{\sqrt{72}}{\sqrt{2}}$ 6

19. $\sqrt{\dfrac{81}{100}}$ $\dfrac{9}{10}$

20. $\sqrt{\dfrac{9}{121}}$ $\dfrac{3}{11}$

21. $\dfrac{\sqrt{20}}{\sqrt{2000}}$ $\dfrac{1}{10}$

22. $\sqrt{\dfrac{20}{80}}$ $\dfrac{1}{2}$

23. $\sqrt{\dfrac{48x^3}{2x}}$ $2x\sqrt{6}$

24. $\sqrt{\dfrac{9ab^4}{3b^3}}$ $\sqrt{3ab}$

25. $\sqrt{\dfrac{45x^2}{16x^2y^4}}$ $\dfrac{3\sqrt{5}}{4y^2}$

26. $\sqrt{\dfrac{60a^3b^6}{10a^3b^8}}$ $\dfrac{\sqrt{6}}{b}$

27. $\sqrt{\dfrac{16x^5y^3}{81x^7y}}$ $\dfrac{4y}{9x}$

28. $\sqrt{\dfrac{13xyz^5}{52x^3y^3z^4}}$ $\dfrac{\sqrt{z}}{2xy}$

29. $\sqrt{\dfrac{14ab}{14a^5b^3}}$ $\dfrac{1}{a^2b}$

30. $\sqrt{\dfrac{48x^3y}{48x^7y^3}}$ $\dfrac{1}{x^2y}$

31. $\dfrac{\sqrt{32n^5}}{\sqrt{8n}}$ $2n^2$

32. $\dfrac{\sqrt{44x^2y^2}}{\sqrt{11x^2y^4}}$ $\dfrac{2}{y}$

33. $\dfrac{\sqrt{81w^5z}}{\sqrt{144wz^3}}$ $\dfrac{3w^2}{4z}$

34. $\dfrac{\sqrt{66}}{\sqrt{22m^4n^6}}$ $\dfrac{\sqrt{3}}{m^2n^3}$

35. $\dfrac{\sqrt{50ab^6}}{\sqrt{10ab^4c^2}}$ $\dfrac{b\sqrt{5}}{c}$

36. $\dfrac{\sqrt{21x^2y^6}}{\sqrt{7x^4z^4}}$ $\dfrac{y^3\sqrt{3}}{xz^2}$

37. $\dfrac{\sqrt{125a^6b^8}}{\sqrt{5a^2b^2}}$ $5a^2b^3$

38. $\dfrac{\sqrt{144x^{60}y^{32}}}{\sqrt{12x^{40}y^{18}}}$ $2x^{10}y^7\sqrt{3}$

Simplify each expression.

39. $\dfrac{1}{\sqrt{7}}$ $\dfrac{\sqrt{7}}{7}$

40. $\dfrac{1}{\sqrt{6}}$ $\dfrac{\sqrt{6}}{6}$

41. $\dfrac{4}{\sqrt{2}}$ $2\sqrt{2}$

42. $\dfrac{6}{\sqrt{3}}$ $2\sqrt{3}$

43. $\dfrac{6}{\sqrt{12}}$ $\sqrt{3}$

44. $\dfrac{3}{\sqrt{50}}$ $\dfrac{3\sqrt{2}}{10}$

45. $\sqrt{\dfrac{2}{5}}$ $\dfrac{\sqrt{10}}{5}$

46. $\sqrt{\dfrac{3}{5}}$ $\dfrac{\sqrt{15}}{5}$

47. $\sqrt{\dfrac{2}{7}}$ $\dfrac{\sqrt{14}}{7}$ **48.** $\sqrt{\dfrac{11}{12}}$ $\dfrac{\sqrt{33}}{6}$ **49.** $\sqrt{\dfrac{6}{18}}$ $\dfrac{\sqrt{3}}{3}$ **50.** $\sqrt{\dfrac{6}{7}}$ $\dfrac{\sqrt{42}}{7}$

51. $\sqrt{\dfrac{5}{8}}$ $\dfrac{\sqrt{10}}{4}$ **52.** $\sqrt{\dfrac{7}{18}}$ $\dfrac{\sqrt{14}}{6}$ **53.** $\sqrt{\dfrac{6}{x}}$ $\dfrac{\sqrt{6x}}{x}$ **54.** $\sqrt{\dfrac{5}{a}}$ $\dfrac{\sqrt{5a}}{a}$

55. $\dfrac{\sqrt{a}}{\sqrt{b}}$ $\dfrac{\sqrt{ab}}{b}$ **56.** $\sqrt{\dfrac{c}{d}}$ $\dfrac{\sqrt{cd}}{d}$ **57.** $\dfrac{\sqrt{m}}{\sqrt{n}}$ $\dfrac{\sqrt{mn}}{n}$ **58.** $\sqrt{\dfrac{r}{5}}$ $\dfrac{\sqrt{5r}}{5}$

59. $\sqrt{\dfrac{3x}{11}}$ $\dfrac{\sqrt{33x}}{11}$ **60.** $\sqrt{\dfrac{5w}{18}}$ $\dfrac{\sqrt{10w}}{6}$ **61.** $\sqrt{\dfrac{x^2}{7}}$ $\dfrac{x\sqrt{7}}{7}$ **62.** $\sqrt{\dfrac{x^2}{3}}$ $\dfrac{x\sqrt{3}}{3}$

63. $\sqrt{\dfrac{a^2}{18}}$ $\dfrac{a\sqrt{2}}{6}$ **64.** $\sqrt{\dfrac{a^3}{18}}$ $\dfrac{a\sqrt{2a}}{6}$ **65.** $\sqrt{\dfrac{t^5}{6}}$ $\dfrac{t^2\sqrt{6t}}{6}$ **66.** $\sqrt{\dfrac{x^3}{10}}$ $\dfrac{x\sqrt{10x}}{10}$

67. $\sqrt{\dfrac{a^8}{14b}}$ $\dfrac{a^4\sqrt{14b}}{14b}$ **68.** $\sqrt{\dfrac{a^7b}{24b^4}}$ $\dfrac{a^3\sqrt{6ab}}{12b^2}$ **69.** $\sqrt{\dfrac{6c^2d^4}{30c^2d^7}}$ $\dfrac{\sqrt{5d}}{5d^2}$ **70.** $\sqrt{\dfrac{27xz^4}{6y^5}}$ $\dfrac{3z^2\sqrt{2xy}}{2y^3}$

71. $\sqrt{\dfrac{50yz}{24x^4y^5z^9}}$ $\dfrac{5\sqrt{3}}{6x^2y^2z^4}$ **72.** $\dfrac{\sqrt{21x^5}}{\sqrt{84xy^7}}$ $\dfrac{x^2\sqrt{y}}{2y^4}$ **73.** $\dfrac{\sqrt{90x^4y}}{\sqrt{2x^5y^5}}$ $\dfrac{3\sqrt{5x}}{xy^2}$ **74.** $\dfrac{\sqrt{120xyz^2}}{\sqrt{9xy^4}}$ $\dfrac{2z\sqrt{30y}}{3y^2}$

Find the product of the given binomial and its conjugate.

75. $6 + \sqrt{3}$ 33 **76.** $\sqrt{5} - 2$ 1 **77.** $\sqrt{3} - \sqrt{11}$ −8 **78.** $\sqrt{7} + \sqrt{6}$ 1

79. $\sqrt{x} - y$ $x - y^2$ **80.** $\sqrt{x} + y$ $x - y^2$ **81.** $\sqrt{a} + \sqrt{b}$ $a - b$ **82.** $\sqrt{x} - \sqrt{y}$ $x - y$

Simplify each expression.

83. $\dfrac{3}{\sqrt{5} + 2}$ $3\sqrt{5} - 6$ **84.** $\dfrac{5}{4 - \sqrt{3}}$ $\dfrac{20 + 5\sqrt{3}}{13}$ **85.** $\dfrac{4}{\sqrt{6} - 1}$ $\dfrac{4\sqrt{6} + 4}{5}$

86. $\dfrac{3}{\sqrt{2} - 7}$ $\dfrac{-3\sqrt{2} - 21}{47}$ **87.** $\dfrac{12}{\sqrt{3} + \sqrt{5}}$ $-6\sqrt{3} + 6\sqrt{5}$ **88.** $\dfrac{7}{\sqrt{6} + \sqrt{3}}$ $\dfrac{7\sqrt{6} - 7\sqrt{3}}{3}$

89. $\dfrac{8}{\sqrt{5} - \sqrt{8}}$ $\dfrac{-8\sqrt{5} - 16\sqrt{2}}{3}$ **90.** $\dfrac{3}{\sqrt{17} - \sqrt{8}}$ $\dfrac{\sqrt{17} + 2\sqrt{2}}{3}$ **91.** $\dfrac{4}{\sqrt{y} + 3}$ $\dfrac{4\sqrt{y} - 12}{y - 9}$

92. $\dfrac{10}{6 - \sqrt{x}}$ $\dfrac{60 + 10\sqrt{x}}{36 - x}$ **93.** $\dfrac{7}{4 - \sqrt{y}}$ $\dfrac{28 + 7\sqrt{y}}{16 - y}$ **94.** $\dfrac{2}{3 + \sqrt{x}}$ $\dfrac{6 - 2\sqrt{x}}{9 - x}$

95. $\dfrac{16}{\sqrt{y} + x}$ $\dfrac{16\sqrt{y} - 16x}{y - x^2}$ **96.** $\dfrac{9}{r + \sqrt{t}}$ $\dfrac{9r - 9\sqrt{t}}{r^2 - t}$ **97.** $\dfrac{9}{\sqrt{x} + \sqrt{y}}$ $\dfrac{9\sqrt{x} - 9\sqrt{y}}{x - y}$

98. $\dfrac{\sqrt{3}}{\sqrt{x} - \sqrt{3}}$ $\dfrac{\sqrt{3x} + 3}{x - 3}$ **99.** $\dfrac{\sqrt{3}}{\sqrt{3} - \sqrt{n}}$ $\dfrac{3 + \sqrt{3n}}{3 - n}$ **100.** $\dfrac{5}{\sqrt{x} - y}$ $\dfrac{5\sqrt{x} + 5y}{x - y^2}$

101. $\dfrac{2\sqrt{x}}{6 - \sqrt{x}}$ $\dfrac{12\sqrt{x} + 2x}{36 - x}$ **102.** $\dfrac{8\sqrt{r}}{2 + \sqrt{r}}$ $\dfrac{16\sqrt{r} - 8r}{4 - r}$ **104.** no; $\dfrac{\sqrt{75}}{\sqrt{3}} = \sqrt{25} = 5$

Problem Solving

103. Will the quotient of two rational numbers (denominator not equal to 0) always be a rational number? Explain and give an example to support your answer. yes

104. Will the quotient of two irrational numbers (denominator not equal to 0) always be an irrational number? Explain and give an example to support your answer.

In Exercises 105–108, if $\sqrt{5} \approx 2.236$ and $\sqrt{10} \approx 3.162$, find to the nearest hundredth:

105. $\sqrt{5} + \sqrt{10}$ 5.40 **106.** $\sqrt{5} \cdot \sqrt{10}$ 7.07 **107.** $\dfrac{\sqrt{5}}{\sqrt{10}}$ 0.71 **108.** $\dfrac{\sqrt{10}}{\sqrt{5}}$ 1.41

In Exercises 109–112, if $\sqrt{7} \approx 2.646$ and $\sqrt{21} \approx 4.583$, find to the nearest hundredth:

109. $\sqrt{7} + \sqrt{21}$ 7.23 **110.** $\sqrt{7} \cdot \sqrt{21}$ 12.13 **111.** $\dfrac{\sqrt{7}}{\sqrt{21}}$ 0.58 **112.** $\dfrac{\sqrt{21}}{\sqrt{7}}$ 1.73

In Exercises 113 and 114, find the width of each rectangle whose area and length are given. Give the answer in simplified form with integer denominator.

113.

$A = 24$

$l = 4 + \sqrt{3}$

$\dfrac{24(4 - \sqrt{3})}{13}$

114. $A = \sqrt{70}$

$l = 7 - \sqrt{2}$

$\dfrac{7\sqrt{70} + 2\sqrt{35}}{47}$

Challenge Problems

119. $\dfrac{-\sqrt{x} - \sqrt{3x}}{2}$ **120.** $\dfrac{2\sqrt{x} - \sqrt{2x}}{2}$

Fill in the shaded area to make the expression true. Explain how you determined your answer.

115. $\dfrac{1}{\sqrt{\blacksquare}} = \dfrac{\sqrt{2}}{2}$ 2   **116.** $\dfrac{9x}{\sqrt{\blacksquare}} = \dfrac{9\sqrt{2x}}{2}$ 2x   **117.** $\sqrt{\dfrac{\blacksquare}{4x^2}} = 4x^4$ $64x^{10}$ **118.** $\dfrac{\sqrt{32x^5}}{\sqrt{\blacksquare}} = 2x^2$ 8x

119. Simplify $\dfrac{\sqrt{x}}{1 - \sqrt{3}}$ by rationalizing the denominator.

120. Simplify $\dfrac{\sqrt{x}}{2 + \sqrt{2}}$ by rationalizing the denominator.

Group Activity

121. Consider $\dfrac{\sqrt{x}}{x + \sqrt{x}}$, where $x > 0$.

   a) Individually, simplify $\dfrac{\sqrt{x}}{x + \sqrt{x}}$ by rationalizing the denominator. Compare and correct your answer if necessary.

   b) Group Member 1: Substitute $x = 4$ in the original expression and in the results found in part **a)**. Evaluate each expression.

   c) Group Member 2: Repeat part **b)** for $x = 6$.

   d) Group Member 3: Repeat part **b)** for $x = 9$. $\dfrac{1}{4}; \dfrac{1}{4}$

   e) As a group, determine what relationship exists between the given expression and the rationalized expression you obtained in part **b)**.   equal

121. a) $\dfrac{x\sqrt{x} - x}{x^2 - x} = \dfrac{\sqrt{x} - 1}{x - 1}$ **b)** both are $\dfrac{1}{3}$ **c)** $\dfrac{\sqrt{6} - 1}{5}, \dfrac{\sqrt{6} - 1}{5}$

Cumulative Review Exercises

[6.6] **122.** Divide $\dfrac{3x^2 + 4x - 26}{x + 4}$ $3x - 8 + \dfrac{6}{x + 4}$

[7.6] **123.** Solve the equation $2x^2 - x - 36 = 0$. $\dfrac{9}{2}, -4$

[8.4] **124.** Subtract $\dfrac{1}{x^2 - 4} - \dfrac{3}{x - 2}$, $\dfrac{-3x - 5}{(x + 2)(x - 2)}$

[8.7] **125.** **Stacking Wood** Mark DeGroat can stack a cord of wood in 20 minutes. With his wife's help, they can stack the wood in 12 minutes. How long would it take his wife, Terry, to stack the wood by herself?   30 min

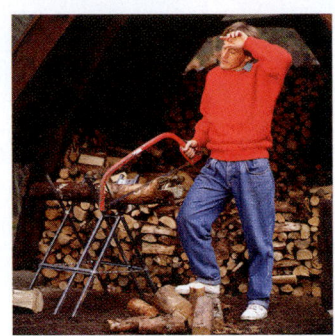

See Exercise 125.

Mid-Chapter Test: 9.1–9.4

To find out how well you understand the chapter material to this point, take this brief test. The answers, and the section where the material was initially discussed, are given in the back of the book. Review any questions that you answered incorrectly.

Evaluate each square root.   **4. a)** irrational **b)** rational **c)** imaginary **d)** rational   **11.** $12\sqrt{x} + 6\sqrt{5} + 17$

1. $\sqrt{81}$ 9   **2.** $-\sqrt{121}$ -11 **3.** $\sqrt{\dfrac{169}{49}}$ $\dfrac{13}{7}$

14. Multiply $(\sqrt{x} - 4z)(\sqrt{x} + 5z)$. $x + z\sqrt{x} - 20z^2$

15. Multiply $(\sqrt{3a} + \sqrt{2b})(\sqrt{3a} - \sqrt{2b})$. $3a - 2b$

4. Determine whether the following numbers are rational, irrational, or imaginary.

   a) $\sqrt{17}$ **b)** $\sqrt{36}$ **c)** $\sqrt{-36}$ **d)** $-\sqrt{36}$

5. Write $\sqrt{53xy^2}$ in exponential form. $(53xy^2)^{1/2}$

16. When asked to add $\sqrt{8} + \sqrt{32}$, Robert Jones decided to add the two radicands together to obtain $\sqrt{8 + 32}$ or $\sqrt{40}$. This is incorrect. Why is this incorrect? Explain your answer. Then, add $\sqrt{8} + \sqrt{32}$ correctly.   can add only like radicals, $6\sqrt{2}$

Simplify.

6. $\sqrt{40}$ $2\sqrt{10}$ **7.** $\sqrt{63}$ $3\sqrt{7}$

8. $\sqrt{a^2b^5c^8}$ $ab^2c^4\sqrt{b}$ **9.** $\sqrt{128x^9y^{14}}$ $8x^4y^7\sqrt{2x}$

Divide.

17. $\dfrac{\sqrt{17}}{\sqrt{68}}$ $\dfrac{1}{2}$ **18.** $\dfrac{\sqrt{45x^5y^6}}{\sqrt{5xy^8}}$ $\dfrac{3x^2}{y}$

10. $\sqrt{6x^2y^3}\sqrt{9x^3y^6}$ $3x^2y^4\sqrt{6xy}$

11. Add $3\sqrt{x} + 2\sqrt{5} + 9\sqrt{x} + 4\sqrt{5} + 17$.

12. Subtract $4\sqrt{75} - 2\sqrt{108}$. $8\sqrt{3}$

13. Multiply $(5 - \sqrt{2})(7 + \sqrt{3})$. $35 + 5\sqrt{3} - 7\sqrt{2} - \sqrt{6}$

Rationalize the denominator.

19. $\dfrac{7}{\sqrt{6} - 2}$ $\dfrac{7\sqrt{6} + 14}{2}$ **20.** $\dfrac{3\sqrt{x}}{\sqrt{x} + 5}$ $\dfrac{3x - 15\sqrt{x}}{x - 25}$

9.5 Solving Radical Equations

1. Solve radical equations containing only one square root term.

2. Solve radical equations containing two square root terms.

1 Solve Radical Equations Containing Only One Square Root Term

A **radical equation** is an equation that contains a variable in a radicand. Some examples of radical equations are

$$\sqrt{x} = 5 \qquad \sqrt{x + 4} = 6 \qquad \sqrt{x - 2} = x - 8$$

In this section we will assume that all radicands represent nonnegative numbers. This will allow us to write statements such as $(\sqrt{x})^2 = x$ and $(\sqrt{z - 3})^2 = z - 3$.

In the process of solving radical equations we will need to **square both sides of the equation**. An example of squaring both sides of an equation is illustrated below.

$$\sqrt{y} = 5$$
$$(\sqrt{y})^2 = 5^2 \qquad \text{\textit{Square both sides of the equation.}}$$
$$y = 25$$

Now we will give a general procedure for solving radical equations containing only one square root term.

> ### To Solve a Radical Equation Containing Only One Square Root Term
>
> 1. Use the appropriate properties to rewrite the equation with the square root term by itself on one side of the equation. We call this **isolating the square root**.
> 2. Combine like terms.
> 3. Square both sides of the equation to eliminate the square root.
> 4. Solve the equation for the variable.
> 5. Check the solution in the *original* equation for extraneous roots.

Step 3 of the procedure, squaring both sides of the equation, has the effect of removing a radical sign from the expression so that the variable can be isolated. For example, consider the following radical equation:

$$\sqrt{y - 4} = 8 \qquad \text{\textit{Given equation}}$$
$$(\sqrt{y - 4})^2 = 8^2 \qquad \text{\textit{Square both sides.}}$$
$$y - 4 = 64 \qquad \text{\textit{Square root has been removed.}}$$
$$y = 68 \qquad \text{\textit{Solve for y.}}$$

Now we will work some additional examples.

EXAMPLE 1 ▸ Solve the equation $\sqrt{x} = 7$.

Solution   The square root containing the variable is already by itself on one side of the equation. Square both sides of the equation.

$$\sqrt{x} = 7$$
$$(\sqrt{x})^2 = 7^2 \qquad \text{\textit{Square both sides.}}$$
$$x = 49$$

Check $\sqrt{x} = 7$

$$\sqrt{49} \overset{?}{=} 7$$
$$7 = 7 \qquad \text{\textit{True}}$$

▸ **Now Try Exercise 13**

EXAMPLE 2 ▶ Solve the equation $\sqrt{x - 3} = 4$.

Solution   The square root containing the variable is already by itself on one side of the equation. Square both sides of the equation.

$$\sqrt{x - 3} = 4$$
$$\left(\sqrt{x - 3}\right)^2 = 4^2 \qquad \textcolor{red}{\textit{Square both sides.}}$$
$$x - 3 = 16 \qquad \textcolor{red}{\textit{Simplify.}}$$
$$x = 19$$

Check $\sqrt{x - 3} = 4$
$$\sqrt{19 - 3} \stackrel{?}{=} 4$$
$$\sqrt{16} \stackrel{?}{=} 4$$
$$4 = 4 \quad \textit{True}$$

▶ **Now Try Exercise 17**

In the next example, the square root term containing the variable is not by itself on one side of the equation.

EXAMPLE 3 ▶ Solve the equation $\sqrt{a} + 7 = 10$.

Solution   In this equation we are solving for the variable a. Since the 7 is outside the square root sign, we first subtract 7 from both sides of the equation to isolate the square root term.

$$\sqrt{a} + 7 = 10$$
$$\sqrt{a} + 7 - 7 = 10 - 7$$
$$\sqrt{a} = 3$$

Now we square both sides of the equation.

$$(\sqrt{a})^2 = 3^2$$
$$a = 9$$

A check will show that 9 is the solution.

▶ **Now Try Exercise 21**

Helpful Hint

When you square both sides of an equation, you may introduce extraneous roots. An **extraneous root** is a number obtained when solving an equation that is not a solution to the original equation. Equations where both sides are squared in the process of finding their solutions should always be checked for extraneous roots by substituting the numbers found back in the **original** equation.

Consider the equation

$$x = 6$$

Now square both sides.

$$x^2 = 36$$

Note that the original equation $x = 6$ is true only when x is 6. However, the equation $x^2 = 36$ is true for both 6 and -6. When we squared $x = 6$, we introduced the extraneous root -6.

EXAMPLE 4 ▶ Solve the equation $\sqrt{x} = -5$.

Solution   Begin by squaring both sides of the equation

$$\sqrt{x} = -5$$
$$(\sqrt{x})^2 = (-5)^2$$
$$x = 25$$

Check $\qquad \sqrt{x} = -5$

$$\sqrt{25} \stackrel{?}{=} -5$$

$$5 = -5 \qquad \textit{False}$$

Since the check results in a false statement, the number 25 is an extraneous root and is not a solution to the given equation. Thus, the equation $\sqrt{x} = -5$ has **no real solution**.

▶ **Now Try Exercise 19**

In Example 4, you might have realized without working the problem that there is no solution to the equation. In the original, the left side cannot be a negative number and the right side is a negative number. Thus, the equation cannot have a solution.

EXAMPLE 5 ▶ Solve the equation $\sqrt{2x - 3} = x - 3$.

Solution Square both sides of the equation.

$$\left(\sqrt{2x - 3}\right)^2 = (x - 3)^2$$

$$2x - 3 = x^2 - 6x + 9 \qquad \textit{Simplify on left. Write } (x - 3)^2 \textit{ as } x^2 - 6x + 9.$$

Now solve the quadratic equation as explained in Section 7.6. Make one side of the equation equal to zero by subtracting $2x$ and adding 3 to both sides of the equation. This gives the following quadratic equation.

$$0 = x^2 - 8x + 12 \quad \text{or} \quad x^2 - 8x + 12 = 0$$

Solve for x by factoring.

$$x^2 - 8x + 12 = 0$$

$$(x - 6)(x - 2) = 0 \qquad \textit{Factor.}$$

$$x - 6 = 0 \qquad \text{or} \qquad x - 2 = 0 \qquad \textit{Zero-factor property}$$

$$x = 6 \qquad\qquad\qquad x = 2 \qquad \textit{Solve for x.}$$

Check $\qquad\qquad x = 6 \qquad\qquad\qquad\qquad x = 2$

$$\sqrt{2x - 3} = x - 3 \qquad\qquad \sqrt{2x - 3} = x - 3$$

$$\sqrt{2(6) - 3} \stackrel{?}{=} 6 - 3 \qquad\qquad \sqrt{2(2) - 3} \stackrel{?}{=} 2 - 3$$

$$\sqrt{9} \stackrel{?}{=} 3 \qquad\qquad\qquad\qquad \sqrt{1} \stackrel{?}{=} -1$$

$$3 = 3 \quad \textit{True} \qquad\qquad\qquad 1 = -1 \quad \textit{False}$$

The solution is 6; 2 is not a solution to the equation.

▶ **Now Try Exercise 27**

Remember, when solving a radical equation, begin by isolating the radical, as is shown in Example 6.

EXAMPLE 6 ▶ Solve the equation $2x - 5\sqrt{x} - 3 = 0$.

Solution First rewrite the equation so that the square root containing the variable is by itself on one side of the equation.

$$2x - 5\sqrt{x} - 3 = 0$$

$$-5\sqrt{x} = -2x + 3$$

$$\text{or} \quad 5\sqrt{x} = 2x - 3 \qquad \textit{Multiplied both sides by } -1$$

Now square both sides of the equation.

$$\left(5\sqrt{x}\right)^2 = (2x - 3)^2$$

$$5^2\left(\sqrt{x}\right)^2 = (2x - 3)^2$$

$$25x = 4x^2 - 12x + 9 \qquad \textit{Simplify on left. Write } (2x - 3)^2 \textit{ as } 4x^2 - 12x + 9.$$

$$0 = 4x^2 - 37x + 9 \qquad \textit{Set one side of equation equal to zero.}$$

$$\text{or} \quad 4x^2 - 37x + 9 = 0$$
$$(4x - 1)(x - 9) = 0 \qquad \textit{Factor.}$$
$$4x - 1 = 0 \quad \text{or} \quad x - 9 = 0 \qquad \textit{Zero-factor property}$$
$$4x = 1 \qquad\qquad x = 9 \qquad \textit{Solve for x.}$$
$$x = \frac{1}{4}$$

Check
$$x = \frac{1}{4} \qquad\qquad\qquad x = 9$$
$$2x - 5\sqrt{x} - 3 = 0 \qquad\qquad 2x - 5\sqrt{x} - 3 = 0$$
$$2\left(\frac{1}{4}\right) - 5\sqrt{\frac{1}{4}} - 3 \stackrel{?}{=} 0 \qquad\qquad 2(9) - 5\sqrt{9} - 3 \stackrel{?}{=} 0$$
$$\frac{1}{2} - 5\left(\frac{1}{2}\right) - 3 \stackrel{?}{=} 0 \qquad\qquad 18 - 5(3) - 3 \stackrel{?}{=} 0$$
$$\frac{1}{2} - \frac{5}{2} - 3 \stackrel{?}{=} 0 \qquad\qquad 18 - 15 - 3 \stackrel{?}{=} 0$$
$$-\frac{4}{2} - 3 \stackrel{?}{=} 0 \qquad\qquad\qquad 0 = 0 \quad \textit{True}$$
$$-2 - 3 \stackrel{?}{=} 0$$
$$-5 = 0 \quad \textit{False}$$

The solution is 9; $\frac{1}{4}$ is not a solution.

▶ **Now Try Exercise 39**

---

2 Solve Radical Equations Containing Two Square Root Terms

Consider the radical equations

$$\sqrt{x - 4} = \sqrt{x + 9} \quad \text{and} \quad \sqrt{2x + 5} - \sqrt{3x + 8} = 0$$

These equations are different from those previously discussed because they have two square root terms containing the variable x. To solve equations of this type, rewrite the equation, when necessary, so that there is only one term containing a square root on each side of the equation. Then square both sides of the equation. Examples 7 and 8 illustrate this procedure.

EXAMPLE 7 ▶ Solve the equation $\sqrt{2x + 4} = \sqrt{3x - 2}$.

Solution Since each side of the equation already contains one square root, it is not necessary to rewrite the equation. Square both sides of the equation, then solve for x.

$$\left(\sqrt{2x + 4}\right)^2 = \left(\sqrt{3x - 2}\right)^2$$
$$2x + 4 = 3x - 2$$
$$4 = x - 2$$
$$6 = x$$

Check
$$\sqrt{2x + 4} = \sqrt{3x - 2}$$
$$\sqrt{2(6) + 4} \stackrel{?}{=} \sqrt{3(6) - 2}$$
$$\sqrt{16} \stackrel{?}{=} \sqrt{16}$$
$$4 = 4 \qquad \textit{True}$$

The solution is 6.

▶ **Now Try Exercise 29**

EXAMPLE 8 ▶ Solve the equation $4\sqrt{r-4} - \sqrt{10r+14} = 0$.

INSTRUCTOR EXAMPLE
Solve $2\sqrt{x-1} - \sqrt{3x+6} = 0$.
Ans.: 10

Solution Add $\sqrt{10r+14}$ to both sides of the equation to get one square root on each side of the equation. Then square both sides of the equation.

$$4\sqrt{r-4} - \sqrt{10r+14} \;\boxed{+\; \sqrt{10r+14}} = 0 \;\boxed{+\; \sqrt{10r+14}}$$

$$
\begin{aligned}
4\sqrt{r-4} &= \sqrt{10r+14} \\
\left(4\sqrt{r-4}\right)^2 &= \left(\sqrt{10r+14}\right)^2 &&\text{\textit{Square both sides.}}\\
16(r-4) &= 10r+14 &&\text{\textit{Simplify.}}\\
16r - 64 &= 10r+14 &&\text{\textit{Distributive property}}\\
6r - 64 &= 14 &&\text{\textit{Subtract 10r from both sides.}}\\
6r &= 78 &&\text{\textit{Add 64 to both sides.}}\\
r &= 13
\end{aligned}
$$

Check

$$
\begin{aligned}
4\sqrt{r-4} - \sqrt{10r+14} &= 0 \\
4\sqrt{13-4} - \sqrt{10(13)+14} &\overset{?}{=} 0 \\
4\sqrt{9} - \sqrt{130+14} &\overset{?}{=} 0 \\
4(3) - \sqrt{144} &\overset{?}{=} 0 \\
12 - 12 &= 0 \quad \text{\textit{True}}
\end{aligned}
$$

The solution is 13.

▶ **Now Try Exercise 49**

Helpful Hint

In Example 6 when we simplified $(5\sqrt{x})^2$ we obtained $25x$ and in Example 8 when we simplified $\left(4\sqrt{r-4}\right)^2$ we obtained $16(r-4)$. Remember, by the power rule for exponents (discussed in Section 6.1) that when a product of factors is raised to a power, each of the factors is raised to that power. Thus, we see that

$$(5\sqrt{x})^2 = 5^2(\sqrt{x})^2 = 25x \quad \text{and} \quad \left(4\sqrt{r-4}\right)^2 = 4^2\left(\sqrt{r-4}\right)^2 = 16(r-4)$$

---

1. an equation that contains a variable in a radicand 2. a number obtained when solving an equation that is not a solution to the original equation

EXERCISE SET 9.5

MathXL MathXL®   *MyMathLab* MyMathLab

Concept/Writing Exercises

1. What is a radical equation?

2. What is an extraneous root?

3. Why is it necessary to always check solutions to radical equations? because they may be extraneous

4. a) Write a step-by-step procedure for solving equations containing a single square root term. Answers will vary.

   b) Solve the equation $\sqrt{x+1} - 1 = 1$ using the procedure you gave in part **a)**. 3

Determine whether the given value is the solution to the equation. If it is not a solution, state why.

5. $\sqrt{x} = 7, x = 49$ yes

6. $\sqrt{x} = -7, x = 49$ no

7. $-\sqrt{p} = 8, p = 64$ no

8. $-\sqrt{x} = -8, x = 64$ yes

9. $\sqrt{x+4} = 3, x = 5$ yes

10. $\sqrt{-y-5} = 3, y = 4$ no

11. $-3 = \sqrt{t-9}, t = 0$ no

12. $\sqrt{x+5} = 0, x = -5$ yes

Practice the Skills

Solve each equation. If the equation has no real solution, so state.

13. $\sqrt{x} = 5$ 25

14. $\sqrt{x} = 10$ 100

15. $\sqrt{m} = 11$ 121

16. $\sqrt{m} = -3$ no solution

 17. $\sqrt{x+5} = 3$ 4

18. $\sqrt{2x-4} = 2$ 4

19. $\sqrt{x} + 5 = -7$ no solution

20. $\sqrt{x} = -6$ no solution

21. $\sqrt{z} - 3 = 6$ 81

22. $9 + \sqrt{w} = 12$ 9

23. $11 = 6 + \sqrt{x}$ 25

24. $7 = 9 - \sqrt{x}$ 4

25. $8 + \sqrt{n} = 4$ no solution

26. $\sqrt{3x + 4} = x - 2$ 7

27. $\sqrt{2x - 5} = x - 4$ 7

28. $\sqrt{x + 8} = x + 2$ 1

29. $\sqrt{2r - 3} = \sqrt{r + 3}$ 6

30. $\sqrt{3x - 2} = \sqrt{x + 10}$ 6

31. $\sqrt{4x + 4} = \sqrt{6x - 2}$ 3

32. $6\sqrt{x - 4} = 24$ 20

33. $\sqrt{x^2 + 5} = x + 1$ 2

34. $\sqrt{4t + 8} = 2\sqrt{t}$ no solution

35. $\sqrt{3x - 5} = \sqrt{x + 9}$ 7

36. $\sqrt{3k + 5} = 2\sqrt{k}$ 5

37. $3\sqrt{x} = \sqrt{x + 8}$ 1

38. $x - 5 = \sqrt{x^2 - 35}$ 6

39. $4\sqrt{x} = x + 3$ 1, 9

40. $5 + \sqrt{x - 5} = x$ 5, 6

41. $\sqrt{3f - 4} = 2\sqrt{3f - 2}$ no solution

42. $16 - 4\sqrt{2x} = 0$ 8

43. $\sqrt{x^2 - 25} = x + 5$ -5

44. $6\sqrt{3x - 2} = 24$ 6

45. $3 + \sqrt{3x - 5} = x$ 7

46. $\sqrt{4x + 5} + 5 = 2x$ 5

47. $\sqrt{8 - 7x} = x - 3$ no solution

48. $5 + \sqrt{x + 1} = x$ 8

49. $2\sqrt{3b - 5} - \sqrt{2b + 10} = 0$ 3

50. $2\sqrt{m + 4} - \sqrt{7m + 1} = 0$ 5

51. $4\sqrt{2w + 3} = 4w$ 3

52. $2\sqrt{4c - 7} = c + 2$ 4, 8

Problem Solving

Exercises 53–56 show rectangles with areas. Find the value of the indicated variable.

53.
$A = 24$ 7
6
$\sqrt{w + 9}$

54.
$A = 32$ 10
8
$\sqrt{2s - 4}$

55.
$\sqrt{3n + 3}$ $A = 37.2$ 11
6.2

56.
$\sqrt{3p + 1}$ $A = 29.2$ 5
7.3

In Section 9.1, we indicated that we could write a square root expression in exponential form. For example, $\sqrt{25}$ can be written $(25)^{1/2}$. Similarly, we can write certain exponential expressions as square roots. For example $(25)^{1/2}$ can be written $\sqrt{25}$, and $(x - 5)^{1/2}$ can be written $\sqrt{x - 5}$. Rewrite the following equations as equations containing square roots. Then solve each equation.

57. $(x + 4)^{1/2} = 7$
$\sqrt{x + 4} = 7; 45$

58. $(x - 8)^{1/2} = 5$
$\sqrt{x - 8} = 5; 33$

59. $(x - 2)^{1/2} = (2x - 9)^{1/2}$
$\sqrt{x - 2} = \sqrt{2x - 9}; 7$

60. $3(x - 9)^{1/2} = 21$
$3\sqrt{x - 9} = 21; 58$

In Exercises 61–64, a) Use the FOIL method to multiply the factors on the left-hand side of the equation. b) Solve the equation. Remember to check your answer in the original equation.

61. $(\sqrt{x} - 3)(\sqrt{x} + 3) = 40$ **a)** $x - 9 = 40$ **b)** 49

62. $(\sqrt{x} + 5)(\sqrt{x} - 5) = 11$ **a)** $x - 25 = 11$ **b)** 36

63. $(7 - \sqrt{x})(5 + \sqrt{x}) = 35$ **a)** $35 + 2\sqrt{x} - x = 35$ **b)** 0, 4

64. $(6 - \sqrt{x})(2 + \sqrt{x}) = 15$ **a)** $12 + 4\sqrt{x} - x = 15$ **b)** 1, 9

65. The sum of a natural number and its square root is 2. Find the number.   1

66. The product of 3 and the square root of a number is 15. Find the number.   25

Challenge Problems

Solve each equation. (Hint: You will need to square both sides of the equation, then isolate the square root containing the variable, then square both sides of the equation again.)

67. $\sqrt{x} + 1 = \sqrt{x + 11}$ 25

68. $\sqrt{x + 1} = 2 - \sqrt{x}$ $\frac{9}{16}$

69. $\sqrt{x + 7} = 3 + \sqrt{x - 8}$ 9

Group Activity

Discuss and answer Exercises 70–72 as a group.

70. Radical equations in two variables can be graphed by selecting values for x and finding the corresponding values of y, as was done in Section 4.2 when we graphed linear equations.

a) As a group, discuss what values would be appropriate to select for x if you wanted to graph $y = \sqrt{x}$. Explain your answer.   Answers will vary.

b) Select four values for x that will result in y being a whole number. List your values for x and y in a table.

c) Individually, plot the points and sketch the graph. Compare your graphs.   See graphing answer section.

d) Is the graph linear? Explain.   no

e) Is the graph a function? (See Section 4.6.) Explain.   yes

f) Can you determine whether $y = \sqrt{x}$ has an x-intercept and a y-intercept from the graph? If so, give the intercepts.   yes, $(0, 0)$

As a group, repeat parts a)–f) of exercise 70 for each the following equations.

71. $y = \sqrt{x - 2}$ **71. a)–b)** Answers will vary.   **c)** See graphing answer section.   **d)** no   **e)** yes   **f)** yes; x-int. $(2, 0)$, no y-int.

72. $y = \sqrt{x + 4}$ **72. a)–b)** Answers will vary.   **c)** See graphing answer section.   **d)** no   **e)** yes   **f)** yes; x-int. $(-4, 0)$, y-int. $(0, 2)$

Cumulative Review Exercises

[5.1] **73.** Solve the following system of equations graphically.

$$3x - 2y = 6$$
$$y = 2x - 4$$ $(2, 0)$

[5.2] **74.** Solve the following system of equations by substitution.

$$3x - 2y = 6$$
$$y = 2x - 4$$ $(2, 0)$

[5.3] **75.** Solve the following system of equations using the addition method.

$$3x - 2y = 6$$
$$y = 2x - 4$$ $(2, 0)$

[5.4] **76. Boat Ride** A ferry boat on the Hudson River can travel at a speed of 18 miles per hour with the current and 14 miles per hour against the current. Find the speed of the ferry boat in still water and the speed of the current.   ferry: 16 mph; current, 2 mph

9.6 Radicals: Applications and Problem Solving

1 Use the Pythagorean Theorem.

2 Use the distance formula.

3 Use radicals to solve application problems.

In this section we will focus on some of the many interesting applications of radicals. We will use the Pythagorean Theorem and introduce the distance formula, and then give a few additional applications of radicals.

1 Use the Pythagorean Theorem

In Section 7.7 we introduced the Pythagorean Theorem. For your convenience we state the Pythagorean Theorem again.

Pythagorean Theorem

The square of the hypotenuse of a right triangle is equal to the sum of the squares of the two legs.

$$(\text{leg})^2 + (\text{leg})^2 = (\text{hypotenuse})^2$$

If a and b represent the legs, and c represents the hypotenuse, then

$$a^2 + b^2 = c^2$$

In Section 9.5, when we solved equations containing square roots, we raised both sides of the equation to the second power to eliminate the square roots. When we solve problems using the Pythagorean Theorem, we will raise both sides of the equation to the $\frac{1}{2}$ power to remove the square on one of the variables. We can do this because the rules of exponents presented in Sections 6.1 and 6.2 also apply to fractional exponents. Since lengths are positive, the values of a, b, and c in the Pythagorean Theorem must represent positive values.

FIGURE 9.2

EXAMPLE 1 ▸ **Right Triangle Problem** Find the hypotenuse of a right triangle whose legs are $\sqrt{3}$ feet and 4 feet.

Solution   Draw a picture of the problem (**Fig. 9.2**). It makes no difference which leg is called a and which leg is called b.

$$a^2 + b^2 = c^2$$
$$4^2 + \left(\sqrt{3}\right)^2 = c^2 \qquad \textit{Substitute values for a and b.}$$
$$16 + 3 = c^2$$
$$19 = c^2$$
$$\sqrt{19} = \sqrt{c^2} \qquad \textit{Take the square root of both sides.}$$
$$\sqrt{19} = c \qquad \textit{Since c > 0, } \sqrt{c^2} = c$$

Thus the hypotenuse is $\sqrt{19}$ feet or approximately 4.36 feet.

Check $a^2 + b^2 = c^2$
$$4^2 + \left(\sqrt{3}\right)^2 \overset{?}{=} \left(\sqrt{19}\right)^2$$
$$16 + 3 \overset{?}{=} 19$$
$$19 = 19 \qquad \textit{True}$$

▸ **Now Try Exercise 15**

EXAMPLE 2 ▸ **Basketball Court** A professional basketball court is a rectangle whose overall dimensions are 94 feet by 50 feet. Find the length of the diagonal of the court.

Solution   **Understand and Translate**   First, we draw the court (**Fig. 9.3**). We are asked to find the length of the diagonal. This length is the hypotenuse, c, of the triangle shown in **Figure 9.4.**

FIGURE 9.3   **FIGURE 9.4**

$$a^2 + b^2 = c^2$$
Carry Out $$(50)^2 + (94)^2 = c^2$$
$$2500 + 8836 = c^2$$
$$11{,}336 = c^2$$
$$c = \sqrt{11{,}336}$$

Answer   The length of the diagonal of the court is approximately 106.47 feet.

▸ **Now Try Exercise 25**

2 Use the Distance Formula

The **distance formula** can be used to find the distance between two points, (x_1, y_1) and (x_2, y_2), in the Cartesian coordinate system.

   It can be derived using the Pythagorean Theorem. In **Figure 9.5**, three points are indicated. The length of side a is $x_2 - x_1$ and the length of side b is $y_2 - y_1$. The

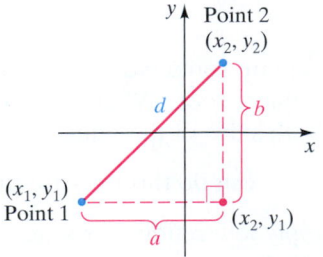

FIGURE 9.5

distance between points 1 and 2 can be determined using the Pythagorean Theorem. In this case we let the hypotenuse be represented by the letter d, for distance.

$$d^2 = a^2 + b^2$$
$$d^2 = (x_2 - x_1)^2 + (y_2 - y_1)^2$$
$$d = \sqrt{(x_2 - x_1)^2 + (y_2 - y_1)^2}$$

Distance Formula

$$d = \sqrt{(x_2 - x_1)^2 + (y_2 - y_1)^2}$$

INSTRUCTOR EXAMPLE
Find the length of the line segment between the points $(-1, -2)$ and $(4, -5)$.

Ans.: $\sqrt{34} \approx 5.83$

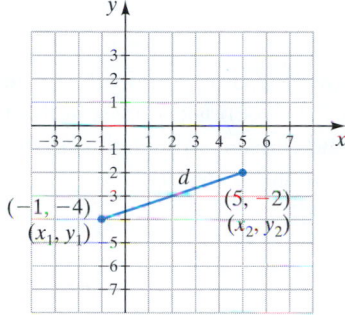

FIGURE 9.6

EXAMPLE 3 ▶ Find the length of the line segment between the points $(-1, -4)$ and $(5, -2)$.

Solution The two points are illustrated in **Figure 9.6**. It makes no difference which point is labeled (x_1, y_1), and which is labeled (x_2, y_2). Let $(5, -2)$ be (x_2, y_2) and $(-1, -4)$ be (x_1, y_1). Thus $x_2 = 5$, $y_2 = -2$ and $x_1 = -1$, $y_1 = -4$.

$$\begin{aligned}
d &= \sqrt{(x_2 - x_1)^2 + (y_2 - y_1)^2} \\
&= \sqrt{[5 - (-1)]^2 + [-2 - (-4)]^2} \\
&= \sqrt{(5 + 1)^2 + (-2 + 4)^2} \\
&= \sqrt{6^2 + 2^2} \\
&= \sqrt{36 + 4} = \sqrt{40}, \text{ or approximately } 6.32
\end{aligned}$$

Thus, the distance between $(-1, -4)$ and $(5, -2)$ is approximately 6.32 units.

▶ **Now Try Exercise 21**

3 Use Radicals to Solve Application Problems

Radicals are often used in science and mathematics courses. Examples 4 through 6 illustrate some scientific applications that use radicals.

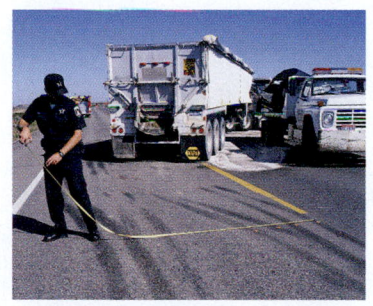

INSTRUCTOR EXAMPLE
Find the speed of a car that leaves a 30-foot-long skid mark. Use $c = 0.71$.
Ans.: ≈ 25.4 mph

TEACHING TIP
Ask, "If the road surface is wet, will the value of c increase or decrease? Why?"

EXAMPLE 4 ▶ **Accident Investigation** Traffic accident investigators are trained in accident reconstruction. They use, among other things, formulas derived from the laws of physics in their work. One task they face is to try to determine the speed at which a vehicle is traveling before hitting an object. The accident investigators use the formula

$$S = 5.5\sqrt{cl}$$

to estimate the original speed of the vehicle, S, in miles per hour, where c represents the coefficient of friction between the road surface and the tire, and l represents the length of the longest skid mark measured in feet. On dry roads, the value of the coefficient of friction is between 0.69 and 0.75 for most cars. Find the speed of a car that leaves a 40-foot-long skid mark before stopping. Use $c = 0.72$.

Solution **Understand and Translate** Begin by substituting 0.72 for c and 40 for the length in the given formula.

Carry Out
$$\begin{aligned}
S &= 5.5\sqrt{cl} \\
&= 5.5\sqrt{0.72 \times 40} \\
&= 5.5\sqrt{28.8} \\
&\approx 29.5
\end{aligned}$$

Answer A car leaving a 40-foot-long skid mark on a dry surface before stopping is originally traveling at approximately 29.5 miles per hour.

▶ **Now Try Exercise 45**

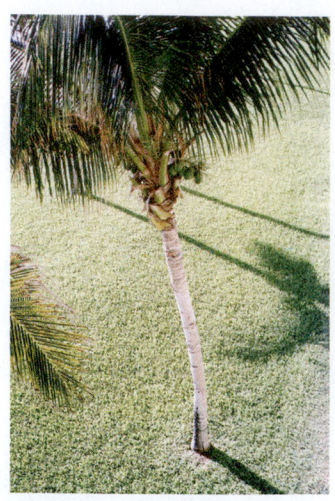

EXAMPLE 5 ▶ Gravity A formula for the velocity of an object in feet per second (neglecting air resistance) after it has fallen a certain distance is

$$v = \sqrt{2gh}$$

where g is the acceleration due to gravity and h is the height the object has fallen in feet. On Earth the acceleration due to gravity, g, is approximately 32 feet per second squared. Find the velocity of a coconut after it has fallen 20 feet.

Solution **Understand and Translate** Begin by substituting 32 for g in the given equation.

$$v = \sqrt{2gh} = \sqrt{2(32)(h)} = \sqrt{64h}$$

Carry Out   At $h = 20$ feet,

$$v = \sqrt{64(20)} = \sqrt{1280} \approx 35.78$$

Answer   After a coconut has fallen 20 feet, its velocity is approximately 35.78 feet per second.

▶ **Now Try Exercise 49**

INSTRUCTOR EXAMPLE 5
Find the velocity of an object that has dropped 16 feet.
Ans.: 32 ft/sec

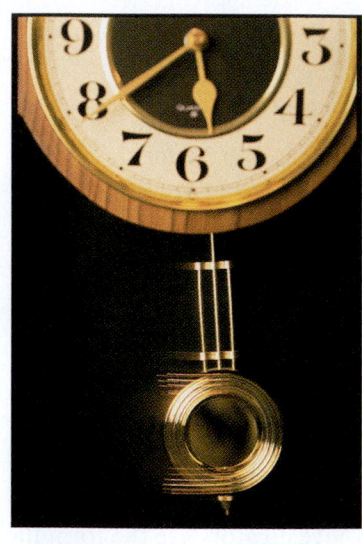

EXAMPLE 6 ▶ A Pendulum The *period of a pendulum* (the time required for the pendulum to make one complete swing both back and forth) depends on the length of the pendulum. Finding the length for a pendulum that would cause it to swing back and forth 60 times in one minute was a first step in creating more accurate clocks.

The formula for the period, T (in seconds), of a pendulum is

$$T = 2\pi\sqrt{\frac{L}{32}}$$

where L is the length of the pendulum in feet (**Fig. 9.7**). Find the period of the pendulum if its length is 8 feet. Use 3.14 as an approximation for π.

Solution **Understand and Translate** Substitute 3.14 for π and 8 for L in the formula.

$$T \approx 2(3.14)\sqrt{\frac{8}{32}}$$

Carry Out

$$\approx 6.28\sqrt{\frac{1}{4}}$$

$$\approx 6.28\left(\frac{1}{2}\right) = 3.14 \text{ seconds}$$

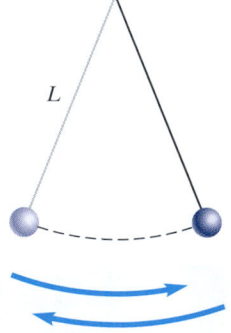

FIGURE 9.7

INSTRUCTOR EXAMPLE 6
Find the period of a pendulum if its length is 16 feet.
Ans.: ≈4.44 sec

Answer   A pendulum 8 feet long takes about 3.14 seconds to make one complete swing.

▶ **Now Try Exercise 39**

EXERCISE SET 9.6

4. b) to find the distance between two points in the Cartesian coordinate system   **5.** the two points in the coordinate plane that you are trying to find the distance between

Concept/Writing Exercises

1. What is a right triangle?   a triangle that contains a 90° angle

2. State the Pythagorean Theorem and describe what relationship it expresses about a right triangle. $a^2 + b^2 = c^2$

3. Can the Pythagorean Theorem be used with any triangle? Explain.   no

4. a) Write the distance formula. $d = \sqrt{(x_2 - x_1)^2 + (y_2 - y_1)^2}$

 b) When do we use the distance formula?

5. What do the following ordered pairs represent in the distance formula: (x_1, y_1) and (x_2, y_2)?

6. Determine the distance between the points $(4, 0)$ and $(-5, 0)$.   9

7. Determine the distance between the points $(0, -4)$ and $(0, -11)$.   7

8. What is meant by the period of a pendulum?   the time required for the pendulum to make one complete swing back and forth

Practice the Skills

Use the Pythagorean Theorem to find each indicated quantity. Give the exact value, then round your answer to the nearest hundredth.

9. $\sqrt{33} \approx 5.74$ **10.** $\sqrt{73} \approx 8.54$ **11.** $\sqrt{170} \approx 13.04$ **12.** $\sqrt{63} \approx 7.94$

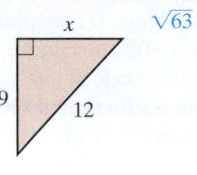

13. $\sqrt{151} \approx 12.29$ **14.** $\sqrt{175} \approx 13.23$ **15.** $\sqrt{67} \approx 8.19$ **16.** $\sqrt{176} \approx 13.27$

17. $\sqrt{202} \approx 14.21$ **18.** $\sqrt{100} = 10$

19. $\sqrt{180} \approx 13.42$ **20.** $\sqrt{128} \approx 11.31$

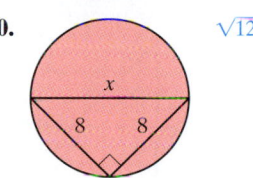

Use the distance formula to find the length of the line segments between each pair of points.

21. $(8, 7)$ and $(3, 10)$ $\sqrt{34} \approx 5.83$

22. $(6, -1)$ and $(-3, 8)$ $\sqrt{162} \approx 12.73$

23. $(-8, 4)$ and $(4, 11)$ $\sqrt{193} \approx 13.89$

24. $(2, 7)$ and $(-4, -2)$ $\sqrt{117} \approx 10.82$

Problem Solving

25. Football Field Dimensions Pro Player Stadium in Miami, Florida, is home to both the Florida Marlins and the Miami Dolphins. The football field is 120 yards long from end zone to end zone. Find the length of the diagonal, to the nearest hundredth, from one end zone to the opposite corner of the other if the width of the field is 53.3 yards. $\sqrt{17{,}240.89} \approx 131.30$ yd

26. Rugby Field According to information provided by the Austin Rugby Football Club Website, the dimensions of a rugby field are 69 meters by 100 meters. What is the length of the diagonal, to the nearest hundredth, from one corner of the field to the opposite corner of the field? $\sqrt{14{,}761} \approx 121.49$ m

27. Ladder on a House Pedro and Vanessa are planning to paint their house. The instructions on an 8-meter extension ladder indicate that the base of the ladder should be two meters from the house when in use. If they follow the instructions, how high will the top of the ladder reach on the house? $\sqrt{60} \approx 7.75$ m

28. Guy Wire to a Pole A local cable company crew must run a guy wire to support a pole. The wire will go from the top of a 14-meter pole to a point 6 meters from the base of the pole. How long will the guy wire be? $\sqrt{232} \approx 15.23$ m

29. Boxing Ring The length of the side of a square, s, can be found by the formula $s = \sqrt{A}$, where A is the area of the square. Find the length of the side of a square boxing ring whose area is 256 square feet.   16 ft

30. Square Window (See Exercise 29.) Find the length of a side of a square window having an area 1600 square centimeters.   40 cm

31. Helicopter Pad The formula for the area of a circle is $A = \pi r^2$, where π is approximately 3.14 and r is the radius of the circle. Find the radius of a circular helicopter pad if its area is 1965 square feet. $\approx \sqrt{625.80} \approx 25.02$ ft

32. Radius of a Circle Find the radius of a circle whose area is 80 square feet. $\approx\sqrt{25.48} \approx 5.05$ ft

33. Birdbath A birdbath can hold water 2 inches deep, as shown in the figure. If the volume of water that can be held in the birdbath is 402 cubic inches, find the radius of the birdbath. Water volume is calculated by finding the area of the circular bottom of the birdbath and then multiplying the area by the depth of the water. Use the formula $V = \pi r^2 h$. $\approx\sqrt{64.01} \approx 8.00$ in.

$V = 402$ in^3

34. Baseball A regulation baseball diamond is a square with 90 feet between bases. How far is second base from home plate? $\sqrt{16,200} \approx 127.28$ ft

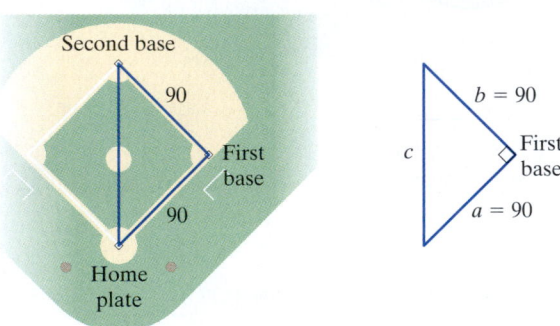

35. Shoe Box The top of a shoe box is a rectangular piece of cardboard with a length of 12 inches and a width of 5 inches. Find the length of the diagonal across the top of the shoe box. $\sqrt{169} = 13$ in.

36. Sheet of Paper A large sheet of paper measures 8 inches by 15 inches. Find the length of the diagonal.   17 in.

37. Diagonal of Rectangular Solid The length of the diagonal of a rectangular solid (see the figure below) is given by

$$d = \sqrt{a^2 + b^2 + c^2}$$

Find the length of the diagonal of the suitcase shown below. $\sqrt{932} \approx 30.53$ in.

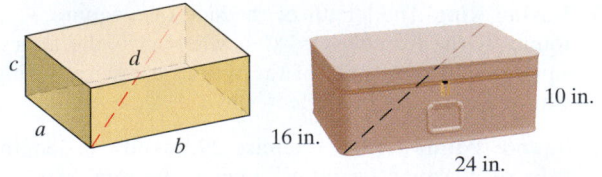

38. Carry-On Luggage The maximum dimensions of a carry-on suitcase on most airlines is length: 24 inches, height: 16 inches, and depth: 10 inches. If the suitcase is lying flat, determine the length of the diagonal across the surface of the suitcase. $\sqrt{832} \approx 28.84$ in.

39. Pendulum The period of a simple pendulum is determined by the length of the string, not the material composing the bob (or ball). Mikel Finn made a pendulum with a string measuring 43 inches. What is the period for this pendulum? (Use $T = 2\pi\sqrt{L/32}$; refer to Example 6.) $6.28\sqrt{0.11} \approx 2.08$ sec

40. Foucault Pendulum An example of a Foucault pendulum is on display in the Smithsonian Institute in Washington, D.C. It is used to demonstrate the earth's rotation. It has a cable 52 feet long and a symmetrical, hollow brass bob weighing about 240 pounds. Find the period of the pendulum. $6.28\sqrt{1.625} \approx 8.01$ sec

41. Another Pendulum The Houston Museum of Natural Science also has a Foucault pendulum on display. It has a cable 61.6 feet long and a bob weighing 180 pounds. Find the period of the pendulum. $6.28\sqrt{1.925} \approx 8.71$ sec

Earth Days

For any planet, its "year" is the time it takes for the planet to revolve once around the sun. The number of "Earth days," N, in a given planet's year, is approximated by the formula

$$N = 0.2(\sqrt{R})^3$$

where R is the mean distance from the sun in millions of kilometers. The mean distance from the sun, in millions of kilometers, for three planets is illustrated below.   **43.** about 365 Earth days

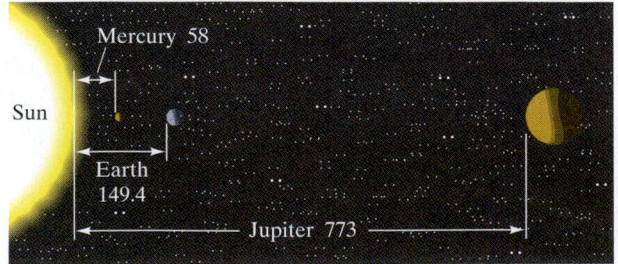

42. Find the number of Earth days in the year of Mercury.   about 88 Earth days

43. Find the number of Earth days in the year of Earth.

44. Find the number of Earth days in the year of Jupiter.   about 4298 Earth days

Speed *In Exercises 45–48, use the formula $S = 5.5\sqrt{cl}$ to find the speed of a vehicle, S, in miles per hour given the coefficient of friction, c, between the road surface and the tires, and the length, l, of the skid mark, measured in feet; see Example 4.*

45. $c = 0.72$
$l = 50$ feet   33 mph

46. $c = 0.70$
$l = 70$ feet   38.5 mph

47. $c = 0.75$
$l = 120$ feet   ≈52.2 mph

48. $c = 0.65$
$l = 180$ feet   ≈59.5 mph

Escape velocity, v_e, is the velocity needed for a spacecraft to escape a planet's gravitational field. This is found by the formula, $v_e = \sqrt{2gR}$, where g is the acceleration due to gravity of the planet and R is the radius of the planet in meters.

49. Earth's Escape Velocity Find the escape velocity for Earth where $g = 9.81$ meters per second squared and $R = 6,370,000$ meters. $\sqrt{19.62(6,370,000)} \approx 11,179.42$ m/sec

50. Mars's Escape Velocity Future Mars exploration may include sending spacecraft that will land on the surface of the planet and leave after scientific work has been completed. What is the approximate velocity needed for a spacecraft to escape the gravitational field of Mars? The acceleration due to gravity on Mars is approximately 3.6835 meters per second squared. The radius of Mars is approximately 3,393,500 meters. $\sqrt{2(3.6835)(3,393,500)} \approx 4999.99$ m/sec

51. Freefall If a pair of glasses was dropped from the Sears Tower at a height of 1431 feet (the highest occupied floor), determine the velocity of the glasses when they strike the ground. Neglect air resistance. (Use $v = \sqrt{2gh}$; refer to Example 5.) $\sqrt{91,584} \approx 302.63$ ft/sec

52. Resultant Force When two forces, F_1 and F_2, pull at right angles to each other as illustrated, the resultant, or the effective force, R, can be found by the formula $R = \sqrt{F_1^2 + F_2^2}$.

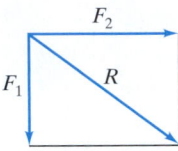

Two cars at a 90° angle to each other are trying to pull a third car out of the mud, as shown. If car A exerts 600 pounds of force and car B exerts 800 pounds of force, find the resulting force on the car stuck in the mud. $\sqrt{1,000,000} = 1000$ lb

Body Surface Area *The amount of skin that covers our bodies is called **body surface area** (BSA). The formula to calculate BSA, in square meters, is*

$$\text{BSA} = \sqrt{\frac{HW}{3600}}$$

where H is the height, in centimeters, and W is the weight, in kilograms.

In Exercises 53 and 54, calculate the BSA for a person with the given height and weight.

53. $H = 120$ centimeters
$W = 165$ kilograms   ≈2.35 m²

54. $H = 182$ centimeters
$W = 390$ kilograms   ≈4.44 m²

Challenge Problems

55. Rectangle The length of a rectangle is 3 inches more than its width. If the length of the diagonal is 15 inches, find the dimensions of the rectangle.   9 in. by 12 in.

56. Gravity on the Moon The acceleration due to gravity on the moon is $\frac{1}{6}$ of that on earth. If a camera falls from a rocket 100 feet above the surface of the moon, with what velocity will it strike the moon? (Use $v = \sqrt{2gh}$; see Example 5.)   ≈32.66 ft/sec

57. Length of a Pendulum Find the length of a pendulum if the period is 2 seconds. (Use $T = 2\pi\sqrt{L/32}$; refer to Example 6.)   ≈3.25 ft

Cumulative Review Exercises

[2.8] **58.** Solve the inequality $2(x + 3) < 4x - 6$. $x > 6$

[6.2] **59.** Simplify $(8x^{-4}y^3)^{-1}$. $\dfrac{x^4}{8y^3}$

[5.3] **60.** Solve the following system of equations using the addition method.

$$3x + 4y = 12$$
$$\frac{1}{2}x - 2y = 8 \qquad \left(7, -\frac{9}{4}\right)$$

[8.6] **61.** Solve $5 + \dfrac{6}{x} = \dfrac{2}{3x}$. $-\dfrac{16}{15}$

9.7 Higher Roots and Rational Exponents

1 Evaluate cube and fourth roots.

2 Simplify cube and fourth roots.

3 Write radical expressions in exponential form.

TEACHING TIP
You may want to begin this section by having students write a response to the following question. "Knowing what you know about square roots, what do you think $\sqrt[3]{x}$ means?"

1 Evaluate Cube and Fourth Roots

In this section we will use the same basic concepts used in Sections 9.1 through 9.4 to work with radicals with indices of 3 and 4. Now we introduce **cube** and **fourth roots**.

$\sqrt[3]{a}$ is read "the cube root of a."

$\sqrt[4]{a}$ is read "the fourth root of a."

Note that

$$\sqrt[3]{a} = b \quad \text{if} \quad b^3 = a$$

and

$$\sqrt[4]{a} = b \quad \text{if} \quad b^4 = a, \qquad a \geq 0$$

Examples

$\sqrt[3]{8} = 2$ since $2^3 = 2 \cdot 2 \cdot 2 = 8$

$\sqrt[3]{-8} = -2$ since $(-2)^3 = (-2)(-2)(-2) = -8$

$\sqrt[3]{27} = 3$ since $3^3 = 3 \cdot 3 \cdot 3 = 27$

$\sqrt[4]{16} = 2$ since $2^4 = 2 \cdot 2 \cdot 2 \cdot 2 = 16$

$\sqrt[4]{81} = 3$ since $3^4 = 3 \cdot 3 \cdot 3 \cdot 3 = 81$

$\sqrt[3]{\dfrac{1}{27}} = \dfrac{1}{3}$ since $\left(\dfrac{1}{3}\right)^3 = \dfrac{1}{3} \cdot \dfrac{1}{3} \cdot \dfrac{1}{3} = \dfrac{1}{27}$

EXAMPLE 1 ▶ Evaluate. **a)** $\sqrt[3]{-64}$ **b)** $\sqrt[3]{216}$

INSTRUCTOR EXAMPLE
Evaluate.
 a) $\sqrt[3]{-125}$ **b)** $\sqrt[4]{256}$
Ans.:
 a) -5 **b)** 4

Solution

a) To find $\sqrt[3]{-64}$, we must find the number that when cubed is -64.
$$\sqrt[3]{-64} = -4 \quad \text{since } (-4)^3 = -64$$

b) To find $\sqrt[3]{216}$, we must find the number that when cubed is 216.
$$\sqrt[3]{216} = 6 \quad \text{since } 6^3 = 216$$

▶ **Now Try Exercise 11**

Note that the cube root of a positive number is a positive number and the cube root of a negative number is a negative number. The radicand of a fourth root (or any even root) must be a nonnegative number for the expression to be a real number. For example, $\sqrt[4]{-16}$ is not a real number because no real number raised to the fourth power can be a negative number.

It will be helpful in the explanations that follow if we define perfect cubes. A **perfect cube** is a number that is the cube of a natural number.

1,	2,	3,	4,	5,	6,	7,	8,	9,	10,	...	*Natural numbers*
1^3,	2^3,	3^3,	4^3,	5^3,	6^3,	7^3,	8^3,	9^3,	10^3,	...	*Cubes of natural numbers*
1,	8,	27,	64,	125,	216,	343,	512,	729,	1000,	...	*Perfect cubes*

Note that $\sqrt[3]{1} = 1$, $\sqrt[3]{8} = 2$, $\sqrt[3]{27} = 3$, $\sqrt[3]{64} = 4$, and so on.

Perfect fourth powers can be expressed in a similar manner.

1,	2,	3,	4,	5,	6,	...	*Natural numbers*
1^4,	2^4,	3^4,	4^4,	5^4,	6^4,	...	*Fourth powers of natural numbers*
1,	16,	81,	256,	625,	1296,	...	*Perfect fourth powers*

Note that $\sqrt[4]{1} = 1$, $\sqrt[4]{16} = 2$, $\sqrt[4]{81} = 3$, $\sqrt[4]{256} = 4$, and so on.

Table 9.2 illustrates some perfect cube and perfect fourth power numbers. This table may prove helpful when simplifying cube and fourth power roots.

You may wish to refer to **Table 9.2** when evaluating cube and fourth roots.

Table 9.2

Perfect Cubes	Cube Root		Value	Perfect Fourth Powers	Fourth Root		Value
1	$\sqrt[3]{1}$	=	1	1	$\sqrt[4]{1}$	=	1
8	$\sqrt[3]{8}$	=	2	16	$\sqrt[4]{16}$	=	2
27	$\sqrt[3]{27}$	=	3	81	$\sqrt[4]{81}$	=	3
64	$\sqrt[3]{64}$	=	4	256	$\sqrt[4]{256}$	=	4
125	$\sqrt[3]{125}$	=	5	625	$\sqrt[4]{625}$	=	5
216	$\sqrt[3]{216}$	=	6	1296	$\sqrt[4]{1296}$	=	6
343	$\sqrt[3]{243}$	=	7				
512	$\sqrt[3]{512}$	=	8				

USING YOUR CALCULATOR   Evaluating Cube and Higher Roots on a Scientific Calculator

If your scientific calculator contains a $\boxed{y^x}$ or $\boxed{x^y}$ key, then you can find cube and higher roots. To find cube and higher roots, you need to use both the second function key, $\boxed{2^{nd}}$, and either the $\boxed{y^x}$ or $\boxed{x^y}$ key. Some calculators use an inverse key $\boxed{INV}$, in place of the $\boxed{2^{nd}}$ key. To evaluate $\sqrt[3]{216}$ press the following keys:

$$216 \;\boxed{2^{nd}}\; \boxed{y^x}\; 3 \;\boxed{=}\; 6$$

radicand   index   answer displayed

Thus $\sqrt[3]{216} = 6$. To evaluate $\sqrt[4]{158}$, press the following keys:

$$158 \;\boxed{2^{nd}}\; \boxed{y^x}\; 4 \;\boxed{=}\; 3.54539$$

radicand   index   answer displayed

Thus $\sqrt[4]{158} \approx 3.54539$.

To find the odd root of a negative number, find the odd root of that positive number and then place a negative sign before the value. For example, to find $\sqrt[3]{-64}$, find $\sqrt[3]{64}$, which is 4; then place a negative sign before the value to get -4. Thus $\sqrt[3]{-64} = -4$.

EXERCISES

Evaluate each of the following.

1. $\sqrt[3]{729}$ 9

2. $\sqrt[4]{16}$ 2

3. $\sqrt[4]{200}$ ≈ 3.76060

4. $\sqrt[3]{1000}$ 10

5. $\sqrt[3]{-216}$ -6

6. $\sqrt[5]{-1200}$ ≈ -4.12892

USING YOUR GRAPHING CALCULATOR   Evaluating Cube and Higher Roots on a Graphing Calculator

The procedure to use to find cube and higher roots depends upon your graphing calculator. Read the manual that comes with your graphing calculator for instructions.

On a TI-84 Plus calculator you use the $\boxed{\text{MATH}}$ menu to find both cube roots and roots greater than cube roots. To find a cube root you use the $\boxed{\text{MATH}}$ menu option 4: $\sqrt[3]{\ }$ (.

To evaluate $\sqrt[3]{216}$ press the following keys:

$$\boxed{\text{MATH}}\quad\boxed{4}\quad 216\ \boxed{)}\ \boxed{\text{ENTER}}\ 6$$

| ↑ | ↑ | ↑ | ↑ |
| MATH menu | TI-84 Plus then shows $\sqrt[3]{\ }$ (| Enter radicand | answer displayed |

To evaluate $\sqrt[3]{-216}$, you press the following keys:

$$\boxed{\text{MATH}}\ \boxed{4}\ \boxed{(-)}\ 216\ \boxed{)}\ \boxed{\text{ENTER}}\ -6$$

Thus $\sqrt[3]{-216} = -6$.

To evaluate roots greater than 3, you use the $\boxed{\text{MATH}}$ menu, option 5: $\sqrt[x]{\ }$. You enter the index before you press the $\boxed{\text{MATH}}$ key. To evaluate $\sqrt[4]{158}$ press the following keys.

$$\boxed{4}\quad\boxed{\text{MATH}}\quad\boxed{5}\quad 158\ \boxed{\text{ENTER}}\ 3.545392093$$

| ↑ | ↑ | ↑ | ↑ | ↑ |
| Index | MATH menu | calculator shows $4\sqrt[x]{\ }$ | Enter radicand | answer displayed |

EXERCISES

Evaluate each of the following.

1. $\sqrt[3]{343}$ 7

2. $\sqrt[4]{1296}$ 6

3. $\sqrt[4]{76}$ ≈2.952591724

4. $\sqrt[3]{2744}$ 14

5. $\sqrt[3]{-512}$ −8

6. $\sqrt[5]{-1000}$ ≈−3.981071706

---

2 **Simplify Cube and Fourth Roots**

The product rule used in simplifying square roots can be expanded to indices greater than 2.

Product Rule for Radicals

$$\sqrt[n]{a}\ \sqrt[n]{b} = \sqrt[n]{ab}, \qquad \text{for } a \geq 0, b \geq 0 \text{ and } n \text{ is even}$$
$$\sqrt[n]{a}\ \sqrt[n]{b} = \sqrt[n]{ab}, \qquad \text{when } n \text{ is odd}$$

To simplify a cube root whose radicand is a constant, write the radicand as the product of a perfect cube and another number. Then simplify, using the product rule.

EXAMPLE 2 ▶ Simplify. **a)** $\sqrt[3]{40}$ **b)** $\sqrt[3]{54}$ **c)** $\sqrt[4]{48}$

Solution

a) Eight is a perfect cube that is a factor of the radicand, 40. Therefore, we simplify as follows:

$$\sqrt[3]{40} = \sqrt[3]{8 \cdot 5}$$
$$= \sqrt[3]{8}\ \sqrt[3]{5} \qquad \textcolor{red}{\textit{Product rule}}$$
$$= 2\sqrt[3]{5} \qquad \textcolor{red}{\textit{Simplify.}}$$

b) Twenty-seven is a perfect cube factor of 54. Therefore we simplify as follows.

$$\sqrt[3]{54} = \sqrt[3]{27 \cdot 2} = \sqrt[3]{27}\ \sqrt[3]{2} = 3\sqrt[3]{2}$$

c) Write $\sqrt[4]{48}$ as a product of a perfect fourth power and another number, then simplify. From the listing above, we see that 16 is a perfect fourth power. Since 16 is a factor of 48, we simplify as follows:

$$\sqrt[4]{48} = \sqrt[4]{16 \cdot 3}$$
$$= \sqrt[4]{16} \ \sqrt[4]{3} \qquad \textcolor{red}{\textit{Product rule}}$$
$$= 2\sqrt[4]{3} \qquad \textcolor{red}{\textit{Simplify.}}$$

▶ **Now Try Exercise 27**

3 Write Radical Expressions in Exponential Form

A radical expression can be written in **exponential form** by using the following rule.

Exponential Form of a Radical Expression

$$\sqrt[n]{a} = a^{1/n}, \qquad a \geq 0 \text{ and } n \text{ is even} \qquad \text{Rule 4}$$
$$\sqrt[n]{a} = a^{1/n}, \qquad \text{when } n \text{ is odd}$$

Examples

$$\sqrt{8} = 8^{1/2} \qquad\qquad \sqrt{x} = x^{1/2}$$
$$\sqrt[3]{7} = 7^{1/3} \qquad\qquad \sqrt[4]{9} = 9^{1/4}$$
$$\sqrt[3]{x} = x^{1/3} \qquad\qquad \sqrt[4]{y} = y^{1/4}$$
$$\sqrt[3]{5z^2} = (5z^2)^{1/3} \qquad\qquad \sqrt[4]{3y^2} = (3y^2)^{1/4}$$

Notice $\sqrt{8} = 8^{1/2}$ and $\sqrt{x} = x^{1/2}$, which is consistent with what we learned in Section 9.1. This concept can be expanded as follows.

Exponential Form of a Radical Expression

Power   *Index*

$$\sqrt[n]{a^m} = (\sqrt[n]{a})^m = a^{m/n}, \text{ for } a \geq 0 \text{ and } m \text{ and } n \text{ integers} \qquad \text{Rule 5}$$

As long as the radicand is nonnegative, we can change from one form to another.

Examples

$$\sqrt[3]{27^4} = \left(\sqrt[3]{27}\right)^4 = 3^4 = 81 \qquad\qquad \sqrt[3]{x^3} = x^{3/3} = x^1 = x$$
$$8^{2/3} = \left(\sqrt[3]{8}\right)^2 = 2^2 = 4 \qquad\qquad \sqrt[4]{y^8} = y^{8/4} = y^2$$

EXAMPLE 3 ▶ Write each radical in exponential form.

a) $\sqrt[3]{a^5}$ **b)** $\sqrt[4]{y^7}$ **c)** $\sqrt[4]{x^{13}}$

INSTRUCTOR EXAMPLE

Write $\sqrt[3]{c^7}$ in exponential form.
Ans.: $c^{7/3}$

Solution

a) $\sqrt[3]{a^5} = a^{5/3}$

b) $\sqrt[4]{y^7} = y^{7/4}$

c) $\sqrt[4]{x^{13}} = x^{13/4}$

▶ **Now Try Exercise 31**

EXAMPLE 4 ▶ Simplify. **a)** $\sqrt[4]{x^{12}}$ **b)** $\sqrt[3]{y^{21}}$

INSTRUCTOR EXAMPLE

Simplify $\sqrt[3]{m^{12}}$.
Ans.: m^4

Solution Write each radical expression in exponential form, then simplify.

a) $\sqrt[4]{x^{12}} = x^{12/4} = x^3$ **b)** $\sqrt[3]{y^{21}} = y^{21/3} = y^7$

▶ **Now Try Exercise 41**

The rules of exponents discussed in Sections 6.1 and 6.2 also apply when the exponents are fractions. In Example 5c) we use the negative exponent rule and in Example 8 we use the product and power rules with fractional exponents.

EXAMPLE 5 ▶ Evaluate. **a)** $8^{4/3}$ **b)** $16^{5/4}$ **c)** $8^{-2/3}$

Solution   To evaluate, we write each exponential expression in radical form.

a) $8^{4/3} = \left(\sqrt[3]{8}\right)^4 = 2^4 = 16$

b) $16^{5/4} = \left(\sqrt[4]{16}\right)^5 = 2^5 = 32$

c) Recall from Section 6.2 that $x^{-m} = \dfrac{1}{x^m}$. Thus,

$$8^{-2/3} = \frac{1}{8^{2/3}} = \frac{1}{\left(\sqrt[3]{8}\right)^2} = \frac{1}{2^2} = \frac{1}{4}$$

▶ **Now Try Exercise 67**

Avoiding Common Errors

Students may make mistakes simplifying expressions that contain negative exponents. Be careful when working such problems. The following is a common error.

CORRECT	INCORRECT
$27^{-2/3} = \dfrac{1}{27^{2/3}}$	$27^{-2/3} = -27^{2/3}$

The expression $27^{-2/3}$ simplifies to $\dfrac{1}{9}$. Can you show how?

EXAMPLE 6 ▶ Simplify. **a)** $\sqrt[4]{36^2}$ **b)** $\sqrt[6]{27^2}$

Solution   Write each expression in exponential form, then simplify.

a) $\sqrt[4]{36^2} = 36^{2/4} = 36^{1/2} = \sqrt{36} = 6$

b) $\sqrt[6]{27^2} = 27^{2/6} = 27^{1/3} = \sqrt[3]{27} = 3$

▶ **Now Try Exercise 79**

EXAMPLE 7 ▶ Simplify and write the answer in radical form.

a) $\sqrt[8]{y^4}$ **b)** $\sqrt[9]{z^3}$

Solution   Write the expression in exponential form, then simplify.

a) $\sqrt[8]{y^4} = y^{4/8} = y^{1/2} = \sqrt{y}$

b) $\sqrt[9]{z^3} = z^{3/9} = z^{1/3} = \sqrt[3]{z}$

▶ **Now Try Exercise 51**

EXAMPLE 8 ▶ Simplify. **a)** $\sqrt{x} \cdot \sqrt[4]{x}$. **b)** $\left(\sqrt[4]{a^2}\right)^6$.

Solution   To simplify, we change each radical expression to exponential form, then apply the rules of exponents.

a) $\sqrt{x} \cdot \sqrt[4]{x} = x^{1/2} \cdot x^{1/4}$

$= x^{(1/2)+(1/4)}$

$= x^{(2/4)+(1/4)}$

$= x^{3/4}$ $\left(\text{or } \sqrt[4]{x^3} \text{ in radical form}\right)$

b) $\left(\sqrt[4]{a^2}\right)^6 = \left(a^{2/4}\right)^6$

$= \left(a^{1/2}\right)^6$

$= a^3$

▶ **Now Try Exercise 89**

USING YOUR CALCULATOR

In Chapter 1, page 70, we learned how to use the y^x key or $\wedge$ key to raise a value to an integer exponent greater than 2. You can also use these keys if the exponent is a fraction. We demonstrate how in the following examples.

EXAMPLE 1 Evaluate $27^{2/3}$.

Solution Scientific calculator:

$$27 \boxed{y^x} \boxed{(} \boxed{2} \boxed{\div} \boxed{3} \boxed{)} \boxed{=} 9 \qquad \leftarrow \textit{Answer displayed}$$

Graphing calculator:

$$27 \boxed{\wedge} \boxed{(} \boxed{2} \boxed{\div} \boxed{3} \boxed{)} \boxed{ENTER} 9 \qquad \leftarrow \textit{Answer displayed}$$

The answer is 9. Thus, $27^{2/3} = 9$.

EXAMPLE 2 Evaluate $16^{-3/4}$.

Solution Scientific calculator:

$$16 \boxed{y^x} \boxed{(} \boxed{3} \boxed{+/-} \boxed{\div} \boxed{4} \boxed{)} \boxed{=} .125 \qquad \leftarrow \textit{Answer displayed}$$

Graphing calculator:

$$16 \boxed{\wedge} \boxed{(} \boxed{(-)} \boxed{3} \boxed{\div} \boxed{4} \boxed{)} \boxed{ENTER} .125 \qquad \leftarrow \textit{Answer displayed}$$

The answer is 0.125. Thus, $16^{-3/4} = 0.125$.

EXERCISES

Use your calculator to evaluate each expression.

1. $4^{3/2}$ 8
2. $64^{4/3}$ 256
3. $125^{-2/3}$ .04
4. $81^{-3/4}$ .037

This section was meant to give you a brief introduction to roots other than square roots. If you take a course in intermediate algebra, you may study these concepts in more depth.

EXERCISE SET 9.7

MathXL® MyMathLab

In this exercise set, assume all variables represent nonnegative real numbers.

2. Answers will vary. **3.** Write the radicand as the product of a perfect cube and another number. **4.** Write the radicand as a product of a perfect fourth power and another number.

Concept/Writing Exercises

1. Write how the following radicals would be read.
 a) $\sqrt{8}$ the square root of 8
 b) $\sqrt[3]{8}$ the cube root of 8
 c) $\sqrt[4]{8}$ the fourth root of 8

2. Describe a perfect cube and a perfect fourth power.

3. How do you simplify a cube root whose radicand is a constant?

4. How do you simplify a fourth root whose radicand is a constant?

5. a) Explain how to change an expression written in radical form to exponential form. Answers will vary.

 b) Using the procedure you wrote in part **a)**, write $\sqrt[3]{y^7}$ in exponential form. $y^{7/3}$

6. a) Explain how to change an expression written in exponential form to radical form. Answers will vary.

 b) Using the procedure you wrote in part **a)**, write $x^{5/4}$ in radical form. $\sqrt[4]{x^5}$

7. Will the odd root of a positive number always be a positive number? Explain. yes

8. Can the odd root of a negative number ever be a positive number? Explain. no

Practice the Skills

Evaluate.

9. $\sqrt[3]{8}$ 2
10. $\sqrt[3]{27}$ 3
11. $\sqrt[3]{-27}$ −3
12. $\sqrt[3]{-125}$ −5
13. $\sqrt[3]{216}$ 6
14. $\sqrt[3]{-1000}$ −10
15. $\sqrt[3]{1}$ 1
16. $\sqrt[3]{-1}$ −1

17. $\sqrt[4]{81}$ 3   **18.** $\sqrt[4]{1}$ 1   **19.** $\sqrt[4]{16}$ 2   **20.** $\sqrt[4]{625}$ 5

Simplify.

21. $\sqrt[3]{40}$ $2\sqrt[3]{5}$ **22.** $\sqrt[3]{48}$ $2\sqrt[3]{6}$ **23.** $\sqrt[3]{16}$ $2\sqrt[3]{2}$ **24.** $\sqrt[3]{32}$ $2\sqrt[3]{4}$

25. $\sqrt[3]{108}$ $3\sqrt[3]{4}$ **26.** $\sqrt[3]{192}$ $4\sqrt[3]{3}$ **27.** $\sqrt[3]{32}$ $2\sqrt[3]{2}$ **28.** $\sqrt[3]{80}$ $2\sqrt[3]{5}$

29. $\sqrt[4]{1250}$ $5\sqrt[4]{2}$ **30.** $\sqrt[5]{96}$ $2\sqrt[5]{3}$

Write each radical in exponential form.

31. $\sqrt[3]{x^7}$ $x^{7/3}$ **32.** $\sqrt[3]{x^4}$ $x^{4/3}$ **33.** $\sqrt[5]{a^2}$ $a^{2/5}$ **34.** $\sqrt[5]{x^{11}}$ $x^{11/5}$

35. $\sqrt[4]{y^{15}}$ $y^{15/4}$ **36.** $\sqrt[4]{w^{15}}$ $w^{15/4}$ **37.** $\sqrt[3]{y^8}$ $y^{8/3}$ **38.** $\sqrt[4]{x^7}$ $x^{7/4}$

Write each radical in exponential form and then simplify.

39. $\sqrt[3]{x^3}$ x **40.** $\sqrt[3]{y^6}$ y^2 **41.** $\sqrt[3]{y^{12}}$ y^4 **42.** $\sqrt[3]{m^{18}}$ m^6

43. $\sqrt[4]{x^4}$ x **44.** $\sqrt[4]{m^8}$ m^2 **45.** $\sqrt[4]{a^{20}}$ a^5 **46.** $\sqrt[4]{a^{60}}$ a^{15}

47. $\sqrt[3]{x^{15}}$ x^5 **48.** $\sqrt[3]{r^{30}}$ r^{10}

Write each radical in exponential form and then simplify. Write the answer in simplified radical form.

49. $\sqrt[4]{m^2}$ $\sqrt{m}$ **50.** $\sqrt[8]{y^4}$ $\sqrt{y}$ **51.** $\sqrt[10]{c^5}$ $\sqrt{c}$ **52.** $\sqrt[12]{p^6}$ $\sqrt{p}$

53. $\sqrt[9]{x^3}$ $\sqrt[3]{x}$ **54.** $\sqrt[12]{r^3}$ $\sqrt[4]{r}$ **55.** $\sqrt[8]{w^4}$ $\sqrt{w}$ **56.** $\sqrt[16]{z^4}$ $\sqrt[4]{z}$

57. $\sqrt[6]{x^4}$ $\sqrt[3]{x^2}$ **58.** $\sqrt[6]{y^4}$ $\sqrt[3]{y^2}$ **59.** $\sqrt[8]{z^6}$ $\sqrt[4]{z^3}$ **60.** $\sqrt[12]{n^9}$ $\sqrt[4]{n^3}$

Write each expression in radical form and then evaluate.

61. $8^{4/3}$ 16   **62.** $27^{2/3}$ 9   **63.** $27^{4/3}$ 81   **64.** $64^{2/3}$ 16

65. $1^{2/3}$ 1   **66.** $49^{3/2}$ 343   **67.** $9^{3/2}$ 27   **68.** $64^{3/2}$ 512

69. $27^{5/3}$ 243   **70.** $25^{3/2}$ 125   **71.** $256^{3/4}$ 64   **72.** $256^{2/4}$ 16

73. $8^{-1/3}$ $\dfrac{1}{2}$ **74.** $16^{-3/4}$ $\dfrac{1}{8}$ **75.** $27^{-4/3}$ $\dfrac{1}{81}$ **76.** $64^{-2/3}$ $\dfrac{1}{16}$

Write each radical in exponential form and then simplify.

77. $\sqrt[4]{4^2}$ 2   **78.** $\sqrt[4]{36^2}$ 6   **79.** $\sqrt[6]{9^3}$ 3   **80.** $\sqrt[6]{16^3}$ 4

81. $\sqrt[8]{64^4}$ 8   **82.** $\sqrt[8]{81^4}$ 9   **83.** $\sqrt[4]{7^8}$ 49   **84.** $\sqrt[4]{3^8}$ 9

85. $\sqrt[4]{3^{12}}$ 27   **86.** $\sqrt[6]{2^{18}}$ 8   **87.** $\sqrt[5]{6^{10}}$ 36   **88.** $\sqrt[5]{5^{15}}$ 125

Write each radical in exponential form and then simplify. Write the answer in exponential form.

89. $\sqrt[4]{x} \cdot \sqrt[4]{x^3}$ x **90.** $\sqrt[3]{x} \cdot \sqrt[4]{x}$ $x^{7/12}$ **91.** $\sqrt[4]{t} \cdot \sqrt[4]{t^3}$ t **92.** $\sqrt[3]{x^4} \cdot \sqrt[3]{x^5}$ x^3

93. $\left(\sqrt[3]{r^4}\right)^6$ r^8 **94.** $\left(\sqrt[4]{x^3}\right)^4$ x^3 **95.** $\left(\sqrt[4]{a^2}\right)^4$ a^2 **96.** $\left(\sqrt[3]{x^6}\right)^2$ x^4

97. Show that $(\sqrt[3]{x})^2 = \sqrt[3]{x^2}$ for $x = 27$.   both equal 9   **98.** Show that $(\sqrt[4]{x})^3 = \sqrt[4]{x^3}$ for $x = 16$.   both equal 8

Problem Solving

The product $\sqrt[3]{2} \cdot \sqrt[3]{2}$ is not an integer, but $\sqrt[3]{2} \cdot \sqrt[3]{2^2} = \sqrt[3]{2^3} = 2^{3/3} = 2$. *Use this information to determine by what radical expression you can multiply each radical so that the result is an integer.*

99. $\sqrt[3]{4}$ $\sqrt[3]{4^2}$ **100.** $\sqrt[3]{5^2}$ $\sqrt[3]{5}$ **101.** $\sqrt[3]{6}$ $\sqrt[3]{6^2}$

102. $\sqrt[4]{6^3}$ $\sqrt[4]{6}$ **103.** $\sqrt[4]{7}$ $\sqrt[4]{7^3}$ **104.** $\sqrt[4]{3^2}$ $\sqrt[4]{3^2}$

Fill in the shaded area(s) in each equation to make a true statement.

105. $\sqrt{6^2} \cdot \sqrt{6} = 6$ 3   **106.** $\sqrt{7^2} \cdot \sqrt{7^2} = 7$ 4   **107.** $\sqrt[3]{5^\blacksquare} \cdot \sqrt[3]{5^2} = 5$ 1   **108.** $\sqrt[5]{2^3} \cdot \sqrt[5]{2^\blacksquare} = 2$ 2

Challenge Problems

Simplify.

109. $\sqrt[3]{xy} \cdot \sqrt[3]{x^2y^2}$ xy **110.** $\sqrt[4]{3x^2y} \cdot \sqrt[4]{27x^6y^3}$ $3x^2y$ **111.** $\sqrt[4]{32} - \sqrt[4]{2}$ $\sqrt[4]{2}$ **112.** $\sqrt[3]{3x^3y} + \sqrt[3]{24x^3y}$ $3x\sqrt[3]{3y}$

113. a) Explain why multiplying both the numerator and denominator of $\dfrac{1}{\sqrt[3]{2}}$ by $\sqrt[3]{2^2}$ will give an integer in the denominator. $\sqrt[3]{2^3} = 2$

b) Rationalize the denominator of $\dfrac{1}{\sqrt[3]{2}}$ by multiplying both the numerator and denominator by $\sqrt[3]{2^2}$. $\dfrac{\sqrt[3]{4}}{2}$

Cumulative Review Exercises

116. $m = \dfrac{2}{3}$, y-intercept: $\left(0, -\dfrac{4}{3}\right)$

[1.9] **114.** Evaluate $-x^2 + 4xy - 8$ when $x = 2$ and $y = -4$. -44

[7.4] **115.** Factor $3x^2 - 28x + 32$. $(3x - 4)(x - 8)$

[4.2] **116.** Determine the slope and the y-intercept of the graph of the equation $2x - 3y = 4$.

[9.4] **117.** Simplify $\sqrt{\dfrac{36x^3y^7}{2x^4}}$. $\dfrac{3y^3\sqrt{2xy}}{x}$

Chapter 9 Summary

IMPORTANT FACTS AND CONCEPTS	EXAMPLES
Section 9.1	

The **positive** or **principal square root** of a positive number a is written as $\sqrt{a}$. The negative square root is written as $-\sqrt{a}$. $\qquad \sqrt{a} = b$ if $b^2 = a$ The $\sqrt{}$ is called the **radical sign**. The number or expression inside the radical sign is called the **radicand**.	$\sqrt{36} = 6$ since $36 = 6 \cdot 6$ $\sqrt{\dfrac{25}{49}} = \dfrac{5}{7}$ since $\dfrac{25}{49} = \dfrac{5}{7} \cdot \dfrac{5}{7}$ In the radical expression $\sqrt{50}$, the 50 is the radicand.
If $a \geq 0$, then $\sqrt{a}$ is a real number. If $a < 0$, then $\sqrt{a}$ is an imaginary number.	$\sqrt{31}$, $\sqrt{19.42}$ are real numbers. $\sqrt{-101}$, $\sqrt{-1.63}$ are imaginary numbers.
The square of a natural number is a perfect square. The square root of a perfect square is an integer.	$1, 4, 9, 16, 25, 36, \ldots$ are perfect squares $\sqrt{16} = 4$, $\sqrt{81} = 9$
A **rational number** is a number that can be written in the form $\dfrac{a}{b}$, where a and b are integers and $b \neq 0$. When written as a decimal, a rational number is either a **terminating** or **repeating decimal**. **Irrational numbers** are numbers that are not rational.	$\dfrac{1}{4} = 0.25$ and $\dfrac{21}{99} = 0.212121\ldots = 0.\overline{21}$ are rational numbers. $\sqrt{15}$, $\sqrt{23}$ are irrational numbers.
When writing a square root in exponential form, $\qquad \sqrt{x} = x^{1/2}$	$\sqrt{36} = 36^{1/2}$, $\qquad \sqrt{3x} = (3x)^{1/2}$
Section 9.2	

Product Rule for Square Roots $\qquad \sqrt{a} \cdot \sqrt{b} = \sqrt{a \cdot b}$, provided $a \geq 0, b \geq 0$ Rule 1	$\sqrt{3} \cdot \sqrt{5} = \sqrt{15}$
To Simplify the Square Root of a Constant 1. Write the constant as a product of the largest perfect square factor and another factor. 2. Use the product rule to write the expression as a product of square roots, with each square root containing one of the factors. 3. Find the square root of the perfect square factor.	Simplify $\sqrt{54}$. $\qquad \sqrt{54} = \sqrt{9 \cdot 6} = \sqrt{9} \cdot \sqrt{6} = 3\sqrt{6}$
$\qquad \sqrt{a^{2n}} = a^n, a \geq 0$ Rule 2	$\sqrt{x^6} = x^3$

IMPORTANT FACTS AND CONCEPTS	EXAMPLES

Section 9.2 (continued)

To Simplify the Square Root of a Radicand Containing a Variable Raised to an Odd Power

1. Express the variable as the product of two factors, one of which has an exponent of 1 (the other will therefore be a perfect square factor).
2. Use the product rule to simplify.

$$\sqrt{75y^7} = \sqrt{25y^6 \cdot 3y} = \sqrt{25y^6} \cdot \sqrt{3y}$$
$$= 5y^3\sqrt{3y}$$

Section 9.3

Like square roots are square roots having the same radicands. To add, combine like square roots.

$$3\sqrt{5} + 8\sqrt{5} + \sqrt{5} = 12\sqrt{5}$$
$$2\sqrt{x} + y + 7\sqrt{x} = 9\sqrt{x} + y$$

Unlike square roots are square roots having different radicands. Sometimes unlike square roots can be changed to like square roots by simplifying the radicals in the expression.

$$3\sqrt{2} + \sqrt{32} = 3\sqrt{2} + \sqrt{16} \cdot \sqrt{2}$$
$$= 3\sqrt{2} + 4\sqrt{2}$$
$$= 7\sqrt{2}$$

To multiply radical expressions, use the distributive property.

$$\sqrt{5x}\left(\sqrt{x} - \sqrt{3y}\right) = \left(\sqrt{5x}\right)\left(\sqrt{x}\right) - \left(\sqrt{5x}\right)\left(\sqrt{3y}\right)$$
$$= \sqrt{5x^2} - \sqrt{15xy}$$
$$= x\sqrt{5} - \sqrt{15xy}$$

To multiply two binomials with radical expressions, use the FOIL method.

$$\left(2 + \sqrt{3}\right)\left(5 - 4\sqrt{3}\right) = 2 \cdot 5 + 2\left(-4\sqrt{3}\right) + 5\sqrt{3}$$
$$+ \left(\sqrt{3}\right)\left(-4\sqrt{3}\right)$$
$$= 10 - 8\sqrt{3} + 5\sqrt{3} - 12$$
$$= -2 - 3\sqrt{3}$$

Section 9.4

A Square Root Is Simplified When

1. No radicand has a factor that is a perfect square.

2. No radicand contains a fraction.

3. No denominator contains a square root.

1. $\sqrt{32}$ is not simplified.

2. $\sqrt{\dfrac{1}{3}}$ is not simplified.

3. $\dfrac{1}{\sqrt{11}}$ is not simplified.

Quotient Rule for Square Roots

$$\frac{\sqrt{a}}{\sqrt{b}} = \sqrt{\frac{a}{b}}, \quad \text{provided} \quad a \geq 0, b > 0 \quad \text{Rule 3}$$

$$\frac{\sqrt{35}}{\sqrt{5}} = \sqrt{\frac{35}{5}} = \sqrt{7}$$

To **rationalize a denominator** means to remove all radicals from the denominator. To rationalize a denominator with a square root, multiply *both* the numerator and the denominator of the fraction by the square root that appears in the denominator or by the square root of a number that makes the denominator a perfect square.

$$\frac{1}{\sqrt{7}} = \frac{1}{\sqrt{7}} \cdot \frac{\sqrt{7}}{\sqrt{7}} = \frac{\sqrt{7}}{7}$$

$$\frac{9}{\sqrt{c}} = \frac{9}{\sqrt{c}} \cdot \frac{\sqrt{c}}{\sqrt{c}} = \frac{9\sqrt{c}}{c}$$

IMPORTANT FACTS AND CONCEPTS	EXAMPLES

Section 9.4 (continued)

The **conjugate of a binomial** is a binomial having the same two terms with the sign of the second term changed.

$13 - \sqrt{2}$ is the conjugate of $13 + \sqrt{2}$

$-\sqrt{5} + \sqrt{3}$ is the conjugate of $-\sqrt{5} - \sqrt{3}$

To rationalize a denominator that has a binomial, multiply the numerator and denominator by the conjugate of the denominator.

$$\frac{9}{5 + \sqrt{2}} = \frac{9}{5 + \sqrt{2}} \cdot \frac{5 - \sqrt{2}}{5 - \sqrt{2}} = \frac{9(5 - \sqrt{2})}{25 - 2} = \frac{45 - 9\sqrt{2}}{23}$$

$$\frac{y}{\sqrt{x} + y} = \frac{y}{\sqrt{x} + y} \cdot \frac{\sqrt{x} - y}{\sqrt{x} - y} = \frac{y(\sqrt{x} - y)}{x - y^2} = \frac{y\sqrt{x} - y^2}{x - y^2}$$

Section 9.5

A **radical equation** is an equation that contains a variable in a radicand.

$\sqrt{x} = 5, \quad \sqrt{y - 10} = 8$

To Solve a Radical Equation Containing Only One Square Root Term

1. Rewrite the equation with the square root term by itself on one side of the equation.
2. Combine like terms.
3. Square both sides of the equation to eliminate the square root.
4. Solve the equation for the variable.
5. Check the solution in the *original* equation for extraneous roots.

Solve $\sqrt{x} + 4 = 6$.

$$\sqrt{x} + 4 = 6$$
$$\sqrt{x} = 2$$
$$(\sqrt{x})^2 = 2^2$$
$$x = 4$$

A check shows that 4 is the solution.

Section 9.6

Pythagorean Theorem
In a right triangle, if a and b represent the legs, and c represents the hypotenuse, then $a^2 + b^2 = c^2$.

Find the hypotenuse of a right triangle whose legs are $\sqrt{15}$ and 3.

$$a^2 + b^2 = c^2$$
$$(\sqrt{15})^2 + 3^2 = c^2$$
$$15 + 9 = c^2$$
$$24 = c^2$$
$$\sqrt{24} = c \quad \text{or} \quad c = 2\sqrt{6}$$

Distance Formula
The distance between two points (x_1, y_1) and (x_2, y_2) is

$$d = \sqrt{(x_2 - x_1)^2 + (y_2 - y_1)^2}$$

The length of the line segment joining the points $(-3, 4)$ and $(1, 7)$ is

$$d = \sqrt{[1 - (-3)]^2 + (7 - 4)^2}$$
$$= \sqrt{4^2 + 3^2} = \sqrt{16 + 9} = \sqrt{25} = 5$$

Section 9.7

The **cube root of a** is $\sqrt[3]{a}$.
$\sqrt[3]{a} = b$ if $b^3 = a$

$\sqrt[3]{27} = 3, \sqrt[3]{-27} = -3$

The **fourth root of a** is $\sqrt[4]{a}$.
$\sqrt[4]{a} = b$ if $b^4 = a$ $a \geq 0$
$\sqrt[4]{a}$ is not a real number if $a < 0$.

$\sqrt[4]{16} = 2,$

$\sqrt[4]{-16}$ is not a real number

IMPORTANT FACTS AND CONCEPTS	EXAMPLES

Section 9.7 (continued)

Product Rule for Radicals

$\sqrt[n]{a}\,\sqrt[n]{b} = \sqrt[n]{ab}$, for $a \geq 0, b \geq 0$ and n is even

$\sqrt[n]{a}\,\sqrt[n]{b} = \sqrt[n]{ab}$, when n is odd

$\sqrt[3]{4} \cdot \sqrt[3]{2} = \sqrt[3]{8} = 2$

$\sqrt[4]{96} = \sqrt[4]{16 \cdot 6} = \sqrt[4]{16} \cdot \sqrt[4]{6} = 2\sqrt[4]{6}$

Exponential Form of a Radical Expression

$\sqrt[n]{a} = a^{1/n}$, for $a \geq 0$ and n is even   Rule 4

$\sqrt[n]{a} = a^{1/n}$, when n is odd

$\sqrt[n]{a^m} = \left(\sqrt[n]{a}\right)^m = a^{m/n}$, for $a \geq 0$ and m and n integers   Rule 5

$\sqrt{z} = z^{1/2},\ \sqrt[3]{7b^2} = \left(7b^2\right)^{1/3}$

$\sqrt[3]{27^2} = \left(\sqrt[3]{27}\right)^2 = 3^2 = 9,$

$8^{4/3} = \left(\sqrt[3]{8}\right)^4 = 2^4 = 16$

$\sqrt[4]{x^{20}} = x^{20/4} = x^5$

Negative Exponent Rule

$$x^{-m} = \frac{1}{x^m}$$

$$3^{-4} = \frac{1}{3^4} = \frac{1}{81}$$

Chapter 9 Review Exercises

[9.1] *Evaluate.*

1. $\sqrt{81}$ 9

2. $\sqrt{121}$ 11

3. $-\sqrt{49}$ -7

Write in exponential form.

4. $\sqrt{15}$ $15^{1/2}$

5. $\sqrt{41x}$ $(41x)^{1/2}$

6. $\sqrt{23x^2y}$ $(23x^2y)^{1/2}$

[9.2] *Simplify.*

7. $\sqrt{24}$ $2\sqrt{6}$

8. $\sqrt{52}$ $2\sqrt{13}$

9. $\sqrt{48x^7y^5}$ $4x^3y^2\sqrt{3xy}$

10. $\sqrt{125x^4y^8}$ $5x^2y^4\sqrt{5}$

11. $\sqrt{60ab^5c^4}$ $2b^2c^2\sqrt{15ab}$

12. $\sqrt{72a^2b^2c^7}$ $6abc^3\sqrt{2c}$

Simplify.

13. $\sqrt{144}\,\sqrt{10}$ $12\sqrt{10}$

14. $\sqrt{3y}\,\sqrt{3y}$ $3y$

15. $\sqrt{32x}\,\sqrt{2xy}$ $8x\sqrt{y}$

16. $\sqrt{25x^2y}\,\sqrt{2y}$ $5xy\sqrt{2}$

17. $\sqrt{12a^3b^4}\,\sqrt{3b^4}$ $6ab^4\sqrt{a}$

18. $\sqrt{2ab^3}\,\sqrt{50ab^4}$ $10ab^3\sqrt{b}$

[9.3] *Simplify.*

19. $9\sqrt{3} - 4\sqrt{3}$ $5\sqrt{3}$

20. $4\sqrt{5} - 6\sqrt{5} - 3\sqrt{5}$ $-5\sqrt{5}$

21. $11\sqrt{x} - 5\sqrt{x}$ $6\sqrt{x}$

22. $\sqrt{k} + 3\sqrt{k} - 8\sqrt{k}$ $-4\sqrt{k}$

23. $2\sqrt{18} - \sqrt{27}$ $6\sqrt{2} - 3\sqrt{3}$

24. $7\sqrt{40} - 3\sqrt{10}$ $11\sqrt{10}$

25. $2\sqrt{98} - 4\sqrt{72}$ $-10\sqrt{2}$

26. $7\sqrt{50} + 2\sqrt{18} - 4\sqrt{32}$ $25\sqrt{2}$

Multiply.

27. $\sqrt{6}\left(2 + \sqrt{6}\right)$ $2\sqrt{6} + 6$

28. $\sqrt{2}\left(\sqrt{2} + 3\right)$ $2 + 3\sqrt{2}$

29. $\sqrt{y}\left(x - 8\sqrt{y}\right)$ $x\sqrt{y} - 8y$

30. $4a\left(3a + \sqrt{2a}\right)$ $12a^2 + 4a\sqrt{2a}$

31. $\left(\sqrt{7} - 2\right)\left(\sqrt{7} + 2\right)$ 3

32. $\left(9 - \sqrt{5}\right)\left(9 + \sqrt{5}\right)$ 76

33. $(x - 5\sqrt{y})(x + 5\sqrt{y})$ $x^2 - 25y$

34. $\left(\sqrt{c} - 3\sqrt{d}\right)\left(\sqrt{c} + 3\sqrt{d}\right)$ $c - 9d$

35. $(m + 2\sqrt{r})(m - 5\sqrt{r})$

36. $\left(\sqrt{t} + 2s\right)(3\sqrt{t} - s)$ $3t + 5s\sqrt{t} - 2s^2$

37. $\left(\sqrt{5m} + 6\sqrt{n}\right)(3\sqrt{5m} - \sqrt{n})$

38. $\left(\sqrt{7} - 3\sqrt{p}\right)(2\sqrt{7} - 3\sqrt{p})$

35. $m^2 - 3m\sqrt{r} - 10r$ **37.** $15m + 17\sqrt{5mn} - 6n$ **38.** $14 - 9\sqrt{7p} + 9p$

[9.4] *Simplify.*

39. $\dfrac{\sqrt{48}}{\sqrt{3}}$ 4

40. $\sqrt{\dfrac{5}{245}}$ $\dfrac{1}{7}$

41. $\sqrt{\dfrac{6}{24}}$ $\dfrac{1}{2}$

42. $\dfrac{2}{\sqrt{3}}$ $\dfrac{2\sqrt{3}}{3}$

43. $\sqrt{\dfrac{n}{7}}$ $\dfrac{\sqrt{7n}}{7}$

44. $\sqrt{\dfrac{10a}{24}}$ $\dfrac{\sqrt{15a}}{6}$

45. $\sqrt{\dfrac{x^2}{5}}$ $\dfrac{x\sqrt{5}}{5}$

46. $\sqrt{\dfrac{z^6}{8}}$ $\dfrac{z^3\sqrt{2}}{4}$

47. $\sqrt{\dfrac{28x^3y^7}{4x^3y^3}}$ $y^2\sqrt{7}$

48. $\sqrt{\dfrac{20x^4y}{10x^2y^4}}$ $\dfrac{x\sqrt{2y}}{y^2}$

49. $\dfrac{\sqrt{60}}{\sqrt{27a^3b^2}}$ $\dfrac{2\sqrt{5a}}{3a^2b}$

50. $\dfrac{\sqrt{2a^4bc^4}}{\sqrt{7a^5bc^2}}$ $\dfrac{c\sqrt{14a}}{7a}$

Simplify.

51. $\dfrac{2}{1 - \sqrt{6}}$ $\dfrac{-2 - 2\sqrt{6}}{5}$

52. $\dfrac{4}{3 - \sqrt{6}}$ $\dfrac{12 + 4\sqrt{6}}{3}$

53. $\dfrac{\sqrt{3}}{2 + \sqrt{y}}$ $\dfrac{2\sqrt{3} - \sqrt{3y}}{4 - y}$

54. $\dfrac{3}{\sqrt{x} - 5}$ $\dfrac{3\sqrt{x} + 15}{x - 25}$

55. $\dfrac{\sqrt{10}}{\sqrt{x} + \sqrt{3}}$ $\dfrac{\sqrt{10x} - \sqrt{30}}{x - 3}$

56. $\dfrac{\sqrt{7}}{\sqrt{5} - x}$ $\dfrac{\sqrt{35} + x\sqrt{7}}{5 - x^2}$

[9.5] *Solve.*

57. $\sqrt{x} = 7$ 49

58. $\sqrt{g} = -2$ no solution

59. $\sqrt{h - 6} = 3$ 15

60. $\sqrt{3x + 4} = 5$ 7

61. $\sqrt{5x + 7} = \sqrt{4x + 9}$ 2

62. $4\sqrt{x} - x = 4$ 4

63. $\sqrt{x^2 + 7} = x + 1$ 3

64. $\sqrt{4x + 8} - \sqrt{7x - 13} = 0$ 7

65. $\sqrt{4p + 1} = 2p - 1$ 2

[9.6] *Find each length indicated by x. Round answers to nearest hundredth.*

67. $\sqrt{125} \approx 11.18$ **68.** $\sqrt{12} \approx 3.46$

66.   26 24 x 10

67.   15 x 10

68. x $\sqrt{3}$ $\sqrt{15}$

69.   6 5 x $\sqrt{61} \approx 7.81$

70. Ladder on a Cottage Adam Kurtz leans a 12-foot ladder against his grandfather's cottage. If the base of the ladder is 4 feet from the cottage how high is the ladder on the cottage? $\sqrt{128} \approx 11.31$ ft

71. Diagonal of a Rectangle Find the diagonal of a rectangle of length 15 inches and width 10 inches. $\sqrt{325} \approx 18.03$ in.

72. Find the straight-line distance between the points $(4, -3)$ and $(1, 7)$. $\sqrt{109} \approx 10.44$

73. Find the length of the line segment between the points $(6, 5)$ and $(-6, 8)$. $\sqrt{153} \approx 12.37$

74. Right-of-Way Sign An **equilateral triangle** is a triangle with three sides of the same length. A yield-right-of-way sign in the United States is an equilateral triangle with each side, s, measuring 36 inches. Use the formula for the area of an equilateral triangle

$$\text{Area} = \frac{s^2\sqrt{3}}{4}$$

to find an approximation of the area of a yield sign. Round the area to the nearest hundredth.   561.18 sq in.

75. Distance Seen The farthest distance, in miles, that a person looking at the horizon can see is approximated by the formula $distance = \sqrt{(3/2)h}$, where h represents the height of the vantage point measured in feet. Approximately how far can a person see, correct to the nearest hundredth of a mile, if the person is at a vantage point 40 feet high? $\sqrt{60} \approx 7.75$ mi

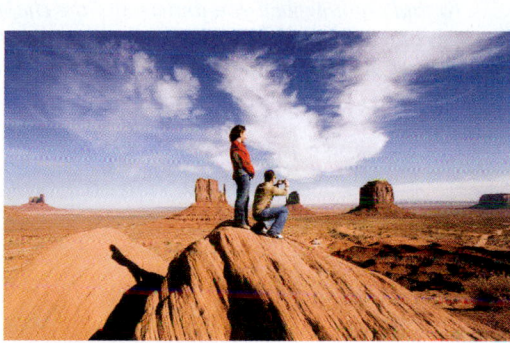

See Exercise 75.

76. Luxor Hotel The Luxor Hotel in Las Vegas, Nevada, is the world's second largest hotel. It is a pyramid with a square base and a height of 350 feet. The length, s, of each side of the base of any pyramid with a square base can be found by the formula $s = \sqrt{(3V)/h}$, where V represents the volume, in cubic feet, of the pyramid and h represents the height, in feet. The volume of the Luxor is approximately 48,686,866.67 cubic feet. Find the length of each side of the square base of the Luxor Hotel. ≈ 646 feet

[9.7] *Evaluate.*

77. $\sqrt[3]{8}$ 2

78. $\sqrt[3]{-64}$ -4

79. $\sqrt[4]{16}$ 2

80. $\sqrt[4]{81}$ 3

Simplify.

81. $\sqrt[3]{16}$ $2\sqrt[3]{2}$

82. $\sqrt[3]{-16}$ $-2\sqrt[3]{2}$

83. $\sqrt[3]{48}$ $2\sqrt[3]{6}$

84. $\sqrt[4]{32}$ $2\sqrt[4]{2}$

85. $\sqrt[3]{54}$ $3\sqrt[3]{2}$

86. $\sqrt[4]{80}$ $2\sqrt[4]{5}$

87. $\sqrt[3]{x^{21}}$ x^7

88. $\sqrt[4]{s^{48}}$ s^{12}

Evaluate.

89. $27^{2/3}$ 9

90. $36^{1/2}$ 6

91. $27^{-2/3}$ $\dfrac{1}{9}$

92. $64^{4/3}$ 256

93. $125^{-4/3}$ $\dfrac{1}{625}$

94. $9^{5/2}$ 243

Write in exponential form.

95. $\sqrt{x^5}$ $x^{5/2}$

96. $\sqrt{a^7}$ $a^{7/2}$

97. $\sqrt[3]{z^{11}}$ $z^{11/3}$

98. $\sqrt[3]{x^{10}}$ $x^{10/3}$

99. $\sqrt[4]{y^{13}}$ $y^{13/4}$

100. $\sqrt[4]{m^6}$ $m^{6/4} = m^{3/2}$

Simplify.

101. $\sqrt[3]{x} \cdot \sqrt[3]{x^2}$ x

102. $\sqrt[3]{x} \cdot \sqrt[3]{x}$ $\sqrt[3]{x^2}$

103. $\sqrt[3]{a^4} \cdot \sqrt[3]{a^8}$ a^4

104. $\sqrt[4]{x^2} \cdot \sqrt[4]{x^6}$ x^2

105. $\left(\sqrt[3]{q^3}\right)^3$ q^3

106. $\left(\sqrt[4]{b^2}\right)^4$ b^2

107. $\left(\sqrt[4]{x^8}\right)^3$ x^6

108. $\left(\sqrt[4]{x^5}\right)^8$ x^{10}

Chapter 9 Practice Test

To find out how well you understand the chapter material, take this practice test. The answers, and the section where the material was initially discussed, are given in the back of the book. Each problem is also fully worked out on the **Chapter Test Prep Video CD.** *Review any questions that you answered incorrectly.*

1. Write $\sqrt{5x}$ exponential form. $(5x)^{1/2}$

2. Write $x^{3/4}$ in radical form. $\sqrt[4]{x^3}$

Simplify.

3. $\sqrt{169}$ 13

4. $\sqrt{90}$ $3\sqrt{10}$

5. $\sqrt{12x^2}$ $2x\sqrt{3}$

6. $\sqrt{75x^7y^3}$ $5x^3y\sqrt{3xy}$

7. $\sqrt{4x^2y}\sqrt{20xy}$ $4xy\sqrt{5x}$

8. $\sqrt{10xy^2}\sqrt{5x^3y^3}$ $5x^2y^2\sqrt{2y}$

9. $\sqrt{\dfrac{5}{125}}$ $\dfrac{1}{5}$

10. $\dfrac{\sqrt{3c^4d}}{\sqrt{3d^3}}$ $\dfrac{c^2}{d}$

11. $\dfrac{1}{\sqrt{5}}$ $\dfrac{\sqrt{5}}{5}$

12. $\sqrt{\dfrac{9r}{5}}$ $\dfrac{3\sqrt{5r}}{5}$

13. $\sqrt{\dfrac{40x^2y^5}{3x^3y^7}}$ $\dfrac{2\sqrt{30x}}{3xy}$

14. $\dfrac{6}{2-\sqrt{7}}$ $-4-2\sqrt{7}$

15. $\dfrac{7}{\sqrt{x}-3}$ $\dfrac{7\sqrt{x}+21}{x-9}$

16. $\sqrt{48}+5\sqrt{12}+2\sqrt{3}$ $16\sqrt{3}$

17. $9\sqrt{y}-3\sqrt{y}-\sqrt{y}$ $5\sqrt{y}$

Solve.

18. $\sqrt{x-10}=4$ 26

19. $2\sqrt{x-4}+4=x$ 4, 8

Solve.

20. Find the value of x in the right triangle. $\sqrt{106} \approx 10.30$

21. Find the length of the line segment between the points $(3, 2)$ and $(-4, -1)$. $\sqrt{58} \approx 7.62$

22. Evaluate $27^{-4/3}$. $\dfrac{1}{81}$

23. Simplify $\sqrt[4]{x^5} \cdot \sqrt[4]{x^7}$. x^3

24. Side of a Square Find the side of a square whose area is 169 square meters.   13 m

25. Dropping Eggs Mary Ellen Baker and her brother, Michael, were in the tree house in their backyard. They were dropping raw eggs (much to their mother's dismay) from a ledge in the tree house 10 feet in the air. At what velocity did the eggs hit the ground? Use the formula $v = \sqrt{2gh}$ with $g = 32$ feet per second squared. The velocity will be in feet per second. $\sqrt{640} \approx 25.30$ ft/sec

Cumulative Review Test

Take the following test and check your answers with those given in the back of the book. Review any questions that you answered incorrectly. The section where the material was covered is indicated after the answer.

1. Consider the set of numbers

$$\left\{-5, \sqrt{12}, 735, 0.5, 4, \frac{1}{2}\right\}.$$

List those that are

a) integers; $-5, 735, 4$

b) whole numbers; $735, 4$

c) rational numbers; $-5, 735, 0.5, 4, \frac{1}{2}$

d) irrational numbers; $\sqrt{12}$

e) real numbers.   all

2. Evaluate $7a^2 - 4b^2 + 3ab$ when $a = -3$ and $b = 2$.   29

3. Solve $-7(3 - x) = 4(x + 2) - 3x$. $\dfrac{29}{6}$

4. Solve the inequality $3(x + 2) > 5 - 4(2x - 7)$ and graph the solution on a number line.

5. Factor $4x^3 + x^2 + 8x + 2$. $(4x + 1)(x^2 + 2)$

6. Factor $2x^2 - 19x + 24$. $(2x - 3)(x - 8)$

7. Use factoring to solve $r^2 - 9r = 0$. $0, 9$

8. Simplify $\dfrac{4a^3b^{-5}}{20a^8b}$. $\dfrac{1}{5a^5b^6}$

9. Graph $4x - 6y = 24$.   See graphing answer section.

10. Write the equation of the graph below. $y = 3x - 2$

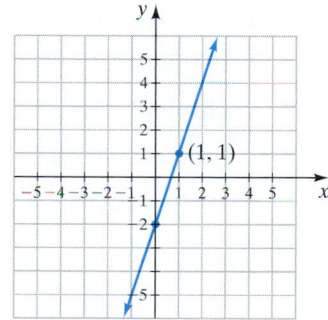

11. Find the equation of the line, in slope–intercept form, that has a slope of $\dfrac{2}{5}$ and goes through the point $(5, 6)$. $y = \dfrac{2}{5}x + 4$

12. Solve the following system of equations.

$$-2x + 3y = 6$$
$$4x - 2y = -4 \quad (0, 2)$$

13. Simplify $\dfrac{y + 9}{8} + \dfrac{2y - 14}{8}$. $\dfrac{3y - 5}{8}$

14. Solve $\dfrac{3}{5} + \dfrac{1}{z} = 2$. $\dfrac{5}{7}$

15. Simplify $7\sqrt{11} - 4\sqrt{11}$. $3\sqrt{11}$

16. Simplify $\sqrt{\dfrac{3z}{28y^5}}$. $\dfrac{\sqrt{21yz}}{14y^3}$

17. Solve $\sqrt{x + 10} = 6$.   26   **18.** $2\dfrac{8}{11}$ cups

18. Making a Fruitcake Susan Effing is planning her first holiday meal. She has decided to make her grandmother's famous fruitcake. The recipe calls for 10 cups of flour and will make an 11-pound fruitcake. She would like to make a 3-pound fruitcake. How many cups of flour should Susan use?

19. Special Promotion During a special promotion, the rooms in the Hyatt Hotel in Oklahoma City cost $75. If this is a 40% discount off the hotel's regular room rate, determine the Hyatt's regular room rate. $125

20. Distance between Cities Alan Heard is in the process of getting his pilot's license. As part of his training, he flew his instructor from a small airport near Pasadena, California, to another small airport near San Diego at an average speed of 100 miles per hour. On the return trip, his average speed was 125 miles per hour. How far apart were the two airports if Alan's total flying time was 2 hours? ≈ 111.1 mi

4. $x > \dfrac{27}{11}$,

Quadratic Equations

10

WE SEE OBJECTS PROJECTED upward often but rarely think of the mathematics that describes the projected motion. For example, when a ball hits a bat, or a child kicks a football or a soccer ball, the ball is projected upward. In Exercises 69 and 70 on page 613, we will determine the height a model rocket obtains when launched upward.

10.1 The Square Root Property

1 Know that every positive real number has two square roots.

2 Solve quadratic equations using the square root property.

In Section 7.6 we solved quadratic equations by factoring. Recall that **quadratic equations** are equations of the form

$$ax^2 + bx + c = 0$$

where a, b, and c are real numbers, $a \neq 0$. A quadratic equation in this form is said to be in **standard form**. Solving quadratic equations by factoring is the preferred technique when the factors can be found quickly. To refresh your memory, below we will solve the equation $x^2 - 3x - 10 = 0$ by factoring. If you need further examples, review Section 7.6.

TEACHING TIP
Point out that a quadratic equation can be created from 2 solutions by working backward. Ask students to write a quadratic equation that has solutions 5 and −2.

$$x^2 - 3x - 10 = 0$$

$$(x - 5)(x + 2) = 0$$

$$x - 5 = 0 \quad \text{or} \quad x + 2 = 0$$

$$x = 5 \qquad \qquad x = -2$$

The solutions to this equation are 5 and −2.

Not every quadratic equation can be factored easily, and many cannot be factored at all. In this chapter we give two techniques, completing the square and the quadratic formula, for solving quadratic equations that cannot be solved by factoring.

1 Know That Every Positive Real Number Has Two Square Roots

In Section 9.1 we stated that every positive number has two square roots. Thus far we have been using only the positive or principal square root. In this section we use both the positive and negative square roots of a number. For example, the positive square root of 49 is 7.

$$\sqrt{49} = 7$$

The negative square root of 49 is −7.

$$-\sqrt{49} = -7$$

TEACHING TIP
Point out that a solution to $x^2 = 49$ is any number that results in 49 when squared, and a solution to $x = \sqrt{49}$ is the positive number that results in 49 when squared.

Notice that $7 \cdot 7 = 49$ and $(-7)(-7) = 49$. The two square roots of 49 are +7 and −7. A convenient way to indicate the two square roots of a number is to use the plus or minus symbol, $\pm$. For example, the square roots of 49 can be indicated ± 7, read "plus or minus 7."

Number	Both Square Roots
64	± 8
100	± 10
3	$\pm \sqrt{3}$
7	$\pm \sqrt{7}$

The value of a number like $-\sqrt{5}$ can be found by finding the value of $\sqrt{5}$ on your calculator and then taking its opposite or negative value.

$$\sqrt{5} = 2.24 \qquad \textit{(rounded to the nearest hundredth)}$$

$$-\sqrt{5} = -2.24$$

Now consider the equation

$$x^2 = 49$$

We can see by substitution that this equation has two solutions, 7 and -7.

Check

$x = 7$	$x = -7$
$x^2 = 49$	$x^2 = 49$
$7^2 \overset{?}{=} 49$	$(-7)^2 \overset{?}{=} 49$
$49 = 49$ *True*	$49 = 49$ *True*

Therefore, the solutions to the equation $x^2 = 49$ are 7 and -7 (or ± 7).

2 Solve Quadratic Equations Using the Square Root Property

TEACHING TIP
Before discussing Example 1, have
students solve $y - 5 = 0$ and
$y^2 - 25 = 0$.

In general, for any quadratic equation of the form $x^2 = a$, we can use the **square root property** to obtain the solution.

> **Square Root Property**
>
> If $x^2 = a$, then $x = \sqrt{a}$ or $x = -\sqrt{a}$ (abbreviated $x = \pm\sqrt{a}$).

For example, if $x^2 = 7$, then by the square root property, $x = \sqrt{7}$ or $x = -\sqrt{7}$. We may also write $x = \pm\sqrt{7}$.

EXAMPLE 1 ▶ Solve the equation $x^2 - 25 = 0$.

INSTRUCTOR EXAMPLE
Solve $x^2 - 49 = 0$.
Ans.: ± 7

Solution   Before we use the square root property we must isolate the squared variable. Add 25 to both sides of the equation to get the variable by itself on one side of the equation.

$$x^2 = 25$$

Now use the square root property to isolate the variable.

$$x = \pm\sqrt{25}$$
$$x = \pm 5$$

Check in the original equation.

Check

$x = 5$	$x = -5$
$x^2 - 25 = 0$	$x^2 - 25 = 0$
$5^2 - 25 \overset{?}{=} 0$	$(-5)^2 - 25 = 0$
$25 - 25 \overset{?}{=} 0$	$25 - 25 \overset{?}{=} 0$
$0 = 0$ *True*	$0 = 0$ *True*

▶ **Now Try Exercise 7**

EXAMPLE 2 ▶ Solve the equation $x^2 + 10 = 74$.

INSTRUCTOR EXAMPLE
Solve $x^2 - 5 = 20$.
Ans.: ± 5

Solution   Begin by subtracting 10 from both sides of the equation.

$$x^2 + 10 = 74$$
$$x^2 = 64 \qquad \text{\color{magenta}\textit{Isolate } x^2.}$$
$$x = \pm\sqrt{64} \qquad \text{\color{magenta}\textit{Square root property}}$$
$$x = \pm 8$$

▶ **Now Try Exercise 13**

EXAMPLE 3 ▶ Solve the equation $a^2 - 13 = 0$.

INSTRUCTOR EXAMPLE
Solve $m^2 - 19 = 0$.
Ans.: $\pm\sqrt{19}$

Solution
$$a^2 - 13 = 0$$
$$a^2 = 13 \qquad \text{\color{magenta}\textit{Isolate } a^2.}$$
$$a = \pm\sqrt{13} \qquad \text{\color{magenta}\textit{Square root property}}$$

▶ **Now Try Exercise 15**

EXAMPLE 4 ▶ Solve the equation $(x - 3)^2 = 4$.

Solution   Begin by using the square root property.

$$(x - 3)^2 = 4$$
$$x - 3 = \pm\sqrt{4} \qquad \textcolor{red}{\textit{Square root property}}$$
$$x - 3 = \pm 2$$
$$x - 3 \boxed{+3} = \boxed{3} \pm 2 \qquad \textcolor{red}{\textit{Add 3 to both sides.}}$$
$$x = 3 \pm 2$$
$$x = 3 + 2 \quad \text{or} \quad x = 3 - 2$$
$$x = 5 \qquad\qquad x = 1$$

The solutions are 1 and 5.

▶ **Now Try Exercise 27**

EXAMPLE 5 ▶ Solve the equation $(5x + 4)^2 - 2 = 16$.

Solution   We must first isolate the squared term. We do so by adding 2 to both sides of the equation.

$$(5x + 4)^2 - 2 = 16$$
$$(5x + 4)^2 = 18 \qquad \textcolor{red}{\substack{\textit{Add 2 to both sides to} \\ \textit{isolate the squared term.}}}$$
$$5x + 4 = \pm\sqrt{18} \qquad \textcolor{red}{\textit{Square root property}}$$
$$5x + 4 = \pm\sqrt{9}\,\sqrt{2} \qquad \textcolor{red}{\textit{Simplify } \sqrt{18}.}$$
$$5x + 4 = \pm 3\sqrt{2}$$
$$5x + 4 \boxed{-4} = \boxed{-4} \pm 3\sqrt{2} \qquad \textcolor{red}{\textit{Subtract 4 from both sides.}}$$
$$5x = -4 \pm 3\sqrt{2}$$
$$x = \frac{-4 \pm 3\sqrt{2}}{5} \qquad \textcolor{red}{\textit{Divide both sides by 5.}}$$

The solutions are $\dfrac{-4 + 3\sqrt{2}}{5}$ and $\dfrac{-4 - 3\sqrt{2}}{5}$.

▶ **Now Try Exercise 43**

Now let's look at one of many applications of quadratic equations.

EXAMPLE 6 ▶ **Creating Advertisements** When creating advertisements, the shape of the ad as well as its coloring and print style must be considered. When Antoinette LeMans approached an advertising firm to design a magazine ad for her company, she learned that one of the most appealing shapes is a rectangle whose length is about 1.62 times its width. Any rectangle with these proportions is called a *golden rectangle*. She decided that the ad would have the dimensions of a golden rectangle. Find the dimensions of the ad if it is to have an area of 20 square inches, see **Figure 10.1**.

1.62x

x

FIGURE 10.1

Solution   **Understand and Translate**   Let x = width of rectangle.

Then $1.62x$ = length of rectangle.

$$\text{area} = \text{length} \cdot \text{width}$$
$$20 = (1.62x)x$$

Carry Out $20 = 1.62x^2$

or $1.62x^2 = 20$

$$x^2 = \frac{20}{1.62} \approx 12.3$$

$$x \approx \pm\sqrt{12.3} \approx \pm 3.51 \text{ inches}$$

Check and Answer   Since the width cannot be negative, the width, x, is approximately 3.51 inches. The length is about $1.62(3.51) = 5.69$ inches.

Check

$$\text{area} = \text{length} \cdot \text{width}$$
$$20 \overset{?}{=} (5.69)(3.51)$$
$$20 \approx 19.97 \qquad \textit{True} \qquad \textit{(There is a slight round-off error due to rounding off decimal answers.)}$$

▶ **Now Try Exercise 57**

Note that the answer to Example 6 is not a whole number. In many real-life situations this is the case. You should not feel uncomfortable when this occurs.

EXERCISE SET 10.1   Math XL   MyMathLab
MathXL®   MyMathLab

Concept/Writing Exercises

1. If $x^2 = a$, then $x = \sqrt{a}$ or $x = -\sqrt{a}$.

1. State the square root property.

2. Explain how to solve the quadratic equation $x^2 = 13$ using the square root property.   Answers will vary.

3. What is the relationship between the length and width of any golden rectangle?   The length is about 1.62 times its width.

4. If a golden rectangle has a width of 7 centimeters, what is its length? ≈ 11.34 cm

5. How many different real solutions would you expect for each of the following quadratic equations? Explain.

a) $x^2 = 9$ 2   **b)** $x^2 = 0$ 1
c) $(x - 2)^2 = 2$ 2   **d)** $(x - 3)^2 = -4$ no real solution

6. Write the standard form of a quadratic equation.
$ax^2 + bx + c = 0, a \neq 0$

Practice the Skills

Solve.

7. $x^2 - 64 = 0$ 8, −8

8. $x^2 - 36 = 0$ 6, −6

9. $x^2 = 81$ 9, −9

10. $x^2 = 1$ 1, −1

11. $y^2 = 169$ 13, −13

12. $z^2 = 196$ 14, −14

13. $x^2 + 3 = 103$ 10, −10

14. $x^2 - 4 = 60$ 8, −8

15. $x^2 + 10 = 30$ $2\sqrt{5}, -2\sqrt{5}$

16. $w^2 + 20 = 44$ $2\sqrt{6}, -2\sqrt{6}$

17. $3x^2 = 12$ 2, −2

18. $2x^2 = 32$ 4, −4

19. $3w^2 = 51$ $\sqrt{17}, -\sqrt{17}$

20. $4n^2 = 64$ 4, −4

21. $3z^2 + 4 = 31$ 3, −3

22. $3x^2 - 4 = 8$ 2, −2

23. $9w^2 + 5 = 20$ $\sqrt{15}/3, -\sqrt{15}/3$

24. $3y^2 + 10 = 94$ $2\sqrt{7}, -2\sqrt{7}$

25. $16x^2 - 7 = 66$ $\sqrt{73}/4, -\sqrt{73}/4$

26. $2x^2 + 5 = 53$ $2\sqrt{6}, -2\sqrt{6}$

Solve.

27. $(x - 4)^2 = 1$ 3, 5

28. $(y - 2)^2 = 49$ −5, 9

29. $(a + 3)^2 = 36$ 3, −9

30. $(x + 5)^2 = 25$ 0, −10

31. $(x + 2)^2 = 64$ 6, −10

32. $(x + 4)^2 = 100$ 6, −14

33. $(r + 6)^2 = 32$ $-6 \pm 4\sqrt{2}$

34. $(x + 7)^2 = 18$ $-7 \pm 3\sqrt{2}$

35. $(d + 1)^2 = 20$ $-1 \pm 2\sqrt{5}$

36. $(k - 9)^2 = 40$ $9 \pm 2\sqrt{10}$

37. $(n - 8)^2 = 49$ 1, 15

38. $(x - 10)^2 = 28$ $10 \pm 2\sqrt{7}$

39. $(x + 9)^2 = 100$ 1, −19

40. $(x - 2)^2 = 15$ $2 \pm \sqrt{15}$

41. $(2x + 3)^2 = 18$ $\left(-3 \pm 3\sqrt{2}\right)/2$

42. $(3a - 2)^2 = 29$ $\left(2 \pm \sqrt{29}\right)/3$

43. $(4x + 1)^2 - 3 = 17$ $\left(-1 \pm 2\sqrt{5}\right)/4$

44. $(5s - 6)^2 - 30 = 70$ $\dfrac{16}{5}, -\dfrac{4}{5}$

45. $(2p - 7)^2 + 6 = 24$ $\left(7 \pm 3\sqrt{2}\right)/2$

46. $(5x + 9)^2 + 10 = 50$ $\left(-9 \pm 2\sqrt{10}\right)/5$

Problem Solving

47. Write an equation that has the solutions 7 and −7. $x^2 = 49$

48. Write an equation that has the solutions $\sqrt{5}$ and $-\sqrt{5}$. $x^2 = 5$

49. Fill in the shaded area to make a true statement. Explain how you determined your answer. The equation $x^2 - \blacksquare = 17$ has the solutions 6 and −6.   19

50. Fill in the shaded area to make a true statement. Explain how you determined your answer. The equation $x^2 + \blacksquare = 35$ has the solutions 8 and -8. -29

51. a) Rewrite $-3x^2 + 9x - 6 = 0$ so that the coefficient of the x^2-term is positive. $3x^2 - 9x + 6 = 0$

   b) Rewrite $-3x^2 + 9x - 6 = 0$ so that the coefficient of the x^2-term is 1. $x^2 - 3x + 2 = 0$

52. a) Rewrite $-\dfrac{1}{4}x^2 + 3x - 4 = 0$ so that the coefficient of the x^2-term is positive. $\dfrac{1}{4}x^2 - 3x + 4 = 0$

   b) Rewrite $-\dfrac{1}{4}x^2 + 3x - 4 = 0$ so that the coefficient of the x^2-term is 1. $x^2 - 12x + 16 = 0$

53. Product of Numbers The product of two positive numbers is 68. Determine the numbers if the larger number is 4.25 times the smaller number.   4 and 17

54. Product of Numbers The product of two positive numbers is 140. Determine the numbers if the larger number is 5.6 times the smaller number.   5 and 28

55. Newspaper Page The area of a newspaper page (opened up) is about 631.92 square inches. Determine the length and width of the page if its length is about 1.21 times its width.

56. Kitchen Table The area of a rectangular kitchen table is 2478 square inches. Determine the length and width of the table if its width is 0.71 times its length.

57. Enlarging a Garden Paul Martin decided to plant a rectangular garden so that it has the length-to-width ratio found in a golden rectangle. Determine the length and width of the garden if it is to have an area of 2000 square feet.

58. Mailing Envelope The length of a priority mailing envelope is about 1.33 times its width. Determine the length and width of the envelope if its area is approximately 112 square inches.   length, $\approx$12.21 in.; width, $\approx$9.18 in.

59. Comparing Areas Consider the two squares with sides x and $x + 3$ shown below.

a) Write a quadratic expression for the area of each square.   left, x^2; right, $(x + 3)^2$

b) If the area of the square on the left is 36 square inches, what is the length of each side of the square?   6 in.

c) If the area of the square on the left is 50 square inches, what is the length of each side of the square? $\sqrt{50} \approx 7.07$ in.

d) If the area of the square on the right is 81 square inches, what is the length of each side of the square?   9 in.

e) If the area of the square on the right is 92 square inches, what is the length of each side of the square? $\sqrt{92} \approx 9.59$ in.

60. Area Consider the figure below. If the area shaded in pink is approximately 153.94 square inches, find x (to the nearest hundredth).   4.62 in.

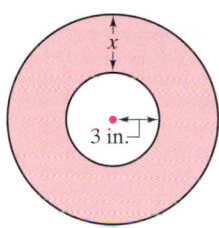

3 in.

55. $l \approx 1.21\sqrt{522.25}$ or ≈ 27.65 in., $w \approx \sqrt{522.25}$ or ≈ 22.85 in.

56. $l \approx \sqrt{3490.14}$ or ≈ 59.08 in., $w \approx 0.71\sqrt{3490.14}$ or ≈ 41.94 in.

57. width, ≈ 35.14 ft; length, ≈ 56.93 ft

Challenge Problems

Use the square root property to solve for the indicated variable. Assume that all variables represent positive numbers. You may wish to review Section 2.6 before working these problems. List only the positive square root.

61. $A = s^2$, for s $s = \sqrt{A}$

62. $I = p^2 r$, for p $p = \sqrt{\dfrac{I}{r}}$

63. $A = \pi r^2$, for r $r = \sqrt{\dfrac{A}{\pi}}$

64. $a^2 + b^2 = c^2$, for b $b = \sqrt{c^2 - a^2}$

65. $I = \dfrac{k}{d^2}$, for d $d = \sqrt{\dfrac{k}{I}}$

66. $A = p(1 + r)^2$, for r $r = \sqrt{\dfrac{A}{p}} - 1$

Cumulative Review Exercises

[7.4]   **67.** Factor $6x^2 - 15x - 36$. $3(2x + 3)(x - 4)$

[8.5]   **68.** Simplify $\dfrac{5 - \dfrac{1}{y}}{6 - \dfrac{1}{y}}$. $\dfrac{5y - 1}{6y - 1}$

[4.4]   **69.** Determine the equation of the line illustrated in the graph on the right. $y = 4x - 1$

[9.3]   **70.** Simplify $\dfrac{\sqrt{135a^4b}}{\sqrt{3a^5b^7}}$. $\dfrac{3\sqrt{5a}}{ab^3}$

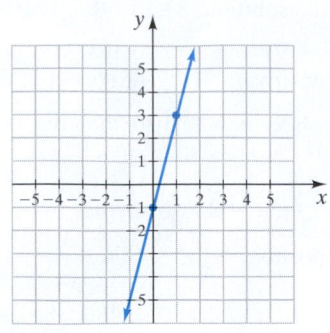

Exercise 69

10.2 Solving Quadratic Equations by Completing the Square

1 Write perfect square trinomials.

2 Solve quadratic equations by completing the square.

Quadratic equations that cannot be solved by factoring can be solved by completing the square or by the quadratic formula. In this section we focus on completing the square.

1 Write Perfect Square Trinomials

A **perfect square trinomial** is a trinomial that can be expressed as the square of a binomial. Some examples follow.

Perfect Square Trinomials		Factors		Square of a Binomial
$x^2 + 6x + 9$	$=$	$(x + 3)(x + 3)$	$=$	$(x + 3)^2$
$x^2 - 6x + 9$	$=$	$(x - 3)(x - 3)$	$=$	$(x - 3)^2$
$x^2 + 10x + 25$	$=$	$(x + 5)(x + 5)$	$=$	$(x + 5)^2$
$x^2 - 10x + 25$	$=$	$(x - 5)(x - 5)$	$=$	$(x - 5)^2$

Notice that each of the squared terms in the preceding perfect square trinomials has a numerical coefficient of 1. When the coefficient of the squared term is 1, there is an important relationship between the coefficient of the x-term and the constant. In every perfect square trinomial of this type, *the constant term is the square of one-half the coefficient of the x-term.*

Consider the perfect square trinomial $x^2 + 6x + 9$. The coefficient of the x-term is 6 and the constant is 9. Note that the constant, 9, is the square of one-half the coefficient of the x-term.

$$x^2 \boxed{+\, 6}\, x \boxed{+\, 9}$$

$$\left[\frac{1}{2}\boxed{(6)}\right]^2 = 3^2 = \boxed{9}$$

Consider the perfect square trinomial $x^2 - 10x + 25$. The coefficient of the x-term is -10 and the constant is 25. Note again that the constant, 25, is the square of one-half of the coefficient of the x-term.

$$x^2 \boxed{-\, 10}\, x \boxed{+\, 25}$$

$$\left[\frac{1}{2}\boxed{(-10)}\right]^2 = (-5)^2 = \boxed{25}$$

TEACHING TIP
Have students rewrite each of the perfect square trinomials with the constant term as a square. Then ask, "How is the constant term related to the coefficient of x?"

TEACHING TIP
Another method to use is to remind students that
$(x + a)^2 = x^2 + 2ax + a^2$, then
$2a = 6$
$a = 3$
$a^2 = 9$

Consider the expression $x^2 + 8x + $ ▨. Can you determine what number must be placed in the colored box to make the trinomial a perfect square trinomial? If you answered 16, you answered correctly.

$$x^2 + 8x + \boxed{}$$

$$\left[\frac{1}{2}(8)\right]^2 = 4^2 = \boxed{16}$$

The perfect square trinomial is $x^2 + 8x + 16$. Note that $x^2 + 8x + 16 = (x + 4)^2$. Let's examine perfect square trinomials a little further.

Perfect Square Trinomial		Square of a Binomial
$x^2 + 6x + 9$	$=$	$(x + 3)^2$
$\frac{1}{2}(6) = 3$		
$x^2 - 10x + 25$	$=$	$(x - 5)^2$
$\frac{1}{2}(-10) = -5$		

Note that when a perfect square trinomial is written as the square of a binomial *the constant in the binomial is one-half the value of the coefficient of the x-term in the perfect square trinomial.*

2 Solve Quadratic Equations by Completing the Square

The procedure for solving a quadratic equation by **completing the square** is illustrated in the following example. Some of the equations that you will be solving in the examples could be easily solved by factoring, but they are being solved by completing the square as a means of illustrating the procedure on easy problems before moving on to more difficult problems.

EXAMPLE 1 ▶ Solve the equation $x^2 + 6x - 7 = 0$ by completing the square.

Solution First we make sure that the squared term has a coefficient of 1. (In Example 5 we explain what to do if the coefficient is not 1.) Next we wish to get the terms containing a variable by themselves on the left side of the equation. Therefore, we add 7 to both sides of the equation.

$$x^2 + 6x - 7 = 0$$
$$x^2 + 6x = 7$$

Now we determine one-half the numerical coefficient of the x-term. In this example, the x-term is $6x$.

$$\frac{1}{2}(6) = \boxed{3}$$

We square this number,

$$(3)^2 = (3)(3) = \boxed{9}$$

and then add this product to both sides of the equation.

$$x^2 + 6x \boxed{+9} = 7 \boxed{+9}$$

or

$$x^2 + 6x + 9 = 16$$

INSTRUCTOR EXAMPLE
Solve $x^2 + 6x - 16 = 0$ by completing the square.
Ans.: 2, −8

TEACHING TIP
While discussing Example 1, ask, "We add 9 to the left side of the equation to make a perfect square trinomial, but why do we add 9 to the right side?"

By following this procedure, we produce a perfect square trinomial on the left side of the equation. The expression $x^2 + 6x + 9$ is a perfect square trinomial that can be expressed as $(x + 3)^2$. Therefore,

$$x^2 + 6x + 9 = 16$$

can be written

$$(x \boxed{+ 3})^2 = 16$$

Now we use the square root property,

$$x + 3 = \pm\sqrt{16}$$
$$x + 3 = \pm 4$$

Finally, we solve for x by subtracting 3 from both sides of the equation.

$$x + 3 - 3 = -3 \pm 4$$
$$x = -3 \pm 4$$
$$x = -3 + 4 \quad \text{or} \quad x = -3 - 4$$
$$x = 1 \qquad\qquad x = -7$$

Thus, the solutions are 1 and -7. We check both solutions in the original equation.

Check

$x = 1$	$x = -7$
$x^2 + 6x - 7 = 0$	$x^2 + 6x - 7 = 0$
$(1)^2 + 6(1) - 7 \stackrel{?}{=} 0$	$(-7)^2 + 6(-7) - 7 \stackrel{?}{=} 0$
$1 + 6 - 7 \stackrel{?}{=} 0$	$49 - 42 - 7 \stackrel{?}{=} 0$
$0 = 0$ *True*	$0 = 0$ *True*

▶ **Now Try Exercise 11**

Now let's summarize the procedure.

To Solve a Quadratic Equation by Completing the Square

1. Use the multiplication (or division) property of equality if necessary to make the numerical coefficient of the squared term equal to 1.

2. Rewrite the equation with the constant by itself on the right side of the equation.

3. Take one-half the numerical coefficient of the first-degree term, square it, and add this quantity to both sides of the equation.

4. Replace the trinomial with its equivalent squared binomial.

5. Use the square root property.

6. Solve for the variable.

7. Check your answers in the *original* equation.

EXAMPLE 2 ▶ Solve the equation $x^2 - 10x + 21 = 0$ by completing the square.

Solution

INSTRUCTOR EXAMPLE
Solve $x^2 - 8x + 15 = 0$ by completing the square.
Ans.: $3, 5$

$$x^2 - 10x + 21 = 0$$
$$x^2 - 10x = -21 \quad \textit{Step 2}$$

Take half the numerical coefficient of the x-term, square it, and add this product to both sides of the equation.

$$\frac{1}{2}(-10) = \boxed{-5}, \quad (-5)^2 = \boxed{25}$$

Now add 25 to both sides of the equation.

$$x^2 - 10x \boxed{+ 25} = -21 \boxed{+ 25} \qquad \textit{Step 3}$$
$$x^2 - 10x + 25 = 4$$
$$\text{or } (x \boxed{- 5})^2 = 4 \qquad \textit{Step 4}$$
$$x - 5 = \pm\sqrt{4} \qquad \textit{Step 5}$$
$$x - 5 = \pm 2$$
$$x = 5 \pm 2 \qquad \textit{Step 6}$$
$$x = 5 + 2 \quad \text{or} \quad x = 5 - 2$$
$$x = 7 \qquad\qquad x = 3$$

A check will show that the solutions are 7 and 3.

▸ **Now Try Exercise 13**

INSTRUCTOR EXAMPLE
Solve $x^2 - 7x + 12 = 0$ by
completing the square.
Ans.: 3, 4

EXAMPLE 3 ▸ Solve the equation $x^2 = 3x + 18$ by completing the square.

Solution   Place all terms except the constant on the left side of the equation.

$$x^2 = 3x + 18$$
$$x^2 - 3x = 18 \qquad \textit{Step 2}$$

Take half the numerical coefficient of the x-term, square it, and add this product to both sides of the equation.

$$\frac{1}{2}(-3) = \boxed{-\frac{3}{2}}, \quad \left(-\frac{3}{2}\right)^2 = \boxed{\frac{9}{4}}$$

$$x^2 - 3x + \boxed{\frac{9}{4}} = \boxed{+\frac{9}{4}} \qquad \textit{Step 3}$$

$$\left(x - \frac{3}{2}\right)^2 = 18 + \frac{9}{4} \qquad \textit{Step 4}$$

$$\left(x - \frac{3}{2}\right)^2 = \frac{72}{4} + \frac{9}{4}$$

$$\left(x - \frac{3}{2}\right)^2 = \frac{81}{4}$$

$$x - \frac{3}{2} = \pm\sqrt{\frac{81}{4}} \qquad \textit{Step 5}$$

$$x - \frac{3}{2} = \pm\frac{9}{2}$$

$$x = \frac{3}{2} \pm \frac{9}{2} \qquad \textit{Step 6}$$

$$x = \frac{3}{2} + \frac{9}{2} \quad \text{or} \quad x = \frac{3}{2} - \frac{9}{2}$$

$$x = \frac{12}{2} = 6 \qquad\qquad x = -\frac{6}{2} = -3$$

The solutions are 6 and -3.

▸ **Now Try Exercise 21**

In the following examples we will not show some of the intermediate steps.

EXAMPLE 4 ▶ Solve the equation $x^2 - 16x + 12 = 0$ by completing the square.

Solution

$$x^2 - 16x + 12 = 0$$
$$x^2 - 16x = -12 \qquad \text{\textit{Step 2}}$$
$$x^2 - 16x + 64 = -12 + 64 \qquad \text{\textit{Step 3}}$$
$$(x - 8)^2 = 52 \qquad \text{\textit{Step 4}}$$
$$x - 8 = \pm\sqrt{52} \qquad \text{\textit{Step 5}}$$
$$x - 8 = \pm\sqrt{4}\,\sqrt{13}$$
$$x - 8 = \pm 2\sqrt{13}$$
$$x = 8 \pm 2\sqrt{13} \qquad \text{\textit{Step 6}}$$

The solutions are $8 + 2\sqrt{13}$ and $8 - 2\sqrt{13}$.

▶ **Now Try Exercise 29**

EXAMPLE 5 ▶ Solve the equation $5z^2 - 25z + 10 = 0$ by completing the square.

Solution To solve an equation by completing the square, the numerical coefficient of the squared term must be 1. Since the coefficient of the squared term is 5, we multiply both sides of the equation by $\dfrac{1}{5}$ (or divide every term by 5) to make the coefficient equal to 1.

$$5z^2 - 25z + 10 = 0$$
$$\frac{1}{5}(5z^2 - 25z + 10) = \frac{1}{5}(0) \qquad \text{\textit{Step 1}}$$
$$z^2 - 5z + 2 = 0$$

Now we proceed as in earlier examples.

$$z^2 - 5z = -2 \qquad \text{\textit{Step 2}}$$
$$z^2 - 5z + \frac{25}{4} = -2 + \frac{25}{4} \qquad \text{\textit{Step 3}}$$
$$\left(z - \frac{5}{2}\right)^2 = -\frac{8}{4} + \frac{25}{4} \qquad \text{\textit{Step 4}}$$
$$\left(z - \frac{5}{2}\right)^2 = \frac{17}{4}$$
$$z - \frac{5}{2} = \pm\sqrt{\frac{17}{4}} \qquad \text{\textit{Step 5}}$$
$$z - \frac{5}{2} = \pm\frac{\sqrt{17}}{2}$$
$$z = \frac{5}{2} \pm \frac{\sqrt{17}}{2} \qquad \text{\textit{Step 6}}$$

$$z = \frac{5}{2} + \frac{\sqrt{17}}{2} \quad \text{or} \quad z = \frac{5}{2} - \frac{\sqrt{17}}{2}$$

$$z = \frac{5 + \sqrt{17}}{2} \qquad\qquad z = \frac{5 - \sqrt{17}}{2}$$

The solutions are $\dfrac{5 + \sqrt{17}}{2}$ and $\dfrac{5 - \sqrt{17}}{2}$.

▶ **Now Try Exercise 33**

EXERCISE SET 10.2

MathXL®   MyMathLab

1. a) a trinomial that can be expressed as the square of a binomial
3. constant is the square of half the coefficient

Concept/Writing Exercises

1. a) What is a perfect square trinomial?
b) Fill in the shaded area to make a perfect square trinomial and explain how you determined your answer.
$$x^2 + 8x \quad +16$$

2. Fill in the shaded area to make a perfect square trinomial and explain how you determined your answer.
$$x^2 - 12x \quad +36$$

3. In a perfect square trinomial, what is the relationship between the constant and the coefficient of the x-term?

4. In a perfect square trinomial, if the coefficient of the x-term is 4, what is the constant?   4

5. In a perfect square trinomial, if the coefficient of the x-term is -14, what is the constant?   49

6. a) Explain how to solve a quadratic equation by completing the square.   Answers will vary.
b) Compare your answer to part **a)** with the procedure given on page 600. Did you omit any steps in your explanation?   Answers will vary.

Practice the Skills

Solve by completing the square.

7. $x^2 + 7x + 10 = 0$ $-5, -2$

8. $x^2 + 5x + 6 = 0$ $-2, -3$

9. $x^2 - 8x + 7 = 0$ $7, 1$

10. $r^2 - r - 30 = 0$ $6, -5$

11. $x^2 + 13x + 12 = 0$ $-1, -12$

12. $x^2 + 12x + 32 = 0$ $-4, -8$

13. $z^2 - 6z + 8 = 0$ $2, 4$

14. $m^2 - 9m + 14 = 0$ $7, 2$

15. $n^2 = -6n - 9$ -3

16. $k^2 = 12k - 36$ 6

17. $x^2 = 2x + 15$ $5, -3$

18. $x^2 = -5x - 6$ $-2, -3$

19. $x^2 + 10x + 24 = 0$ $-4, -6$

20. $-45 = n^2 + 14n$ $-5, -9$

21. $x^2 = 10x - 16$ $8, 2$

22. $x^2 = 3x + 28$ $7, -4$

23. $-60 = -p^2 + 4p$ $10, -6$

24. $-x^2 - 3x + 54 = 0$ $6, -9$

25. $z^2 - 4z = -2$ $2 \pm \sqrt{2}$

26. $z^2 + 2z = 9$ $-1 \pm \sqrt{10}$

27. $w^2 + 6w = -3$ $-3 \pm \sqrt{6}$

28. $g^2 - 2g = 4$ $1 \pm \sqrt{5}$

29. $m^2 + 7m + 2 = 0$ $\left(-7 \pm \sqrt{41}\right)/2$

30. $x^2 + 3x - 3 = 0$ $\left(-3 \pm \sqrt{21}\right)/2$

31. $3x^2 + 6x - 9 = 0$ $1, -3$

32. $2x^2 + 2x - 24 = 0$ $3, -4$

33. $2x^2 + 18x + 4 = 0$ $\left(-9 \pm \sqrt{73}\right)/2$

34. $3x^2 + 21x - 12 = 0$ $\left(-7 + \sqrt{65}\right)/2$

35. $3h^2 - 15h = 18$ $6, -1$

36. $4x^2 = -28x + 32$ $1, -8$

37. $3x^2 - 11x - 4 = 0$ $4, -\dfrac{1}{3}$

38. $3x^2 - 8x + 4 = 0$ $2, 2/3$

39. $9t^2 + 6t = 6$ $\left(-1 \pm \sqrt{7}\right)/3$

40. $4x^2 - 2x = 10$ $\left(1 \pm \sqrt{41}\right)/4$

41. $x^2 - 8x = 0$ $8, 0$

42. $2x^2 - 14x = 0$ $7, 0$

43. $2x^2 = 18x$ $9, 0$

44. $5x^2 = 20x$ $4, 0$

Problem Solving   **45. a)** $x^2 + 10x + 25$

45. a) Write a perfect square trinomial that has a term of $10x$.
b) Explain how you constructed your perfect square trinomial.   Answers will vary.

46. a) Write a perfect square trinomial that has a term of $-16x$. $x^2 - 16x + 64$
b) Explain how you constructed your perfect square trinomial.   Answers will vary.

47. Numbers When 3 times a number is added to the square of a number, the sum is 4. Find the number(s). $1, -4$

48. Numbers When 5 times a number is subtracted from 2 times the square of a number, the difference is 12. Find the number(s). $-\dfrac{3}{2}, 4$

49. Numbers If the square of 3 more than a number is 9, find the number(s). $0, -6$

50. Numbers If the square of 2 less than an integer is 16, find the number(s). $6, -2$

51. Numbers The product of two positive numbers is 21. Find the two numbers if the larger is 4 greater than the smaller. $3, 7$

52. Supporting a Pole A guy wire 20 feet long is supporting a pole as shown in the figure. Determine the height of the pole.   16 ft

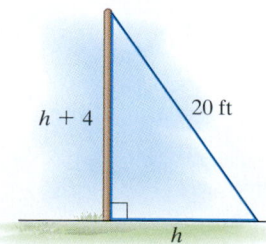

53. Ladder Leaning on a House A 30-foot ladder is leaning against a house, as shown. Determine the vertical distance from the ground to where the ladder rests on the house. $\left(9 + 3\sqrt{41}\right)$ or ≈28.21 ft

54. Sum of Integers The sum of the first n integers, s, can be found by the formula $s = \dfrac{n^2 + n}{2}$. Find the value of n if the sum is 28.   7

55. Height of an Object When an object is thrown straight up from Earth with an initial velocity of 128 feet per second, its height above the ground, s, in feet, in t seconds is given by the formula $s = -16t^2 + 128t$. How long will it take the object to reach a height of 240 feet? (Therefore, $s = 240$.)   3 sec and 5 sec

56. Height of an Object Repeat Exercise 55 for a height of 112 feet.   1 sec and 7 sec

Challenge Problems

57. Fill in the shaded area to make a perfect square trinomial and explain how you determined your answer.
$$x^2 \; \rule{0.6cm}{0.35cm} \; + 81 \quad +18x \text{ or } -18x$$

58. Fill in the shaded area to make a perfect square trinomial and explain how you determined your answer.
$$x^2 \; \rule{0.6cm}{0.35cm} \; + \frac{9}{100} \quad +\frac{3}{5}x \text{ or } -\frac{3}{5}x$$

59. a) Solve the equation $x^2 - 14x - 1 = 0$ by completing the square. $7 \pm 5\sqrt{2}$

b) Check your solution (it will not be a rational number) by substituting the value(s) you obtained in part **a)** for each x in the equation in part **a)**.

60. a) Solve the equation $x^2 + 3x - 7 = 0$ by completing the square. $\dfrac{-3 \pm \sqrt{37}}{2}$

b) Check your solution (it will not be a rational number) by substituting the value(s) you obtained in part **a)** for each x in the equation in part **a)**.

Solve by completing the square.

61. $x^2 + \dfrac{3}{5}x - \dfrac{1}{2} = 0.$ $\left(-3 \pm \sqrt{59}\right)/10$

62. $x^2 - \dfrac{2}{3}x - \dfrac{1}{5} = 0.$ $\left(5 \pm \sqrt{70}\right)/15$

63. $3x^2 + \dfrac{1}{2}x = 4.$ $\left(-1 \pm \sqrt{193}\right)/12$

64. $0.1x^2 + 0.2x - 0.54 = 0$ $-1 \pm \sqrt{6.4}$

65. $-5.26x^2 + 7.89x + 15.78 = 0$ $0.75 \pm \sqrt{3.5625}$

Cumulative Review Exercises

[8.4] **66.** Simplify $\dfrac{x^2}{x^2 - x - 6} - \dfrac{x - 2}{x - 3}.$ $\dfrac{4}{(x + 2)(x - 3)}$

[4.4] **67.** Explain how you can determine whether two equations represent parallel lines without graphing the equations.   If slopes are same and y-intercepts are different, equations represent parallel lines.

[5.2, 5.3] **68.** Solve the following system of equations.
$$2x + 3y = 6$$
$$-x + 4y = 19 \quad (-3, 4)$$

[9.5] **69.** Solve the equation $\sqrt{2x + 3} = 2x - 3.$ 3

10.3 Solving Quadratic Equations by the Quadratic Formula

1 Solve quadratic equations by the quadratic formula.

2 Determine the number of solutions to a quadratic equation using the discriminant.

1 Solve Quadratic Equations by the Quadratic Formula

Another method that can be used to solve any quadratic equation is the **quadratic formula**. It is the most useful and versatile method of solving quadratic equations.

The standard form of a quadratic equation is $ax^2 + bx + c = 0$, where a is the coefficient of the squared term, b is the coefficient of the first-degree term, and c is the constant.

Quadratic Equation in Standard Form	Values of a, b, and c		
$x^2 - 5x + 6 = 0$	$a = 1,$	$b = -5,$	$c = 6$
$5x^2 + 3x = 0$	$a = 5,$	$b = 3,$	$c = 0$
$-\dfrac{1}{2}x^2 + 5 = 0$	$a = -\dfrac{1}{2},$	$b = 0,$	$c = 5$

We can derive the quadratic formula by starting with a quadratic equation in standard form and completing the square, as discussed in the preceding section.

$$ax^2 + bx + c = 0$$

Standard form of quadratic equation

$$\frac{ax^2}{a} + \frac{b}{a}x + \frac{c}{a} = 0$$

Divide both sides by a.

$$x^2 + \frac{b}{a}x = -\frac{c}{a}$$

Subtract c/a from both sides.

$$x^2 + \frac{b}{a}x + \frac{b^2}{4a^2} = -\frac{c}{a} + \frac{b^2}{4a^2}$$

Take 1/2 of b/a; that is, b/2a, and square it to get $b^2/4a^2$. Then add this expression to both sides.

$$\left(x + \frac{b}{2a}\right)^2 = \frac{b^2}{4a^2} - \frac{c}{a}$$

Rewrite the left side of the equation as the square of a binomial.

$$\left(x + \frac{b}{2a}\right)^2 = \frac{b^2 - 4ac}{4a^2}$$

Write the right side with a common denominator.

$$x + \frac{b}{2a} = \pm\sqrt{\frac{b^2 - 4ac}{4a^2}}$$

Square root property

$$x + \frac{b}{2a} = \pm\frac{\sqrt{b^2 - 4ac}}{2a}$$

Quotient rule for radicals, $\sqrt{4a^2} = 2a$

$$x = \frac{-b}{2a} \pm \frac{\sqrt{b^2 - 4ac}}{2a}$$

Subtract b/2a, from both sides.

$$x = \frac{-b \pm \sqrt{b^2 - 4ac}}{2a}$$

Write with a common denominator to get the quadratic formula.

To Solve a Quadratic Equation by the Quadratic Formula

1. Write the equation in standard form, $ax^2 + bx + c = 0$, and determine the numerical values for a, b, and c.

2. Substitute the values for a, b, and c from step 1 in the quadratic formula below and then evaluate to obtain the solution.

THE QUADRATIC FORMULA

$$x = \frac{-b \pm \sqrt{b^2 - 4ac}}{2a}$$

EXAMPLE 1 ▶ Use the quadratic formula to solve the equation $x^2 + 4x + 3 = 0$.

Solution In this equation $a = 1, b = 4$, and $c = 3$. Substitute these values into the quadratic formula and then evaluate.

$$x = \frac{-b \pm \sqrt{b^2 - 4ac}}{2a}$$

$$= \frac{-(4) \pm \sqrt{(4)^2 - 4(1)(3)}}{2(1)}$$

$$= \frac{-4 \pm \sqrt{16 - 12}}{2}$$

$$= \frac{-4 \pm \sqrt{4}}{2}$$

$$= \frac{-4 \pm 2}{2}$$

$$x = \frac{-4 + 2}{2} \quad \text{or} \quad x = \frac{-4 - 2}{2}$$

$$= \frac{-2}{2} = -1 \qquad\qquad = \frac{-6}{2} = -3$$

Check

$$x = -1$$
$$x^2 + 4x + 3 = 0$$
$$(-1)^2 + 4(-1) + 3 \overset{?}{=} 0$$
$$1 - 4 + 3 \overset{?}{=} 0$$
$$0 = 0 \quad \textit{True}$$

$$x = -3$$
$$x^2 + 4x + 3 = 0$$
$$(-3)^2 + 4(-3) + 3 \overset{?}{=} 0$$
$$9 - 12 + 3 \overset{?}{=} 0$$
$$0 = 0 \quad \textit{True}$$

▶ **Now Try Exercise 29**

Avoiding Common Errors

The **entire numerator** of the quadratic formula must be divided by $2a$.

CORRECT

$$x = \frac{-b \pm \sqrt{b^2 - 4ac}}{2a}$$

INCORRECT

EXAMPLE 2 ▶ Use the quadratic formula to solve the equation $8x^2 + 2x - 1 = 0$.

Solution

$$8x^2 + 2x - 1 = 0$$
$$a = 8, \qquad b = 2, \qquad c = -1$$

$$x = \frac{-b \pm \sqrt{b^2 - 4ac}}{2a}$$

$$= \frac{-(2) \pm \sqrt{(2)^2 - 4(8)(-1)}}{2(8)}$$

$$= \frac{-2 \pm \sqrt{4 + 32}}{16}$$

$$= \frac{-2 \pm \sqrt{36}}{16}$$

$$= \frac{-2 \pm 6}{16}$$

$$x = \frac{-2 + 6}{16} \quad \text{or} \quad x = \frac{-2 - 6}{16}$$

$$= \frac{4}{16} = \frac{1}{4} \qquad\qquad = \frac{-8}{16} = -\frac{1}{2}$$

Check

$$x = \frac{1}{4}$$
$$8x^2 + 2x - 1 = 0$$
$$8\left(\frac{1}{4}\right)^2 + 2\left(\frac{1}{4}\right) - 1 \overset{?}{=} 0$$
$$8\left(\frac{1}{16}\right) + \frac{1}{2} - 1 \overset{?}{=} 0$$
$$\frac{1}{2} + \frac{1}{2} - 1 \overset{?}{=} 0$$
$$0 = 0 \quad \textit{True}$$

$$x = -\frac{1}{2}$$
$$8x^2 + 2x - 1 = 0$$
$$8\left(-\frac{1}{2}\right)^2 + 2\left(-\frac{1}{2}\right) - 1 \overset{?}{=} 0$$
$$8\left(\frac{1}{4}\right) - 1 - 1 \overset{?}{=} 0$$
$$2 - 1 - 1 \overset{?}{=} 0$$
$$0 = 0 \quad \textit{True}$$

▶ **Now Try Exercise 43**

EXAMPLE 3 ▶ Use the quadratic formula to solve the equation $2w^2 + 6w - 3 = 0$.

Solution The variable in this equation is w. The procedure to solve the equation is the same.

$$a = 2, \quad b = 6, \quad c = -3$$

$$w = \frac{-b \pm \sqrt{b^2 - 4ac}}{2a}$$

$$= \frac{-(6) \pm \sqrt{(6)^2 - 4(2)(-3)}}{2(2)}$$

$$= \frac{-6 \pm \sqrt{36 + 24}}{4}$$

$$= \frac{-6 \pm \sqrt{60}}{4}$$

$$= \frac{-6 \pm \sqrt{4}\sqrt{15}}{4}$$

$$= \frac{-6 \pm 2\sqrt{15}}{4}$$

Now factor out 2 from both terms in the numerator; then divide out common factors as explained in Section 9.4.

$$w = \frac{\overset{1}{2}\left(-3 \pm \sqrt{15}\right)}{\underset{2}{\cancel{4}}}$$

$$w = \frac{-3 \pm \sqrt{15}}{2}$$

Thus, the solutions are $w = \dfrac{-3 + \sqrt{15}}{2}$ and $w = \dfrac{-3 - \sqrt{15}}{2}$.

▶ **Now Try Exercise 49**

INSTRUCTOR EXAMPLE
Use the quadratic formula to solve $5n^2 + 2n - 1 = 0$.

Ans.: $\dfrac{-1 \pm \sqrt{6}}{5}$.

TEACHING TIP
After discussing the solution to Example 3, have students solve it by completing the square. Show that the equation cannot be solved by factoring.

Now let's try two examples where the equation is not in standard form.

EXAMPLE 4 ▶ Use the quadratic formula to solve the equation $x^2 = 6x - 4$.

Solution First write the equation in standard form.

INSTRUCTOR EXAMPLE
Use the quadratic formula to solve $x^2 = 4x - 1$.

Ans.: $2 \pm \sqrt{3}$

$$x^2 - 6x + 4 = 0$$

Set one side of the equation equal to zero.

$$a = 1, \quad b = -6, \quad c = 4$$

$$x = \frac{-b \pm \sqrt{b^2 - 4ac}}{2a}$$

$$= \frac{-(-6) \pm \sqrt{(-6)^2 - 4(1)(4)}}{2(1)}$$

Substitute.

$$= \frac{6 \pm \sqrt{36 - 16}}{2}$$

Simplify.

$$= \frac{6 \pm \sqrt{20}}{2}$$

$$= \frac{6 \pm \sqrt{4}\sqrt{5}}{2}$$

Product rule

$$= \frac{6 \pm 2\sqrt{5}}{2}$$

$$= \frac{\overset{1}{\cancel{2}}\left(3 \pm \sqrt{5}\right)}{\underset{1}{\cancel{2}}}$$ *Factor out 2.*

$$= 3 \pm \sqrt{5}$$

The solutions are $x = 3 + \sqrt{5}$ and $x = 3 - \sqrt{5}$.

▶ **Now Try Exercise 41**

Avoiding Common Errors

Many students solve quadratic equations correctly until the last step, when they make an error. Do not make the mistake of trying to simplify an answer that cannot be simplified any further. The following are answers that cannot be simplified, along with some common errors.

ANSWERS THAT CANNOT BE SIMPLIFIED   INCORRECT

$$\frac{3 + 2\sqrt{5}}{2}$$ $$\frac{3 + 2\sqrt{5}}{2} = \frac{3 + \overset{1}{\cancel{2}}\sqrt{5}}{\underset{1}{\cancel{2}}} = 3 + \sqrt{5}$$

$$\frac{4 + 3\sqrt{5}}{2}$$ $$\frac{\overset{2}{\cancel{4}} + 3\sqrt{5}}{\underset{1}{\cancel{2}}} = 2 + 3\sqrt{5}$$

EXAMPLE 5 ▶ Use the quadratic formula to solve the equation $t^2 = 36$.

INSTRUCTOR EXAMPLE
Use the quadratic formula to solve
$m^2 = 64$.
Ans.: $-8, 8$

Solution   First write the equation in standard form.

$$t^2 - 36 = 0$$ *Set one side of the*
equation equal to 0.

$$a = 1, \qquad b = 0, \qquad c = -36$$

$$t = \frac{-b \pm \sqrt{b^2 - 4ac}}{2a}$$

$$= \frac{-0 \pm \sqrt{0^2 - 4(1)(-36)}}{2(1)}$$ *Substitute.*

$$= \frac{\pm\sqrt{144}}{2} = \frac{\pm 12}{2} = \pm 6$$ *Simplify and solve for t.*

Thus, the solutions are 6 and -6.

▶ **Now Try Exercise 33**

The solution to Example 5 could have been solved more quickly by using the Square Root Property discussed in Section 10.1. We worked Example 5 using the Quadratic Formula to give you more practice using the formula.

The next example illustrates a quadratic equation that has no real number solution.

EXAMPLE 6 ▶ Use the quadratic formula to solve the equation $3x^2 = x - 1$.

INSTRUCTOR EXAMPLE
Use the quadratic formula to solve
$4x^2 = 2x - 3$.
Ans.: no real number solution

Solution

$$3x^2 - x + 1 = 0$$

$$a = 3, \qquad b = -1, \qquad c = 1$$

$$x = \frac{-b \pm \sqrt{b^2 - 4ac}}{2a}$$

$$= \frac{-(-1) \pm \sqrt{(-1)^2 - 4(3)(1)}}{2(3)}$$

$$= \frac{1 \pm \sqrt{1 - 12}}{6}$$

$$= \frac{1 \pm \sqrt{-11}}{6}$$

Since $\sqrt{-11}$ is not a real number, we stop here. This equation has no real number solution. *When given a problem of this type, your answer should be "no real number solution." Do not leave the answer blank, and do not write 0 for the answer.* We will study numbers like $\sqrt{-11}$ and $\dfrac{1 \pm \sqrt{-11}}{6}$ further in Section 10.5 when we study a number system that includes numbers of this type.

▶ **Now Try Exercise 47**

2 Determine the Number of Solutions to a Quadratic Equation Using the Discriminant

TEACHING TIP
Before discussing the discriminant, ask students to suggest values for $a, b,$ and $c,$ such that

$b^2 - 4ac > 0$
$b^2 - 4ac = 0$
$b^2 - 4ac < 0$

Then have them write quadratic equations using those values and solve them.

The expression under the square root sign in the quadratic formula is called the **discriminant**.

$$\underbrace{b^2 - 4ac}_{\textit{Discriminant}}$$

The discriminant can be used to determine the number of real solutions to a quadratic equation.

> **When the Discriminant Is:**
>
> 1. **Greater than zero**, $b^2 - 4ac > 0$, the quadratic equation has **two distinct real number solutions**.
> 2. **Equal to zero**, $b^2 - 4ac = 0$, the quadratic equation has **one real number solution**.
> 3. **Less than zero**, $b^2 - 4ac < 0$, the quadratic equation has **no real number solution**.

TEACHING TIP
Have students describe the number of solutions a quadratic equation will have if

$a = 1$ and $c < 0$
$b \neq 0$ and $c = 0$
$b = 0,$ and $a, c > 0$

We indicate this information in a shortened form in the chart below.

$b^2 - 4ac$	Number of Solutions
Positive	Two distinct real number solutions
0	One real number solution
Negative	No real number solution

EXAMPLE 7 ▶

a) Find the discriminant of the equation $x^2 - 12x + 36 = 0$.

b) Use the discriminant to determine the number of solutions to the equation.

c) Use the quadratic formula to find the solutions, if any exist.

INSTRUCTOR EXAMPLE
Repeat Example 7 for
$25x^2 - 10x + 1 = 0$.

Ans.: a) 0 **b)** 1 **c)** $\dfrac{1}{5}$

Solution

a) $a = 1, \qquad b = -12, \qquad c = 36$

$$b^2 - 4ac = (-12)^2 - 4(1)(36) = 144 - 144 = 0$$

b) Since the discriminant is equal to zero, there is one real number solution.

c)
$$x = \frac{-b \pm \sqrt{b^2 - 4ac}}{2a}$$
$$= \frac{-(-12) \pm \sqrt{0}}{2(1)}$$
$$= \frac{12 \pm 0}{2} = \frac{12}{2} = 6$$

The only solution is 6.

▶ **Now Try Exercise 9**

EXAMPLE 8 ▶ Without actually finding the solutions, determine whether the following equations have two distinct real number solutions, one real number solution, or no real number solution.

a) $4x^2 - 4x + 1 = 0$ **b)** $2x^2 + 13x = -10$ **c)** $6p^2 = -5p - 3$

Solution   We use the discriminant of the quadratic formula to answer these equations.

a) $b^2 - 4ac = (-4)^2 - 4(4)(1) = 16 - 16 = 0$

Since the discriminant is equal to zero, this equation has one real number solution.

b) First, rewrite $2x^2 + 13x = -10$ as $2x^2 + 13x + 10 = 0$.

$$b^2 - 4ac = (13)^2 - 4(2)(10) = 169 - 80 = 89$$

Since the discriminant is positive, this equation has two distinct real number solutions.

c) First rewrite $6p^2 = -5p - 3$ as $6p^2 + 5p + 3 = 0$

$$b^2 - 4ac = (5)^2 - 4(6)(3) = 25 - 72 = -47$$

Since the discriminant is negative, this equation has no real number solution.

▶ **Now Try Exercise 19**

Now let's look at one of many applications that may be solved using the quadratic formula.

FIGURE 10.2

EXAMPLE 9 ▶ **Building a Border** The Johnsons have a rectangular swimming pool that measures 30 feet by 16 feet. They want to add a cement border of uniform width around all sides of the pool. How wide can they make the border if they want the area of the border to be 200 square feet?

Solution   Let's make a diagram of the pool, see **Figure 10.2.** Let $x = $ uniform width of the border. Then the total length of the pool and border is $2x + 30$. The total width of the pool and border is $2x + 16$. The area of the border can be found by subtracting the area of the pool (the smaller rectangle area) from the area of the pool and border (the larger rectangle area).

$$\text{area of pool} = l \cdot w = (30)(16) = 480$$

$$\text{area of pool and border} = l \cdot w = (2x + 30)(2x + 16)$$

$$= 4x^2 + 92x + 480$$

$$\text{area of border} = \text{area of pool and border} - \text{area of pool}$$

$$= (4x^2 + 92x + 480) - 480$$

$$= 4x^2 + 92x$$

The total area of the border is 200 square feet. Therefore,

$$\text{area of border} = 4x^2 + 92x$$

$$200 = 4x^2 + 92x$$

or $4x^2 + 92x - 200 = 0$ *Write equation in standard form.*

$4(x^2 + 23x - 50) = 0$ *Factor out 4.*

$\dfrac{1}{4} \cdot 4(x^2 + 23x - 50) = \dfrac{1}{4} \cdot 0$ *Multiply both sides by $\dfrac{1}{4}$ to eliminate 4.*

$x^2 + 23x - 50 = 0$

Now use the quadratic formula.

$$a = 1 \qquad b = 23 \qquad c = -50$$

$$x = \frac{-b \pm \sqrt{b^2 - 4ac}}{2a}$$

$$= \frac{-23 \pm \sqrt{(23)^2 - 4(1)(-50)}}{2(1)}$$

$$= \frac{-23 \pm \sqrt{529 + 200}}{2}$$

$$= \frac{-23 \pm \sqrt{729}}{2}$$

$$= \frac{-23 \pm 27}{2}$$

$$x = \frac{-23 - 27}{2} \qquad \text{or} \qquad x = \frac{-23 + 27}{2}$$

$$= \frac{-50}{2} \qquad\qquad\qquad = \frac{4}{2}$$

$$= -25 \qquad\qquad\qquad = 2$$

Since lengths are positive, the only possible answer is $x = 2$. Thus the uniform cement border will be 2 feet wide all around the pool.

▸ **Now Try Exercise 63**

In Example 9, the answer came out to be an integer value. However, many times when working with application problems the answer comes out to be an irrational number. When this occurs in the exercise set we will round radical values to two decimal places to determine our answer.

Helpful Hint

Notice in Example 9 that when we had the quadratic equation $4x^2 + 92x - 200 = 0$ we factored out the common factor 4 to get

$$4x^2 + 92x - 200 = 0$$
$$4(x^2 + 23x - 50) = 0$$

We then multiplied both sides of the equation by $\frac{1}{4}$ and used the quadratic equation $x^2 + 23x - 50 = 0$, where $a = 1, b = 23$, and $c = -50$ in the quadratic formula. If all the terms in a quadratic equation have a common factor, it will be easier to factor it out first so that you will have smaller numbers when you use the quadratic formula. Consider the quadratic equation $4x^2 + 8x - 12 = 0$.

In this equation $a = 4, b = 8$, and $c = -12$. If you solve this equation with the quadratic formula, after simplification you will get the solutions -3 and 1. Try this and see. If you factor out 4 to get

$$4x^2 + 8x - 12 = 0$$
$$4(x^2 + 2x - 3) = 0$$

and then use the quadratic formula with the equation $x^2 + 2x - 3 = 0$, where $a = 1, b = 2$, and $c = -3$, you get the same solution. Try this and see.

EXERCISE SET 10.3

MathXL®   MyMathLab

1. b) discriminant: greater than 0, two solutions; equal to 0, one solution; less than 0, no real solution   **3.** $x = \dfrac{-b \pm \sqrt{b^2 - 4ac}}{2a}$

Concept/Writing Exercises

6. Did not leave the -5 in the numerator   **7.** Values used for b and c are incorrect   **8.** Evaluated $\sqrt{-16}$ as 4

1. a) What is the discriminant? $b^2 - 4ac$

   b) Explain how the discriminant can be used to determine the number of real number solutions a quadratic equation has.

2. How many real number solutions does a quadratic equation have if the discriminant equals

   a) -4?   none   **b)** 0?   one   **c)** $\dfrac{1}{2}$?   two

3. Write down the quadratic formula. You must memorize this formula.

4. Explain why a quadratic equation will have two real number solutions when the discriminant is greater than 0, one real number solution when the discriminant is equal to 0, and no real number solution when the discriminant is less than 0. Use the quadratic formula in explaining your answer.   Answers will vary.

5. What is the first step in solving a quadratic equation using the quadratic formula?   Write the equation in standard form.

6. A student using the quadratic formula to solve $2x^2 + 5x + 1 = 0$ wrote down the following steps. What is wrong with the student's work?

$$x = \frac{-5 \pm \sqrt{5^2 - 4(2)(1)}}{2(2)}$$

$$= -5 \pm \frac{\sqrt{25 - 8}}{4}$$

$$= -5 \pm \frac{\sqrt{17}}{4}$$

7. A student using the quadratic formula to solve $x^2 = 4x + 7$ wrote down the following steps. What is wrong with the student's work?

$$x = \frac{-4 \pm \sqrt{4^2 - 4(1)(7)}}{2(1)}$$

$$= \frac{-4 \pm \sqrt{16 - 28}}{2}$$

$$= \frac{-4 \pm \sqrt{-12}}{2}$$

8. A student using the quadratic formula to solve $x^2 + 4 = 0$ listed the following steps. What is wrong with the student's work?

$$x = \frac{0 \pm \sqrt{0^2 - 4(1)(4)}}{2(1)}$$

$$= \frac{\pm\sqrt{-16}}{2}$$

$$= \frac{\pm 4}{2}$$

$$= \pm 2$$

9., 10., 13., 16., 18., 21., 23., 24.: two real number solutions
14., 15., 25., 26., one real number solution
11., 12., 17., 19., 20., 22., 47., 48., 57., 58. no real number solution

Practice the Skills

42. $\dfrac{-5 \pm \sqrt{13}}{6}$ **43.** $\dfrac{1}{3}, -\dfrac{1}{2}$ **44.** $\dfrac{3}{4}, -\dfrac{1}{2}$ **45.** $\dfrac{7}{2}, -1$ **46.** $\dfrac{5}{4}, -1$ **51.** $\dfrac{9}{2}, -1$ **52.** $\dfrac{5}{2}, 3$

Determine whether each equation has two distinct real number solutions, one real number solution, or no real number solution.

9. $x^2 + 5x - 9 = 0$ **10.** $x^2 + 3x - 7 = 0$ **11.** $2x^2 + x + 1 = 0$ **12.** $r^2 + r + 5 = 0$

13. $6n^2 + 3n - 5 = 0$ **14.** $4x^2 - 24x = -36$ **15.** $2m^2 - 16m = -32$ **16.** $5x^2 - 4x = 2$

17. $2x^2 - 7x + 10 = 0$ **18.** $z^2 = 5z + 11$ **19.** $4x = 8 + x^2$ **20.** $5x - 8 = 3x^2$

21. $x^2 + 7x - 2 = 0$ **22.** $2x^2 - 6x + 5 = 0$ **23.** $2.1x^2 - 0.5 = 0$ **24.** $0.6x^2 - 1.3x = 0$

25. $9 = -t^2 + 6t$ **26.** $-25 = w^2 + 10w$

Use the quadratic formula to solve each equation. If the equation has no real number solution, so state.

27. $x^2 - 10x + 24 = 0$ $4, 6$ **28.** $x^2 - 11x + 10 = 0$ $1, 10$ **29.** $x^2 + 9x + 18 = 0$ $-3, -6$

30. $x^2 - 3x - 10 = 0$ $5, -2$ **31.** $m^2 - 8m = -15$ $5, 3$ **32.** $x^2 + 5x - 24 = 0$ $3, -8$

33. $x^2 - 49 = 0$ $7, -7$ **34.** $m^2 = 121$ $11, -11$ **35.** $x^2 - 6x = 0$ $6, 0$

36. $t^2 - 5t = 0$ $5, 0$ **37.** $30 = -z^2 - 11z$ $-5, -6$ **38.** $z^2 - 14z + 45 = 0$ $9, 5$

39. $x^2 - 7x - 8 = 0$ $8, -1$ **40.** $n^2 - 7n + 10 = 0$ $5, 2$ **41.** $2y^2 - 7y + 4 = 0$ $(7 \pm \sqrt{17})/4$

42. $3x^2 + 5x + 1 = 0$ **43.** $6x^2 = -x + 1$ **44.** $8x^2 - 2x - 3 = 0$

45. $2x^2 = 5x + 7$ **46.** $4x^2 = x + 5$ **47.** $2s^2 - 4s + 5 = 0$

48. $3w^2 - 4w + 2 = 0$ **49.** $x^2 - 7x + 3 = 0$ $(7 \pm \sqrt{37})/2$ **50.** $x^2 - 3x - 1 = 0$ $(3 \pm \sqrt{13})/2$

51. $2x^2 - 7x = 9$ **52.** $-2x^2 + 11x - 15 = 0$ **53.** $-x^2 + 2x + 15 = 0$ $-3, 5$

54. $36 = -4s^2 + 40s$ $1, 9$ **55.** $2t^2 - 6t - 56 = 0$ $7, -4$ **56.** $2r^2 - 18r + 36 = 0$ $3, 6$

57. $6y^2 + 9 = -5y$ **58.** $15 = -5p^2 - 5p$

Problem Solving

59. Product of Integers The product of two consecutive positive integers is 56. Find the two consecutive integers. 7, 8

60. Dimensions of Rectangle The length of a rectangle is 5 feet longer than its width. Find the dimensions of the rectangle if its area is 36 square feet. $w = 4$ ft, $l = 9$ ft

61. Dimensions of Rectangle The length of a rectangle is 3 feet smaller than twice its width. Find the length and width of the rectangle if its area is 20 square feet. $w = 4$ ft, $l = 5$ ft

62. Rectangular Garden Sean McDonald's rectangular garden measures 20 feet by 30 feet. He wishes to build a uniform width brick walkway around his garden that covers an area of 336 square feet. What will be the width of the walkway? 3 ft

63. Swimming Pool Harold Goldstein and his wife Elaine recently installed a built-in rectangular swimming pool measuring 25 feet by 35 feet. They want to add a decorative tile border of uniform width around all sides of the pool. How wide can they make the tile border if they purchased enough tile to cover 256 square feet? 2 ft

64. Pottery Studio Julie Bonds is planning to plant a grass lawn of uniform width around her rectangular pottery studio, which measures 48 feet by 36 feet. How far will the lawn extend from the studio if Julie has only enough seed to plant 4000 square feet of grass? ≈ 16.96 ft

65. Diagonals in a Polygon The number of diagonals, d, in a polygon with n sides is given by the formula $d = \dfrac{n^2 - 3n}{2}$. For example, a pentagon, a polygon with 5 sides, has $d = \dfrac{5^2 - 15}{2} = 5$ diagonals; see the figure.

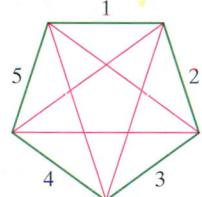

If a polygon has 14 diagonals, how many sides does it have? 7 sides

66. Diagonals in a Polygon If a polygon has 20 diagonals, how many sides does it have? See Exercise 65. 8 sides

67. Flags The cost, c, for manufacturing x American flags is given by $c = x^2 - 16x + 40$. Find the number of flags manufactured if the cost is $120. 20 flags

68. Manufacturing Cost Repeat Exercise 67 for a cost of $2680. 60 flags

69. Model Rocket Phil Chefetz launches a model rocket from the ground. The height, s, of the rocket above the ground at time t seconds after it is launched can be found by the formula $s = -16t^2 + 90t$. Find how long it will take for the rocket to reach a height of 80 feet. ≈ 1.11 sec and ≈ 4.52 sec

70. Model Rocket Repeat Exercise 69 for a height of 100 feet. ≈ 1.52 sec and ≈ 4.10 sec

71. a) $c < 16$ **b)** $c = 16$ **c)** $c > 16$

72. a) $c < \dfrac{9}{8}$ **b)** $c = \dfrac{9}{8}$ **c)** $c > \dfrac{9}{8}$

73. a) $c > -3$ **b)** $c = -3$ **c)** $c < -3$

Challenge Problems

*Find all the values of c that will result in each equation having **a)** two real number solutions, **b)** one real number solution, and **c)** no real number solution.*

71. $x^2 + 8x + c = 0$

72. $2x^2 + 3x + c = 0$

73. $-3x^2 + 6x + c = 0$

74. Fenced in Area Farmer Justina Wells wishes to form a rectangular region along a river bank by constructing fencing on three sides, as illustrated in the diagram. If she has only 400 feet of fencing and wishes to enclose an area of 15,000 square feet, find the dimensions of the rectangular region.

300 ft by 50 ft, or 100 ft by 150 ft

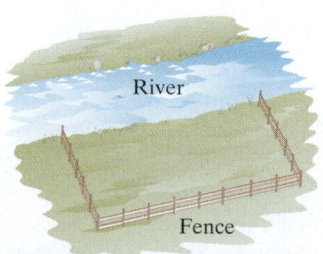

Group Activity

75. In Section 10.4 we will graph quadratic equations. We will learn that the graphs of quadratic equations are *parabolas*. The graph of the quadratic equation $y = x^2 - 2x - 8$ is illustrated below.

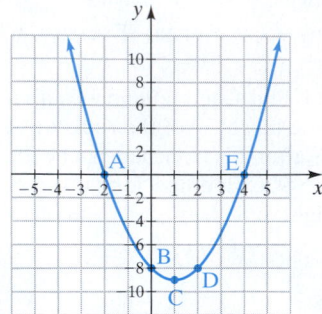

a) Each member of the group, copy the graph in your notebook.

b) Group Member 1: List the ordered pairs corresponding to points A and B. Verify that each ordered pair is a solution to the equation $y = x^2 - 2x - 8$.   A, $(-2, 0)$; B, $(0, -8)$

c) Group Member 2: List the ordered pairs corresponding to points C and D. Verify that each ordered pair is a solution to the equation $y = x^2 - 2x - 8$.   C, $(1, -9)$; D, $(2, -8)$

d) Group Member 3: List the ordered pair corresponding to point E. Verify that the ordered pair is a solution to the equation $y = x^2 - 2x - 8$.   E, $(4, 0)$

e) Individually, graph the equation $y = 2x - 3$ on the same axes that you used in part **a)**. Compare your graphs with the other members of your group.   See graphing answer section.

f) The two graphs represent the system of equations

$$y = x^2 - 2x - 8$$
$$y = 2x - 3$$

As a group, estimate the points of intersection of the graphs. $(-1, -5), (5, 7)$

g) If we set the two equations equal to each other, we obtain the following quadratic equation in only the variable x.

$$x^2 - 2x - 8 = 2x - 3$$

As a group, solve this quadratic equation. Does your answer agree with the x-coordinates of the points of intersection from part **f)**? $-1, 5$; yes

h) As a group, use the values of x found in part **g)** to find the values of y in $y = x^2 - 2x - 8$ and $y = 2x - 3$. Does your answer agree with the y-coordinates of the points of intersection from part **f)**? $x = -1, y = -5$; $x = 5, y = 7$; yes

Cumulative Review Exercises

78. cannot be solved by factoring; $\left(-3 \pm \sqrt{41}\right)/4$

[7.6, 10.2, 10.3] *Solve the following quadratic equations by **a)** factoring, **b)** completing the square, and **c)** the quadratic formula. If the equation cannot be solved by factoring, so state.*

76. $x^2 - 14x + 40 = 0$ $10, 4$ **77.** $6x^2 + 11x - 35 = 0$ $\dfrac{5}{3}, -\dfrac{7}{2}$ **78.** $2x^2 + 3x - 4 = 0$ **79.** $3x^2 = 48$ $4, -4$

[8.4]   **80.** Subtract $\dfrac{x}{2x^2 + 7x - 4} - \dfrac{2}{x^2 - x - 20}$ $\dfrac{x^2 - 9x + 2}{(2x - 1)(x + 4)(x - 5)}$

Mid-Chapter Test: 10.1–10.3

To find out how well you understand the chapter material to this point, take this brief test. The answers, and the section where the material was initially discussed, are given in the back of the book. Review any questions that you answered incorrectly.

Solve.

1. $x^2 = 64$ $8, -8$

2. $a^2 = 19$ $\sqrt{19}, -\sqrt{19}$

3. $16m^2 + 10 = 25$ $\dfrac{\sqrt{15}}{4}, -\dfrac{\sqrt{15}}{4}$

4. $(y - 3)^2 = 4$ $1, 5$

5. $(z + 6)^2 = 81$ $3, -15$

6. $(b - 7)^2 = 24$ $7 \pm 2\sqrt{6}$

7. Numbers The product of two positive numbers is 40. Determine the numbers if the larger number is 2.5 times the smaller number. $4, 10$

8. Numbers When 2 times a number is added to the square of the number, the sum is 8. Find the number(s). $2, -4$

Solve by completing the square.

9. $x^2 + 2x - 15 = 0$ $3, -5$

10. $x^2 - 11x + 18 = 0$ $2, 9$

11. $p^2 - 7p = 0$ $0, 7$

12. $h^2 + 2h - 6 = 0$ $-1 \pm \sqrt{7}$

13. $x^2 - 9x + 1 = 0$ $\dfrac{9 \pm \sqrt{77}}{2}$

Solve by using the quadratic formula.

14. $x^2 - 5x - 24 = 0$ $8, -3$

15. $x^2 + 11x + 30 = 0$ $-6, -5$

16. $m^2 - 5m - 3 = 0$ $\dfrac{5 \pm \sqrt{37}}{2}$

17. Under what conditions will a quadratic equation have
   a) two real number solutions $b^2 - 4ac > 0$
   b) one real number solution, $b^2 - 4ac = 0$
   c) no real number solutions? $b^2 - 4ac < 0$

Determine whether each equation has two distinct real number solutions, one real number solution, or no real number solution.

18. $3x^2 - x - 2 = 0$ two distinct real number solutions

19. $\frac{1}{2}x^2 + 4x + 11 = 0$ no real number solution

20. Rectangle The length of the rectangular screen on a portable DVD player is 3 inches longer than the width. Find the length and width if the screen's area is 88 square inches.
l: 11 in., *w:* 8 in.

10.4 Graphing Quadratic Equations

1 Graph quadratic equations in two variables.

2 Find the coordinates of the vertex of a parabola.

3 Use symmetry to graph quadratic equations.

4 Find the *x*-intercepts of the graph of a quadratic equation.

TEACHING TIP
Point out that in the last section we were solving quadratic equations for the specific case when $y = 0$. Now we are graphing all the cases.

1 Graph Quadratic Equations in Two Variables

Helpful Hint *Study Tip*

In this section we will graph quadratic equations. Quadratic equations can be graphed solely by plotting points, as we did in Chapter 4 when we graphed linear equations. However, there are certain things we can do to make graphing quadratic equations easier. These include finding the vertex of the graph, finding the *x*-intercepts of the graph, and using symmetry to draw the graph. We will discuss each of these items shortly.

In Section 4.2 we learned how to graph linear equations. In this section we graph quadratic equations of the form

$$y = ax^2 + bx + c, \quad a \neq 0$$

The graph of every quadratic equation of this form is a **parabola**. The graph of $y = ax^2 + bx + c$ will have one of the shapes indicated in **Figure 10.3**. When a quadratic equation is in the form $y = ax^2 + bx + c$, the sign of *a*, the numerical coefficient of the squared term, will determine whether the parabola will open upward (**Fig. 10.3a**) or downward (**Fig. 10.3b**). When *a* is positive, the parabola will open upward, and when *a* is negative, the parabola will open downward.

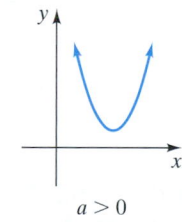

$a > 0$
Parabola opens upward
(a)

$a < 0$
Parabola opens downward
(b)

FIGURE 10.3

TEACHING TIP
Have students use a graphing calculator to investigate how the *a* and the *c* in a quadratic equation of the form $y = ax^2 + bx + c$ influence the graph of the equation.

The **vertex** is the lowest point on a parabola that opens upward or the highest point on a parabola that opens downward (**Fig. 10.4**). Graphs of quadratic equations of the form $y = ax^2 + bx + c$ have **symmetry** about a line through the vertex. This means that if we fold the paper along this imaginary line, called the **axis of symmetry**, the right and left sides of the graph will coincide.

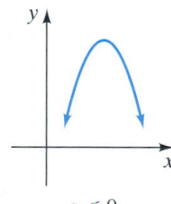

FIGURE 10.4

One method you can use to graph a quadratic equation is to plot it point by point. When determining points to plot, select values for x and determine the corresponding values for y.

EXAMPLE 1 ▶ Graph $y = x^2$.

Solution   Since $a = 1$, which is positive, this parabola opens upward.

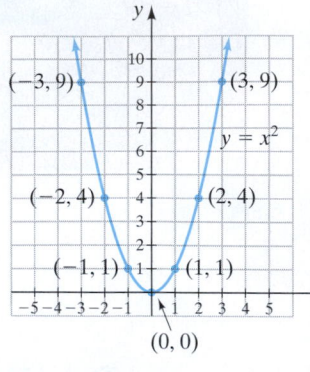

			x	y
Let $x = 3$,	$y = (3)^2 = 9$		3	9
Let $x = 2$,	$y = (2)^2 = 4$		2	4
Let $x = 1$,	$y = (1)^2 = 1$		1	1
Let $x = 0$,	$y = (0)^2 = 0$		0	0
Let $x = -1$,	$y = (-1)^2 = 1$		−1	1
Let $x = -2$,	$y = (-2)^2 = 4$		−2	4
Let $x = -3$,	$y = (-3)^2 = 9$		−3	9

FIGURE 10.5

Connect the points with a smooth curve (**Fig. 10.5**). Note how the graph is symmetric about the line $x = 0$ (or the y-axis).

▶ **Now Try Exercise 21**

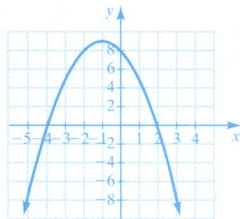

EXAMPLE 2 ▶ Graph $y = -2x^2 + 4x + 6$.

Solution   Since $a = -2$, which is negative, this parabola opens downward.

$y = -2x^2 + 4x + 6$		x	y
Let $x = 5$,	$y = -2(5)^2 + 4(5) + 6 = -24$	5	−24
Let $x = 4$,	$y = -2(4)^2 + 4(4) + 6 = -10$	4	−10
Let $x = 3$,	$y = -2(3)^2 + 4(3) + 6 = 0$	3	0
Let $x = 2$,	$y = -2(2)^2 + 4(2) + 6 = 6$	2	6
Let $x = 1$,	$y = -2(1)^2 + 4(1) + 6 = 8$	1	8
Let $x = 0$,	$y = -2(0)^2 + 4(0) + 6 = 6$	0	6
Let $x = -1$,	$y = -2(-1)^2 + 4(-1) + 6 = 0$	−1	0
Let $x = -2$,	$y = -2(-2)^2 + 4(-2) + 6 = -10$	−2	−10
Let $x = -3$,	$y = -2(-3)^2 + 4(-3) + 6 = -24$	−3	−24

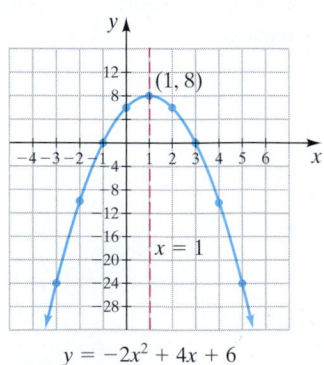

$y = -2x^2 + 4x + 6$

FIGURE 10.6

Note how the graph (**Fig. 10.6**) is symmetric about the line $x = 1$, which is dashed because it is not part of the graph. The vertex of this parabola is the point $(1, 8)$. Since the y-values are large, the y-axis has been marked with 4-unit intervals to allow us to graph the points $(-3, -24)$ and $(5, -24)$. The arrows on the ends of the graph indicate that the parabola continues indefinitely.

▶ **Now Try Exercise 23**

2   Find the Coordinates of the Vertex of a Parabola

When graphing quadratic equations, how do we decide what values to use for x? When the location of the vertex is unknown, this is a difficult question to answer. When the location of the vertex is known, it becomes more obvious which values to use.

In Example 2, the axis of symmetry is $x = 1$, and the x-coordinate of the vertex is also 1. For a quadratic equation in the form $y = ax^2 + bx + c$, both the axis of symmetry and the x-coordinate of the vertex can be found by using the following formula.

Axis of Symmetry and x-Coordinate of the Vertex

$$x = -\frac{b}{2a}$$

TEACHING TIP
Point out the duplicate y-values in the table in Example 2. Then ask, "Can you find the x-coordinate of the vertex if you know the x-values for duplicate y-values? Explain." Point out that the quadratic formula gives x-values for both occurrences of $y = 0$. Then have them average the two x-values to determine the x-coordinate of the vertex.

In the quadratic equation in Example 2, $a = -2$, $b = 4$, and $c = 6$. Substituting these values in the formula for the axis of symmetry gives

$$x = -\frac{b}{2a} = -\frac{4}{2(-2)} = -\frac{4}{-4} = 1$$

Thus, the graph is symmetric about the line $x = 1$, and the x-coordinate of the vertex is 1.

The y-coordinate of the vertex can be found by substituting the value of the x-coordinate of the vertex into the quadratic equation and solving for y.

$$
\begin{aligned}
y &= -2x^2 + 4x + 6 \\
&= -2(1)^2 + 4(1) + 6 \\
&= -2(1) + 4 + 6 \\
&= -2 + 4 + 6 \\
&= 8
\end{aligned}
$$

Thus, the vertex is at the point $(1, 8)$.

For a quadratic equation of the form $y = ax^2 + bx + c$, the y-coordinate of the vertex can also be found by the following formula.

y-Coordinate of the Vertex

$$y = \frac{4ac - b^2}{4a}$$

For Example 2,

$$
\begin{aligned}
y &= \frac{4ac - b^2}{4a} \\
&= \frac{4(-2)(6) - 4^2}{4(-2)} \\
&= \frac{-48 - 16}{-8} = \frac{-64}{-8} = 8
\end{aligned}
$$

You may use the method of your choice to find the y-coordinate of the vertex. Both methods result in the same value of y.

3 Use Symmetry to Graph Quadratic Equations

One method to use in selecting points to plot when graphing parabolas is to determine the axis of symmetry and the vertex of the graph. Then select nearby values of x on either side of the axis of symmetry. When graphing the equation, make use of the symmetry of the graph.

EXAMPLE 3 ▶

a) Find the axis of symmetry of the graph of the equation $y = x^2 + 6x + 5$.

b) Find the vertex of the graph.

c) Graph the equation.

Solution

a) $a = 1,$ $b = 6,$ $c = 5.$

$$x = -\frac{b}{2a} = -\frac{6}{2(1)} = -3$$

The parabola is symmetric about the line $x = -3$. The x-coordinate of the vertex is -3.

b) Now find the y-coordinate of the vertex. Substitute -3 for x in the quadratic equation.

$$y = x^2 + 6x + 5$$
$$y = (-3)^2 + 6(-3) + 5 = 9 - 18 + 5 = -4$$

The vertex is at the point $(-3, -4)$.

c) Since the axis of symmetry is $x = -3$, we will select values for x that are greater than or equal to -3. It is often helpful to plot each point as it is determined. If a point does not appear to lie on the parabola, check it.

	$y = x^2 + 6x + 5$		x	y
Let $x = -2,$	$y = (-2)^2 + 6(-2) + 5 = -3$		-2	-3
Let $x = -1,$	$y = (-1)^2 + 6(-1) + 5 = 0$		-1	0
Let $x = 0,$	$y = (0)^2 + 6(0) + 5 = 5$		0	5

These points are plotted in **Figure 10.7a**. The entire graph of the equation is illustrated in **Figure 10.7b**. Note how we use symmetry to complete the graph. The points $(-2, -3)$ and $(-4, -3)$ are each 1 horizontal unit from the axis of symmetry, $x = -3$. The points $(-1, 0)$ and $(-5, 0)$ are each 2 horizontal units from the axis of symmetry, and the points $(0, 5)$ and $(-6, 5)$ are each 3 horizontal units from the axis of symmetry.

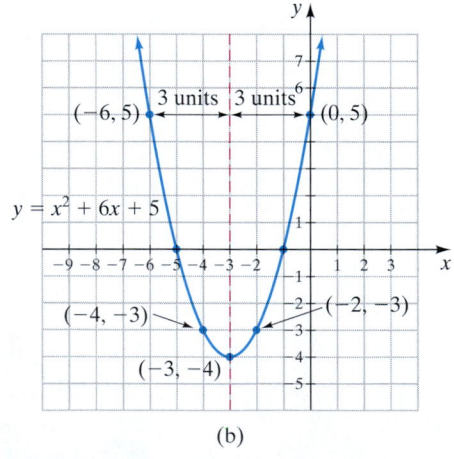

FIGURE 10.7   (a)   (b)

▶ **Now Try Exercise 25**

EXAMPLE 4 ▶ Graph $y = -2x^2 + 5x - 4$.

Solution $a = -2,$ $b = 5,$ $c = -4.$
Since $a < 0$, this parabola will open downward.

$$\text{Axis of symmetry: } x = -\frac{b}{2a}$$

$$= -\frac{5}{2(-2)} = -\frac{5}{-4} = \frac{5}{4} \; \left(\text{or } 1\frac{1}{4}\right)$$

Since the *x*-value of the vertex is a fraction, we would need to add fractions if we wished to find *y* by substituting $\frac{5}{4}$ for *x* in the given equation. Therefore, we will use the formula to find the *y*-coordinate of the vertex.

$$y = \frac{4ac - b^2}{4a}$$

$$= \frac{4(-2)(-4) - 5^2}{4(-2)} = \frac{32 - 25}{-8} = \frac{7}{-8} = -\frac{7}{8}$$

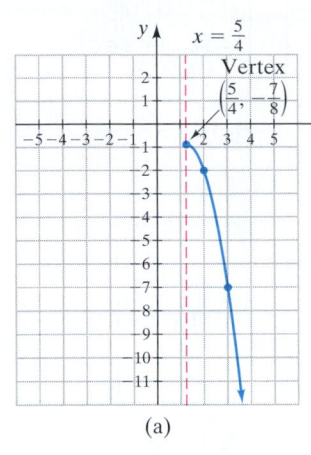

The vertex of this graph is at the point $\left(\frac{5}{4}, -\frac{7}{8}\right)$. Since the axis of symmetry is $x = \frac{5}{4}$, we will begin by selecting values of *x* that are greater than $\frac{5}{4}$, or $1\frac{1}{4}$.

$$y = -2x^2 + 5x - 4$$

Let $x = 2$, $y = -2(2)^2 + 5(2) - 4 = -2$

Let $x = 3$, $y = -2(3)^2 + 5(3) - 4 = -7$

Let $x = 4$, $y = -2(4)^2 + 5(4) - 4 = -16$

x	*y*
2	−2
3	−7
4	−16

When the axis of symmetry is a fractional value, be very careful when constructing the graph. You should plot as many additional points as needed. Following we determine some values of *y* when *x* is less than $\frac{5}{4}$.

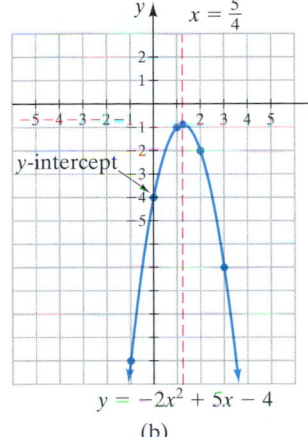

Let $x = 1$ $y = -2(1)^2 + 5(1) - 4 = -1$

Let $x = 0$ $y = -2(0)^2 + 5(0) - 4 = -4$

Let $x = -1$ $y = -2(-1)^2 + 5(-1) - 4 = -11$

x	*y*
1	−1
0	−4
−1	−11

$y = -2x^2 + 5x - 4$

(b)

FIGURE 10.8

Figure 10.8a shows the points plotted on the right side of the axis of symmetry. **Figure 10.8b** shows the completed graph. The point $(4, -16)$ is not shown on the graphs.

▶ **Now Try Exercise 19**

When graphing, we will often have to evaluate quadratic expressions to obtain values for *y*. You may wish to review *Evaluating Expressions* as explained in the Using Your Calculator box in Section 1.9, page 76.

(a)

(b)

FIGURE 10.9 Not every shape that resembles a parabola is a parabola. For example, the St. Louis Arch, **Figure 10.9a** resembles a parabola, but it is not a parabola. However, the bridge over the Mississippi near Jefferson Barracks, Missouri, which connects Missouri and Illinois, **Figure 10.9b**, is a parabola.

Let's discuss how to find the vertex of a parabola. In Example 3 we graphed $y = x^2 + 6x + 5$. This graph is shown on the window of a TI-84 Plus in **Figure 10.10** using the standard window settings.

We can use the CALC (calculate) menu to find the vertex. The vertex of a parabola is also called the minimum point (if the parabola opens upward) or the maximum point (if the parabola opens downward). To obtain the CALC menu press $\boxed{2^{nd}}$ $\boxed{\text{TRACE}}$. The CALC menu is shown in **Figure 10.11**.

FIGURE 10.10

FIGURE 10.11

Since this graph opens upward, it has a minimum point. Scroll down the CALC menu to option 3: minimum, and press $\boxed{\text{ENTER}}$, which gives you the graph shown in **Figure 10.12**. Notice the cursor is at the y-intercept, $(0, 5)$. Use the left-arrow key to move the cursor to the left. Notice the values of X and Y changing as you move the cursor. The value of Y will decrease until the cursor reaches the vertex. When the cursor moves past the vertex, the value of Y will begin to increase. Move the cursor just to the left of the vertex, and press $\boxed{\text{ENTER}}$. Notice the words *Left Bound?* change to *Right Bound?*. Now move the cursor just to the right of the vertex and press $\boxed{\text{ENTER}}$. The screen now shows *Guess?*. Press $\boxed{\text{ENTER}}$ again and you get the screen shown in **Figure 10.13**.

FIGURE 10.12

Figure 10.13 shows that the minimum point of the graph occurs when $x = -3$ and $y = -4$. Thus, the vertex is at $(-3, -4)$.

If the parabola opened downward, the graph would have a maximum point. To obtain the vertex in this case we would use the CALC menu, option 4: maximum, to obtain the vertex. You then would follow the same basic procedure to find the maximum point.

EXERCISES

Use your graphing calculator to find the vertex of the graph of each equation. You may need to adjust your window settings to show the vertex.

FIGURE 10.13

1. $y = x^2 - 2x - 3$ $(1, -4)$
2. $y = x^2 - 7x + 10$ $(3.5, -2.25)$
3. $y = -2x^2 - 2x + 12$ $(-0.5, 12.5)$
4. $y = 2x^2 - 7x - 15$ $(1.75, -21.125)$

▣4 Find the x-Intercepts of the Graph of a Quadratic Equation

In Example 4 the graph crossed the y-axis at $y = -4$. Recall from earlier sections that to find the y-intercept we let $x = 0$ and solve the resulting equation for y. The locations of the x and y-intercepts are often helpful when graphing quadratic equations.

To find the x-intercept when graphing straight lines in Section 4.2, we set $y = 0$ and found the corresponding value of x. We did this because the value of y where a graph crosses the x-axis is 0. We use the same procedure here when finding the x-intercepts of a quadratic equation of the form $y = ax^2 + bx + c$. To find the x-intercepts of the graph of $y = ax^2 + bx + c$, we set y equal to 0 and solve the resulting equation, $ax^2 + bx + c = 0$. The real number solutions of the equation $ax^2 + bx + c = 0$ are called the *zeros* (or *roots*) of the equation, for when they are substituted for x in $y = ax^2 + bx + c$, y has a value of zero. The zeros can be used to determine the x-intercepts of the graph of $y = ax^2 + bx + c$ because the zeros are the x-coordinates of the x-intercepts. To solve equations of the form $ax^2 + bx + c = 0$, we can use factoring as explained in Section 7.6; completing the square as explained in Section 10.2; or the quadratic formula as explained in Section 10.3.

In Section 10.3 we mentioned that when solving quadratic equations of the form $ax^2 + bx + c = 0$, when the discriminant, $b^2 - 4ac$, is greater than zero, there are two distinct real number solutions; when it is equal to zero, there is one real number solution; and when it is less than zero, there is no real number solution.

A quadratic equation of the form $y = ax^2 + bx + c$ will have either two distinct x-intercepts (**Fig. 10.14a**), one x-intercept (**Fig. 10.14b**), or no x-intercepts (**Fig. 10.14c**). The number of x-intercepts may be determined by the discriminant.

$b^2 - 4ac > 0$
Two distinct x-intercepts

$b^2 - 4ac = 0$
One x-intercept

$b^2 - 4ac < 0$
No x-intercepts

or

or

or

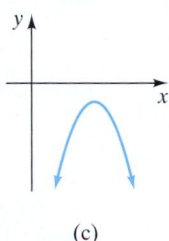

FIGURE 10.14   (a)   (b)   (c)

The x-intercepts can be found graphically. They may also be found algebraically by setting y equal to 0 and solving the resulting equation, as in Example 5.

EXAMPLE 5 ▶

a) Find the x-intercepts of the graph of the equation $y = x^2 - 6x - 7$ by factoring, by completing the square, and by the quadratic formula.

b) Graph the equation.

Solution   **a)** To find the x-intercepts algebraically we set y equal to 0 and solve the resulting equation, $x^2 - 6x - 7 = 0$. We will solve this equation by all three algebraic methods.

Method 1:   Factoring.

$$x^2 - 6x - 7 = 0$$
$$(x - 7)(x + 1) = 0$$
$$x - 7 = 0 \quad \text{or} \quad x + 1 = 0$$
$$x = 7 \qquad\qquad x = -1$$

Method 2:   Completing the square.

$$x^2 - 6x - 7 = 0$$
$$x^2 - 6x = 7$$
$$x^2 - 6x + 9 = 7 + 9$$
$$(x - 3)^2 = 16$$
$$x - 3 = \pm 4$$
$$x = 3 \pm 4$$
$$x = 3 + 4 \quad \text{or} \quad x = 3 - 4$$
$$x = 7 \qquad\qquad x = -1$$

Method 3:   Quadratic formula.

$$x^2 - 6x - 7 = 0$$

$$a = 1, \qquad b = -6, \qquad c = -7$$

$$x = \frac{-b \pm \sqrt{b^2 - 4ac}}{2a}$$

$$= \frac{-(-6) \pm \sqrt{(-6)^2 - 4(1)(-7)}}{2(1)}$$

$$= \frac{6 \pm \sqrt{36 + 28}}{2}$$

$$= \frac{6 \pm \sqrt{64}}{2}$$

$$= \frac{6 \pm 8}{2}$$

$$x = \frac{6 + 8}{2} \qquad \text{or} \qquad x = \ = \frac{6 - 8}{2}$$

$$= \frac{14}{2} = 7 \qquad\qquad = \frac{-2}{2} = -1$$

Note that the same solutions, 7 and -1, were obtained by all three methods. The graph of the equation $y = x^2 - 6x - 7$ will have two distinct x-intercepts. The graph will cross the x-axis at 7 and -1. The x-intercepts are $(7, 0)$ and $(-1, 0)$.

b) Since $a > 0$, this parabola opens upward.

$$\text{axis of symmetry:} \quad x = -\frac{b}{2a} = -\frac{-6}{2(1)} = \frac{6}{2} = 3$$

x	y
3	-16
4	-15
5	-12
6	-7
7	0
8	9

$$y = x^2 - 6x - 7$$

Let $x = 3$, $y = 3^2 - 6(3) - 7 = -16$

Let $x = 4$, $y = 4^2 - 6(4) - 7 = -15$

Let $x = 5$, $y = 5^2 - 6(5) - 7 = -12$

Let $x = 6$, $y = 6^2 - 6(6) - 7 = -7$

Let $x = 7$, $y = 7^2 - 6(7) - 7 = 0$

Let $x = 8$, $y = 8^2 - 6(8) - 7 = 9$

FIGURE 10.15

The vertex is at $(3, -16)$. Again we use symmetry to complete the graph (**Fig. 10.15**). The x-intercepts $(7, 0)$ and $(-1, 0)$ agree with the answer obtained in part **a)**.

▸ **Now Try Exercise 31**

USING YOUR GRAPHING CALCULATOR

The x-intercepts of a parabola can be found using a graphing calculator. Read the manual that comes with your graphing calculator to find out how to determine the x-intercepts of a parabola. On the TI-84 Plus, you can use the CALC (calculate) menu with option 2: *zero* (see **Fig. 10.11** on page 620).

EXERCISE SET 10.4

MathXL®   MyMathLab

2. highest point on a parabola that opens downward, lowest point on a parabola that opens upward   **4.** the sign of a; $a > 0$, upward; $a < 0$, downward   **5. a)** where the graph crosses the x-axis

Concept/Writing Exercises

6. If you fold the paper along the line, the right and left sides of the graph will coincide.   **7. a)** $x = -\dfrac{b}{2a}$

1. What do we call the graph of a quadratic equation of the form $y = ax^2 + bx + c$, $a \neq 0$?   a parabola

2. What is the vertex of a parabola?

3. Explain how to find the coordinates of the vertex of a parabola.   Answers will vary.

4. What determines whether the graph of a quadratic equation of the form $y = ax^2 + bx + c$, $a \neq 0$, is a parabola that opens upward or downward? Explain your answer.

5. a) What are the x-intercepts of a graph?

b) How can you find the x-intercepts of a graph algebraically?   Let $y = 0$ and solve for x.

6. What does it mean when we say that graphs of quadratic equations of the form $y = ax^2 + bx + c$ have symmetry about an imaginary vertical line through the vertex?

7. a) When graphing a quadratic equation of the form $y = ax^2 + bx + c$, what is the equation of the vertical line about which the parabola will be symmetric?

b) What is this vertical line called?   axis of symmetry

8. How many x-intercepts will the graph of a quadratic equation have if the discriminant has a value of

a) 25   two   **b)** -2 none   **c)** 0   one

Practice the Skills

Indicate the axis of symmetry, the coordinates of the vertex, and whether the parabola opens upward or downward.

9. $y = x^2 + 2x - 7$ $x = -1$, $(-1, -8)$, upward

10. $y = x^2 + 4x - 5$ $x = -2$, $(-2, -9)$, upward

11. $y = 4x^2 + 8x + 3$ $x = -1$, $(-1, -1)$, upward

12. $y = -x^2 + 8x - 15$ $x = 4$, $(4, 1)$, downward

13. $y = -3x^2 + 2x + 1$ $x = \dfrac{1}{3}$, $\left(\dfrac{1}{3}, \dfrac{4}{3}\right)$, downward

14. $y = x^2 + 3x - 6$ $x = -\dfrac{3}{2}$, $\left(-\dfrac{3}{2}, -\dfrac{33}{4}\right)$, upward

15. $y = -x^2 + 3x - 4$ $x = \dfrac{3}{2}$, $\left(\dfrac{3}{2}, -\dfrac{7}{4}\right)$, downward

16. $y = 3x^2 - 2x + 2$ $x = \dfrac{1}{3}$, $\left(\dfrac{1}{3}, \dfrac{5}{3}\right)$, upward

17. $y = 2x^2 + 3x + 4$ $x = -\dfrac{3}{4}$, $\left(-\dfrac{3}{4}, \dfrac{23}{8}\right)$, upward

18. $y = -2x^2 - 6x - 1$ $x = -\dfrac{3}{2}$, $\left(-\dfrac{3}{2}, \dfrac{7}{2}\right)$, downward

19. $y = -x^2 + x + 8$ $x = \dfrac{1}{2}$, $\left(\dfrac{1}{2}, \dfrac{33}{4}\right)$, downward

20. $y = -5x^2 + 6x - 3$ $x = \dfrac{3}{5}$, $\left(\dfrac{3}{5}, -\dfrac{6}{5}\right)$, downward

Graph each quadratic equation and determine the x-intercepts, if they exist.   **21.–48.** See graphing answer section.

21. $y = x^2 + 3$

22. $y = -x^2 - 1$

23. $y = -x^2 + 5$

24. $y = x^2 - 1$

25. $y = x^2 + 4x + 3$

26. $y = 2x^2 + 1$

27. $y = x^2 + 4x + 4$

28. $y = x^2 - 4x + 4$

29. $y = -x^2 - 5x - 4$

30. $y = -x^2 - 5x + 6$

31. $y = x^2 + 5x - 6$

32. $y = x^2 - 4x - 5$

33. $y = x^2 + 5x - 14$

34. $y = 2x^2 + 4x + 2$

35. $y = x^2 - 6x + 9$

36. $y = x^2 + 8x + 16$

37. $y = x^2 - 6x$

38. $y = -x^2 + 5x$

39. $y = x^2 - 2x + 1$

40. $y = x^2 + x + 1$

41. $y = -x^2 + 7x - 10$

42. $y = x^2 - 2x - 16$

43. $y = 4x^2 + 12x + 9$

44. $y = 2x^2 + 3x - 2$

45. $y = -2x^2 + 3x - 2$

46. $y = -4x^2 - 6x + 4$

47. $y = 2x^2 - x - 15$

48. $y = 6x^2 + 10x - 4$

Using the discriminant, determine the number of x-intercepts the graph of each equation will have. Do not graph the equation.

49. $y = 4x^2 - 2x - 7$ two   **50.** $y = -x^2 - 8$ none   **51.** $y = 4x^2 - 6x - 5$ two   **52.** $y = x^2 - 6x + 9$ one

53. $y = x^2 - 22x + 121$ one   **54.** $y = -4.3x^2 + 2.4x$ two   **55.** $y = 5.7x^2 + 2x - 1.5$ two   **56.** $y = 5x^2 - 7.1x + 6.3$ none

Problem Solving

57. none; the vertex is below the x-axis, the parabola opens downward   **58.** two; the vertex is below the x-axis, the parabola opens upward   **59.** one; the vertex of the parabola is on the x-axis   **60.** none; the vertex is below the x-axis, the parabola opens downward

The graph of a quadratic equation of the form $y = ax^2 + bx + c$ is a parabola. The value of a (the coefficient of the squared term in the equation) and the vertex of the parabola are given. Determine the number of x-intercepts the parabola will have. Explain how you determined your answer.   **61.** yes; if y is set to 0, both equations have the same solutions 5 and -3 **62. a)** The graphs will be symmetric about the x-axis.

57. $a = -2$, vertex at $(0, -4)$

58. $a = 2$, vertex at $(1, -3)$

59. $a = -3$, vertex at $(-5, 0)$

60. $a = -1$, vertex at $(2, -7)$

61. Will the equations below have the same x-intercepts when graphed? Explain how you determined your answer.

$$y = x^2 - 2x - 15 \quad \text{and} \quad y = -x^2 + 2x + 15$$

62. a) How will the graphs of the following equations compare? Explain how you determined your answer.

$$y = x^2 - 2x - 8 \quad \text{and} \quad y = -x^2 + 2x + 8$$

b) Graph $y = x^2 - 2x - 8$ and $y = -x^2 + 2x + 8$ on the same axes.   See graphing answer section.

63. Height above Ground An object is projected upward from the ground. The height of the object above the ground, in feet, at time t, in seconds, is illustrated in the following graph.

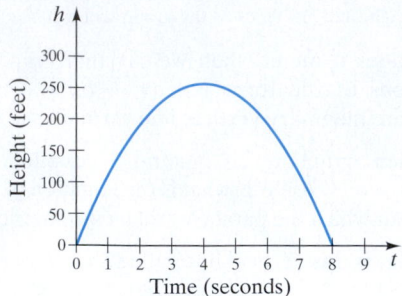

a) Estimate the maximum height the object will obtain.   ≈255 ft

b) How long will it take for the object to reach its maximum height?   4 sec

c) Estimate how long will it take for the object to strike the ground.   8 sec

d) Estimate the object's height at 2 seconds and at 5 seconds.   ≈190 ft, ≈240 ft

64. Height above Ground An object is projected straight upward from a platform that is 100 feet above the ground. The height of the object above the ground, in feet, at time t, in seconds, is illustrated in the following graph.

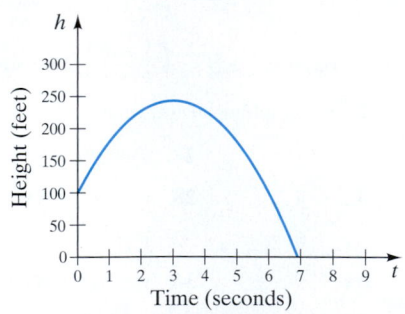

a) Estimate the maximum height the object will obtain.   ≈245 ft

b) How long will it take for the object to reach its maximum height?   3 sec

c) Approximately how long will it take for the object to strike the ground?   ≈7 sec

d) Estimate the object's height above the ground at 2 seconds and at 5 seconds.   ≈230 ft, ≈180 ft

65. Maximum Area An area is to be fenced in along a river as shown in the figure. Only 180 feet of fencing is available. The fenced-in area is $A = $ length · width or $A = x(180 - 2x) = -2x^2 + 180x$.

a) Graph $A = -2x^2 + 180x$.   See graphing answer section.

b) Using the graph, estimate the value of x that will yield the maximum area.   45 ft

c) Estimate the maximum area.   4050 ft^2

66. Maximum Area Read Exercise 65. If 260 feet of fencing is available, the fenced-in area is $A = x(260 - 2x) = -2x^2 + 260x$.

a) Graph $A = -2x^2 + 260x$.   See graphing answer section.

b) Using the graph, estimate the value of x that yields the maximum area.   65 ft

c) Estimate the maximum area.   8450 ft^2

Challenge Problems
67. a), 68. a) See graphing answer section.

67. a) Graph the quadratic equation $y = -x^2 + 6x$.

 b) On the same axes, graph the quadratic equation $y = x^2 - 2x$.   See graphing answer section.

 c) Estimate the points of intersection of the graphs. The points represent the solution to the system of equations. $(0, 0), (4, 8)$

68. a) Graph the quadratic equation $y = x^2 + 2x - 3$.

 b) On the same axes, graph the quadratic equation $y = -x^2 + 1$.   See graphing answer section.

 c) Estimate the points of intersection of the graphs. The points represent the solution to the system of equations. $(-2, -3), (1, 0)$

Cumulative Review Exercises

[8.4] **69.** Subtract $\dfrac{5}{x + 3} - \dfrac{x - 2}{x - 4}$. $\dfrac{-x^2 + 4x - 14}{(x + 3)(x - 4)}$

[8.6] **70.** Solve $\dfrac{1}{3}(x + 6) = 3 - \dfrac{1}{4}(x - 5)$. $\dfrac{27}{7}$

[5.3] **71.** Solve the system of equations.
$$2x + 3y = -3$$
$$3x + 5y = -7 \quad (6, -5)$$

[9.5] **72.** Solve $\sqrt{x + 9} - x = -3$.   7

10.5 Complex Numbers

1 Write complex numbers using i.

2 Add and subtract complex numbers.

3 Solve quadratic equations with complex number solutions.

1 Write Complex Numbers Using i

In Section 10.3 we stated that the square roots of negative numbers, such as $\sqrt{-11}$, are not real numbers. Numbers like $\sqrt{-11}$ are called **imaginary numbers**. Such numbers are called imaginary because when they were introduced many mathematicians refused to believe that they existed. Although they do not belong to the set of real numbers, the imaginary numbers do exist and are very useful in mathematics and science.

Every imaginary number has $\sqrt{-1}$ as a factor. The $\sqrt{-1}$, called the **imaginary unit**, is often denoted by the letter i.

> ### Imaginary Unit
> $$i = \sqrt{-1}$$

TEACHING TIP
Stress that i is a shorthand for $\sqrt{-1}$.

We can therefore write

$$\sqrt{-4} = \sqrt{4}\,\sqrt{-1} = 2\sqrt{-1} = 2i$$
$$\sqrt{-9} = \sqrt{9}\,\sqrt{-1} = 3\sqrt{-1} = 3i$$
$$\sqrt{-11} = \sqrt{11}\,\sqrt{-1} = \sqrt{11}i \quad \text{or} \quad i\sqrt{11}$$

We will generally write $i\sqrt{11}$ rather than $\sqrt{11}i$ to avoid confusion with $\sqrt{11i}$.

To help in writing square roots of negative numbers using i, we give the following rule.

> ### Square Root of a Negative Number
> For any positive real number n,
> $$\sqrt{-n} = i\sqrt{n}$$

Examples

$$\sqrt{-16} = i\sqrt{16} = 4i \qquad \sqrt{-6} = i\sqrt{6}$$
$$\sqrt{-100} = i\sqrt{100} = 10i \qquad \sqrt{-10} = i\sqrt{10}$$

The real number system is a part of a larger number system, called the *complex number system*. Now we will discuss **complex numbers**.

> ### Complex Number
> Every number of the form
> $$a + bi$$
> where a and b are real numbers, is a **complex number**.

Every real number and every imaginary number are also complex numbers. A complex number has two parts: a real part, a, and an imaginary part, b.

Real part ⟶ ↓   ↓ ⟵ *Imaginary part*

$$a + b\,i$$

If $b = 0$, the complex number is a real number. If $a = 0$, the complex number is a *pure imaginary number*.

Examples of Complex Numbers

$3 + 8i$	$a = 3, \quad b = 8$	
$5 - i\sqrt{3}$	$a = 5, \quad b = -\sqrt{3}$	
2	$a = 2, \quad b = 0$	(real number, $b = 0$)
$9i$	$a = 0, \quad b = 9$	(imaginary number, $a = 0$)
$-i\sqrt{7}$	$a = 0, \quad b = -\sqrt{7}$	(imaginary number, $a = 0$)

We stated that all real numbers and imaginary numbers are also complex numbers. The relationship between the various sets of numbers is illustrated in **Figure 10.16**. As the figure illustrates, the real numbers include both the rational numbers and the irrational numbers, and the complex numbers include both the real numbers and the nonreal numbers.

Complex Numbers		
Real Numbers		**Nonreal Numbers**
Rational numbers $\frac{1}{2}, -\frac{3}{5}, \frac{9}{4}$	Irrational numbers $\sqrt{2}, \sqrt{3}$	$\sqrt{-4}$ $2 + 3i$
Integers $-4, -9$	$-\sqrt{7}, \pi$	$6 - 4i$ $\sqrt{2} + i\sqrt{3}$
Whole numbers $0, 4, 12$		$i\sqrt{5}$ $6i$

FIGURE 10.16

EXAMPLE 1 ▶ Write each of the following complex numbers in the form $a + bi$.

a) $5 + \sqrt{-4}$ **b)** $9 - \sqrt{-12}$

Solution

a) $5 + \sqrt{-4} = 5 + \sqrt{4}\,\sqrt{-1}$.
$$= 5 + 2i$$

b) $9 - \sqrt{-12} = 9 - \sqrt{12}\,\sqrt{-1}$
$$= 9 - \sqrt{4}\,\sqrt{3}\,\sqrt{-1}$$
$$= 9 - 2\sqrt{3}i \quad \text{or} \quad 9 - 2i\sqrt{3}$$

▶ **Now Try Exercise 21**

INSTRUCTOR EXAMPLE
Write $5 + \sqrt{-18}$ in the form $a + bi$.
Ans.: $5 + 3i\sqrt{2}$

In Section 10.3, Example 6, we obtained the answers $\dfrac{1 + \sqrt{-11}}{6}$ and $\dfrac{1 - \sqrt{-11}}{6}$. We indicated that since $\sqrt{-11}$ is not a real number we would stop there. Now we can rewrite these answers as $\dfrac{1 + i\sqrt{11}}{6}$ and $\dfrac{1 - i\sqrt{11}}{6}$, or $\dfrac{1 \pm i\sqrt{11}}{6}$.

2 Add and Subtract Complex Numbers

Complex numbers can be added, subtracted, multiplied, and divided. To add (or subtract) complex numbers, add (or subtract) their real parts and add (or subtract) their complex parts.

EXAMPLE 2 ▶ Add each of the following.

a) $3 + 6i$ and $-2 - 3i$ **b)** $-4 - 5i$ and $-3 - 7i$

INSTRUCTOR EXAMPLE
Add $2 - 7i$ and $-5 + 3i$.
Ans.: $-3 - 4i$

Solution

a) $(3 + 6i) + (-2 - 3i) = (3 - 2) + (6i - 3i)$
$$= 1 + 3i$$

b) $(-4 - 5i) + (-3 - 7i) = (-4 - 3) + (-5i - 7i)$
$$= -7 - 12i$$

▶ **Now Try Exercise 37**

Complex numbers can also be multiplied and divided, but we will not multiply and divide complex numbers in this text.

3 Solve Quadratic Equations with Complex Number Solutions

Before we leave this section, let's solve a quadratic equation that does not have real numbers as solutions. We will write the answers as complex numbers.

EXAMPLE 3 ▶ Solve $2x^2 - 4x + 7 = 0$.

Solution   We will use the quadratic formula.

$$a = 2, \quad b = -4, \quad c = 7$$

$$x = \frac{-b \pm \sqrt{b^2 - 4ac}}{2a} \qquad \textit{Quadratic formula}$$

$$= \frac{-(-4) \pm \sqrt{(-4)^2 - 4(2)(7)}}{2(2)}$$

$$= \frac{4 \pm \sqrt{16 - 56}}{4}$$

$$= \frac{4 \pm \sqrt{-40}}{4} \qquad \textit{These are complex numbers.}$$

$$= \frac{4 \pm \sqrt{4}\sqrt{10}\sqrt{-1}}{4}$$

$$= \frac{4 \pm 2i\sqrt{10}}{4} \qquad \textit{Write complex numbers using i.}$$

$$= \frac{\overset{1}{2}\left(2 \pm i\sqrt{10}\right)}{\underset{2}{\cancel{4}}} \qquad \textit{Factor numerator, divide out common factors.}$$

$$= \frac{2 \pm i\sqrt{10}}{2}$$

The solutions, $\dfrac{2 + i\sqrt{10}}{2}$ and $\dfrac{2 - i\sqrt{10}}{2}$, are complex numbers.

▶ **Now Try Exercise 51**

EXERCISE SET 10.5   *Math XL* *MyMathLab*
MathXL®   MyMathLab

Concept/Writing Exercises

1. Is every real number a complex number? Explain.   yes

2. Are there any complex numbers that are real numbers? If so, how many complex numbers are real numbers? Explain.   yes, an infinite number of them

3. What is the value of i? $\sqrt{-1}$

4. a) Is $\sqrt{-11}$ a member of the real number system? Explain.   no

   b) Is $\sqrt{-11}$ a member of the complex number system? Explain.   yes

5. What is the general form of a complex number? $a + bi$

6. Explain how to add or subtract complex numbers.   add real parts, add imaginary parts

Practice the Skills

Write each imaginary number in terms of i.

7. $\sqrt{-16}$ $4i$

8. $\sqrt{-49}$ $7i$

9. $\sqrt{-100}$ $10i$

10. $\sqrt{-144}$ $12i$

11. $\sqrt{-15}$ $i\sqrt{15}$

12. $\sqrt{-10}$ $i\sqrt{10}$

13. $\sqrt{-13}$ $i\sqrt{13}$

14. $\sqrt{-23}$ $i\sqrt{23}$

15. $\sqrt{-32}$ $4i\sqrt{2}$

16. $\sqrt{-27}$ $3i\sqrt{3}$

17. $\sqrt{-45}$ $3i\sqrt{5}$

18. $\sqrt{-200}$ $10i\sqrt{2}$

Write each complex number in the form of a + bi.

19. $8 + \sqrt{-4}$ $8 + 2i$

20. $9 + \sqrt{-16}$ $9 + 4i$

21. $10 + \sqrt{-25}$ $10 + 5i$

22. $-5 + \sqrt{-64}$ $-5 + 8i$

23. $-3 - \sqrt{-9}$ $-3 - 3i$

24. $-2 - \sqrt{-81}$ $-2 - 9i$

25. $-7 - \sqrt{-15}$ $-7 - i\sqrt{15}$

26. $12 - \sqrt{-6}$ $12 - i\sqrt{6}$

27. $5.2 + \sqrt{-48}$ $5.2 + 4i\sqrt{3}$

28. $11.9 - \sqrt{-32}$ $11.9 - 4i\sqrt{2}$

29. $\frac{1}{4} + \sqrt{-75}$ $\frac{1}{4} + 5i\sqrt{3}$

30. $-\frac{3}{5} + \sqrt{-80}$ $-\frac{3}{5} + 4i\sqrt{5}$

Add or subtract the following complex numbers.

31. $(2 + 3i) + 8$ $10 + 3i$

32. $(3 - 5i) + 4$ $7 - 5i$

33. $(4 - 2i) - 9i$ $4 - 11i$

34. $(11 - 5i) - 7i$ $11 - 12i$

35. $(5 + 3i) + (6 + 2i)$ $11 + 5i$

36. $(7 - 5i) + (4 - 2i)$ $11 - 7i$

37. $(4 - 3i) - (6 + 4i)$ $-2 - 7i$

38. $(10 - 13i) - (10 - 4i)$ $-9i$

39. $(13 - 6i) - (13 - 6i)$ 0

40. $(17 - 4i) - (4 - 4i)$ 13

41. $(35 - 3i) - (26 + i)$ $9 - 4i$

42. $(6 - 5i) - (11 + 8i)$ $-5 - 13i$

Solve the quadratic equation and write the solutions in terms of i.

43. $x^2 = -16$ $\pm 4i$

44. $x^2 = -64$ $\pm 8i$

45. $3x^2 = -30$ $\pm i\sqrt{10}$

46. $2a^2 = -24$ $\pm 2i\sqrt{3}$

47. $x^2 - 4x + 5 = 0$ $2 \pm i$

48. $x^2 + 6x + 15 = 0$ $-3 \pm i\sqrt{6}$

49. $2r^2 + 3r + 5 = 0$ $\dfrac{-3 \pm i\sqrt{31}}{4}$

50. $3w^2 - 5w + 8 = 0$ $\dfrac{5 \pm i\sqrt{71}}{6}$

51. $2p^2 + 4p + 7 = 0$ $\dfrac{-2 \pm i\sqrt{10}}{2}$

52. $4m^2 - 6m + 3 = 0$ $\dfrac{3 \pm i\sqrt{3}}{4}$

53. $-4w^2 + 7w - 6 = 0$ $\dfrac{7 \pm i\sqrt{47}}{8}$

54. $-3z^2 - 2w - 10 = 0$ $\dfrac{-1 \pm i\sqrt{29}}{3}$

Problem Solving

55. Under what conditions will an equation of the form $x^2 = c$ have imaginary number solutions?   when $c < 0$

56. Can an equation of the form $x^2 = c$ ever have only one imaginary solution? Explain.   no

57. Under what conditions will an equation of the form $ax^2 + bx + c = 0$ have non-real number solutions?

58. Is it possible for a quadratic equation to have only one non-real number solution? Explain.   no

57. when $b^2 - 4ac < 0$

Cumulative Review Exercises

[1.9] 59. Evaluate $-\{[3(x - 4)^2 - 5] - 2x\}$ when $x = 6$.   5

[2.5] 60. Solve the equation $\frac{1}{2}x + \frac{3}{5}x = \frac{1}{2}(x - 2)$. $-\frac{5}{3}$

[8.6] 61. Solve the equation $\dfrac{w - 2}{w - 5} = \dfrac{3}{w - 6} + \dfrac{3}{4}$.   2, 9

[9.5] 62. Solve the equation $2\sqrt{r - 4} + 5 = 11$.   13

Chapter 10 Summary

IMPORTANT FACTS AND CONCEPTS	**EXAMPLES**
Section 10.1	
A **quadratic equation in standard form** is one of the form $ax^2 + bx + c = 0, a \neq 0$.	$3x^2 - x + 10 = 0$
Square Root Property If $x^2 = a$, then $x = \sqrt{a}$ or $x = -\sqrt{a}$ (abbreviated $x = \pm\sqrt{a}$).	If $x^2 = 5$, then $x = \sqrt{5}$ or $x = -\sqrt{5}$ (or $x = \pm\sqrt{5}$).
Section 10.2	
A **perfect square trinomial** is a trinomial that can be expressed as the square of a binomial.	$x^2 - 10x + 25 = (x - 5)^2$

IMPORTANT FACTS AND CONCEPTS	**EXAMPLES**

Section 10.2 (continued)

To Solve a Quadratic Equation by Completing the Square

1. Use the multiplication (or division) property of equality if necessary to make the numerical coefficient of the squared term equal to 1.
2. Rewrite the equation with the constant by itself on the right side of the equation.
3. Take one-half the numerical coefficient of the first-degree term, square it, and add this quantity to both sides of the equation.
4. Replace the trinomial with its equivalent squared binomial.
5. Use the square root property.
6. Solve for the variable.
7. Check your answers in the *original* equation.

Solve $x^2 + 2x - 35$ by completing the square.

$$x^2 + 2x - 35 = 0$$

$$x^2 + 2x = 35$$

$$x^2 + 2x + \boxed{1} = 35 + \boxed{1}$$

$$(x + 1)^2 = 36$$

$$x + 1 = \pm\sqrt{36}$$

$$x + 1 = \pm 6$$

$$x = -1 \pm 6$$

$$x = -1 + 6 = 5 \quad \text{or} \quad x = -1 - 6 = -7.$$

A check shows that 5 and -7 are the solutions.

Section 10.3

To Solve a Quadratic Equation by the Quadratic Formula

1. Write the equation in standard form, $ax^2 + bx + c = 0$, and determine the numerical values for a, b, and c.
2. Substitute the values for a, b, and c from step 1 in the quadratic formula below and then evaluate to obtain the solution.

The Quadratic Formula

$$x = \frac{-b \pm \sqrt{b^2 - 4ac}}{2a}$$

Solve $x^2 + 4x - 21 = 0$ by *the quadratic formula*.

a)

$$x^2 + 4x - 21 = 0$$

$$a = 1, \quad b = 4, \quad c = -21$$

$$x = \frac{-b \pm \sqrt{b^2 - 4ac}}{2a}$$

$$= \frac{-4 \pm \sqrt{4^2 - 4(1)(-21)}}{2(1)}$$

$$= \frac{-4 \pm \sqrt{100}}{2} = \frac{-4 \pm 10}{2}$$

$$x = \frac{-4 + 10}{2} = \frac{6}{2} = 3 \quad \text{or} \quad x = \frac{-4 - 10}{2} = \frac{-14}{2} = -7.$$

A check shows that 3 and -7 are the solutions.

The expression under the square root sign in the quadratic formula, $b^2 - 4ac$, is called the **discriminant**.

When the Discriminant Is

1. **Greater than zero**, $b^2 - 4ac > 0$, the quadratic equation has **two distinct real number solutions**.
2. **Equal to zero**, $b^2 - 4ac = 0$, the quadratic equation has **one real number solution**.
3. **Less than zero**, $b^2 - 4ac < 0$, the quadratic equation has **no real number solution**.

$$5x^2 - 3x + 2 = 0: \quad (-3)^2 - 4(5)(2) = -31$$

The discriminant is -31. Therefore, the equation has no real number solution.

$$t^2 - 18t + 81 = 0: \quad (-18)^2 - 4(1)(81) = 0$$

The discriminant is 0. Therefore, the equation has one real number solution.

$$2d^2 + 7d - 3 = 0: \quad (7)^2 - 4(2)(-3) = 73$$

The discriminant is 73. Therefore, the equation has two real number solutions.

IMPORTANT FACTS AND CONCEPTS	EXAMPLES

Section 10.4

The graph of an equation of the form $y = ax^2 + bx + c, a \neq 0$, is called a **parabola**. The parabola **opens upward** when $a > 0$ and **downward** when $a < 0$. The **vertex** is the lowest point on a parabola that opens upward or the highest point on a parabola that opens downward.

The **axis of symmetry** is a line through the vertex where the left and right sides have symmetry.

Axis of Symmetry and x-Coordinate of the Vertex

$$x = -\frac{b}{2a}$$

y-Coordinate of the Vertex

$$y = \frac{4ac - b^2}{4a}$$

Find the axis of symmetry and the vertex of the graph of $y = x^2 - 4x + 9$.

$$x = -\frac{b}{2a} = -\frac{-4}{2(1)} = 2$$

axis of symmetry: $x = 2$

$$y = \frac{4ac - b^2}{4a} = \frac{4(1)(9) - (-4)^2}{4(1)}$$

$$= \frac{36 - 16}{4} = \frac{20}{4} = 5$$

vertex: $(2, 5)$

Section 10.5

The **imaginary unit**, *i*, is defined as $i = \sqrt{-1}$. For any positive number, n, $\sqrt{-n} = i\sqrt{n}$.

$$\sqrt{-4} = 2i, \quad \sqrt{-10} = i\sqrt{10}$$

A **complex number** is of the form $a + bi$, where a and b are real numbers.

$$2 + 6i, \quad 9 - i\sqrt{13}$$

To add (or subtract) complex numbers, add (or subtract) their real parts and add (or subtract) their imaginary parts.

$$(2 + 3i) + (8 - 7i) = (2 + 8) + (3 - 7)i$$
$$= 10 - 4i$$

Chapter 10 Review Exercises

[10.1] *Solve using the square root property.*

1. $x^2 = 25$ 5, −5

2. $x^2 = 121$ 11, −11

3. $x^2 + 4 = 9$ $\sqrt{5}, -\sqrt{5}$

4. $2x^2 = 12$ $\sqrt{6}, -\sqrt{6}$

5. $2x^2 - 3 = 11$ $\sqrt{7}, -\sqrt{7}$

6. $x^2 - 2 = 18$ $2\sqrt{5}, -2\sqrt{5}$

7. $4a^2 - 31 = 1$ $2\sqrt{2}, -2\sqrt{2}$

8. $(r - 3)^2 = 24$ $3 \pm 2\sqrt{6}$

9. $(4t - 9)^2 = 50$ $\left(9 \pm 5\sqrt{2}\right)/4$

10. $(3x + 4)^2 = 30$ $\left(-4 \pm \sqrt{30}\right)/3$

[10.2] *Solve by completing the square.*

11. $x^2 - 7x + 10 = 0$ 5, 2

12. $x^2 - 11x + 28 = 0$ 7, 4

13. $x^2 + 18x + 17 = 0$ −17, −1

14. $x^2 + 19x + 90 = 0$ −10, −9

15. $t^2 - 3t - 54 = 0$ 9, −6

16. $x^2 = -5x + 6$ 1, −6

17. $2x^2 - 8x = 64$ 8, −4

18. $30 = 2n^2 - 4n$ 5, −3

19. $x^2 + 2x - 12 = 0$ $-1 \pm \sqrt{13}$

20. $y^2 - 5y - 2 = 0$ $\left(5 \pm \sqrt{33}\right)/2$

21. $3p^2 = -2p + 8$ $\frac{4}{3}, -2$

22. $12x^2 - 11x + 2 = 0$ $\frac{2}{3}, \frac{1}{4}$

[10.3] *Determine whether each equation has two distinct real number solutions, one real number solution, or no real number solution.*

23. $-4x^2 + 4x - 9 = 0$ no real solution
24. $-3x^2 + 4x = 10$ no real solution
25. $x^2 - 12x + 36 = 0$ one solution

26. $y^2 + 5y - 8 = 0$ two solutions
27. $4z^2 - 3z = 2$ two solutions
28. $3x^2 - 2x + 4 = 0$ no real solution

29. $-3x^2 - 4x + 1 = 0$ two solutions
30. $x^2 - 9x + 7 = 0$ two solutions

Use the quadratic formula to solve. If an equation has no real number solution, so state.

31. $x^2 - 10x + 16 = 0$ $2, 8$
32. $x^2 + 11x = -18$ $-9, -2$
33. $x^2 - 7x - 44 = 0$ $11, -4$

34. $5x^2 - 9x = -4$ $1, \dfrac{4}{5}$
35. $21 = r^2 + 4r$ $3, -7$
36. $x^2 - x + 1 = 0$ no real solution

37. $6x^2 + x - 15 = 0$ $\dfrac{3}{2}, -\dfrac{5}{3}$
38. $-2x^2 + 3x + 6 = 0$ $(3 \pm \sqrt{57})/4$
39. $-2x^2 - 4x + 3 = 0$ $(-2 \pm \sqrt{10})/2$

40. $y^2 - 6y + 3 = 0$ $3 \pm \sqrt{6}$
41. $3x^2 - 4x + 5 = 0$ no real solution
42. $3x^2 - 6x - 8 = 0$ $(3 \pm \sqrt{33})/3$

43. $7x^2 - 4x = 0$ $0, \dfrac{4}{7}$
44. $4z^2 = 10z$ $0, \dfrac{5}{2}$

[10.1–10.3] *Solve each quadratic equation using the method of your choice.*

45. $x^2 - 10x + 24 = 0$ $4, 6$
46. $x^2 - 16x + 55 = 0$ $5, 11$
47. $r^2 - 3r - 70 = 0$ $10, -7$

48. $x^2 + 6x = 27$ $-9, 3$
49. $x^2 - 4x - 60 = 0$ $-6, 10$
50. $x^2 - 13x + 22 = 0$ $2, 11$

51. $y^2 + 9y - 36 = 0$ $3, -12$
52. $t^2 = 8t$ $0, 8$
53. $x^2 = 64$ $8, -8$

54. $x^2 = 169$ $13, -13$
55. $2x^2 = 9x - 10$ $\dfrac{5}{2}, 2$
56. $6x^2 + 5x = 6$ $\dfrac{2}{3}, -\dfrac{3}{2}$

57. $4x^2 - 11x = 0$ $0, \dfrac{11}{4}$
58. $3x^2 + 10x = 0$ $0, -\dfrac{10}{3}$
59. $-5w = 3w^2 - 8$ $1, -\dfrac{8}{3}$

60. $3x^2 - 11x + 10 = 0$ $2, \dfrac{5}{3}$
61. $6n = 2n^2 - 9$ $(3 \pm 3\sqrt{3})/2$
62. $x^2 + 3x = 6$ $(-3 \pm \sqrt{33})/2$

[10.4] *Indicate the axis of symmetry, the coordinates of the vertex, and whether the parabola opens upward or downward.*

63. $y = x^2 - 4x - 5$ $x = 2, (2, -9)$, upward
64. $y = x^2 - 12x + 17$ $x = 6, (6, -19)$, upward

65. $y = x^2 - 3x + 7$ $x = \dfrac{3}{2}, \left(\dfrac{3}{2}, \dfrac{19}{4}\right)$, upward
66. $y = -x^2 - 2x + 13$ $x = -1, (-1, 14)$, downward

67. $y = 3x^2 + 7x + 3$ $x = -\dfrac{7}{6}, \left(-\dfrac{7}{6}, -\dfrac{13}{12}\right)$, upward
68. $y = -x^2 - 5x$ $x = -\dfrac{5}{2}, \left(-\dfrac{5}{2}, \dfrac{25}{4}\right)$, downward

69. $y = -x^2 - 10$ $x = 0, (0, -10)$, downward
70. $y = -2x^2 - x + 15$ $x = -\dfrac{1}{4}, \left(-\dfrac{1}{4}, \dfrac{121}{8}\right)$, downward

71. $y = -4x^2 + 8x + 9$ $x = 1, (1, 13)$, downward
72. $y = 3x^2 + 5x - 6$ $x = -\dfrac{5}{6}, \left(-\dfrac{5}{6}, -\dfrac{97}{12}\right)$, upward

73.–84. See graphing answer section.

Graph each quadratic equation and determine the x-intercepts, if they exist. If they do not exist, so state.

73. $y = x^2 - 2x$
74. $y = -x^2 - 6x$
75. $y = -x^2 + 9$
76. $y = -3x^2 + 6$

77. $y = x^2 - x + 1$
78. $y = x^2 + 5x + 4$
79. $y = -x^2 + 2x - 3$
80. $y = -x^2 + 5x - 6$

81. $y = x^2 + 4x + 3$
82. $y = 3x^2 - 4x - 8$
83. $y = -2x^2 + 7x - 3$
84. $y = x^2 - 5x + 4$

[10.1–10.4] *Solve.*

85. Product of Integers The product of two positive consecutive even integers is 35. Find the integers. $5, 7$

86. Product of Integers The product of two positive integers is 96. Find the two integers if the larger one is 4 greater than the smaller. $8, 12$

87. Rectangular Table Samuel Jones is making a table with a rectangular top for the kitchen. He determines that the length of the table top should be 6 inches more than twice its width. What will be the dimensions of the table top if its area is to be 920 square inches?   width, 20 in.; length, 46 in.

88. Wood Desk Jordan and Patricia Wells recently purchased an oak desk for their son's room. To protect the rectangular writing surface of the desk, they decided to cover the top with a piece of glass. The length of the desktop is 16 inches greater than its width. Find the dimensions of the glass piece Jordan and Patricia should order if the area of the desktop is 960 square inches.   width, 24 in.; length, 40 in.

[10.5] *Write each imaginary number or complex number in terms of i.*

89. $\sqrt{-9}$ $3i$

90. $\sqrt{-26}$ $i\sqrt{26}$

91. $8 - \sqrt{-25}$ $8 - 5i$

92. $6 - \sqrt{-60}$ $6 - 2i\sqrt{15}$

Add or subtract the complex numbers.

93. $(4 - 6i) + (7 - 3i)$ $11 - 9i$

94. $(9 + 5i) - (6 - 3i)$ $3 + 8i$

Solve the quadratic equations and write the complex solutions in terms of i.

95. $3x^2 = -48$ $\pm 4i$

96. $5a^2 = -30$ $\pm i\sqrt{6}$

97. $2r^2 - 5r + 6 = 0$ $\dfrac{5 \pm i\sqrt{23}}{4}$

98. $4w^2 - 8w + 9 = 0$ $\dfrac{2 \pm i\sqrt{5}}{2}$

1. $4\sqrt{2}, -4\sqrt{2}$ **2.** $(3 \pm \sqrt{13})/2$ **6.** $(-4 \pm \sqrt{6})/2$ **8.** $x = \dfrac{-b \pm \sqrt{b^2 - 4ac}}{2a}$ **9.** Answers will vary.
16. lowest point on a parabola that opens upward, highest point on a parabola that opens downward

Chapter 10 Practice Test

*To find out how well you understand the chapter material, take this practice test. The answers, and the section where the material was initially discussed, are given in the back of the book. Each problem is also fully worked out on the **Chapter Test Prep Video CD**. Review any questions that you answered incorrectly.*

1. Solve $x^2 - 2 = 30$ using the square root property.

2. Solve $(2p - 3)^2 = 13$ using the square root property.

3. Solve $x^2 - 5x = 50$ by completing the square. $10, -5$

4. Solve $r^2 + 8r = 33$ by completing the square. $3, -11$

5. Solve $k^2 = 13k - 42$ by the quadratic formula. $6, 7$

6. Solve $2x^2 + 5 = -8x$ by the quadratic formula.

7. Solve $16x^2 = 25$ by the method of your choice. $\dfrac{5}{4}, -\dfrac{5}{4}$

8. Write the quadratic formula.

9. Give an example of a perfect square trinomial.

10. Determine whether $-2x^2 - 4x + 7 = 0$ has two distinct real solutions, one real solution, or no real solution. Explain your answer.   two real solutions

11. Determine whether $x^2 + 10x + 25 = 0$ has two distinct real solutions, one real solution, or no real solution. Explain your answer.   one real solution

12. Find the equation of the axis of symmetry of the graph of $y = -x^2 - 8x + 11$. $x = -4$

13. Find the equation of the axis of symmetry of the graph of $y = 4x^2 - 16x + 9$. $x = 2$

14. Determine whether the graph of $y = -x^2 - 10x + 3$ opens upward or downward. Explain your answer.   downward; $a < 0$

15. Determine whether the graph of $y = 5x^2 - 2x + 9$ opens upward or downward. Explain your answer.   upward; $a > 0$

16. What is the vertex of the graph of a parabola?

17. Find the vertex of the graph of $y = -x^2 - 4x - 12$. $(-2, -8)$

18. Find the vertex of the graph of $y = 3x^2 - 8x + 9$. $\left(\dfrac{4}{3}, \dfrac{11}{3}\right)$

19. Graph the equation $y = x^2 + 2x - 8$ and determine the x-intercepts, if they exist.   See graphing answer section.

20. Graph the equation $y = 2x^2 - 6x$ and determine the x-intercepts, if they exist.   See graphing answer section.

21. Graph the equation $y = -x^2 + 6x - 9$ and determine the x-intercepts, if they exist.   See graphing answer section.

22. **Wall Mural** The length of a rectangular wall mural is 2 feet greater than 3 times its width. Find the length and width of the mural if its area is 33 square feet. $w = 3$ ft, $l = 11$ ft

23. **Consecutive Odd Integers** The product of two positive consecutive odd integers is 35. Find the larger of the two integers.   7

24. **Shawn's Age** Shawn Goodwin is 6 years older than his cousin, Aaron. The product of their ages is 55. How old is Shawn?   11

25. Solve the quadratic equation $3p^2 - 2p + 6 = 0$ and write the answer in terms of i. $\dfrac{1 \pm i\sqrt{17}}{3}$

Cumulative Review Test

Take the following test and check your answers with those given in the back of the book. Review any questions that you answered incorrectly. The section where the material was covered is indicated after the answer.

1. Evaluate $-5x^2y + 3y^2 + xy$ when $x = 4$ and $y = -3$. 255

2. Solve $\dfrac{1}{2}z - \dfrac{2}{7}z = \dfrac{1}{5}(3z - 1)$. $\dfrac{14}{27}$

3. Find the length of side x. $5\dfrac{1}{3}$ in.

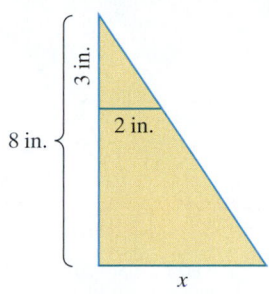

4. Solve the inequality $2(x - 3) \le 6x - 5$ and graph the solution on a number line. $x \ge -\dfrac{1}{4}$,

5. Solve the formula $A = \dfrac{m + n + P}{6}$ for P. $P = 6A - m - n$

6. Simplify $(2a^4b^5)^3(3a^2b^5)^2$. $72a^{16}b^{25}$

7. Divide $\dfrac{x^2 + 6x - 1}{x + 2}$. $x + 4 - \dfrac{9}{x + 2}$

8. Factor by grouping $2x^2 - 3xy - 4xy + 6y^2$.

9. Factor $6x^2 - 27x - 54$. $3(2x + 3)(x - 6)$

10. Add $\dfrac{4}{a^2 - 16} + \dfrac{5}{(a - 4)^2}$. $\dfrac{9a + 4}{(a + 4)(a - 4)^2}$

11. Solve the equation $x + \dfrac{24}{x} = 11$. $3, 8$

12. Graph the equation $4x - y = 8$. See graphing answer section.

13. Solve the system of equations by the addition method.

$$5x - 3y = 12$$
$$4x - 2y = 6 \qquad (-3, -9)$$

14. Simplify $\sqrt{\dfrac{2x^2y^3}{12x}}$. $\dfrac{y\sqrt{6xy}}{6}$

15. Add $2\sqrt{28} - 3\sqrt{7} + \sqrt{63}$. $4\sqrt{7}$

16. Solve the equation $x - 1 = \sqrt{x^2 - 7}$. 4

17. Solve the equation $2x^2 + 3x - 8 = 0$ using the quadratic formula.

18. **Fertilizer** If 4 pounds of fertilizer can fertilize 500 square feet of lawn, how many pounds of fertilizer are needed to fertilize 3200 square feet of lawn? 25.6 lb

19. **Vegetable Garden** The length of a rectangular vegetable garden is 3 feet less than four times its width. Find the width and length of the garden if its perimeter is 64 feet.

20. **Jogging** Robert McCloud jogs 3 miles per hour faster than he walks. He jogs for 2 miles and then walks for 2 miles. If the total time of his outing is 1 hour, find the rate at which he walks and jogs. walks, 3 mph; jogs, 6 mph

8. $(2x - 3y)(x - 2y)$ **17.** $\dfrac{-3 \pm \sqrt{73}}{4}$ **19.** $w = 7$ ft, $l = 25$ ft

Appendices

Appendix A Review of Decimals and Percent

Decimals

To Add or Subtract Numbers Containing Decimal Points

1. Align the numbers by the decimal points.

2. Add or subtract the numbers as if they were whole numbers.

3. Place the decimal point in the sum or difference directly below the decimal points in the numbers being added or subtracted.

EXAMPLE 1 ▶ Add $4.6 + 13.813 + 9.02$.

Solution

$$
\begin{array}{r}
4.600 \\
13.813 \\
+\ 9.020 \\
\hline
27.433
\end{array}
$$

EXAMPLE 2 ▶ Subtract 3.062 from 34.9.

Solution

$$
\begin{array}{r}
34.900 \\
-\ 3.062 \\
\hline
31.838
\end{array}
$$

To Multiply Numbers Containing Decimal Points

1. Multiply as if the factors were whole numbers.

2. Determine the total number of digits to the right of the decimal points in the factors.

3. Place the decimal point in the product so that the product contains the same number of digits to the right of the decimal as the total found in step 2. For example, if there are a total of three digits to the right of the decimal points in the factors, there must be three digits to the right of the decimal point in the product.

EXAMPLE 3 ▶ Multiply 2.34×1.9.

Solution

$$
\begin{array}{r}
2.34 \quad \longleftarrow \quad \text{\textit{two digits to the right of the decimal point}} \\
\times\ \ 1.9 \quad \longleftarrow \quad \text{\textit{one digit to the right of the decimal point}} \\
\hline
2106 \\
234 \\
\hline
4.446 \quad \longleftarrow \quad \text{\textit{three digits to the right of the decimal point in the product}}
\end{array}
$$

EXAMPLE 4 ▶ Multiply 2.13×0.02.

Solution

$$
\begin{array}{r}
2.13 \\
\times\ 0.02 \\
\hline
0.0426
\end{array}
$$

← two digits to the right of the decimal point
← two digits to the right of the decimal point
← four digits to the right of the decimal point in the product

Note that it was necessary to add a zero preceding the digit 4 in the answer in order to have four digits to the right of the decimal point.

To Divide Numbers Containing Decimal Points

1. Multiply both the dividend and divisor by a power of 10 that will make the divisor a whole number.
2. Divide as if working with whole numbers.
3. Place the decimal point in the quotient directly above the decimal point in the dividend.

To make the divisor a whole number, multiply *both* the dividend and divisor by 10 if the divisor is given in tenths, by 100 if the divisor is given in hundredths, by 1000 if the divisor is given in thousandths, and so on. Multiplying both the numerator and denominator by the same nonzero number is the same as multiplying the fraction by 1. Therefore, the value of the fraction is unchanged.

EXAMPLE 5 ▶ Divide $\dfrac{1.956}{0.12}$.

Solution Since the divisor, 0.12, is twelve-hundredths, we multiply both the divisor and dividend by 100.

$$\frac{1.956}{0.12} \times \frac{100}{100} = \frac{195.6}{12.}$$

Now we divide.

$$
\begin{array}{r}
16.3 \\
12\overline{)195.6} \\
\underline{12} \\
75 \\
\underline{72} \\
36 \\
\underline{36} \\
0
\end{array}
$$

The decimal point in the answer is placed directly above the decimal point in the dividend. Thus, $\dfrac{1.956}{0.12} = 16.3$.

EXAMPLE 6 ▶ Divide 0.26 by 10.4.

Solution First, multiply both the dividend and divisor by 10.

$$\frac{0.26}{10.4} \times \frac{10}{10} = \frac{2.6}{104.}$$

Now divide.

$$
\begin{array}{r}
0.025 \\
104\overline{)2.600} \\
\underline{2\ 08} \\
520 \\
\underline{520} \\
0
\end{array}
$$

Note that a zero had to be placed before the digit 2 in the quotient.

$$\frac{0.26}{10.4} = 0.025$$

Rounding Decimal Numbers

Now we will explain how to round decimal numbers. The explanation of the procedure will refer to the positional values to the right of the decimal point, as illustrated here:

To Round a Decimal Number

1. Identify the number in the problem to the right of the positional value to which the number is to be rounded. For example, if you wish to round to tenths, you identify the number in the hundredths position. If you wish to round to hundredths, you identify the number in the thousandths position, and so on.

2. **a)** If the number you identified in step 1 is greater than or equal to 5, the number in the preceding position is increased by 1 unit, and all numbers to the right of the number that has been increased by 1 unit are eliminated.

   b) If the number you identified in step 1 is less than 5, the number you identified in step 1 and all numbers to its right are eliminated.

EXAMPLE 7 ▶ Round 4.863 to tenths.

Solution: Since we are rounding to tenths, we identify the number in the hundredths position as 6. Because the number 6 is greater than or equal to 5, we increase the number in the preceding position by 1 unit and drop the remaining digits. Therefore, 4.863 when rounded to tenths is 4.9.

EXAMPLE 8 ▶ Round 5.4738 to hundredths.

Solution: Since we are rounding to hundredths, we identify the number in the thousandths position as 3. Because the number 3 is less than 5, we drop the 3 and all numbers to the right of 3. Therefore, 5.4738 when rounded to hundredths is 5.47.

Percent

The word *percent* means "per hundred." The symbol % means percent. One percent means "one per hundred".

One Percent

$$1\% = \frac{1}{100} \quad \text{or} \quad 1\% = 0.01$$

EXAMPLE 9 ▶ Convert 16% to a decimal.

Solution   Since 1% = 0.01,

$$16\% = 16(0.01) = 0.16$$

EXAMPLE 10 ▶ Convert 4.7% to a decimal.

Solution   4.7% = 4.7(0.01) = 0.047

EXAMPLE 11 ▶ Convert 1.14 to a percent.

Solution   To change a decimal number to a percent, we multiply the number by 100%.

$$1.14 = 1.14 \times 100\% = 114\%$$

Often, you will need to find an amount that is a certain percent of a number. For example, when you purchase an item in a state or county that has a sales tax you must often pay a percent of the item's price as the sales tax. Examples 12 and 13 show how to find a certain percent of a number.

EXAMPLE 12 ▶ Find 32% of 300.

Solution   To find a percent of a number, use multiplication. Change 32% to a decimal number, then multiply by 300.

$$(0.32)(300) = 96$$

Thus, 32% of 300 is 96.

EXAMPLE 13 ▶ Johnson County charges an 8% sales tax.

a) Find the sales tax on a stereo system that cost $580.

b) Find the total cost of the system, including tax.

Solution

a) The sales tax is 8% of 580.

$$(0.08)(580) = 46.40$$

The sales tax is $46.40.

b) The total cost is the purchase price plus the sales tax:

$$\text{total cost} = \$580 + \$46.40 = \$626.40$$

Appendix B Finding the Greatest Common Factor and Least Common Denominator

Prime Factorization

In Section 1.3, we mentioned that to simplify fractions you can divide both the numerator and denominator by the *greatest common factor* (GCF). One method to find the GCF is to use *prime factorization*. Prime factorization is the process of writing a given number as a product of prime numbers. *Prime numbers* are natural numbers, excluding

1, that can be divided by only themselves and 1. The first ten prime numbers are 2, 3, 5, 7, 11, 13, 17, 19, 23, and 29. Can you find the next prime number? If you answered 31, you answered correctly.

To write a number as a product of primes, we can use a *tree diagram*. Begin by selecting any two numbers whose product is the given number. Then continue factoring each of these numbers into prime numbers, as shown in Example 1.

EXAMPLE 1 ▶ Determine the prime factorization of the number 120.

Solution   We will use three different tree diagrams to illustrate the prime factorization of 120.

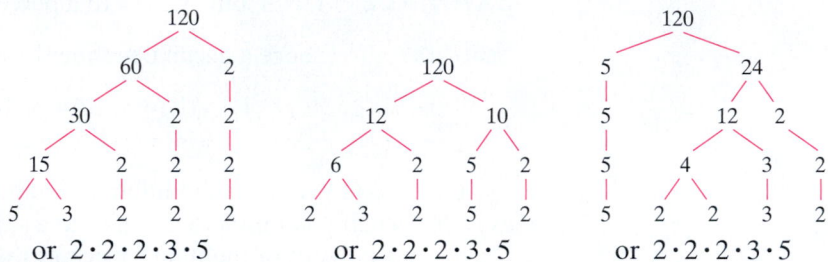

or $2 \cdot 2 \cdot 2 \cdot 3 \cdot 5$ or $2 \cdot 2 \cdot 2 \cdot 3 \cdot 5$ or $2 \cdot 2 \cdot 2 \cdot 3 \cdot 5$

Note that no matter how you start, if you do not make a mistake, you find that the prime factorization of 120 is $2 \cdot 2 \cdot 2 \cdot 3 \cdot 5$. There are other ways 120 can be factored but all will lead to the prime factorization $2 \cdot 2 \cdot 2 \cdot 3 \cdot 5$.

Greatest Common Factor

The greatest common factor (GCF) of two natural numbers is the greatest integer that is a factor of both numbers. We use the GCF when simplifying fractions.

> **To Find the Greatest Common Factor of a Given Numerator and Denominator**
>
> 1. Write both the numerator and the denominator as a product of primes.
> 2. Determine all the prime factors that are common to both prime factorizations.
> 3. Multiply the prime factors found in step 2 to obtain the GCF.

EXAMPLE 2 ▶ Consider the fraction $\dfrac{108}{156}$.

a) Find the GCF of 108 and 156.   **b)** Simplify $\dfrac{108}{156}$.

Solution

a) First determine the prime factorizations of both 108 and 156.

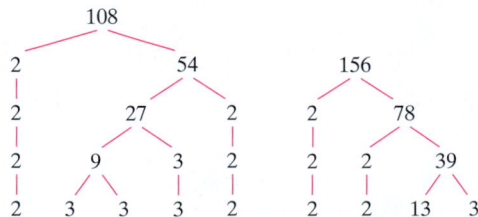

There are two 2s and one 3 common to both prime factorizations; thus

$$\text{GCF} = 2 \cdot 2 \cdot 3 = 12$$

The greatest common factor of 108 and 156 is 12. Twelve is the greatest integer that divides into both 108 and 156.

b) To simplify $\dfrac{108}{156}$, we divide both the numerator and denominator by the GCF, 12.

$$\frac{108 \div 12}{156 \div 12} = \frac{9}{13}$$

Thus, $\dfrac{108}{156}$ simplifies to $\dfrac{9}{13}$.

Least Common Denominator

When adding two or more fractions, you must write each fraction with a common denominator. The best denominator to use is the *least common denominator* (LCD). The LCD is the smallest number that each denominator divides into. Sometimes the least common denominator is referred to as the *least common multiple* of the denominators.

To Find the Least Common Denominator of Two or More Fractions

1. Write each denominator as a product of prime numbers.

2. For each prime number, determine the maximum number of times that prime number appears in any of the prime factorizations.

3. Multiply all the prime numbers found in step 2. Include each prime number the maximum number of times it appears in any of the prime factorizations. The product of all these prime numbers will be the LCD.

Example 3 illustrates the procedure to determine the LCD.

EXAMPLE 3 ▶ Consider $\dfrac{7}{108} + \dfrac{5}{156}$.

a) Determine the least common denominator.

b) Add the fractions.

Solution

a) We found in Example 2 that

$$108 = 2 \cdot 2 \cdot 3 \cdot 3 \cdot 3 \quad \text{and} \quad 156 = 2 \cdot 2 \cdot 3 \cdot 13$$

We can see that the maximum number of 2s that appear in either prime factorization is two (there are two 2s in both factorizations), the maximum number of 3s is three, and the maximum number of 13s is one. Multiply as follows:

$$2 \cdot 2 \cdot 3 \cdot 3 \cdot 3 \cdot 13 = 1404$$

Thus, the least common denominator is 1404. This is the smallest number that both 108 and 156 divide into.

b) To add the fractions, we need to write both fractions with a common denominator. The best common denominator to use is the LCD. Since $1404 \div 108 = 13$, we will multiply $\dfrac{7}{108}$ by $\dfrac{13}{13}$. Since $1404 \div 156 = 9$, we will multiply $\dfrac{5}{156}$ by $\dfrac{9}{9}$.

$$\frac{7}{108} \cdot \frac{13}{13} + \frac{5}{156} \cdot \frac{9}{9} = \frac{91}{1404} + \frac{45}{1404} = \frac{136}{1404} = \frac{34}{351}$$

Thus, $\dfrac{7}{108} + \dfrac{5}{156} = \dfrac{34}{351}$.

Appendix C Geometry

This appendix introduces or reviews important geometric concepts. **Table C.1** gives the names and descriptions of various types of angles.

Angles

Table C.1	
Angle	**Sketch of Angle**
An **acute angle** is an angle whose measure is between 0° and 90°.	
A **right angle** is an angle whose measure is 90°.	
An **obtuse angle** is an angle whose measure is between 90° and 180°.	
A **straight angle** is an angle whose measure is 180°.	
Two angles are **complementary angles** when the sum of their measures is 90°. Each angle is the complement of the other. Angles A and B are complementary angles.	60° A B 30°
Two angles are **supplementary angles** when the sum of their measures is 180°. Each angle is the supplement of the other. Angles A and B are supplementary angles.	130° A B 50°

When two lines intersect, four angles are formed as shown in **Figure C.1**. The pair of opposite angles formed by the intersecting lines are called **vertical angles**.

Angles 1 and 3 are vertical angles. Angles 2 and 4 are also vertical angles. *Vertical angles have equal measures.* Thus, angle 1, symbolized by $\angle 1$, is equal to angle 3, symbolized by $\angle 3$. We can write $\angle 1 = \angle 3$. Similarly, $\angle 2 = \angle 4$.

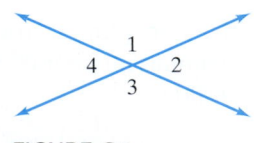

FIGURE C.1

Parallel and Perpendicular Lines

Parallel lines are two lines in the same plane that do not intersect (**Fig. C.2**). **Perpendicular lines** are lines that intersect at right angles (**Fig. C.3**).

Parallel lines

FIGURE C.2

Perpendicular lines

FIGURE C.3

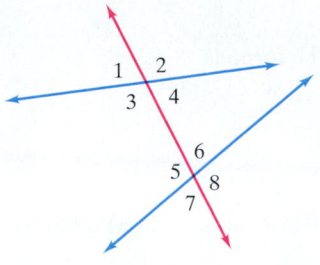

FIGURE C.4

A **transversal** is a line that intersects two or more lines at different points. When a transversal line intersects two other lines, eight angles are formed, as illustrated in **Figure C.4**. Some of these angles are given special names.

Interior angles: 3, 4, 5, 6

Exterior angles: 1, 2, 7, 8

Pairs of corresponding angles: 1 and 5; 2 and 6; 3 and 7; 4 and 8

Pairs of alternate interior angles: 3 and 6; 4 and 5

Pairs of alternate exterior angles: 1 and 8; 2 and 7

Parallel Lines Cut by a Transversal

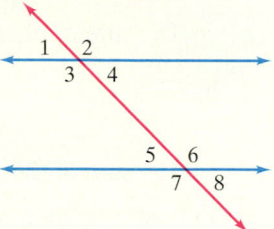

When two parallel lines are cut by a transversal,

1. Corresponding angles are equal ($\angle 1 = \angle 5$, $\angle 2 = \angle 6$, $\angle 3 = \angle 7$, $\angle 4 = \angle 8$).
2. Alternate interior angles are equal ($\angle 3 = \angle 6$, $\angle 4 = \angle 5$).
3. Alternate exterior angles are equal ($\angle 1 = \angle 8$, $\angle 2 = \angle 7$).

EXAMPLE 1 ▶ If line 1 and line 2 are parallel lines and $m\angle 1 = 112°$, find the measure of angles 2 through 8.

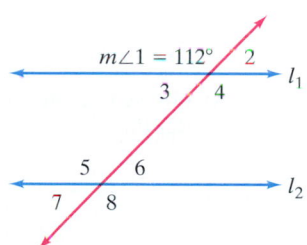

Solution   Angles 1 and 2 are supplementary, so $m\angle 2$ is $180° - 112° = 68°$. The measures of angles 1 and 4 are equal since they are vertical angles. Thus, $m\angle 4 = 112°$. Angles 1 and 5 are corresponding angles. Thus, $m\angle 5 = 112°$. It is equal to its vertical angle, $\angle 8$, so $m\angle 8 = 112°$. The measures of angles 2, 3, 6, and 7 are all equal and measure $68°$.

Polygons

A **polygon** is a closed figure in a plane determined by three or more line segments. Some polygons are illustrated in **Figure C.5**.

A **regular polygon** has sides that are all the same length, and interior angles that all have the same measure. In **Figure C.5**, (b) and (d) are regular polygons.

FIGURE C.5   (a)   (b)   (c)   (d)

Sum of the Interior Angles of a Polygon

The sum of the interior angles of a polygon can be found by the formula

$$\text{Sum} = (n - 2)180°$$

where n is the number of sides of the polygon.

EXAMPLE 2 ▶ Find the sum of the measures of the interior angles of **a)** a triangle; **b)** a quadrilateral (4 sides); **c)** an octagon (8 sides).

Solution

a) Since $n = 3$, we write

$$\text{Sum} = (n - 2)180°$$
$$= (3 - 2)180° = 1(180°) = 180°$$

The sum of the measures of the interior angles in a triangle is 180°.

b)
$$\text{Sum} = (n - 2)180°$$
$$= (4 - 2)180° = 2(180°) = 360°$$

The sum of the measures of the interior angles in a quadrilateral is 360°.

c)
$$\text{Sum} = (n - 2)(180°) = (8 - 2)180° = 6(180°) = 1080°$$

The sum of the measures of the interior angles in an octagon is 1080°.

Now we will briefly define several types of triangles in **Table C.2.**

Triangles

Table C.2

Triangle	Sketch of Triangle
An **acute triangle** is one that has three acute angles (angles of less than 90°).	
An **obtuse triangle** has one obtuse angle (an angle greater than 90°).	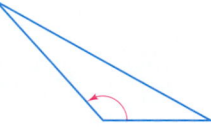
A **right triangle** has one right angle (an angle equal to 90°). The longest side of a right triangle is opposite the right angle and is called the **hypotenuse**. The other two sides are called the **legs**.	
An **isosceles triangle** has two sides of equal length. The angles opposite the equal sides have the same measure.	
An **equilateral triangle** has three sides of equal length. It also has three equal angles that measure 60° each.	

When two sides of a *right triangle* are known, the third side can be found using the **Pythagorean Theorem**, $a^2 + b^2 = c^2$, where a and b are the legs and c is the hypotenuse of the triangle. (See Section 7.7 for examples.)

Congruent and Similar Figures

If two triangles are **congruent**, it means that the two triangles are identical in size and shape. Two congruent triangles could be placed one on top of the other if we were able to move and rearrange them.

Two Triangles Are Congruent If Any One of the Following Statements Is True

1. Two angles of one triangle are equal to two corresponding angles of the other triangle, and the lengths of the sides between each pair of angles are equal. This method of showing that triangles are congruent is called the *angle, side, angle* method.

$\angle 1 = \angle 3$
$\angle 2 = \angle 4$
$a = x$

2. Corresponding sides of both triangles are equal. This is called the *side, side, side* method.

$a = x$
$b = y$
$c = z$

3. Two corresponding pairs of sides are equal, and the angle between them is equal. This is referred to as the *side, angle, side* method.

$a = x$
$\angle 1 = \angle 2$
$b = y$

EXAMPLE 3 ▶ Determine whether the two triangles are congruent.

Solution   The unknown angle in the figure on the right must measure 100° since the sum of the angles of a triangle is 180°. Both triangles have the same two angles (100° and 50°), with the same length side between them, 8 units. Thus, these two triangles are congruent by the angle, side, angle method.

Two triangles are **similar** if all three pairs of corresponding angles are equal and corresponding sides are in proportion. Similar figures do not have to be the same size but must have the same general shape.

Two Triangles Are Similar If Any One of the Following Statements Is True

1. Two angles of one triangle equal two angles of the other triangle.

$\angle 1 = \angle 4$
$\angle 2 = \angle 5$
(also $\angle 3 = \angle 6$)

2. Corresponding sides of the two triangles are proportional.

$\dfrac{a}{x} = \dfrac{b}{y} = \dfrac{c}{z}$

3. Two pairs of corresponding sides are proportional, and the angles between them are equal.

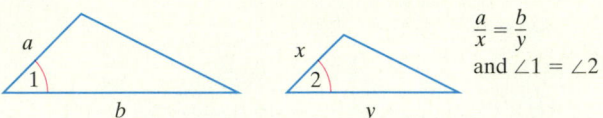

$\dfrac{a}{x} = \dfrac{b}{y}$
and $\angle 1 = \angle 2$

EXAMPLE 4 ▶ Are the triangles ABC and $AB'C'$ similar?

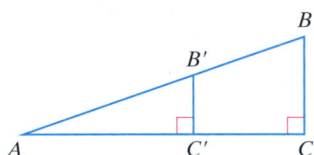

Solution   Angle A is common to both triangles. Since angle C and angle C' are equal (both 90°), then $\angle B$ and $\angle B'$ must be equal. Since the three angles of triangle ABC equal the three angles of triangle $AB'C'$, the two triangles are similar.

Answers

Chapter 1

Exercise Set 1.1 **1.** Answers will vary. **3.** Answers will vary. **5.** Answers will vary. **7.** Answers will vary. **9.** Answers will vary. **11.** Do all the homework carefully and completely and preview the new material that is to be covered in class. **13.** At least 2 hours of study and homework time for each hour of class time is generally recommended. **15. a)** You need to do the homework in order to practice what was presented in class. **b)** When you miss class, you miss important information; therefore, it is important that you attend class regularly. **17.** Answers will vary.

Exercise Set 1.2 **1.** Understand, translate, calculate, check, state answer **3.** is approximately equal to **5.** Rank the data. The median is the value in the middle. **7.** Divide the sum of the data by the number of pieces of data. **9.** He actually missed a B by 10 points. **11. a)** 76.4 **b)** 74 **13. a)** $87.32 **b)** $86.57 **15. a)** 11.593 **b)** 11.68 **17.** $470 **19. a)** $1336 **b)** $18,036 **21.** 1,610,000,000 operations **23. a)** 19.375 minutes **b)** 88 minutes **c)** 10 minutes **25.** ≈18.49 miles per gallon **27.** $153 **29.** On the 3 on the right **31. a)** 4106.25 gallons **b)** ≈$21.35 **33. a)** $193 **b)** $172 **35. a)** Hong Kong–China; 550 **b)** Mexico; 385 **c)** 165 **37. a)** 0.275 million or 275,000; 1.05 million or 1,050,000 **b)** 0.775 million or 775,000 **c)** ≈3.82 times greater **39. a)** 1.394 million **b)** 0.255 million **c)** 0.051 million **41. a)** 48 **b)** He cannot get a C. **43.** Bachelor's degree **45.** One example is 50, 60, 70, 80, 90.

Exercise Set 1.3 **1. a)** Variables are letters that represent numbers. **b)** x, y, and z **3. a)** Numerator **b)** Denominator **5.** Divide out the common factors. **7. a)** The smallest number that is divisible by the two denominators **b)** Answers will vary. **9.** Part **b)** shows simplification. **11.** Part **a)** is incorrect. **13. c)** **15.** Divide out common factors, then multiply the numerators, and multiply the denominators. **17.** Write fractions with a common denominator, then add or subtract the numerators while keeping the common denominator. **19.** Yes, the numerator and denominator have no common factors (other than 1). **21.** Yes **23.** $\frac{2}{3}$

25. $\frac{1}{4}$ **27.** $\frac{9}{19}$ **29.** $\frac{3}{7}$ **31.** Simplified **33.** Simplified **35.** $\frac{43}{15}$ **37.** $\frac{23}{3}$ **39.** $\frac{59}{18}$ **41.** $\frac{159}{17}$ **43.** $1\frac{3}{4}$ **45.** $3\frac{1}{4}$ **47.** $4\frac{4}{7}$ **49.** $6\frac{1}{7}$

51. $\frac{8}{15}$ **53.** $\frac{1}{9}$ **55.** $\frac{3}{2}$ or $1\frac{1}{2}$ **57.** $\frac{1}{2}$ **59.** 6 **61.** $\frac{5}{2}$ or $2\frac{1}{2}$ **63.** $\frac{43}{10}$ or $4\frac{3}{10}$ **65.** $\frac{8}{13}$ **67.** $\frac{5}{8}$ **69.** $\frac{1}{7}$ **71.** $\frac{6}{5}$ or $1\frac{1}{5}$ **73.** $\frac{9}{17}$

75. $\frac{7}{12}$ **77.** $\frac{13}{36}$ **79.** $\frac{65}{24}$ or $2\frac{17}{24}$ **81.** $\frac{17}{6}$ or $2\frac{5}{6}$ **83.** $\frac{29}{10}$ or $2\frac{9}{10}$ **85.** $\frac{277}{30}$ or $9\frac{7}{30}$ **87.** $\frac{11}{24}$ mile **89.** $8\frac{15}{16}$ inches **91.** $\frac{19}{50}$ **93.** $\frac{3}{40}$

95. 11 feet, $11\frac{1}{4}$ inches or $143\frac{1}{4}$ inches or ≈11.94 feet **97.** $2\frac{1}{10}$ minutes **99.** $1\frac{9}{16}$ inches **101.** 5 mg **103.** 40 times **105.** $1\frac{1}{2}$ inches

107. 6 strips **109. a)** Yes **b)** $\frac{5}{8}$ inches **c)** $52\frac{3}{4}$ inches **111. a)** $\frac{*+?}{a}$ **b)** $\frac{\odot - \square}{?}$ **c)** $\frac{\triangle + 4}{\square}$ **d)** $\frac{x-2}{3}$ **e)** $\frac{8}{x}$ **113.** 270 pills

115. Answers will vary. **116.** 16 **117.** 15 **118.** Variables are letters used to represent numbers.

Exercise Set 1.4 **1.** A set is a collection of elements. **3.** Answers will vary. **5.** The set of natural numbers does not contain the number 0. The set of whole numbers contains the number 0. **7. a)–c)** All natural numbers are whole numbers, rational numbers, and real numbers. **9. a)** Yes **b)** No **c)** No **d)** Yes **11.** $\{\ldots, -3, -2, -1, 0, 1, 2, 3, \ldots\}$ **13.** $\{0, 1, 2, 3, \ldots\}$ **15.** $\{\ldots, -3, -2, -1\}$ **17.** True **19.** True **21.** False **23.** False **25.** True **27.** True **29.** False **31.** True **33.** True **35.** False **37.** True **39.** True **41.** False **43.** True **45.** False **47.** True **49. a)** 13 **b)** $-2, 13$ **c)** $-2, 13$ **d)** 13 **51. a)** 3, 77

b) $0, 3, 77$ **c)** $0, -2, 3, 77$ **d)** $-\frac{5}{7}, 0, -2, 3, 6\frac{1}{4}, 1.63, 77$ **e)** $\sqrt{7}, -\sqrt{3}$ **f)** $-\frac{5}{7}, 0, -2, 3, 6\frac{1}{4}, \sqrt{7}, -\sqrt{3}, 1.63, 77$

53. Answers will vary; three examples are 0, 1, and 2. **55.** Answers will vary; three examples are $-\sqrt{2}, -\sqrt{3}$, and $-\sqrt{7}$.

57. Answers will vary; three examples are $-\frac{2}{3}, \frac{1}{2}$, and 6.3. **59.** Answers will vary; three examples are $-13, -5$, and -1.

61. Answers will vary; three examples are $\sqrt{2}, \sqrt{3}$, and $-\sqrt{5}$. **63.** Answers will vary; three examples are $-7, 1$, and 5. **65.** 87 **67. a)** $\{1, 3, 4, 5, 8\}$ **b)** $\{2, 5, 6, 7, 8\}$ **c)** $\{5, 8\}$ **d)** $\{1, 2, 3, 4, 5, 6, 7, 8\}$ **69. a)** Set B continues beyond 4. **b)** 4

c) An infinite number of elements **d)** An infinite set **71. a)** An infinite number **b)** An infinite number **73.** $\frac{27}{5}$ **74.** $5\frac{1}{3}$

75. $\frac{5}{24}$ **76.** $\frac{4}{45}$

Exercise Set 1.5 **1. a)** ← ——|——→ **b)** ←+|●+|●++→ **c)** Greater than **d)** $-4 < -2$ **e)** $-2 > -4$
$\quad\quad\quad\quad\quad\quad\quad\quad 0 \quad\quad\quad\quad\quad -5 \quad\quad 0$

3. a) 4 is 4 units from 0 on the number line. **b)** -4 is 4 units from 0 on the number line. **c)** 0 is 0 units from 0 on the number line. **5.** Yes **7.** No, $-4 < -3$ but $|-4| > |-3|$. **9.** No, $|-3| < |-4|$ but $-3 > -4$. **11.** 7 **13.** 15 **15.** 0 **17.** -5 **19.** -21 **21.** > **23.** < **25.** > **27.** < **29.** > **31.** < **33.** < **35.** > **37.** < **39.** > **41.** > **43.** < **45.** > **47.** < **49.** <

51. $<$ **53.** $>$ **55.** $>$ **57.** $>$ **59.** $<$ **61.** $<$ **63.** $<$ **65.** $<$ **67.** $=$ **69.** $=$ **71.** $<$ **73.** $<$ **75.** $-|-1|, \frac{3}{7}, \frac{4}{9}, 0.46, |-5|$

77. $\frac{5}{12}, 0.6, \frac{2}{3}, \frac{19}{25}, |-2.6|$ **79.** $4, -4$ **81.** Not possible   **83.** Answers will vary: one example is $-3, -4$, and -5.   **85.** Answers will

vary: one example is $4, 5$, and 6.   **87.** Answers will vary: one example is $3, 4$, and 5.   **89. a)** Does not include the endpoints

b) Answers will vary: one example is $4.1, 5$, and $5\frac{1}{2}$.   **c)** No   **d)** Yes   **e)** True   **91. a)** Dietary fiber and thiamin

b) Vitamin E, niacin, and riboflavin   **93.** Greater than   **95.** No   **98.** $\frac{89}{15}$ or $5\frac{14}{15}$ **99.** $\{\ldots, -3, -2, -1, 0, 1, 2, 3, \ldots\}$

100. $\{0, 1, 2, 3, \ldots\}$ **101. a)** 5 **b)** $5, 0$ **c)** $5, -2, 0$ **d)** $5, -2, 0, \frac{1}{3}, -\frac{5}{9}, 2.3$ **e)** $\sqrt{3}$ **f)** $5, -2, 0, \frac{1}{3}, \sqrt{3}, -\frac{5}{9}, 2.3$

Mid-Chapter Test.*   **1.** At least two hours of study and homework for each hour of class time is generally

recommended. [1.1]   **2. a)** \$80.63   **b)** \$83.81 [1.2]   **3.** \$824.59 [1.2]   **4. a)** Natwora's   **b)** \$24 [1.2]   **5.** \$62.35 [1.2]   **6.** $\frac{1}{6}$ [1.3]
7. $\frac{39}{64}$ [1.3]   **8.** $\frac{49}{40}$ or $1\frac{9}{40}$ [1.3]   **9.** $\frac{61}{20}$ or $3\frac{1}{20}$ [1.3]   **10.** $54\frac{1}{3}$ feet [1.3]   **11.** False [1.4]   **12.** True [1.4]   **13.** False [1.4]

14. True [1.4]   **15.** False [1.4]   **16.** $-\frac{7}{10}$ [1.5]   **17.** $>$ [1.5]   **18.** $>$ [1.5]   **19.** $<$ [1.5]   **20.** $=$ [1.5]

Exercise Set 1.6   **1.** Addition, subtraction, multiplication, and division   **3. a)** No   **b)** $\frac{2}{3}$ **5.** Negative   **7.** Answers will vary.

9. a) Answers will vary.   **b)** -77 **c)** Answers will vary.   **11.** Correct   **13.** -9 **15.** 28 **17.** 0 **19.** $-\frac{5}{3}$ **21.** $-2\frac{3}{5}$ **23.** -3.72

25. 11 **27.** 1 **29.** -6 **31.** 0 **33.** 0 **35.** -10 **37.** -4 **39.** -13 **41.** 0 **43.** -6 **45.** 9 **47.** -64 **49.** 16 **51.** -12 **53.** 3

55. -6 **57.** -20 **59.** -31 **61.** -39 **63.** 91 **65.** -9.9 **67.** -144.0 **69.** -141.91 **71.** -53.65 **73.** $\frac{26}{35}$ **75.** $\frac{107}{84}$ or $1\frac{23}{84}$ **77.** $\frac{4}{55}$

79. $-\frac{26}{45}$ **81.** $-\frac{16}{15}$ or $-1\frac{1}{15}$ **83.** $\frac{3}{10}$ **85.** $-\frac{13}{15}$ **87.** $\frac{19}{56}$ **89.** $-\frac{43}{60}$ **91.** $-\frac{23}{21}$ or $-1\frac{2}{21}$ **93. a)** Positive   **b)** 390 **c)** Yes

95. a) Negative   **b)** -373 **c)** Yes   **97. a)** Negative   **b)** -452 **c)** Yes   **99. a)** Negative   **b)** -1300 **c)** Yes   **101. a)** Negative
b) -112 **c)** Yes   **103. a)** Negative   **b)** -3880 **c)** Yes   **105. a)** Positive   **b)** 1111 **c)** Yes   **107. a)** Negative   **b)** -2050 **c)** Yes
109. True   **111.** True   **113.** False   **115.** \$277   **117.** 21 yards   **119.** 61 feet   **121.** 13,796 feet   **123. a)** $-\$12$ million

b) 1999-2001: surplus, \$5 million   **125.** -22 **127.** 20 **129.** 0 **131.** $\frac{11}{30}$ **133.** 55 **135.** $\frac{19}{14}$ or $1\frac{5}{14}$ **136.** $\frac{43}{16}$ or $2\frac{11}{16}$ **137.** False

138. $>$ **139.** $<$

Exercise Set 1.7   **1.** $2 - 7$ **3.** ☺ $- ?$ **5. a)** Answers will vary.   **b)** $5 + (-14)$ **c)** -9 **7. a)** $a + b$ **b)** $-4 + 12$ **c)** 8
9. a) $3 + 6 - 5$ **b)** 4 **11.** Correct   **13.** 6 **15.** 7 **17.** -1 **19.** 12 **21.** -12 **23.** -7 **25.** 0 **27.** -4 **29.** -3 **31.** 9 **33.** -20
35. 9.8 **37.** 0.3 **39.** 7 **41.** 4 **43.** 22 **45.** -11 **47.** -131.0 **49.** -82 **51.** 140 **53.** -7.4 **55.** -3.93 **57.** -11 **59.** 0
61. 6.1 **63.** 18.2 **65.** -11 **67.** -18.1 **69.** $\frac{13}{72}$ **71.** $\frac{17}{45}$ **73.** $-\frac{67}{60}$ or $-1\frac{7}{60}$ **75.** $-\frac{5}{12}$ **77.** $-\frac{17}{24}$ **79.** $\frac{1}{4}$ **81.** $\frac{7}{45}$ **83.** $\frac{13}{16}$ **85.** $-\frac{13}{63}$

87. $-\frac{7}{60}$ **89. a)** Positive   **b)** 99 **c)** Yes   **91. a)** Negative   **b)** -619 **c)** Yes   **93. a)** Positive   **b)** 1588 **c)** Yes
95. a) Positive   **b)** 196 **c)** Yes   **97. a)** Negative   **b)** -448 **c)** Yes   **99. a)** Positive   **b)** 116.1 **c)** Yes   **101. a)** Negative
b) -69 **c)** Yes   **103. a)** Negative   **b)** -1670 **c)** Yes   **105. a)** Zero   **b)** 0 **c)** Yes   **107.** 4 **109.** -6 **111.** -15 **113.** -2

115. 13 **117.** -5 **119.** -32 **121.** -4 **123.** 9 **125.** -12 **127.** 12 **129.** -18 **131. a)** 43 **b)** 143 **133.** $1\frac{7}{8}$ inches

135. Dropped $100°$ F   **137. a)** 281 **b)** 3 strokes less   **139.** -5 **141. a)** 8 units   **b)** $-3 - (-11)$ **143. a)** 9 feet   **b)** -3 feet
144. $\{1, 2, 3, \ldots\}$ **145.** The set of rational numbers together with the set of irrational numbers form the set of real numbers.

146. $>$ **147.** $<$ **148.** $-\frac{1}{24}$

Exercise Set 1.8   **1.** Like signs: product is positive. Unlike signs: product is negative.   **3.** Even number of negatives: product is
positive, odd number of negatives: product is negative   **5. a)** 0 **b)** Undefined   **7. a)** With $3 - 5$ you subtract, but with $3(-5)$ you
multiply.   **b)** $-2, -15$ **9. a)** With $x - y$ you subtract, but with $x(-y)$ you multiply.   **b)** 7 **c)** 10 **d)** -3 **11.** Negative
13. Positive   **15.** Negative   **17.** 20 **19.** -18 **21.** 80 **23.** -12.6 **25.** 42 **27.** -81 **29.** 30 **31.** 0 **33.** -84 **35.** -72 **37.** 140

39. 0 **41.** $-\frac{3}{10}$ **43.** $\frac{7}{27}$ **45.** 4 **47.** $-\frac{1}{10}$ **49.** 7 **51.** 4 **53.** 4 **55.** -18 **57.** 9.9 **59.** -10 **61.** -6 **63.** -8 **65.** 16.2

67. 0 **69.** -5.5 **71.** 6 **73.** $-\frac{2}{5}$ **75.** $\frac{5}{36}$ **77.** 1 **79.** $-\frac{144}{5}$ or $-28\frac{4}{5}$ **81.** -32 **83.** 20 **85.** -14 **87.** -9.3 **89.** -20 **91.** 1 **93.** 0

95. Undefined   **97.** 0 **99.** Undefined   **101. a)** Negative   **b)** -3496 **c)** Yes   **103. a)** Negative   **b)** -16 **c)** Yes

---

105. a) Negative **b)** −9 **c)** Yes **107. a)** Positive **b)** 6174 **c)** Yes **109. a)** Zero **b)** 0 **c)** Yes **111. a)** Undefined **b)** Undefined **c)** Yes **113. a)** Positive **b)** 3.2 **c)** Yes **115. a)** Positive **b)** 226.8 **c)** Yes **117.** False **119.** False **121.** True **123.** True **125.** False **127.** True **129.** 45 yard loss or −45 yards **131. a)** $104 **b)** −$416 **133.** $143.85 **135. a)** 20 point loss or −20 points **b)** 80 **137. a)** 102 to 128 beats per minute **b)** Answers will vary. **139.** −125 **141.** 1

143. Positive **146.** > **147.** $-\dfrac{41}{60}$ **148.** −2 **149.** −3 **150.** 3

Exercise Set 1.9 **1.** Base; exponent **3. a)** 1 **b)** 1, 3, 2, 1 **5. a)** $4y$ **b)** y^4 **7.** Parentheses, exponents, multiplication or division, then addition or subtraction **9.** No **11. a)** 13 **b)** 1 **c) b)** **13. a)** Answers will vary. **b)** −180 **15. a)** Answers will vary. **b)** −91 **17.** 25 **19.** 1 **21.** −64 **23.** 9 **25.** −1 **27.** −100 **29.** 81 **31.** 27 **33.** 256 **35.** −16 **37.** $\dfrac{9}{16}$ **39.** $-\dfrac{1}{32}$ **41.** 225 **43.** 576 **45. a)** Positive **b)** 343 **c)** Yes **47. a)** Positive **b)** 1296 **c)** Yes **49. a)** Negative **b)** −243 **c)** Yes **51. a)** Positive **b)** 625 **c)** Yes **53. a)** Negative **b)** −81 **c)** Yes **55. a)** Negative **b)** −0.140625 **c)** Yes **57.** 15 **59.** 8 **61.** 57 **63.** 0 **65.** 16 **67.** 29 **69.** −19 **71.** −77 **73.** $\dfrac{83}{100}$ **75.** 2 **77.** 10 **79.** −34 **81.** 103 **83.** 169 **85.** 13 **87.** 36.75 **89.** $\dfrac{5}{8}$ **91.** $\dfrac{1}{4}$ **93.** $\dfrac{49}{30}$ or $1\dfrac{19}{30}$ **95.** $\dfrac{5}{27}$ **97.** $\dfrac{32}{53}$ **99.** 9 **101.** −4 **103.** 1 **105. a)** 25 **b)** −25 **c)** 25 **107. a)** 4 **b)** −4 **c)** 4 **109. a)** 36 **b)** −36 **c)** 36 **111. a)** $\dfrac{1}{9}$ **b)** $-\dfrac{1}{9}$ **c)** $\dfrac{1}{9}$ **113.** 4 **115.** −45 **117.** 3 **119.** −4 **121.** −1 **123.** $\dfrac{15}{4}$ or $3\dfrac{3}{4}$ **125.** 994 **127.** −5 **129.** 193 **131.** −25 **133.** $[(6 \cdot 3) - 4] - 2; 12$ **135.** $\{[(10 \cdot 4) + 9] - 6\} \div 7; \dfrac{43}{7}$ or $6\dfrac{1}{7}$ **137.** $\left(\dfrac{4}{5} + \dfrac{3}{7}\right) \cdot \dfrac{2}{3}; \dfrac{86}{105}$ **139.** All real numbers **141.** 162.5 miles **143.** 102 feet **145. a)** .08 **b)** .16 **147.** 1.71 inches **149.** $12 - (4 - 6) + 10 = 24$

155. a) 3 **b)**

Dogs	Number of Houses
0	4
1	5
2	3
3	1
4	1

c) 18 **d)** ≈1.29 dogs per house **156.** $6.40 **157.** $-\dfrac{5}{36}$ **158.** $\dfrac{10}{3}$ or $3\dfrac{1}{3}$

Exercise Set 1.10 **1.** The commutative property of addition states that the sum of two numbers is the same regardless of the order in which they are added; $3 + 4 = 4 + 3$. **3.** The associative property of addition states that the sum of three numbers is the same regardless of the way the numbers are grouped; $(2 + 3) + 4 = 2 + (3 + 4)$ **5. a)** Answers will vary. **b)** 15 **c)** 44 **7.** The associative property involves changing parentheses, and uses only one operation whereas the distributive property uses two operations, multiplication and addition. **9.** 0 **11. a)** −6 **b)** $\dfrac{1}{6}$ **13. a)** 3 **b)** $-\dfrac{1}{3}$ **15. a)** $-x$ **b)** $\dfrac{1}{x}$ **17. a)** −1.6 **b)** $\dfrac{1}{1.6}$ or 0.625 **19. a)** $-\dfrac{1}{5}$ **b)** 5 **21. a)** $\dfrac{5}{6}$ **b)** $-\dfrac{6}{5}$ **23.** Distributive property **25.** Associative property of addition **27.** Commutative property of multiplication **29.** Associative property of multiplication **31.** Distributive property **33.** Identity property of multiplication **35.** Inverse property of multiplication **37.** $1 + (-4)$ **39.** $(-6 \cdot 4) \cdot 2$ **41.** $-2 \cdot x + -2 \cdot y$ or $-2x - 2y$ **43.** $y \cdot x$ **45.** $3y + 4x$ **47.** $a + (b + 3)$ **49.** $3x + (4 + 6)$ **51.** $(m + n)3$ **53.** $4x + 4y + 12$ **55.** 0 **57.** $\dfrac{5}{2}n$ **59.** Yes **61.** Yes **63.** No **65.** Yes **67.** No **69.** No **71.** The $(3 + 4)$ is treated as one value. **73.** Commutative property of addition **75.** No; Associative property of addition **77.** $\dfrac{49}{15}$ or $3\dfrac{4}{15}$ **78.** $\dfrac{23}{16}$ or $1\dfrac{7}{16}$ **79.** −11.2 **80.** $-\dfrac{7}{8}$

Chapter 1 Review Exercises **1.** 28 **2.** $551.25 **3. a)** $74.25 **b)** $974.24 **4.** $30 **5. a)** 78.4 **b)** 79 **6. a)** 11 **b)** 9.5 **7. a)** 30 minutes **b)** 27 minutes **8. a)** 1.0192 million **b)** 0.5187 million **9.** $\dfrac{1}{2}$ **10.** $\dfrac{127}{21}$ or $6\dfrac{1}{21}$ **11.** $\dfrac{25}{36}$ **12.** $\dfrac{7}{6}$ or $1\dfrac{1}{6}$ **13.** $\dfrac{23}{12}$ or $1\dfrac{11}{12}$ **14.** $\dfrac{177}{10}$ or $17\dfrac{7}{10}$ **15.** $\{1, 2, 3, \ldots\}$ **16.** $\{0, 1, 2, 3, \ldots\}$ **17.** $\{\ldots, -3, -2, -1, 0, 1, 2, 3, \ldots\}$ **18.** The set of all numbers which can be expressed as the quotient of two integers, denominator not zero **19. a)** $3, 426$ **b)** $3, 0, 426$ **c)** $3, -5, -12, 0, 426$ **d)** $3, -5, -12, 0, \dfrac{1}{2}, -0.62, 426, -3\dfrac{1}{4}$ **e)** $\sqrt{7}$ **f)** $3, -5, -12, 0, \dfrac{1}{2}, -0.62, \sqrt{7}, 426, -3\dfrac{1}{4}$ **20. a)** 1 **b)** 1 **c)** $-8, -9$ **d)** $-8, -9, 1$ **e)** $-2.3, -8, -9, 1\dfrac{1}{2}, 1, -\dfrac{3}{17}$ **f)** $-2.3, -8, -9, 1\dfrac{1}{2}, \sqrt{2}, -\sqrt{2}, 1, -\dfrac{3}{17}$ **21.** < **22.** > **23.** < **24.** > **25.** < **26.** > **27.** = **28.** > **29.** −14 **30.** 0 **31.** −3 **32.** −6 **33.** −6 **34.** 2 **35.** 8 **36.** 0 **37.** −5 **38.** 14 **39.** 4 **40.** −12 **41.** $\dfrac{7}{12}$ **42.** $\dfrac{11}{10}$ or $1\dfrac{1}{10}$ **43.** $-\dfrac{7}{36}$ **44.** $-\dfrac{19}{56}$ **45.** $-\dfrac{5}{4}$ or $-1\dfrac{1}{4}$ **46.** $-\dfrac{37}{84}$ **47.** $-\dfrac{7}{90}$ **48.** $\dfrac{61}{60}$ or $1\dfrac{1}{60}$ **49.** 8 **50.** −13 **51.** −12 **52.** −7 **53.** 6 **54.** 11 **55.** −63 **56.** 25.42 **57.** −120 **58.** $-\dfrac{6}{35}$ **59.** $-\dfrac{6}{11}$ **60.** $\dfrac{15}{56}$ **61.** 0 **62.** 144 **63.** −5 **64.** −6 **65.** −3.2 **66.** 4.3 **67.** 8 **68.** 9 **69.** $\dfrac{56}{27}$ or $2\dfrac{2}{27}$

70. $-\frac{35}{9}$ or $-3\frac{8}{9}$ **71.** 0 **72.** 0 **73.** Undefined **74.** Undefined **75.** Undefined **76.** 0 **77.** 25 **78.** -8 **79.** 1 **80.** 3 **81.** -6

82. -32 **83.** 6 **84.** -4 **85.** 10 **86.** 1 **87.** 15 **88.** -4 **89.** -36 **90.** 36 **91.** 16 **92.** -27 **93.** -1 **94.** -32 **95.** $\frac{16}{25}$

96. $\frac{8}{125}$ **97.** 500 **98.** 4 **99.** 12 **100.** -256 **101.** 7 **102.** 32 **103.** 6.36 **104.** -17 **105.** -39 **106.** -2.3 **107.** 0 **108.** $\frac{9}{7}$ or $1\frac{2}{7}$

109. -60 **110.** 10 **111.** 20 **112.** 20 **113.** 14 **114.** 9 **115.** -4 **116.** 50 **117.** 5 **118.** 26 **119.** 45 **120.** 0 **121.** -11
122. -3 **123.** -3 **124.** 39 **125.** -215 **126.** 353.6 **127.** -2.88 **128.** 117.8 **129.** 65,536 **130.** -74.088 **131.** Associative property of addition **132.** Distributive property **133.** Commutative property of addition **134.** Commutative property of multiplication **135.** Distributive property **136.** Associative property of addition **137.** Identity property of multiplication **138.** Inverse property of addition

Chapter 1 Practice Test **1. a)** \$10.65 **b)** \$0.23 **c)** \$10.88 **d)** \$39.12 [1.2] **2.** ≈ 2.5 times greater [1.2]
3. a) ≈ 13 thousand **b)** During this specific time, half the time KFUN had more than 8.8 thousand listeners and half the time KFUN had less than 8.8 thousand listeners. [1.2] **4. a)** 42 **b)** 42, 0 **c)** $-6, 42, 0, -7, -1$ **d)** $-6, 42, -3\frac{1}{2}, 0, 6.52, \frac{5}{9}, -7, -1$ **e)** $\sqrt{5}$

f) $-6, 42, -3\frac{1}{2}, 0, 6.52, \sqrt{5}, \frac{5}{9}, -7, -1$ [1.4] **5.** $<$ [1.5] **6.** $>$ [1.5] **7.** -15 [1.6] **8.** -11 [1.7] **9.** -14 [1.7] **10.** 8 [1.9]

11. -24 [1.8] **12.** $\frac{16}{63}$ [1.8] **13.** -3 [1.9] **14.** $-\frac{53}{56}$ [1.7] **15.** 12 [1.9] **16.** $-\frac{32}{243}$ [1.9] **17.** 100 [1.9]

18. $-x^2$ means $-(x^2)$ and x^2 will always be positive for any nonzero value of x. Therefore, $-x^2$ will always be negative. [1.9] **19.** 37 [1.9]
20. 11 [1.9] **21.** 10 [1.9] **22.** 1 [1.9] **23.** Commutative property of addition [1.10] **24.** Distributive property [1.10]
25. Associative property of addition [1.10]

Chapter 2

Exercise Set 2.1 **1. a)** Terms are the parts that are added. **b)** $3x, -4y,$ and -5 **c)** $6xy, 3x, -y,$ and -9 **3. a)** A variable **b)** A constant **c)** Coefficient **5. a)** Yes **b)** No, they don't have the same variable with the same exponent. **c)** Yes **d)** Yes
7. a) The signs of all the terms inside the parentheses change when the parentheses are removed. **b)** $-x + 8$

9. $9x$ **11.** $3x + 6$ **13.** $5y + 3$ **15.** $\frac{9}{44}a$ **17.** $-6x + 7$ **19.** $-5w + 5$ **21.** $-2x$ **23.** 0 **25.** $-2x + 11$ **27.** $-2r - 8$

29. $10x^2 - 10y^2 - 7$ **31.** $2x - 3$ **33.** $b + \frac{23}{5}$ **35.** $0.8n + 6.42$ **37.** $\frac{1}{2}a + 3b + 1$ **39.** $14.6x + 8.3$ **41.** $x^2 + y$

43. $-3x - 5y$ **45.** $-3n^2 - 2n + 13$ **47.** $21.72x - 7.11$ **49.** $-\frac{23}{20}x - 5$ **51.** $5w^3 + 2w^2 + w + 3$ **53.** $-7z^3 - z^2 + 2z$

55. $6x^2 - 6xy + 3y^2$ **57.** $4a^2 + 3ab + b^2$ **59.** $5x + 10$ **61.** $5x + 20$ **63.** $3x - 18$ **65.** $-x + 2$ **67.** $x - 4$ **69.** $\frac{4}{5}s - 4$

71. $-0.9x - 1.5$ **73.** $-r + 4$ **75.** $1.4x + 0.35$ **77.** $x - y$ **79.** $-2x - 4y + 8$ **81.** $3.41x - 5.72y + 3.08$ **83.** $10x - 45y$
85. $x + 3y - 9$ **87.** $3x - 6y - 12$ **89.** $-3x + 1$ **91.** $2x + 1$ **93.** $14x + 18$ **95.** $4x - 2y + 3$ **97.** $5c$ **99.** $7x + 3$

101. $\frac{5}{4}x + \frac{1}{3}$ **103.** $\frac{19}{6}x - 2$ **105.** $-4s - 6$ **107.** $2x - 2$ **109.** 0 **111.** $-y - 6$ **113.** $3x - 5$ **115.** $x + 15$

117. $0.2x - 4y - 2.8$ **119.** $-6x + 7y$ **121.** $\frac{3}{2}x + \frac{7}{2}$ **123.** $2\square + 3\ominus$ **125.** $2x + 3y + 2\triangle$ **127.** $2\triangle + 2\square$ **129.** $1, 2, 3, 6, 9, 18$
131. $22x^2 - 25y^2 - 4x + 3$ **133.** $9x - 39$ **135.** 7 **136.** -16 **137.** -1 **138.** Answers will vary. **139.** -12

Exercise Set 2.2 **1.** An equation is a statement that shows two algebraic expressions are equal. **3.** Substitute the value in the equation and then determine if it results in a true statement. **5.** Equivalent equations are two or more equations with the same solution. **7.** Subtract 2 from both sides of the equation. **9.** One example is $x + 2 = 1$. **11.** They all have the same solution, 1.
13. Yes **15.** No **17.** Yes **19.** Yes **21.** No **23.** Yes **25.** 5 **27.** -7 **29.** -4 **31.** 43 **33.** 15 **35.** 11 **37.** -4 **39.** -5
41. -13 **43.** -30 **45.** 0 **47.** -57 **49.** -4 **51.** -20 **53.** 0 **55.** 17 **57.** -26 **59.** 28 **61.** -46.1 **63.** 46.5 **65.** -8.23
67. 5.57 **69.** No, the equation is equivalent to $1 = 2$, a false statement. **71.** $x = \square + \triangle$ **73.** $\square = \odot - \triangle$

76. $\frac{11}{30}$ **77.** $-\frac{31}{24}$ **78.** $2x - 13$ **79.** $7t - 19$

Exercise Set 2.3 **1.** Answers will vary. **3. a)** $x = -a$ **b)** $x = -5$ **c)** $x = 5$ **5.** Divide by 3 to isolate the variable.

7. Multiply both sides by 2. **9.** 3 **11.** 21 **13.** -3 **15.** -8 **17.** 5 **19.** -3 **21.** $-\frac{7}{3}$ **23.** -13 **25.** 8 **27.** 39 **29.** $-\frac{1}{3}$ **31.** 6

33. $\frac{26}{43}$ **35.** 2 **37.** $\frac{1}{5}$ **39.** $-\frac{3}{40}$ **41.** -60 **43.** 240 **45.** -35 **47.** 20 **49.** -50 **51.** 0 **53.** 0 **55.** 22.5 **57.** 6 **59.** -20.2

61. 7 **63.** 9 **65.** In $5 + x = 10$, 5 is added to the variable, whereas in $5x = 10$, 5 is multiplied by the variable. **b)** $x = 5$

c) $x = 2$ **67.** Multiply by $\dfrac{3}{2}$; 6 **69.** Multiply by $\dfrac{7}{3}$; $\dfrac{28}{15}$ **71. a)** ⊡ **b)** Divide both sides of the equation by △. **c)** ⊡ $= \dfrac{☺}{△}$
73. −4 **74.** −30 **75.** 6 **76.** Associative property of addition **77.** −57

Exercise Set 2.4
1. No, there is an x on both sides of the equation. **3.** $x = \dfrac{1}{3}$ **5.** $x = -\dfrac{1}{2}$ **7.** $x = \dfrac{4}{9}$ **9.** Evaluate

11. a) Answers will vary. **b)** Answers will vary. **13. a)** Answers will vary. **b)** $x = -2$ **15.** 5 **17.** −4 **19.** 2 **21.** $\dfrac{12}{5}$

23. 3 **25.** 3 **27.** $\dfrac{11}{3}$ **29.** $-\dfrac{19}{16}$ **31.** −10 **33.** 2 **35.** $-\dfrac{51}{5}$ **37.** 3 **39.** 6.8 **41.** 4 **43.** 12 **45.** 22 **47.** 60 **49.** −13

51. −11 **53.** −1 **55.** $\dfrac{19}{8}$ **57.** 0 **59.** −10 **61.** −1 **63.** 6 **65.** −21 **67.** $-\dfrac{19}{7}$ **69.** −4 **71.** 4 **73.** 5 **75.** 0.8 **77.** −1

79. $\dfrac{2}{7}$ **81.** −2.6 **83.** $-\dfrac{14}{5}$ **85.** 23 **87.** $-\dfrac{1}{15}$ **89.** 3 **91.** $-\dfrac{16}{21}$ **93.** 10 **95.** 5 **97.** $-\dfrac{23}{3}$ **99.** 2 **101.** $\dfrac{25}{3}$ **103.** $\dfrac{88}{135}$

105. a) You will not have to work with fractions. **b)** $x = 3$ **107.** $\dfrac{35}{6}$ **109.** −4 **113.** False **114.** 64 **115.** Isolate the variable on one side of the equation. **116.** Divide both sides of the equation by −4 to isolate the variable.

Mid-Chapter Test
1. $-2x - 5y - 6$ [2.1] **2.** $-\dfrac{7}{20}x - \dfrac{15}{2}$ [2.1] **3.** $-8a + 12b - 24$ [2.1]
4. $3.36x - 5.44y - 8.32$ [2.1] **5.** $2t - 38$ [2.1] **6.** Yes [2.2] **7.** No [2.2] **8.** −4 [2.2] **9.** −16 [2.2] **10.** −23 [2.2]
11. Multiply both sides by 4. [2.3] **12.** $\dfrac{1}{2}$ [2.3] **13.** 24 [2.3] **14.** 10 [2.3] **15.** $-\dfrac{3}{7}$ [2.3] **16.** $\dfrac{5}{2}$ [2.4] **17.** $-\dfrac{3}{2}$ [2.4] **18.** $\dfrac{11}{8}$ [2.4]
19. −6 [2.4] **20.** $-\dfrac{20}{9}$ [2.4]

Exercise Set 2.5
1. Answers will vary. **3. a)** An identity is an equation that is true for infinitely many values of the variable.
b) All real numbers **5.** Both sides of the equation are identical. **7.** You will obtain a false statement. **9. a)** Answers will vary.
b) $x = -8$ **11.** 3 **13.** 1 **15.** $\dfrac{3}{5}$ **17.** 3 **19.** 2 **21.** No Solution **23.** 6.5 **25.** 3.2 **27.** 3 **29.** −2 **31.** No solution **33.** $\dfrac{34}{5}$
35. $\dfrac{7}{9}$ **37.** 5 **39.** 30 **41.** $\dfrac{3}{4}$ **43.** $\dfrac{5}{2}$ **45.** 25 **47.** All real numbers **49.** 23 **51.** 0 **53.** All real numbers **55.** $\dfrac{21}{20}$ **57.** 14
59. $-\dfrac{35}{6}$ **61.** 5 **63.** 4 **65.** 0 **67.** 16 **69.** $-\dfrac{12}{5}$ **71.** $-\dfrac{4}{21}$ **73.** $\dfrac{10}{3}$ **75.** 30 **77.** 4 **79. a)** One example is $x + x + 1 = x + 2$.
b) It has a single solution. **c)** For the example given in part **a)**, $x = 1$. **81. a)** One example is $x + x + 1 = 2x + 1$. **b)** Both
sides simplify to the same expression. **c)** All real numbers **83. a)** One example is $x + x + 1 = 2x + 2$. **b)** It simplifies to a
false statement. **c)** No solution **85.** ✳ $= -\dfrac{1}{4}$ **87.** All real numbers **89.** $x = -4$ **91. a)** 4 **b)** 7 **c)** 0 **92.** ≈0.131687243

93. Factors are expressions that are multiplied. Terms are expressions that are added. **94.** $7x - 10$ **95.** $\dfrac{10}{7}$ **96.** −3

Exercise Set 2.6
1. A formula is an equation used to express a relationship mathematically. **3.** $i = prt$; i: simple interest,
p: principal, r: rate, t: time **5.** $d = rt$; d: distance, r: rate, t: time **7.** No, 3.14 is an approximation for π. **9.** When you multiply a unit
by the same unit, you get a square unit. **11.** 240 **13.** 96 **15.** 360 **17.** 26 **19.** 78.54 **21.** 82 **23.** 2 **25.** 8 **27.** 6.00 **29.** 127.03
31. ≈50.27 square feet **33.** 16.5 square feet **35.** ≈452.39 cubic centimeters **37.** $C = 10°$ **39.** $F = 77°$ **41.** $P = 40$ **43.** $V = 5$
45. $w = A/l$ **47.** $t = d/r$ **49.** $t = i/(pr)$ **51.** $b = 2A/h$ **53.** $w = (P - 2l)/2$ **55.** $r = (-n + 3)/2$ **57.** $b = y - mx$
59. $b = d - a - c$ **61.** $y = (-ax - c)/b$ **63.** $h = 3V/(\pi r^2)$ **65.** $m = 2A - d$ **67.** $y = -2x + 5$ **69.** $y = x - 5$
71. $y = \dfrac{2}{3}x + \dfrac{4}{3}$ **73.** $y = \dfrac{3}{5}x - 2$ **75.** $y = \dfrac{1}{2}x - \dfrac{5}{2}$ **77.** $y = -\dfrac{1}{2}x + 4$ **79.** $y = -\dfrac{1}{3}x - \dfrac{5}{3}$ **81.** $y = 2x + \dfrac{13}{15}$
83. The distance stays the same. **85.** The area is 4 times as large; $(2s)^2 = 4s^2$ **87.** Square; **89.** $1440 **91.** $5000
93. 50 miles per hour **95.** 7.632 miles **97.** 48 square inches **99.** 558 square inches
101. ≈75.40 feet **103.** 3 square feet **105.** 7 square feet **107.** ≈124.1 feet

109. ≈381.7 cubic inches **111. a)** $B = \dfrac{703w}{h^2}$ **b)** ≈23.91 **113. a)** $V = 18x^3 - 3x^2$ **b)** 6027 cubic centimeters **c)** $S = 54x^2 - 8x$

d) 2590 square centimeters **115.** $\dfrac{2}{15}$ **116.** −6 **117.** 0 **118.** 8

Exercise Set 2.7
1. A ratio is a quotient of two quantities. **3.** c to d, $c:d$, $\dfrac{c}{d}$ **5.** Need a given ratio and one of the two parts
of a second ratio **7.** Yes, their corresponding angles must be equal and their corresponding sides must be in proportion. **9.** Yes
11. No **13.** 2:3 **15.** 1:2 **17.** 8:1 **19.** 7:4 **21.** 1:3 **23.** 6:1 **25.** 7:6 **27.** 8:1 **29. a)** 50:23 **b)** ≈2.17:1
31. a) 5.15:3.35 or 1.03:0.67 **b)** ≈1.54:1 **33. a)** 19.2:2.2 or 9.6:1.1 **b)** 6.7:3.1 **35. a)** 40:32 or 5:4 **b)** 15:11 **37.** 12
39. 45 **41.** −9 **43.** −2 **45.** −54 **47.** 6 **49.** 32 inches **51.** 15.75 inches **53.** 19.5 inches **55.** 25 loads **57.** 269.8 miles
59. 1.5 feet **61.** 24 teaspoons **63.** ≈0.43 feet **65.** 3.75 cups **67.** ≈9.49 feet **69.** 0.55 milliliter **71.** 570 minutes or 9 hours 30 minutes
73. ≈339 children **75.** 6.5 feet **77.** 2.9 square yards **79.** 20 inches **81.** ≈23 **83.** $307 **85.** 2113.4 pesos
87. Yes, her ratio is 2.12 : 1. **89.** It must increase. **91.** ≈41,667 miles **93.** 0.625 cubic centimeters **96.** Commutative property of
addition **97.** Associative property of multiplication **98.** Distributive property **99.** All real numbers. **100.** $m = (y - b)/x$

Exercise Set 2.8   1. $>$: is greater than; $\geq$: is greater than or equal to; $<$: is less than; $\leq$: is less than or equal to
3. a) False **b)** True **5.** When multiplying or dividing by a negative number **7.** All real numbers **9. a)** $28 > -12$ **b)** $\dfrac{7}{4} > -\dfrac{3}{4}$

11. $x > 4$; **13.** $x > 4$; **15.** $x > -5$; **17.** $r \leq -6$;

19. $x > -\dfrac{3}{2}$; **21.** $x \leq 1$; **23.** $x < -2$; **25.** $x < \dfrac{3}{2}$;

27. $x > \dfrac{35}{9}$; **29.** $x < -\dfrac{3}{2}$; **31.** No solution; **33.** $x \geq -6$;

35. $x < 1$; **37.** All real numbers; **39.** All real numbers; **41.** $x > \dfrac{3}{4}$;

43. No solution; **45.** $x \geq -\dfrac{7}{11}$; **47.** $x > 3$; **49.** $m \geq 2.5$;

51. $x \geq 30$; **53.** $t > -\dfrac{1}{2}$; **55.** $r \geq 2$; **57.** $t \leq -17$;

59. a) May, September, June, August, and July **b)** January, February, December, March, November, and April **c)** January, February, and December **d)** June, August, and July **61.** $\neq$ **63.** We do not know that y is positive. If y is negative, we must reverse the sign of the inequality. **65.** $x > 4$ **66.** -9 **67.** -25 **68.** $\dfrac{14}{5}$ **69.** 500 kilowatt-hours

Chapter 2 Review Exercises
1. $3x + 12$ **2.** $5x - 10$ **3.** $-2x - 8$ **4.** $-x - 2$ **5.** $-m - 3$ **6.** $-16 + 4x$ **7.** $25 - 5p$
8. $24x - 30$ **9.** $-25x + 25$ **10.** $-4x + 12$ **11.** $x + 2$ **12.** $-1 - 2y$ **13.** $-x - 2y + z$ **14.** $-6a + 15b - 21$ **15.** $4x$
16. $-3y + 8$ **17.** $5x + 1$ **18.** $-3x + 3y$ **19.** $8m + 8n$ **20.** $9x + 3y + 2$ **21.** $4x + 3y + 6$ **22.** 3 **23.** $-12x^2 + 3$ **24.** 0
25. $5x + 7$ **26.** $-3b + 2$ **27.** 0 **28.** $4x - 4$ **29.** $22x - 42$ **30.** $6x^2 - 3x + y$ **31.** $-\dfrac{7}{20}d + 7$ **32.** 3 **33.** $\dfrac{1}{6}x + 2$
34. $-\dfrac{7}{12}n$ **35.** 1 **36.** -13 **37.** 11 **38.** -27 **39.** $\dfrac{11}{5}$ **40.** $\dfrac{11}{2}$ **41.** -6 **42.** -3 **43.** 12 **44.** 4 **45.** 2 **46.** -3 **47.** $\dfrac{3}{2}$ **48.** -3
49. $-\dfrac{1}{2}$ **50.** -1 **51.** All real numbers **52.** 2 **53.** -5 **54.** -35.5 **55.** -1.125 **56.** 0.6 **57.** $-\dfrac{21}{4}$ **58.** $\dfrac{78}{7}$ **59.** $-\dfrac{3}{2}$ **60.** $-\dfrac{6}{11}$
61. 2 **62.** $\dfrac{10}{7}$ **63.** 0 **64.** -1 **65.** 10 **66.** No solution **67.** All real numbers **68.** -4 **69.** No solution **70.** All real numbers
71. $\dfrac{17}{3}$ **72.** $-\dfrac{20}{7}$ **73.** No solution **74.** 6 **75.** 52 **76.** 32 **77.** 7 **78.** -18 **79.** 3 **80.** 48 **81.** 12 square centimeters
82. ≈ 33.51 cubic inches **83.** $l = (P - 2w)/2$ **84.** $m = \dfrac{y - y_1}{x - x_1}$ **85.** $y = \dfrac{1}{3}x + \dfrac{2}{3}$ **86.** 308.5 miles **87.** 240 square feet
88. ≈ 25.13 cubic inches **89.** $3:5$ **90.** $5:12$ **91.** $6:1$ **92.** 2 **93.** 20 **94.** 9 **95.** $\dfrac{135}{4}$ **96.** -10 **97.** -16 **98.** $\dfrac{108}{7}$ **99.** 90
100. 40 inches **101.** 1 foot **102.** $x \geq 2$; **103.** $a < 1$; **104.** $r \geq -2$;

105. No solution; **106.** All real numbers; **107.** $x < -3$; **108.** $x \leq \dfrac{17}{4}$;

109. $x > \dfrac{8}{5}$; **110.** $x > -12$; **111.** $t \geq -3$; **112.** 6.3 hours **113.** 72 dishes

114. 440 pages **115.** $6\dfrac{1}{3}$ inches **116.** 15.75 feet **117.** $\approx \$0.109$ **118.** 192 bottles

Chapter 2 Practice Test
1. $6x - 12$ [2.1] **2.** $-x - 3y + 4$ [2.1] **3.** $-3x + 4$ [2.1] **4.** $-x + 10$ [2.1] **5.** $-5x - y - 6$ [2.1]
6. $7a - 8b - 3$ [2.1] **7.** $2x^2 + 6x - 1$ [2.1] **8.** $x = 3$ [2.4] **9.** $x = 8$ [2.5] **10.** $x = -\dfrac{1}{7}$ [2.5] **11.** No solution [2.5]
12. All real numbers [2.5] **13.** $x = \dfrac{-by - c}{a}$ [2.6] **14.** $y = \dfrac{6}{5}x - \dfrac{2}{5}$ [2.6] **15.** $x = 0$ [2.5] **16.** $x = -45$ [2.7]
17. a) Conditional equation **b)** Contradiction **c)** Identity [2.5] **18.** $x > -7$; [2.8] **19.** $x \leq 12$; [2.8]
20. No solution; [2.8] **21.** All real numbers; [2.5] **22.** $x = \dfrac{32}{3}$ feet or $10\dfrac{2}{3}$ feet [2.7] **23.** 4% [2.6]
24. ≈ 28.27 inches [2.6] **25.** 175 minutes or 2 hours 55 minutes [2.6]

Cumulative Review Test   **1.** $\frac{8}{3}$ [1.3]   **2.** $\frac{15}{16}$ [1.3]   **3.** > [1.5]   **4.** 3 [1.7]   **5.** −1 [1.7]   **6.** 16 [1.9]   **7.** 3 [1.9]   **8.** 12 [1.9]
9. Distributive property [1.10]   **10.** $12x + y$ [2.1]   **11.** $\frac{1}{12}x + 25$ [2.1]   **12.** −1 [2.4]   **13.** $-\frac{5}{4}$ [2.5]   **14.** $\frac{12}{5}$ [2.5]
15. $b = 3A - a - c$ [2.6]   **16.** $\frac{9}{4}$ or 2.25 [2.7]   **17.** $x > 10$; [2.8]   **18.** $x \geq -12$; [2.8]
19. ≈380.13 square feet [2.6]   **20.** $42 [2.7]

Chapter 3

Exercise Set 3.1   **1.** add to, more than, increased by, sum   **3.** multiplied by, product of, twice, three times   **5.** need $0.25c$
7. $25 - x$ **9.** is, was, will be, yields, gives   **11.** $h + 4$ **13.** $a - 5$ **15.** $5h$ **17.** $2d$ **19.** $\frac{1}{2}a$ **21.** $r - 5$ **23.** $8 - m$ **25.** $2w + 8$
27. $5a - 4$ **29.** $\frac{1}{3}w - 7$ **31.** $x =$ Sonya's height   **33.** $x =$ length of Jones Beach   **35.** $x =$ number of medals Finland won
37. $x =$ cost of the Chevy   **39.** $x =$ Teri's grade   **41.** $x =$ amount Kristen receives or $x =$ amount Yvonne receives
43. $x =$ Don's weight or $x =$ Angela's weight   **45.** Let $c =$ cost of chair, then $3c =$ cost of table.   **47.** Let $a =$ area of the kitchen,
then $2a + 20 =$ area of the living room.   **49.** Let $w =$ width of rectangle, then $5w - 2 =$ length of rectangle.   **51.** Let $w =$ number
of medals won by Sweden, then $38 - w =$ number of medals won by Brazil, or let $w =$ number of medals won by Brazil, then
$38 - w =$ number of medals won by Sweden.   **53.** Let $g =$ George's age, then $\frac{1}{2}g + 2 =$ Mike's age.   **55.** Let $m =$ number of
miles Jan walked, then $6.4 - m =$ number of miles Edward walked, or let $m =$ number of miles Edward walked, then
$6.4 - m =$ number of miles Jan walked.   **57.** $n + 8$ **59.** $\frac{1}{2}x$ **61.** $2a - 1$ **63.** $2t - 30$ **65.** $2p - 2.3$ **67.** $80{,}000 - m$
69. $2r - 673$ **71.** $10x$ **73.** $100d$ **75.** $45 + 0.40x$ **77.** $s + 0.20s$ **79.** $e - 0.12e$ **81.** $c + 0.07c$ **83.** $m - 0.313m$
85. $f + (f + 15)$ **87.** $(2l - 1) - l$ **89.** $n - (3n - 40)$ **91.** $w + (2w - 3)$ **93.** $r + (479r + 462)$ **95.** $n + (n + 0.06n)$
97. $a - (a - 0.023a)$ **99.** $x + 4x = 20$ **101.** $x + (x + 1) = 41$ **103.** $2x - 8 = 12$ **105.** $\frac{1}{5}(x + 10) = 150$
107. $x + 2(x + 2) = 22$ **109.** $12.50h = 150$ **111.** $2.99x = 17.94$ **113.** $25q = 175$ **115.** $a + (2a + 1) = 52$
117. $(2s + 300) - s = 420$ **119.** $s + (2s - 4) = 890$ **121.** $m + (3m - 2) = 12.6$ **123.** $c + 0.023c = 89{,}600$
125. $p - 0.019p = 12{,}087$ **127.** $c + 0.07c = 32{,}600$ **129.** $c + 0.15c = 42.50$ **131.** **a)** $86{,}400d + 3600h + 60m + s$
b) 368,125 seconds   **134.** 4   **135.** 15   **136.** $y = \frac{3x - 6}{2}$ or $y = \frac{3}{2}x - 3$ **137.** 2.52   **138.** $x > \frac{7}{2}$;

Exercise Set 3.2   **1.** Answers will vary.   **3.** 5   **5.** 43, 44   **7.** 47, 49   **9.** 8, 19   **11.** 2, 6   **13.** 25, 42   **15.** 65 cards
17. 22.2 hours   **19.** 13 weeks   **21.** 9.6 years   **23.** December: 22, June: 226   **25.** $14.74   **27.** Northern China: $0.86, Mexico $2.42
29. 15 gallons   **31.** 18,100 copies   **33.** 6 movies   **35.** 150 miles   **37.** 6 years   **39.** 4000 pages   **41.** 2000 newsletters   **43.** $261.68
45. $23,230.77   **47.** ≈371 thousand bushels   **49.** $25,000   **51.** $39,387.76   **53.** $49,867   **55.** $7500   **57.** 500 pages
59. $1071.43   **61.** $24.59   **63.** $77,777.78   **65.** **a)** $80 = \frac{74 + 88 + 76 + x}{4}$ **b)** 82   **67.** 4   **68.** Commutative property of addition
69. $h = \frac{2A}{b}$ **70.** 12

Mid-Chapter Test   **1.** $6w$ [3.1]   **2.** $3h + 5$ [3.1]   **3.** $c + 0.20c$ [3.1]   **4.** $40 + 0.25m$ [3.1]
5. $50n$ [3.1]   **6.** $25 - x$ [3.1]   **7.** $c - 0.25c$ [3.1]   **8.** $x =$ length of Poison Dart Frog [3.1]   **9.** Let $p =$ distance Pedro traveled, then
$4p + 6 =$ distance Mary traveled. [3.1]   **10.** $v - (v - 0.18v)$ [3.1]   **11.** $p + 0.12p = 38{,}619$ [3.2]   **12.** $x + 3(x + 2) = 26$ [3.2]
13. 46, 47 [3.2]   **14.** 4, 11 [3.2]   **15.** 18 days [3.2]   **16.** 15 hours [3.2]   **17.** $700 [3.2]   **18.** Betty: 196 clients, Anita: 404 clients [3.2]
19. 52 miles [3.2]   **20.** $5000 [3.2]

Exercise Set 3.3   **1.** The area remains the same.   **3.** The volume is eight times as great.   **5.** The area is nine times as great.
7. An isosceles triangle is a triangle with two equal sides.   **9.** 180°   **11.** 46°, 46°, 88°   **13.** 11.5 inches   **15.** $A = 67°, B = 23°$
17. $A = 47°, B = 133°$ **19.** 88°   **21.** 50°, 60°, 70°   **23.** Length is 14 feet, width is 8 feet.   **25.** Length is 78 feet, width is 36 feet.
27. Smaller angles are 50°; larger angles are 130°   **29.** 30°, 30°, 150°, 150°   **31.** 63°, 73°, 140°, 84°   **33.** Width is 4 feet, height is 7 feet.
35. Width is 2.5 feet, height is 5 feet.   **37.** Width is 11 feet, length is 16 feet.   **39.** $ac + ad + bc + bd$ **41.** <   **42.** >   **43.** −10
44. $-2x - 5y + 6$ **45.** $y = -2x + 3$

Exercise Set 3.4   **1.** 1 hour   **3.** 6 mph   **5.** ≈0.72 hour   **7.** 2.4 hours   **9.** 70 mph   **11.** ≈44.4 seconds   **13.** 35 mph, 40 mph
15. ≈0.61 hour   **17.** 1.5 miles/day, 2.25 miles/day   **19.** *Apollo*: 5 mph, *Pythagoras*: 9 mph   **21.** 1.5 hours   **23.** **a)** 2.4 miles
b) 112.0 miles   **c)** 26.2 miles   **d)** 140.6 miles   **e)** 9.01 hours   **25.** $10,000 at 7%; $2000 at 5%   **27.** $2400 at 6%; $3600 at 4%
29. $2000 at 4%; $8000 at 5%   **31.** November   **33.** 8 hours at Home Depot; 10 hours at clinic   **35.** 1200 adults   **37.** **a)** 41 shares of
Nike, 205 shares of Kellogg   **b)** $37   **39.** 11.25 pounds almonds, 18.75 pounds walnuts   **41.** $160: 6 cubic yards, $120: 2 cubic yards

43. \$2.74 per pound   **45.** $\approx 11.1\%$ **47.** $1\frac{2}{3}$ liters   **49.** 18.96%   **51.** $\approx 11.1\%$ **53.** 40% pure juice   **55.** ≈ 3.77 cups Clorox,

≈ 2.23 cups shock treatment   **57.** 11.25 pints   **59.** ≈ 5.74 hours   **62. a)** $\frac{22}{13}$ or $1\frac{9}{13}$ **b)** $\frac{35}{8}$ or $4\frac{3}{8}$ **63.** All real numbers

64. $\frac{3}{4}$ or 0.75   **65.** $x \le \frac{1}{4}$

Chapter 3 Review Exercises
1. $3n + 7$ **2.** $1.2g$ **3.** $d - 0.25d$ **4.** $16y$ **5.** $200 - x$ **6.** Let d = Dino's age, then $7d + 6$ = Mario's age.   **7.** $c - (c - 0.12c)$ **8.** $n - (3n - 24) = 8$ **9.** 33 and 41   **10.** 118 and 119   **11.** 38 and 7   **12.** \$21,738.32   **13.** 19 months   **14.** \$2000   **15.** \$618.75   **16.** 10 hours   **17.** $\approx$\$171,000   **18.** \$684   **19.** $45°, 55°, 80°$ **20.** $30°, 40°, 150°, 140°$ **21.** Width is 15.5 feet; length is 19.5 feet   **22.** Width is 50 feet; length is 80 feet   **23.** $45°, 45°, 135°, 135°$ **24.** Height is 2 feet; length is 4 feet

25. 2 hours   **26.** 4 hours   **27.** ≈ 8.8 feet per second   **28.** \$4000 at 8%; \$8000 at $7\frac{1}{4}\%$ **29.** \$700 at 3%; \$3300 at 3.5%

30. ≈ 0.67 gallon   **31.** 9 smaller and 21 larger   **32.** 1.2 liters of 10%; 0.8 liters of 5%   **33.** 103 and 105   **34.** \$450   **35.** \$12,000   **36.** $42°, 50°, 88°$ **37.** 8 years   **38.** $70°, 70°, 110°, 110°$ **39.** 500 copies   **40.** 0.6 mph   **41.** 60 pounds of \$3.50; 20 pounds of \$4.10   **42.** Older brother: 55 mph; younger brother: 60 mph   **43.** 0.4 liters   **44.** Width is 16 feet; length is 24 feet   **45.** 1.5 liters

Chapter 3 Practice Test
1. $500 - n$ [3.1]   **2.** $2w + 6000$ [3.1]   **3.** $60t$ [3.1]   **4.** $c + 0.06c$ [3.1]   **5.** Let n = number of packages of orange, then $7n - 105$ = number of packages of peppermint. [3.1]   **6.** Let x = number of men, then $600 - x$ = number of women, or let x = number of women, then $600 - x$ = number of men. [3.1]   **7.** $(2n - 1) - n$ [3.1]   **8.** $n + (n + 18)$ [3.1]   **9.** $(c + 0.84c) - c$ [3.1]   **10.** 56 and 102 [3.2]   **11.** 5 and 7 [3.2]   **12.** 9 and 33 [3.2]   **13.** \$2500 [3.2]   **14.** \$34.78 [3.2]   **15.** Peter: \$40,000, Julie: \$80,000 [3.2]   **16.** 6 times [3.2]   **17.** 7450 pages [3.2]   **18.** 15 inches, 30 inches, 30 inches [3.3]   **19.** Width is 6 feet, length is 8 feet [3.3]   **20.** $59°, 59°, 121°, 121°$ [3.3]   **21.** Harlene: 0.3 feet per minute, Ellis: 0.5 feet per minute [3.4]   **22.** 6 mph [3.4]   **23.** Jelly Belly: ≈ 1.91 pounds, Kits: ≈ 1.09 pounds [3.4]   **24.** 20 liters [3.4]   **25.** 1 liter of 8%; 2 liters of 5% [3.4]

Cumulative Review Test
1. \$16,000 [1.2]   **2. a)** 34%   **b)** ≈ 0.06 million or $\approx 60,000$ [1.2]   **3. a)** 7.2 parts per million

b) 6 parts per million [1.2]   **4.** $\frac{5}{9}$ [1.3]   **5.** $\frac{13}{24}$ inch [1.3]   **6. a)** $\{1, 2, 3, 4, \dots\}$ **b)** $\{0, 1, 2, 3, \dots\}$ **c)** A rational number is a quotient of two integers where the denominator is not 0. [1.4]   **7. a)** 4   **b)** $|-5|$ [1.5]   **8.** -34 [1.9]   **9.** $2x - 28$ [2.1]   **10.** 5 [2.5]

11. $\frac{1}{5}$ [2.5]   **12.** No solution [2.5]   **13.** ≈ 113.10 [2.6]   **14. a)** $y = -\frac{1}{2}x + 2$ **b)** 4 [2.6]   **15.** $w = \frac{P - 2l}{2}$ [2.6]   **16.** 9 gallons [2.7]

17. $x \le 1$;   [2.8]   **18.** 40 minutes [3.7]   **19.** 6, 23 [3.2]   **20.** $40°, 45°, 90°, 185°$ [3.3]

Chapter 4

Using Your Graphing Calculator, 4.1
1.   **2.**   **3.** 40   **4.** 100

$-20, 40, 5, -10, 60, 10$ $-200, 400, 100, -500, 1000, 200$

Exercise Set 4.1
1. The x-coordinate   **3. a)** x-axis   **b)** y-axis   **5.** Axis is singular; axes is plural.   **7.** An illustration of the set of points whose coordinates satisfy the equation   **9. a)** Two   **b)** To catch errors   **11.** $ax + by = c$

13.   **15.** II   **17.** IV   **19.** I   **21.** III   **23.** III   **25.** II   **27.** $A(3, 1)$; $B(-3, 0)$; $C(1, -3)$; $D(-2, -3)$; $E(0, 3)$; $F\left(\frac{3}{2}, -1\right)$ **29.**   **31.**

33. The points are collinear.   **35.** $(-5, -3)$ is not on the line.   **37. a)** Point c) does not satisfy the equation.   **b)**   **39. a)** Point a) does not satisfy the equation.   **b)**   **41. a)** Point a) does not satisfy the equation.   **b)**

43. 2   **45.** -4 **47.** 3   **49.** $\frac{1}{2}$ **51.** 0   **53. a)** Latitude, 16° N; Longitude, 56° W   **b)** Latitude, 29° N; Longitude, 90.5° W

c) Latitude, 26° N; Longitude, 80.5° W   d) Answers will vary.   **57.** A linear equation is an equation of the form $ax + b = c$.

58. A conditional equation is a linear equation that has only one solution.   **59.** -2 **60.** $C = 6\pi \approx 18.84$ inches,

$A = 9\pi \approx 28.27$ square inches   **61.** $y = \dfrac{2x - 6}{5} = \dfrac{2}{5}x - \dfrac{6}{5}$

Using Your Graphing Calculator, 4.2

1.

2.

3.

4.

$-10, 10, 1, -10, 10, 1$ $-10, 10, 1, -10, 10, 1$ $-10, 10, 1, -10, 10, 1$ $-10, 10, 1, -10, 10, 1$

Using Your Graphing Calculator, 4.2   **1.** $(2, 0), (0, -8)$ **2.** $(-3, 0), (0, -6)$ **3.** $(2.5, 0), (0, -2)$ **4.** $(1.5, 0), (0, -4.5)$

Exercise Set 4.2   **1.** x-intercept: substitute 0 for y and find the corresponding value of x; y-intercept: substitute 0 for x and find the corresponding value of y **3.** A horizontal line   **5.** You may not be able to read exact answers from a graph.

7. Yes   **9.** 0   **11.** 5   **13.** 3   **15.** 2   **17.** $\dfrac{8}{3}$ **19.** -7

21.   **23.**   **25.**   **27.**   **29.**   **31.**

33.   **35.**   **37.**   **39.**   **41.**

43.   **45.**   **47.**   **49.**   **51.**   **53.**

55.   **57.**   **59.**   **61.**   **63.**   **65.** $x = -2$

67. $y = 6$ **69.** 5   **71.** 2   **73.** Yes

75. a) $C = 0.10n + 15$

b)

c) $19

d) 100 minutes

77. a) $C = m + 40$

b)

c) $100

d) 30 miles

79. a)

b) $550 **c)** 800 tapes   **81.** 3,2   **83.** 6,4

85. a)   **b)** (2, 3) **c)** Yes **d)** No

88. −57 **89.** 18 **90.** 6.67 ounces

91. 9, 28

Exercise Set 4.3   **1.** The slope of a line is the ratio of the vertical change to the horizontal change between any two points on the line.   **3.** Rises from left to right   **5.** Lines that rise from the left to right have a positive slope; lines that fall from left to right have a negative slope.   **7.** No, since we cannot divide by 0, the slope is undefined.   **9.** The slopes are the same.

11. 2   **13.** $\frac{1}{2}$ **15.** 0   **17.** 1   **19.** Undefined   **21.** $-\frac{3}{8}$ **23.** $\frac{2}{3}$ **25.** $m = 2$ **27.** $m = -2$ **29.** $m = -\frac{4}{7}$ **31.** $m = \frac{7}{4}$ **33.** $m = 0$

35. $m = -\frac{2}{3}$ **37.** Undefined   **39.**   **41.**   **43.**   **45.**   **47.**

49. Parallel   **51.** Perpendicular   **53.** Perpendicular   **55.** Neither   **57.** Neither   **59.** Parallel   **61.** Parallel

63. Perpendicular   **65.** 3   **67.** $\frac{1}{4}$ **69.** First   **71. a)** $-\frac{23}{4}$ **b)** 11   **73.** −4   **75.** $-\frac{1}{8}$ **77.** $\frac{225}{68}$

79. a)   **b)** AC, $m = \frac{3}{5}$; CB, $m = -2$; DB, $m = \frac{3}{5}$; AD, $m = -2$ **c)** Yes, opposite sides are parallel.

81. a) AB, $m = 4$; BC, $m = -2$; CD, $m = 4$ **b)** $[4 + (-2) + 4]/3 = 2$
c) AD, $m = 2$ **d)** Yes   **e)** Answers will vary.

83. 0   **84. a)** $\frac{5}{2}$ **b)** 0   **85.** $\frac{84}{17}$ **86.** $c = d - a - b$ **87.** x-intercept: (6, 0); y-intercept: (0, −10)

Mid-Chapter Test   **1.** IV [4.1]   **2.**   [4.1]   **3. b)** [4.1]
4. −4 [4.1]
5. 3 [4.1]
6. A graph of an equation in two variables is an illustration of a set of points whose coordinates satisfy the equation. [4.1]

7. [4.2]   **8.** [4.2]   **9.** [4.2]   **10.** [4.2]   **11.** [4.2]

12. [4.2]   **13.** $-\frac{2}{7}$ [4.3]   **16.** [4.3]   **17.** [4.3]   **18.** Neither [4.3]
19. Perpendicular [4.3]
14. 0 [4.3]   **20.** 10 [4.3]
15. Undefined [4.3]

Using Your Graphing Calculator, 4.4

1. a)   **b)**   **c)**

−10, 10, 1, −10, 10, 1   −15.2, 15.2, 1, −10, 10, 1   −4.7, 4.7, 1, −3.1, 3.1, 1

2. a)

                       b)   **c)**

$-10, 10, 1, -10, 10, 1$ $-15.2, 15.2, 1, -10, 10, 1$ $-4.7, 4.7, 1, -3.1, 3.1, 1$

Exercise Set 4.4

1. $y = mx + b$ **3.** $y = 3x - 5$ **5.** Write the equations in slope-intercept form. If slopes are the same and the y-intercepts are different, the lines are parallel.   **7.** $y - y_1 = m(x - x_1)$ **9.** $2; (0, -6)$ **11.** $\dfrac{4}{3}; (0, -7)$

13. $1; (0, -3)$ **15.** $3; (0, 2)$ **17.** $2; (0, 0)$ **19.** $2; (0, -3)$

21. $\dfrac{5}{2}; (0, -5)$ **23.** $-\dfrac{1}{2}; \left(0, \dfrac{3}{2}\right)$ **25.** $3; (0, 4)$ **27.** $\dfrac{3}{2}; (0, 2)$

29. $y = x - 2$ **31.** $y = -\dfrac{1}{3}x + 2$ **33.** $y = -3x - 5$ **35.** $y = \dfrac{1}{3}x + 5$ **37.** Parallel   **39.** Perpendicular   **41.** Parallel

43. Neither   **45.** Perpendicular   **47.** Neither   **49.** $y = 3x + 2$ **51.** $y = -3x - 7$ **53.** $y = \dfrac{1}{2}x - \dfrac{5}{2}$ **55.** $y = \dfrac{2}{3}x + 6$

57. $y = 3x + 10$ **59.** $y = -\dfrac{3}{2}x$ **61.** $y = \dfrac{1}{2}x - 2$ **63.** $y = 7.4x - 4.5$ **65. a)** $y = 5x + 60$ **b)** $\$210$

67. a) Slope-intercept form   **b)** Point-slope form   **c)** Point-slope form
69. a) No   **b)** $y + 4 = 2(x + 5)$ **c)** $y - 12 = 2(x - 3)$ **d)** $y = 2x + 6$ **e)** $y = 2x + 6$ **f)** Yes

71. a) 1.465 **b)** $f = 1.465m$ **c)** ≈ 209.06 feet per second   **d)** 150 feet per second   **e)** 55 miles per hour

73. $y = -2x + 5$ **75.** $y = \dfrac{3}{4}x + 5$ **78.** $<$ **79.** True   **80.** True   **81.** False   **82.** False   **83.** 64   **84.** $r = \dfrac{i}{pt}$

Exercise Set 4.5

1. Points on the line satisfy the $=$ part of the inequality.   **3.** The shading is on opposite sides of the line.

5.   **7.**   **9.**   **11.**   **13.**

15.   **17.**   **19.**   **21.**   **23.**

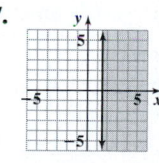

25. a) No   **b)** No   **c)** Yes   **d)** Yes   **27.** No, it could be a solution to $ax + by = c$.   **29.** No, the location of an ordered pair which satisfies the first inequality lies on one side of the line while an ordered pair which satisfies the other inequality lies either on the line or on the other side of the line.   **31. a)** Less than or equal to   **b)** Greater than or equal to   **c)** Less than or equal to

d) Greater than or equal to   **33.** a), b), and c)   **34. a)** 2   **b)** 2, 0   **c)** $2, -5, 0, \dfrac{2}{5}, -6.3, -\dfrac{23}{34}$ **d)** $\sqrt{7}, \sqrt{3}$

e) $2, -5, 0, \sqrt{7}, \dfrac{2}{5}, -6.3, \sqrt{3}, -\dfrac{23}{34}$ **35.** 2   **36.** 14 miles   **37.** Slope: $\dfrac{3}{4}$; y-intercept: $(0, -5)$

Exercise Set 4.6   **1.** A relation is any set of ordered pairs.   **3.** A function is a set of ordered pairs in which each first component corresponds to exactly one second component   **5. a)** The domain is the set of first components in the set of ordered pairs.   **b)** The range is the set of second components in the set of ordered pairs.   **7.** No, each x must have a unique y for it to be a function.   **9.** Function; Domain: $\{1, 2, 3, 4, 5\}$; Range: $\{1, 2, 3, 4, 5\}$ **11.** Relation; Domain: $\{1, 2, 3, 5, 7\}$; Range: $\{-2, 0, 2, 4, 5\}$ **13.** Function; Domain: $\{0, 1, 3, 4, 5\}$; Range: $\{-4, -1, 0, 1, 2\}$ **15.** Relation; Domain: $\{0, 1, 3\}$; Range: $\{-3, 0, 2, 5\}$ **17.** Function; Domain: $\{0, 1, 2, 3, 4\}$; Range: $\{3\}$ **19. a)** $\{(1, 4), (2, 5), (3, 5), (4, 7)\}$ **b)** Function   **21. a)** $\{(-5, 4), (0, 7), (6, 9), (6, 3)\}$ **b)** Not a function   **23.** Function   **25.** Not a function   **27.** Function   **29.** Function   **31.** Not a function   **33.** Function   **35. a)** 14   **b)** -2 **37. a)** 31   **b)** 4   **39. a)** 4   **b)** 6   **41. a)** 3   **b)** 8

43.   **45.**   **47.**   **49.**   **51.** $c = 0.35n$

53. No, some value of x must correspond to two values of y.

55. Yes, it passes the vertical line test.

57. a)

b) $160

59. a)

b) $11,000

61. a)

b) $240

63. a)

b) $11,600

65. Yes, it passes the vertical line test.   **67.** No, the vertical line $x = 1$ intersects the graph at more than one point.

69. a) $\dfrac{29}{8}$ **b)** $\dfrac{29}{9}$ **c)** 3.88   **73.** $\dfrac{1}{63}$ **74. a)** Commutative property of addition   **b)** Associative property of addition   **c)** Distributive property   **75.** -14 **76.** A graph is an illustration of a set of points whose coordinates satisfy an equation.

Chapter 4 Review Exercises

1.   **2.** Not collinear

3. a), b), and **d)**

4. a) -1 **b)** -4 **c)** 6   **d)** $\dfrac{8}{3}$

5.   **6.**   **7.**   **8.**   **9.**   **10.**

11.   **12.** $5x + 2y + 10 = 0$ **13.**   **14.**   **15.** $-\dfrac{9}{5}$ **16.** $-\dfrac{1}{12}$

17. -2 **18.** 0

19. Undefined

20. The slope of a line is the ratio of the vertical change to the horizontal change between any two points on the line.   **21.** -2 **22.** $\frac{1}{4}$

23. Neither   **24.** Perpendicular   **25. a)** 214   **b)** -49 **26.** $m = -\frac{6}{7}; (0, 3)$ **27.** Slope is undefined; no y-intercept

28. $m = 0; (0, -3)$ **29.** $y = 3x - 3$ **30.** $y = -\frac{1}{2}x + 2$ **31.** Parallel   **32.** Perpendicular

33. $y = 3x + 1$ **34.** $y = -\frac{2}{3}x + 4$ **35.** $y = 2$ **36.** $x = 4$ **37.** $y = -\frac{7}{2}x - 3$ **38.** $x = -5$

39.   **40.**   **41.**   **42.**   **43.**   **44.**

45. Function; Domain: {1, 2, 3, 4, 6}; Range: {−3, −1, 2, 4, 5}   **46.** Not a function; Domain: {3, 4, 6, 7}; Range: {0, 1, 2, 5}
47. Not a function; Domain: {3, 4, 5, 6}; Range: {−3, 1, 2}   **48.** Function; Domain: {−2, 3, 4, 5, 9}; Range: {−2}
49. a) {(1, 3), (4, 5), (7, 2), (9, 2)}   **b)** Function   **50. a)** {(4, 1), (6, 3), (6, 5), (8, 7)}   **b)** Not a function
51. a) Domain: {Mary, Pete, George, Carlos}; Range: {Apple, Orange, Grape}   **b)** Not a function
52. a) Domain: {Sarah, Jacob, Kristen, Erin}; Range: {Seat 1, Seat 2, Seat 3, Seat 4}   **b)** Not a function
53. a) Domain: {Blue, Green, Yellow}; Range: {Paul, Maria, Lalo, Duc}   **b)** Function
54. a) Domain: {1, 2, 3, 4,}; Range: {A, B, C}   **b)** Function   **55.** Function   **56.** Function   **57.** Not a function   **58.** Function
59. a) 5   **b)** −31   **60. a)** 9   **b)** −39   **61. a)** −4   **b)** −8   **62. a)** 12   **b)** 76   **63.** Yes, each year has a unique dollar amount.
64. Yes, it passes the vertical line test.   **65.**   **66.**

67. a)   **b)** $145   **68. a)**   **b)** $400

Chapter 4 Practice Test
1. A graph is an illustration of the set of points whose coordinates satisfy an equation. [4.1]
2. a) IV   **b)** II [4.1]   **3. a)** $ax + by = c$ **b)** $y = mx + b$ **c)** $y - y_1 = m(x - x_1)$ [4.1-4.4]

4. b) and **d)** [4.1]   **5.** $-\frac{4}{3}$ [4.3]   **6.** $\frac{4}{9}; \left(0, -\frac{5}{3}\right)$ [4.4]   **7.** $y = -x - 1$ [4.4]

8. [4.2]   **9.** [4.2]   **10.** [4.2]   **11. a)** $y = \frac{1}{2}x - 2$ **b)** [4.2]

12. [4.2]   **13.** $y = 4x - 13$ [4.4]   **14.** $y = -\frac{3}{7}x + \frac{2}{7}$ [4.4]   **15.** The lines are parallel since they have the same slope but different y-intercepts. [4.3]

16. [4.4]   **17.** [4.4]   **18.** A set of ordered pairs in which each first component corresponds to exactly one second component. [4.4]

19. a) Not a function; 3, a first component, is paired with more than one value
  b) Domain: {1, 3, 5, 6}; Range: {−4, 0, 2, 3, 5} [4.6]

20. a) Function; it passes the vertical line test   **b)** Not a function; a vertical line can be drawn that intersects the graph at more than one point [4.6]   **21. a)** 15   **b)** 10 [4.6]

22. [4.6]   **23.** [4.5]   **24.** [4.5]

25. a)   **b)** $450 [4.2]

Cumulative Review Test   **1. a)** {1, 2, 3, 4, …}   **b)** {0, 1, 2, 3,…} [1.4]   **2.** 18 [1.7]   **3.** 35 [1.9]   **4.** 100 [1.9]
5. a) Distributive property   **b)** Commutative property of addition [1.10]   **6.** 20 [2.5]   **7.** All real numbers [2.5]

8. $x < -5$, [2.8]   **9.** $4.00 [2.7]   **10.** $w = \dfrac{v}{lh}$ [2.6]   **11.** 4 [3.2]   **12.** width: 5 feet, length: 13 feet [3.3]   **13.** 2 hours [3.4]

14. Answers will vary. [4.1]   **15.** [4.1]   **16.** [4.2]   **17.** [4.4]   **18.** $y - 2 = 3(x - 5)$ [4.4]

19. 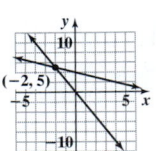 [4.5]   **20. a)** No.   **b)** Yes [4.6]

Chapter 5

Using Your Graphing Calculator, 5.1   **1.** $(-3, -4)$ **2.** $(-4, 3)$ **3.** $(3.1, -1.5)$ **4.** $(-0.6, 4.8)$

Exercise Set 5.1   **1.** The solution to a system of equations represents the ordered pairs that satisfy all the equations in the system.
3. Write the equations in slope-intercept form and compare their slopes and y-intercepts. If the slopes are different, the system has exactly one solution. If the slopes are the same and the y-intercepts are different, the system has no solution. If the slopes and y-intercepts are the same, the system has an infinite number of solutions.   **5.** The point of intersection can only be estimated.   **7.** c)   **9.** a)
11. None   **13.** a), b)   **15.** a)   **17.** Consistent; one solution   **19.** Dependent; infinite number of solutions   **21.** Consistent; one solution
23. Inconsistent; no solution   **25.** One solution   **27.** No solution   **29.** One solution   **31.** No solution   **33.** Infinite number of solutions   **35.** No solution   **37.**   **39.**   **41.**   **43.**   **45.**

Inconsistent

47. 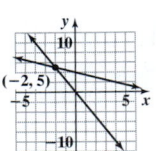   **49.**   **51.**   **53.**   **55.**   **57.**

Dependent   Dependent   Inconsistent

59.

61. Lines are parallel; they have the same slope and different y-intercepts.
63. The system has an infinite number of solutions. If the two lines have two points in common then they must be the same line.
65. The system has no solution. Parallel lines do not intersect.
67. One; $(5, 3)$

69. 6 years   **71.** 7 hours   **79.** $2x + 18$ **80.** 1   **81.** 0.05   **82.** $h = \dfrac{2A}{b}$ **83. a)** $(6, 0), (0, 4)$ **b)**

Exercise Set 5.2

1. The x in the first equation, since both 6 and 12 are divisible by 3.   **3.** You will obtain a false statement, such as $3 = 0$.   **5.** $(4, 1)$ **7.** $(-1, -1)$ **9.** No solution   **11.** $(3, -8)$ **13.** $(-2, -3)$ **15.** $(3, 5)$ **17.** Infinite number of solutions

19. $(2, 1)$ **21.** $(5, -3)$ **23.** $(-1, 0)$ **25.** $\left(-\dfrac{12}{7}, \dfrac{6}{35}\right)$ **27.** No solution   **29.** $\left(\dfrac{1}{8}, -\dfrac{1}{2}\right)$ **31.** $36, 44$ **33.** Width: 8 feet, length: 17 feet

35. 1561 attendees   **37.** \$30,000   **39. a)** 16 months   **b)** Yes   **41. a)** 1.25 hours   **b)** 155 mile marker   **43. a)** $T = 180 - 10t$
b) $T = 20 + 6t$ **c)** 10 minutes   **d)** 80°F   **45.** 23 years   **46.** 2   **47.**

48. Slope: $\dfrac{3}{5}$; y-intercept: $(0, -5)$ **49.** $y = 2x + 4$

Exercise Set 5.3

1. Multiply the top equation by 2.   **3.** You will obtain a false statement, such as $0 = 6$.   **5.** $(5, 1)$ **7.** $(4, 5)$

9. $(5, 8)$ **11.** No solution   **13.** $(-8, -26)$ **15.** $\left(-\dfrac{3}{2}, -3\right)$ **17.** $(-2, 2)$ **19.** $(3, -1)$ **21.** Infinite number of solutions   **23.** $(1, 2)$

25. No solution   **27.** $(0, 0)$ **29.** $\left(10, \dfrac{15}{2}\right)$ **31.** $(-6, -12)$ **33.** $\left(\dfrac{20}{39}, -\dfrac{16}{39}\right)$ **35.** $\left(\dfrac{14}{5}, -\dfrac{12}{5}\right)$ **37.** No solution

39. First number: 14, second number: 6   **41.** First number: 6, second number: 4   **43.** Width: 3 inches, length: 6 inches
45. Width: 8 inches, length: 10 inches   **47.** Answers will vary.   **49. a)** $(200, 100)$ **b)** Same solution; dividing both sides of an equation by a nonzero number does not change the solution.   **51.** $(8, -1)$ **53.** $(1, 2, 3)$ **55.** 125   **56.** 7
57. $x > -1$;   **58.** $y = 3x + 2$ **59.** 14

Mid-Chapter Test

1. b) [5.1]   **2.** a) [5.1]   **3.** One solution [5.1]   **4.** Infinite number of solutions [5.1]   **5.** No solution [5.1]

6.   [5.1]   **7.**   [5.1]   **8.** $(-2, 4)$ [5.2]   **9.** $\left(1, -\dfrac{1}{3}\right)$ [5.2]   **10.** No solution [5.2]

11. Length: 15 feet, width: 7 feet [5.2]   **12.** $(4, -1)$ [5.3]   **13.** $\left(-\dfrac{1}{2}, 2\right)$ [5.3]

14. Infinite number of solutions [5.3]

15. Solution must have two values, one for x and one for y. The solution is $x = 3$ and $y = 5$ or $(3, 5)$. [5.1–5.3]

Exercise Set 5.4

1. $17, 26$ **3.** $A = 36°, B = 54°$ **5.** $A = 112°, B = 68°$ **7.** Width: 390 feet, length: 740 feet
9. 20 years   **11.** kayak: 4.05 miles per hour, current: 0.65 miles per hour   **13.** 60 acres corn, 40 acres wheat   **15.** adults: 12, children: 15
17. a) 1400 copies   **b)** Office Copier Depot   **19.** \$2500 at 4%; \$5500 at 5%   **21. a)** 15 square yards   **b)** Tom Taylor's
23. Dave: 57 miles per hour, Alice: 72 miles per hour   **25.** Melissa, 30 miles per hour; Elizabeth, 34 miles per hour   **27.** 2 hours
29. ≈ 0.68 hour   **31.** 8 liters of 15%; 12 liters of 40%   **33.** 180 tiles   **35.** 140 gallons 5%, 60 gallons skim

37. $2\dfrac{2}{3}$ ounces drink, $5\dfrac{1}{3}$ ounces juice   **39.** 2010   **41.** 1.125 miles   **43.** 45 minutes   **45. a)** Commutative property of addition

b) Associative property of multiplication   **c)** Distributive property   **46.** $\dfrac{1}{2}$ **47.** Width: 3 feet, length: 8 feet   **48.** $(-1, -3)$

Exercise Set 5.5

1. Yes, the solution to a system of linear inequalities contains all of the ordered pairs which satisfy both inequalities.   **3.** Yes, when the lines are parallel. One possible system is $x + y > 2, x + y < 1$.   **5.**   **7.**

9.   **11.**   **13.**   **15.**

17.   **19.**   **21.**   **23.**

25. No, the system can have no solution or infinitely many solutions.   **29.** All real numbers;

30. $y = \dfrac{3}{5}x - \dfrac{6}{5}$ **31.**   **32.** $-\dfrac{8}{7}$

Chapter 5 Review Exercises

1. c)   **2.** a)   **3.** Consistent, one solution   **4.** Inconsistent, no solution   **5.** Dependent, infinite number of solutions   **6.** Consistent, one solution   **7.** No solution   **8.** One solution   **9.** Infinite number of solutions   **10.** One solution

11.   **12.**   **13.**   **14.**   **15.**   **16.**   **17.**

18.   **19.** $(5, 2)$ **20.** $(-3, 2)$ **21.** $(4, 1)$ **22.** $(-15, 5)$ **23.** No solution   **24.** Infinite number of solutions

25. $\left(\dfrac{5}{2}, -1\right)$ **26.** $\left(-\dfrac{2}{7}, \dfrac{29}{7}\right)$ **27.** $(-6, -2)$ **28.** $(1, -2)$ **29.** $(-7, 19)$ **30.** $\left(\dfrac{32}{13}, \dfrac{8}{13}\right)$ **31.** $\left(-1, \dfrac{13}{3}\right)$

32. No solution   **33.** Infinite number of solutions   **34.** $\left(-\dfrac{78}{7}, -\dfrac{48}{7}\right)$ **35.** 10 and 12

36. plane: 550 miles per hour; wind: 30 miles per hour   **37.** 50 miles   **38.** \$10,000 at 4%, \$6000 at 6%   **39.** Liz: 57 miles per hour; Mary: 63 miles per hour   **40.** 20 pounds of Green Turf's, 30 pounds of Agway's   **41.** 5 liters of each

42.   **43.**   **44.**   **45.**

Chapter 5 Practice Test

1. b) [5.1]   **2.** Consistent, one solution [5.1]   **3.** Inconsistent, no solution [5.1]   **4.** Dependent, infinite number of solutions [5.1]   **5.** No solution [5.1]   **6.** One solution [5.1]   **7.** Infinite number of solutions [5.1]
8. a) You will obtain a false statement, such as $6 = 0$.   **b)** You will obtain a true statement, such as $0 = 0$. [5.1]

9. [5.1]   **10.** [5.1]   **11.** [5.1]   **12.** $(6, 21)$ [5.2]   **13.** $\left(\dfrac{7}{2}, -\dfrac{5}{2}\right)$ [5.2]

14. $(4, 5)$ [5.2]   **15.** $(-2, 2)$ [5.3]   **16.** $\left(\dfrac{1}{2}, -6\right)$ [5.3]
17. Infinite number of solutions [5.3]   **18.** $(3, 2)$ [5.1–5.3]

19. $(-5, -4)$ [5.1–5.3]   **20.** $\left(-\dfrac{40}{7}, \dfrac{52}{7}\right)$ [5.1–5.3]   **21.** 100 miles [5.4]   **22.** butterscotch: $13\dfrac{1}{3}$ pounds; lemon: $6\dfrac{2}{3}$ pounds [5.4]

23. Deja's boat, 20 miles per hour; Dante's boat, 24 miles per hour [5.4]   **24.** [5.5]   **25.** 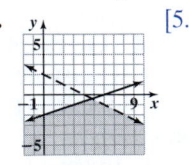 [5.5]

Cumulative Review Test

1. a) Air Force, Army   **b)** Air Force, Army, Navy [1.2]   **2.** 87 [1.2]   **3.** 85.2 [1.2]   **4.** $\dfrac{5}{12}$ [1.3]

5. a) 7   **b)** $-5, -0.6, \dfrac{3}{5}, 7, 0, -\dfrac{5}{9}, 1.34$ **c)** $\sqrt{10}, -\sqrt{2}$ **d)** $-5, -0.6, \dfrac{3}{5}, \sqrt{10}, -\sqrt{2}, 7, 0, -\dfrac{5}{9}, 1.34$ [1.4]   **6.** $=$ [1.5]   **7.** -244 [1.7]

8. $a + 24$ [2.1]   **9.** -2 [2.5]   **10.** $w = \dfrac{P - 2l}{2}$ [2.6]   **11.** $x \le 5$; [2.8]   **12.** $39 - y$ [3.1]   **13.** \$5800 [3.2]

14. $15°, 45°, 120°$ [3.3]

15. [4.2]   **16.** [4.2]   **17.** $-\dfrac{10}{9}$ [4.3]   **18.** An infinite number of solutions [5.1]

19. [5.1]   **20.** $\left(\dfrac{11}{3}, -1\right)$ [5.3]

Chapter 6

Exercise Set 6.1 **1.** In the expression t^p, t is the base, p is the exponent. **3. a)** $\dfrac{x^m}{x^n} = x^{m-n}, x \neq 0$ **b)** Answers will vary.
5. a) $(x^m)^n = x^{m \cdot n}$ **b)** Answers will vary. **7.** a^2b^5 **9.** Answers will vary. **11.** x^9 **13.** $-z^5$ **15.** y^5 **17.** $3^5 = 243$ **19.** z^8
21. 6 **23.** x^7 **25.** $3^4 = 81$ **27.** $\dfrac{1}{y^2}$ **29.** 1 **31.** $\dfrac{1}{a^6}$ **33.** 1 **35.** 3 **37.** 4 **39.** -9 **41.** $6x^3y^2$ **43.** $-8r$ **45.** x^8 **47.** x^{25}
49. x^3 **51.** x^{12} **53.** n^{18} **55.** $-8w^6$ **57.** $-27x^9$ **59.** $64x^9y^6$ **61.** $\dfrac{x^2}{9}$ **63.** $\dfrac{y^4}{x^4}$ **65.** $-\dfrac{216}{x^3}$ **67.** $\dfrac{8x^3}{y^3}$ **69.** $\dfrac{16p^2}{25}$ **71.** $\dfrac{27x^{12}}{y^3}$ **73.** $\dfrac{a^7}{b^3}$
75. $\dfrac{x^{11}}{2y^7}$ **77.** $\dfrac{6y^4}{z^3}$ **79.** $\dfrac{7}{3x^5y^3}$ **81.** $-\dfrac{3y^2}{x^3}$ **83.** $-\dfrac{2}{x^3y^2z^5}$ **85.** $\dfrac{8}{x^6}$ **87.** $27y^9$ **89.** 1 **91.** $\dfrac{x^4}{y^4}$ **93.** $\dfrac{z^{24}}{16y^{28}}$ **95.** $\dfrac{125}{s^6t^9}$ **97.** $9x^2y^8$
99. $5ab^4$ **101.** $-6x^2y^2$ **103.** $15x^3y^6$ **105.** $-9p^6q^3$ **107.** $49r^6s^4$ **109.** x^2 **111.** x^{12} **113.** $6.25x^6$ **115.** $\dfrac{x^7}{y^4}$ **117.** $-\dfrac{m^{12}}{n^9}$
119. $-216x^9y^6$ **121.** $-8x^{12}y^6z^3$ **123.** $729r^{12}s^{15}$ **125.** $108x^5y^7$ **127.** $53.29x^4y^8$ **129.** $x^{11}y^{13}$ **131.** x^8z^8
133. Cannot be simplified **135.** Cannot be simplified **137.** $6z^2$ **139.** Cannot be simplified **141.** 40 **143.** 1 **145.** The sign will be positive because a negative number with an even exponent will be positive. This is because $(-1)^m = 1$ when m is even.
147. $8x^2$ **149.** $ab + a^2 + b^2$ **151.** $576y^8z^{13}$ **154.** 13 **155.** $x + 10$ **156.** All real numbers **157. a)** 4 inches, 4 inches, 9 inches, 9 inches
b) $w = \dfrac{P - 2l}{2}$

Exercise Set 6.2 **1.** Answers will vary. **3.** No, it is not simplified because of the negative exponent; $\dfrac{x^5}{y^3}$ **5.** The given simplification
is not correct since $5^{-2} = \dfrac{1}{25}$. **7. a)** The numerator has one term, x^5y^2. **b)** The factors of the numerator are x^5 and y^2. **9.** The sign of
the exponent changes when a factor is moved from the numerator to the denominator of a fraction. **11.** $\dfrac{1}{x^6}$ **13.** $\dfrac{1}{5}$ **15.** x^3 **17.** a
19. 36 **21.** $\dfrac{1}{x^6}$ **23.** $\dfrac{1}{y^{20}}$ **25.** $\dfrac{1}{x^8}$ **27.** 9 **29.** y^2 **31.** x^2 **33.** 9 **35.** $\dfrac{1}{r}$ **37.** p^3 **39.** $\dfrac{1}{x^4}$ **41.** 27 **43.** $\dfrac{1}{125}$ **45.** z^9 **47.** p^{24}
49. y^6 **51.** $\dfrac{1}{x^4}$ **53.** $\dfrac{1}{x^{15}}$ **55.** $-\dfrac{1}{16}$ **57.** $-\dfrac{1}{16}$ **59.** $-\dfrac{1}{8}$ **61.** $\dfrac{1}{36}$ **63.** $\dfrac{1}{x^{10}}$ **65.** n^2 **67.** 1 **69.** 1 **71.** 64 **73.** x^8 **75.** 1 **77.** $\dfrac{1}{4}$
79. $\dfrac{1}{49}$ **81.** x^3 **83.** $\dfrac{1}{16}$ **85.** 125 **87.** $\dfrac{1}{9}$ **89.** 1 **91.** $\dfrac{1}{36x^4}$ **93.** $\dfrac{3y^2}{x^2}$ **95.** 4 **97.** $\dfrac{64}{125}$ **99.** $\dfrac{d^4}{c^8}$ **101.** $-\dfrac{s^4}{r^{16}}$ **103.** $-\dfrac{7}{a^3b^4}$
105. $\dfrac{y^9}{64x^{15}}$ **107.** $\dfrac{18}{z^9}$ **109.** -8 **111.** $12x^5$ **113.** $-\dfrac{20z^5}{y}$ **115.** $8d^4$ **117.** $\dfrac{4}{x^2}$ **119.** $\dfrac{x^4}{2y^5}$ **121.** $\dfrac{8x^6}{y^2}$ **123.** $\dfrac{y^{14}z^6}{25x^8}$ **125.** $\dfrac{r^{20}t^{48}}{16s^{36}}$
127. $\dfrac{y^{12}}{x^{18}z^6}$ **129.** $\dfrac{1}{16p^4q^6}$ **131. a)** Yes **b)** No **133.** $16\dfrac{1}{16}$ **135.** $125\dfrac{1}{125}$ **137.** $\dfrac{2}{3}$ **139.** $-\dfrac{7}{8}$ **141.** $-\dfrac{5}{6}$ **143.** $\dfrac{22}{9}$ **145.** -2
147. -3 **149.** -2 **151.** $2, -3$ **153.** The product rule is $(xy)^m = x^my^m$, not $(x + y)^m = x^m + y^m$. **155.** 186 miles **156.** 94, 96
157. 12 feet by 16 feet **158.** $3400 at 4%, $5600 at 3% **159.** $18x^3y^9$

Exercise Set 6.3 **1.** A number in scientific notation is written as a number greater than or equal to 1 and less than 10 that is
multiplied by some power of 10. **3. a)** Answers will vary. **b)** 7.23×10^{-5} **5.** 6 places to the right **7.** The exponent is positive
when the number is 10 or greater. **9.** Negative since $0.000937 < 1$. **11.** 1.0×10^{-6} **13.** 3.5×10^5 **15.** 7.950×10^3
17. 5.3×10^{-2} **19.** 7.26×10^{-4} **21.** 5.26×10^9 **23.** 9.14×10^{-6} **25.** 2.203×10^5 **27.** 5.104×10^{-3} **29.** 43,000
31. 0.00000932 **33.** 0.0000213 **35.** 625,000 **37.** 9,000,000 **39.** 535 **41.** 0.000000773 **43.** 10,000 **45.** 0.000008 meter
47. 125,000,000,000 watts **49.** 15,300 meters **51.** 0.0482 meter **53.** 60,000,000 **55.** 0.243 **57.** 0.000064 **59.** 0.0013 **61.** 2500
63. 250,000 **65.** 4.2×10^{12} **67.** 1.28×10^{-1} **69.** 7.0×10^2 **71.** 1.75×10^2 **73.** $3.3 \times 10^{-4}, 5.3, 7.3 \times 10^2, 1.75 \times 10^6$
75. a) $\approx 6{,}251{,}000{,}000$ **b)** ≈ 21.9 **77.** 8,640,000,000 cubic feet **79.** 1.6×10^7 seconds **81. a)** 1.68×10^8 **b)** ≈ 1.39
83. a) $36,600,000,000 **b)** ≈ 4.7 **85. a)** Earth, 5.794×10^{24} metric tons; Moon, 7.34×10^{19} metric tons; Jupiter, 1.899×10^{27} metric
tons; **b)** $\approx 7.89 \times 10^4$ **c)** $\approx 3.28 \times 10^2$ **87.** $\approx 1.316 \times 10^9$ **89. a)** 55–59: 2.0×10^5; 20–24: 5.0×10^4 **b)** 2.48×10^5 **c)** 1.52×10^5
91. 17 **93.** Answers will vary. **95.** 1,000,000 times greater **98.** 0 **99. a)** $\dfrac{3}{2}$ **b)** 0 **100.** 2 **101.** $-\dfrac{y^{12}}{64x^9}$

Mid-Chapter Test: Sections 6.1–6.3 **1.** y^{13} [6.1] **2.** x^3 [6.1] **3.** $6x^6y^{13}$ [6.1] **4.** $\dfrac{2a^5b^6}{3}$ [6.1] **5.** $-64x^6y^{12}$ [6.1]
6. $\dfrac{t^6}{4s^4}$ [6.1] **7.** $63x^{11}y^{13}$ [6.1] **8.** $\dfrac{1}{p^8}$ [6.2] **9.** $\dfrac{1}{x^{10}}$ [6.2] **10.** 1 [6.2] **11.** $\dfrac{49}{9}$ [6.2] **12.** $\dfrac{32x}{y}$ [6.2] **13.** $\dfrac{3}{m^4n^6}$ [6.2] **14.** $\dfrac{x^{12}y^{10}}{4z^4}$ [6.2]
15. a) and **b)** Answers will vary. [6.3] **16.** 6.54×10^9 [6.3] **17.** 0.0000327 [6.3] **18.** 18,900 meters [6.3] **19.** 0.0238 [6.3]
20. 3.0×10^{-7} [6.3]

Exercise Set 6.4 **1.** A polynomial is an expression containing the sum of a finite number of terms of the form ax^n, where a is a
real number and n is a whole number. **3.** No, it contains a negative exponent. **5. a)** A monomial is a one-termed polynomial.
Examples will vary. **b)** A binomial is a two-termed polynomial. Examples will vary. **c)** A trinomial is a three-termed polynomial.
Examples will vary. **7.** Answers will vary. **9. b)** and **c)** **11.** Write the polynomial with exponents on the variable decreasing from

left to right.   **13.** Combine like terms.   **15.** Use the distributive property to remove parentheses and then combine like terms.
17. Fifth   **19.** Eighth   **21.** Third   **23.** Tenth   **25.** Ninth   **27.** Trinomial   **29.** Monomial   **31.** Binomial   **33.** Monomial
35. Not a polynomial   **37.** Polynomial   **39.** Trinomial   **41.** Not a polynomial   **43.** Already in descending order, 0 degree
45. $x^2 - 2x - 4$, second   **47.** $3x^2 + x - 8$, second   **49.** Already in descending order, first   **51.** Already in descending order,
second   **53.** $4x^3 - 3x^2 + x - 4$, third   **55.** $-2x^4 + 3x^2 + 5x - 6$, fourth   **57.** $10x - 9$ **59.** $-x + 11$ **61.** $-2t - 1$

63. $x^2 + 6.6x + 0.8$ **65.** $5m^2 + 4$ **67.** $x^2 + 3x - 3$ **69.** $-3x^2 + x + \dfrac{17}{2}$ **71.** $8.2n^2 - 4.8n - 0.6$ **73.** $-2x^3 - 3x^2 + 4x - 3$

75. $11x^2 - 7x - y + 5$ **77.** $5x^2y - 3x + 2$ **79.** $11x - 3$ **81.** $7y^2 - 2y + 5$ **83.** $4x^2 + 2x - 4$ **85.** $2x^3 - x^2 + 6x - 2$
87. $3n^3 - 11n^2 - n + 2$ **89.** $2x - 6$ **91.** $3x + 4$ **93.** $-3r$ **95.** $-6y^2 + 1.9y - 12.7$ **97.** $8x^2 + x + 4$ **99.** $-6.4n^2 + 6n - 7.6$

101. $8x^3 - 7x^2 - 4x - 3$ **103.** $2x^3 - \dfrac{23}{5}x^2 + 2x - 2$ **105.** $x - 2$ **107.** $2x^2 - 9x + 14$ **109.** $-5c^3 - 4c^2 - 7c + 14$

111. $3x + 8$ **113.** $3a^2 - 16a + 28$ **115.** $x^2 - 3x - 3$ **117.** $-4x^2$ **119.** $4x^3 - 7x^2 + x - 2$ **121.** Answers will vary.
123. Answers will vary.   **125.** Sometimes   **127.** Sometimes   **129.** Answers will vary; one example is: $x^4 - 2x^3 + x$.
131. No, all three terms would have to be degree 4 or 1. Therefore at least two of the terms would be like terms.   **133.** $a^2 + 2ab + b^2$

135. $4x^2 + 3xy$ **137.** $-12x + 18$ **139.** $8x^2 + 28x - 24$ **141.** 4.5   **142.** $n - 5$ **143.**   **144.**

145. $\dfrac{y^3}{27x^{12}}$ **146.** 0.035

Exercise Set 6.5   **1.** Answers will vary.   **3.** First, Outer, Inner, Last   **5.** Yes
7. $(a + b)^2 = a^2 + 2ab + b^2$; $(a - b)^2 = a^2 - 2ab + b^2$ **9.** No, $(x - 2)^2 = x^2 - 4x + 4$ **11.** Answers will vary.
13. Answers will vary.   **15.** $-24x^6$ **17.** $20x^5y^6$ **19.** $-28x^3y^{15}$ **21.** $54x^6y^{14}$ **23.** $3x^6y$ **25.** $5.94x^8y^3$ **27.** $9x - 45$
29. $-6x^2 + 6x$ **31.** $-16y - 10$ **33.** $-2x^3 + 4x^2 - 10x$ **35.** $-20x^3 + 30x^2 - 20x$ **37.** $0.5x^5 - 3x^4 - 0.5x^2$
39. $0.6x^2y + 1.5x^2 - 1.8xy$ **41.** $x^2y^4 - 4y^7 - 3y^4$ **43.** $5x^2 + 18x - 8$ **45.** $6x^2 + 3x - 30$ **47.** $4x^2 - 16$ **49.** $-5x^2 - 22x + 48$
51. $-12x^2 + 32x - 5$ **53.** $4x^2 - 10x + 4$ **55.** $12k^2 - 30k + 12$ **57.** $x^2 - 4$ **59.** $4x^2 - 12x + 9$ **61.** $-6z^2 + 46z - 28$
63. $8x^2 - 50x + 63$ **65.** $xy - 3x + 7y - 21$ **67.** $6x^2 - 5xy - 6y^2$ **69.** $-27x^2 - 3xy + 36x + 4y$ **71.** $x^2 + 0.9x + 0.18$

73. $x^2 + \dfrac{7}{2}x - 2$ **75.** $x^2 - 36$ **77.** $9x^2 - 64$ **79.** $x^2 + 2xy + y^2$ **81.** $x^2 - 0.4x + 0.04$ **83.** $16x^2 + 40x + 25$

85. $0.16x^2 + 0.8xy + y^2$ **87.** $16c^2 - 25d^2$ **89.** $4x^2 - 36$ **91.** $49s^2 - 42st + 9t^2$ **93.** $16m^3 - 8m^2 + 9m + 18$
95. $12x^3 + 5x^2 + 13x + 10$ **97.** $-14x^3 - 22x^2 + 19x - 3$ **99.** $a^3 + b^3$ **101.** $6x^4 + 5x^3 + 5x^2 + 10x + 4$
103. $x^4 - 3x^3 + 5x^2 - 6x$ **105.** $2x^5 + 2x^4 - 23x^3 + x^2 - 12x$ **107.** $b^3 - 3b^2 + 3b - 1$ **109.** $27a^3 - 135a^2 + 225a - 125$
111. Yes   **113.** No   **115.** 6, 3, 1   **117. a)** $(x + 2)(2x + 1)$ or $2x^2 + 5x + 2$ **b)** 54 square feet   **c)** 1 foot   **119. a)** $3x^2 + 19x + 20$

b) $6x^3 + 32x^2 + 2x - 40$ **c)** 864 cubic feet   **d)** 864 cubic feet   **e)** Yes   **121.** $\dfrac{1}{3}x^2 + \dfrac{11}{45}x - \dfrac{4}{15}$ **123.** No solution

124. $C = 53°, D = 37°$ **125.** $\dfrac{x^4}{16y^8}$ **126. a)** -216 **b)** $\dfrac{1}{216}$ **127.** $-5x^2 - 2x + 14$

Exercise Set 6.6   **1.** To divide a polynomial by a monomial, divide each term in the polynomial by the monomial.   **3.** $x + 4$

5. The terms should be listed in descending order.   **7.** $\dfrac{x^2 + 0x - 7}{x - 2}$ **9.** $(x + 5)(x - 3) - 2 = x^2 + 2x - 17$

11. $\dfrac{x^2 - x - 42}{x - 7} = x + 6$ or $\dfrac{x^2 - x - 42}{x + 6} = x - 7$ **13.** $\dfrac{2x^2 + 5x + 3}{2x + 3} = x + 1$ or $\dfrac{2x^2 + 5x + 3}{x + 1} = 2x + 3$

15. $\dfrac{4x^2 - 9}{2x + 3} = 2x - 3$ or $\dfrac{4x^2 - 9}{2x - 3} = 2x + 3$ **17.** $x + 2$ **19.** $2n + 5$ **21.** $\dfrac{7}{3}x + 2$ **23.** $-3x + 2$ **25.** $3x + 1$ **27.** $\dfrac{1}{2}x + 4$

29. $-1 + \dfrac{5}{2}w$ **31.** $1 + \dfrac{2}{x} - \dfrac{3}{x^2}$ **33.** $-2x^3 + \dfrac{3}{x} + \dfrac{4}{x^2}$ **35.** $x^2 + 3x - \dfrac{3}{x^3}$ **37.** $3x^2 - 2x + 6 - \dfrac{5}{2x}$ **39.** $-2k^2 - \dfrac{3}{2}k + \dfrac{2}{k}$

41. $-4x^3 - x^2 + \dfrac{10}{3} + \dfrac{3}{x^2}$ **43.** $x + 3$ **45.** $5y + 1$ **47.** $2x + 4$ **49.** $x + 4$ **51.** $x + 5 - \dfrac{3}{2x - 3}$ **53.** $x + 6$

55. $3x^2 + 4x + 5 + \dfrac{4}{3x - 4}$ **57.** $4x - 3 - \dfrac{3}{2x + 3}$ **59.** $7x^2 - 5$ **61.** $2x^2 + \dfrac{12}{x - 2}$ **63.** $w^2 + 3w + 9 + \dfrac{19}{w - 3}$ **65.** $x^2 + 3x + 9$

67. $2x^2 + x - 2 - \dfrac{2}{2x - 1}$ **69.** $-m^2 - 7m - 5 - \dfrac{8}{m - 1}$ **71.** $4t^2 - 8t + 15 - \dfrac{26}{t + 2}$ **73.** No; for example $\dfrac{x + 2}{x} = 1 + \dfrac{2}{x}$ which

is not a binomial.   **75.** $2x^2 + 11x + 16$ **77.** Third degree   **79.** $4x$ **81.** Since the shaded areas minus 2 must equal 3, 1, 0, and -1,

respectively, the shaded areas are 5, 3, 2, and 1, respectively.   **83.** $x^2 + \dfrac{2}{3}x + \dfrac{4}{9} - \dfrac{37}{9(3x - 2)}$ **85.** $-3x + 3 + \dfrac{1}{x + 3}$ **88. a)** 2 **b)** 2, 0

c) $2, -5, 0, \dfrac{2}{5}, -6.3, -\dfrac{23}{34}$ **d)** $\sqrt{7}, \sqrt{3}$ **e)** $2, -5, 0, \sqrt{7}, \dfrac{2}{5}, -6.3, \sqrt{3}, -\dfrac{23}{34}$ **89. a)** 0   **b)** Undefined   **90.** Parentheses, exponents,

multiplication or division from left to right, addition or subtraction from left to right   **91.** $-\dfrac{2}{3}$ **92.** \$39.50   **93.** x^{13}

Chapter 6 Review Exercises   **1.** x^7 **2.** x^6 **3.** 243   **4.** 32   **5.** x^3 **6.** 1   **7.** 25   **8.** 64   **9.** $\dfrac{1}{x^2}$ **10.** y^3 **11.** 1   **12.** 7

13. 1   **14.** 1   **15.** $25x^2$ **16.** $27a^3$ **17.** $-27x^3$ **18.** $216s^3$ **19.** $16x^8$ **20.** x^{24} **21.** p^{32} **22.** $\dfrac{4x^6}{y^2}$ **23.** $\dfrac{25y^4}{4b^2}$ **24.** $24x^5$ **25.** $\dfrac{4x}{y}$

26. $54x^4y^9$ **27.** $9x^2$ **28.** $24x^7y^7$ **29.** $16x^8y^{11}$ **30.** $6c^6d^3$ **31.** $\dfrac{27a^6}{b^{15}}$ **32.** $27x^{12}y^3$ **33.** $\dfrac{1}{b^9}$ **34.** $\dfrac{1}{27}$ **35.** $\dfrac{1}{25}$ **36.** z^2 **37.** x^7

38. 16 **39.** $\dfrac{1}{y^3}$ **40.** $\dfrac{1}{x^5}$ **41.** $\dfrac{1}{p^2}$ **42.** $\dfrac{1}{a^5}$ **43.** m^{10} **44.** x^7 **45.** $\dfrac{1}{x^6}$ **46.** $\dfrac{1}{9x^8}$ **47.** $\dfrac{x^9}{64y^3}$ **48.** $\dfrac{4n^2}{m^6}$ **49.** $12y^2$ **50.** $-\dfrac{125z^3}{y^9}$

51. $\dfrac{x^4}{16y^6}$ **52.** $\dfrac{6}{x}$ **53.** $10x^2y^2$ **54.** $\dfrac{12x^2}{y}$ **55.** $\dfrac{24y^2}{x^2}$ **56.** $3y^5$ **57.** $\dfrac{4y}{x^3}$ **58.** $\dfrac{7x^5}{y^4}$ **59.** $\dfrac{x}{2y^5}$ **60.** $\dfrac{4y^{10}}{x}$ **61.** 1.72×10^6

62. 1.53×10^{-1} **63.** 7.63×10^{-3} **64.** 4.7×10^4 **65.** 5.76×10^3 **66.** 3.14×10^{-4} **67.** 0.0075 **68.** 0.000652 **69.** $8,900,000$
70. $51,200$ **71.** 0.0000314 **72.** $11,030,000$ **73.** 0.092 liter **74.** $6,000,000,000$ meters **75.** 0.0000128 gram **76.** $19,200$ grams
77. 0.085 **78.** 1260 **79.** 245 **80.** $397,000,000$ **81.** 0.00003 **82.** 0.0325 **83.** 3.64×10^9 **84.** 2.12×10^1 **85.** 5.0×10^9
86. 5.0×10^{-4} **87.** 3.4×10^{-3} **88.** 3.4×10^7 **89.** $50,000$ gallons **90. a)** $1,500,000,000,000$ **b)** $\$1.125 \times 10^{11}$
91. Not a polynomial **92.** Monomial, zero **93.** $x^2 + 3x - 4$, trinomial, second **94.** $4x^2 - x - 3$, trinomial, second
95. Not a polynomial **96.** Binomial, third **97.** $-4x^2 + x$, binomial, second **98.** Not a polynomial **99.** $2x^3 + 4x^2 - 3x - 7$,
polynomial, third **100.** $5x - 3$ **101.** $7d + 4$ **102.** $-3x - 5$ **103.** $-4x^2 + 11x - 7$ **104.** $5m^2 - 10$ **105.** $8.1p + 2.8$
106. $-3y - 15$ **107.** $4x^2 - 12x - 15$ **108.** $3a^2 - 5a - 21$ **109.** $4x + 2$ **110.** $-5x^2 + 8x - 19$ **111.** $3x^2 + 3x$
112. $-15x^2 - 12x$ **113.** $6x^3 - 12x^2 + 21x$ **114.** $-2c^3 + 3c^2 - 5c$ **115.** $28b^3 + 21b^2 + 35b$ **116.** $x^2 + 9x + 20$
117. $-12x^2 - 21x + 6$ **118.** $25x^2 - 30x + 9$ **119.** $-6x^2 + 14x + 12$ **120.** $r^2 - 25$ **121.** $3x^3 + x^2 - 10x + 6$

122. $3x^3 + 7x^2 + 14x + 4$ **123.** $-12x^3 + 10x^2 - 30x + 14$ **124.** $x + 2$ **125.** $4y + 6$ **126.** $8x + 4$ **127.** $2x^2 + 3x - \dfrac{4}{3}$

128. $2w - \dfrac{5}{3} + \dfrac{1}{w}$ **129.** $4x^5 - 2x^4 - \dfrac{3}{4}x^2 + \dfrac{1}{4x}$ **130.** $-4m + 2$ **131.** $\dfrac{5}{2}x + \dfrac{5}{x} + \dfrac{1}{x^2}$ **132.** $\dfrac{5}{3}x - 2 + \dfrac{5}{x}$ **133.** $x + 4$

134. $5x - 2 + \dfrac{2}{x + 6}$ **135.** $n + 3$ **136.** $2x^2 + 3x - 4$ **137.** $2x - 3$

Chapter 6 Practice Test

1. $15x^6$ [6.1] **2.** $27x^3y^6$ [6.1] **3.** $8p^5$ [6.1] **4.** $\dfrac{x^3}{8y^6}$ [6.1] **5.** $\dfrac{y^4}{4x^6}$ [6.2] **6.** 4 [6.1] **7.** $\dfrac{2x^7y}{3}$ [6.2]

8. 1.425×10^{10} [6.3] **9.** 2.0×10^{-7} [6.3] **10.** Monomial [6.4] **11.** Binomial [6.4] **12.** Not a polynomial [6.4]
13. $6x^3 - 2x^2 + 5x - 5$, third degree [6.4] **14.** $2x^2 + x - 7$ [6.4] **15.** $-3y^2 - 2y + 5$ [6.4] **16.** $3x^2 - x + 3$ [6.4]
17. $15d^2 - 40d$ [6.5] **18.** $15x^2 + 4x - 32$ [6.5] **19.** $-12c^2 + 7c + 45$ [6.5] **20.** $6x^3 + 2x^2 - 35x + 25$ [6.5] **21.** $4x^2 + 2x - 1$ [6.6]

22. $4x + 2 - \dfrac{5}{3x}$ [6.6] **23.** $4x + 5$ [6.6] **24.** $3x - 2 - \dfrac{2}{4x + 5}$ [6.6] **25. a)** 5.73×10^3 **b)** $\approx 7.78 \times 10^5$ [6.3]

Cumulative Review Test

1. 17 [1.9] **2.** $8x + 2$ [2.1] **3.** -25 [1.9] **4.** 0 [2.5] **5.** $x > -\dfrac{9}{2}$; ![number line with open circle at $-\frac{9}{2}$] [2.8]

6. $y = 3x + 5$ [2.6] **7.** $-\dfrac{1}{2}$ [4.3] **8.** Function: Domain, $\{-4, 1, 2, 5\}$, Range, $\{-5, 5, 7, 13\}$ [4.6]

9. $(4, -1)$ [5.2] **10.** $\dfrac{25x^6}{y^{16}}$ [6.1] **11.** $-7x^2 - 5x + 2$, second [6.4] **12.** $3x^2 + 9x - 2$ [6.4] **13.** $5a^2 + 6a + 5$ [6.4]

14. $10t^2 - 11t + 3$ [6.5] **15.** $6x^3 - 13x^2 + 9x - 2$ [6.5] **16.** $\dfrac{5}{2}d + 3 - \dfrac{2}{d}$ [6.6] **17.** $2x + 5$ [6.6] **18.** $\$3.33$ [2.7]

19. Bob, 56.5 mph; Nick, 63.5 mph [3.4] **20.** $l = 10$ feet, $w = 4$ feet [3.3]

Chapter 7

Exercise Set 7.1 **1.** To factor an expression means to write the expression as the product of its factors. **3.** A composite number is a positive integer other than 1 that is not prime. **5.** The greatest common factor is the greatest number that divides into all the numbers. **7.** $1, 2, 4, x, 2x, 4x, x^2, 2x^2, 4x^2$, and the opposites of these factors **9.** $2^3 \cdot 7$ **11.** $2 \cdot 3^2 \cdot 5$ **13.** $2^3 \cdot 31$ **15.** 4 **17.** 14
19. 2 **21.** x **23.** $3x$ **25.** a **27.** qr **29.** x^3y^5 **31.** 1 **33.** x^2y^2 **35.** x **37.** $x - 4$ **39.** $2x - 3$ **41.** $3w + 5$ **43.** $x - 4$
45. $x - 1$ **47.** $x - 9$ **49.** $4(x - 2)$ **51.** $5(3x - 1)$ **53.** $7(q + 4)$ **55.** $3x(3x - 4)$ **57.** $x^4(7x - 9)$ **59.** $3x^2(x^3 - 4)$
61. $12x^8(3x^4 + 2)$ **63.** $9y^3(3y^{12} - 1)$ **65.** $y(1 + 6x^3)$ **67.** $a^2(7a^2 + 3)$ **69.** $4xy(4yz + x^2)$ **71.** $4x^2yz^3(20x^3y^2z - 9)$
73. $25x^2yz(z^2 + x)$ **75.** $x^4y^3z^9(19y^9z^4 - 8x)$ **77.** $4(2c^2 - c - 8)$ **79.** $3(3x^2 + 6x + 1)$ **81.** $4x(x^2 - 2x + 3)$
83. $8(5b^2 - 6c + 3)$ **85.** $3(5p^2 - 2p + 3)$ **87.** $3a(3a^3 - 2a^2 + b)$ **89.** $xy(8x + 12y + 5)$ **91.** $(x - 7)(x + 6)$
93. $(a - 2)(3b - 4)$ **95.** $(2x + 1)(4x + 1)$ **97.** $(2x + 1)(5x + 1)$ **99.** $(6c + 7)(3c - 2)$ **101.** $6\nabla(2 - \nabla)$
103. $4\square(3\square^2 - \square + 1)$ **105.** $2x^2(2x + 7)(3x^3 + 2x - 1)$ **107.** $(x + 2)(x + 3)$ **108.** $-3x + 17$ **109.** 2

110. $y = \dfrac{4x - 20}{5}$ or $y = \dfrac{4}{5}x - 4$ **111.** ≈ 201.06 cubic inches **112.** $14, 27$ **113.** $\dfrac{9y^2}{4x^6}$

Exercise Set 7.2 **1.** The first step is to factor out a common factor, if one exists. **3.** $x^2 - 3x - 2xy + 6y$; found by multiplying the factors. **5.** -1 **7.** $(x + 3)(x + 2)$ **9.** $(x + 5)(x + 4)$ **11.** $(x + 2)(x + 5)$ **13.** $(c - 4)(c + 7)$ **15.** $(2x - 3)(2x + 3)$
17. $(x + 3)(3x + 1)$ **19.** $(2x + 1)(3x - 1)$ **21.** $(x + 4)(8x + 1)$ **23.** $(3t - 2)(4t - 1)$ **25.** $(x + 9)(x - 1)$
27. $(2p + 5)(3p - 2)$ **29.** $(x + 2y)(x - 3y)$ **31.** $(3x + 2y)(x - 3y)$ **33.** $(5x - 6y)(2x - 5y)$ **35.** $(x - b)(x - a)$

37. $(y + 9)(x - 5)$ **39.** $(a + 3)(a + b)$ **41.** $(y - 1)(x + 5)$ **43.** $(3 + 2y)(4 - x)$ **45.** $(z + 5)(z^2 + 1)$ **47.** $(x - 5)(x^2 + 8)$
49. $2(x - 6)(x + 4)$ **51.** $4(x + 2)(x + 2) = 4(x + 2)^2$ **53.** $x(2x + 3)(3x - 1)$ **55.** $p(p - 6q)(p + 2q)$ **57.** $(y + 5)(x + 3)$
59. $(x + 5)(y + 6)$ **61.** $(a + b)(x + y)$ **63.** $(r + 6)(s - 7)$ **65.** $(c - a)(d + 3)$ **67.** No; $xy + 2x + 5y + 10$ is factorable;
$xy + 10 + 2x + 5y$ is not factorable in this arrangement.   **69.** $(\odot + 3)(\odot - 5)$ **71. a)** $2x^2 - 5x - 6x + 15$ **b)** $(2x - 5)(x - 3)$
73. a) $2x^2 - 6x - 5x + 15$ **b)** $(x - 3)(2x - 5)$ **75. a)** $4x^2 + 3x - 20x - 15$ **b)** $(4x + 3)(x - 5)$ **77.** $(\odot + 3)(\star + 2)$
79. $\dfrac{6}{5}$ **80.** 30 pounds of jelly beans; 20 pounds of gumdrops   **81.** $5x^2 - 2x - 3 + \dfrac{5}{3x}$ **82.** $a - 4$

Exercise Set 7.3   **1.** Since 960 is positive, both signs will be the same. Since 92 is positive, both signs will be positive.   **3.** Since
-1500 is negative, one sign will be positive, the other will be negative.   **5.** Since 8000 is positive, both signs will be the same. Since
-240 is negative, both signs will be negative.   **7.** The trinomial $x^2 - 11x + 24$ is obtained by multiplying the factors using the FOIL
method.   **9.** The trinomial $2x^2 - 8xy - 10y^2$ is obtained by multiplying all the factors and combining like terms.   **11.** It is not completely factored. It factors to $2(x - 2)(x - 1)$.   **13.** A trinomial factoring problem can be checked by multiplying the factors.
15. $(x - 5)(x - 2)$ **17.** $(x + 2)(x + 4)$ **19.** $(x + 8)(x - 3)$ **21.** Prime   **23.** $(y - 12)(y - 1)$ **25.** $(a - 4)(a + 2)$
27. $(r - 5)(r + 3)$ **29.** $(b - 9)(b - 2)$ **31.** Prime   **33.** $(q + 9)(q - 5)$ **35.** $(x - 10)(x + 3)$ **37.** $(x + 2)^2$ **39.** $(s - 4)^2$
41. $(p - 6)^2$ **43.** $(w - 15)(w - 3)$ **45.** $(x + 13)(x - 3)$ **47.** $(x - 5)(x + 4)$ **49.** $(y + 5)(y + 8)$ **51.** $(x + 16)(x - 4)$
53. Prime   **55.** $(x - 16)(x - 4)$ **57.** $(a - 9)(a - 11)$ **59.** $(x + 2)(x + 1)$ **61.** $(w + 9)(w - 2)$ **63.** $(x - 3y)(x - 5y)$
65. $(m - 3n)^2$ **67.** $(x + 6y)(x + 2y)$ **69.** $(m + 3n)(m - 8n)$ **71.** $6(x - 4)(x - 1)$ **73.** $5(x + 3)(x + 1)$
75. $2(x - 4)(x - 5)$ **77.** $b(b - 5)(b - 2)$ **79.** $3z(z - 9)(z + 2)$ **81.** $x(x + 4)^2$ **83.** $7(a - 2b)(a - 3b)$
85. $3r(r + 4t)(r - 2t)$ **87.** $x^2(x - 7)(x + 3)$ **89.** Both negative; one positive and one negative; one positive and one negative;
both positive   **91.** $x^2 - 12x + 32 = (x - 8)(x - 4)$ **93.** $x^2 - 2x - 35 = (x - 7)(x + 5)$ **95.** $(x + 0.4)(x + 0.2)$
97. $\left(x + \dfrac{1}{5}\right)\left(x + \dfrac{1}{5}\right) = \left(x + \dfrac{1}{5}\right)^2$ **99.** $(x + 8)(x - 32)$ **101.** 9   **102.** 19.6%   **103.**   **104.** $2x^3 + x^2 - 16x + 12$
105. $3x + 2 - \dfrac{2}{x - 4}$ **106.** $(5x + 2)(4x - 3)$

Using Your Graphing Calculator, 7.4   **1.** $(3x + 4)(2x - 7)$ **2.** $(5x - 8)(2x + 3)$ **3.** $(6x - 7)(2x + 5)$ **4.** $(9x + 4)(3x + 5)$

Exercise Set 7.4   **1.** Factoring trinomials is the reverse process of multiplying binomials.   **3.** The first term of the trinomial, ax^2
5. $(2x + 1)(x + 5)$ **7.** $(3x + 2)(x + 4)$ **9.** $(5x + 1)(x - 2)$ **11.** $(3r - 2)(r + 5)$ **13.** $(2z - 3)^2$ **15.** $(2z + 3)(3z - 4)$
17. Prime   **19.** $(8x + 3)(x + 2)$ **21.** Prime   **23.** $(5y - 1)(y - 3)$ **25.** $(7x + 1)(x + 6)$ **27.** $(2x + 5)(2x - 3)$ **29.** $(7t - 1)^2$
31. $(5z + 4)(z - 2)$ **33.** $(4y - 3)(y + 2)$ **35.** $(5x - 1)(2x - 5)$ **37.** $(5d + 4)(2d - 3)$ **39.** $2(4x + 1)(x - 6)$
41. $(7t + 3)(t + 1)$ **43.** $2(3x + 5)(x + 1)$ **45.** $x(2x + 1)(3x - 4)$ **47.** $4x(3x + 1)(x + 2)$ **49.** $2x(2x + 3)(x - 2)$
51. $8(2c - 1)(3c + 2)$ **53.** $4(2p + 3)(p - 1)$ **55.** $(8c + d)(c + 5d)$ **57.** $(5x + 3y)(3x - 2y)$ **59.** $2(2x - y)(3x + 4y)$
61. $(7p + 6q)(p + q)$ **63.** $(3m - 2n)(2m + n)$ **65.** $x(4x + 3y)(2x + y)$ **67.** $x^2(2x + y)(2x + 3y)$ **69.** $3x^2 - 20x - 7$; obtained by multiplying the factors.   **71.** $10x^2 + 35x + 15$; obtained by multiplying the factors.   **73.** $3t^4 + 11t^3 - 4t^2$; obtained by multiplying the factors.   **75. a)** Dividing the trinomial by the binomial gives the second factor.   **b)** $6x + 11$ **77.** $(6x - 5)(3x + 4)$
79. $(5x - 8)(3x - 20)$ **81.** $5(3a - 8)(7a + 4)$ **83.** $2x + 45$, the product of the three first terms must equal $6x^3$, and the product
of the constants must equal 2250.   **85.** 49   **86.** ≈ 142.56 mph   **87.** $12xy^2(3x^3y - 1 + 2x^4y^4)$ **88.** $(b + 12)(b - 8)$

Mid-Chapter Test: Sections 7.1–7.4   **1.** A factoring problem may be checked by multiplying the factors. [7.1]
2. $3xy^2$ [7.1]   **3.** $4a^2b(b^2 - 6a)$ [7.1]   **4.** $(d - 6)(5c - 3)$ [7.1]   **5.** $(2x + 9)(7x + 1)$ [7.1]   **6.** $(x + 4)(x + 7)$ [7.2]
7. $(x + 5)(x - 3)$ [7.2]   **8.** $(2a + 5b)(3a - b)$ [7.2]   **9.** $(5x - 2y)(x - 9)$ [7.2]   **10.** $4x(2x + 1)(x - 6)$ [7.2]
11. $(x - 3)(x - 7)$ [7.3]   **12.** $(t + 4)(t + 5)$ [7.3]   **13.** Prime [7.3]   **14.** $(x + 8)^2$ [7.3]   **15.** $(m + 5n)(m - 9n)$ [7.3]
16. $(3x + 2)(x + 5)$ [7.4]   **17.** $(4z - 3)(z - 2)$ [7.4]   **18.** Prime [7.4]   **19.** $(3x - 1)^2$ [7.4]   **20.** $3(2a - b)(a + b)$ [7.4]

Exercise Set 7.5   **1. a)** $a^2 - b^2 = (a + b)(a - b)$ **b)** Answers will vary.   **3. a)** $a^3 + b^3 = (a + b)(a^2 - ab + b^2)$
b) Answers will vary.   **5.** No   **7.** Prime   **9.** $3(b^2 + 16)$ **11.** $4(4m^2 + 9n^2)$ **13.** $(y + 5)(y - 5)$ **15.** $(9 + z)(9 - z)$
17. $(x + 7)(x - 7)$ **19.** $(x + y)(x - y)$ **21.** $(3y + 5z)(3y - 5z)$ **23.** $4(4a + 3b)(4a - 3b)$ **25.** $(6 + 7x)(6 - 7x)$
27. $(z^2 + 9x)(z^2 - 9x)$ **29.** $(5x^2 + 7y^2)(5x^2 - 7y^2)$ **31.** $(6m^2 + 7n)(6m^2 - 7n)$ **33.** $2(x^2 + 5y)(x^2 - 5y)$
35. $(x^2 + 9)(x + 3)(x - 3)$ **37.** $(x + y)(x^2 - xy + y^2)$ **39.** $(x - y)(x^2 + xy + y^2)$ **41.** $(x + 4)(x^2 - 4x + 16)$
43. $(x - 3)(x^2 + 3x + 9)$ **45.** $(a + 1)(a^2 - a + 1)$ **47.** $(3x - 1)(9x^2 + 3x + 1)$ **49.** $(3a - 5)(9a^2 + 15a + 25)$
51. $(3 - 2y)(9 + 6y + 4y^2)$ **53.** $(4m + 3n)(16m^2 - 12mn + 9n^2)$ **55.** $(2a - 3b)(4a^2 + 6ab + 9b^2)$ **57.** $4(x - 3)^2$
59. $2(5x + 2)(5x - 3)$ **61.** $2(d + 4)^2$ **63.** $5(x - 3)(x + 1)$ **65.** $5(x + 2)(x - 2)$ **67.** $2(x + 5)(x - 5)$
69. $2y(x + 3)(x - 3)$ **71.** $3y^2(x + 1)(x^2 - x + 1)$ **73.** $2(x - 2)(x^2 + 2x + 4)$ **75.** $2(3x + 5)(3x - 5)$ **77.** $3r(2t^2 - 5t + 7)$
79. $2(3x - 2)(x + 4)$ **81.** $2r(s + 3)(s - 8)$ **83.** $(x + 2)(4x - 3)$ **85.** $25(b + 2)(b - 2)$ **87.** $a^3b^2(a + 2b)(a - 2b)$
89. $5x^2(x + 1)^2$ **91.** $x(x^2 + 25)$ **93.** $(y^2 + 4)(y + 2)(y - 2)$ **95.** $2(2m + 5)(4m^2 - 10m + 25)$ **97.** $(a + b)(c + 2)$
99. $9(1 + y^2)(1 + y)(1 - y)$ **101.** You cannot divide both sides of the equation by $a - b$ because it equals 0.
103. $2\blacklozenge^4(\blacklozenge^2 + 2\maltese^2)$ **105.** $(x^2 - 3y^3)(x^4 + 3x^2y^3 + 9y^6)$ **107.** $(x - 3 + 2y)(x - 3 - 2y)$ **109.** $(x + y + 3)(x - y + 7)$
110. $x \le 1$;   ⟵———•⟶   **111.** 4 inches   **112.** -9 **113.** $\dfrac{8x^9}{27y^{12}}$ **114.** $\dfrac{1}{a^{11}}$

Using Your Graphing Calculator, 7.6   **1.** $4, -2$ **2.** $2, 5$ **3.** $2, 1$ **4.** $-1, 5$

Exercise Set 7.6   **1.** Answers will vary.   **3.** $ax^2 + bx + c = 0, a \neq 0$ **5. a)** The zero-factor property may only be used when one side of the equation is equal to 0.   **b)** $-2, 3$ **7.** $-6, 7$ **9.** $0, 8$ **11.** $-\frac{7}{3}, \frac{11}{2}$ **13.** $4, -4$ **15.** $0, 12$ **17.** $0, -7$ **19.** 4

21. $-2, -10$ **23.** $-2, -10$ **25.** $-3, 4$ **27.** $1, -24$ **29.** $-5, -6$ **31.** $5, -3$ **33.** $30, -1$ **35.** $-3, -\frac{5}{4}$ **37.** $-\frac{1}{3}, -2$ **39.** $\frac{2}{3}, -5$

41. $-4, 3$ **43.** $-\frac{3}{4}, \frac{1}{2}$ **45.** $8, -8$ **47.** $0, 25$ **49.** $10, -10$ **51.** $-2, 5$ **53.** $-2, \frac{1}{3}$ **55.** $\frac{3}{2}, 6$

57. $x^2 - 2x - 24 = 0$ (other answers are possible)   **59.** $x^2 - 6x = 0$ (other answers are possible)   **61. a)** $(2x - 1)$ and $(3x + 1)$

b) $6x^2 - x - 1 = 0$ **63.** $4, 5$ **65.** $0, 3, -2$ **67.** $\frac{17}{45}$ **68. a)** Identity   **b)** Contradiction   **69.** ≈ 738 people   **70.** $\frac{9}{p^8 q^2}$
71. Monomial   **72.** Binomial   **73.** Not a polynomial   **74.** Trinomial

Exercise Set 7.7   **1.** A triangle with a 90° angle   **3.** $(\text{leg})^2 + (\text{leg})^2 = (\text{hypotenuse})^2$ or $a^2 + b^2 = c^2$ **5.** 3 **7.** 13 **9.** 18
11. 39 **13.** $9, 13$ **15.** $6, 14$ **17.** $16, 18$ **19.** Width: 3 feet; length: 12 feet   **21.** Width: 10 feet; length: 15 feet   **23.** 4 meters
25. 4 seconds   **27.** Yes   **29.** Yes   **31.** 16 feet   **33.** 41 feet   **35.** 6 feet, 8 feet, 10 feet   **37.** Width: 9 inches; length: 12 inches
39. Width: 7 feet; length: 24 feet   **41.** 30 books   **43. a)** 4 **b)** 9 **45.** 432 square feet   **47.** $0, 8, -4$ **49.** $x^3 - x^2 - 6x = 0$
51. 3 and 6   **55.** $3x - 7$ **56.** $-x^2 + 7x - 4$ **57.** $6x^3 + x^2 - 10x + 4$ **58.** $2x - 3$ **59.** $2x - 3$

Chapter 7 Review Exercises   **1.** y^3 **2.** $3p$ **3.** $6c^2$ **4.** $5x^2 y^2$ **5.** 1 **6.** s **7.** $x - 3$ **8.** $x + 5$ **9.** $7(x - 5)$
10. $5(7x - 1)$ **11.** $4y(6y - 1)$ **12.** $5p^2(11p - 4)$ **13.** $12ab(5a - 3b)$ **14.** $9xy(1 - 4x^2 y)$ **15.** $4x^3 y^2(5 + 2x^6 y - 4x^2)$
16. Prime   **17.** Prime   **18.** $(5x + 3)(x - 2)$ **19.** $(x - 1)(3x + 4)$ **20.** $(4x - 3)(2x + 1)$ **21.** $(x + 6)(x + 2)$
22. $(x - 5)(x + 4)$ **23.** $(y - 6)^2$ **24.** $(y + 1)(3x + 2)$ **25.** $(a - b)(4a - 1)$ **26.** $(x + 6)(2x - 1)$ **27.** $(x + 3)(x - 2y)$
28. $(5x - y)(x + 4y)$ **29.** $(x + 3y)(4x - 5y)$ **30.** $(3a - 5b)(2a - b)$ **31.** $(p - 3)(q + 4)$ **32.** $(x - 3y)(3x + 2y)$
33. $(a + 2b)(7a - b)$ **34.** $(2x - 1)(4x + 3)$ **35.** $(x - 3)(x + 2)$ **36.** Prime   **37.** $(x + 2)(x + 9)$ **38.** $(n + 8)(n - 5)$
39. $(b + 5)(b - 4)$ **40.** $(x - 8)(x - 7)$ **41.** Prime   **42.** Prime   **43.** $x(x - 9)(x - 8)$ **44.** $t(t - 9)(t + 4)$
45. $(x + 3y)(x - 5y)$ **46.** $4x(x + 5y)(x + 3y)$ **47.** $(2x + 5)(x - 3)$ **48.** $(6x + 1)(x - 5)$ **49.** $(4x - 5)(x - 1)$
50. $(5m - 4)(m - 2)$ **51.** $(4y + 3)(4y - 1)$ **52.** $(5x - 2)(x - 6)$ **53.** Prime   **54.** $(5x - 3)(x + 8)$ **55.** $(2s + 1)(3s + 5)$
56. $(3x - 2)(2x + 5)$ **57.** $2(3x + 2)(2x - 1)$ **58.** $(5x - 3)^2$ **59.** $x(3x - 2)^2$ **60.** $2x(3x + 4)(3x - 2)$
61. $(2a - 3b)(2a - 5b)$ **62.** $(8a + b)(2a - 3b)$ **63.** $(x + 10)(x - 10)$ **64.** $(x + 6)(x - 6)$ **65.** $3(x + 4)(x - 4)$
66. $9(3x + y)(3x - y)$ **67.** $(9 + a)(9 - a)$ **68.** $(8 + x)(8 - x)$ **69.** $(4x^2 + 7y)(4x^2 - 7y)$ **70.** $(8x^3 + 7y^3)(8x^3 - 7y^3)$
71. $(a + b)(a^2 - ab + b^2)$ **72.** $(x - y)(x^2 + xy + y^2)$ **73.** $(x - 1)(x^2 + x + 1)$ **74.** $(x + 2)(x^2 - 2x + 4)$
75. $(a + 3)(a^2 - 3a + 9)$ **76.** $(b - 4)(b^2 + 4b + 16)$ **77.** $(5a + b)(25a^2 - 5ab + b^2)$ **78.** $(3 - 2y)(9 + 6y + 4y^2)$
79. $3(x - 4y)(x^2 + 4xy + 16y^2)$ **80.** $3(3x^2 + 5y)(3x^2 - 5y)$ **81.** $(x - 6)(x - 8)$ **82.** $3(x - 3)^2$ **83.** $5(q + 1)(q - 1)$
84. $8(x + 3)(x - 1)$ **85.** $4(y + 3)(y - 3)$ **86.** $(x - 9)(x + 3)$ **87.** $(3x - 1)^2$ **88.** $(7x - 3)(x + 4)$
89. $6(b - 1)(b^2 + b + 1)$ **90.** $y(x - 3)(x^2 + 3x + 9)$ **91.** $b(a + 3)(a - 5)$ **92.** $3x(2x + 3)(x + 5)$ **93.** $(x - 3y)(x - y)$
94. $(3m - 4n)(m + 2n)$ **95.** $(2x + 3y)^2$ **96.** $(5a + 7b)(5a - 7b)$ **97.** $(x + 2)(y - 7)$ **98.** $y^5(4 + 5y)(4 - 5y)$
99. $(2x - 3y)(3x + 7y)$ **100.** $2x(2x + 5y)(x + 2y)$ **101.** $x^2(4x + 1)(4x - 3)$ **102.** $(d^2 + 4)(d + 2)(d - 2)$ **103.** $0, -9$

104. $2, -6$ **105.** $-5, \frac{3}{4}$ **106.** $0, -7$ **107.** $0, -5$ **108.** $0, -3$ **109.** $-3, -6$ **110.** $1, 2$ **111.** $-4, 3$ **112.** $-1, -4$ **113.** $2, 4$

114. $3, -5$ **115.** $\frac{1}{4}, -\frac{3}{2}$ **116.** $-\frac{1}{3}, 4$ **117.** $2, -2$ **118.** $\frac{10}{7}, -\frac{10}{7}$ **119.** $\frac{3}{2}, \frac{1}{4}$ **120.** $\frac{3}{2}, \frac{5}{2}$ **121.** $a^2 + b^2 = c^2$ **122.** Hypotenuse
123. 10 feet   **124.** 12 meters   **125.** $9, 11$ **126.** $4, 14$ **127.** Width: 12 feet; length: 15 feet   **128.** 8 feet, 15 feet, 17 feet
129. 9 inches   **130.** 10 feet   **131.** 1 second   **132.** 80 dozen

Chapter 7 Practice Test   **1.** $3y^3$ [7.1]   **2.** $8p^2 q^2$ [7.1]   **3.** $5x^2 y^2(y - 3x^3)$ [7.1]   **4.** $4a^2 b(2a - 3b + 7)$ [7.1]

5. $(x - 5)(4x + 1)$ [7.2]   **6.** $(a - 4b)(a - 5b)$ [7.2]   **7.** $(r + 8)(r - 3)$ [7.3]   **8.** $(5a - 3b)(5a + 2b)$ [7.4]   **9.** $4(x + 2)(x - 6)$ [7.4]

10. $y(2y - 3)(y + 1)$ [7.4]   **11.** $(3x + 2)(4x - 3y)$ [7.4]   **12.** $(x + 3y)(x - 3y)$ [7.5]   **13.** $(x - 4)(x^2 + 4x + 16)$ [7.5]

14. $\frac{5}{6}, -3$ [7.6]   **15.** $0, 6$ [7.6]   **16.** $-8, 8$ [7.6]   **17.** -9 [7.6]   **18.** $3, 4$ [7.6]   **19.** $-2, -3$ [7.6]   **20.** 24 inches [7.7]   **21.** 34 feet [7.7]

22. $4, 9$ [7.7]   **23.** $12, 14$ [7.7]   **24.** Length: 6 meters; width: 4 meters [7.7]   **25.** 10 seconds [7.7]

Cumulative Review Test   **1.** -171 [1.9]   **2.** 9 [1.9]   **3.** \$90 [3.2]   **4. a)** 7 **b)** $-6, -0.2, \frac{3}{5}, 7, 0, -\frac{5}{9}, 1.34$ **c)** $\sqrt{7}, -\sqrt{2}$

d) $-6, -0.2, \frac{3}{5}, \sqrt{7}, -\sqrt{2}, 7, 0, -\frac{5}{9}, 1.34$ [1.4]   **5.** $|-8|$ [1.5]   **6.** 13 [2.5]   **7.** 19.2 [2.7]   **8.** $x \geq 5$; [2.8]

9. $y = -\frac{4}{3}x + \frac{7}{3}$ [2.6]   **10.** 6 liters [3.4]   **11.** $\frac{1}{4}$ hour [3.4]   **12.** $y = \frac{3}{5}x + \frac{26}{5}$ [4.4]   **13.** $(-3, -4)$ [5.2]   **14.** $\frac{16y^6}{x^3}$ [6.2]

15. $-3x^3 + 2x^2 + 6x - 12$ [6.4]   **16.** $3x^3 + 13x^2 - 28x + 12$ [6.5]   **17.** $x - 5 + \frac{21}{x + 3}$ [6.6]   **18.** $(r + 2)(q - 8)$ [7.2]

19. $(5x + 3)(x - 2)$ [7.4]   **20.** $7y(y + 3)(y - 3)$ [7.5]

Chapter 8

Using Your Graphing Calculator, 8.1　**1.** Yes　**2.** Yes　**3.** No　**4.** Yes

Exercise Set 8.1　**1. a–b)** Answers will vary.　**3.** We assume that the value of the variable does not make the denominator equal to 0.　**5.** There is no factor common in both the numerator and the denominator.　**7.** The denominator cannot be 0.
9. $x \neq 2$　**11.** No　**13.** All real numbers except $x = 0$.　**15.** All real numbers except $n = 4$.　**17.** All real numbers except $x = 2$ and $x = -2$.　**19.** All real numbers except $x = \dfrac{3}{2}$ and $x = 3$.　**21.** All real numbers　**23.** All real numbers except $p = \dfrac{5}{2}$ and $p = -\dfrac{5}{2}$

25. $\dfrac{x}{3y^4}$　**27.** $\dfrac{4}{b^5}$　**29.** $\dfrac{2}{1+y}$　**31.** 5　**33.** $\dfrac{x^2 + 6x + 7}{2}$　**35.** $r + 1$　**37.** $\dfrac{x}{x+2}$　**39.** $\dfrac{z-5}{z+5}$　**41.** $\dfrac{x+1}{x+2}$　**43.** -1

45. $-(x+2)$　**47.** $-\dfrac{x+6}{2x}$　**49.** $-(x+3)$　**51.** $\dfrac{1}{4m-5}$　**53.** $\dfrac{x-5}{x+5}$　**55.** $2x - 3$　**57.** $x - 3$　**59.** $\dfrac{x-4}{x+4}$

61. $a^2 + 2a + 4$　**63.** $3s + 4t$　**65.** $\dfrac{3}{x-y}$　**67.** $\dfrac{\smiley}{5}$　**69.** $\dfrac{\Delta}{2\Delta + 9}$　**71.** -1　**73.** $x + 2; (x+2)(x-3) = x^2 - x - 6$

75. $x^2 + 9x + 20; (x+5)(x+4) = x^2 + 9x + 20$　**77. a)** $x \neq -3, x \neq 2$　**b)** $\dfrac{1}{x+3}$　**79. a)** $x \neq 0, x \neq -5, x \neq \dfrac{3}{2}$

b) $\dfrac{1}{x(2x-3)}$　**81.** 1, the numerator and denominator are identical.　**84.** $y = x - 4z$　**85.** $28°, 58°$, and $94°$　**86.** $\dfrac{25}{81x^4y^2}$

87. $8x^2 - 10x - 19$　**88.** $3(a+4)(a-6)$　**89.** 13 inches

Exercise Set 8.2　**1.** Answers will vary.　**3.** $x^2 + x - 20$; the numerator must be $(x-4)(x+5)$

5. $x^2 + 2x - 35$; the denominator must be $(x+7)(x-5)$　**7.** $\dfrac{6}{19}$　**9.** $-\dfrac{15}{18}$　**11.** $\dfrac{5}{16}$　**13.** $\dfrac{3}{5}$　**15.** $-\dfrac{13}{48}$　**17.** $\dfrac{xy}{8}$　**19.** $\dfrac{70x^4}{y^6}$

21. $\dfrac{36x^9y^2}{25z^7}$　**23.** $\dfrac{-3x+2}{3x+2}$　**25.** 1　**27.** $\dfrac{1}{a^2 - b^2}$　**29.** 1　**31.** $\dfrac{x+2}{x+3}$　**33.** $x + 9$　**35.** $4x^2y$　**37.** $\dfrac{9z}{x}$　**39.** $\dfrac{11}{6ab^2}$　**41.** $6r^2$　**43.** $x + 9$

45. $\dfrac{x-8}{x+2}$　**47.** $\dfrac{x+3}{x-1}$　**49.** -1　**51.** $\dfrac{x+1}{x-4}$　**53.** $4x^2y^2$　**55.** $\dfrac{7c}{5ab^2}$　**57.** $\dfrac{3y^2}{a^2}$　**59.** $\dfrac{8mx^7}{3y^2}$　**61.** $\dfrac{2(x+3)}{x(x-3)}$　**63.** $\dfrac{7x}{y}$　**65.** $\dfrac{4}{m^4n^{11}}$

67. $\dfrac{r+2}{r-3}$　**69.** $\dfrac{x-6}{x-3}$　**71.** $\dfrac{2w-7}{w+1}$　**73.** $\dfrac{q-5}{2q+3}$　**75.** $\dfrac{2n+3}{3n-1}$　**77.** $\dfrac{1}{6\Delta^3}$　**79.** $\dfrac{\Delta + \smiley}{9(\Delta - \smiley)}$　**81.** $x^2 + 5x + 6$　**83.** $x^2 - 4x - 12$

85. $x^2 - 3x + 2$　**87.** $\dfrac{x-3}{x+3}$　**89.** $\dfrac{x-1}{x-3}$　**91.** $x^2 - 5x + 6, x^2 - x - 20$　**94.** 1 hour　**95.** $12x^4y^5z^{11}$　**96.** $2x^2 + x - 2 - \dfrac{2}{2x-1}$
97. $6(x-5)(x+2)$　**98.** $5, -2$

Exercise Set 8.3　**1.** Answers will vary.　**3.** Answers will vary.　**5.** $x(x+6)$　**7.** $4x(x+3)$　**9. a)** The negative sign in $-(2x-7)$ was not distributed.　**b)** $\dfrac{4x - 3 - 2x + 9}{5x + 4}$　**11. a)** The negative sign in $-(3x^2 - 4x + 5)$ was not distributed.

b) $\dfrac{8x - 2 - 3x^2 + 4x - 5}{x^2 - 4x + 3}$　**13.** $\dfrac{6}{7}$　**15.** $\dfrac{5r-1}{4}$　**17.** $\dfrac{x+6}{x}$　**19.** $\dfrac{n+8}{n+1}$　**21.** $\dfrac{5x+9}{x-3}$　**23.** $\dfrac{t+3}{5t^2}$　**25.** $\dfrac{1}{x-4}$　**27.** $\dfrac{1}{m-3}$

29. $\dfrac{p-12}{p-5}$　**31.** $x - 3$　**33.** $\dfrac{1}{2}$　**35.** 1　**37.** 4　**39.** $\dfrac{5}{x-2}$　**41.** $\dfrac{3}{4}$　**43.** $\dfrac{x-5}{x+2}$　**45.** $\dfrac{3x+2}{x-4}$　**47.** $\dfrac{6x+1}{x-8}$　**49.** 5　**51.** $9n$
53. $15x$　**55.** p^3　**57.** $3m - 4$　**59.** $6x^2$　**61.** $36x^3y$　**63.** $18r^4s^7$　**65.** $m(m+2)$　**67.** $x(x+1)$　**69.** $4n - 1$ or $1 - 4n$

71. $4k - 5r$ or $-4k + 5r$　**73.** $18q(q+1)$　**75.** $120x^2y^3$　**77.** $6(x+4)(x+2)$　**79.** $(x+1)(x+8)$　**81.** $(x-8)(x+3)(x+8)$

83. $(a-4)^2(a-3)$　**85.** $(x+5)(x+1)(x+3)$　**87.** $(x-3)^2$　**89.** $(x-6)(x-1)$　**91.** $(3t-2)(t+4)(3t-1)$

93. $(2x+1)^2(4x+3)$　**95.** $\dfrac{19}{35}$　**97.** $\dfrac{35}{36}$　**99.** $\dfrac{1}{18}$　**101.** $x^2 + x - 9$; the sum of the numerators must be $2x^2 - 5x - 6$

103. $x^2 + 9x - 10$; the sum of the numerators must be $5x - 7$　**105.** $5\smiley$　**107.** $(\Delta + 3)(\Delta - 3)$　**109.** $\dfrac{-3x^2 + 12x}{x^2 - 25}$　**111.** $30x^{12}y^9$

113. $(x-4)(x+3)(x-2)$　**115.** $\dfrac{92}{45}$ or $2\dfrac{2}{45}$　**116.** $-\dfrac{1}{5}$　**117.** 2.25 ounces　**118.** 70 hours　**119.** 1　**120.** 4.0×10^{11}　**121.** $\dfrac{3}{2}, -1$

Exercise Set 8.4　**1.** For each fraction, divide the LCD by the denominator.　**3. a)** Answers will vary.

b) $\dfrac{x^2 + x - 9}{(x+2)(x-3)(x-2)}$　**5. a)** $12z^2$　**b)** $\dfrac{3yz + 10}{12z^2}$　**c)** Yes　**7.** $\dfrac{3x+2y}{xy}$　**9.** $\dfrac{x+10}{2x^2}$　**11.** $\dfrac{3x+8}{x}$　**13.** $\dfrac{3x+10}{5x^2}$

15. $\dfrac{45y + 12x}{20x^2y^2}$ **17.** $\dfrac{4y^2 + x}{y}$ **19.** $\dfrac{9a + 1}{6a}$ **21.** $\dfrac{6x^2 + 2y}{xy}$ **23.** $\dfrac{45a^2 - 4b}{5a^2b}$ **25.** $\dfrac{13x - 12}{x(x - 3)}$ **27.** $\dfrac{11p + 6}{p(p + 3)}$ **29.** $\dfrac{-d^2 + 14d + 25}{(d + 1)(3d + 5)}$

31. $\dfrac{6}{p - 3}$ **33.** $\dfrac{14}{x + 7}$ **35.** $\dfrac{a + 16}{2(a - 2)}$ **37.** $\dfrac{20x}{(x - 5)(x + 5)}$ **39.** $\dfrac{-7n - 6}{3n(2n + 1)}$ **41.** $\dfrac{15w + 66}{2(w + 5)(w + 2)}$ **43.** $\dfrac{5z - 16}{(z + 4)(z - 4)}$

45. $\dfrac{-x + 6}{(x + 2)(x - 2)}$ **47.** $\dfrac{r + 12}{(r - 4)(r - 6)}$ **49.** $\dfrac{6x - 11}{(x + 4)(x - 2)}$ **51.** $\dfrac{x^2 + 3x - 21}{(x + 5)^2}$ **53.** $\dfrac{-a + 16}{(a - 8)(a - 1)(a + 2)}$

55. $\dfrac{9x + 17}{(x + 3)^2(x - 2)}$ **57.** $\dfrac{3x^2 - 12x - 5}{(2x + 1)(3x - 2)(x + 3)}$ **59.** $\dfrac{2x^2 - 3x - 4}{(4x + 3)(x + 2)(2x - 1)}$ **61.** $\dfrac{1}{w - 3}$ **63.** $\dfrac{6}{r - 3}$ **65.** $-\dfrac{x + 4}{4x}$

67. All real numbers except $x = 0$.   **69.** All real numbers except $x = 4$ and $x = -6$.   **71.** $\dfrac{7}{\Delta - 2}$ **73.** All real numbers except

$a = -b$ and $a = 0$.   **75.** 0   **77.** $\dfrac{2x - 3}{2 - x}$ **79.** $\dfrac{6x + 5}{(x + 2)(x - 3)(x + 1)}$ **82.** ≈ 1.53 hours   **83.** $x > -8$; $\xleftarrow{\quad\bullet\quad}{\xrightarrow{}}$
$\qquad\;\; -8$

84. $4x - 3 - \dfrac{6}{2x + 3}$ **85.** -1

Mid-Chapter Test

1. All real numbers except $x = \dfrac{2}{3}$ [8.1]   **2.** All real numbers except $x = -2, x = 7$ [8.1]   **3.** 9 [8.1]

4. $\dfrac{2x + 3}{3x - 1}$ [8.1]   **5.** $5r + 6t$ [8.1]   **6.** $\dfrac{6y^3}{x^3}$ [8.2]   **7.** $-(m + 4)$ or $-m - 4$ [8.2]   **8.** $x - 2$ [8.2]   **9.** $\dfrac{x + 7}{2(x + 1)}$ [8.2]

10. $\dfrac{5x + 2}{7x + 3}$ [8.2]   **11.** $x - 6$ [8.3]   **12.** $x - 3$ [8.3]   **13.** $\dfrac{3x + 2}{4x - 1}$ [8.3]   **14.** $3m(2m + 1)$ [8.3]   **15.** $(2x + 3)(x - 4)(x - 5)$ [8.3]

16. $\dfrac{13x - 1}{10x}$ [8.4]   **17.** $-\dfrac{a^2 + 13a + 23}{a^2 - a - 12}$ [8.4]   **18.** $\dfrac{4x^2 + 17x - 1}{2x^2 + 13x + 6}$ [8.4]   **19.** $\dfrac{x^2 - 7x - 4}{(x + 1)(x + 2)(x - 3)}$ [8.4]

20. Need common denominator of $x(x + 1)$, $\dfrac{15x + 8}{x(x + 1)}$ [8.4]

Exercise Set 8.5

1. A complex fraction is a fraction whose numerator or denominator (or both) contains a fraction.

3. a) Numerator, $\dfrac{x + 9}{4}$; denominator, $\dfrac{7}{x^2 + 5x + 6}$ **b)** Numerator, $\dfrac{1}{2y} + x$; denominator, $\dfrac{3}{y} + x^2$ **5.** $\dfrac{7}{8}$ **7.** $\dfrac{57}{32}$ **9.** $\dfrac{11}{6}$ **11.** $\dfrac{x^3y^2}{21}$

13. $\dfrac{2ab^3}{21c^2}$ **15.** $\dfrac{ab - a}{3 + a}$ **17.** $\dfrac{3}{x}$ **19.** $\dfrac{5x - 1}{4x - 1}$ **21.** $\dfrac{m - n}{m}$ **23.** $-\dfrac{a}{b}$ **25.** -1 **27.** 1   **29.** $b - a$ **31.** $\dfrac{a^2 + b}{b(b + 1)}$ **33.** $\dfrac{x^2y}{y - x}$

35. $\dfrac{ab^2 + b^2}{a^2(b + 1)}$ **37. b)–c)** $-\dfrac{224}{155}$ **39. b)–c)** $\dfrac{x - y + 6}{2x + 2y - 7}$ **41. a)** $\dfrac{\dfrac{5}{12x}}{\dfrac{8}{x^2} - \dfrac{4}{3x}}$ **b)** $\dfrac{5x}{96 - 16x}$ **43.** $\dfrac{y + x}{3xy}$ **45.** $x + y$ **47. a)** $\dfrac{2}{7}$ **b)** $\dfrac{4}{13}$

49. $\dfrac{a^3b + a^2b^3 - ab^2}{a^3 - ab^3 + 3b^2}$ **51.** $\dfrac{17}{2}$ **52.** A polynomial is an expression containing a finite number of terms of the form ax^n where a is a

real number and n is a whole number.   **53.** $(x - 5)(x - 8)$ **54.** $\dfrac{x^2 - 9x + 2}{(3x - 1)(x + 6)(x - 3)}$

Exercise Set 8.6

1. a) Answers will vary.   **b)** $\dfrac{2}{3}$ **3. a)** The problem on the left is an expression to be simplified while the

problem on the right is an equation to be solved.   **b)** Left: Write the fractions with the LCD, $12(x - 1)$, then combine numerators;

Right: Multiply both sides of the equation by the LCD, $12(x - 1)$, then solve.   **c)** Left: $\dfrac{x^2 - x + 12}{12(x - 1)}$; Right: $4, -3$ **5.** You need to

check for extraneous solutions when there is a variable in a denominator.   **7.** 2   **9.** No   **11.** Yes   **13.** 12   **15.** -4 **17.** -20 **19.** 30

21. 4   **23.** $\dfrac{25}{6}$ **25.** 36   **27.** 8   **29.** -8 **31.** 3   **33.** 4   **35.** 2   **37.** 5   **39.** No solution   **41.** 7   **43.** 15   **45.** No solution   **47.** -3

49. 38   **51.** $-\dfrac{1}{3}, 3$ **53.** $6, -1$ **55.** $4, -4$ **57.** $-4, -5$ **59.** 4   **61.** $-\dfrac{5}{2}$ **63.** No solution   **65.** 24   **67.** -12 **69.** -3 **71.** 3

73. 5   **75.** 0   **77.** x can be any real number since the sum on the left is also $\dfrac{2x - 4}{3}$.   **79.** 15 centimeters   **81.** -4 **83.** No, it is

impossible for both sides of the equation to be equal.   **85.** More than $6\dfrac{1}{3}$ hours   **86.** 150 minutes   **87.** $40°, 140°$ **88.** 6.8×10^8

89. Linear equation: $ax + b = c$, $a \neq 0$; quadratic equation: $ax^2 + bx + c = 0$, $a \neq 0$

Exercise Set 8.7

1. Some examples are $A = \dfrac{1}{2}bh$, $A = \dfrac{1}{2}h(b_1 + b_2)$, $V = \dfrac{1}{3}\pi r^2h$, and $V = \dfrac{4}{3}\pi r^3$

3. It represents 1 complete task.   **5.** length $= 11$ inches, width $= 9$ inches   **7.** base $= 12$ centimeters, height $= 7$ centimeters

9. Base: 8 feet   **11.** $\dfrac{8}{9}, 8$ **13.** 7   **15.** 9 miles per hour   **17.** 15 miles   **19.** 150 miles per hour, 600 miles per hour

21. No wake zone: ≈ 1.83 miles; zone to Island: ≈ 34.77 miles   **23.** 3 hours at 600 miles per hour and 2 hours at 550 miles per hour

25. 1200 feet   **27.** $3\dfrac{3}{7}$ hours   **29.** 4 hours   **31.** 24 minutes   **33.** 120 minutes or 2 hours.   **35.** 60 minutes or 1 hour   **37.** $8\dfrac{3}{4}$ days

39. $\dfrac{6}{5}$ hours or 1 hour, 12 minutes   **41.** 300 hours   **43.** 3 or $\dfrac{1}{2}$ **45.** 8 pints   **47.** $-\dfrac{3}{2}x - \dfrac{7}{2}$ **48.**

49. 1   **50.** $\dfrac{3x^2 - 9x - 15}{(2x + 3)(3x - 5)(3x + 1)}$

Exercise Set 8.8

1. 30   **3.** $y = kx$ **5.** Direct   **7.** Inverse   **9.** Inverse   **11.** Direct   **13.** Direct   **15.** 44   **17.** $\dfrac{1}{5}$ **19.** 75

21. 2.5   **23.** 20   **25.** 3.5   **27.** 36   **29.** 80   **31.** It will be doubled.   **33.** It will be halved.   **35.** 110 miles   **37.** 3 hours

39. $57   **41.** 4.2 hours   **43.** 1000 people   **45.** ≈ 766.9 tons   **47.** ≈ 452.16 square inches   **49.** ≈ 44.44 ohms   **51.** $50

53. 6400 cubic centimeters   **55. a)** $x = kyz$ **b)** 216   **57.** $2x - 3 + \dfrac{6}{4x + 9}$ **58.** $(z - 2)(y + 8)$ **59.** $-4, 2$ **60.** $x + 8$

Chapter 8 Review Exercises

1. All real numbers except $x = 9$ **2.** All real numbers except $x = 3$ and $x = 5$

3. All real numbers except $x = \dfrac{1}{5}$ and $x = -1$ **4.** $\dfrac{1}{x - 3}$ **5.** $x^2 + 5x + 12$ **6.** $3x + y$ **7.** $x + 4$ **8.** $a + 9$ **9.** $-(2x + 1)$

10. $\dfrac{b - 2}{b + 2}$ **11.** $\dfrac{x - 3}{x - 2}$ **12.** $\dfrac{x - 8}{2x + 3}$ **13.** $\dfrac{5}{12b^2}$ **14.** $12xz^2$ **15.** $\dfrac{8b^3c^4}{a^2}$ **16.** $-\dfrac{1}{9}$ **17.** $-\dfrac{2}{3}$ **18.** 1   **19.** $\dfrac{36x^2}{y}$ **20.** $\dfrac{20z}{x^3}$ **21.** $\dfrac{6}{a - b}$

22. $\dfrac{1}{8(a + 3)}$ **23.** 1   **24.** $6y(x - y)$ **25.** $\dfrac{n - 2}{n + 5}$ **26.** 4   **27.** 5   **28.** $\dfrac{4}{x + 10}$ **29.** $4h - 3$ **30.** $3x + 4$ **31.** 24   **32.** $x + 3$

33. $20x^2y^3$ **34.** $x(x - 3)$ **35.** $(n + 5)(n - 4)$ **36.** $x(x + 2)$ **37.** $(r + s)(r - s)$ **38.** $x - 9$ **39.** $(x + 7)(x - 5)(x + 2)$

40. $\dfrac{3y^2 + 10}{6y^2}$ **41.** $\dfrac{12x + y}{4xy}$ **42.** $\dfrac{5x^2 - 18y}{3x^2y}$ **43.** $\dfrac{7x + 12}{x + 2}$ **44.** $\dfrac{x^2 - 2xy - y^2}{xy}$ **45.** $\dfrac{9x + 8}{x(x + 4)}$ **46.** $\dfrac{-x - 4}{3x(x - 2)}$ **47.** $\dfrac{z + 14}{(z + 5)^2}$

48. $\dfrac{2x - 8}{(x - 3)(x - 5)}$ **49.** $\dfrac{5x + 38}{(x + 6)(x + 2)}$ **50.** $\dfrac{3x - 8}{x - 4}$ **51.** $\dfrac{5ab + 10b}{a - 2}$ **52.** $\dfrac{3x - 1}{(x + 3)(x - 3)}$ **53.** $\dfrac{6p^2}{q}$ **54.** $\dfrac{2x + 2}{(x + 2)(x - 3)(x - 2)}$

55. $\dfrac{8x - 29}{(x + 2)(x - 7)(x + 7)}$ **56.** $\dfrac{x}{x + y}$ **57.** $\dfrac{3(x + 3y)}{5(x - 3y)}$ **58.** $a - 3$ **59.** $\dfrac{3a^2 - 8a + 3}{(a + 1)(a - 1)(3a - 5)}$ **60.** $\dfrac{4x - 8}{x}$ **61.** $\dfrac{68}{9}$ **62.** $\dfrac{2}{3}$

63. $\dfrac{bc}{3}$ **64.** $\dfrac{8x^3z^2}{y^3}$ **65.** $\dfrac{ab - a}{a + 1}$ **66.** $\dfrac{r^2s + 7}{s^3}$ **67.** $\dfrac{3x + 2}{x(5x - 1)}$ **68.** $\dfrac{4}{x}$ **69.** x **70.** $\dfrac{2a + 1}{4}$ **71.** $\dfrac{-x + 1}{x + 1}$ **72.** $\dfrac{8x^2 - x^2y}{y(y - x)}$ **73.** 15

74. 6   **75.** 12   **76.** 20   **77.** -16 **78.** $\dfrac{1}{2}$ **79.** -6 **80.** 28   **81.** No solution   **82.** 2.4 hours   **83.** $16\dfrac{4}{5}$ hours   **84.** $\dfrac{1}{6}, 1$

85. Robert: 2.1 miles per hour; Tran: 5.6 miles per hour   **86.** 273 milligrams   **87.** 1.68 hours

Chapter 8 Practice Test

1. 1 [8.1]   **2.** $\dfrac{x^2 + x + 1}{x + 1}$ [8.1]   **3.** $\dfrac{8x^2z}{y}$ [8.2]   **4.** $a + 3$ [8.2]   **5.** $\dfrac{x^2 - 6x + 9}{(x + 3)(x + 2)}$ [8.2]

6. -1 [8.2]   **7.** $\dfrac{x - 2y}{5}$ [8.2]   **8.** $\dfrac{3}{y + 5}$ [8.2]   **9.** $-\dfrac{m + 6}{m - 5}$ [8.2]   **10.** $\dfrac{3x - 1}{4y}$ [8.3]   **11.** $\dfrac{7x^2 - 6x - 13}{x + 3}$ [8.3]   **12.** $\dfrac{2y^2 - 8}{xy^3}$ [8.4]

13. $-\dfrac{2z + 15}{z - 5}$ [8.4]   **14.** $\dfrac{-1}{(x + 4)(x - 4)}$ [8.4]   **15.** $\dfrac{25}{28}$ [8.5]   **16.** $\dfrac{x^2 + x^2y}{7y}$ [8.5]   **17.** $\dfrac{4x + 3}{9 - 5x}$ [8.5]   **18.** 2 [8.6]   **19.** $-\dfrac{12}{7}$ [8.6]

20. 12 [8.6]   **21.** 6 hours [8.7]   **22.** 1 [8.7]   **23.** Base: 6 inches; height: 10 inches [8.7]   **24.** 2 miles [8.7]   **25.** ≈ 1.13 feet [8.8]

Cumulative Review Test

1. 121 [1.9]   **2.** 36 [1.9]   **3.** $\dfrac{17}{8}$ [2.5]   **4.** $c + (c + 0.012c)$ [3.1]   **5.** 0 [4.3]   **6.** $y = \dfrac{3}{4}x - 3$ [4.4]

7. $8x^2 + 5x + 14$ [6.4]   **8.** $6n^3 - 23n^2 + 26n - 15$ [6.5]   **9.** $\dfrac{1}{2}x - \dfrac{19}{4}$ [6.6]   **10.** $(8a - 5)(a - 1)$ [7.2]   **11.** $13(x + 3)(x - 1)$ [7.3]

12. $4, \dfrac{3}{2}$ [7.6]   **13.** $\dfrac{x + 4}{2x + 1}$ [8.2]   **14.** $\dfrac{r^2 - 8r - 6}{(r + 2)(r - 5)}$ [8.4]   **15.** $\dfrac{10x - 18}{(x - 5)(x + 2)(x + 3)}$ [8.4]   **16.** $-\dfrac{3}{2}$ [8.6]   **17.** No solution [8.6]

18. $3000 [3.2]   **19.** 20 pounds sunflower seed, 30 pounds premixed assorted seed mix; [3.4]   **20.** First leg: 3.25 miles, second leg: 9.5 miles [3.4]

Chapter 9

Using Your Calculator, 9.1   **1.** 3.872983346   **2.** 12.28820573   **3.** Error   **4.** 5.196152423

Exercise Set 9.1   **1.** The principal square root of a positive real number, a, is the positive number whose square equals a.
3. Answers will vary.   **5. a)** Answers will vary.   **b)** Check Table 9.1   **7.** Yes, since $5^2 = 25$.   **9.** No, because the square root of a
negative number is not a real number.   **11.** Yes, since $\sqrt{\dfrac{16}{25}} = \dfrac{4}{5}$ which is a rational number.   **13.** 0   **15.** 6   **17.** -7 **19.** 20

21. -4 **23.** 12   **25.** 15   **27.** -1 **29.** -12 **31.** -11 **33.** $\dfrac{1}{2}$ **35.** $\dfrac{5}{2}$ **37.** $-\dfrac{5}{6}$ **39.** $\dfrac{9}{10}$ **41.** 3.4641016   **43.** 3.8729833

45. 8.9442719   **47.** 18   **49.** 9.8488578   **51.** 5.4772256   **53.** False   **55.** True   **57.** False   **59.** True   **61.** True   **63.** True   **65.** $7^{1/2}$

67. $(29)^{1/2}$ **69.** $(8x)^{1/2}$ **71.** $(12x^2)^{1/2}$ **73.** $(17ab^2)^{1/2}$ **75.** $(38n^3)^{1/2}$ **77.** Rational: $9.83, \dfrac{3}{5}, 0.333\ldots, 5, \sqrt{\dfrac{4}{49}}, \dfrac{3}{7}, -\sqrt{9}$;

Irrational: $\sqrt{\dfrac{5}{16}}$; Imaginary: $\sqrt{-4}, -\sqrt{-16}$ **79.** 6 and 7   **81. a)** Square 4.6 and compare the result to 20.   **b)** 4.6

83. $-\sqrt{9}, -\sqrt{7}, -\dfrac{1}{2}, 2.5, \sqrt{16}, 4.01, 5, 12$ **85.** $\sqrt{4} = 2; 6^{1/2} \approx 2.45; -\sqrt{9} = -3; -(25)^{1/2} = -5; (30)^{1/2} \approx 5.48; (-4)^{1/2}$,

imaginary number   **87. a)** Yes   **b)** No   **c)** No   **d)** Yes   **e)** No   **89. a)** Yes   **b)** Yes   **c)** a **d)** Answers will vary.   **91.** $x^{3/2}$ **93.** x^3

95. 52 jumps   **96.** -6 **97.** -1 **98.** $\dfrac{5}{11}$ **99.** 6

Exercise Set 9.2   **1.** Answers will vary.   **3.** The product rule cannot be used when radicands are negative.   **5. a)** Express the
variable as the product of two factors, one of which has an exponent of 1. Use the product rule to simplify.   **b)** $x^6\sqrt{x}$
7. a) There can be no perfect square factors nor any exponents greater than 1 in the radicand of a simplified square root expression.
b) $5x^2\sqrt{3x}$ **9.** Yes   **11.** No; $4\sqrt{2}$ **13.** $3\sqrt{2}$ **15.** $2\sqrt{2}$ **17.** $2\sqrt{7}$ **19.** $2\sqrt{5}$ **21.** $4\sqrt{10}$ **23.** $4\sqrt{5}$ **25.** $6\sqrt{2}$ **27.** $2\sqrt{30}$
29. $9\sqrt{3}$ **31.** $5\sqrt{6}$ **33.** x^3 **35.** xy^4 **37.** $a^6b^4\sqrt{b}$ **39.** $ab^2\sqrt{c}$ **41.** $n\sqrt{3n}$ **43.** $6ab\sqrt{3a}$ **45.** $10a^2b^5\sqrt{3ab}$ **47.** $9xy^2\sqrt{3x}$
49. $6ab^4\sqrt{3bc}$ **51.** $6rs^5t^2\sqrt{5rt}$ **53.** 7   **55.** $6\sqrt{2}$ **57.** $12\sqrt{5}$ **59.** $x\sqrt{14}$ **61.** $4ab\sqrt{3a}$ **63.** $6xy^2\sqrt{2x}$ **65.** $3r^5s^6\sqrt{7}$
67. $3xy^3\sqrt{10yz}$ **69.** $3a^3b^5\sqrt{6}$ **71.** $2x$ **73.** $13x^4y^6$ **75.** $35a^2$ **77.** 8   **79.** Exponent on x, 12, on y, 5   **81.** Coefficient, 8; exponent
on x, 12; exponent on y, 7   **83. a)** $7x^4$ **b)** $7x^4$ **c)** Yes   **85.** $x^{1/6}$ **87.** $2x^{2/5}$ **89.** Rational, since $\sqrt{6.25} = 2.5$ and 2.5 is a terminating decimal number.   **91. a)** 4 feet   **b)** No; the area increased $\sqrt{2}$ or ≈ 1.414 times   **c)** 4 times   **93. a)** Yes   **b)** No, for example
$\sqrt{2} \cdot \sqrt{2} = 2$.   **98.** 148.5 square inches   **99.** ≈ 25.13 cubic feet   **100.** $\dfrac{3x+1}{x-1}$ **101.** $y = -\dfrac{1}{2}x + \dfrac{3}{2}; m = -\dfrac{1}{2}; \left(0, \dfrac{3}{2}\right)$

102.

103. $\left(\dfrac{1}{2}, -3\right)$

Exercise Set 9.3   **1.** Like square roots are square roots having the same radicand. One example is $\sqrt{3}$ and $5\sqrt{3}$.   **3.** Only like
square roots can be added or subtracted.   **5.** $3\sqrt{5}$ **7.** $-2\sqrt{5}$ **9.** $2\sqrt{7} + 8$ **11.** $7\sqrt{x}$ **13.** $-4\sqrt{y}$ **15.** $-4\sqrt{t} - 11$
17. $\sqrt{x} + 8\sqrt{y} + x$ **19.** $5m - 2\sqrt{m} + 9$ **21.** $-2\sqrt{7} - 9\sqrt{x}$ **23.** $2\sqrt{10} + 3\sqrt{2}$ **25.** $8\sqrt{3}$ **27.** $11\sqrt{3}$ **29.** $16\sqrt{2}$
31. $-15\sqrt{5} + 40\sqrt{3}$ **33.** $28\sqrt{10}$ **35.** $28 - 4\sqrt{3}$ **37.** $2\sqrt{3} + 3$ **39.** $3\sqrt{x} - 3\sqrt{2}$ **41.** $y\sqrt{y} + y^2$ **43.** $2\sqrt{10} - 3\sqrt{5}$
45. $x + \sqrt{3x}$ **47.** $9\sqrt{a} - a\sqrt{2}$ **49.** $x^2 + 8x\sqrt{y}$ **51.** $12x^2 - 9x\sqrt{x}$ **53.** $6 - 6\sqrt{2} + \sqrt{3} - \sqrt{6}$
55. $\sqrt{30} + 3\sqrt{5} - 4\sqrt{6} - 12$ **57.** $76 - 28\sqrt{7}$ **59.** $16 - 8\sqrt{x} + x$ **61.** $z\sqrt{15} + \sqrt{3z} - 4\sqrt{5z} - 4$ **63.** $2r^2 + 9r\sqrt{s} - 18s$
65. $2x^2 - 4x\sqrt{2y} + 4y$ **67.** $4p^2 + 6p\sqrt{3q} - 12q$ **69.** -2 **71.** 23   **73.** $x - 4$ **75.** $7 - m^2$ **77.** $5x - y$ **79.** $36x - 9y$
81. a) No   **b)** $2\sqrt{5}$ **83.** $x + 3$ **85.** Yes   **87.** 343   **89.** Perimeter: $4(\sqrt{2} + \sqrt{3})$ units; area: $5 + 2\sqrt{6}$ square units

91. Perimeter: $\sqrt{7} + \sqrt{15} + \sqrt{22}$ units; area: $\dfrac{1}{2}\sqrt{105}$ square units   **93.** 1   **95.** $\sqrt{216} = 6\sqrt{6}$ **97.** $\sqrt{72} = 6\sqrt{2}$ **99.** 48

101. 0.05 hour or 3 minutes   **102.** $3(x+4)(x-8)$ **103.** $\dfrac{x+1}{x^2+x+1}$ **104.** $6, -4$ **105.**

Exercise Set 9.4   **1.** Cannot be simplified   **3.** Simplifies to $x\sqrt{3}$ **5.** Cannot be simplified   **7.** No perfect square factors in
any radicand, no radicand contains a fraction, no square roots in any denominator   **9. a)** $\sqrt{27}$ has a perfect square factor, 9.

b) The radicand contains a fraction.   **c)** There is a square root in the denominator.   **11.** 3.   **13.** 3   **15.** 3   **17.** $\dfrac{1}{2}$ **19.** $\dfrac{9}{10}$ **21.** $\dfrac{1}{10}$

23. $2x\sqrt{6}$ **25.** $\dfrac{3\sqrt{5}}{4y^2}$ **27.** $\dfrac{4y}{9x}$ **29.** $\dfrac{1}{a^2b}$ **31.** $2n^2$ **33.** $\dfrac{3w^2}{4z}$ **35.** $\dfrac{b\sqrt{5}}{c}$ **37.** $5a^2b^3$ **39.** $\dfrac{\sqrt{7}}{7}$ **41.** $2\sqrt{2}$ **43.** $\sqrt{3}$ **45.** $\dfrac{\sqrt{10}}{5}$

47. $\dfrac{\sqrt{14}}{7}$ **49.** $\dfrac{\sqrt{3}}{3}$ **51.** $\dfrac{\sqrt{10}}{4}$ **53.** $\dfrac{\sqrt{6x}}{x}$ **55.** $\dfrac{\sqrt{ab}}{b}$ **57.** $\dfrac{\sqrt{mn}}{n}$ **59.** $\dfrac{\sqrt{33x}}{11}$ **61.** $\dfrac{x\sqrt{7}}{7}$ **63.** $\dfrac{a\sqrt{2}}{6}$ **65.** $\dfrac{t^2\sqrt{6t}}{6}$ **67.** $\dfrac{a^4\sqrt{14b}}{14b}$

69. $\dfrac{\sqrt{5d}}{5d^2}$ **71.** $\dfrac{5\sqrt{3}}{6x^2y^2z^4}$ **73.** $\dfrac{3\sqrt{5x}}{xy^2}$ **75.** 33 **77.** -8 **79.** $x-y^2$ **81.** $a-b$ **83.** $3\sqrt{5}-6$ **85.** $\dfrac{4\sqrt{6}+4}{5}$ **87.** $-6\sqrt{3}+6\sqrt{5}$

89. $\dfrac{-8\sqrt{5}-16\sqrt{2}}{3}$ **91.** $\dfrac{4\sqrt{y}-12}{y-9}$ **93.** $\dfrac{28+7\sqrt{y}}{16-y}$ **95.** $\dfrac{16\sqrt{y}-16x}{y-x^2}$ **97.** $\dfrac{9\sqrt{x}-9\sqrt{y}}{x-y}$ **99.** $\dfrac{3+\sqrt{3n}}{3-n}$ **101.** $\dfrac{12\sqrt{x}+2x}{36-x}$

103. Yes **105.** 5.40 **107.** 0.71 **109.** 7.23 **111.** 0.58 **113.** $\dfrac{24(4-\sqrt{3})}{13}$ **115.** 2 **117.** $64x^{10}$ **119.** $\dfrac{-\sqrt{x}-\sqrt{3x}}{2}$

122. $3x-8+\dfrac{6}{x+4}$ **123.** $\dfrac{9}{2},-4$ **124.** $\dfrac{-3x-5}{(x+2)(x-2)}$ **125.** 30 minutes

Mid-Chapter Test

1. 9 [9.1] **2.** -11 [9.1] **3.** $\dfrac{13}{7}$ [9.1] **4. a)** Irrational **b)** Rational **c)** Imaginary **d)** Rational [9.1]

5. $(53xy^2)^{1/2}$ [9.1] **6.** $2\sqrt{10}$ [9.2] **7.** $3\sqrt{7}$ [9.2] **8.** $ab^2c^4\sqrt{b}$ [9.2] **9.** $8x^4y^7\sqrt{2x}$ [9.2] **10.** $3x^2y^4\sqrt{6xy}$ [9.2]

11. $12\sqrt{x}+6\sqrt{5}+17$ [9.3] **12.** $8\sqrt{3}$ [9.3] **13.** $35+5\sqrt{3}-7\sqrt{2}-\sqrt{6}$ [9.3] **14.** $x+z\sqrt{x}-20z^2$ [9.3] **15.** $3a-2b$ [9.3]

16. Can add only like radicals; $\sqrt{8}$ and $\sqrt{32}$ are not like radicals. $\sqrt{8}+\sqrt{32}=2\sqrt{2}+4\sqrt{2}=6\sqrt{2}$ [9.3] **17.** $\dfrac{1}{2}$ [9.4]

18. $\dfrac{3x^2}{y}$ [9.4] **19.** $\dfrac{7\sqrt{6}+14}{2}$ [9.4] **20.** $\dfrac{3x-15\sqrt{x}}{x-25}$ [9.4]

Exercise Set 9.5

1. A radical equation is an equation that contains a variable in a radicand. **3.** It is necessary to check solutions because they may be extraneous. **5.** Yes **7.** No; $-\sqrt{64}=-8$ **9.** Yes **11.** No, $\sqrt{-9}\neq-3$ **13.** 25 **15.** 121 **17.** 4 **19.** No solution **21.** 81 **23.** 25 **25.** No solution **27.** 7 **29.** 6 **31.** 3 **33.** 2 **35.** 7 **37.** 1 **39.** 1, 9 **41.** No solution **43.** -5 **45.** 7 **47.** No solution **49.** 3 **51.** 3 **53.** 7 **55.** 11 **57.** $\sqrt{x+4}=7;45$ **59.** $\sqrt{x-2}=\sqrt{2x-9};7$ **61. a)** $x-9=40$ **b)** 49 **63. a)** $35+2\sqrt{x}-x=35$ **b)** 0, 4 **65.** 1 **67.** 25 **69.** 9 **73.**

Graph: y-axis, value 5; point (2, 0); x-axis marks -5, 5; lines labeled $3x-2y=6$ and $y=2x-4$; -5.

74. $(2,0)$ **75.** $(2,0)$
76. Ferryboat: 16 mph; current: 2 mph

Exercise Set 9.6

1. A right triangle is a triangle that contains a 90° angle. **3.** No; only with right triangles. **5.** They represent the two points in the coordinate plane that you are trying to find the distance between. **7.** 7 **9.** $\sqrt{33}\approx5.74$ **11.** $\sqrt{170}\approx13.04$
13. $\sqrt{151}\approx12.29$ **15.** $\sqrt{67}\approx8.19$ **17.** $\sqrt{202}\approx14.21$ **19.** $\sqrt{180}\approx13.42$ **21.** $\sqrt{34}\approx5.83$ **23.** $\sqrt{193}\approx13.89$
25. $\sqrt{17{,}240.89}\approx131.30$ yards **27.** $\sqrt{60}\approx7.75$ meters **29.** 16 feet **31.** $\approx\sqrt{625.80}\approx25.02$ feet **33.** $\approx\sqrt{64.01}\approx8.00$ inches
35. $\sqrt{169}=13$ inches **37.** $\sqrt{932}\approx30.53$ inches **39.** $6.28\sqrt{0.11}\approx2.08$ seconds **41.** $6.28\sqrt{1.925}\approx8.71$ seconds
43. About 365 Earth days **45.** 33 miles per hour **47.** ≈52.2 miles per hour **49.** $\sqrt{19.62(6{,}370{,}000)}\approx11{,}179.42$ meters per second
51. $\sqrt{91{,}584}\approx302.63$ feet per second **53.** ≈2.35 square meters **55.** 9 inches by 12 inches **57.** ≈3.25 feet **58.** $x>6$
59. $\dfrac{x^4}{8y^3}$ **60.** $\left(7,-\dfrac{9}{4}\right)$ **61.** $-\dfrac{16}{15}$

Using Your Calculator, 9.7 (page 576)
1. 9 **2.** 2 **3.** ≈3.76060 **4.** 10 **5.** -6 **6.** ≈-4.12892

Using Your Graphing Calculator, 9.7 (page 577)
1. 7 **2.** 6 **3.** ≈2.952591724 **4.** 14 **5.** -8 **6.** ≈-3.981071706

Using Your Calculator, 9.7 (page 580)
1. 8 **2.** 256 **3.** .04 **4.** $.0\overline{37}$

Exercise Set 9.7

1. a) The square root of 8 **b)** The cube root of 8 **c)** The fourth root of 8 **3.** Write the radicand as a product of a perfect cube and another number. **5. a)** Answers will vary. **b)** $y^{7/3}$ **7.** Yes **9.** 2 **11.** -3 **13.** 6 **15.** 1 **17.** 3 **19.** 2
21. $2\sqrt[3]{5}$ **23.** $2\sqrt[3]{2}$ **25.** $3\sqrt[4]{4}$ **27.** $2\sqrt[4]{2}$ **29.** $5\sqrt[4]{2}$ **31.** $x^{7/3}$ **33.** $a^{2/5}$ **35.** $y^{15/4}$ **37.** $y^{8/3}$ **39.** x **41.** y^4 **43.** x **45.** a^5 **47.** x^5
49. $\sqrt{m}$ **51.** $\sqrt{c}$ **53.** $\sqrt[3]{x}$ **55.** $\sqrt{w}$ **57.** $\sqrt[3]{x^2}$ **59.** $\sqrt[4]{z^3}$ **61.** 16 **63.** 81 **65.** 1 **67.** 27 **69.** 243 **71.** 64 **73.** $\dfrac{1}{2}$ **75.** $\dfrac{1}{81}$

77. 2 **79.** 3 **81.** 8 **83.** 49 **85.** 27 **87.** 36 **89.** x **91.** t **93.** r^8 **95.** a^2 **97.** both equal 9 **99.** $\sqrt[3]{4^2}$ **101.** $\sqrt[3]{6^2}$ **103.** $\sqrt[4]{7^3}$

105. 3 **107.** 1 **109.** xy **111.** $\sqrt[4]{2}$ **113. a)** $\sqrt[3]{2^3}=2$ **b)** $\dfrac{\sqrt[3]{4}}{2}$ **114.** -44 **115.** $(3x-4)(x-8)$

116. slope: $\dfrac{2}{3}$, y intercept: $\left(0,-\dfrac{4}{3}\right)$ **117.** $\dfrac{3y^3\sqrt{2xy}}{x}$

Chapter 9 Review Exercises
1. 9 **2.** 11 **3.** -7 **4.** $(15)^{1/2}$ **5.** $(41x)^{1/2}$ **6.** $(23x^2y)^{1/2}$ **7.** $2\sqrt{6}$ **8.** $2\sqrt{13}$
9. $4x^3y^2\sqrt{3xy}$ **10.** $5x^2y^4\sqrt{5}$ **11.** $2b^2c^2\sqrt{15ab}$ **12.** $6abc^3\sqrt{2c}$ **13.** $12\sqrt{10}$ **14.** $3y$ **15.** $8x\sqrt{y}$ **16.** $5xy\sqrt{2}$ **17.** $6ab^4\sqrt{a}$
18. $10ab^3\sqrt{b}$ **19.** $5\sqrt{3}$ **20.** $-5\sqrt{5}$ **21.** $6\sqrt{x}$ **22.** $-4\sqrt{k}$ **23.** $6\sqrt{2} - 3\sqrt{3}$ **24.** $11\sqrt{10}$ **25.** $-10\sqrt{2}$ **26.** $25\sqrt{2}$
27. $2\sqrt{6} + 6$ **28.** $2 + 3\sqrt{2}$ **29.** $x\sqrt{y} - 8y$ **30.** $12a^2 + 4a\sqrt{2a}$ **31.** 3 **32.** 76 **33.** $x^2 - 25y$ **34.** $c - 9d$
35. $m^2 - 3m\sqrt{r} - 10r$ **36.** $3t + 5s\sqrt{t} - 2s^2$ **37.** $15m + 17\sqrt{5mn} - 6n$ **38.** $14 - 9\sqrt{7p} + 9p$ **39.** 4 **40.** $\dfrac{1}{7}$ **41.** $\dfrac{1}{2}$
42. $\dfrac{2\sqrt{3}}{3}$ **43.** $\dfrac{\sqrt{7n}}{7}$ **44.** $\dfrac{\sqrt{15a}}{6}$ **45.** $\dfrac{x\sqrt{5}}{5}$ **46.** $\dfrac{z^3\sqrt{2}}{4}$ **47.** $y^2\sqrt{7}$ **48.** $\dfrac{x\sqrt{2y}}{y^2}$ **49.** $\dfrac{2\sqrt{5a}}{3a^2b}$ **50.** $\dfrac{c\sqrt{14a}}{7a}$ **51.** $\dfrac{-2 - 2\sqrt{6}}{5}$
52. $\dfrac{12 + 4\sqrt{6}}{3}$ **53.** $\dfrac{2\sqrt{3} - \sqrt{3y}}{4 - y}$ **54.** $\dfrac{3\sqrt{x} + 15}{x - 25}$ **55.** $\dfrac{\sqrt{10x} - \sqrt{30}}{x - 3}$ **56.** $\dfrac{\sqrt{35} + x\sqrt{7}}{5 - x^2}$ **57.** 49 **58.** No solution **59.** 15
60. 7 **61.** 2 **62.** 4 **63.** 3 **64.** 7 **65.** 2 **66.** 26 **67.** $\sqrt{125} \approx 11.18$ **68.** $\sqrt{12} \approx 3.46$ **69.** $\sqrt{61} \approx 7.81$
70. $\sqrt{128} \approx 11.31$ feet **71.** $\sqrt{325} \approx 18.03$ inches **72.** $\sqrt{109} \approx 10.44$ **73.** $\sqrt{153} \approx 12.37$ **74.** 561.18 square inches
75. $\sqrt{60} \approx 7.75$ miles **76.** ≈ 646 feet **77.** 2 **78.** -4 **79.** 2 **80.** 3 **81.** $2\sqrt[3]{2}$ **82.** $-2\sqrt[3]{2}$ **83.** $2\sqrt[3]{6}$ **84.** $2\sqrt[4]{2}$ **85.** $3\sqrt[3]{2}$
86. $2\sqrt[4]{5}$ **87.** x^7 **88.** s^{12} **89.** 9 **90.** 6 **91.** $\dfrac{1}{9}$ **92.** 256 **93.** $\dfrac{1}{625}$ **94.** 243 **95.** $x^{5/2}$ **96.** $a^{7/2}$ **97.** $z^{11/3}$ **98.** $x^{10/3}$ **99.** $y^{13/4}$
100. $m^{6/4} = m^{3/2}$ **101.** x **102.** $\sqrt[3]{x^2}$ **103.** a^4 **104.** x^2 **105.** q^3 **106.** b^2 **107.** x^6 **108.** x^{10}

Chapter 9 Practice Test
1. $(5x)^{1/2}$ [9.1] **2.** $\sqrt[4]{x^3}$ [9.1] **3.** 13 [9.1] **4.** $3\sqrt{10}$ [9.2] **5.** $2x\sqrt{3}$ [9.2] **6.** $5x^3y\sqrt{3xy}$ [9.2]
7. $4xy\sqrt{5x}$ [9.3] **8.** $5x^2y^2\sqrt{2y}$ [9.3] **9.** $\dfrac{1}{5}$ [9.4] **10.** $\dfrac{c^2}{d}$ [9.4] **11.** $\dfrac{\sqrt{5}}{5}$ [9.4] **12.** $\dfrac{3\sqrt{5r}}{5}$ [9.4] **13.** $\dfrac{2\sqrt{30x}}{3xy}$ [9.4] **14.** $-4 - 2\sqrt{7}$ [9.4]
15. $\dfrac{7\sqrt{x} + 21}{x - 9}$ [9.4] **16.** $16\sqrt{3}$ [9.3] **17.** $5\sqrt{y}$ [9.3] **18.** 26 [9.5] **19.** 4, 8 [9.5] **20.** $\sqrt{106} \approx 10.30$ [9.6] **21.** $\sqrt{58} \approx 7.62$ [9.6]
22. $\dfrac{1}{81}$ [9.7] **23.** x^3 [9.6] **24.** 13 meters [9.6] **25.** $\sqrt{640} \approx 25.30$ feet per second [9.6]

Cumulative Review Test
1. a) $-5, 735, 4$ **b)** $735, 4$ **c)** $-5, 735, 0.5, 4, \dfrac{1}{2}$ **d)** $\sqrt{12}$ **e)** $-5, \sqrt{12}, 735, 0.5, 4, \dfrac{1}{2}$ [1.4]
2. 29 [1.9] **3.** $\dfrac{29}{6}$ [2.5] **4.** $x > \dfrac{27}{11}$; [2.8] **5.** $(4x + 1)(x^2 + 2)$ [7.2] **6.** $(2x - 3)(x - 8)$ [7.4] **7.** $0, 9$ [7.6]
8. $\dfrac{1}{5a^5b^6}$ [6.2] **9.** [4.2] **10.** $y = 3x - 2$ [4.4] **11.** $y = \dfrac{2}{5}x + 4$ [4.4] **12.** $(0, 2)$ [5.3] **13.** $\dfrac{3y - 5}{8}$ [8.3] **14.** $\dfrac{5}{7}$ [8.6]
15. $3\sqrt{11}$ [9.3] **16.** $\dfrac{\sqrt{21yz}}{14y^3}$ [9.4] **17.** 26 [9.5] **18.** $2\dfrac{8}{11}$ cups [2.7] **19.** $\$125$ [3.2]
20. ≈ 111.1 miles [8.7]

Chapter 10

Exercise Set 10.1
1. If $x^2 = a$, then $x = \sqrt{a}$ or $x = -\sqrt{a}$. **3.** In any golden rectangle, the length is about 1.62 times its width.
5. a) 2 **b)** 1 **c)** 2 **d)** No real solution **7.** $8, -8$ **9.** $9, -9$ **11.** $13, -13$ **13.** $10, -10$ **15.** $2\sqrt{5}, -2\sqrt{5}$ **17.** $2, -2$
19. $\sqrt{17}, -\sqrt{17}$ **21.** $3, -3$ **23.** $\dfrac{\sqrt{15}}{3}, -\dfrac{\sqrt{15}}{3}$ **25.** $\dfrac{\sqrt{73}}{4}, -\dfrac{\sqrt{73}}{4}$ **27.** $3, 5$ **29.** $3, -9$ **31.** $6, -10$ **33.** $-6 + 4\sqrt{2}, -6 - 4\sqrt{2}$
35. $-1 + 2\sqrt{5}, -1 - 2\sqrt{5}$ **37.** $1, 15$ **39.** $1, -19$ **41.** $\dfrac{-3 + 3\sqrt{2}}{2}, \dfrac{-3 - 3\sqrt{2}}{2}$ **43.** $\dfrac{-1 + 2\sqrt{5}}{4}, \dfrac{-1 - 2\sqrt{5}}{4}$
45. $\dfrac{7 + 3\sqrt{2}}{2}, \dfrac{7 - 3\sqrt{2}}{2}$ **47.** $x^2 = 49$ **49.** 19 **51. a)** $3x^2 - 9x + 6 = 0$ **b)** $x^2 - 3x + 2 = 0$ **53.** $4, 17$
55. Width $\approx \sqrt{522.25}$ or ≈ 22.85 inches, length $\approx 1.21\sqrt{522.25}$ or ≈ 27.65 inches **57.** Width ≈ 35.14 feet, length ≈ 56.93 feet
59. a) Left, x^2; right, $(x + 3)^2$ **b)** 6 inches **c)** $\sqrt{50} \approx 7.07$ inches **d)** 9 inches **e)** $\sqrt{92} \approx 9.59$ inches **61.** $s = \sqrt{A}$
63. $r = \sqrt{\dfrac{A}{\pi}}$ **65.** $d = \sqrt{\dfrac{k}{I}}$ **67.** $3(2x + 3)(x - 4)$ **68.** $\dfrac{5y - 1}{6y - 1}$ **69.** $y = 4x - 1$ **70.** $\dfrac{3\sqrt{5a}}{ab^3}$

Exercise Set 10.2
1. a) A perfect square trinomial is a trinomial that can be expressed as the square of a binomial.
b) $+16$; The constant term is the square of half the coefficient of the x-term. **3.** The constant is the square of half the coefficient of the x-term. **5.** 49 **7.** $-5, -2$ **9.** $7, 1$ **11.** $-1, -12$ **13.** $2, 4$ **15.** -3 **17.** $5, -3$ **19.** $-4, -6$ **21.** $8, 2$ **23.** $10, -6$

25. $2 + \sqrt{2}, 2 - \sqrt{2}$ **27.** $-3 + \sqrt{6}, -3 - \sqrt{6}$ **29.** $\dfrac{-7 + \sqrt{41}}{2}, \dfrac{-7 - \sqrt{41}}{2}$ **31.** $1, -3$ **33.** $\dfrac{-9 + \sqrt{73}}{2}, \dfrac{-9 - \sqrt{73}}{2}$

35. $6, -1$ **37.** $4, -\dfrac{1}{3}$ **39.** $\dfrac{-1 + \sqrt{7}}{3}, \dfrac{-1 - \sqrt{7}}{3}$ **41.** $8, 0$ **43.** $9, 0$ **45. a)** $x^2 + 10x + 25$ **b)** Answers will vary.   **47.** $1, -4$

49. $0, -6$ **51.** $3, 7$ **53.** $9 + 3\sqrt{41}$ or ≈ 28.21 feet   **55.** 3 seconds and 5 seconds   **57.** $+18x$ or $-18x$ **59.** $7 + 5\sqrt{2}, 7 - 5\sqrt{2}$

61. $\dfrac{-3 + \sqrt{59}}{10}, \dfrac{-3 - \sqrt{59}}{10}$ **63.** $\dfrac{-1 + \sqrt{193}}{12}, \dfrac{-1 - \sqrt{193}}{12}$ **65.** $0.75 + \sqrt{3.5625}, 0.75 - \sqrt{3.5625}$ **66.** $\dfrac{4}{(x+2)(x-3)}$

67. If the slopes are the same and the y-intercepts are different, the equations represent parallel lines.   **68.** $(-3, 4)$ **69.** 3

Exercise Set 10.3   **1. a)** $b^2 - 4ac$ **b)** Discriminant: greater than 0, two solutions; equal to 0, one solution; less than 0,
no real solution.   **3.** $x = \dfrac{-b \pm \sqrt{b^2 - 4ac}}{2a}$ **5.** The first step is to write the equation in standard form.   **7.** The values used for b
and c are incorrect because the equation was not first put in standard form.   **9.** Two distinct real number solutions   **11.** No real
number solution   **13.** Two distinct real number solutions   **15.** One real number solution   **17.** No real number solution
19. No real number solution   **21.** Two distinct real number solutions   **23.** Two distinct real number solutions   **25.** One real number

solution   **27.** $4, 6$ **29.** $-3, -6$ **31.** $5, 3$ **33.** $7, -7$ **35.** $6, 0$ **37.** $-5, -6$ **39.** $8, -1$ **41.** $\dfrac{7 + \sqrt{17}}{4}, \dfrac{7 - \sqrt{17}}{4}$

43. $\dfrac{1}{3}, -\dfrac{1}{2}$ **45.** $\dfrac{7}{2}, -1$ **47.** No real number solution   **49.** $\dfrac{7 + \sqrt{37}}{2}, \dfrac{7 - \sqrt{37}}{2}$ **51.** $\dfrac{9}{2}, -1$ **53.** $-3, 5$ **55.** $7, -4$

57. No real number solution   **59.** $7, 8$ **61.** Width = 4 feet; length = 5 feet   **63.** 2 feet   **65.** 7 sides   **67.** 20 flags
69. ≈ 1.11 seconds and ≈ 4.52 seconds   **71. a)** $c < 16$ **b)** $c = 16$ **c)** $c > 16$ **73. a)** $c > -3$ **b)** $c = -3$ **c)** $c < -3$

76. $10, 4$ **77.** $\dfrac{5}{3}, -\dfrac{7}{2}$ **78.** Cannot be solved by factoring; $\dfrac{-3 + \sqrt{41}}{4}, \dfrac{-3 - \sqrt{41}}{4}$ **79.** $4, -4$ **80.** $\dfrac{x^2 - 9x + 2}{(2x-1)(x+4)(x-5)}$

Mid-Chapter Test   **1.** $8, -8$ [10.1]   **2.** $\sqrt{19}, -\sqrt{19}$ [10.1]   **3.** $\dfrac{\sqrt{15}}{4}, -\dfrac{\sqrt{15}}{4}$ [10.1]   **4.** $1, 5$ [10.1]   **5.** $3, -15$ [10.1]
6. $7 + 2\sqrt{6}, 7 - 2\sqrt{6}$ [10.1]   **7.** $4, 10$ [10.1]   **8.** $2, -4$ [10.2]   **9.** $3, -5$ [10.2]   **10.** $2, 9$ [10.2]   **11.** $0, 7$ [10.2]

12. $-1 + \sqrt{7}, -1 - \sqrt{7}$ [10.2]   **13.** $\dfrac{9 + \sqrt{77}}{2}, \dfrac{9 - \sqrt{77}}{2}$ [10.2]   **14.** $8, -3$ [10.3]   **15.** $-6, -5$ [10.3]   **16.** $\dfrac{5 + \sqrt{37}}{2}, \dfrac{5 - \sqrt{37}}{2}$ [10.3]
17. a) $b^2 - 4ac > 0$ **b)** $b^2 - 4ac = 0$ **c)** $b^2 - 4ac < 0$ [10.3]   **18.** Two distinct real number solutions [10.3]
19. No real number solution [10.3]   **20.** length is 11 inches, width is 8 inches [10.3]

Using Your Graphing Calculator, 10.4   **1.** $(1, -4)$ **2.** $(3.5, -2.25)$ **3.** $(-0.5, 12.5)$ **4.** $(1.75, -21.125)$

Exercise Set 10.4   **1.** A parabola   **3.** Answers will vary.   **5. a)** The x-intercepts are where the graph crosses the x-axis.
b) The x-intercepts are found by setting $y = 0$ and solving for x.   **7. a)** $x = -\dfrac{b}{2a}$ **b)** This line is called the axis of symmetry.

9. $x = -1$ $(-1, -8)$, upward   **11.** $x = -1, (-1, -1)$, upward   **13.** $x = \dfrac{1}{3}, \left(\dfrac{1}{3}, \dfrac{4}{3}\right)$, downward

15. $x = \dfrac{3}{2}, \left(\dfrac{3}{2}, -\dfrac{7}{4}\right)$, downward   **17.** $x = -\dfrac{3}{4}, \left(-\dfrac{3}{4}, \dfrac{23}{8}\right)$, upward   **19.** $x = \dfrac{1}{2}, \left(\dfrac{1}{2}, \dfrac{33}{4}\right)$, downward

21.   **23.**   **25.**   **27.**   **29.**   **31.**

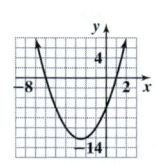

33.   **35.**   **37.**   **39.**   **41.**   **43.**

45.   **47.**

49. Two   **51.** Two   **53.** One   **55.** Two
57. None; the vertex is below the x-axis and the parabola opens downward
59. One; the vertex of the parabola is on the x-axis.
61. Yes; if y is set to 0, both equations have the same solutions, 5 and -3.
63. a) ≈ 255 feet   **b)** 4 seconds   **c)** 8 seconds   **d)** ≈ 190 feet, ≈ 240 feet

65. a)

67. a)

b)

69. $\dfrac{-x^2 + 4x - 14}{(x + 3)(x - 4)}$ **70.** $\dfrac{27}{7}$

71. $(6, -5)$ **72.** 7

b) 45 feet   **c)** 4050 square feet   **c)** $(0, 0), (4, 8)$

Exercise Set 10.5   **1.** Yes, every real number is a complex number.   **3.** $\sqrt{-1}$ **5.** $a + bi$ **7.** $4i$ **9.** $10i$ **11.** $i\sqrt{15}$

13. $i\sqrt{13}$ **15.** $4i\sqrt{2}$ **17.** $3i\sqrt{5}$ **19.** $8 + 2i$ **21.** $10 + 5i$ **23.** $-3 - 3i$ **25.** $-7 - i\sqrt{15}$ **27.** $5.2 + 4i\sqrt{3}$ **29.** $\dfrac{1}{4} + 5i\sqrt{3}$

31. $10 + 3i$ **33.** $4 - 11i$ **35.** $11 + 5i$ **37.** $-2 - 7i$ **39.** 0   **41.** $9 - 4i$ **43.** $4i, -4i$ **45.** $i\sqrt{10}, -i\sqrt{10}$ **47.** $2 + i, 2 - i$

49. $\dfrac{-3 + i\sqrt{31}}{4}, \dfrac{-3 - i\sqrt{31}}{4}$ **51.** $\dfrac{-2 + i\sqrt{10}}{2}, \dfrac{-2 - i\sqrt{10}}{2}$ **53.** $\dfrac{7 + i\sqrt{47}}{8}, \dfrac{7 - i\sqrt{47}}{8}$ **55.** When $c < 0$

57. When $b^2 - 4ac < 0$ **59.** 5   **60.** $-\dfrac{5}{3}$ **61.** 2, 9   **62.** 13

Chapter 10 Review Exercises   **1.** $5, -5$ **2.** $11, -11$ **3.** $\sqrt{5}, -\sqrt{5}$ **4.** $\sqrt{6}, -\sqrt{6}$ **5.** $\sqrt{7}, -\sqrt{7}$ **6.** $2\sqrt{5}, -2\sqrt{5}$

7. $2\sqrt{2}, -2\sqrt{2}$ **8.** $3 + 2\sqrt{6}, 3 - 2\sqrt{6}$ **9.** $\dfrac{9 + 5\sqrt{2}}{4}, \dfrac{9 - 5\sqrt{2}}{4}$ **10.** $\dfrac{-4 + \sqrt{30}}{3}, \dfrac{-4 - \sqrt{30}}{3}$ **11.** $5, 2$ **12.** $7, 4$ **13.** $-17, -1$

14. $-10, -9$ **15.** $9, -6$ **16.** $1, -6$ **17.** $8, -4$ **18.** $5, -3$ **19.** $-1 + \sqrt{13}, -1 - \sqrt{13}$ **20.** $\dfrac{5 + \sqrt{33}}{2}, \dfrac{5 - \sqrt{33}}{2}$ **21.** $\dfrac{4}{3}, -2$

22. $\dfrac{2}{3}, \dfrac{1}{4}$ **23.** No real solution   **24.** No real solution   **25.** One solution   **26.** Two solutions   **27.** Two solutions

28. No real solution   **29.** Two solutions   **30.** Two solutions   **31.** $8, 2$ **32.** $-9, -2$ **33.** $11, -4$ **34.** $1, \dfrac{4}{5}$ **35.** $3, -7$

36. No real solution   **37.** $\dfrac{3}{2}, -\dfrac{5}{3}$ **38.** $\dfrac{3 + \sqrt{57}}{4}, \dfrac{3 - \sqrt{57}}{4}$ **39.** $\dfrac{-2 + \sqrt{10}}{2}, \dfrac{-2 - \sqrt{10}}{2}$ **40.** $3 + \sqrt{6}, 3 - \sqrt{6}$

41. No real solution   **42.** $\dfrac{3 + \sqrt{33}}{3}, \dfrac{3 - \sqrt{33}}{3}$ **43.** $0, \dfrac{4}{7}$ **44.** $0, \dfrac{5}{2}$ **45.** $4, 6$ **46.** $5, 11$ **47.** $10, -7$ **48.** $-9, 3$ **49.** $-6, 10$

50. $2, 11$ **51.** $3, -12$ **52.** $0, 8$ **53.** $8, -8$ **54.** $13, -13$ **55.** $\dfrac{5}{2}, 2$ **56.** $\dfrac{2}{3}, -\dfrac{3}{2}$ **57.** $0, \dfrac{11}{4}$ **58.** $0, -\dfrac{10}{3}$ **59.** $1, -\dfrac{8}{3}$ **60.** $2, \dfrac{5}{3}$

61. $\dfrac{3 + 3\sqrt{3}}{2}, \dfrac{3 - 3\sqrt{3}}{2}$ **62.** $\dfrac{-3 + \sqrt{33}}{2}, \dfrac{-3 - \sqrt{33}}{2}$ **63.** $x = 2, (2, -9)$, upward   **64.** $x = 6, (6, -19)$, upward

65. $x = \dfrac{3}{2}, \left(\dfrac{3}{2}, \dfrac{19}{4}\right)$, upward   **66.** $x = -1, (-1, 14)$, downward   **67.** $x = -\dfrac{7}{6}, \left(-\dfrac{7}{6}, -\dfrac{13}{12}\right)$, upward

68. $x = -\dfrac{5}{2}, \left(-\dfrac{5}{2}, \dfrac{25}{4}\right)$, downward   **69.** $x = 0, (0, -10)$, downward   **70.** $x = -\dfrac{1}{4}, \left(-\dfrac{1}{4}, \dfrac{121}{8}\right)$, downward

71. $x = 1, (1, 13)$, downward   **72.** $x = -\dfrac{5}{6}, \left(-\dfrac{5}{6}, -\dfrac{97}{12}\right)$, upward

73.

74.

75.

76.

77.

78.

79.

80.

81.

82.

83.

84.

85. $5, 7$ **86.** $8, 12$ **87.** Width = 20 inches, length = 46 inches   **88.** Width = 24 inches, length = 40 inches   **89.** $3i$ **90.** $i\sqrt{26}$

91. $8 - 5i$ **92.** $6 - 2i\sqrt{15}$ **93.** $11 - 9i$ **94.** $3 + 8i$ **95.** $4i, -4i$ **96.** $i\sqrt{6}, -i\sqrt{6}$ **97.** $\dfrac{5 + i\sqrt{23}}{4}, \dfrac{5 - i\sqrt{23}}{4}$

98. $\dfrac{2 + i\sqrt{5}}{2}, \dfrac{2 - i\sqrt{5}}{2}$

Chapter 10 Practice Test

1. $4\sqrt{2}, -4\sqrt{2}$ [10.1]   **2.** $\dfrac{3 + \sqrt{13}}{2}, \dfrac{3 - \sqrt{13}}{2}$ [10.1]   **3.** $10, -5$ [10.2]   **4.** $3, -11$ [10.2]

5. $6, 7$ [10.3]   **6.** $\dfrac{-4 + \sqrt{6}}{2}, \dfrac{-4 - \sqrt{6}}{2}$ [10.3]   **7.** $\dfrac{5}{4}, -\dfrac{5}{4}$ [10.1–10.3]   **8.** $x = \dfrac{-b \pm \sqrt{b^2 - 4ac}}{2a}$ [10.3]

9. Answers will vary. [10.2]   **10.** Two real solutions. [10.3]   **11.** One real solution [10.3]   **12.** $x = -4$ [10.4]   **13.** $x = 2$ [10.4]

14. Downward; $a < 0$ [10.4]   **15.** Upward; $a > 0$ [10.4]   **16.** The vertex is the lowest point on a parabola that opens upward; highest point on a parabola that opens downward. [10.4]   **17.** $(-2, -8)$ [10.4]   **18.** $\left(\dfrac{4}{3}, \dfrac{11}{3}\right)$ [10.4]

19. [10.4]   **20.** [10.4]   **21.** [10.4]   **22.** Width = 3 feet, length = 11 feet [10.2–10.3]

23. 7 [10.2–10.3]

24. 11 [10.2–10.3]   **25.** $\dfrac{1 + i\sqrt{17}}{3}, \dfrac{1 - i\sqrt{17}}{3}$ [10.5]

Cumulative Review Test

1. 255 [1.9]   **2.** $\dfrac{14}{27}$ [2.5]   **3.** $5\dfrac{1}{3}$ inches [2.7]   **4.** $x \geq -\dfrac{1}{4}$; [2.8]

5. $P = 6A - m - n$ [2.6]   **6.** $72a^{16}b^{25}$ [6.1]   **7.** $x + 4 - \dfrac{9}{x + 2}$ [6.6]   **8.** $(2x - 3y)(x - 2y)$ [7.2]   **9.** $3(2x + 3)(x - 6)$ [7.4]

10. $\dfrac{9a + 4}{(a + 4)(a - 4)^2}$ [8.4]   **11.** $3, 8$ [8.6]   **12.** [4.2]   **13.** $(-3, -9)$ [5.3]   **14.** $\dfrac{y\sqrt{6xy}}{6}$ [9.4]   **15.** $4\sqrt{7}$ [9.3]

16. 4 [9.5]   **17.** $\dfrac{-3 + \sqrt{73}}{4}, \dfrac{-3 - \sqrt{73}}{4}$ [10.3]   **18.** 25.6 pounds [2.7]   **19.** Width = 7 feet, length = 25 feet [3.3]

20. Walks: 3 miles per hour, jogs: 6 miles per hour [8.7]

Graphing Answer Section

Using Your Graphing Calculator, 4.1

1.   **2.**

Exercise Set 4.1

13.   **29.**   **30.**   **31.**   **32.**   **37. b)**

38. b)   **39. b)**   **40. b)**   **41. b)**   **42. b)**

54.   **55.**   **56.**

Using Your Graphing Calculator, 4.2

1.   **2.**   **3.**   **4.**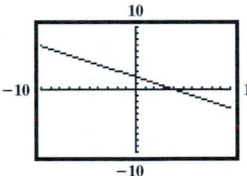

Exercise Set 4.2

21.   **22.**   **23.**   **24.**   **25.**   **26.**

27.   **28.**   **29.**   **30.**   **31.**   **32.**

33.   **34.**   **35.**   **36.**   **37.**

38.

39.

40.

41.

42.

43.

44.

45.

46.

47.

48.

49.

50.

51.

52.

53.

54.

55.

56.

57.

58.

59.

60.

61.

62.

63.

64.

75. b)

76. b)

77. b)

78. b)

79. a)

80. b)

85. a)

86.

87. a–d)

Exercise Set 4.3

39.

40.

41.

42.

43.

44.

45.

46.

47.

48.

79. a)

Mid-Chapter Test

2.

7.

8.

9.

10.

11.

12.

16.

17.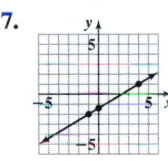

Using Your Graphing Calculator, 4.4

1. a)

b)

c)

2. a)

b)

c)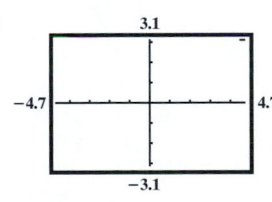

Exercise Set 4.4

13.

14.

15.

16.

17.

18.

19.

20.

21.

22.

23.

24.

25.

26.

27.

28.

77. d)

Exercise Set 4.5

5.   **6.** **7.** **8.** **9.** **10.** **11.**

12. **13.** **14.** **15.** **16.** **17.**

18. **19.** **20.** **21.** **22.** **23.**

24. **32. d)**

Exercise Set 4.6

43. **44.** **45.** **46.** **47.**

48. **49.** **50.**

57. a) **58. a)**

59. a)

60. a)

61. a)

62. a)

63. a)

64. a)

Chapter 4 Review Exercises

1.   **5.**   **6.**   **7.**   **8.**   **9.**

10.   **11.**   **12.** $5x + 2y + 10 = 0$ **13.**   **14.**

39.   **40.**   **41.**   **42.**   **43.**   **44.**

65.   **66.**

67. a)

68. a)

Chapter 4 Practice Test

8.

9.

10.

11. b)

12.

16.

17.

22.

23.

24.

25. a)

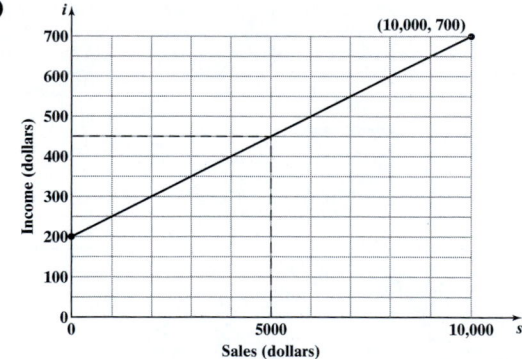

Chapter 4 Cumulative Review Test

15.

16.

17.

19.

Exercise Set 5.1

83. b)

Exercise Set 5.2

47.

Exercise Set 5.5

5.   **6.**   **7.**   **8.**   **9.**   **10.**   **11.**

12.   **13.**   **14.**   **15.**   **16.**   **17.**

18.   **19.**   **20.**   **21.**   **22.**   **23.**

24.   **27.**   **28.**   **31.**

Chapter 5 Review Exercises

42.   **43.**   **44.**   **45.**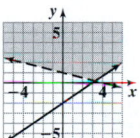

Chapter 5 Practice Test

24.   **25.**

Chapter 5 Cumulative Review Test

15.   **16.**   **19.**

Exercise Set 6.4

143.   **144.**

Exercise Set 7.3

103.

Exercise Set 8.7

48.

Exercise Set 9.2

102.

Exercise Set 9.5

70. c)   **71. c)**   **72. c)**

Chapter 9 Cumulative Review Test

9.

Exercise Set 10.3

75. e)

Exercise Set 10.4

21.

22.

23.

24.

25.

26.

27.

28.

29.

30.

31.

32.

33.

34.

35.

36.

37.

38.

39.

40.

41.

42.

43.

44.

45.

46.

47.

48.

62. b)

65. a)

66. a)

67. a)

67. b)

68. a)

68. b)

Chapter 10 Review Exercises

73.

74.

75.

76.

77.

78.

79.

80.

81.

82.

83.

84.

Chapter 10 Practice Test

19.   **20.**   **21.**

Chapter 10 Cumulative Review Test

12.

Applications Index

Index

Photo Credits

Chapter 1 p. 1 © Jose Luis Pelaez/CORBIS All Rights Reserved;   **p. 5** Gary Connor, PhotoEdit, Inc.;   **p. 7** AP World Wide Photos;   **p. 8** William Thomas Cain, Getty Images Inc.;   **p. 16** Pictor, ImageState/International Stock Photography Ltd.;   **p. 19** Jeopardy Productions, Getty Images Inc.;   **p. 34** Allen R. Angel;   **p. 40** Rhoda Peacher, R Photographs; **p. 462 (left)** Tom Pantages and **(right)** DLP ®/Courtesy of Texas Instruments Incorporated;   **p. 54** Bob Daemmrich, PhotoEdit, Inc.;   **p. 59** James Blank, Stock Boston;   **p. 67** © Jose Luis Pelaez/CORBIS All Rights Reserved; **p. 78** Ross M. Horowitz, Getty Images Inc.;   **p. 79** Doug Menuez, Getty Images, Inc.—Photodisc; **p. 85** © Zave Smith/CORBIS All Rights Reserved

Chapter 2 p. 95 Ryan McVay, Getty Images, Inc.–Photodisc;   **p. 140** Getty Images – Stockbyte;   **p. 143** Allen R. Angel; **p. 144** Steve Vidler, SuperStock, Inc.;   **p. 149** AP Photo/Dusan Vranic;   **p. 150** SuperStock, Inc.;   **p. 151** Allen R. Angel; **p. 152** © Walt Disney Pictures/Pixar Animation Studios 07000;   **p. 155** Johner Images, Getty Images Inc.; **p. 156** Allen R. Angel;   **p. 162 (left)** Allen R. Angel;   **(right)** Allen R. Angel;   **p. 163 (left)** Robert Glusic, Getty Images, Inc.;   **(right)** Gary Wiepert/Reuters, Landov LLC;   **p. 176** Steve Mason, Getty Images, Inc.-Photodisc; **p.177** Allen R. Angel

Chapter 3 p. 179 Dennis MacDonald, PhotoEdit, Inc.;   **p. 183** Dale Pollinger;   **p. 184 (top)** Allen R. Angel; **(bottom)** John A. Rizzo, Getty Images, Inc. – Photodisc;   **p. 188** W. Bliss/HOA-QUI, Photo Researchers, Inc.; **p. 190** Allen R. Angel;   **p. 191 (top left)** Jeff Greenberg, The Image Works;   **(bottom left)** Allen R. Angel; **(right/column 1)** Allen R. Angel;   **(right/column 2)** Allen R. Angel;   **p. 192 (left)** Allen R. Angel; **(right)** Pictor, ImageState/International Stock Photography Ltd.;   **p. 193 (left)** Allen R. Angel; **(top right)** Allen R. Angel **(bottom right)** Allen R. Angel;   **p. 194** Allen R. Angel;   **p. 197 (top)** © Erich Schlegel/Dallas Morning News/CORBIS All Rights Reserved;   **(bottom)** Allen R. Angel;   **p. 198** Dennis MacDonald, PhotoEdit, Inc.; **p. 199 (top)** Dave King © Dorling Kindersley;   **(bottom)** Allen R. Angel;   **p. 200** Laima Druskis, Pearson Education/PH College;   **p. 202 (left)** Allen R. Angel;   **(top right)** Getty Images, Inc.–Photodisc; **(bottom right)** EyeWire Collection, Getty Images, Inc.–Photodisc;   **p. 203** Michael Newman, PhotoEdit, Inc.; **p. 204 (top left)** Nick Rowe, Getty Images, Inc.–Photodisc;   **(bottom left)** Doug Menuez, Getty Images, Inc.–Photodisc; **(bottom right)** J. Gerard Smith, Photo Researchers, Inc.;   **p. 205 (left)** Jeff Maloney, Getty Images, Inc.– Photodisc; **(right)** Jose Carrillo, PhotoEdit, Inc.;   **p. 206 (top left)** Allen R. Angel;   **(bottom left)** Allen R. Angel; **(right)** Karl Weatherly, Getty Images–Photodisc;   **p. 209** Allen R. Angel;   **p. 215** Allen R. Angel; **p. 221 (top left)** Allen R. Angel;   **(bottom left)** Justin Sullivan, Getty Images, Inc.;   **(right)** Allen R. Angel; **p. 222 (left)** EyeWire Collection, Getty Images, Inc.–Photodisc;   **(right)** Glenn Cratty, Getty Images, Inc.; **p. 223** Peter Wilson © Dorling Kindersley Media Library, Courtesy of the Baseball Hall of Fame, Tokyo; **p. 224 (left)** © Dann Tardif/CORBIS All Rights Reserved;   **(right)** © Holger Winkler/Zefa/CORBIS All Rights Reserved;   **p. 228** Gary Randall, Getty Images, Inc.–Photodisc;   **p. 229 (left)** © Tim McGuire/CORBIS All Rights Reserved;   **(right)** © James D. Smith/Icon SMI/CORBIS All Rights Reserved

Chapter 4 p. 232 Tony Garcia, Getty Images, Inc.;   **p. 233** Sheila Terry/Science Photo Library, Photo Researchers, Inc.; **p. 247** Corbis Royalty Free;   **p. 250** © R. W. Jones/CORBIS;   **p. 262** Sylvie Chappaz, Photo Researchers, Inc.; **p. 267** Allen R. Angel;   **p. 274** Chris Oxley, Corbis/Bettmann;   **p. 275** David Graham, AP Wide World Photos; **p. 284** Pictor, Image State/International Stock Photography Ltd.;   **p. 287** Corbis Digital Stock; **p. 293** Allen R. Angel

Chapter 5 p. 298 Tomas del Amo, Index Stock Imagery, Inc. Royalty Free;   **p. 308** Allen R. Angel; **p. 313** Dennis MacDonald, PhotoEdit, Inc.;   **p. 314** Adam Jones, Photo Researchers, Inc.;   **p. 325** Allen R. Angel; **p. 326** Allen R. Angel;   **p. 331 (left)** Corbis/Reuters America LLC;   **(right)** Peter Skinner, Photo Researchers, Inc.; **p. 332 (top right)** Ed Lallo, Index Stock Imagery, Inc.;   **(bottom right)** Tom Prettyman, PhotoEdit, Inc.; **p. 333** Eric Dreyer, Getty Images, Inc.

Allen R. Angel
Chapter Test Prep Video t/a Elementary Algebra for College Students Early Graphing, 3e
0-13-159446-X
© 2008 Pearson Education, Inc.
Pearson Prentice Hall
Pearson Education, Inc.
Upper Saddle River, NJ 07458
Pearson Prentice Hall™ is a trademark of Pearson Education, Inc.

YOU SHOULD CAREFULLY READ THE TERMS AND CONDITIONS BEFORE USING THE CD-ROM PACKAGE. USING THIS CD-ROM PACKAGE INDICATES YOUR ACCEPTANCE OF THESE TERMS AND CONDITIONS.

Pearson Education, Inc. provides this program and licenses its use. You assume responsibility for the selection of the program to achieve your intended results, and for the installation, use, and results obtained from the program. This license extends only to use of the program in the United States or countries in which the program is marketed by authorized distributors.

LICENSE GRANT

You hereby accept a nonexclusive, nontransferable, permanent license to install and use the program ON A SINGLE COMPUTER at any given time. You may copy the program solely for backup or archival purposes in support of your use of the program on the single computer. You may not modify, translate, disassemble, decompile, or reverse engineer the program, in whole or in part.

TERM

The License is effective until terminated. Pearson Education, Inc. reserves the right to terminate this License automatically if any provision of the License is violated. You may terminate the License at any time. To terminate this License, you must return the program, including documentation, along with a written warranty stating that all copies in your possession have been returned or destroyed.

LIMITED WARRANTY

THE PROGRAM IS PROVIDED "AS IS" WITHOUT WARRANTY OF ANY KIND, EITHER EXPRESSED OR IMPLIED, INCLUDING, BUT NOT LIMITED TO, THE IMPLIED WARRANTIES OF MERCHANTABILITY AND FITNESS FOR A PARTICULAR PURPOSE. THE ENTIRE RISK AS TO THE QUALITY AND PERFORMANCE OF THE PROGRAM IS WITH YOU. SHOULD THE PROGRAM PROVE DEFECTIVE, YOU (AND NOT PEARSON EDUCATION, INC. OR ANY AUTHORIZED DEALER) ASSUME THE ENTIRE COST OF ALL NECESSARY SERVICING, REPAIR, OR CORRECTION. NO ORAL OR WRITTEN INFORMATION OR ADVICE GIVEN BY PEARSON EDUCATION, INC., ITS DEALERS, DISTRIBUTORS, OR AGENTS SHALL CREATE A WARRANTY OR INCREASE THE SCOPE OF THIS WARRANTY. SOME STATES DO NOT ALLOW THE EXCLUSION OF IMPLIED WARRANTIES, SO THE ABOVE EXCLUSION MAY NOT APPLY TO YOU. THIS WARRANTY GIVES YOU SPECIFIC LEGAL RIGHTS AND YOU MAY ALSO HAVE OTHER LEGAL RIGHTS THAT VARY FROM STATE TO STATE.

Pearson Education, Inc. does not warrant that the functions contained in the program will meet your requirements or that the operation of the program will be uninterrupted or error-free. However, Pearson Education, Inc. warrants the CD-ROM(s) on which the program is furnished to be free from defects in material and workmanship under normal use for a period of ninety (90) days from the date of delivery to you as evidenced by a copy of your receipt. The program should not be relied on as the sole basis to solve a problem whose incorrect solution could result in injury to person or property. If the program is employed in such a manner, it is at the user's own risk and Pearson Education, Inc. explicitly disclaims all liability for such misuse.

LIMITATION OF REMEDIES

Pearson Education, Inc.'s entire liability and your exclusive remedy shall be:

1. the replacement of any CD-ROM not meeting Pearson Education, Inc.'s "LIMITED WARRANTY" and that is returned to Pearson Education, or

2. if Pearson Education is unable to deliver a replacement CD-ROM that is free of defects in materials or workmanship, you may terminate this agreement by returning the program.

IN NO EVENT WILL PEARSON EDUCATION, INC. BE LIABLE TO YOU FOR ANY DAMAGES, INCLUDING ANY LOST PROFITS, LOST SAVINGS, OR OTHER INCIDENTAL OR CONSEQUENTIAL DAMAGES ARISING OUT OF THE USE OR INABILITY TO USE SUCH PROGRAM EVEN IF PEARSON EDUCATION, INC. OR AN AUTHORIZED DISTRIBUTOR HAS BEEN ADVISED OF THE POSSIBILITY OF SUCH DAMAGES, OR FOR ANY CLAIM BY ANY OTHER PARTY. SOME STATES DO NOT ALLOW FOR THE LIMITATION OR EXCLUSION OF LIABILITY FOR INCIDENTAL OR CONSEQUENTIAL DAMAGES, SO THE ABOVE LIMITATION OR EXCLUSION MAY NOT APPLY TO YOU.

GENERAL

You may not sublicense, assign, or transfer the license of the program. Any attempt to sublicense, assign or transfer any of the rights, duties, or obligations hereunder is

void. This Agreement will be governed by the laws of the State of New York. Should you have any questions concerning this Agreement, you may contact Pearson Education, Inc. by writing to:

ESM Media Development
Higher Education Division
Pearson Education, Inc.
1 Lake Street
Upper Saddle River, NJ 07458

Should you have any questions concerning technical support, you may write to:

New Media Production
Higher Education Division
Pearson Education, Inc.
1 Lake Street
Upper Saddle River, NJ 07458

YOU ACKNOWLEDGE THAT YOU HAVE READ THIS AGREEMENT, UNDERSTAND IT, AND AGREE TO BE BOUND BY ITS TERMS AND CONDITIONS. YOU FURTHER AGREE THAT IT IS THE COMPLETE AND EXCLUSIVE STATEMENT OF THE AGREEMENT BETWEEN US THAT SUPERSEDES ANY PROPOSAL OR PRIOR AGREEMENT, ORAL OR WRITTEN, AND ANY OTHER COMMUNICATIONS BETWEEN US RELATING TO THE SUBJECT MATTER OF THIS AGREEMENT.

System Requirements

-Windows
Pentium II 300 MHz processor
Windows 2000 (Service Pack 4) or XP
64 MB RAM (128 MB RAM required for Windows XP)
7.2 MB available hard drive space (optional—for minimum QuickTime installation)
800 x 600 resolution
8x or faster CD-ROM drive
QuickTime 7.x
Sound card

-Macintosh
PowerPC G3 233 MHz or better
Mac OS 10.x
64 MB RAM
19 MB on OS X (optional—if QuickTime installation is needed)
800 x 600 resolution
8x or faster CD-ROM drive
QuickTime 6 or 7

Support Information

If you are having problems with this software, call (800) 677-6337 between 8:00 a.m. and 8:00 p.m. EST, Monday through Friday, and 5:00 p.m. through Midnight EST on Sundays. You can also get support by filling out the web form located at: http://247.prenhall.com/mediaform

Our technical staff will need to know certain things about your system in order to help us solve your problems more quickly and efficiently. If possible, please be at your computer when you call for support. You should have the following information ready:

- Textbook ISBN
- CD-ROM ISBN
- corresponding product and title
- computer make and model
- Operating System (Windows or Macintosh) and Version
- RAM available
- hard disk space available
- Sound card? Yes or No
- printer make and model
- network connection
- detailed description of the problem, including the exact wording of any error messages.

NOTE: Pearson does not support and/or assist with the following:

- third-party software (i.e. Microsoft including Microsoft Office suite, Apple, Borland, etc.)
- homework assistance
- Textbooks and CD-ROMs purchased used are not supported and are non-replaceable. To purchase a new CD-ROM, contact Pearson Individual Order Copies at 1-800-282-0693.

Chapter 1 Real Numbers

Fractions

Addition

$$\frac{a}{c} + \frac{b}{c} = \frac{a+b}{c}$$

Subtraction

$$\frac{a}{c} - \frac{b}{c} = \frac{a-b}{c}$$

Multiplication

$$\frac{a}{b} \cdot \frac{c}{d} = \frac{a \cdot c}{b \cdot d}$$

Division

$$\frac{a}{b} \div \frac{c}{d} = \frac{a}{b} \cdot \frac{d}{c} = \frac{a \cdot d}{b \cdot c}$$

Natural numbers $\{1, 2, 3, 4, \ldots\}$

Whole numbers $\{0, 1, 2, 3, \ldots\}$

Integers $\{\ldots, -3, -2, -1, 0, 1, 2, 3, \ldots\}$

Rational numbers {quotient of two integers, denominator not 0}

The sum of two positive numbers will be a positive number.
The sum of two negative numbers will be a negative number.
The sum of a positive number and a negative number can be either a positive or negative number.

The product (or quotient) of two numbers with like signs will be a positive number.
The product (or quotient) of two numbers with unlike signs will be a negative number.

$a - b$ means $a + (-b)$

$$\frac{a}{-b} = \frac{-a}{b} = -\frac{a}{b}$$

$$b^n = \underbrace{b \cdot b \cdot b \cdot \cdots \cdot b}_{n \text{ factors of } b}$$

Order of Operations

1. Evaluate expressions within parentheses.
2. Evaluate expressions with exponents.
3. Perform multiplications or divisions moving from left to right.
4. Perform additions or subtractions moving from left to right.

Properties of the Real Numbers

Commutative: $a + b = b + a, a \cdot b = b \cdot a$

Associative: $(a + b) + c = a + (b + c), (a \cdot b) \cdot c = a \cdot (b \cdot c)$

Distributive: $a(b + c) = a \cdot b + a \cdot c$

Identity: $a + 0 = 0 + a = a, 1 \cdot a = a \cdot 1 = a$

Inverse: $a + (-a) = -a + a = 0, a \cdot \dfrac{1}{a} = \dfrac{1}{a} \cdot a = 1$

Chapter 2 Solving Linear Equations and Inequalities

Addition property of equality: If $a = b$, then $a + c = b + c$ for any real numbers $a, b,$ and c.

Multiplication property of equality: If $a = b$, then $a \cdot c = b \cdot c$ for any real numbers $a, b,$ and c.

Linear equation: $ax + b = c$, for real numbers $a, b,$ and c.

To Solve Linear Equations with the Variable on Both Sides of the Equal Sign

1. If the equation contains fractions, multiply both sides of the equation by the LCD.
2. Use the distributive property to remove parentheses.
3. Combine like terms on the same side of the equal sign.
4. Use the addition property to rewrite the equation with all terms containing the variable on one side of the equal sign and all terms not containing the variable on the other side of the equal sign. Repeated use of the addition property will eventually result in an equation of the form $ax = b$.
5. Use the multiplication property to isolate the variable. This will give a solution of the form $x =$ some number.
6. Check the solution in the original equation.

Simple interest formula: $i = prt$

Distance formula: $d = rt$

Geometric formulas: See Section 2.6 and Appendix C.

Cross multiplication: If $\dfrac{a}{b} = \dfrac{c}{d}$, then $ad = bc$.

Inequalities

If $a > b$, then $a + c > b + c$.
If $a > b$, then $a - c > b - c$.
If $a > b$ and $c > 0$, then $ac > bc$.

If $a > b$ and $c > 0$, then $\dfrac{a}{c} > \dfrac{b}{c}$.

If $a > b$ and $c < 0$, then $ac < bc$.

If $a > b$ and $c < 0$, then $\dfrac{a}{c} < \dfrac{b}{c}$.

Chapter 3 Applications of Algebra

Problem-Solving Procedure for Solving Applications Problems

1. **Understand the problem.**
   Identify the quantity or quantities you are being asked to find.
2. **Translate the problem into mathematical language (express the problem as an equation).**
   a) Choose a variable to represent one quantity, *and write down exactly what it represents*. Represent any other quantity to be found in terms of this variable.
   b) Using the information from step a) write an equation that represents the application.
3. **Carry out the mathematical calculations (solve the equation).**
4. **Check the answer (using the original application).**
5. **Answer the question asked.**

Chapter 4 Graphing Linear Equations

Linear equation in two variables: $ax + by = c$

A **graph** is an illustration of the set of points whose coordinates satisfy the equation.

Every **linear equation** of the form $ax + by = c$ will be a straight line when graphed.

To find the y-intercept (where the graph crosses the y-axis) set $x = 0$ and solve for y.

To find the x-intercept (where the graph crosses the x-axis) set $y = 0$ and solve for x.

$$\text{slope } (m) = \frac{\text{change in } y}{\text{change in } x} = \frac{y_2 - y_1}{x_2 - x_1}$$

Positive slope
(rises to right)

Negative slope
(falls to right)

Slope is 0.
(horizontal line)

Slope is undefined.
(vertical line)

Linear Equations

Standard form of a linear equation: $ax + by = c$

Slope–intercept form of a linear equation: $y = mx + b$, where m is the slope and $(0, b)$ is the y-intercept.

Point–slope form of a linear equation: $y - y_1 = m(x - x_1)$, where m is the slope and (x_1, y_1) is a point on the line.

A **relation** is any set of ordered pairs.

A **function** is a set of ordered pairs in which each first component corresponds to exactly one second component.

Chapter 5 Systems of Linear Equations

The **solution** to a system of linear equations is the ordered pair or pairs that satisfy all equations in the system. A system of linear equations may have no solution, exactly one solution, or an infinite number of solutions.

Exactly 1 solution
(Nonparallel lines)

No solution
(Parallel lines)

Infinite number of solutions
(Same line)

Line 1   Line 2
Consistent system

Inconsistent system

Dependent system

A system of linear equations may be solved graphically, or algebraically by the substitution method or by the addition (or elimination) method.

Chapter 6 Exponents and Polynomials

Rules of Exponents

1. $x^m \cdot x^n = x^{m+n}$ **product rule**

2. $\dfrac{x^m}{x^n} = x^{m-n}, x \neq 0$ **quotient rule**

3. $(x^m)^n = x^{m \cdot n}$ **power rule**

4. $x^0 = 1, x \neq 0$ **zero exponent rule**

5. $x^{-m} = \dfrac{1}{x^m}, x \neq 0$ **negative exponent rule**

6. $\left(\dfrac{ax}{by}\right)^m = \dfrac{a^m x^m}{b^m y^m}, b \neq 0, y \neq 0$ **expanded power rule**

7. $\left(\dfrac{a}{b}\right)^{-m} = \left(\dfrac{b}{a}\right)^m, a \neq 0, b \neq 0$ **a fraction raised to a negative exponent rule**

FOIL method (First, Outer, Inner, Last) of multiplying binomials:
$$(a + b)(c + d) = ac + ad + bc + bd$$

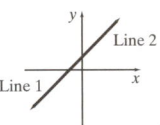

Product of the sum and difference of the same two terms:
$$(a + b)(a - b) = a^2 - b^2$$

Squares of binomials:
$$(a + b)^2 = a^2 + 2ab + b^2$$
$$(a - b)^2 = a^2 - 2ab + b^2$$

Chapter 7 Factoring

If $a \cdot b = c$, then a and b are **factors** of c.

Difference of two squares: $a^2 - b^2 = (a + b)(a - b)$

Sum of two cubes: $a^3 + b^3 = (a + b)(a^2 - ab + b^2)$

Difference of two cubes: $a^3 - b^3 = (a - b)(a^2 + ab + b^2)$

To Factor a Polynomial

1. If all the terms of the polynomial have a greatest common factor other than 1, factor it out.

2. If the polynomial has two terms, determine if it is a difference of two squares or a sum or a difference of two cubes. If so, factor using the appropriate formula.

3. If the polynomial has three terms, factor the trinomial using one of the procedures discussed.

4. If the polynomial has more than three terms, try factoring by grouping.

5. As a final step, examine your factored polynomial to see if the terms in any factors listed have a common factor. If you find a common factor, factor it out at this point.